SCHOLARSHIPS,

FELLOWSHIPS

AND LOANS

ISSN 1058-5699

SCHOLARSHIPS, FELLOWSHIPS AND LOANS

A GUIDE TO EDUCATION-RELATED FINANCIAL AID PROGRAMS FOR STUDENTS AND PROFESSIONALS

Volume Three

Sponsors and Their Scholarships: U–Z
and Indexes

Thirtieth Edition

GALE
CENGAGE Learning®

Detroit • New York • San Francisco • New Haven, Conn • Waterville, Maine • London

Scholarships, Fellowships and Loans, 30th Edition

Product Management: Jerry Moore

Project Editor: Bohdan Romaniuk

Editorial Support Services: Wayne Fong

Composition and Electronic Prepress: Gary Leach

Manufacturing: Rita Wimberley

For product information and technology assistance, contact us at
Gale Customer Support, 1-800-877-4253.
For permission to use material from this text or product,
submit all requests online at **www.cengage.com/permissions.**
Further permissions questions can be emailed to
permissionrequest@cengage.com

While every effort has been made to ensure the reliability of the information presented in this publication, Gale, a part of Cengage Learning,does not guarantee the accuracy of the data contained herein. Gale accepts no payment for listing; and inclusion in the publication of any organization, agency, institution, publication, service, or individual does not imply endorsement of the editors or publisher. Errors brought to the attention of the publisher, and verified to the satisfaction of the publisher, will be corrected in future editions.

EDITORIAL DATA PRIVACY POLICY: Does this product contain information about you as an individual? If so, for more information about our editorial data privacy policies, please see our Privacy Statement at www.gale.cengage.com.

Gale
27500 Drake Rd.
Farmington Hills, MI, 48331-3535

ISBN-13: 978-1-4144-6916-4 (3 vol. set)
ISBN-10: 1-4144-6916-0 (3 vol. set)
ISBN-13: 978-1-4144-6917-1 (vol. 1)
ISBN-10: 1-4144-6917-9 (vol. 1)
ISBN-13: 978-1-4144-6918-8 (vol. 2)
ISBN-10: 1-4144-6918-7 (vol. 2)
ISBN-13: 978-1-4144-8894-3 (vol. 3)
ISBN-10: 1-4144-8894-7 (vol. 3)

ISSN 1058-5699

This title is also available as an e-book.
ISBN-13: 978-1-4144-7420-5
ISBN-10: 1-4144-7420-2
Contact your Gale sales representative for ordering information.

Printed in the United States of America
1 2 3 4 5   17 16 15 14 13

Contents

This edition of *Scholarships, Fellowships, and Loans (SFL)* provides access to nearly 7,400 sources of education-related financial aid for students and professionals at all levels. *SFL*'s scope ranges from undergraduate and vocational/technical education through post-doctoral and professional studies. Students and others interested in education funding will find comprehensive information on a variety of programs in all educational areas, including:

▪ Architecture	▪ Law
▪ Area and Ethnic Studies	▪ Literature
▪ Art	▪ Liberal Arts
▪ Business	▪ Library Science
▪ Communications	▪ Life Science
▪ Computer Science	▪ Medicine
▪ Education	▪ Mathematics
▪ Engineering	▪ Performing Arts
▪ Health Science	▪ Philosophy
▪ Humanities	▪ Physical Sciences
▪ Industrial Arts	▪ Social Sciences
▪ Language	▪ Theology and Religion

SFL Provides Detailed Information on Awards

SFL provides all the information students need to complete their financial aid search. Entries include: administering organization name and address; purpose of award; qualifications and restrictions; selection criteria; award amount and number of awards granted; application details and deadlines; detailed contact information.

Additionally, look for the section on federal financial aid following the User's Guide for a quick summary of programs sponsored by the U.S. government, as well as information on the AmeriCorps program. There is also a section that lists higher education agencies by state.

Five Indexes Allow Quick and Easy Access to Awards

Whether you are a high school student looking for basic undergraduate financial aid, a scientist investigating research grants, or a professional attempting to finance additional career training, SFL aids your search by providing access to awards through the following indexes:

Field of Study Index categorizes awards by very specific subject fields.

Legal Resident Index targets awards restricted to applicants from specific geographic locations.

Place of Study Index provides a handy guide to awards granted for study within specific states, provinces, or countries.

Special Recipient Index lists awards that are reserved for candidates who qualify by virtue of their gender, organizational affiliation, minority or ethnic background.

Sponsor and Scholarship Index provides a complete alphabetical listing of all awards and their administering organizations.

Catchwords

SFL includes catchwords of the organization on each corresponding page, to aid the user in finding a particular entry.

As we make our way through difficult economic times, there is a growing need for a more highly-trained and educated work force. From political discussions and debates to reports from future-oriented think tanks and other groups, there is agreement that postsecondary education is a key to success. Yet how are students and their families to afford the already high (and constantly rising) cost of higher education? Searching for financial aid can be very tedious and difficult, even though hundreds of millions of dollars in aid reportedly go unclaimed every year.

Scholarships, Fellowships and Loans (SFL), the most comprehensive single directory of education-related financial aid available, can save you time, effort, and money by helping you to focus your search within the largest pool of awards and avoid pursuing aid for which you do not qualify. In most cases, the detailed descriptions contain enough information to allow you to decide if a particular scholarship is right for you to begin the application process. *SFL* lists almost 7,400 major awards available to U.S. and Canadian students for study throughout the world. Included are:

- scholarships, fellowships, and grants, which do not require repayment;

- loans, which require repayment either monetarily or through service;

- scholarship loans, which are scholarships that become loans if the recipient does not comply with the award's terms;

- internships and work study programs, which provide training, work experience, and (usually) monetary compensation; and

- awards and prizes that recognize excellence in a particular field.

Also included are other forms of assistance offered by associations, corporations, religious groups, fraternal organizations, foundations, and other private organizations and companies. *SFL* includes a broad representation of government-funded awards at the national and state levels, as well as a representative sampling of lesser-known and more narrowly focused awards, such as those of a strictly local nature or programs sponsored by small organizations. Financial aid programs administered and funded by individual colleges or universities are not included in *SFL*. Both need- and merit-based awards are included. Competition-based awards and prizes are included when they offer funds that support study or research and are intended to encourage further educational or professional growth.

Students of All Types Can Benefit

Traditional students as well as those returning to school, non-degree learners, those in need of retraining, and established professionals can use the funding sources listed in *SFL* for formal and non-formal programs of study at all levels:

- high school

- vocational

- undergraduate

- graduate

- postgraduate

- doctorate

- postdoctorate

- professional development

Content and Arrangement

Scholarships, Fellowships and Loans is organized into a main section containing descriptive listings of award programs and their administering organizations, and five indexes.

The main section, Sponsors and Their Scholarships, is arranged alphabetically by name of administering organization. Entries for each organization's awards appear immediately following the entry on the organization. Each entry contains detailed contact and descriptive information, often providing users with all the information they need to make a decision about applying.

The indexes provide a variety of specific access points to the information contained within the organization and award listings, allowing users to easily identify awards of interest.

Practical Tips on How to Find Financial Aid

While there are many education-related financial aid programs for students of all types and study levels, the competition for available funds is steadily increasing. You will improve the likelihood of meeting your financial aid goals if you:

- carefully assess your particular needs and preferences;
- consider any special circumstances or conditions that might qualify you for aid; and
- carefully research available aid programs.

The following pages list some general guidelines for making your way through the search and application process.

Start Your Search Early

Any search for financial aid is likely to be more successful if you begin early. If you allow enough time to complete all of the necessary steps, you will be more likely to identify a wide variety of awards for which you qualify with plenty of time to meet their application deadlines. This can increase your chances of obtaining aid.

Some experts recommend that you start this process up to two years before you think you will need financial assistance. While you will probably be able to obtain some support if you allow less time, you might overlook some important opportunities.

Some awards are given on a first-come, first-served basis, and if you do not file your application early enough, the aid will already be distributed. In many cases, if your application is late you will not be considered, even if you have met all of the other criteria.

An early start will also allow you to identify organizations that offer scholarships to members or participants, such as student or professional associations, in time to establish membership or otherwise meet their qualifying criteria.

Assess Your Needs and Goals

The intended recipients for financial aid programs and the purposes for which awards are established can vary greatly. Some programs are open to almost anyone, while others are restricted to very specific categories of recipients. The majority of awards fall somewhere in between. Your first step in seeking financial aid is to establish your basic qualifications as a potential recipient. The following are some general questions to ask yourself to help define your educational and financial needs and goals:

- What kinds of colleges or universities interest me?
- What careers or fields of study interest me?
- Do I plan to earn a degree?
- Am I only interested in financial aid that is a gift, or will I consider a loan or work study?
- In what parts of the country am I willing to live and study?

Leave No Stone Unturned

After you have defined your goals, the next step is to identify any special factors that might make you eligible for aid programs offered only to a restricted group. Examine this area carefully, and remember that even minor or unlikely connections may be worth checking. The most common qualifications and restrictions involve:

- citizenship
- community involvement or volunteer work
- creative or professional accomplishment
- employer
- financial need
- gender
- merit or academic achievement
- military or veteran status
- organization membership (such as a union, association, or fraternal group)
- place of residence
- race or ethnic group
- religious affiliation

With many awards, you may be eligible if your spouse, parents, or guardians meet certain criteria by status or affiliations. You should be aware of your parents' affiliations even if you don't live with one (or both) of them, or if they are deceased. And given enough lead time, it may be possible for you (or your parents) to join a particular organization, or establish necessary residence, in time for you to be eligible for certain funds.

Contact Financial Aid Offices

Most colleges, universities, and other educational institutions offer their own financial aid programs. Their financial aid offices may also have information on privately sponsored awards that are specifically designated for students at those institutions. Contact their respective financial aid offices to request applications and details for all of the aid programs they sponsor and/or administer.

Use *SFL* to Identify Awards Sponsored by Private Organizations and Corporations

Scholarships, Fellowships and Loans (SFL) is the most comprehensive single source of information on major education-related financial aid programs sponsored and administered by private organizations and companies for use by students and professionals. Using *SFL* as a starting point, you can quickly compile a substantial list of financial aid programs for which you may qualify by following these simple steps:

- Compile an initial list of awards offered in your field of study.

- If you have already chosen your field of study, look in the Field of Study Index to find listings of awards grouped by more precise disciplines (such as Accounting or Journalism). If you choose this approach, your initial list is likely to be shorter but more focused. Eliminate awards that cannot be used at your chosen level of study or that do not meet your financial needs. Are you an undergraduate only interested in scholarships? Are you a graduate student willing to participate in an internship or take out a loan? Consult the User's Guide to determine which of the study level categories and award types apply to your particular situation. Both indexes clearly note the study levels at which awards may be used. The Field of Study Index also lists the type of financial aid provided.

- Eliminate awards by citizenship, residence, and other restrictions (minority status, ethnic background, gender, organizational affiliation) that make you ineligible.

- If your list is based on the Field of Study Index, you will need to look under the section for qualifications in each descriptive listing to see what requirements apply.

- Read the descriptive listings for each of the award programs left on your list. The descriptive listings should contain all the information you need to decide if you qualify and should apply for each of the awards on your list.

Expand Your List of Possibilities

If you are willing to take the initiative and do a little extra digging, you should be able to add to your list of institution-related and privately sponsored programs. In most cases, the best possibilities fall into these two areas:

Government Agencies and Programs. The Sponsors and Their Scholarships main section includes a broad representation of award programs sponsored by federal and state governments. Since these listings are not meant to be exhaustive, you should be able to identify additional programs by contacting the government agencies responsible for education-related financial aid programs listed here. On the federal level, contact the U.S. Department of Education at 400 Maryland Ave., SW, Washington, DC 20202, or on their website at http://www.ed.gov, for up-to-date information on U.S. Government award programs. For a broad overview of federal financial aid, consult the Federal

Programs section. Similarly, you may contact your state department of education for details on what is offered in your particular state. Please see the State Higher Education Agencies section for state-by-state listings.

Local Sources of Awards. A surprisingly large number of financial aid programs are sponsored by small and/or local organizations. *SFL* contains a representative sampling of such programs to encourage you to seek similar programs in your own geographic area. High school guidance counselors are often aware of local programs as well, and they can usually tell you how to get in touch with the sponsoring or administering organizations. Local newspapers are also rich sources of information on financial aid programs.

Allow Enough Time for the Application Process

The amount of time needed to complete the application process for individual awards will vary, so you should pay close attention to application deadlines. Some awards carry application deadlines that require you to apply a year or more before your studies will begin. In general, allow plenty of time to:

- Write for official applications. You may not be considered for some awards unless you apply with the correct forms.

- Read all instructions carefully.

- Take note of application deadlines.

- Accurately and completely file all required supporting material, such as essays, school transcripts, and financial records. If you fail to answer certain questions, you may be disqualified even if you are a worthy candidate.

- Give references enough time to submit their recommendations. Teachers in particular get many requests for letters of recommendation and should be given as much advance notice as possible.

Make Sure You Qualify

Finally, don't needlessly submerge yourself in paperwork. If you find you don't qualify for a particular award, don't apply for it. Instead, use your time and energy to find and apply for more likely sources of aid.

Available in Electronic Formats

Licensing. Scholarships, Fellowships and Loans is available for licensing. The complete database is provided in a fielded format and is deliverable on such media as disk or CD-ROM. For more information, contact Gale's Business Development group at 1-800-877-GALE, or visit our website at http://gale.cengage.com/bizdev/.

The Directory is also available online as part of the Gale Directory Library. For more information, call 1-800-877-GALE.

Comments and Suggestions Welcome

We welcome reader suggestions regarding new and previously unlisted organizations and awards. Please send your suggestions to:

Scholarships, Fellowships and Loans

Gale, Cengage Learning

27500 Drake Rd.

Farmington Hills, MI 48331-3535

Phone: (248) 699-4253

Toll-free: 800-347-4253

Fax: (248) 699-8070

Email: Bob.Romaniuk@cengage.com

Scholarships, Fellowships and Loans is comprised of a main section containing descriptive listings on award programs and their administering organizations, and five indexes that aid users in identifying relevant information. Each of these sections is described in detail below.

Sponsors and Their Scholarships

SFL contains two types of descriptive listings:

- brief entries on the organizations that sponsor or administer specific award programs

- descriptive entries on the award programs themselves

Entries are arranged alphabetically by administering organization; awards administered by each organization follow that organization's listings. Entries contain detailed contact and descriptive information. Users are strongly encouraged to read the descriptions carefully and pay particular attention to the various eligibility requirements before applying for awards.

The following sample organization and award entries illustrate the kind of information that is or might be included in these entries. Each item of information is preceded by a number, and is explained in the paragraph with the same number on the following pages.

Sample Entry

▮ 1 ▮ 3445
▮ 2 ▮ Microscopy Society of America
▮ 3 ▮ 4 Barlows Landing Rd., Ste. 8 Woods Hole, MA 02543
▮ 4 ▮ *Ph:* (508) 563-1155
▮ 5 ▮ *Fax:* (508) 563-1211
▮ 6 ▮ *Free:* 800-538-3672
▮ 7 ▮ *E-mail:* businessofficemsa.microscopy.com
▮ 8 ▮ *URL:* http://www.msa.microscopy.com
▮ 9 ▮ 3446
▮ 10 ▮ MSA Presidential Student Awards
▮ 11 ▮ *(Graduate, Undergraduate/*
▮ 12 ▮ *Award*

▮ 13 ▮ Purpose: To recognize outstanding original research by students. ▮ 14 ▮ Focus: Biological Clinical Sciences—Microscopy, Physical Sciences—Microscopy. ▮ 15 ▮ Qualif.: Candidate may be of any nationality, but must be enrolled at a recognized college or university in the United States at the time of the MSA annual meeting. ▮ 16 ▮ Criteria: Selection is done based on the applicant's career objectives, academic record, and financial need. ▮ 17 ▮ Funds Avail.: Registration and round-trip travel to the MSA annual meeting,

plus a stipend to defray lodging and other expenses. ▮ 18 ▮ Number awarded: 5. ▮ 19 ▮ To Apply: Write to MSA for application form and guidelines. ▮ 20 ▮ Deadline: March 15. ▮ 21 ▮ Remarks: Established in 1979. ▮ 22 ▮ Contact: Alternate phone number: 800-538-EMSA.

Descriptions of Numbered Elements

▮ 1 ▮ **Organization Entry Number.** Administering organizations are listed alphabetically. Each entry is followed by an alphabetical listing of its awards. All entries (organization and award) are numbered in a single sequence. These numbers are used as references in the indexes.

▮ 2 ▮ **Organization Name.** The name of the organization administering the awards that follow.

▮ 3 ▮ **Mailing Address.** The organization's permanent mailing address is listed when known; in some cases an award address is given.

▮ 4 ▮ **Telephone Number.** The general telephone number for the administering organization. Phone numbers pertaining to specific awards are listed under "Contact" in the award description.

▮ 5 ▮ **Fax Number.** The facsimile number for the administering organization. Fax numbers pertaining to specific awards are included under "Contact" in the award description.

▮ 6 ▮ **Toll-free Number.** The toll-free number for the administering organization. Toll-free numbers pertaining to specific awards are included under "Contact" in the award description.

▮ 7 ▮ **E-mail Address.** The electronic mail address for the administering organization. Electronic mail addresses pertaining to specific awards are included under "Contact" in the award description.

▮ 8 ▮ **URL.** The web address for the administering organization.

▮ 9 ▮ **Award Entry Number.** Awards are listed alphabetically following the entry for their administering organizations. All entries (organization and award) are numbered in a single sequence. These numbers are used as references in the indexes.

▮ 10 ▮ **Award Name.** Names of awards are always listed. Organization titles or acronyms have been added to generic award names (for example, MSA Undergraduate Scholarships, Canadian Council Fiction Writing Grant, etc.) to avoid confusion.

❚11❚ Study Level. The level of study for which the award may be used. One or more of the following terms will be listed:

- All: not restricted to a particular level.

- High School: study at the secondary level.

- Vocational: study leading to postsecondary awards, certificates, or diplomas requiring less than two years of study.

- 2 Year: study leading to a bachelor's degree within two years

- 4 Year: study leading to a bachelor's degree within four years

- Undergraduate: study immediately beyond the secondary level, including associate, colleges and universities, junior colleges, technical institutes leading to a bachelor's degree, and vocational technical schools.

- Graduate: study leading to an M.A., M.S., LL.B., LL.M., and other intermediate degrees.

- Master's: study leading specifically to a master's degree, such as a M.A., M.S., or M.B.A.

- Postgraduate: study beyond the graduate level not specifically leading to a degree.

- Doctorate: study leading to a Ph.D., Ed.D., Sc.D., M.D., D.D.S., D.O., J.D., and other terminal degrees.

- Postdoctorate: study beyond the doctorate level; includes awards intended for professional development when candidates must hold a doctoral degree to qualify.

- Professional Development: career development not necessarily restricted by study.

❚12❚ Award Type. The type or category of award. One or more of the following terms will be listed:

- Award: generally includes aid given in recognition and support of excellence, including awards given through music and arts competitions. Non-monetary awards and awards given strictly for recognition are not included.

- Fellowship: awards granted for graduate- or postgraduate-level research or education that do not require repayment.

- Grant: includes support for research, travel, and creative, experimental, or innovative projects.

- Internship: training and work experience programs. Internships that do not include compensation of some type are not included.

- Loan: aid that must be repaid either monetarily or through service. Some loans are interest-free, others are not.

- Prize: funds awarded as the result of a competition or contest. Prizes that are not intended to be used for

study or to support professional development are not included.

- Scholarships: support for formal educational programs that does not require repayment.

- Scholarship Loan: a scholarship that becomes a loan if the recipient does not comply with the terms.

- Work Study: combined study and work program for which payment is received.

- Other: anything that does not fit the other categories, such as a travel award.

❚13❚ Purpose. The purpose for which the award is granted is listed here when known.

❚14❚ Focus. The field(s) of study that the recipient must be pursuing.

❚15❚ Qualif. Information regarding applicant eligibility. Some examples of qualification requirements include the following: academic record, citizenship, financial need, organizational affiliation, minority or ethnic background, residency, and gender.

❚16❚ Criteria Information concerning selection criteria.

❚17❚ Funds Avail. The award dollar amounts are included here along with other relevant funding information, such as the time period covered by the award, a breakdown of expenses covered (e.g., stipends, tuition and fees, travel and living allowances, equipment funds, etc.), the amount awarded to the institution, loan repayment schedules, service-in-return-for-funding agreements, and other obligations.

❚18❚ Number awarded. Typical number of awards distributed.

❚19❚ To Apply. Application guidelines, requirements, and other information.

❚20❚ Deadline. Application due dates, notification dates (the date when the applicant will be notified of receipt or denial of award), disbursement dates, and other relevant dates.

❚21❚ Remarks. Any additional information concerning the award.

❚22❚ Contact. When contact information differs from that given for the administering organization, relevant addresses, telephone and fax numbers, and names of specific contact persons are listed here. When the address is that of the administering organization, the entry number for the organization is provided.

Indexes

Field of Study Index classifies awards by one or more of 450 specific subject categories, allowing users to easily target their search by specific area of study. Citations are arranged alphabetically under all appropriate subject terms. Each citation is followed by the study level and award type, which appear in parentheses and can be used to narrow the search even further.

Legal Residence Index lists awards that are restricted by the applicant's residence of legal record. Award citations are arranged alphabetically by country and subarranged by region, state or province (for U.S. and Canada). Each citation is followed by the study level and award type, which appear in parentheses and can be used to eliminate inappropriate awards.

Place of Study Index lists awards that carry restrictions on where study can take place. Award citations are arranged alphabetically under the following geographic headings:

- United States
- United States—by Region
- United States—by State
- Canada
- Canada—by Province
- International
- International—by Region
- International—by Country

Each citation is followed by the study level and award type, which appear in parentheses.

Special Recipient Index lists awards that carry restrictions or special qualifying factors relating to applicant affiliation. This index allows users to quickly identify awards relating to the following categories:

- African American
- Asian American
- Association Membership
- Disabled
- Employer Affiliation
- Ethnic Group Membership
- Fraternal Organization Membership
- Hispanic American
- Military
- Minority
- Native American
- Religious Affiliation
- Union Affiliation
- Veteran

Awards are listed under all appropriate headings. Each citation includes information on study level and award type, which appear in parentheses and can be used to further narrow the search. Users interested in awards restricted to particular minorities should also look under the general Minorities heading, which lists awards targeted for minorities but not restricted to any particular minority group.

Sponsor and Scholarship Index lists, in a single alphabetic sequence, all of the administering organizations, awards, and acronyms included in *SFL*.

Federal aid for college students is available through a variety of programs administered by the U.S. Department of Education. Most colleges and universities participate in federal programs, but there are exceptions. Contact a school's financial aid office to find out if it is a participating institution. If it participates, the student works with financial aid counselors to determine how much aid can be obtained.

Aid for students comes in three forms: grants (gifts to the student), loans (which must be repaid), and work-study jobs (a job for the student while enrolled in which his/her pay is applied to his school account). These types of aid are further explained below. More information can be found at http://www.ed.gov.

Grants

Pell Grants are intended to provide funds for any undergraduate student (who does not already have a degree) who wishes to attend college regardless of family financial background. They are available through the financial aid office at the school. The maximum Pell Grant award for the 2012-2013 award year (July 1, 2012 to June 30, 2013) is $5,550

Federal Supplemental Educational Opportunity Grants (FSEOG) are intended for students with exceptional financial need, these grants are typically for smaller amounts (between $100 and $4,000) than Pell Grants. They are available on a limited basis.

Loans

Student loans are available a variety of ways. Loans may not be taken out for more than the cost of attendance at the school, which is determined by the financial aid administrator. Grants and other forms of aid are taken into consideration when determining the amount a student will be allowed to borrow. Loan amounts may be reduced if a student receives other forms of aid. Loans are divided into two types, subsidized and unsubsidized:

Subsidized loans: the federal government pays the interest on the loan until after schooling is complete.

Unsubsidized loans: the student incurs the interest charges while in school, but payment of the charges may be deferred until schooling is complete. The advantage of unsubsidized loans is that there are usually fewer restrictions against obtaining them. Amounts available through these programs vary depending on academic level. The total debt a student or a student's parents may accumulate for that student is $31,000 for a dependent undergraduate student, $57,500 for an independent undergraduate student (with a limit of $23,000 in subsidized loans), and $138,500 for a graduate or professional student (with a limit of $65,500 in subsidized loans) or $224,000 for health professionals.

Available Funding Programs Direct Loan Program

These low-interest loans bypass lending institutions such as banks. They are a direct arrangement between the government and the student (administered by the school). There are four repayment options for the Direct Loan program: the Income Contingent Repayment Plan, the Extended Repayment Plan, the Graduated Repayment Plan, and the Standard Repayment Plan.

Direct subsidized loans may be taken out for a maximum of $3,500 by incoming freshmen, while juniors and seniors may borrow up to a maximum of $5,500. The amounts for independent undergraduate students range from $9,500 to $12,500 per year for direct loans. Independent students face some restrictions on the amount of subsidized funds they can receive from the program. At least half of the funds borrowed through the Direct Loan program by independent students must come from unsubsidized loans. Graduate students may borrow up to $20,500 directly, with a maximum of $8,500 in subsidized loans.

Federal Family Education Loans (FFEL)/Stafford Loans This program provides funds to the lending institution(s) of the student's choice. Before borrowing the funds, the student must complete a Free Application for Federal Student Aid (FAFSA) and a Federal Stafford Loan Application (FSLA). Both forms are available at participating schools' financial aid offices and on the Internet at http://www.ed.gov. There are three repayment options for FFEL/Stafford Loans:

Fixed, Graduated, and Income-Sensitive. Any FFEL/Stafford loan must be paid back within ten years.

This program is also divided into subsidized and unsubsidized loans. However, students may not borrow simultaneously from this program and the Direct Loan program. Students may borrow separately subsidized and unsubsidized funds from either program. The maximum amounts that can be borrowed through this program are the same as through the Direct Loan program.

Direct and FFEL/Stafford Program Loans for Parents (PLUS)

Parents may borrow for their children's education through the aforementioned Federal Loan programs. They are responsible for the repayment of the loans. The maximum amount to be borrowed is the cost of attending the school minus other forms of aid already obtained. For 2012-2013, the fixed rate for a Direct PLUS loan is 7.9% and for a FFEL PLUS loan is 8.5%. Parents who borrow through the FFEL/Stafford program make arrangements with the lender for repayment.

With the Direct PLUS loan, parents fill out a Direct PLUS Loan Application, available at the school's financial aid office. The funds are disbursed to the school. Parents may choose from three repayment plans: Standard, Extended, or Graduated. To obtain funds for their children through the FFEL/Stafford Program, parents make the arrangements with the lending institution. The school is not involved in the application process.

Perkins Loan Program The Perkins Loan program allows students who have unusual financial need to borrow funds not otherwise available from other loan or grant programs. Up to $5,500 is available to undergraduates each year (up to $8,000 for graduate students). These loans have a fixed interest rate of 5%. Perkins Loans must be repaid within ten years.

Federal Work-Study Program Work-study is an arrangement that allows students to work on campus while they are enrolled to help pay their expenses. The federal government pays the majority of the student's wages, although the department where the student works also contributes. The employment must be relevant to the student's field of study and only so much time per semester may be devoted to the job. If the student earns the amount of aid prior to the end of the semester, work is terminated for the duration of the award period.

Other Considerations

Application: Applying for federal student aid is free. All federal aid is obtained by first completing a Free Application for Federal Student Aid (FAFSA). After the application is submitted, it will be processed by the Department of Education. The student then receives a Student Aid Report (SAR), which contains a figure for Expected Family Contribution. This is the amount that the student should plan on providing from non-federal sources in order to attend school.

Dependency: If a student is eligible for independent status, more money may be available in the form of loans. The interest rates and the programs for repayment, however, are the same. Independent status provides more financial aid for students who do not have the benefit of parental financial contributions.

Deadline: FAFSA deadlines are set by federal and state agencies, as well as individual schools, and vary widely. Applicants are encouraged to apply as soon as possible after January 1 of the year they plan to enroll, but no earlier.

Special Circumstances: The financial aid counselor at the school will often listen to extenuating circumstances such as unexpected medical expenses, private education expenses for other family members, or recent unemployment when evaluating requests for assistance.

Contact Information for Federal Financial Aid Programs

Call (800)433-3243 to have questions answered or to request the *Student Guide to Financial Aid*; (319) 337-5665 to find out if your application has been processed; (800) 730-8913 (TTY) if you are hearing impaired; (800) 647-8733 to report fraud, waste, or abuse of federal student aid funds; or visit http://www.ed.gov for application forms, guidelines, and general information.

President Clinton launched this volunteer community service program in September 1993 through the *National and Community Service Trust Act*, aimed at helping college-bound young people pay for their education while serving their communities. AmeriCorps volunteers receive minimum wage, health benefits, and a grant toward college for up to two years.

Funds for the program are distributed by the federal government in the form of grants to qualifying organizations and community groups with the goal of achieving direct results in addressing the nation's critical education, human services, public safety, and environmental needs at the community level. The program provides meaningful opportunities for Americans to serve their country in organized efforts, fostering citizen responsibility, building community, and providing educational opportunities for those who make a substantial commitment to service.

The AmeriCorps programs are run by not-for-profit organizations or partnerships, institutions of higher learning, local governments, school or police districts, states, Native American tribes, and federal agencies. Examples of participating programs include Habitat for Humanity, the American Red Cross, Boys and Girls Clubs, and local community centers and places of worship. Volunteers have nearly 1,000 different groups from which to choose. The AmeriCorps Pledge: "I will get things done for America to make our people safer, smarter, and healthier. I will bring Americans together to strengthen our communities. Faced with apathy, I will take action. Faced with conflict, I will seek a common ground. Faced with adversity, I will persevere. I will carry this commitment with me this year and beyond. I am an AmeriCorps Member and I am going to get things done."

Eligibility and Selection for Service in AmeriCorps

Citizens and legal resident aliens who are 17 years of age or older are eligible to serve in AmeriCorps before, during, or after post-secondary education. In general, participants must be high school graduates or agree to achieve their GED prior to receiving education awards. Individual programs select service participants on a nondiscriminatory and nonpolitical basis. There are national and state-wide recruit

ing information systems and a national pool of potential service volunteers.

Term of Service

One full-time term of service is a minimum of 1,700 hours over the course of one year or less; one part-time term of service is at least 900 hours over two years or less. Short-term service (such as a summer program) provides eligibility for reduced part-time status.

Compensation

You will receive a modest living allowance, health insurance, student loan deferment, and training. After you complete your term of service, you will receive an education award to help pay for your education. Serve part-time and you will receive a portion of the full amount. The amount is tied to the maximum amount of the U.S. Department of Education's Pell Grant. For terms of service that are approved using 2009 funds (or earlier funds) the award continues to be $4,725 for a year of full-time service, and is pro-rated for part-time service based on the full-time amount. For terms of service that are supported with 2010 funds the award value increased to $5,350. For terms of service that are supported with 2011 funds the award value increased to $5,550.

How Can I Use an Award?

These awards may be used to repay qualified existing or future student loans, to pay all or part of the cost of attending a qualified institute of higher education (including some vocational programs), or to pay expenses while participating in an approved school-to-work program. Awards must be used within seven years of completion of service.

Contact

Individuals interested in participating in AmeriCorps national service programs should apply directly. For basic program information, individuals can call the AmeriCorps Information Hotline at 1-800-942-2677 or visit their Web site at http://www.americorps.gov.

The following is an alphabetic state-by-state listing of agencies located in the United States. Many of these agencies administer special federal award programs, as well as state-specific awards, such as the Tuition Incentive Program (TIP) offered by the state of Michigan for low-income students to receive free tuition at community colleges. Financial aid seekers should contact the agency in their home state for more information.

ALABAMA

Alabama Comm. on Higher Education
P.O. Box 302000
Montgomery, AL 36130-2000
(334)242-1998
http://www.ache.state.al.us

ALASKA

Alaska Comm. on Postsecondary Education
P.O. Box 110505
Juneau, AK 99811-0505
(907)465-2962
http://www.alaskadvantage.state.ak.us/

ARIZONA

Arizona Comm. for Postsecondary Education
2020 N. Central Ave.,
Ste. 650
Phoenix, AZ 85004-4503
(602)258-2435
http://www.azhighered.org

ARKANSAS

Arkansas Dept. of Higher Education
114 E. Capitol Ave.
Little Rock, AR 72201-3818
(501)371-2000
http://www.adhe.edu

CALIFORNIA

California Student Aid Comm.
PO Box 419026
Rancho Cordova, CA 95741-9026
(916)526-8047
http://www.csac.ca.gov

COLORADO

Colorado Dept. of Higher Education
1560 Broadway, Ste. 1600
Denver, CO 80202
(303)866-2723
http://highered.colorado.gov

CONNECTICUT

Connecticut Dept. of Higher Education
61 Woodland St.
Hartford, CT 06105-2326
(860)947-1800
http://www.ctdhe.org

DELAWARE

Delaware Higher Education Office
The Townsend Building
401 Federal St., Ste. 2
Dover, DE 19901
(302)735-4120
http://www.doe.k12.de.us/infosuites/students_family/dheo/about.shtml

DISTRICT OF COLUMBIA

District of Columbia Dept. of Human Services
Office of Postsecondary Education, Research, and Assistance
810 1st St., NE, 9th Fl.
Washington, DC 20002
(202)727-6436
http://osse.dc.gov/seo/cwp

FLORIDA

Office of Student Financial Assistance
Dept. of Education
325 W. Gaines St.

Turlington Bldg., Ste. 1514
Tallahassee, FL 32399-0400
(800)336-3475
http://www.floridastudentfinancialaid.org

GEORGIA

Georgia Student Finance Comm.
2082 E. Exchange Pl., Ste. 200
Tucker, GA 30084
(770)724-9000
http://www.gsfc.org/gsfcnew/index.cfm

HAWAII

Hawaii State Postsecondary Education Comm.
2444 Dole St., Rm. 209
Honolulu, HI 96822-2302
(808)956-8213

IDAHO

Idaho State Board of Education
PO Box 83720
Boise, ID 83720-0037
(208)334-2270
http://www.boardofed.idaho.gov

ILLINOIS

Illinois Student Assistance Comm.
1755 Lake Cook Rd.
Deerfield, IL 60015-5209
(800)899-4722
http://www.collegezone.com

INDIANA

State Student Assistance Comm. of Indiana
W462 Indiana Government Center South
402 W. Washington St.
Indianapolis, IN 46204

(317)232-2350
www.in.gov/ssaci/

IOWA

Iowa College Student Aid Comm.
603 E. 12th St., 5th Fl.
Des Moines, IA 50319
(877)272-4456
http://www.iowacollegeaid.org

KANSAS

Kansas Board of Regents
1000 SW Jackson St., Ste. 520
Topeka, KS 66612-1368
(785)296-3421
http://www.kansasregents.org

KENTUCKY

Kentucky Higher Education Assistance Authority
PO Box 798
Frankfort, KY 40602-0798
(800)928-8926
http://www.kheaa.com

LOUISIANA

Louisiana Office of Student Financial Assistance
602 N. Fifth St.
Baton Rouge, LA 70802
(225)219-1012
http://www.osfa.state.la.us

MAINE

Maine Education Assistance Division
Finance Authority of Maine (FAME)
5 Community Dr.
P.O. Box 0949
Augusta, ME 04332-0949
(207)623-3263
http://www.famemaine.com

MARYLAND

Maryland Higher Education Comm.
6 N. Liberty St.
Baltimore, MD 21201
(410)767-3301
http://www.mhec.state.md.us

MASSACHUSETTS

Massachusetts Dept. of Higher Education
One Ashburton Pl., Rm. 1401
Boston, MA 02108-1696

(617)994-6950
http://www.mass.edu

MICHIGAN

Michigan Higher Education Student Loan Authority
Student Scholarships and Grants
P.O. Box 30462
Lansing, MI 48909-7962
(888)447-2687
http://www.michigan.gov/mistudentaid

MINNESOTA

Minnesota Office of Higher Education
1450 Energy Park Dr., Ste. 350
St. Paul, MN 55108-5227
(651)642-0567
http://www.ohe.state.mn.us/index.cfm

MISSISSIPPI

Mississippi Institutions of Higher Learning
3825 Ridgewood Rd.
Jackson, MS 39211
(601)432-6198
http://www.ihl.state.ms.us

MISSOURI

Missouri Dept. of Higher Education
205 Jefferson St.
P.O.Box 1469
Jefferson City, MO 65102-1469
(573)751-2361
http://www.dhe.mo.gov/

MONTANA

Montana Board of Regents
Office of Commissioner of Higher Education
Montana University System
2500 Broadway St.
PO Box 203201
Helena, MT 59620-3201
(406)444-6570
http://www.mus.edu

NEBRASKA

Nebraska Coordinating Comm. for Postsecondary Education
P.O. Box 95005
Lincoln, NE 68509-5005
(402)471-2847
http://www.ccpe.state.ne.us/
PublicDoc/CCPE/Default.asp

NEVADA

Nevada Department of Education
700 E. Fifth St.
Carson City, NV 89701
(775)687-9200
http://www.doe.nv.gov

NEW HAMPSHIRE

New Hampshire Higher Education Comm.
101 Pleasant St.
Concord, NH 03301-3494
(603)271-3494
http://www.state.nh.us/postsecondary

NEW JERSEY

Higher Education Student Assistance Authority
P.O. Box 545
Trenton, NJ 08625-0545
(800)792-8670
http://www.hesaa.org

NEW MEXICO

New Mexico Higher Education Dept.
2048 Galisteo St.
Santa Fe, NM 87505-2100
(505)476-8400
http://www.hed.state.nm.us

NEW YORK

New York State Higher Education Svcs. Corp.
99 Washington Ave.
Albany, NY 12255
(888)697-4372
http://www.hesc.com

NORTH CAROLINA

North Carolina State Education Assistance Authority
PO Box 14103
Research Triangle Park, NC 27709
(919)549-8614
http://www.ncseaa.edu

NORTH DAKOTA

North Dakota University System
North Dakota Student Financial Assistance Program

10th Fl., State Capitol
600 E. Boulevard Ave., Dept. 215
Bismarck, ND 58505-0230
(701)328-2960
http://www.ndus.edu

OHIO

Ohio Board of Regents
State Grants and Scholarships Dept.
30 E. Broad St., 36th Fl.
Columbus, OH 43215
(614)466-7420
http://www.ohiohighered.org

OKLAHOMA

Oklahoma State Regents for Higher Education
Oklahoma Guaranteed Loan Program
655 Research Pkwy.
Suite 200
Oklahoma City, OK 73104
(405)225-9100
http://www.okhighered.org

OREGON

Oregon Student Access Comm.
1500 Valley River Dr., Ste. 100
Eugene, OR 97401
(541)687-7400
http://www.osac.state.or.us

PENNSYLVANIA

Pennsylvania Higher Education Assistance Agency
1200 N. 7th St.
Harrisburg, PA 17102-1444
(800)233-0557
http://www.pheaa.org

RHODE ISLAND

Rhode Island Higher Education Assistance Authority
560 Jefferson Blvd., Ste. 100
Warwick, RI 02886-1304
(401)736-1100
http://www.riheaa.org

SOUTH CAROLINA

South Carolina Comm. on Higher Education
1122 Lady St., Ste. 300
Columbia, SC 29201
(803)737-2297
http://www.che400.state.sc.us

SOUTH DAKOTA

South Dakota Education Access Foundation
115-1st Ave., SW
Aberdeen, SD 57401
(888)502-5902
http://www.sdeducationaccess.org/

TENNESSEE

Tennessee Higher Education Comm.
Parkway Towers
404 James Robertson Pkwy., Ste. 1900
Nashville, TN 37243-0830
(615)741-3605
http://www.state.tn.us/thec

TEXAS

Texas Higher Education Coordinating Board
P.O. Box 12788
Austin, TX 78711-2788
(512)427-6101
http://www.thecb.state.tx.us

UTAH

Utah State Board of Regents
Board of Regents Building, The Gateway
60 South 400 West
Salt Lake City, UT 84101-1284
(801)321-7101
http://www.utahsbr.edu

VERMONT

Vermont Student Assistance Corp.
10 E. Allen St.
P.O. Box 2000

Winooski, VT 05404
(802)655-9602
http://www.vsac.org

VIRGINIA

State Council of Higher Education for Virginia
James Monroe Bldg.
101 N. 14th St., 10th Fl.
Richmond, VA 23219
(804)225-2600
http://www.schev.edu

WASHINGTON

Washington State Higher Education Coordinating Board
917 Lakeridge Way
P.O. Box 43430
Olympia, WA 98540-3430
(360)753-7800
http://www.hecb.wa.gov

WEST VIRGINIA

West Virginia Higher Education Policy Comm.
1018 Kanawha Blvd., E., Ste. 700
Charleston, WV 25301-2800
(304)558-2101
http://www.hepc.wvnet.edu

WISCONSIN

Wisconsin Higher Education Aids Board
131 W. Wilson St., Ste. 902
P.O. Box 7885
Madison, WI 53707-7885
(608)267-2206
http://heab.state.wi.us

WYOMING

Wyoming Community College Comm.
2020 Carey Ave., 8th Fl.
Cheyenne, WY 82002
(307)777-7763
http://www.communitycolleges.wy.edu

U.S. State Abbreviations

AK	Alaska
AL	Alabama
AR	Arkansas
AZ	Arizona
CA	California
CO	Colorado
CT	Connecticut
DC	District of Columbia
DE	Delaware
FL	Florida
GA	Georgia
GU	Guam
HI	Hawaii
IA	Iowa
ID	Idaho
IL	Illinois
IN	Indiana
KS	Kansas
KY	Kentucky
LA	Louisiana
MA	Massachusetts
MD	Maryland
ME	Maine
MI	Michigan
MN	Minnesota
MO	Missouri
MS	Mississippi
MT	Montana
NC	North Carolina
ND	North Dakota
NE	Nebraska
NH	New Hampshire
NJ	New Jersey
NM	New Mexico
NV	Nevada
NY	New York
OH	Ohio
OK	Oklahoma
OR	Oregon
PA	Pennsylvania
PR	Puerto Rico
RI	Rhode Island
SC	South Carolina
SD	South Dakota
TN	Tennessee
TX	Texas
UT	Utah
VA	Virginia
VI	Virgin Islands
VT	Vermont
WA	Washington
WI	Wisconsin
WV	West Virginia
WY	Wyoming

Canadian Province Abbreviations

AB	Alberta
BC	British Columbia
MB	Manitoba
NB	New Brunswick
NL	Newfoundland and Labrador
NS	Nova Scotia
NT	Northwest Territories
ON	Ontario
PE	Prince Edward Island
QC	Quebec
SK	Saskatchewan
YT	Yukon Territory

Other Abbreviations

ACT	American College Testing Program
B.A.	Bachelor of Arts
B.Arch.	Bachelor of Architecture
B.F.A.	Bachelor of Fine Arts
B.S.	Bachelor of Science
B.Sc.	Bachelor of Science
CSS	College Scholarship Service
D.D.S.	Doctor of Dental Science/Surgery
D.O.	Doctor of Osteopathy
D.Sc.	Doctor of Science
D.S.W.	Doctor of Social Work
D.V.M.	Doctor of Veterinary Medicine
D.V.M.S.	Doctor of Veterinary Medicine and Surgery
D.V.S.	Doctor of Veterinary Science
FAFSA	Free Application for Federal Student Aid
FWS	Federal Work Study
GED	General Education Development Certificate
GPA	Grade Point Average
GRE	Graduate Record Examination
J.D.	Doctor of Jurisprudence
LL.B.	Bachelor of Law
LL.M.	Master of Law
LSAT	Law School Admission Test
M.A.	Master of Arts
M.Arch.	Master of Architecture
M.B.A.	Master of Business Administration
M.D.	Doctor of Medicine
M.Div.	Master of Divinity
M.F.A.	Master of Fine Arts
MIA	Missing in Action
M.L.S.	Master of Library Science
M.N.	Master of Nursing
M.S.	Master of Science
M.S.W.	Master of Social Work
O.D.	Doctor of Optometry
Pharm.D.	Doctor of Pharmacy
Ph.D.	Doctor of Philosophy
POW	Prisoner of War
PSAT	Preliminary Scholastic Aptitude Test
ROTC	Reserve Officers Training Corps
SAR	Student Aid Report
SAT	Scholastic Aptitude Test
Sc.D.	Doctor of Science
TDD	Telephone Device for the Deaf
Th.d.	Doctor of Theology
U.N.	United Nations
U.S.	United States

8982 ■ UAF Community and Technical College

604 Barnette St.
Fairbanks, AK 99701
Ph: (907) 455-2800
Free: 877-882-8827
URL: www.tvc.uaf.edu

8983 ■ Mary Ghezzi Nursing Scholarships
(Undergraduate/Scholarship)

Purpose: To provide financial support for qualified students intending to pursue their nursing education. **Focus:** Nursing. **Qualif.:** Applicants must be enrolled in Tahana Valley Campus; must be students who want to pursue their career in Nursing. **Criteria:** Applicants will be selected based on their application requirements.

Funds Avail.: No specific amount. **To Apply:** Applicants are advised to contact Allied Health at 455-2822 for further information about the scholarship application.

8984 ■ Stacy Kaiser Memorial Funds
(Undergraduate/Scholarship)

Purpose: To provide support for deserving students intending to pursue their careers in radiologic technology. **Focus:** Radiology. **Qualif.:** Applicants must be residents of Alaska; must be in the second year of program in radiologic technology. **Criteria:** Applicants will be selected based on their application requirements.

Funds Avail.: No specific amount. **To Apply:** Scholarship applications are available online and must be completed and sent to: uaonline.alaska.edu (to access the scholarship application, applicant must choose to "Login to secured area "if they have a UA ID or apply for admission for the new students).

8985 ■ William C. Leary Memorial Emergency Services Scholarships *(Undergraduate/ Scholarship)*

Purpose: To encourage students to pursue their career in emergency service program. **Focus:** Emergency and disaster services. **Qualif.:** Applicants must be students enrolled in emergency service program. **Criteria:** Selection of applicants will be based on the decision of the scholarship committee.

Funds Avail.: No specific amount. **To Apply:** Scholarship applications are available at uaonline.alaska.edu (to access the scholarship application, you must choose "Login to secure area" if they have a UA ID or apply for admission for the new students).

8986 ■ Ruth Lister Scholarships *(Undergraduate, Vocational/Occupational/Scholarship)*

Purpose: To provide financial support for deserving individuals intending to pursue their educational goals. **Focus:** General studies. **Qualif.:** Applicants must be residents of Alaska; must be enrolled in a vocational program. **Criteria:** Preference will be given to Alaska residents and students enrolled in vocational programs.

Funds Avail.: No specific amount. **To Apply:** Scholarship applications are available online at uaonline.alaska.edu (to access the scholarship application, applicant must choose "Login to secured area" if they have a UA ID or apply for admission for the new students).

8987 ■ Rachael Patterson Memorial Scholarships *(Undergraduate/Scholarship)*

Purpose: To provide educational support for qualified students intending to pursue their education. **Focus:** Technology, Criminal justice, Fires and fire prevention. **Qualif.:** Applicants must be sophomores or above; must be enrolled in justice, fire science or office management and technology; must be residents of Alaska (at least two years) and are intending to remain in Alaska. **Criteria:** Preference will be given to residents of Alaska.

Funds Avail.: No specific amount. **To Apply:** Scholarship applications are available online at uaonline.alaska.edu (to access the scholarship application, applicant must choose "Login to secured area" if they have a UA ID or apply for admission for the new students). **Deadline:** February 16.

8988 ■ Schaible Health Care Services Scholarships *(Undergraduate/Scholarship)*

Purpose: To assist students in the health care services field at Tahana Valley Campus and/or Kuskokwim Campus within the college of Rural and Community Development at UAF. **Focus:** Health care services. **Qualif.:** Applicants must be attending at Kuskokwom Campus or Tahana Valley Campus; must be enrolled in health care service. **Criteria:** Selection of applicants will be based on their application requirements.

Funds Avail.: No specific amount. **To Apply:** Scholarship applications are available online at uaonline.alaska.edu (to access the scholarship application, applicant must choose "Login to secured area" if they have a UA ID or apply for admission for the new students).

8989 ■ Tanana Valley Campus Culinary Arts Scholarships *(Undergraduate/Scholarship)*

Purpose: To provide support for deserving students intending to pursue their study in culinary arts. **Focus:** Culinary

Awards are arranged alphabetically below their administering organizations

arts. **Qualif.:** Applicants must be students intending to pursue a career in culinary arts in Alaska. **Criteria:** Applicants will be selected based on their application requirements.

Funds Avail.: Varies. **To Apply:** Applicants are advised to contact the Culinary Arts at 455-2903 for further information about the application requirements and procedure.

8990 ■ Morris K. Udall Foundation

130 S Scott Ave.
Tucson, AZ 85701-1922
Ph: (520) 901-8500
Fax: (520) 670-5530
E-mail: info@udall.gov
URL: www.udall.gov

8991 ■ Morris K. Udall Scholarships
(Undergraduate/Scholarship)

Purpose: To provide scholarship assistance for qualified individuals. **Focus:** Environmental technology; Native American studies. **Qualif.:** Applicant must be a student who has demonstrated commitment to a career related to the environment; or must be a Native American or Alaska Native student who has demonstrated commitment to a career related to tribal public policy or Native health care; must be a sophomore or junior level college student; must have a college GPA of at least 3.0 or the equivalent; and must be a U.S citizen, U.S national or U.S permanent resident. **Criteria:** Recipients will be selected based on the following criteria: (1) demonstrated commitment to environmental or natural resources, tribal public policy, or Native American health care; (2) course of study and proposed career; (3) leadership, character, desire to make a difference, and general wellroundedness.

Funds Avail.: No specific amount. **To Apply:** Applicants must complete and sign Udall Scholarship Application and submit along with an 800-word essay (signed and dated), a current official college transcript and transcripts for other colleges attended, and three letters of recommendation. **Deadline:** March 5.

8992 ■ Unitarian Universalist Association of Congregations (UUA)

25 Beacon St.
Boston, MA 02108
Ph: (617) 742-2100
E-mail: info@uua.org
URL: www.uua.org

8993 ■ Martha and Robert Atherton Ministerial Scholarships *(Graduate, Master's/Scholarship)*

Purpose: To provide financial assistance to promising ministerial students in their second or third year of seminary. **Focus:** Ministry. **Qualif.:** Applicant must be student in the second or third year of seminary; and a citizen of the United States or Canada. **Criteria:** Priority is given to students that have demonstrated outstanding ministerial ability secondarily to students with the greatest financial need, especially persons of color.

Funds Avail.: No specific amount. **To Apply:** Applicants must apply for financial aid to be automatically considered for scholarships with no additional material is required, except where noted. **Deadline:** April 15. **Remarks:** Established in 1997, through the generous contributions of Mar-

tha and Robert Atherton. **Contact:** mco@uua.org.

8994 ■ Olympia Brown and Max Kapp Awards
(Graduate/Scholarship)

Purpose: To support the education of a student in a Masters of Divinity degree program leading to fellowship as a Unitarian Universalist (UU) minister. **Focus:** Ministry. **Qualif.:** Applicant must be student enrolled full-time or at least half time in a Masters of Divinity degree program leading to fellowship as a Unitarian Universalist (UU) minister; and a citizen of the United States or Canada. **Criteria:** Priority will be given to students who have demonstrated outstanding ministerial ability secondarily to students with the greatest financial need, especially persons of color. Entries will be evaluated by an outside reader.

Funds Avail.: $2,500. **Number Awarded:** 1. **To Apply:** Applicants must apply for financial aid to be automatically considered for scholarships. In addition, applicants must submit a winning paper, sermon, or other special project on some aspect of Universalism. **Deadline:** April 15. **Contact:** mco@uua.org.

8995 ■ Children of Unitarian Universalist Ministers College Scholarships *(Undergraduate/ Scholarship)*

Purpose: To defray undergraduate college expenses of the children of Unitarian Universalist Ministers. **Focus:** General studies. **Qualif.:** Applicant must be college undergraduate and a dependent of a Unitarian Universalist Minister. **Criteria:** Priority is given to applicants with family income not exceeding $50,000.

Funds Avail.: No specific amount. **To Apply:** Applicants must complete the online Application process and submit a proof of college enrollment to the UUA Office of Church Staff Finances. **Deadline:** September 30.

8996 ■ Pauly D'Orlando Memorial Art Scholarships *(Graduate, Undergraduate/Scholarship)*

Purpose: To support Unitarian Universalist students with their educational pursuit. **Focus:** Fine arts. **Qualif.:** Applicant must be a Unitarian Universalist graduate or undergraduate student pursuing a career in fine arts. Performing arts majors are not eligible. **Criteria:** Selection is based on active relationship with Unitarian Universalism, financial need, and enrollment in an accredited institution.

Funds Avail.: Varies. **Number Awarded:** Varies. **To Apply:** Applicants must submit a completed application form along with the supporting documentation. **Deadline:** February 15. **Remarks:** Funded by a trust set up by the First Unitarian Church of New Orleans.

8997 ■ David Eaton Scholarships *(Graduate, Master's/Scholarship)*

Purpose: To support the education of a student in a Masters of Divinity degree program leading to fellowship as a Unitarian Universalist (UU) minister. **Focus:** Ministry. **Qualif.:** Applicant must be a student enrolled full-time or at least half time in a Masters of Divinity degree program leading to fellowship as a Unitarian Universalist (UU) minister; a citizen of the United States or Canada; and a woman from a historically marginalized group who share the same vision as David Eaton. **Criteria:** Priority is given to students that have demonstrated outstanding ministerial ability secondarily to students with the greatest financial need, especially persons of color.

Awards are arranged alphabetically below their administering organizations

Funds Avail.: No specific amount. **To Apply:** Applicants must apply for financial aid to be automatically considered for scholarships with no additional materials required, except where noted. **Deadline:** April 15. **Remarks:** Established in memory of Rev. David Hilliard Eaton. **Contact:** mco@uua.org.

8998 ■ David Pohl Scholarships (Graduate, Master's/Scholarship)

Purpose: To support the education of a student in a Masters of Divinity degree program leading to fellowship as a Unitarian Universalist (UU) minister. **Focus:** Ministry. **Qualif.:** Applicant must be student enrolled full-time or at least half time in a Masters of Divinity degree program leading to fellowship as a Unitarian Universalist (UU) minister; and a citizen of the United States or Canada. **Criteria:** Priority is given to students that have demonstrated outstanding ministerial ability secondarily to students with the greatest financial need, especially persons of color.

Funds Avail.: No specific amount. **To Apply:** Applicants must apply for financial aid to be automatically considered for scholarships with no additional material is required, except where noted. **Deadline:** April 15. **Remarks:** Established in memory of Rev. David Pohl. **Contact:** mco@uua.org.

8999 ■ Roy H. Pollack Scholarships (Graduate, Master's/Scholarship)

Purpose: To support the education of a student in a Masters of Divinity degree program leading to fellowship as a Unitarian Universalist (UU) minister. **Focus:** Ministry. **Qualif.:** Applicant must be a second or third-year student having strong academic records and a promising candidate for the Unitarian Universalist ministry; must be a citizen of the United States or Canada. **Criteria:** Priority is given to students that have demonstrated outstanding ministerial ability secondarily to students with the greatest financial need, especially persons of color.

Funds Avail.: No specific amount. **To Apply:** Applicants must apply for financial aid to be automatically considered for scholarships with no additional material is required, except where noted. **Deadline:** April 15. **Remarks:** Created in 1998. **Contact:** mco@uua.org.

9000 ■ Alice Southworth Schulman Simmons Scholarships for UU Women (Undergraduate/Scholarship)

Purpose: To support the education of a UU woman with education. **Focus:** General studies. **Qualif.:** Applicant must be a Unitarian Universalist Women attending Simmons College in Boston. **Criteria:** UUA will validate all candidates.

Funds Avail.: $25,000. **Number Awarded:** 2. **To Apply:** Applicants must apply and submit the Information Profile for Endowed Scholarships through the Office of Student Financial Services at Simmons College. **Contact:** Stewardship and Development Office, at 617-948-4655.

9001 ■ Joseph Sumner Smith Scholarships (All/Scholarship)

Purpose: To support the education of a Unitarian Universalist (UU) student. **Focus:** General studies. **Qualif.:** Applicant must be a Unitarian Universalist student attending Antioch or Harvard. **Criteria:** Priority is given to students who will pursue the ministry after graduation.

Funds Avail.: $250-$1000. **To Apply:** Applicants must

contact the Scholarship Administrator of the UU Funding Program for the application process. **Deadline:** July 31. **Contact:** uufp@aol.com.

9002 ■ Marion Barr Stanfield Art Scholarships (Graduate, Undergraduate/Scholarship)

Purpose: To support Unitarian Universalist students with their educational pursuit. **Focus:** Fine arts. **Qualif.:** Applicant must be a Unitarian Universalist graduate or undergraduate student pursuing a career in fine arts. Performing arts majors are not eligible. **Criteria:** Selection is based on active relationship with Unitarian Universalism, financial need, and enrollment in an accredited institution.

Funds Avail.: Varies. **Number Awarded:** Varies. **To Apply:** Applicants must submit a completed application form along with the supporting documentation. **Deadline:** February 15.

9003 ■ Otto M. Stanfield Law Scholarships (Graduate/Scholarship)

Purpose: To support Unitarian Universalist students with their educational pursuits. **Focus:** Law. **Qualif.:** Applicant must be a Unitarian Universalist student entering or in law school. Pre-law students or political science majors are not eligible. **Criteria:** Selection is based on active relationship with Unitarian Universalism, financial need, and enrollment in an accredited institution.

Funds Avail.: No specific amount. **Number Awarded:** Varies. **To Apply:** Applicants must submit a completed application form along with the supporting documentation. **Remarks:** Established by Marion Barr Stanfield in memory of her husband.

9004 ■ Rev. Chuck and Nancy Thomas Scholarships (Graduate, Master's/Scholarship)

Purpose: To support the education of a student in a Masters of Divinity degree program leading to fellowship as a Unitarian Universalist (UU) minister. **Focus:** Ministry. **Qualif.:** Applicant must be a first-year student showing an outstanding commitment to Unitarian Universalism as a lay leader before preparing for ordained ministry; and must be a citizen of the United States or Canada. **Criteria:** Priority is given to students that have demonstrated outstanding ministerial ability secondarily to students with the greatest financial need, especially persons of color.

Funds Avail.: $11,000. **Number Awarded:** 1. **To Apply:** Applicants must apply for financial aid to be automatically considered for scholarships. In addition, applicants must submit a completed application form with the required materials. Those who wish to submit a nomination should write a letter of recommendation showing a connection between the applicant's ministry and their life goals along with examples of their strong leadership skills. **Deadline:** April 1. **Remarks:** Established in 1998 by Lorella and Todd Hess in honor of Lorella's father, Rev. Charles Thomas.

9005 ■ Von Ogden Vogt Scholarships (Graduate, Master's/Scholarship)

Purpose: To support the intellectual, spiritual, and professional development of future Unitarian Universalist ministers attending Meadville Lombard Theological School. **Focus:** Ministry. **Qualif.:** Applicant must be student enrolled full-time or at least half time in a Masters of Divinity degree program leading to fellowship as a Unitarian Universalist (UU) minister; attending Meadville Lombard Theological School; and a citizen of the United States or Canada.

Awards are arranged alphabetically below their administering organizations

Criteria: Priority is given to students that have demonstrated outstanding ministerial ability secondarily to students with the greatest financial need, especially persons of color.

Funds Avail.: No specific amount. **To Apply:** Applicants must apply for financial aid to be automatically considered for scholarships with no additional material is required, except where noted. **Deadline:** April 15. **Remarks:** Established in 2001 by Ogden and Carolyn Vogt to honor Carolyn's father, Rev. Dr. Von Ogden Vogt. **Contact:** mco@uua.org.

9006 ■ United Agribusiness League (UAL)
54 Corporate Park
Irvine, CA 92606-5105
Ph: (949) 975-1424
Fax: (949) 975-1573
Free: 800-223-4590
E-mail: info@aul.org
URL: www.ual.org

9007 ■ UAL/UABT Scholarship Program
(Undergraduate/Scholarship)

Purpose: To provide financial assistance to students who wish to pursue their education. **Focus:** General studies. **Qualif.:** Applicants must be affiliated with UAL or UABT either through members or employees of a member organization; must be enrolled at an accredited college or university; and have a minimum of 2.5 GPA. **Criteria:** Recipients will be selected based on submitted application materials.

Funds Avail.: No specific amount. **To Apply:** Applicants submit an application form; resume; three letters of recommendation; transcript of records; and financial statement (optional). Applicants must also submit a two-page, double-spaced essay with a one-page bibliography explaining "how the economic recession impacted the agricultural industry." **Deadline:** March 31. **Contact:** For further information, applicants must send an e-mail to scholarship@ual.org.

9008 ■ United Engineering Foundation (UEF)
PO Box 70
Mount Vernon, VA 22121-0070
Ph: (973) 244-2328
Fax: (973) 882-5155
E-mail: engfnd@aol.com
URL: www.uefoundation.org

9009 ■ United Engineering Foundation Grants
(All/Grant)

Purpose: To support engineering and education for the advancement of engineering arts and sciences. **Focus:** Engineering. **Qualif.:** Any non-profit organization, individual and group is eligible for the grant. **Criteria:** The UEF Grants Committee will prioritize the proposals and forward prioritized proposals to the UEF Board of Trustees. Preference will be given to proposals demonstrating U.S. based organizations having 501(c)(3) status, established deadlines and with page limitation.

Funds Avail.: No specific amount. **To Apply:** Applicants must submit a detailed proposal and a two-page concept paper (submitted in PDF format to engfnd@aol.com, and a copy to davidlbelden@cs.com). **Deadline:** June 1.

9010 ■ United Foods and Commercial Workers International Union
1775 K St. NW
Washington, DC 20006
Ph: (202) 223-3111
Free: 800-551-4010
URL: www.ufcw.org

9011 ■ UFCW Scholarships *(Undergraduate/Scholarship)*

Purpose: To financially support UFCW members and their unmarried dependents with their educational pursuit. **Focus:** General studies. **Qualif.:** Applicants must be UFCW members or their unmarried dependents under age of 20. **Criteria:** Selection is based on scholastic achievements, community involvement and on submitted essay.

Funds Avail.: No specific amount. **To Apply:** Applicants must fill-out, sign and date the requested UFCW Scholarship Application. An academic counselor must complete the application form and mail it along the grade transcript as well as proof of graduation, intent to graduate or GED received. **Contact:** scholarship@ufcw.org.

9012 ■ United Methodist Communications
810 12th Ave. S
Nashville, TN 37203
Ph: (615) 742-5113
Fax: (615) 742-5423
Free: 800-251-8140
E-mail: umcom@umcom.org
URL: www.umcom.org/

9013 ■ Leonard M. Perryman Communications Scholarships for Ethnic Minority Students
(Undergraduate/Scholarship)

Purpose: To provide financial assistance to students who intend to pursue a career in religion journalism for communications. **Focus:** Religion; Journalism; Communications. **Qualif.:** Applicants must be undergraduate United Methodist students, who intend to pursue a career in religion journalism for study at an accredited U.S. college or university. **Criteria:** Applicants are evaluated based on Christian commitment and involvement in the life of the United Methodist Church; academic achievement as revealed by transcripts, GPA and the required letters of reference; journalistic experience and/or evidence of journalistic talent; clarity of purpose in plans and goals for the future; potential professional ability as a religion journalist.

Funds Avail.: $2,500. **Number Awarded:** 1. **To Apply:** Applicants must submit a completed application form along with official transcript(s); three letters of recommendation; personal photo; three samples of journalistic work; and your essay of not more than 500 words. **Deadline:** March 15. **Contact:** scholarships@umcom.org.

9014 ■ United Methodist Youth Organization
1908 Grand Ave.
Nashville, TN 37212
Ph: (615) 340-7079
Free: 877-899-2780
E-mail: youngpeople@gbod.org
URL: www.gbod.org/youngpeople

Awards are arranged alphabetically below their administering organizations

9015 ■ David W. Self Scholarships
(Undergraduate/Scholarship)

Purpose: To aid United Methodist students who are continuing their self-development through higher education. **Focus:** Church occupations. **Qualif.:** Applicant must be U.S. citizen or permanent resident; a racial/ethnic minority youth active in local United Methodist Church for at least one year; graduating high school senior entering first year of undergraduate study; admitted to a full-time degree program in an accredited college or university; maintaining at least "C" average in high school; pursuing a church-related career; and established financial need. **Criteria:** selection is based on the application.

Funds Avail.: Up to $1000. **To Apply:** Applicants must submit a completed application form. **Deadline:** June 1.

9016 ■ Richard S. Smith Scholarships
(Undergraduate/Scholarship)

Purpose: To aid United Methodist students continuing their self-development through higher education. **Focus:** Church occupations. **Qualif.:** Applicant must be a U.S. citizen or permanent resident; a racial/ethnic minority youth active in local United Methodist Church for at least one year; graduating high school senior entering first year of undergraduate study; admitted to a full-time degree program in an accredited college or university; maintaining at least "C" average in high school; pursuing a church-related career; and established financial need. **Criteria:** selection is based on the application.

Funds Avail.: Up to $1000. **To Apply:** Applicants must submit a completed application form. **Deadline:** June 1.

9017 ■ United Parent Support for Down Syndrome
Hartford Plz.
1070 S Roselle Rd.
Schaumburg, IL 60193
Ph: (847) 895-2100
URL: www.upsfordowns.org

9018 ■ Katie MacDonald Memorial Scholarships
(Graduate, Undergraduate/Scholarship)

Purpose: To provide financial assistance to individuals with Down syndrome pursuing their education. **Focus:** Disabilities. **Qualif.:** Applicants must be U.S. citizens; must be individuals with Down syndrome or siblings of individuals with Down syndrome pursuing full or part-time educational or job training opportunities beyond high school or must be pursuing junior college, undergraduate or graduate degrees in disability related fields. **Criteria:** Selection will be based on demonstrated accomplishments; obstacles overcome; leadership and community involvement; life goals.

Funds Avail.: $2,500. **Number Awarded:** 4. **To Apply:** Applicants must submit a completed application form; essay/personal statement; two recommendation letters; additional documentation (transcripts, extra-curricular activities, etc). Two copies of the application packet should be submitted. **Deadline:** April 1.

9019 ■ Eric Martinez Memorial Scholarships
(Graduate, Undergraduate/Scholarship)

Purpose: To provide financial assistance to individuals or siblings affected by Down syndrome pursuing their education. **Focus:** General studies. **Qualif.:** Applicants must be

U.S. citizens; must be individuals with Down syndrome or siblings of individuals with Down syndrome pursuing full or part-time educational or job training opportunities beyond high school or must be pursuing junior college, undergraduate or graduate degrees. **Criteria:** Selection will be based on demonstrated accomplishments; obstacles overcome; leadership and community involvement; life goals.

Funds Avail.: $2,500. **Number Awarded:** 2. **To Apply:** Applicants must submit a completed application form; essay/personal statement; two recommendation letters; additional documentation (transcripts, extra-curricular activities, etc). Two copies of the application packet should be submitted. **Deadline:** April 1.

9020 ■ United South and Eastern Tribes (USET)
711 Stewarts Ferry Pike, Ste. 100
Nashville, TN 37214
Ph: (615) 872-7900
Fax: (615) 872-7417
E-mail: wjanes@usetinc.org
URL: usetinc.org

9021 ■ United South and Eastern Tribes Scholarship Fund *(Undergraduate/Scholarship)*

Purpose: To provide financial assistance to Indian students in the USET service area. **Focus:** General studies. **Qualif.:** Applicants must be Indian students who are enrolled members of one of twenty-four USET member tribes. **Criteria:** Applicants will be judged based on demonstrated need for financial assistance, satisfactory scholastic standing and current enrollment or acceptance in a post-secondary educational institution.

Funds Avail.: $500. **To Apply:** Applicants must complete the application found on the website of USET. **Deadline:** April 30. **Contact:** Callie Leasure at the above address.

9022 ■ U.S. Air Force ROTC
551 E Maxwell Blvd.
Maxwell AFB, AL 36112-5917
Fax: (334) 953-6167
Free: 866-423-7682
E-mail: csp@maxwell.af.mil
URL: www.afrotc.com

9023 ■ Air Force ROTC Enhanced HBCU Scholarships *(Undergraduate/Scholarship)*

Purpose: To meet officer production requirements and enhance enrollment at HBCUs. **Focus:** General studies. **Qualif.:** Applicants must be enrolled at the following colleges/universities: Jackson State University; Tuskegee University; Alabama State University; Howard University; North Carolina A&T State University; Fayetteville State University; Tennessee State University. **Criteria:** Recipients will be selected based on merit.

Funds Avail.: Tuition capped at $18,000; Books at $900. per year. **To Apply:** Applicants may start the application process for the scholarship program by contacting the Air Force ROTC detachment at the school that they wish to enroll in.

9024 ■ Hispanic Serving Institution Scholarships (HSIS) *(Undergraduate/Scholarship)*

Purpose: To meet officer production requirements and enhance enrollment at HSIs. **Focus:** General studies. **Qua-**

Awards are arranged alphabetically below their administering organizations

lif.: Applicants must be students enrolled as HSIs (Hispanic Serving Institution), including those schools which host an Air force ROTC detachment and those which are cross-towns of another school that hosts a detachment. **Criteria:** Applicants do not have to meet a selection board for this scholarship.

Funds Avail.: Tuition capped at $18,000; Books at $900 per year. **To Apply:** Applicants may start the application process for the scholarship program by contacting the Air Force ROTC detachment at the school that they wish to attend.

9025 ■ Historically Black College or University Scholarships (HBCUS) *(Undergraduate/ Scholarship)*

Purpose: To meet officer production requirements and enhance enrollment at HBCUs. **Focus:** General studies. **Qualif.:** Applicants must be enrolled at an HBCU (Historically Black College or University), including those schools which host an Air Force ROTC detachment and those which are crosstowns of another school that hosts a detachment. **Criteria:** Applicants do not have to meet a selection board.

Funds Avail.: Tuition capped at $18,000; Books at $900. **To Apply:** Applications for the HBCU Scholarship are processed and approved at the detachment level. Applicant must contact the detachment serving the school, and the school will work to nominate the applicant for the appropriate scholarship program. Applications are accepted at any time each year.

9026 ■ U.S. Air Force ROTC Enhanced HSI Scholarships *(Undergraduate/Scholarship)*

Purpose: To meet officer production requirements and enhance enrollment at HSIs. **Focus:** General studies. **Qualif.:** Applicants must be enrolled at the following colleges/universities: California State University; New Mexico State University; University of New Mexico; University of Puerto Rico- Rio Piedras; University of Puerto Rico-Mayaguez; University of Texas - San Antonio. **Criteria:** Recipients will be selected based on merit.

Funds Avail.: Tuition capped at $18,000; Books at $900. per year. **To Apply:** Applicants may start the application process for the scholarship program by contacting the Air Force ROTC detachment at the school that they wish to enroll in. at the above address.

9027 ■ U.S. Air Force ROTC Express Scholarships *(Undergraduate/Scholarship)*

Purpose: To provide financial assistance for college students enrolled in specific fields. **Focus:** Engineering; Aerospace sciences; Aeronautics; Atmospheric sciences. **Qualif.:** Applicants must be United States citizens by the end of the projected term of activation; must pass the Air Force Officer Qualifying Test; must pass the Air Force ROTC Physical Fitness Test; must have at least a 2.5 cumulative college grade point average; must pass a physical examination and be certified; must not be a contracted scholarship recipient; and must meet the age, moral and other scholarship eligibility requirements for Air force ROTC. **Criteria:** The Express Scholarship program is operated on a fully qualified basis - those who meet the qualifications are awarded the scholarship and do not meet a scholarship selection board.

Funds Avail.: $15,000. **To Apply:** Applications for the Express Scholarship are processed and approved at the detachment level. Applicant must contact the detachment

serving the school that he/she wishes to attend and the school will work to nominate the student for the appropriate scholarship program.

9028 ■ U.S. Air Force ROTC High School Scholarships *(Undergraduate/Scholarship)*

Purpose: To provide financial assistance to high school seniors. **Focus:** General studies. **Qualif.:** Applicants must be United States citizens or able to obtain citizenship by the last day of the first term of the freshman year for 4-year offers, or the first term of the sophomore year for 3-year offers; must be a high school graduate or have an equivalent certificate; must be 17-31 years old prior to scholarship activation; and must not be enrolled full-time at a college or a university except for joint high school college programs. **Criteria:** Recipient selection will be based on leadership and work experience; extracurricular activities; results from the personal interview; questionnaire results; and academic scores.

Funds Avail.: Type 1-$900; Type 2-$18,000: Type 7-$9,000. **To Apply:** Applicants must submit their application online and include the following forms: Counselor Certification, Personal Statement, Physical Fitness Assessment, and resume. Applicants must have their high school transcripts with raised seal or signature as well as their SAT or ACT scores. **Deadline:** December 1.

9029 ■ U.S. Air Force ROTC In-College Scholarships *(Undergraduate/Scholarship)*

Purpose: To provide scholarships to college freshmen and sophomores in any major. **Focus:** General studies. **Qualif.:** Applicants must be United States citizens by the end of the projected term of activation; must pass the Air Force Officer Qualifying Test; must meet the Air Force ROTC weight and body fat standards; must pass the Air Force ROTC Physical Fitness Test; have at least a 2.5 cumulative college grade point average; pass a physical examination; must not be a contracted scholarship recipient; and must meet the age, moral and other scholarship eligibility requirements for Air force ROTC. **Criteria:** Selection will be based on academic performance.

Funds Avail.: Type 2-$18,000; Type 3-$9,000; Type 6-$3,000. **To Apply:** Applicants must fill out the application request form online.

9030 ■ United States Army Warrant Officers Association (USAWOA)
462 Herndon Pkwy., Ste. 207
Herndon, VA 20170-5235
Ph: (703) 742-7727
Fax: (703) 742-7728
Free: 800-587-2962
E-mail: usawoahq@verizon.net
URL: www.usawoa.org

9031 ■ USAWOASF/Grantham University On-Line Scholarships *(Graduate, Undergraduate, Vocational/Occupational/Scholarship)*

Purpose: To give financial awards to deserving candidates. **Focus:** General studies. **Qualif.:** Applicant must be a member, or a spouse of a member of the association, or their dependents under 23 years of age (high school seniors and above); planning to attend full-time or continue education at an accredited American college or university or a vocational technical institution; and has a GPA of 3.0

Awards are arranged alphabetically below their administering organizations

or higher on a 4.0 scale. **Criteria:** Applicants will be selected based on the application materials.

Funds Avail.: $1,000. **To Apply:** Application form is available at the website. Applicant must submit a complete application packet consisting of: the application form; an essay (800-100 words, include word count) on educational goals; circumstances which may affect the applicant's school attendance; list of extracurricular activities; recommendation letter (from instructor, faculty advisor, etc.); National Test Scores, SAT, ACT, etc.; transcript of grades; and a 4x6 photograph (view head and shoulders). **Deadline:** May 1.

9032 ■ USAWOASF Regular Scholarships
(Undergraduate, Vocational/Occupational/ Scholarship)

Purpose: To give financial awards to deserving candidates. **Focus:** General studies. **Qualif.:** Applicant must be a spouse or dependent of a USAWOA member, 23 years old and below; must be senior high school student planning to attend full-time or continue education at an accredited American college or university, or a vocational technical institution; and has a GPA of 3.0 or higher on a 4.0 scale. **Criteria:** Selection committee's decision is based on the whole-person concept.

Funds Avail.: Amount not specified. **To Apply:** Application form is available on the website. Applicant must submit a complete application packet consisting of: the application form (typewritten format); an essay (800-100 words, include word count) on educational goals; circumstances which may affect the applicant's school attendance; list of extracurricular activities; a recommendation letter (from instructor, faculty advisor, etc.); National Test Scores, SAT, ACT, etc.; and a 4x6 photograph (view head and shoulders). **Deadline:** May 1.

9033 ■ United States Association for Energy Economics (USAEE)
c/o Mr. David L. Williams, Exec. Dir.
28790 Chagrin Blvd., Ste. 350
Cleveland, OH 44122
Ph: (216) 464-2785
Fax: (216) 464-2768
E-mail: usaee@usaee.org
URL: www.usaee.org

9034 ■ Calgary USAEE/IAEE North American Conference Registration Fee Scholarships
(Undergraduate/Scholarship)

Purpose: To offset the conference registration costs for students. **Focus:** Energy-related areas. **Qualif.:** Applicants must be full-time students or students who have completed their degrees within the past six months; and must be members of IAEE in good standing. **Criteria:** Awards will be awarded on a rolling basis.

Funds Avail.: $300. **To Apply:** Applicants must submit a personal letter as well as a letter from their advisor or another faculty member familiar with their research. Personal letter must include the following information: 1) meets all the required qualifications; 2) describes the energy interests and future accomplishments by attending the conference; and, 3) provides name and contact information of a faculty member. Advisor's letter should describe the applicant's research interests, nature of the academic program and progress, and recommendation for the award.

Deadline: September 9. **Contact:** For further information, applicants must contact David Williams. Materials must be submitted in .pdf format to usaee@usaee.org with "Submission for Registration Fee Scholarship" in the subject line.

9035 ■ Dennis J. O'Brien USAEE/IAEE Best Student Paper Awards *(Undergraduate/Award)*

Purpose: To help and encourage students to present their papers. **Focus:** Energy-related areas. **Qualif.:** Applicants must be full-time students or have completed a degree within the past 12 months. Applicants must also be members of IAEE in good standing. **Criteria:** Recipients will be selected based on the submitted papers.

Funds Avail.: $1,000. Other students received a stipend of $750 and $500 together with complimentary conference registration. **To Apply:** Applicants must submit an abstract; a qualification letter with photocopy of student ID; and advisor's letter or letter from a faculty member confirming that the applicant's paper meets the qualifications. Papers must be original. Only papers co-authored by students will be given consideration. **Contact:** For further information, applicants must contact David Williams. Materials must be submitted in .pdf format to usaee@usaee.org with "Submission for Student Paper Award" in the subject line.

9036 ■ U.S. Capitol Historical Society (USCHS)
200 Maryland Ave. NE
Washington, DC 20002-5724
Ph: (202) 543-8919
Fax: (202) 544-8244
Free: 800-887-9318
E-mail: uschs@uschs.org
URL: www.uschs.org

9037 ■ United States Capitol Historical Society Fellowships *(Graduate/Fellowship)*

Purpose: To provide financial support to scholars researching important topics in the art and architectural history of the United States Capitol Complex. **Focus:** History, United States; Art history; American studies; Museum science. **Qualif.:** Applicant must be a graduate student enrolled in a degree program in art or architectural history, American history, American studies, museum studies, or decorative arts, and scholars with a proven record of research and publication. **Criteria:** Applications are judged based on the qualifications of the applicant, the significance of the topic, the degree of need for the proposed research, the feasibility of the research plan, and the likelihood that the research will lead to publication.

Funds Avail.: $2,500 per month, up to $30,000 for a full year. **To Apply:** Applicants must submit a curriculum vitae; transcripts of graduate work; two supporting letters; dates for which the fellowship is requested, with estimated time period for each phase of the proposed research; list of expected sources of income during the proposed period; and research proposal (maximum 5 pages). Submit materials by regular mail to Dr. Donald Kennon, or by fax, or email to Dr. Barbara Wolanin. **Deadline:** March 15. **Contact:** Dr. Barbara Wolanin, 202-228-4602, bwolanin@aoc.gov.

9038 ■ U.S. Department of Homeland Security
12th & C St. SW
Washington, DC 20024
Ph: (202) 245-2499

Awards are arranged alphabetically below their administering organizations

E-mail: dhsed@orau.org
URL: www.orau.gov/dhsed

9039 ■ The Homeland Security Undergraduate Scholarships *(Undergraduate/Scholarship)*

Purpose: To pursue basic science and technology innovations that can be applied to the DHS mission. **Focus:** Science technologies; Engineering; Mathematics and mathematical sciences. **Qualif.:** Applicants must be a U.S. citizens as of the application deadline; applicants must have a cumulative undergraduate GPA of 3.30 or higher on a 4.00 scale; applicants must be majoring in a homeland security science, technology, engineering or mathematics field with interest in a homeland security research area; applicants must be in second year of college if been attending college full-time; applicants must have completed a total of at least 45 but not more than 60 semester hours if been attending on a part-time, or combination or part-time and full-time basis. **Criteria:** Recipients are selected based on the candidate's academic record; reference report; SAT or ACT test scores; research experience essay; current research interests essay; and contribution to public service essay.

Funds Avail.: $1,000;. **To Apply:** Applicants must complete the online application form; applicants must submit two online reference report forms; applicants must submit official academic transcript from all postsecondary institutions attended. **Deadline:** January 5 for online application form; January 12 for documents.

9040 ■ United States Environmental Protection Agency (USEPA)

Ariel Rios Bldg.
1200 Pennsylvania Ave. NW
Washington, DC 20004
Ph: (202) 272-0167
URL: www.epa.gov

9041 ■ Greater Research Opportunities Undergraduate Fellowships (GRO) *(Undergraduate/Fellowship)*

Purpose: To provide financial assistance to bachelor-level students in environmental fields of study. **Focus:** Environmental Science. **Qualif.:** Students must attend a fully accredited U.S. college or university for their last two years of undergraduate studies; must be U.S. citizens or legal residents; must have at least a "B" average overall at the time of application and during the tenure of the fellowship. **Criteria:** Selection will be based on evaluation of submitted requirements and specific criteria.

Funds Avail.: Up to $19,700 per year of academic support plus $9,500 for internship support. **To Apply:** Applicants must submit a completed application for Federal Assistance form; Standard Form; EPA Key Contacts Form; personal statement; proposal description; background information; and letters of recommendation. Applications must be submitted via electronic mail or through paper submissions. **Contact:** Ron Josephson for electronic submissions at josephson.ron@epa.gov or 202-343-964.

9042 ■ Science to Achieve Results Fellowships (STAR) *(Graduate/Fellowship)*

Purpose: To encourage students to obtain advanced degrees and pursue careers in an environmental field. **Focus:** Environmental Science. **Qualif.:** Students must attend a fully accredited U.S. college or university for their

graduate studies; must be U.S. citizens or legal residents. **Criteria:** Selection will be based on evaluation of the submitted requirements and specific criteria.

Funds Avail.: A total of $42,000 available, covering $25,000 for stipend, $5,000 for authorized expenses, and $12,000 for tuition and fees. **Number Awarded:** 105. **To Apply:** Applicants must submit a completed application for Federal Assistance form; Standard Form; EPA Key Contacts Form; personal statement; proposal description; background information; and letters of recommendation. Applications must be submitted either via electronic mail or through paper submissions. **Deadline:** November. **Contact:** Ron Josephson for electronic submissions at josephson.ron@epa.gov or 202-343-964; Brandon Jones at 2011fellowshipsrfa@epa.gov.

9043 ■ United States Geospatial Intelligence Foundation (USGIF)

2325 Dulles Corner Blvd., Ste. 450
Herndon, VA 20171
Fax: (703) 793-9069
Free: 888-698-7443
E-mail: info@usgif.org
URL: www.usgif.org

9044 ■ United States Geospatial Intelligence Foundation Graduate Scholarships *(Postgraduate/Scholarship)*

Purpose: To help further the geospatial tradecraft. To assist promising students interested in the geospatial sciences. **Focus:** Geosciences. **Qualif.:** Applicants must be graduate students interested in geospatial sciences. **Criteria:** Recipients are selected based on academic standing, financial need and quality of the applicant's essay.

Funds Avail.: $5,000. **Number Awarded:** 10. **To Apply:** Applicants must complete the application form. Applicants must submit an essay describing their understanding of the geospatial intelligence tradecraft, future goals and how they relate to geospatial tradecraft, their understanding of the variety of careers and opportunities available within the geospatial intelligence tradecraft and their motivation for pursuing this field. Applicants must submit two letters of recommendation. **Deadline:** May 2. **Contact:** scholarships@usgif.org.

9045 ■ United States Geospatial Intelligence Foundation High School Scholarships *(Undergraduate/Scholarship)*

Purpose: To help further the geospatial tradecraft. To assist promising students interested in the geospatial sciences. **Focus:** Geosciences. **Qualif.:** Applicants must be senior high school students interested in geospatial sciences. **Criteria:** Recipients are selected based on academic standing, financial need and quality of the applicant's essay.

Funds Avail.: $2,000. **Number Awarded:** 3. **To Apply:** Applicants must complete the application form. Applicants must submit an essay describing their understanding of the geospatial intelligence tradecraft, future goals and how they relate to geospatial tradecraft, their understanding of the variety of careers and opportunities available within the geospatial intelligence tradecraft and their motivation for pursuing this field. Applicants must submit two letters of recommendation. **Contact:** scholarships@usgif.org.

Awards are arranged alphabetically below their administering organizations

9046 ■ United States Geospatial Intelligence Foundation Undergraduate Scholarships
(Undergraduate/Scholarship)

Purpose: To help further the geospatial tradecraft. To assist promising students interested in the geospatial sciences. **Focus:** Geosciences. **Qualif.:** Applicants must be undergraduate students interested in geospatial sciences. **Criteria:** Recipients are selected based on academic standing, financial need and quality of the applicant's essay.

Funds Avail.: $5,000. **Number Awarded:** 6. **To Apply:** Applicants must complete the application form. Applicants must submit an essay describing their understanding of the geospatial intelligence tradecraft, future goals and how they relate to geospatial tradecraft, their understanding of the variety of careers and opportunities available within the geospatial intelligence tradecraft and their motivation for pursuing this field. Applicants must submit two letters of recommendation. **Contact:** scholarships@usgif.org.

9047 ■ U.S. Golf Association (USGA)
77 Liberty Corner Rd.
Far Hills, NJ 07931
Ph: (908) 234-2300
Fax: (908) 234-9687
E-mail: membership@usga.org
URL: www.usga.org

9048 ■ United States Golf Association Fellowship Program *(All/Fellowship)*

Purpose: To develop recent college graduates' professional skills such as leadership and organizational efficiency; to educate them in the role of philanthropy and the non-profit sector and offer experience in the golf world. **Focus:** Athletics. **Qualif.:** Applicants must have: strong leadership potential, interest in public service, desire for personal and professional growth; strong analytical, written and verbal skills; appreciation for the impact of the game; personal initiative and commitment to teamwork; willingness and ability to travel; and eligibility to work in the United States. **Criteria:** Recipients are selected based on demonstrated interest in golf.

Funds Avail.: $29,000 plus $1,500 bonus. **To Apply:** Applicants must submit: a one-to-two page cover letter describing their interest in the program; resume or C.V.; an official transcript of records; two letters of recommendation with an index card including the proponents' name and contact information. International applicants must submit a documentation of eligibility to work in the United States. Fax will not be accepted. **Deadline:** January 8. **Contact:** Andrew Brockman, Jack Hendrickson and Meagan Hinns, Fellowship Recruitment and Selection Team Leaders, Phone: 719-471-4810; E-mail: fellowship@usga.org.

9049 ■ United States Golf Association Scholarship Program *(Undergraduate/Scholarship)*

Purpose: To provide opportunity for participants to think critically about leadership skills and become more engaged and invested citizens in their respective communities. **Focus:** Athletics. **Qualif.:** Applicants must be 15 to 19 years old; must be "Honor Roll" students or maintain a strong GPA; must play or be qualified to play at a varsity level; must demonstrate leadership, have an active involvement in community activities/service and have proven ability in an event of size and magnitude. **Criteria:** Recipients are selected based on academic performance and involvement in extracurricular activities.

Funds Avail.: No specific amount. **To Apply:** Applicants must submit a completed application form and reference letter. **Deadline:** May 5. **Contact:** Application form and other supporting documents should be sent at 1631 Mesa Ave., Ste. Colorado Springs, CO 80906.

9050 ■ United States Hunter Jumper Association
4047 Iron Works Pky.
Lexington, KY 40511
Ph: (859) 225-2055
Fax: (859) 258-9033
E-mail: sdotson@ushja.org
URL: www.ushja.org

9051 ■ USHJA General Scholarships
(Undergraduate/Scholarship)

Purpose: To provide financial support to those students who are in need. **Focus:** General Studies. **Qualif.:** Applicants must be graduating high school seniors or current undergraduate students who are pursuing postsecondary studies. **Criteria:** Selection will be based on academic achievement, financial need, extracurricular activities, community service, involvement with American Saddlebred horses and recommendations.

Funds Avail.: $5,000. **Number Awarded:** 4. **To Apply:** Applicants must check the available website for the required materials. **Deadline:** April 30. **Contact:** For more information, please visit: http://www.asha.net.

9052 ■ USHJA Postgraduate Scholarships
(Postgraduate/Scholarship)

Purpose: To recognize intercollegiate student-athletes by supporting them in their educational expenses. **Focus:** General Studies. **Qualif.:** Applicants must be male or female intercollegiate full-time student-athletes who are in the final year of NCAA eligibility and plan to enroll in graduate school upon completion of their four-year degree. Students must have a minimum 3.2 GPA, be nominated by a faculty athletic representative or director of athletics of a NCAA member institution in the final season of competition, and have performed with distinction as a member of a varsity team in the sport for which they are nominated. Awards are seasonal according to sport, as follows: FALL -badminton (W), cross country, equestrian (W), football, soccer, water polo (M), volleyball (W), and field hockey (W); WINTER archery (W), basketball, bowling (W), fencing, gymnastics, ice hockey, rifle, skiing, squash (W), swimming & diving, team handball (W), indoor track & field, and wrestling (M); and SPRING - baseball, golf, lacrosse, rowing (W), softball, synchronized swimming (W), tennis, volleyball (M), outdoor track & field, and water polo. **Criteria:** Recipients will be selected based on the committee's decision.

Funds Avail.: Maximum award amount: $7,500. **Number Awarded:** 174. **To Apply:** Applicants must check the available website for more information. **Contact:** For inquiries please visit: http://www.ncaa.org.

9053 ■ United States Judo Federation (USJF)
PO Box 338
Ontario, OR 97914
Ph: (541) 889-8753
Fax: (541) 889-5836
E-mail: no@usjf.com
URL: www.usjf.com

Awards are arranged alphabetically below their administering organizations

9054 ■ George C. Balch Scholarships *(Graduate, Undergraduate/Scholarship)*

Purpose: To provide financial assistance to judo students. **Focus:** Education. **Qualif.:** Applicants must be judo students who are high school seniors or graduate students pursuing a college degree in Education. **Criteria:** Applicants will be judged based on academic records.

Funds Avail.: $1,000. **To Apply:** Applicants must submit a filled-out application form, personal statement and a letter of recommendation. **Contact:** For further information, applicants must contact Robert Balch at the above address.

9055 ■ Dr. Joseph J. Fitzsimmons Scholarships *(Doctorate/Scholarship)*

Purpose: To help physicians offset their medical school fees while studying Judo. **Focus:** Medicine. **Qualif.:** Applicants must be registered physicians who are in their 1st or 2nd year of medical school; must be USJF members for three consecutive years; must be yudansha and members of USJF charter club at the time of application. **Criteria:** Scholarship will be given to applicants who best meet the criteria.

Funds Avail.: No specific amount. **To Apply:** Applicants must submit a filled-out application form which can be obtained online; and must send a copy of their acceptance letter from the medical school.

9056 ■ Keiko Fukuda Scholarships *(Undergraduate/Scholarship)*

Purpose: To encourage female judoka to continue their formal education and to further their training in judo. **Focus:** General studies. **Qualif.:** Applicants must be female judoka and must be U.S. citizens. Applicants with post-secondary education must have at least a "B" average. **Criteria:** Award will be based on 1) outstanding contribution to the development of judo on a local, yudanshakai, or national level; 2) good competition records (shiai or kata); 3) good moral character and social conduct; and 4) dedication to judo.

Funds Avail.: No specific amount. **To Apply:** Applicants must submit a completed application form.

9057 ■ Tamo Kitaura Scholarships *(Professional development/Scholarship)*

Purpose: To provide financial assistance to USJF referees. **Focus:** General studies. **Qualif.:** Applicants must be USJF referees who have reached a degree of technical proficiency; must show an interest in developing themselves through testing and certification. **Criteria:** Recipients will be selected based on submitted application materials.

Funds Avail.: No specific amount. **To Apply:** Applicants must complete the application form which can be obtained online. **Contact:** For further information, applicants must contact Vaughn Imada, Chm.

9058 ■ Ben Palacio Scholarships *(Undergraduate/Scholarship)*

Purpose: To financially assist students who wish to continue their judo education. **Focus:** General studies. **Qualif.:** Applicants must have plans to enroll in the City College of San Francisco. **Criteria:** Recipients will be selected based on submitted application materials.

Funds Avail.: No specific amount. **To Apply:** Applicants must contact the Board of Trustees for further information.

9059 ■ U.S. Medical Supplies
3901A Commerce Park Dr.
Raleigh, NC 27610

Fax: (919) 231-4217
Free: 800-790-4792
URL: www.usmedicalsupplies.com

9060 ■ Medical Professionals of Tomorrow Scholarships *(Undergraduate, Graduate/Scholarship)*

Purpose: To help students cover the expenses of tuition and books. **Focus:** Education, Medical. **Qualif.:** Applicants must be enrolled in an accredited two-year, four-year school, or a graduate program in the United States; must be enrolled full-time in an educational program that is related to a medical field; must be legal residents of the United States. **Criteria:** Recipients will be selected based on submitted materials.

Funds Avail.: Amount not specified. **To Apply:** Applicants must complete the online application form. **Deadline:** December 31.

9061 ■ U.S. Pan Asian American Chamber of Commerce (USPAACC)
1329 18th St. NW
Washington, DC 20036
Ph: (202) 296-5221
Fax: (202) 296-5225
Free: 800-696-7818
E-mail: info@uspaacc.com
URL: www.uspaacc.com

9062 ■ Paul Shearman Allen and Associate Scholarships *(Undergraduate/Scholarship)*

Purpose: To provide financial assistance to Asian American high school seniors who have demonstrated scholastic achievement and financial need and will pursue post-secondary education at an accredited educational institution in the United States. **Focus:** General studies. **Qualif.:** Applicants must be: at least 16 years of age at the time of application; of Asian Pacific Island heritage; citizens or permanent residents of the United States; beginning full-time study at an accredited post-secondary educational institution in the United States; must have a 3.3 grade point average. **Criteria:** Recipients are selected based on academic achievement; leadership in extracurricular activities; involvement in community service; and financial need.

Funds Avail.: $5,000. **To Apply:** Applicants must submit: completed online application with photo attached on the top right hand corner; (100 words) biography; (500 words) essay; transcript; household tax return (signed by taxpayers); two letters of recommendations; additional attachments; post-secondary institution information.

9063 ■ Asian American Scholarships *(Undergraduate/Scholarship)*

Purpose: To provide financial assistance to Asian American high school seniors who have demonstrated scholastic achievement and financial need and will pursue post-secondary education at an accredited educational institution in the United States. **Focus:** General studies. **Qualif.:** Applicants must be: at least 16 years of age at the time of application; of Asian Pacific Island heritage; citizens or permanent residents of the United States; beginning full-time study at an accredited post-secondary educational institution in the United States; must have a 3.3 grade point average or higher. **Criteria:** Applicants are evaluated on the basis of academic achievement; leadership in extracur-

Awards are arranged alphabetically below their administering organizations

ricular activities; involvement in community service; and financial need.

Funds Avail.: $5,000. **To Apply:** Applicants must submit: completed online application with photo attached on the top right hand corner; short biography; essay; transcript; household tax return; recommendations; additional attachments; and post-secondary institution information.

9064 ■ Bruce Lee Scholarships (Undergraduate/ Scholarship)

Purpose: To provide financial assistance to a student with strong character, who has persevered and prevailed over adversity, and who will pursue post-secondary education at an accredited educational institution in the United States. **Focus:** General studies. **Qualif.:** Applicants must be: at least 16 years of age at the time of application; of Asian Pacific Island heritage; citizens or permanent residents of the United States; beginning full-time study at an accredited post-secondary educational institution in the United States; must have a GPA of 3.3 or higher. **Criteria:** Applicants are evaluated based on strong character; the ability to persevere and prevail over adversity; academic excellence; community service involvement; and financial need.

Funds Avail.: $5,000. **To Apply:** Applicants must submit: completed online application with photo attached on the top right hand corner; short biography; essay; transcript; household tax return (signed by taxpayers); recommendations; additional attachments; post-secondary institution information. **Deadline:** March 20.

9065 ■ Ruth Mu-Lan and James S.C. Chao Scholarships (Undergraduate/Scholarship)

Purpose: To provide financial assistance to female Asian American high school seniors who will be pursuing post-secondary education at an accredited educational institution in the United States. **Focus:** General studies. **Qualif.:** Applicants must be: females and at least 16 years of age at the of application; of Asian Pacific Island heritage; citizens or permanent residents of the United States; beginning full-time study at an accredited post-secondary educational institution in the United States; must have a GPA of 3.3 or higher. **Criteria:** Applicants are evaluated based on academic excellence; leadership in extracurricular activities; involvement in community service; and financial need.

Funds Avail.: $5,000. **To Apply:** Applicants must submit: completed online application with photo attached on the top right hand corner; short biography; essay; transcript; household tax return (signed by taxpayers); recommendations; additional attachments; post-secondary institution information. **Deadline:** march 20.

9066 ■ Pepsico Scholarships (Undergraduate/ Scholarship)

Purpose: To provide financial assistance to Asian American high school seniors who have demonstrated scholastic achievement and financial need and will pursue post-secondary education at an accredited educational institution in the United States. **Focus:** General studies. **Qualif.:** Applicants must be: at least 16 years of age at the time of application; of Asian Pacific Island heritage; citizens or permanent residents of the United States; beginning full-time study at an accredited post-secondary educational institution in the United States; must have a GPA of 3.3 or higher. **Criteria:** Applicants are evaluated based on academic achievement; leadership in extracurricular activities; involvement in community service; and, financial need.

Funds Avail.: $5,000. **To Apply:** Applicants must submit:

completed online application with photo attached on the top right hand corner; short biography; essay; transcript; household tax return (signed by taxpayers); recommendations; additional attachments; post-secondary institution information. **Deadline:** March 20.

9067 ■ Philip Morris USA Scholarships (Undergraduate/Scholarship)

Purpose: To provide financial assistance to Asian American high school seniors who have demonstrated scholastic achievement and financial need and will pursue post-secondary education at an accredited educational institution in the United States. **Focus:** General studies. **Qualif.:** Applicants must be: at least 16 years of age at the time of application; of Asian Pacific Island heritage; citizens or permanent residents of the United States; beginning full-time study at an accredited post-secondary educational institution in the United States; must have a GPA of 3.3 or higher. **Criteria:** Applicants are evaluated based on academic achievement; leadership in extracurricular activities; involvement in community service; and financial need.

Funds Avail.: No specific amount. **To Apply:** Applicants must submit: completed online application with photo attached on the top right hand corner; short biography; essay; transcript; household tax return (signed by taxpayers); recommendations; additional attachments; post-secondary institution information.

9068 ■ Drs. Poh Shien and Judy Young Scholarships (Undergraduate/Scholarship)

Purpose: To provide financial assistance to Asian American high school seniors who have demonstrated scholastic achievement and financial need and will pursue post-secondary education at an accredited educational institution in the United States. **Focus:** General studies. **Qualif.:** Applicants must be: at least 16 years of age at the time of application; of Asian Pacific Island heritage; citizens or permanent residents of the United States; beginning full-time study at an accredited post-secondary educational institution in the United States; must have a GPA of 3.3 or higher. **Criteria:** Applicants are evaluated based on academic achievement; leadership in extracurricular activities; involvement in community service; and financial need.

Funds Avail.: No specific amount. **To Apply:** Applicants must submit: completed online application with photo attached on the top right hand corner; short biography; essay; transcript; household tax return (signed by taxpayers); recommendations; additional attachments; post-secondary institution information.

9069 ■ U.S. Pan Asian American Chamber of Commerce McDonald's Scholarships (Undergraduate/Scholarship)

Purpose: To provide financial assistance to Asian American high school seniors who have demonstrated scholastic achievement and financial need and will pursue post-secondary education at an accredited educational institution in the United States. **Focus:** General studies. **Qualif.:** Applicants must be: at least 16 years of age at the time of application; of Asian Pacific Island heritage; citizens or permanent residents of the United States; beginning full-time study at an accredited post-secondary educational institution in the United States; must have a GPA 3.3 GPA or higher. **Criteria:** Applicants are evaluated based on academic achievement; leadership in extracurricular activities; involvement in community service; and financial need.

Funds Avail.: $5,000. **To Apply:** Applicants must submit

Awards are arranged alphabetically below their administering organizations

completed online application with photo attached on the top right hand corner; short biography; essay; transcript; household tax return (signed by taxpayers); recommendations; additional attachments; post-secondary institution information. **Deadline:** March 20.

9070 ■ U.S. Pan Asian American Chamber of Commerce UPS Scholarships (Undergraduate/Scholarship)

Purpose: To provide financial assistance to Asian American high school seniors who have demonstrated scholastic achievement and financial need and will pursue post-secondary education at an accredited educational institution in the United States. **Focus:** General studies. **Qualif.:** Applicants must be: at least 16 years of age at the time of application; of Asian Pacific Island heritage; citizens or permanent residents of the United States; beginning full-time study at an accredited post-secondary educational institution in the United States; must have a GPA of 3.3 or higher. **Criteria:** Applicants are evaluated based on academic achievement; leadership in extracurricular activities; involvement in community service; and financial need.

Funds Avail.: $5,000. **To Apply:** Applicants must submit: completed online application with photo attached on the top right hand corner; short biography; essay; transcript; household tax return (signed by taxpayers); recommendations; additional attachments; post-secondary institution information.

9071 ■ United States Society on Dams (USSD)
1616 17th St., No. 483
Denver, CO 80202-1277
Ph: (303) 628-5430
Fax: (303) 628-5431
E-mail: stephens@ussdams.org
URL: www.ussdams.org

9072 ■ United States Society on Dams Scholarships (Graduate/Scholarship)

Purpose: To help students pursue their education. **Focus:** Construction. **Qualif.:** Applicants must be student members whose graduate-level research studies have a potential for developing practical solutions to design and construction problems and other dam-related issues and must be U.S. citizens. **Criteria:** Recipients will be selected based on submitted application.

Funds Avail.: No specific amount. **To Apply:** Applicants must submit a completed application form.

9073 ■ U.S.-Ukraine Foundation (USUF)
1 Thomas Cir. NW, 10th Fl., Caplin Mailroom
Washington, DC 20005
Ph: (202) 223-2228
Fax: (202) 223-1224
E-mail: info@usukraine.org
URL: www.usukraine.org

9074 ■ Mychajlo Dmytrenko Fine Arts Foundation Scholarships (Undergraduate/Scholarship)

Purpose: To support the education of Art students from the Academy of Fine Arts in Kyiv. **Focus:** Fine Arts. **Qualif.:** Applicants must be art students at the academy of Fine Arts in Kyiv. **Criteria:** Selection is based on criteria.

Funds Avail.: No specific amount. **To Apply:** Applicants

must submit a completed application form. **Contact:** 1425 La Perla Long Beach CA 90815 USA and look for Mark Dmytrenko, President or call at Tel: 877-813-4591; Fax: 562-986-5770 Email: foundation@dmytrenko.org.

9075 ■ European College of Liberal Arts Scholarships (ECLA) (Undergraduate/Scholarship)

Purpose: To offer full scholarships on a need-blind basis. **Focus:** General Studies. **Qualif.:** Applicants must study German while attending ECLA; must have earned 30 credit hours in a full year program and 8 credits in the summer program; should be between ages 18-24 with the right background and interests, proficient academic performance and good values. **Criteria:** Preference will be given to those students who meet the criteria.

Funds Avail.: No specific amount. **To Apply:** Applicants must check the available website for more information. **Contact:** Dick Shriver at rhsusa@yahoo.com.

9076 ■ University of Maryland International Student Scholarships (Undergraduate/Scholarship)

Purpose: To provide scholarships to those deserving undergraduate international students. **Focus:** General Studies. **Qualif.:** Applicants must be undergraduate international students; must have demonstrated a strong record of academic achievement and proficient English skills. **Criteria:** Preference will be given to students who meet the criteria.

Funds Avail.: No specific amount. **To Apply:** Applicants must check the available website for more information. **Deadline:** June 1. **Contact:** Office of International Admissions at 410-704-6069.

9077 ■ USA/USA-Ukramerazha Scholarships (Undergraduate/Scholarship)

Purpose: To provide financial support to talented high school students in Ukraine. **Focus:** General Studies. **Qualif.:** Applicants must be talented high school students in Ukraine heading to preparatory schools and colleges in the U.S., Canada or the United Kingdom. **Criteria:** Preference will be given to those students who meet the criteria.

Funds Avail.: No specific amount. **To Apply:** Applicants must check the available website for more information. **Remarks:** USA/USA Program services help selected students understand the requirements and procedures of Western educational institutions by offering advisory workshops and scholarships for entrance exams. **Contact:** at the above address.

9078 ■ United Student Aid Funds
Scholarship Management Services
Saint Peter, MN 56082
Free: 866-497-8723
E-mail: contact@usafunds.org
URL: www.usafunds.org

9079 ■ USA Funds Access to Education Scholarships (Graduate, Undergraduate, Vocational/Occupational/Scholarship)

Purpose: To support students with economic need in their educational pursuit. **Focus:** General studies. **Qualif.:** Applicant may be a high school senior, currently enrolled or incoming college or professional degree student; must be

Awards are arranged alphabetically below their administering organizations

planning to enroll or enrolled in full- or half-time undergraduate or full-time graduate or professional degree coursework at an accredited 2 or 4-year college, university or vocational/ technical school; have an annual adjusted gross family income of $35,000 or less; a U.S. citizen or eligible noncitizen; and must not be currently in default on a federal education loan. If studying abroad, student must be attending or planning to attend a postsecondary institution that is eligible to participate in student aid programs under Title IV of the federal Higher Education Act. **Criteria:** Scholarship awards will be based on the applicant's past academic performance and future potential; leadership and participation in school and community activities; work experience; career and educational aspirations and goals and unusual personal or family circumstances.

Funds Avail.: $1,500. **Number Awarded:** Varies. **To Apply:** Applicants are required to apply online. **Deadline:** February 15. **Contact:** 800-537-4180 or scholarship@ usafunds.org or usafunds@scholarshipamerica.org.

9080 ■ Unites States Institute of Peace (USIP)
2301 Constitution Ave.
Washington, DC 20037
Ph: (202) 457-1700
Fax: (202) 429-6063
URL: www.usip.org

9081 ■ The Jennings Randolph Peace Scholar Dissertation Program *(Doctorate/Scholarship)*

Purpose: To recognize practitioners, scholars, policymakers, journalists and other professionals so that they can conduct research on conflict and peace while in residence at the Institute. **Focus:** General studies. **Qualif.:** Applicants must be citizens of any country; must be enrolled in recognized doctoral programs in accredited universities in the United States. **Criteria:** Recipients are selected based on project significance; project design; implementation; potential as a peace scholar.

Funds Avail.: $20,000. **Number Awarded:** 10. **To Apply:** Applicants must complete the application form; applicants must submit a proposed project. **Deadline:** January 5. **Contact:** Questions will be entertained by e-mail at jrprogram@usip.org.

9082 ■ United States Institute of Peace Jennings Randolph Senior Fellowship Program *(All/Fellowship)*

Purpose: To recognize practitioners, scholars, policymakers, journalists and other professionals so that they can conduct research on conflict and peace while in residence at the Institute. **Focus:** General studies. **Qualif.:** Applicants must be citizens of any country. Non-US citizens without permanent resident status must obtain a J-1 exchange visitor visa to participate in the Fellowship Program. J-1 status requires recipients to reside in their home country for two years. **Criteria:** Recipients are selected based on overall project significance; project design; implementation; track record and reputation; potential as fellows.

Funds Avail.: $100,000. **To Apply:** Applicants must complete the application form; applicants must submit a proposed project. **Deadline:** September 8.

9083 ■ University of Alaska Anchorage
3211 Providence Dr.
Anchorage, AK 99508

Ph: (907) 786-1800
URL: www.uaa.alaska.edu/

9084 ■ UAA Elaine Atwood Scholarships
(Undergraduate/Scholarship)

Purpose: To provide financial assistance to University of Alaska Anchorage students who are formally admitted to the journalism & public communication degree-seeking program. **Focus:** Journalism; Public affairs. **Qualif.:** Applicants must demonstrate motivation, academic and leadership potential; must be in good academic standing with a minimum cumulative GPA of 3.0; must be formally admitted to the Journalism and Public Communication degree program at UAA; must plan on enrolling full-time (12 credits) at the University of Alaska Anchorage; may be an incoming or continuing student at the University of Alaska Anchorage; must be an Alaska resident who will pursue a career in Alaska. **Criteria:** Applicants will be selected based on their academic standing and application documents.

Funds Avail.: $5,000. **Number Awarded:** 2. **To Apply:** Applicants must complete the electronics scholarship application available online at www.uaa.alaska.edu/ scholarships/elaine.cfm. **Deadline:** February 15.

9085 ■ UAA Dr. Jon Baker Memorial Scholarships *(Graduate, Undergraduate, Vocational/ Occupational/Scholarship)*

Purpose: To offer financial assistance for tuition and other educational expenses to full-time University of Alaska Anchorage students who are admitted to the Psychology program. **Focus:** Psychology. **Qualif.:** Applicants must demonstrate motivation, academic and leadership potential; must be in good academic standing with a minimum cumulative GPA of 2.0 for undergraduate and 3.0 for graduate; must be formally admitted to an undergraduate, graduate, certificate, and/or vocational degree-seeking program at the University of Alaska Anchorage; may be a U.S. citizen, non U.S. citizen, Alaska resident, or out-of-state resident. **Criteria:** Preference will be given to students who are formally admitted to the Psychology program.

Funds Avail.: $500. **To Apply:** Applicants must complete the electronic scholarship application available online at www.uaa.alaska.edu/scholarships/jon.cfm. **Deadline:** February 15.

9086 ■ UAA Michael Baring-Gould Memorial Scholarships *(Graduate, Undergraduate/ Scholarship)*

Purpose: To provide financial assistance for tuition and other educational expenses to full-time students who are formally admitted to an undergraduate social sciences program or enrolled in an interdisciplinary masters program which includes sociology as one of the disciplines. **Focus:** Social sciences; Sociology. **Qualif.:** Applicants must be in good academic standing with a minimum cumulative GPA of 2.5 for undergraduates and 3.0 for graduates; must be formally admitted to an undergraduate social sciences major or an Interdisciplinary Master's degree program that includes sociology as one of the disciplines at the University of Alaska Anchorage; must have completed at least thirty credits (undergraduate applicants); must have completed at least six credits prior to the semester of the award at the University of Alaska Anchorage; must plan on enrolling full-time (12 credits for undergraduates and nine credits for graduates) at the University of Alaska Anchorage the semester the award is granted; must demonstrate involve-

Awards are arranged alphabetically below their administering organizations

ment in a project or area of study which reflects a commitment to social justice, peace, equality, and/or empowerment of minorities; may be a U.S. citizen, non-U.S. citizen, Alaska resident, or out-of-state resident. **Criteria:** Applicants will be selected based on their application materials, financial need and academic standing.

Funds Avail.: $500. **To Apply:** Applicants must submit two letters of recommendation and an essay (250 words) describing the student's involvement in a project or area of study which reflects a commitment to social justice, peace, equality, and/or empowerment of minorities. Application material must be mailed to the UAA Office of Student Financial Assistance, PO Box 141608, Anchorage, AK 99514-1608. **Deadline:** February 15.

9087 ■ UAA Mark A. Beltz Scholarships (Graduate, Undergraduate, Vocational/Occupational/ Scholarship)

Purpose: To provide financial assistance for tuition and other educational expenses to students who are in financial need. **Focus:** Political science; Economics; Business administration; Science technologies. **Qualif.:** Applicants must demonstrate motivation, academic and leadership potential; must be in good academic standing with a minimum cumulative GPA of 2.0 for undergraduates and 3.0 for graduates; must be formally admitted to a political science, economics, business administration, business and corporate law, or science and technology undergraduate, graduate, certificate, and/or vocational degree-seeking program at the University of Alaska Anchorage; must plan on enrolling at least half-time (6 credits) at the University of Alaska Anchorage; may be an incoming or continuing student at the University of Alaska Anchorage; may be a U.S. citizen, non-U.S. citizen, Alaska resident, or out-of-state resident. **Criteria:** Preference will be given to Alaska residents; who demonstrate financial need; and who intend to pursue a career in Alaska.

Funds Avail.: No specific amount. **To Apply:** Applicants must complete the electronics scholarship application available online. **Deadline:** February 15.

9088 ■ UAA Pat Brakke Political Science Scholarships (Undergraduate/Scholarship)

Purpose: To provide financial assistance for tuition and other educational expenses to a full-time student majoring in political science. **Focus:** Political science. **Qualif.:** Applicants must be in good academic standing with a minimum cumulative GPA of 3.0; must be formally admitted to the Political Science program at the University of Alaska Anchorage; must plan on enrolling at least full-time (12 credits) at the University of Alaska Anchorage; may be a U.S. citizen, non-U.S. citizen, Alaska resident, or out-of-state resident; must demonstrate motivation, academic and leadership potential. **Criteria:** Applicants will be selected based on their academic standing and application materials.

Funds Avail.: $500. **To Apply:** Applicants must complete the electronic scholarship application available online at www.uaa.alaska.edu/scholarships/pat.cfm. **Deadline:** February 15.

9089 ■ Chugach Gem & Mineral Society Scholarships (Undergraduate/Scholarship)

Purpose: To provide financial assistance for tuition and other related educational expenses to University of Alaska Anchorage or University of Alaska Fairbanks students who are admitted in a Geology degree-seeking program. **Focus:**

Geology. **Qualif.:** Applicant must be in good academic standing with a minimum cumulative GPA of 2.0; must demonstrate motivation, academic and leadership potential; must be formally admitted to an undergraduate Geology major or minor degree-seeking program at the University of Alaska Anchorage or Fairbanks by the start of the fall semester; must plan on enrolling at least half-time (six credits) at the University of Alaska Anchorage or the University of Alaska Fairbanks; must be junior or senior standing; must be an Alaska resident; must be enrolled in the semester for which the award is made. **Criteria:** Selection of applicants will be based on the application requirement.

Funds Avail.: $1,500. **Number Awarded:** 2. **To Apply:** Applicant must complete the UAA Scholarship Application Form available online; must attach a list of activities/ community service in which the applicant have participated; must submit a resume and personal essay; must have two letters of recommendation and transcript; must provide a proof of Alaska residency. Application must be received by the UAA Office of Student Financial Aid, Attn: CGMS Rasmusson Memorial Earth Science Scholarship, PO Box 141608, Anchorage, AK 99514. **Deadline:** February 15. **Contact:** Andres Macias at sheilam@super70s.com.

9090 ■ UAA Edward Rollin Clinton Memorial for Music (Undergraduate/Scholarship)

Purpose: To provide financial assistance for tuition and other educational expenses to full-time students who are formally admitted to a music degree-seeking program at the University of Alaska Anchorage. **Focus:** Music. **Qualif.:** Applicant must be in good academic standing with a minimum cumulative GPA of 3.0; must be formally admitted to a music degree-seeking program at the University of Alaska Anchorage; must plan on enrolling at least full-time (12 credits) at the University of Alaska Anchorage; may be an incoming or continuing student at the University of Alaska Anchorage; may be a U.S citizen, non-U.S citizen, Alaska resident, or out-of-state resident. **Criteria:** Class standing preferences will be as follows: (1) Preference will be given to an entering freshman planning to study piano; (2) Preference will be given to upper division students studying piano; (3) Preference will be given to freshman planning to study any instrument; (4) Preference will be given to upper division students studying any instrument; (5) Preference will be given to students who demonstrate financial need.

Funds Avail.: Amount not specified. **To Apply:** Applicants must submit a compact disc recording which must include a minimum of two (2) selections from the standard classical repertoire. **Deadline:** February 15. **Contact:** PO Box 141608, Anchorage, AK 99514.

9091 ■ UAA Governor William A. Egan Scholarships (Undergraduate/Scholarship)

Purpose: To provide financial assistance for tuition and other educational expenses to students who are formally admitted to a political science or history degree-seeking program or who are members of the Forty-Ninth State Fellows Program at the University of Alaska Anchorage. **Focus:** Political science; History. **Qualif.:** Applicant must demonstrate motivation, academic and leadership potential; must demonstrate a commitment to their community; must be in good academic standing with a minimum cumulative GPA of 2.0; must be formally admitted to a political science or history degree-seeking program at the University of Alaska Anchorage; must plan on enrolling full-time (12 credits) at the University of Alaska Anchorage; may be an

Awards are arranged alphabetically below their administering organizations

incoming or continuing student at the University of Alaska Anchorage; may be a U.S citizen, non-U.S citizen, Alaska resident, out-of-state resident; must be enrolled in the semester for which the award is made. **Criteria:** Preference will be given to applicants who are Alaska residents and have shown a potential for public service.

Funds Avail.: $500. **To Apply:** Applicants must complete the electronic scholarship application available online at www.uaa.alaska.edu/scholarships/egan.cfm. **Deadline:** February 15.

9092 ■ Alaska Community Foundation Sven E. & Lorraine Eriksson Scholarships
(Undergraduate/Scholarship)

Purpose: To provide financial assistance for tuition and other related educational expenses to full-time students of the University of Alaska Anchorage who are formally admitted to an undergraduate engineering or music degree-seeking program. **Focus:** Engineering; Music. **Qualif.:** Applicant must demonstrate motivation, academic and leadership potential; must be an Alaskan resident who has graduated from an Alaskan high school; must be a United States citizen; must be an incoming college freshman must have a minimum high school GPA of 2.5; must have a minimum cumulative GPA of 3.0 from college and have had a 2.5 GPA from high school; must be formally admitted to an undergraduate engineering or music degree-seeking program at the University of Alaska Anchorage; must demonstrate financial need; must be an incoming or continuing student at the University of Alaska Anchorage. **Criteria:** Applicants will be evaluated based on merit and extracurricular activities. Preference will be given to University of Alaska Anchorage applicants and who plan to pursue a career in Alaska as demonstrated by a personal essay.

Funds Avail.: No specific amount. **To Apply:** Applicants must complete the application form available online. **Deadline:** February 15.

9093 ■ UAA Michael D. Ford Memorial Scholarships *(Graduate, Undergraduate/Scholarship)*

Purpose: To encourage an Alaskan student to enter the field of business and to provide financial assistance for tuition and other educational expenses to full-time students who are formally admitted to a business degree-seeking program at the University of Alaska Anchorage. **Focus:** Business. **Qualif.:** Applicants must have been born in Alaska and be current Alaska residents; must be in good academic standing with a minimum cumulative GPA of 3.0; must be formally admitted to a business degree-seeking program at the University of UAA; must plan on enrolling full-time (12 credits for undergraduate and nine credits for graduate) at the UAA. **Criteria:** Preference will be given to minority students who need financial assistance.

Funds Avail.: $1,000. **To Apply:** Applicants must complete the electronic scholarship application available online at www.uaa.alaska.edu/scholarships/michael.cfm. **Deadline:** February 15.

9094 ■ UAA Jan & Glenn Fredericks Scholarships *(Graduate, Undergraduate/Scholarship)*

Purpose: To provide financial assistance for tuition and other educational expenses to full-time students who are formally admitted to a business degree-seeking program at the UAA. **Focus:** Business. **Qualif.:** Applicants must demonstrate motivation, academic and leadership potential; must be in good academic standing with a minimum

cumulative GPA of 2.0 for undergraduates and 3.0 for graduates; must be formally admitted to a business degree-seeking program at the UAA by the start of the semester; must plan on enrolling full-time (12 credits for undergraduate and nine credits for graduate) at the UAA by the start of the semester of the award; must have at least a junior, senior, or graduate class-standing by the start of the semester of the award; may be a U.S. citizen, non-U.S. citizen, Alaska resident, or out-of-state resident. **Criteria:** Preference will be given to students who are of Alaskan ethnicity.

Funds Avail.: No specific amount. **To Apply:** Applicants must complete the electronic scholarship application available online at www.uaa.alaska.edu/scholarships/jan.cfm. **Deadline:** February 15.

9095 ■ UAA Ardell French Memorial Scholarships *(Undergraduate/Scholarship)*

Purpose: To provide financial assistance for tuition and other educational expenses to full-time students who are formally admitted to a chemistry degree-seeking program at the University of Alaska Anchorage. **Focus:** Chemistry. **Qualif.:** Applicants must demonstrate motivation, academic and leadership potential; must be in good academic standing with a minimum cumulative GPA of 2.0; must be formally admitted to a undergraduate chemistry degree-seeking program at the University of Alaska Anchorage; must plan on enrolling full-time (12 credits) at the University of Alaska Anchorage; may be a U.S citizen, non-U.S citizen, Alaska resident, or out-of-state resident; must be enrolled in the semester for which the award is made. **Criteria:** Preference will be given to applicants who demonstrate financial need and to applicants from Alaska.

Funds Avail.: $500. **To Apply:** Applicants must complete the electronic scholarship application available online at www.uaa.alaska.edu/scholarships/ardell.cfm. **Deadline:** February 15.

9096 ■ Benjamin A. Gilman International Scholarships *(Undergraduate/Scholarship)*

Purpose: To encourage students to choose non-traditional study destinations abroad, especially those outside of Western Europe and Australia; to support students who have been traditionally under-represented in study abroad, including but not limited to, students with high financial need, community college students, students in under-represented fields such as the sciences and engineering, students with diverse ethnic backgrounds, and students with disabilities. **Focus:** Engineering; Science; General studies. **Qualif.:** Applicants must be U.S. citizen undergraduate students who are receiving Federal Pell Grant funding at a 2-year or 4-year college or university to participate in study abroad programs worldwide; must be receiving a Federal Pell Grant or provide proof that he/she will be receiving a Pell Grant at the time of application or during the term of their study abroad; must be applying to or has been accepted into a study abroad program eligible for credit by the student's accredited institution of higher education in the U.S; must be studying abroad for at least 4 weeks in one country; must be studying abroad in any country except Cuba or a country on the State Department's current travel warning list; must be studying in the fall, spring, or academic year terms including winter intersessions. **Criteria:** Selection criteria are based on the Gilman Scholarship Program goals that may differ from other scholarship programs. Award recipients are selected using the following criteria: (1) Diversity of Applicant; (2) Statement of Purpose Essay; (3) Follow-on Project Proposal Es-

Awards are arranged alphabetically below their administering organizations

say; (4) Academic Progress and Performance;(5) Fields of Study; (6) Country of Destination; (7) U.S. Institution and State Distribution; (8) Length of Study; (9) Lack Previous Undergraduate Study Abroad Experience.

Funds Avail.: Award amounts will vary depending on length of study and student need, with the average award being $4,000. **To Apply:** Applicants must submit a completed application form with other requirements or supporting documents. **Deadline:** April and September.

9097 ■ UAA Ken Gray Endowment Scholarships *(Undergraduate/Scholarship)*

Purpose: To provide financial assistance for tuition and other educational expenses to full-time junior or senior students who are formally admitted into a Bachelor of Arts or Bachelor of Fine Arts program in the area of sculpture and/or performance art at the University of Alaska Anchorage. **Focus:** Performing arts, Sculpture. **Qualif.:** Applicants must exhibit an innovative, experimental, and conceptual direction in his/her artwork that stretches the limits of traditional sculpture; must demonstrate motivation, academic and leadership potential; must be in good academic standing with a minimum cumulative GPA of 3.25 and a cumulative GPA of 3.5 in the area of concentration; must formally be admitted to a Bachelor of Arts or Bachelor of Fine Arts at the University of Alaska Anchorage; must plan on enrolling full-time at the University of Alaska Anchorage; must be enrolled in the semester for which the award is made; must be U.S. citizens, non-U.S. citizens, Alaska residents, or out-of-state residents. **Criteria:** Applicants will be selected based on their application materials and academic standing.

Funds Avail.: No specific amount. **To Apply:** Applicants must submit a portfolio of work consisting of 20 slides; must have three letters of reference from practitioners in the sculpture area and/or UAA faculty; must have a two-page artist's statement reflecting the criteria for selection. Application materials must be sent to UAA Office of Student Financial Assistance, Ken Gray Scholarships, PO Box 141608, Anchorage, AK 99514-1608. **Deadline:** February 15.

9098 ■ UAA Muriel Hannah Scholarships in Art *(Undergraduate, Vocational/Occupational/ Scholarship)*

Purpose: To provide financial assistance for tuition and other educational expenses to full-time students who are formally admitted to a degree-seeking program at the University of Alaska Anchorage and who have a demonstrated talent in art. **Focus:** Art. **Qualif.:** Applicants must demonstrate motivation, academic and leadership potential; must be in good academic standing with a minimum cumulative GPA of 2.0 for undergraduate and 3.0 for graduate; must be formally admitted to an undergraduate, graduate, certificate, and/or vocational degree-seeking program at the University of Alaska Anchorage; must plan on enrolling full-time (12 credits) for undergraduate and (nine credits) for graduate at the University of Alaska Anchorage; must be able to demonstrate a talent in art; must be enrolled in the semester for which the award is made; must be an incoming or continuing student at the University of Alaska Anchorage; must be a U.S. citizen, non-U.S. citizen, Alaska resident, or out-of-state resident. **Criteria:** Preference will be given to students of one-quarter or more Alaska Native ethnicity.

Funds Avail.: $500. **To Apply:** Applicants must provide ten (10) slides of artwork to demonstrate their talent in art.

Application forms are available on the website and must be sent to UAA Office of Student Financial Assistance, PO Box 141608, Anchorage, AK 99514-1608. **Deadline:** February 15.

9099 ■ Lenore & George Hedla Accounting Scholarships *(Undergraduate/Scholarship)*

Purpose: To provide financial assistance for tuition and other related educational expenses to a UAA student who is enrolled full-time or part-time with a declared major in accounting. **Focus:** Accounting. **Qualif.:** Applicants must demonstrate motivation, academic and leadership potential; must be in good academic standing with a minimum cumulative GPA of 2.0; must be formally admitted to an undergraduate accounting degree-seeking program at the UAA; must plan on enrolling at least full-time or part-time at the UAA; may be a U.S. citizen, non-U.S. citizen, Alaska resident, or out-of-state resident; must be enrolled in the semester for which the award is made. **Criteria:** Applicants will be selected based on their academic standing and application materials.

Funds Avail.: $1,000. **To Apply:** Applicants must complete the electronic scholarship application available online at www.uaa.alaska.edu/scholarships/hedla.cfm. **Deadline:** February 15.

9100 ■ Killam Fellowships Program *(Undergraduate/Fellowship)*

Purpose: To encourage undergraduate students in the United States and Canada by providing a unique opportunity for academic exchange. **Focus:** General studies. **Qualif.:** Applicant must be a citizen of Canada or the United States; must be a full-time undergraduate student in good standing at a degree-granting institution in Canada or the United States; must meet the eligibility requirements of their home university; must be fluent in English; must have a superior academic record; must complete all the steps of the application process prior to the published deadlines, and, in the case of the direct exchange applicants; must be nominated by his/her university to receive a Killam Fellowship. **Criteria:** Selection is open and competitive, based on a combination of academic standing, personal statement, and letters of reference. Applications are reviewed by an independent adjudication committee comprised of faculty members from Canadian and American universities.

Funds Avail.: $5,000. **To Apply:** Applications and instructions can be obtained online at www.killamfellowships.com. **Deadline:** January 31.

9101 ■ UAA Chris L. Kleinke Scholarships *(Graduate, Undergraduate/Scholarship)*

Purpose: To provide a monetary award to an outstanding student in the UAA Master of Science in Clinical Psychology program. **Focus:** Psychology. **Qualif.:** Applicants must demonstrate motivation, academic and leadership potential; must be in good academic standing with a minimum cumulative GPA of 3.0; must be formally admitted to the Master of Science in Clinical Psychology program at the UAA; must plan on enrolling full-time (nine credits of graduate course work) at the University of Alaska Anchorage; applicant may be an incoming or continuing student at the UAA; may be a U.S citizen, non-U.S. citizen, Alaska resident, or out-of-state resident; must be enrolled in the semester for which the award is made. **Criteria:** Preference will be given to students who have completed at least one year in the Master of Science in Clinical Psychology program. Applicants will be judged by the UAA Clinical

Awards are arranged alphabetically below their administering organizations

Training Committee by the following criteria: (1) Academic performance in the MS in Clinical Psychology program as measured by current UAA graduate GPA, and undergraduate GPA in Psychology courses (not necessarily from UAA); (2) Potential for success in the field of clinical psychology as measured by clinical community, and/or research experience and letters of recommendation from a professional in the field; (3) The strength of personal statement detailing the applicant's plans for a future career in psychology.

Funds Avail.: $500. **To Apply:** Applicants must provide two letters of recommendation from professors and/or professionals in the clinical psychology field; must complete the electronic scholarship application available online at www.uaa.alaska.edu/scholarships/chris.cfm. **Deadline:** February 15.

9102 ■ UAA Kris Knudson Memorial Scholarships (Graduate, Undergraduate/Scholarship)

Purpose: To provide financial assistance for tuition and other educational expenses to full-time students who are formally admitted to a degree-seeking program in the area of biochemistry, immunology, or microbiology at the University of Alaska Anchorage. **Focus:** Biochemistry; Immunology; Microbiology. **Qualif.:** Applicant must demonstrate motivation, academic and leadership potential; must be in good academic standing with a minimum cumulative GPA of 3.0; must be formally admitted to an undergraduate or graduate degree-seeking program in the area of biochemistry, immunology, or microbiology at the University of Alaska Anchorage; must plan on enrolling full-time (12 credits) for undergraduate and (9 credits) for graduate at the University of Alaska Anchorage; must have completed at least fifteen credits in chemistry, biological sciences, and/or natural sciences; must be involved in a research project within the area of biochemistry, immunology, or microbiology; may be a U.S citizen, non-U.S. citizen, Alaska resident, or out-of-state resident; must be enrolled in the semester for which the award is made. **Criteria:** Selection of applicants will be based on the criteria of the scholarship committee and by their academic standing.

Funds Avail.: $1,000-undergraduate; $1,500-graduate. **To Apply:** Graduate applicants must submit a brief essay (250 words max) describing their involvement in a research project related to biochemistry, immunology, or microbiology. Application forms are available at www.uaa.alaska.edu/scholarships/kris.cfm. **Deadline:** February 15.

9103 ■ Arlene Kuhner Memorial Scholarships (Undergraduate/Scholarship)

Purpose: To provide financial assistance for tuition and other related educational expenses to a University of Alaska Anchorage student who has a declared major in English. **Focus:** Education, English as a second language. **Qualif.:** Applicant must demonstrate academic excellence; must be in good academic standing with at least a cumulative GPA of 3.0; must be a student attending the University of Alaska Anchorage with a declared major in English; must take a minimum of six credits per semester. **Criteria:** Preference will be given to students who have been in residence at UAA for at least a year.

Funds Avail.: $500. **To Apply:** For further information about the scholarship, applicants are advised to visit the website at www.uaa.alaska.edu/scholarships/arlene.cfm. **Deadline:** February 15.

9104 ■ UAA Paul G. Landis Scholarships (Undergraduate/Scholarship)

Purpose: To provide an annual scholarship to art majors at the University of Alaska Anchorage. **Focus:** Art. **Qualif.:**

Applicants must demonstrate motivation, talent, academic, and leadership potential; must be in good academic standing with a minimum cumulative GPA of 2.0; must be attending at least part-time (6 credits); must be formally admitted to an art degree-seeking program at the University of Alaska Anchorage; must submit one drawing and/ or painting; may be a U.S citizen, non-U.S citizen, Alaska resident, or out-of-state resident; must be enrolled in the semester for which the award is made. **Criteria:** Recipient will be selected based on merit. Preference will be given to students whose work is focused in painting or drawing.

Funds Avail.: $1,000. **To Apply:** Applicant must submit ten (10) visual examples of their art work in slides or digital imagery using CD ROM/DVD formats; must submit a brief statement (125 words max) indicating the conceptual and formal direction pertinent to the student's current body of work. **Deadline:** February 15.

9105 ■ UAA Diane Olsen Memorial Scholarships (Undergraduate/Scholarship)

Purpose: To provide financial assistance to junior and senior students at UAA to help them pay for tuition and other related expenses. **Focus:** Economics. **Qualif.:** Applicants must demonstrate motivation, academic and leadership potential; must be in good academic standing with a minimum cumulative GPA of 2.75; must have a junior or senior standing; must be a declared economics major or have an interest in economics as demonstrated by the completion of at least 12 credits in economic courses; must plan on enrolling full-time (twelve credits for undergraduate) at the UAA; must be active in student clubs, student organizations or student governance; may be an incoming or continuing student at the UAA; may be a U.S. citizen, non-U.S. citizen, Alaska resident, or out-of-state resident. **Criteria:** Preference will be given to non-traditional students.

Funds Avail.: $500. **To Apply:** Applicants must complete the electronic scholarship application available online at www.uaa.alaska.edu/scholarships/diane.cfm. **Deadline:** February 15.

9106 ■ Providence Alaska Medical Center Auxiliary Scholarships (Undergraduate/Scholarship)

Purpose: To provide financial support to students who want to pursue their degree in the field of medicine. **Focus:** Medicine. **Qualif.:** Applicant must be admitted to a degree-seeking clinical major; must be currently enrolled as a first year student or beyond at one of the institutions of higher education in Alaska; must have a minimum GPA of 2.7. **Criteria:** Selection of applicants will be based on their application and academic standing.

Funds Avail.: $1,000. **Number Awarded:** 4. **To Apply:** Applicants must complete the scholarship application form; must have the current official transcript of grades; must have two letters of recommendation from university or college faculty members; must have a two- or three-page statement that includes: (1) Name, permanent address, phone number, social security number and student ID number; (2) A short history of the applicant and family; (3) A statement of goals; (4) A summary of interest and community involvement; (5) A summary of work experience and financial need. Application must be sent to: Providence Alaska Medical Center Auxiliary, Scholarship Committee, 3200 Providence Dr., PO Box 196604, Anchorage, AK 99519-6604. **Deadline:** June 30.

Awards are arranged alphabetically below their administering organizations

9107 ■ UAA April Relyea Scholarships (Graduate, Undergraduate, Vocational/Occupational/ Scholarship)

Purpose: To provide financial assistance for tuition and other educational expenses to students who are formally admitted to a degree-seeking program at the University of Alaska Anchorage who have an intent to explore human-nature relationships through writing or other creative expression. **Focus:** Human relations. **Qualif.:** Applicants must demonstrate environmental interest with intent to explore the topic of human-nature relationships through writing or other creative expressions; must be in good academic standing with a minimum cumulative GPA of 2.0 for undergraduates and 3.0 for graduates; must be formally admitted to an undergraduate, graduate, certificate, and/or vocational degree-seeking program at the University of Alaska Anchorage; may be a U.S citizen, non-U.S citizen, Alaska resident, or out-of-state resident; must complete a project to receive a second semester scholarship. **Criteria:** Preference will be given to students with an intent to produce work for the Student Showcase and students with a demonstrated interest in writing nature books for children.

Funds Avail.: $500. **To Apply:** Applicants must submit an essay about their interest in human-nature relationships and how they intend to pursue that interest at UAA; must submit two letters of reference from source having knowledge of their environmental interest. Application forms and other supporting documents must be sent to the UAA Office of Student Financial Assistance, April Relyea Scholarship, PO Box 141608, Anchorage, AK 99514. **Deadline:** February 15.

9108 ■ UAA Jack & Martha Roderick Scholarships (Graduate, Undergraduate/Scholarship)

Purpose: To provide financial assistance for tuition and other educational expenses to students who are formally admitted to a degree-seeking program within the College of Arts & Sciences at the University of Alaska Anchorage. **Focus:** Art; Science. **Qualif.:** Applicants must be in good academic standing with a minimum cumulative GPA of 2.0 for undergraduates and 3.0 for graduates; must be formally admitted to an undergraduate, graduate, and/or certificate degree-seeking program within the College of Arts & Science at the University of Alaska Anchorage; must plan on enrolling at least part-time (six credits for undergraduate or five for graduate) at the University of the Alaska Anchorage; may be a U.S citizen, non-U.S citizen, Alaska resident, or out-of-state resident; must be able to demonstrate financial need; must be enrolled in the semester for which the award is made. **Criteria:** Selection of applicants will be based on their financial need and academic standing.

Funds Avail.: $500. **To Apply:** Application forms are available at www.uaa.alaska.edu/scholarships/jack.cfm.

9109 ■ UAA Brown Schoenheit Memorial Scholarships (Undergraduate/Scholarship)

Purpose: To provide financial assistance for tuition and other educational expenses to students who are formally admitted to a music degree-seeking program at the University of Alaska Anchorage. **Focus:** Music. **Qualif.:** Applicants must demonstrate motivation, academic and leadership potential, and musical ability; must be in good academic standing with a minimum cumulative GPA of 2.0; must be formally admitted to a music degree-seeking program at the University of Alaska Anchorage by the start of the semester for which the award is to be made; must be a Music major with emphasis in an orchestral instru-ment; must plan on enrolling at least half-time (6 credits) at the University of Alaska Anchorage for the semester in which the award is made; may be an incoming or continuing student at the University of Alaska Anchorage; may be a U.S. citizen, non-U.S. citizen, Alaska resident, or out-of-state resident. **Criteria:** Preference will be given to a flute student and to applicants who intend to pursue a career in Alaska upon graduating.

Funds Avail.: $500. **To Apply:** Applicants must complete the electronic scholarship application available online at www.uaa.alaska.edu/scholarships/brown.cfm. **Deadline:** February 15.

9110 ■ UAA Eveline Schuster Memorial Award/ Scholarships (Graduate, Undergraduate/ Scholarship)

Purpose: To provide financial assistance to cover a student-designated sociology project to be conducted while the student is enrolled at UAA and to encourage the students to pursue sociology as a career. **Focus:** Sociology. **Qualif.:** Applicants must demonstrate motivation, academic, and leadership potential; must be in good academic standing with a 3.0 GPA and a sociology GPA of 3.3 or better; must be formally admitted to a sociology degree-seeking program or interdisciplinary master's degree-seeking program with sociology as one of the disciplines at the UAA; must plan on enrolling full-time (12 credits for undergraduates, 9 credits for graduates) at the UAA; must have at least a junior class standing; must have been enrolled in at least six (6) credits prior to the semester the award is granted; may be a U.S citizen, non-U.S. citizen, Alaska resident, or out-of-state resident. **Criteria:** Selection of applicants will be based on their academic standing and application documents.

Funds Avail.: $500. **To Apply:** Applicants must submit a cover letter indicating if they are applying for the scholarship or for project funding; must submit two (2) letters of recommendation; must submit a project budget and statement indicating the project intent; must complete the electronic scholarship application available online at www.uaa.alaska.edu/scholarships/eveline.cfm. **Deadline:** February 15.

9111 ■ Lillian Smith Scholarship for Teaching Students (Graduate, Undergraduate/Scholarship)

Purpose: To provide financial assistance to students at UAA who are studying to become teachers. **Focus:** Education. **Qualif.:** Applicants must demonstrate motivation, academic and leadership potential; must be in good academic standing with a minimum cumulative GPA of 2.0 for undergraduate and 3.0 for graduate; must be full-time students attending the UAA (12 credits for undergraduates, 9 credits for graduates); must be fully admitted to the Education degree program at the UAA; may be an incoming or continuing student at the University of Alaska Anchorage; may be a U.S. citizen, non-U.S. citizen, Alaskan resident, or out-of-state resident. **Criteria:** Preference will be given to students who demonstrate financial need.

Funds Avail.: $500. **To Apply:** Applicants must complete the electronic scholarship application available online. **Deadline:** February 15.

9112 ■ Sheri Stears Education Scholarships (Undergraduate/Scholarship)

Purpose: To provide financial assistance for tuition and other educational expenses to students admitted to pre-service teacher education programs at UAA. **Focus:** Edu-

Awards are arranged alphabetically below their administering organizations

cation. **Qualif.:** Applicants must be in good academic standing with a minimum cumulative GPA of 3.0; must be involved in extracurricular activities; must be formally admitted to the College of Education pursuing an undergraduate education degree or the Master of Arts in Teaching at the UAA; must plan on enrolling at least half-time (6 credits) at the UAA; may be an incoming or continuing student at the UAA; may be a U.S. citizen, non-U.S. citizen, Alaska resident, or out-of-state resident. **Criteria:** Preference will be given to: (1) Applicants who are Alaska residents; (2) Applicants who demonstrate financial need; (3) Applicants who address best how they see themselves advancing education in Alaska; (4) Undergraduate applicants.

Funds Avail.: $2,500. **To Apply:** Applicants must submit an essay responding to these questions: (1) How do you see yourself further advancing education in Alaska?; (2) How do your extracurricular activities enhance your educational experience?; Applicants must complete the electronic scholarship application available online at www.uaa.alaska.edu/scholarships/sheri.cfm. **Deadline:** Febraury 15.

9113 ■ Sturgulewski Family Scholarships
*(Graduate, Undergraduate, Vocational/
Occupational/Scholarship)*

Purpose: To provide financial assistance for tuition and other educational expenses to full-time students who are formally admitted to a journalism, engineering, or education degree-seeking program at the University of Alaska Anchorage. **Focus:** Journalism; Engineering; Education. **Qualif.:** Applicants must demonstrate motivation, academic and leadership potential; must be in good academic standing with a minimum cumulative GPA of 2.0 for undergraduates and 3.0 for graduates; must be formally admitted to a journalism, engineering, or education undergraduate, graduate, certificate, and/or vocational degree-seeking program at the University of Alaska Anchorage; must have plan on enrolling full-time (12 credits for undergraduates and 9 for graduates) at the University of Alaska Anchorage; may be an incoming or continuing student at the University of Alaska Anchorage; may be a U.S citizen, non-US citizen, Alaska resident, or out-of-state resident; must be enrolled in the semester for which the award is made. **Criteria:** Selection of applicants will be based on their application materials and academic standing.

Funds Avail.: $500. **To Apply:** Applicants must complete the electronic scholarship application available online at www.uaa.alaska.edu/scholarships/sturgulewski_family.cfm. **Deadline:** February 15.

9114 ■ UAA Accounting Club Scholarships
(Undergraduate/Scholarship)

Purpose: To provide financial assistance for tuition and other related educational expenses to a University of Alaska Anchorage student who is enrolled in at least nine credits with a declared major in accounting, and to encourage non-traditional students to pursue academic endeavors. **Focus:** Accounting. **Qualif.:** Applicants must demonstrate motivation, academic and leadership potential; must be in good academic standing with a minimum cumulative GPA of 3.0; must be formally admitted to an undergraduate Accounting degree-seeking program at the UAA; must plan on enrolling at least nine credits at the UAA; must demonstrate an involvement in extracurricular activities, with specific involvement in the UAA Accounting Club; must be junior or senior standing and have completed a 300-level accounting course or be enrolled in a 300-level accounting course during the semester of the award; may be a U.S. citizen,

non-U.S. citizen, Alaska resident, or out-of-state resident; must be enrolled in the semester for which the award is made. **Criteria:** Preference will be given to applicants demonstrating financial need and to non-traditional students.

Funds Avail.: $500. **To Apply:** Applicants must complete the electronic scholarship application available online. **Deadline:** February 15.

9115 ■ UAA Alaska Kidney Foundation Scholarships *(Graduate, Undergraduate/Scholarship)*

Purpose: To provide scholarships in the name of the Alaska Kidney Foundation to prepare new nurses to provide safe and effective care to individuals experiencing chronic kidney disease in Alaska. **Focus:** Nursing. **Qualif.:** Applicants must have been a resident of Alaska for three years prior to the start of the semester the award is given; must be formally admitted to a nursing degree program that leads to RN licensure; must plan on being enrolled at least part-time (six credits); must have completed one clinical nursing course by the start of the semester the award is given, unless a new student. Applicants who have successfully completed a clinical nursing course must have a minimum cumulative GPA of 2.5 and nursing course minimum cumulative GPA of 2.0. Applicants who are new students beginning clinical studies and have not completed a clinical nursing course must have a minimum cumulative GPA of 2.8. **Criteria:** Preference will be given to applicants who write an essay that: (1) Reflects a career plan that includes working with a clientele that could result in working with individuals with chronic or acute kidney disease or with clients at risk for the development of chronic renal disease; (2) Reflects a plan to remain to practice in Alaska.

Funds Avail.: $1,000. **Number Awarded:** 19. **To Apply:** Applicants must submit a brief essay (250 words max) describing the following: (1) A career plan that includes working with a clientele that could result in working with individuals with chronic or acute kidney disease or with clients at risk for the development of chronic renal disease; (2) A plan to remain in practice in Alaska. Applicants must complete the electronic scholarship application available online at www.uaa.alaska.edu/scholarships/kidney.cfm. **Deadline:** February 15.

9116 ■ UAA Alumni Association Scholarships
(Undergraduate/Scholarship)

Purpose: To provide financial assistance to students who want to pursue their education at UAA. **Focus:** General studies. **Qualif.:** Applicants must demonstrate motivation, academic, and leadership potential; must be in good academic standing with a minimum cumulative GPA of 2.5 for undergraduates and 3.0 for graduates; must be formally admitted to a degree- or certificate-seeking program within one of the following UAA schools/ colleges: College of Business, College of Business and Public Policy, College of Arts and Sciences, College of Health and Social Welfare, Community & Technical College, School of Engineering, and the College of Education; must plan on enrolling full-time (12 credits for undergraduates, 9 credits for graduates) at UAA; must be an incoming or continuing student at UAA; may be a U.S citizen, non-U.S citizen, Alaska resident, or out-of-state resident. **Criteria:** Recipient will be chosen based on their monetary need, scholastic success, community volunteer involvement, and leadership. Preference will be given to students who are Alaska high school graduates, continuing UAA students, and/or students whose parent(s) graduated with a degree from the University of Alaska and to those who demonstrate financial need.

Awards are arranged alphabetically below their administering organizations

Funds Avail.: $1,000. **Number Awarded:** 6. **To Apply:** Application forms are available online. **Deadline:** February 15.

9117 ■ UAA Anchorage Daily News Journalism Scholarships *(Undergraduate/Scholarship)*

Purpose: To provide financial assistance for tuition and other educational expenses to minority students who are formally admitted to the journalism degree-seeking program at the University of Alaska Anchorage. **Focus:** Journalism. **Qualif.:** Applicants must demonstrate motivation, academic and leadership potential; must be in good academic standing with a minimum cumulative GPA of 2.0; must be formally admitted to a journalism degree-seeking program at the University of Alaska Anchorage; must plan on enrolling full-time (12 credits for undergraduates) at the University of Alaska Anchorage; may be an incoming or continuing student at the University of Alaska Anchorage; must be enrolled in the semester for which the award is made. **Criteria:** Preference will be given to Alaska Native students.

Funds Avail.: $500. **To Apply:** Applicants must complete the electronic scholarship application available online at www.uaa.alaska.edu/scholarships/adn.cfm. **Deadline:** February 15.

9118 ■ UAA College of Business & Public Policy Scholarships *(Graduate, Undergraduate, Vocational/Occupational/Scholarship)*

Purpose: To provide financial assistance for tuition and other educational expenses to full-time students who are formally admitted to a degree-seeking program within the College of Business & Public Policy at the UAA. **Focus:** Business; Public service. **Qualif.:** Applicants must demonstrate motivation, academic and leadership potential; must be in good academic standing with a minimum cumulative GPA of 2.0 for undergraduates and 3.0 for graduates; must be formally admitted to an undergraduate, graduate, certificate, and/or vocational degree-seeking program within the College of Business & Public Policy at the UAA; must plan on enrolling full-time (12 credits for undergraduate and nine credits for graduate) at the UAA; may be an incoming or continuing student at the UAA; may be a U.S. citizen, non-U.S. citizen, Alaska resident, or out-of-state resident. **Criteria:** Applicants will be selected based on their academic standing and application materials.

Funds Avail.: No specific amount. **To Apply:** Applicants must complete the electronic scholarship application. **Deadline:** February 15.

9119 ■ UAA Emi Chance Memorial Scholarships *(Undergraduate/Scholarship)*

Purpose: To provide financial assistance for tuition and other related educational expenses to a full-time student attending the University of Alaska Anchorage and who are junior-standing art majors. **Focus:** Art. **Qualif.:** Applicants must demonstrate motivation, talent, academic, and leadership potential; must have demonstrated a commitment to his/her community; must be in good academic standing with a minimum cumulative GPA of 3.0; must be a full-time student (12 credits) at the University of Alaska Anchorage; must be formally admitted to an art degree-seeking program at the University of Alaska Anchorage; must be a drawing and/or painting major with a junior class standing; must submit one drawing and/or painting with application; may be a U.S. citizen, non-U.S. citizen, Alaska resident, or out-of-state resident; must be enrolled in the semester for which the award is made. **Criteria:** Selection of applicants will be

based on their academic standing and application materials.

Funds Avail.: $500. **To Apply:** Applicants must submit one drawing and/or painting to the UAA Office of Student Financial Assistance. Application forms are available online and must be sent to UAA Office of Student Financial Assistance, EMI Chance Memorial Scholarships, PO Box 141608, AK 99514-1608. **Deadline:** February 15.

9120 ■ UAA Friends of the Performing Arts Scholarships *(Undergraduate/Scholarship)*

Purpose: To provide financial assistance for tuition and other education related expenses to a full-time University of Alaska Anchorage student who has shown a proven interest in the performing arts. **Focus:** Performing arts. **Qualif.:** Applicants must demonstrate motivation, academic and leadership potential; must be in good academic standing in an undergraduate performing arts degree-seeking program at the University of Alaska Anchorage; must plan on enrolling full-time (12 credits) at the University of Alaska Anchorage; must show proven interest in the performing arts; may be an incoming or continuing student at the University of Alaska Anchorage; may be a U.S. citizen, non-U.S. citizen, Alaska resident, or out-of-state resident; must be enrolled in the semester for which the award is made. **Criteria:** Applicants will be selected based on their application materials and academic standing.

Funds Avail.: $500. **To Apply:** Applicants must complete the scholarship application available online at www.uaa.alaska.edu/scholarships/friends_arts.cfm. **Deadline:** February 15.

9121 ■ UAA GCI, Inc. Scholarships *(Undergraduate/Scholarship)*

Purpose: To provide financial assistance for tuition and other educational expenses to full-time students who are formally admitted to a journalism & public communications degree-seeking program at the University of Alaska Anchorage and who are in financial need. **Focus:** Journalism; Public affairs. **Qualif.:** Applicants must demonstrate motivation, academic and leadership potential; must be in good academic standing with a minimum cumulative GPA of 3.0; must be formally admitted to a journalism & public communications degree-seeking program at the University of Alaska Anchorage; must plan on enrolling full-time (12 credits) at the University of Alaska Anchorage; must be able to demonstrate financial need; must be enrolled in the semester for which the award is made; may be an incoming or continuing student at the University of Alaska Anchorage; may be a U.S citizen, non-U.S citizen, Alaska resident, or out-of-state resident. **Criteria:** Applicants will be selected based on their application materials and academic standing.

Funds Avail.: $500. **To Apply:** Applicants must complete the electronic scholarship application available online at www.uaa.alaska.edu/scholarships/sturgulewski_family.cfm. **Deadline:** February 15.

9122 ■ UAA Kimura Scholarship Fund Illustration Scholarships *(Undergraduate/Scholarship)*

Purpose: To provide financial assistance for tuition and other related educational expenses to full-time students at the University of Alaska Anchorage with a declared major in art or journalism & public communications. **Focus:** Art; Journalism; Illustrators and illustrations. **Qualif.:** Applicants must be a full-time student (12 credits per semester) attending the University of Alaska Anchorage with a declared

Awards are arranged alphabetically below their administering organizations

major in art with an emphasis in illustration; must be in their junior year and have completed at least nine credits in illustration classes at the 200 level or above; must be in good academic standing with at least a 3.0 GPA. **Criteria:** Applicants will be selected based on their application materials and academic standing.

Funds Avail.: $500. **Number Awarded:** 1. **To Apply:** Applicants must submit a proof of their photography work. Application documents and other supporting documents must submit to UAA Office of Student Financial Assistance, Kimura Scholarships, PO Box 141608, Anchorage, AK 99514. **Deadline:** February 15.

9123 ■ UAA Kimura Scholarship Fund Photography Scholarships *(Undergraduate/ Scholarship)*

Purpose: To provide financial assistance for tuition and other related educational expenses to full-time students at the University of Alaska Anchorage with a declared major in art or journalism & public communications. **Focus:** Art; Journalism; Photography. **Qualif.:** Applicant must be a full-time student attending the University of Alaska Anchorage with a declared major in art or with a declared major in journalism & public communication with an emphasis in photography; must be in their junior year and has completed at least nine credits in studio photography classes at the 200 level or above; must be in good academic standing with at least a 3.0 GPA. **Criteria:** Applicants will be selected based on their application and academic standing.

Funds Avail.: $500. **Number Awarded:** 1. **To Apply:** Applicants must submit a proof of their photography work. Application documents and other supporting documents must submit to UAA Office of Student Financial Assistance, Kimura Scholarships, PO Box 141608, Anchorage, AK 99514. **Deadline:** February 15.

9124 ■ UAA Pignalberi Public Policy Scholarships *(Graduate/Scholarship)*

Purpose: To provide financial assistance for tuition and other educational expenses to students enrolled in a graduate degree program in the UAA College of Business and Public Policy. **Focus:** Business; Public service. **Qualif.:** Applicants must demonstrate motivation, academic and leadership potential; must be in good academic standing with a minimum cumulative GPA of 3.0; must be full-time graduate students (9 credits per semester) formally admitted to the College of Business and Public Policy; must be Alaskan residents with the intent to stay and be involved in local business and/or politics; may be incoming or continuing students at the UAA. **Criteria:** Preference will be given to students who demonstrate financial need.

Funds Avail.: $500. **To Apply:** Applicants must submit a brief essay (250 words) answering the following question: "In your opinion, what is the most important political issue in Alaska today?"; must complete the electronic scholarship application available online at www.uaa.alaska.edu/scholarships/pignalberi_pp.cfm. **Deadline:** February 15.

9125 ■ UAA Quanterra Scholarships *(Undergraduate/Scholarship)*

Purpose: To provide financial assistance for tuition and other educational expenses to full-time or part-time students who are formally admitted to an engineering or science degree-seeking program at the University of Alaska Anchorage and who are of Alaska Native ethnicity. **Focus:** Engineering; Science. **Qualif.:** Applicants must demonstrate motivation, academic and leadership potential; must

be in good academic standing with a minimum cumulative GPA of 2.5 for undergraduate and 3.0 for graduate; must be formally admitted to a engineering or science degree-seeking program at the University of Alaska Anchorage by the start of the semester of the award; may also be in the Masters of Civil Engineering Program, Master of Science Program; Associate of Applied Science Program for Petroleum Engineering Aide or Petroleum Technology, or working toward a Petroleum Technology Certificate; must plan on enrolling at least half-time (6 credits) at the University of Alaska Anchorage; must be able to demonstrate financial need; must be enrolled in the semester for which the award is made; must be Alaska Native ethnicity; must provide proof of Native Corporation Affiliation and Lineage Verification; may be an incoming or continuing student at the University of Alaska Anchorage. **Criteria:** Preference will be given to students in the Petroleum Technology Program or the Chemistry Program.

Funds Avail.: $500. **To Apply:** Applicant must complete the online scholarship application and must provide a proof of Native Corporation Affiliation and Lineage Verification. **Deadline:** February 16.

9126 ■ UAA RRANN Program Scholarships *(Undergraduate/Scholarship)*

Purpose: To provide financial assistance for tuition and other educational expenses to students currently enrolled in a nursing degree program through the Recruitment and Retention of Alaska Natives into Nursing at the UAA. **Focus:** Nursing. **Qualif.:** Applicants must be in good academic standing with a minimum cumulative GPA of 2.0; must be formally admitted to a degree program within the School of Nursing through the RRANN program; may be an incoming or continuing student at the UAA; must be residents of Alaska; must be enrolled in the semester for which the award is to be in effect. **Criteria:** Preference will be given to Alaska Natives or American Indian students.

Funds Avail.: $500. **To Apply:** Applicants must complete the electronic scholarship application available online at www.uaa.alaska.edu/scholarships/rrann.cfm. **Deadline:** February 15.

9127 ■ UAA Wells Fargo Career Scholarships *(Graduate/Scholarship)*

Purpose: To provide financial assistance for tuition and other educational expenses to students who are seriously interested in a career with Wells Fargo. **Focus:** Food service careers. **Qualif.:** Applicants must demonstrate motivation, academic and leadership potential; must be in good academic standing with a minimum cumulative GPA of 3.0; must be seriously interested in a career with Wells Fargo; must meet all internship requirements through the UAA Career Services Center; must be a junior or senior student attending the University of Alaska Anchorage; must be enrolled full-time (12 credits) during the semester of the award; must be admitted to an undergraduate degree program within the College of Business and Public Policy. **Criteria:** Preference will be given to candidates in Business Management, Finance, Economics, or Accounting majors or minors.

Funds Avail.: $5,000-$1,100. **Number Awarded:** 2. **To Apply:** Applicants must submit a brief essay (250 words) describing their interest in a career with Wells Fargo; must complete the electronic scholarship application available online at www.uaa.alaska.edu/scholarships/wells.cfm. **Deadline:** February 15.

Awards are arranged alphabetically below their administering organizations

9128 ■ UAA Melissa J. Wolf Scholarships
(Undergraduate/Scholarship)

Purpose: To provide financial assistance for tuition and other educational expenses to full-time students who are formally admitted to the Accounting degree program at the UAA. **Focus:** Accounting. **Qualif.:** Applicant must demonstrate motivation, academic and leadership potential; must be in good academic standing with a minimum cumulative grade point average of 2.0; must be formally admitted to an Accounting degree at the UAA; must plan on enrolling full-time (twelve credits) at the UAA; may be a U.S. citizen, non-U.S. citizen, Alaska resident, or out-of-state resident; must be enrolled in the semester for which the award is made. **Criteria:** Preference will be given to students who demonstrate a financial need.

Funds Avail.: No specific amount. **To Apply:** Applicants must complete the electronic scholarship application online. **Deadline:** February 15.

9129 ■ University of Alaska Anchorage - Matanuska-Susitna College
PO Box 2889
Palmer, AK 99645
Ph: (907) 745-9774
Fax: (907) 745-9711
E-mail: info@matsu.alaska.edu
URL: matsu.alaska.edu

9130 ■ Alaska Aerospace Development Corporation Scholarships *(Undergraduate/Scholarship)*

Purpose: To provide support to deserving students in Alaska who want to pursue an education in any campus of the University of Alaska. **Focus:** Applied mathematics; Physics; Engineering; Business; Technical communications. **Qualif.:** Applicant must be a freshman student majoring in mathematics, physics, engineering, business, or a technical science field such as computer science who has graduated from the Kodiak Island Borough School District; must be a full-time student enrolled in 14 credits and in good academic standing. **Criteria:** Candidates will be selected based on their academic standing and application documents.

Funds Avail.: $5,000. **To Apply:** Applicants must submit a written statement verifying that he/she has not been convicted of a crime other than a minor traffic violation; must complete the application forms available at the website; must attach a personal essay, two letters of recommendation, and current transcripts. **Deadline:** February 15.

9131 ■ Alaska Native Medical Center Auxiliary Scholarships *(Undergraduate/Scholarship)*

Purpose: To provide support to deserving students in Alaska who want to pursue an education in any campus of the University of Alaska. **Focus:** General studies. **Qualif.:** Applicant must have graduated from a rural Alaska high school that is off the highway system in Alaska; must be a full-time student and in good academic standing with a minimum cumulative GPA of 2.0. **Criteria:** Preference will be given to Alaska Natives and/or individuals of Native American descent.

Funds Avail.: $1,000. **To Apply:** Applicant must complete the application forms available at the website; must attach a personal essay, two letters of recommendation, and current transcripts. **Deadline:** February 15.

9132 ■ Alaska Press Club Scholarships
(Undergraduate/Scholarship)

Purpose: To provide support to deserving students in Alaska who want to pursue an education in any campus of the University of Alaska. **Focus:** Journalism. **Qualif.:** Applicant must be a junior, senior or graduate journalism student with a minimum GPA of 2.0. **Criteria:** Preference will be given to applicants from Rural Alaska communities.

Funds Avail.: $500. **To Apply:** Applicant must complete the application forms available at the website; must attach a personal essay, two letters of recommendation, and current transcripts. **Deadline:** February 15.

9133 ■ Alaska Support Industry Alliance Scholarships *(Undergraduate/Scholarship)*

Purpose: To provide financial support for deserving students in Alaska intending to pursue an education in any campus of the University of Alaska. **Focus:** Resource management; Biology; Wildlife conservation management, and science; Petroleum engineering. **Qualif.:** Applicants must be full-time students and Alaska residents who have at least 3.0 GPA majoring in a field that will support the industry growth in Alaska and at the same time showing concern for the environment and how industry is developed. **Criteria:** Preference will be given to students who are sons or daughters of employees of companies that belong to the Alaska Support Industry Alliance.

Funds Avail.: $500. **To Apply:** Applicants must complete the application forms available in the website; must attach a personal essay, two letters of recommendation, and their current transcripts. **Deadline:** February 17.

9134 ■ Alaska Visitors Association/Gomar Scholarships *(Undergraduate/Scholarship)*

Purpose: To provide support for deserving students in Alaska intending to pursue an education in any campus of the University of Alaska. **Focus:** Travel and tourism. **Qualif.:** Applicants must be enrolled in programs of study emphasizing travel and tourism. **Criteria:** Preference will be given to students of Latin American descent.

Funds Avail.: $500. **To Apply:** Applicants must complete the application forms available in the website; must attach a personal essay, two letters of recommendation, and their current transcripts. **Deadline:** February 17.

9135 ■ Alaska Yukon Pioneer Memorial Scholarships *(Undergraduate/Scholarship)*

Purpose: To provide support for deserving students in Alaska intending to pursue an education in any campus of the University of Alaska. **Focus:** General studies. **Qualif.:** Applicants must be full-time students and residents of Alaska or the Yukon Territory and must have graduated from high school either in Alaska or the Yukon Territory. **Criteria:** Preference will be given to students who plan to remain in Alaska or the Yukon Territory.

Funds Avail.: $500. **To Apply:** Applicants must complete the application forms available on the website; must attach a personal essay, two letters of recommendation, and their current transcripts. **Deadline:** February 17.

9136 ■ Amos Joe Alter ASCE Section Alaska Section Scholarships *(Undergraduate/Scholarship)*

Purpose: To provide support to deserving students in Alaska who want to pursue an education in any campus of

Awards are arranged alphabetically below their administering organizations

the University of Alaska. **Focus:** Civil engineering. **Qualif.:** Applicant must be a full-time student attending the University of Alaska at Anchorage or the University of Alaska at Fairbanks, and must be a civil engineering major. **Criteria:** Preference will be given to college seniors with a minimum GPA of 3.0.

Funds Avail.: $1,000. **To Apply:** Applicant must complete the application forms available at the website; must attach a personal essay, two letters of recommendation, and current transcripts. **Deadline:** February 17.

9137 ■ Mike Ardaw Scholarships
(Undergraduate/Scholarship)

Purpose: To provide support to deserving students in Alaska who want to pursue an education in any campus of the University of Alaska. **Focus:** Science; Education; Engineering. **Qualif.:** Applicant must be a full-time student and have a minimum GPA of 2.5. **Criteria:** Preference will be given to students studying science, education or engineering and to students who have been Alaska residents for at least one year and are from the Navy Lake area.

Funds Avail.: $1,000. **To Apply:** Applicant must complete the application forms available at the website; must attach a personal essay, two letters of recommendation, and current transcripts. Applicants must also submit a paragraph describing their connection to and love for the Nacy Lake area. **Deadline:** February 17.

9138 ■ Lawrence Bayer Business Administration Scholarships *(Undergraduate/Scholarship)*

Purpose: To provide support to deserving students in Alaska who want to pursue an education in any campus of the University of Alaska. **Focus:** Business administration. **Qualif.:** Applicant must be full-time students attending the University of Alaska at Fairbanks or the University of Alaska at Anchorage and have a minimum GPA of 3.0; must be a business administration major active in clubs and/or sports. **Criteria:** Preference will be given to applicants with financial need.

Funds Avail.: $500. **To Apply:** Applicant must complete the application forms available at the website; must attach a personal essay, two letters of recommendation, and current transcripts. Applicants must also submit a list of clubs and/or sports in which he/she is an active participant. **Deadline:** February 17.

9139 ■ Charles E. Behlke Engineering Memorial Scholarships *(Undergraduate/Scholarship)*

Purpose: To provide support to deserving students in Alaska who want to pursue an education in any campus of the University of Alaska. **Focus:** Engineering. **Qualif.:** Applicants must be full-time students entering their sophomore, junior, or senior year; must be engineering majors; must be in good academic standing with a minimum GPA of 2.5. **Criteria:** Selection of applicant will be based on their academic standing and application requirements.

Funds Avail.: $1,000. **To Apply:** Applicant must complete the application forms available at the website; must attach a personal essay, two letters of recommendation, and current transcripts. **Deadline:** February 17.

9140 ■ Bill & Nell Biggs Scholarships
(Undergraduate/Scholarship)

Purpose: To provide support to deserving students in Alaska who want to pursue an education in any campus of

the University of Alaska. **Focus:** Accounting; Business administration; Engineering; Science; Mathematics and mathematical sciences. **Qualif.:** Applicants must be graduates of Juneau-Douglas High School or Juneau residents who have completed a high school equivalency program. **Criteria:** Preference will be given to applicants majoring in accounting, business administration, engineering, science and mathematics, related science subjects or foreign languages areas such as Spanish, German or French.

Funds Avail.: $500. **To Apply:** Applicant must complete the application forms available at the website; must attach a personal essay, two letters of recommendation, and current transcripts. **Deadline:** February 17.

9141 ■ Bolick Foreign Student Scholarships
(Undergraduate/Scholarship)

Purpose: To provide support to deserving students in Alaska who want to pursue an education in any campus of the University of Alaska. **Focus:** General studies. **Qualif.:** Applicant must be a full-time student holding exclusive citizenship in another country and attending the university on a student visa. **Criteria:** Preference will be given to Swedish citizens.

Funds Avail.: $1,000. **To Apply:** Applicant must complete the application forms available at the website; must attach a personal essay, two letters of recommendation, and current transcripts. **Deadline:** February 17.

9142 ■ Dr. Betty J. Boyd-Beu & Edwin G. Beu, Jr. Scholarships *(Undergraduate/Scholarship)*

Purpose: To provide financial assistance for tuition and other educational expenses to non-traditional students who are seeking degree completion or retraining at the Matanuska-Susitna College. **Focus:** General studies. **Qualif.:** Applicant must be a non-traditional student and have graduated from high school; must have worked prior to enrolling or returning to college, thus re-entering college to complete a degree or enrolling to retrain for another position in the workplace; must be in good academic standing with a minimum cumulative GPA of 3.0; must be formally admitted to a degree seeking program; must be enrolled in the semester(s) for which the award is made. **Criteria:** Selection will be based on their academic performance and application documents.

Funds Avail.: $2,500. **To Apply:** Applicants must complete the MSC scholarship application; must attach a list of activities/community service in which they have participated; must attach a resume of their work experience over the past four years; must attach a personal essay; must attach two letters of recommendation and transcripts. Application forms must be submitted to: Dr. Betty Boyd-Beu & Edwin G. Beu Jr. Scholarship, Matanuska-Susitna College, Student Services, FSM 102, PO Box 2889, Palmer, AK 99645. **Deadline:** August 1.

9143 ■ Charles E. Bunnell Scholarships
(Undergraduate/Scholarship)

Purpose: To provide support to deserving students in Alaska who want to pursue an education in any campus of the University of Alaska. **Focus:** General studies. **Qualif.:** Applicants must be full-time students entering his/her junior or senior year with a declared major in an accredited field and have a minimum GPA of 3.2. **Criteria:** Preference will be given to applicants who graduated from an Alaska high school and have lived in Alaska for 3 or more years.

Funds Avail.: $1,000. **To Apply:** Applicant must submit an

Awards are arranged alphabetically below their administering organizations

additional paragraph describing how they emulate the ideals of persistence, vision, self sacrifice, concern for others and love of the North. Applicant must complete the application forms available at the website; must attach a personal essay, two letters of recommendation, and current transcripts. **Deadline:** February 17. **Remarks:** Named after Charles E. Bunnell, the first president of the University of Alaska.

9144 ■ Loyal D. Burkett Memorial Scholarships
(Undergraduate/Scholarship)

Purpose: To provide support to deserving students in Alaska who want to pursue an education in any campus of the University of Alaska. **Focus:** General studies. **Qualif.:** Applicant must be a full-time student in good academic standing and demonstrate motivation, academic and leadership potential. **Criteria:** Applicants will be selected based on their application and academic standing.

Funds Avail.: $500. **To Apply:** Applicant must complete the application forms available at the website; must attach a personal essay, two letters of recommendation, and current transcripts. **Deadline:** February 17.

9145 ■ Lyle Carlson Wildlife Management Scholarships *(Undergraduate/Scholarship)*

Purpose: To provide support to deserving students in Alaska who want to pursue an education in any campus of the University of Alaska. **Focus:** Wildlife conservation, management, and science. **Qualif.:** Applicant must be a student majoring in wildlife management, wildlife biology or another closely related major and have a minimum GPA of 3.0. **Criteria:** Applicants will be selected based on their academic standing.

Funds Avail.: $500. **To Apply:** Applicant must complete the application forms available at the website; must attach a personal essay, two letters of recommendation, and current transcripts. **Deadline:** February 17.

9146 ■ Mable B. Crawford Memorial Scholarships *(Undergraduate/Scholarship)*

Purpose: To provide support to deserving students in Alaska who want to pursue an education in any campus of the University of Alaska. **Focus:** Accounting; Economics; Law; Business. **Qualif.:** Applicants must be students who have been residents of Alaska for at least two years. **Criteria:** Awarded on the basis of both scholastic ability and need. Preference is given to applicants majoring in accounting, economics, law or business.

Funds Avail.: $500. **To Apply:** Applicant must complete the application forms available at the website; must attach a personal essay, two letters of recommendation, and current transcripts. **Deadline:** February 17.

9147 ■ Patricia Ann Hughes Eastaugh Memorial Teaching Scholarships *(Undergraduate/Scholarship)*

Purpose: To provide support to deserving students in Alaska who want to pursue an education in any campus of the University of Alaska. **Focus:** Teaching. **Qualif.:** Applicants must be first-time incoming freshman students enrolled in a baccalaureate degree program; must intend to become an elementary or secondary school teacher in Alaska and be enrolled in academic programs leading toward that end; must be an Alaska resident and a graduate of a public or private school in Alaska. **Criteria:** Preference will be given to student who shows a desire to teach

and is in the top 25% of their class.

Funds Avail.: $8,000. **To Apply:** Applicant must attach an additional statement of 1,000 words or less entitled "Why I Want to become a Teacher of Children in Alaska." Candidates should also briefly express their opinion of Alaska's educational system(s) and their thoughts on changes they would embrace therein. Applicant must complete the application forms available in the website; must attach a personal essay, two letters of recommendation, and current transcripts. **Deadline:** February 15.

9148 ■ Excellence in Geographic Information Systems Scholarships *(Undergraduate/Scholarship)*

Purpose: To provide support to deserving students in Alaska who want to pursue an education in any campus of the University of Alaska. **Focus:** Geography. **Qualif.:** Applicant must be a full-time junior, senior, or graduate student in good standing with a minimum overall cumulative GPA of 2.88 or a major GPA of 3.2; must have declared interest in Geographic Information Systems or Mapping Science and be engaged in a directed or undirected project or class involving Geographic Information Systems during the award period . **Criteria:** Applicants will be selected based on their academic standing.

Funds Avail.: $500. **To Apply:** Applicant must complete the application forms available at the website; must attach a personal essay, two letters of recommendation, and current transcripts. **Deadline:** February 17.

9149 ■ Lydia Fohn-Hansen/Lola Hill Memorial Scholarships *(Undergraduate/Scholarship)*

Purpose: To provide support to deserving students in Alaska who want to pursue an education in any campus of the University of Alaska. **Focus:** Family planning; Consumer affairs. **Qualif.:** Applicant must be full-time undergraduate or degree-seeking graduate students majoring in Family and Consumer Sciences or a related field; must have a minimum GPA of 3.0 and must be a resident of Alaska. **Criteria:** Selection of applicants will be based on their academic performance.

Funds Avail.: $1,000. **To Apply:** Applicant must complete the application forms available at the website; must attach a personal essay, two letters of recommendation, and current transcripts. **Deadline:** February 15.

9150 ■ Johnny and Sarah Frank Scholarships *(Undergraduate/Scholarship)*

Purpose: To provide support to deserving students in Alaska who want to pursue an education in any campus of the University of Alaska. **Focus:** General studies. **Qualif.:** Applicants must be of Gwich in Athabaskan descent; must have a minimum 2.5 GPA and must enroll for at least six credit hours. **Criteria:** Preference will be given to students from Arctic Village or Venetie and students from Ft. Yukon, Chalkyitsik, Birch Creek, Circle, Beaver or Eagle.

Funds Avail.: $500. **To Apply:** Applicant must complete the application forms available at the website; must attach a personal essay, two letters of recommendation, and current transcripts. **Deadline:** February 15.

9151 ■ Charles F. Gould Endowment Scholarships *(Undergraduate/Scholarship)*

Purpose: To provide support to deserving students in Alaska who want to pursue an education in any campus of the University of Alaska. **Focus:** General studies. **Qualif.:**

Awards are arranged alphabetically below their administering organizations

Applicant must be a full-time Alaska Native student, preferably Eskimo, with a minimum GPA of 2.0. **Criteria:** Applicants will be selected based on their academic standing.

Funds Avail.: $1,000. **To Apply:** Applicant must complete the application forms available at the website; must attach a personal essay, two letters of recommendation, and their current transcripts. **Deadline:** February 15.

9152 ■ Patty Hamilton Early Childhood Development Scholarships (Undergraduate/ Scholarship)

Purpose: To provide support to deserving students in Alaska who want to pursue an education in any campus of the University of Alaska. **Focus:** Early childhood education. **Qualif.:** Applicants must be Alaska residents entering their junior or senior year and majoring in early childhood development/ education. **Criteria:** Preference will be given to students who are working with or volunteering for young children.

Funds Avail.: $2,500. **To Apply:** Applicant must complete the application forms available at the website; must attach a personal essay, two letters of recommendation, and current transcripts. Applicants must also submit a paragraph describing his/her experience working with or volunteering with young children. **Deadline:** February 15.

9153 ■ John B. Henderson Scholarships (Undergraduate/Scholarship)

Purpose: To provide support to deserving students in Alaska who want to pursue an education in any campus of the University of Alaska. **Focus:** General studies. **Qualif.:** Applicants must be full-time students attending any campus of the University of Alaska. **Criteria:** Applicants will be selected based on their application requirements.

Funds Avail.: $500. **To Apply:** Applicant must complete the application forms available at the website; must attach a personal essay, two letters of recommendation, and current transcripts. **Deadline:** February 15.

9154 ■ Donald Wills Jacobs Scholarships (Undergraduate/Scholarship)

Purpose: To provide support to deserving students in Alaska who want to pursue an education in any campus of the University of Alaska. **Focus:** Fine arts. **Qualif.:** Applicant must be a full-time junior or senior student enrolled in a Bachelor of Fine Arts program at the University of Alaska. **Criteria:** Applicants will be selected based on their academic performance and application documents.

Funds Avail.: $500. **To Apply:** Applicant must complete the application forms available at the website; must attach a personal essay, two letters of recommendation, and current transcripts. **Deadline:** February 17.

9155 ■ Iver & Cora Knapstad Scholarships (Undergraduate/Scholarship)

Purpose: To provide support to deserving students in Alaska who want to pursue an education in any campus of the University of Alaska. **Focus:** General studies. **Qualif.:** Applicants must be full-time students attending any University of Alaska campus. **Criteria:** Applicants will be selected based on their academic standing.

Funds Avail.: $1,000. **To Apply:** Applicant must complete the application forms available at the website; must attach a personal essay, two letters of recommendation, and current transcripts. **Deadline:** February 15.

9156 ■ Robert Wade Korn Endowed Scholarships (Undergraduate/Scholarship)

Purpose: To provide support to deserving students in Alaska who want to pursue an education in any campus of the University of Alaska. **Focus:** General studies. **Qualif.:** Applicants must be graduates of Cordova Alaska High School with a minimum of 2.0 average. **Criteria:** Selection of applicants must be based on their academic standing.

Funds Avail.: $1,000. **To Apply:** Applicant must complete the application forms available at the website; must attach a personal essay, two letters of recommendation, and current transcripts. **Deadline:** February 17.

9157 ■ Austin E. Lathrop Scholarships (Undergraduate/Scholarship)

Purpose: To provide support to deserving students in Alaska who want to pursue an education in any campus of the University of Alaska. **Focus:** General studies. **Qualif.:** Applicants must be full-time students attending any campus of the University of Alaska. **Criteria:** Preference will be given to students who show a need for financial assistance.

Funds Avail.: $1,000. **To Apply:** Applicant must complete the application forms available at the website; must attach a personal essay, two letters of recommendation, and their current transcripts. **Deadline:** February 15.

9158 ■ Franklin M. Leach Scholarships (Undergraduate/Scholarship)

Purpose: To provide support to deserving students in Alaska who want to pursue an education in any campus of the University of Alaska. **Focus:** General studies. **Qualif.:** Applicants must be full-time students attending any campus of the University of Alaska. **Criteria:** Selection of applicants will be selected based on their academic standing.

Funds Avail.: $1,000. **To Apply:** Applicant must complete the application forms available at the website; must attach a personal essay, two letters of recommendation, and current transcripts. **Deadline:** February 15.

9159 ■ Mat-Su Health Foundation Scholarships (Undergraduate/Scholarship)

Purpose: To provide financial support to qualified individuals. **Focus:** Health care services. **Qualif.:** Applicant must be a US citizen; must be a Matanuske-Susitna Borough resident enrolling or currently enrolled in higher education in any health care field. **Criteria:** Selection of applicants will be based on their application materials.

Funds Avail.: $2,500-$5000. **To Apply:** Applicants must complete the application provided in typed format; an essay of not less than 200 words; financial information; three references including address, telephone number and relationship to applicant; a minimum of three reference letters from either work or volunteer-related supervisors or teachers/professors but not from individuals related to the applicant; and a sealed transcript. Scholarship application forms are available at: Mat-Su Regional Outpatient Center in Wasilla, 950 E Bogard, Ste. 218, online at www.matsu-healthfoundation.org. **Deadline:** April 2.

9160 ■ Matanuska-Susitna College Regent's Scholarships (Undergraduate/Scholarship)

Purpose: To provide support to deserving students in Alaska who want to pursue an education in any campus of the University of Alaska. **Focus:** General studies. **Qualif.:** Applicant must be junior, senior or graduate students in good academic standing whose application reflects demon-

Awards are arranged alphabetically below their administering organizations

strated commitment and involvement in leadership and civic or professional service activities and recognized academic achievement. **Criteria:** Applicants will be selected based on their academic standing and application documents.

Funds Avail.: $5,000. **To Apply:** Applicant must complete the application forms available at the website; must attach a personal essay, two letters of recommendation, and current transcripts. **Deadline:** February 15.

9161 ■ Dave McCloud Aviation Memorial Scholarships *(Undergraduate/Scholarship)*

Purpose: To provide support to deserving students in Alaska who want to pursue an education in any campus of the University of Alaska. **Focus:** General studies. **Qualif.:** Applicants must be full-time students seeking a degree in Aviation and have a minimum cumulative GPA of 2.0; must be a resident of Alaska. **Criteria:** Preference will be given to students who are affiliated with the military.

Funds Avail.: $500. **To Apply:** Applicant must complete the application forms available at the website; must attach a personal essay, two letters of recommendation, and current transcripts. **Deadline:** February 15.

9162 ■ Richard Mellon Endowment Scholarships *(Undergraduate/Scholarship)*

Purpose: To provide support to deserving students in Alaska who want to pursue an education in any campus of the University of Alaska. **Focus:** General studies. **Qualif.:** Applicants must be full-time students. **Criteria:** Preference will be given to students who demonstrate a need for financial assistance.

Funds Avail.: $1,500. **To Apply:** Applicant must complete the application forms available at the website; must attach a personal essay, two letters of recommendation, and current transcripts. **Deadline:** February 15.

9163 ■ Molly Ann Mishler Memorial Scholarships *(Undergraduate/Scholarship)*

Purpose: To provide financial assistance for tuition and other educational expenses to students who are enrolled in Early Childhood Development courses at Matanuska-Susitna College. **Focus:** Early childhood education. **Qualif.:** Applicant must demonstrate motivation, academic and leadership potential; must have a good academic standing with a minimum cumulative GPA of 2.0; must be formally admitted to a degree-seeking program at the University of Alaska at Anchorage or Matanuska-Susitna College; must plan on enrolling at least part-time (6 credits) at Matanuska-Susitna College; must be an incoming or continuing student at Matanuska-Susitna College; must be a U.S. citizen, non-U.S. citizen, Alaska resident, or out-of-state resident; must be enrolled in the semester(s) for which the award is offered; must be enrolled in at least three credits for Early Childhood Development courses. **Criteria:** Preference will be given to applicants formally admitted into the Early Childhood Development program.

Funds Avail.: $500. **To Apply:** Applicant must complete the MSC scholarship application form; must attach a list of activities/community service in which they have participated; must attach a resume of their work experience they have held over the past four years; must attach a personal essay (not more than 500 words); must have two letters of recommendation and transcripts. Application documents must be submitted to Molly Ann Mishler Memorial Scholarships, Matanuska-Susitna College, Student Services, FSM 102,

PO Box 2889, Palmer, AK 99645. **Contact:** 907-745-9762.

9164 ■ Andrew Nerland Endowment Scholarships *(Undergraduate/Scholarship)*

Purpose: To provide support to deserving students in Alaska who want to pursue an education in any campus of the University of Alaska. **Focus:** General studies. **Qualif.:** Applicants must be full-time student. **Criteria:** Preference will be given to students who demonstrate a need for financial assistance.

Funds Avail.: $1,000. **To Apply:** Applicant must complete the application forms available at the website; must attach a personal essay, two letters of recommendation, and current transcripts. **Deadline:** February 15.

9165 ■ Maureen E. Nolan-Cahill Memorial Scholarships *(Undergraduate/Scholarship)*

Purpose: To provide support to deserving students in Alaska who want to pursue an education in any campus of the University of Alaska. **Focus:** Science. **Qualif.:** Applicants must be a female students majoring in science with a GPA of at least 3.0; must demonstrate financial need. **Criteria:** Preference will be given first to applicants who are residents of Southern Alaska and next to graduates of Alaska high schools.

Funds Avail.: $500. **To Apply:** Applicant must complete the application forms available at the website; must attach a personal essay, two letters of recommendation, and current transcripts. **Deadline:** February 15.

9166 ■ Don & Jan O'Dowd/SWAA Scholarships *(Undergraduate/Scholarship)*

Purpose: To provide support to deserving students in Alaska who want to pursue an education in any campus of the University of Alaska. **Focus:** General studies. **Qualif.:** Applicants must be full-time incoming freshmen students with a minimum GPA of 3.0; must be Alaska residents and graduates of an Alaska high school. **Criteria:** Applicants will be selected based on their academic standing.

Funds Avail.: $500. **To Apply:** Applicant must complete the application forms available at the website; must attach a personal essay, two letters of recommendation, and current transcripts. **Deadline:** February 15.

9167 ■ Alvin G. Ott Fish and Wildlife Scholarships *(Undergraduate/Scholarship)*

Purpose: To provide support to deserving students in Alaska who want to pursue an education in any campus of the University of Alaska. **Focus:** General studies. **Qualif.:** Applicants must be full-time students with a minimum GPA of 3.0 and majoring in a field related to fish and wildlife. **Criteria:** Applicants will be selected based on their academic standing.

Funds Avail.: $500. **To Apply:** Applicant must complete the application forms available at the website; must attach a personal essay, two letters of recommendation, and current transcripts. **Deadline:** February 15.

9168 ■ Point Lay Memorial Scholarships *(Undergraduate/Scholarship)*

Purpose: To provide support to deserving students in Alaska who want to pursue an education in any campus of the University of Alaska. **Focus:** General studies. **Qualif.:** Applicants must be full-time students and current or former residents of Pt. Lay, Alaska. **Criteria:** Preference for applicants is given in the following order: (1) Resident or

Awards are arranged alphabetically below their administering organizations

former resident of Pt. Lay, Alaska; (2) Alaska resident of one quarter or more Native ancestry who resides north of the Arctic Circle; (3) Alaska resident of one quarter or more Native ancestry; (4) Alaska resident; (5) undergraduate student.

Funds Avail.: $3,000. **To Apply:** Applicant must complete the application forms available at the website; must attach a personal essay, two letters of recommendation, and current transcripts. **Deadline:** February 15.

9169 ■ A.D. 'Al' Robertson Memorial Scholarships *(Undergraduate/Scholarship)*

Purpose: To provide support to deserving students in Alaska who want to pursue an education in any campus of the University of Alaska. **Focus:** General studies. **Qualif.:** Applicants must be full-time students and a member of the graduating class of Ketchikan High School in the year the scholarship is awarded; must have a minimum GPA of 2.5. **Criteria:** Selection of applicants will be based on their academic standing and application documents.

Funds Avail.: $500. **To Apply:** Applicant must complete the application forms available at the website; must attach a personal essay, two letters of recommendation, and current transcripts. **Deadline:** February 15.

9170 ■ Pat and Cliff Rogers Nursing Scholarships *(Undergraduate/Scholarship)*

Purpose: To provide support to deserving students in Alaska who want to pursue an education in any campus of the University of Alaska. **Focus:** General studies. **Qualif.:** Applicants must be full-time students in his/her junior or senior year of a nursing program at any institution within the U.S. **Criteria:** Applicants will be selected based on their application requirements.

Funds Avail.: $500. **To Apply:** Applicant must complete the application forms available in the website; must attach a personal essay, two letters of recommendation, and current transcripts. **Deadline:** February 15.

9171 ■ Dr. Orrin J. Rongstad Wildlife Management Scholarships *(Undergraduate/Scholarship)*

Purpose: To provide support to deserving students in Alaska who want to pursue an education in any campus of the University of Alaska. **Focus:** Wildlife conservation, management, and science. **Qualif.:** Applicants must be full-time students majoring in wildlife management and be in good academic standing. **Criteria:** Applicants will be selected based on their academic standing and application documents.

Funds Avail.: $500. **To Apply:** Applicant must complete the application forms available at the website; must attach a personal essay, two letters of recommendation, and current transcripts. **Deadline:** February 15.

9172 ■ Russian/Central Asian Student Scholarships *(Undergraduate/Scholarship)*

Purpose: To provide support to deserving students in Alaska who want to pursue an education in any campus of the University of Alaska. **Focus:** General studies. **Qualif.:** Applicants must be residents of Russia, Central Asia or the former Soviet Union, Kazakhstan, Uzbekistan, Turkmenistan, or Kyrgyzstan. **Criteria:** Preference will be given to residents of the Russian Far East.

Funds Avail.: $500. **To Apply:** Applicant must complete the application forms available at the website; must attach a personal essay, two letters of recommendation, and cur-

rent transcripts. **Deadline:** February 17.

9173 ■ Clair Shirey Scholarships *(Undergraduate/Scholarship)*

Purpose: To provide support to deserving students in Alaska who want to pursue an education in any campus of the University of Alaska. **Focus:** Classical studies. **Qualif.:** Applicants must be music majors with a demonstrated interest or emphasis in classical/liturgical organ. **Criteria:** Preference will be given to students who are residents of the following geographical areas: Anchorage Archdiocese, Alaska and Pacific Northwest.

Funds Avail.: $500. **To Apply:** Applicant must complete the application forms available at the website; must attach a personal essay, two letters of recommendation, and current transcripts. Applicants must a paragraph describing his/her interest or emphasis in classical/liturgical organ. **Deadline:** February 15.

9174 ■ Ward Sims Memorial Scholarships *(Undergraduate/Scholarship)*

Purpose: To provide support to deserving students in Alaska who want to pursue an education in any campus of the University of Alaska. **Focus:** Journalism. **Qualif.:** Applicants must be full-time junior or senior students enrolled in the Journalism program with a minimum GPA of 2.0. **Criteria:** Applicants will be selected based on their academic performance and application materials.

Funds Avail.: $1,000. **To Apply:** Applicant must complete the application forms available at the website; must attach a personal essay, two letters of recommendation, and current transcripts. **Deadline:** February 15.

9175 ■ Snodgrass Scholarships *(Undergraduate/Scholarship)*

Purpose: To provide an incentive for Alaska's middle and high school students to achieve academic excellence, and to encourage the top high school graduates from every community in Alaska to attend the University of Alaska. **Focus:** Accounting; Engineering, Architectural; Computer and information sciences; Fires and fire prevention; Heating, air conditioning, and refrigeration; Business administration; Telecommunications systems. **Qualif.:** Applicant must be admitted to the given Matanuska-Susitna College degree programs; must be a continuing student at Matanuska-Susitna College who has earned at least 20 credit hours; must have a cumulative GPA of 3.0 or higher; must exhibit good moral character and conduct; must be registered for eight or more credit hours. **Criteria:** Candidates will be selected based on their academic achievements and scholarship committee criteria.

Funds Avail.: $500-$2,000. **To Apply:** Applicants must complete the MSC scholarship application and attach a resume showing their work experience; must compose an essay of 500 words or less describing their educational and career goals and how they plan to attain them; must have two letters of recommendation, written within the last two years. Application form and other supporting documents must be sent to Snodgrass Scholarships, Matanuska-Susitna College, Student Service, 907-745-9762. **Deadline:** May 31.

9176 ■ Sourdough Reunion Memorial Scholarships *(Undergraduate/Scholarship)*

Purpose: To provide support to deserving students in Alaska who want to pursue an education in any campus of

Awards are arranged alphabetically below their administering organizations

the University of Alaska. **Focus:** General studies. **Qualif.:** Applicants must be full-time students entering his/her junior or senior year with a minimum GPA of 3.0 and be residents of Alaska or the Yukon Territory; must have graduated from a high school in Alaska or the Yukon Territory. **Criteria:** Selection of recipients will be based on academic performance and application materials.

Funds Avail.: $500. **To Apply:** Applicant must complete the application forms available at the website; must attach a personal essay, two letters of recommendation, and current transcripts. **Deadline:** February 15.

9177 ■ Umialik Scholarships *(Undergraduate/ Scholarship)*

Purpose: To provide support to deserving students in Alaska who want to pursue an education in any campus of the University of Alaska. **Focus:** General studies. **Qualif.:** Applicants must be full-time students attending any campus of the University of Alaska and be in good academic standing. **Criteria:** Preference will be given to Alaska Natives.

Funds Avail.: $5,000. **To Apply:** Applicant must complete the application forms available at the website; must attach a personal essay, two letters of recommendation, and current transcripts. **Deadline:** February 15.

9178 ■ University of Alaska Scholars Program *(Undergraduate/Scholarship)*

Purpose: To provide an incentive for Alaska's middle and high school students intending to achieve academic excellence; to nourish efforts of schools to provide high quality education; and to encourage the top high school graduates from every community in Alaska to attend the University of Alaska. **Focus:** General studies. **Qualif.:** Applicants must be US citizens or aliens lawfully admitted for permanent residence in the United States; must have successfully earned a high school diploma from a qualified Alaska high school; must be admitted into a certificate or degree program; must be enrolled as full-time, undergraduate students for the first fall semester following the graduation date of the class with which he or she designated and continuously thereafter; and must participate in or attend any mandatory orientation or program as may be required by the campus. **Criteria:** Selection of recipients will be based on their academic standing at the end of their junior year.

Funds Avail.: No specific amount. **To Apply:** Applicants may contact the UA Scholars Program for application process. **Contact:** 907-474-5105; 877-257-2465; scholars@alaska.edu.

9179 ■ William S. Wilson Memorial Scholarships *(Undergraduate/Scholarship)*

Purpose: To provide support to deserving students in Alaska who want to pursue an education in any campus of the University of Alaska. **Focus:** Science. **Qualif.:** Applicants must be full-time students majoring in science. **Criteria:** Preference will be given to undergraduate students, but graduate students will be considered.

Funds Avail.: $500. **To Apply:** Applicant must complete the application forms available at the website; must attach a personal essay, two letters of recommendation, and current transcripts. Applicants must also submit a paragraph describing his/her research interest and/or evidence of research potential. **Deadline:** February 15.

9180 ■ Guy A. Woodings Scholarships *(Undergraduate/Scholarship)*

Purpose: To provide support to deserving students in Alaska who want to pursue an education in any campus of

the University of Alaska. **Focus:** Natural resources. **Qualif.:** Applicants must be majoring in Natural Resource Management with a 3.1 GPA; must have been enrolled at least 2 years pursuing a 4-year degree. **Criteria:** Preference will be given to students pursuing a degree in Natural Resource Management with an emphasis on planning and land use and those who have performed community service.

Funds Avail.: $500. **To Apply:** Applicant must complete the application forms available at the website. Applicants must submit an essay discussing how they envision the growth and development of the state over the next five years and what part they envision themselves playing in that growth and development. **Deadline:** February 15.

9181 ■ Ralph Yetka Memorial Scholarships *(Undergraduate/Scholarship)*

Purpose: To provide support to deserving students in Alaska who want to pursue an education in any campus of the University of Alaska. **Focus:** Engineering; Education, Elementary; Education, Secondary; Computer and information sciences. **Qualif.:** Applicants must be full-time students and graduates of Ketchikan or Revilla High School with a minimum GPA of 2.5; must be majoring in engineering, elementary or secondary education, computer science or aviation. **Criteria:** Applicants will be selected based on their application materials and academic standing.

Funds Avail.: $500. **To Apply:** Applicant must complete the application forms available at the website; must attach a personal essay, two letters of recommendation, and current transcripts. **Deadline:** February 15.

9182 ■ Joan C. Yoder Memorial Nursing Scholarships *(Undergraduate/Scholarship)*

Purpose: To provide support to deserving students in Alaska who want to pursue an education in any campus of the University of Alaska. **Focus:** Nursing. **Qualif.:** Applicants must be full-time students majoring in nursing who have completed one clinical nursing course and is in good academic standing. **Criteria:** Selection of applicants will be based on their academic standing and application materials.

Funds Avail.: $500. **To Apply:** Applicant must complete the application forms available at the website; must attach a personal essay, two letters of recommendation, and current transcripts. **Deadline:** February 15.

9183 ■ Yukon Delta Fisheries Development Association Scholarships *(Undergraduate/ Scholarship)*

Purpose: To provide support to deserving students in Alaska who want to pursue an education in any campus of the University of Alaska. **Focus:** General studies. **Qualif.:** Applicants must be undergraduate or graduate students from Alakanuk, Emmonak, Grayling, Kotlik, Mountain Village, Nunam Iqua, Pitka's Point, St. Mary's, Pilot Station, Marshall, Russian Mission, Holy Cross, Anvik and Shageluk; must demonstrate a subsistence and/or commercial fishing relationship to the lower Yukon Delta region and maintain a minimum cumulative GPA of 2.5 or higher. **Criteria:** Applicants will be selected based on their application materials and academic standing.

Funds Avail.: $1,500. **To Apply:** Applicant must complete the application forms available at the website; must attach a personal essay, two letters of recommendation, current transcripts, and a letter from his/her city or tribal council

Awards are arranged alphabetically below their administering organizations

stating his/her relationship to the area. **Deadline:** February 15.

9184 ■ University of Alaska Fairbanks Alumni Association (UAFAA)
PO Box 750126
Fairbanks, AK 99775
Ph: (907) 474-7081
Fax: (907) 474-6712
Free: 800-770-ALUM
E-mail: uaf-alumni@alaska.edu
URL: www.uaf.edu/alumni

9185 ■ Jim Doogan Memorial Scholarships
(Undergraduate/Scholarship)

Purpose: To support students with their educational pursuit. **Focus:** General studies. **Qualif.:** Applicant must be a sophomore student or above. **Criteria:** Scholarship recipients are selected based on the volunteer alumni scholarship committee's review of the application materials.

Funds Avail.: No specific amount. **To Apply:** Applicants may apply using the Supplement for Scholarship Application. **Remarks:** Established in memory of Jim Doogan, a supporter of UAF and an active member of the UAF Alumni Association.

9186 ■ Fairbanks Chapter Legacy Scholarships
(Undergraduate/Scholarship)

Purpose: To support students in their educational pursuits. **Focus:** General studies. **Qualif.:** Applicant must be a sophomore student or above with a 3.5 GPA or higher. **Criteria:** Recipients are selected by the volunteer alumni scholarship committee.

Funds Avail.: No specific amount. **To Apply:** Applicants may apply using the Supplement for Scholarship Application.

9187 ■ Jay Hammond Memorial Scholarships
(Undergraduate/Scholarship)

Purpose: To support students with their educational pursuit. **Focus:** General studies. **Qualif.:** Applicants must exhibit leadership and desire to make a difference in Alaska. **Criteria:** Scholarship recipients are selected based on the volunteer alumni scholarship committee's review of the application materials.

Funds Avail.: No specific amount. **To Apply:** Applicants may apply using the Supplement for Scholarship Application. **Remarks:** The scholarship is named after Jay Hammond, former governor.

9188 ■ Audrey Loftus Memorial Scholarships
(Undergraduate/Scholarship)

Purpose: To support students with their educational pursuit. **Focus:** General studies. **Qualif.:** Applicants must be freshmen or transfer students, demonstrated experience in and future commitment to extracurricular/ community activities; and have a GPA of 3.0 and above. **Criteria:** Selection is based on leadership skills and potentiality.

Funds Avail.: No specific amount. **To Apply:** Applicants may apply using the Supplement for Scholarship Application. **Remarks:** Established in memory of Adrey Loftus, founding director of the UAFAA.

9189 ■ UAF Alumni Association Scholarships
(Undergraduate/Scholarship)

Purpose: To support the education of a dependent of an alumni. **Focus:** General studies. **Qualif.:** Applicants must

be undergraduate sophomores, juniors and seniors; dependents of active alumni association members; and have a GPA of 2.5-3.5 range. **Criteria:** Recipients are selected by the volunteer alumni scholarship committee.

Funds Avail.: No specific amount. **To Apply:** Applicants may apply using the Supplement for Scholarship Application. **Remarks:** Recipients are expected to be involved in the alumni development after graduation. Previous awardees may re-apply.

9190 ■ University Aviation Association (UAA)
3410 Skyway Dr.
Auburn, AL 36830-6444
Ph: (334) 844-2434
Fax: (334) 844-2432
E-mail: uaamail@uaa.aero
URL: www.uaa.aero

9191 ■ Joseph Frasca Excellence in Aviation Scholarships *(Undergraduate/Scholarship)*

Purpose: To encourage a high level of achievement in aviation studies through education assistance. **Focus:** Aviation. **Qualif.:** Applicants must have a minimum of 3.0 GPA; must have Federal Aviation Administration certification in either aviation maintenance or flight; a member of at least one Aviation organization; and juniors or seniors currently enrolled in a UAA member institution. **Criteria:** Preference is given to applicants with demonstrated interest or experience in aviation simulation; aircraft restoration; aerobatics; with work experience in aviation; with work experience while in school; and exhibits financial need.

Funds Avail.: 2,000. **Number Awarded:** 2. **To Apply:** Applicants must submit five copies of completed application form; a brief essay; transcript; FAA certificates; one letter of reference; documents about financial status and other supporting documents. **Deadline:** April 9. **Contact:** Dr. David NewMyer, Southern Illinois University Carbondale, College of Applied Sciences and Arts, 1365 Douglas Dr., MC 6623, Carbondale, IL 62901; Phone:618-453-8898; Email: dnewmyer@aviation.siu.edu.

9192 ■ Eugene S. Kropf Scholarships
(Undergraduate/Scholarship)

Purpose: To encourage careers in aviation and other related fields through educational assistance. **Focus:** Aviation. **Qualif.:** Applicants must be U.S. citizens; enrolled in or planning to pursue two- or four-year degrees in the field of aviation; must be officially enrolled in a UAA member institution; and have a 3.0 GPA or above on a 4.0 scale. **Criteria:** Awards are given based on academic merit and character.

Funds Avail.: $500. **To Apply:** Applicants must submit application form; proof of enrollment; transcript; an essay (250 words typewritten, double-spaced) on "How Can I Improve Aviation Education". **Deadline:** May 31. **Contact:** Prof. Kevin R. Kuhlmann, Metropolitan State College of Denver, Campus Box 30, PO Box 173362, Denver, CO 80217-3362.

9193 ■ Paul A. Whelan Aviation Scholarships
(Undergraduate, Graduate/Scholarship)

Purpose: To promote educational pursuits in the field of aviation or space-related fields through financial assistance. **Focus:** Aviation. **Qualif.:** Applicants must be U.S. citizens; sophomore, junior, senior or graduate students; enrolled in

---

Awards are arranged alphabetically below their administering organizations

a UAA member institution; must have 2.5 overall GPA and 3.0 in Aviation; and must demonstrate a love of aviation, leadership and extracurricular involvement/community involvement. **Criteria:** Priority is given to applicants who have an FAA certification as a pilot or mechanic; formerly or currently in military service via active duty, ROTC, the Air National Guard or Reserves while in school; and member of an aviation-related association or professional group such as the UAA.

Funds Avail.: $2,000. **Number Awarded:** 1. **To Apply:** Applicants must submit original copies and five copies of application form; official transcript; and recommendation letter from the institution. **Deadline:** May 15. **Remarks:** Established in memory of Paul A. Whelan, an aviation educator. **Contact:** Dr. David A. NewMyer, Chair, University Aviation Association Scholarship Committee, Southern Illinois University Carbondale, 1365 Douglas Drive, ASA Carbondale, IL 62901-6623.

9194 ■ University of California, Berkeley
F501 Haas School of Business, No. 1900
Berkeley, CA 94720-1900
Ph: (510) 642-7159
Fax: (510) 642-1318
E-mail: cmr@haas.berkeley.edu
URL: cmr.berkeley.edu/

9195 ■ John Gardner Fellowships
(Undergraduate/Fellowship)

Purpose: To encourage the graduating seniors to pursue the public service career of their choice. **Focus:** Public service. **Qualif.:** Applicant must be a senior graduating from the University of California, Berkeley; must be a United States citizen. **Criteria:** Applicants are evaluated based on the following criteria: (1) Demonstrated commitment to public service; (2) Record of academic accomplishment; (3) Maturity, personal integrity, and sense of responsibility; (4) Creativity, energy, and initiative; (5) Leadership potential: the ability to inspire others to action.

Funds Avail.: $27,500. **Number Awarded:** 3. **To Apply:** Applicant must submit one copy of the complete application form (available online); must have a formal resume; must have an official academic transcript; must have three letters of recommendation, at least one of which must be from a faculty member who is familiar with the applicant's university level work. **Deadline:** February 16. **Contact:** Terri Bimes, Assist. Dir. of Research, Institute of Governmental Studies, 122 Moses Hall, No. 2370, Berkely, CA 94720-2370; Phone: 510-642-3233; Fax: 510-642-3020; Email: bimes@berkely.edu.

9196 ■ Donald A. Strauss Scholarships
(Undergraduate/Scholarship)

Purpose: To encourage junior students to pursue a public service career of their choice. **Focus:** Public service. **Qualif.:** Applicant must be a full-time junior; must be in the upper third class (typically a minimum 3.3 GPA); must have a plan to devote a significant part of his/her life to public service. **Criteria:** Applicants will be evaluated based on their public service project proposal, outstanding leadership potential, effective communication skills and who "wish to make a difference" in local, regional, or national communities.

Funds Avail.: $10,000. **To Apply:** Applicant must complete the application form (available online); must have one-page

resume that includes work history and community service experience; must have one-page autobiographical statement; must have four-page proposal for a community service project; must have completed the acceptance form; must have two or three letters of recommendation from individuals who are well-acquainted worth the student's academic and/or service work; must have an official copies of all college transcripts. **Deadline:** February 22. **Contact:** Alicia Hayes at the above address.

9197 ■ Udall Scholarships *(Undergraduate/ Scholarship)*

Purpose: To provide financial support for outstanding sophomore and junior students. **Focus:** Environmental science, Health care services. **Qualif.:** Applicant must be a student who studies the environmental and related fields; must be a Native American or Alaska Native in fields related to health care or tribal public policy; Applicant must be a full-time sophomore or junior students; must be a U.S. citizen or resident alien; must have a minimum of 3.0 GPA. **Criteria:** Applicants will be selected based on how they demonstrate the area of study and public or community service activities, commitment to and potential for making significant contributions to their fields.

Funds Avail.: $5,000 for educational expenses. UC Berkeley selection committee will select the university's nominee based on the application materials and criteria. **To Apply:** Applicant must complete the application form; must have a 800-word essay discussing a significant public speech, legislative act, or public policy statement by Congressman Udall and its relationship to the applicant's interest or coursework; must have a three letters of recommendation from: (1) a faculty member who can discuss the applicant's potential; (2) a faculty member in the applicant's of study; (3) another individual who can attest to the applicant's capabilities; must have the official college transcripts. **Deadline:** February 22. **Contact:** Alicia Hayes at the above address.

9198 ■ University of California Institute for Mexico and the United States
University of California
3324 Olmsted Hall
Riverside, CA 92521-0147
Ph: (951) 827-3519
Fax: (951) 827-3856
E-mail: ucmexus@ucr.edu
URL: ucmexus.ucr.edu

9199 ■ UC MEXUS Grants for Dissertation Research *(Graduate/Grant)*

Purpose: To support dissertation research or MFA final projects by University of California graduate students. **Focus:** Latin American studies. **Qualif.:** Applicants must be University of California graduate students in good standing or Mexican nationals currently enrolled in UC Mexico-related graduate programs. **Criteria:** Recipients will be selected based on submitted proposal.

Funds Avail.: $12,000. **To Apply:** Applicants must submit a proposal. This should include an application cover sheet, project institutional approval sheet, project plan, bibliography, budget request, abbreviated curriculum vitae, letters of intent to participate, attachments and support letters. **Deadline:** September 17 - submission of proposal; September 28 - submission of application and supporting documents.

Awards are arranged alphabetically below their administering organizations

9200 ■ UC MEXUS Short-Term Projects
(Master's, Doctorate, Postdoctorate/Grant)

Purpose: To encourage graduate students and post-doctoral researchers continue academic exchange, research training and scholarly development in Mexico-related studies. **Focus:** Latin American studies. **Qualif.:** Applicants must be University of California graduate students enrolled in a Master's or Doctoral level program who are in good standing or either be Mexican nationals currently enrolled in any UC Mexico-related graduate studies. Post-doctoral researchers are eligible to apply. **Criteria:** Applicants will be selected based on submitted proposal. It should demonstrate clarity, quality and feasibility.

Funds Avail.: $1,500. **To Apply:** Applicants must complete the application form; must submit a cover page, project plan, detailed budget, curriculum vitae, UC faculty sponsor's abbreviated curriculum vitae, letter of support, Mexican academic host's letter of invitation and curriculum vitae, letter of acceptance and two sets of the proposal. **Deadline:** December 3.

9201 ■ University Film and Video Association (UFVA)
PO Box 1777
Edwardsville, IL 62026
Ph: (914) 761-1187
Fax: (914) 761-3115
Free: 866-647-8382
E-mail: ufvahome@aol.com
URL: www.ufva.org

9202 ■ UFVA Carole Fielding Student Grants
(Graduate, Undergraduate/Grant)

Purpose: To support a student research project. **Focus:** Video; Media arts. **Qualif.:** Applicant must be an undergraduate or graduate student (a faculty member who is also a member of the association must sponsor the applicant). **Criteria:** Applicants are selected based on eligibility and merit.

Funds Avail.: $1,000. **To Apply:** Applicants must submit six stapled copies of the application form as cover sheet (available on the website); a one-page description of the project; a one-page resume; a statement by the sponsoring UFVA member; and a one-page budget statement. **Deadline:** December 15. **Contact:** Professor Adrianne Carageorge Rochester Institute of Technology, Bldg. 7B, Rm. 2270, 70 Lomb Memorial Dr., Rochester, NY 14623.

9203 ■ University of Hawaii at Manoa
2445 Campus Rd., Hemenway Hall 107
Honolulu, HI 96822
Ph: (808) 956-7043
Fax: (808) 956-9962
E-mail: kaleo@kaleo.org
URL: www.kaleo.org/

9204 ■ National Security Education Program - David L. Boren Fellowships *(Undergraduate/Fellowship)*

Purpose: To provide support for outstanding U.S. graduate students intending to pursue a career in language study. **Focus:** Foreign languages. **Qualif.:** Applicant must be a U.S graduate student who wants to pursue their area of specialization in language study; must be a U.S. citizen. **Criteria:** Selection of applicants will be based on their application requirements.

Funds Avail.: Up to $30,000. **To Apply:** For applications and information, applicants are advised to contact Dr. Chizuko Allen. **Deadline:** January 31. **Contact:** Dr. Chizuko Allen, Undergraduate and Fellowships Advisor, School of Pacific & Asian Studies, University of Hawaii, Honolulu, HI 96822, 808-956-2210.

9205 ■ Starr Foundation Graduate Fellowships in Asian Studies *(Graduate/Grant)*

Purpose: To support continuing graduate students for such activities as field study, summer language study or research/conference travel. **Focus:** Foreign languages, General studies. **Qualif.:** Applicant must be a graduate student who does not hold FLAS awards. **Criteria:** Selection will be based on the application requirements.

Funds Avail.: $15,000. **Number Awarded:** 2. **To Apply:** For further information and application materials, applicants are advised to contact the SPAS Office of student Academic Services, 315 Moore Hall. **Deadline:** February 21.

9206 ■ University of Hawaii at Manoa East-West Center Graduate Fellowships *(Graduate, Postdoctorate/Fellowship)*

Purpose: To provide support for qualified individuals intending to participate in the educational and research programs at the EWC. **Focus:** General studies. **Qualif.:** Applicant must be a citizen and legal resident of an Asian or Pacific country, or the United States; must be interested in participating in the educational and research programs at EWC while pursuing a master's or doctoral degree at the University of Hawaii. **Criteria:** Preference is given to those in a master's degree program.

Funds Avail.: No specific amount. **To Apply:** Application must be made to the Center's in-country program representative. **Deadline:** November 1. **Contact:** For further information, applicants may write to the EastWest Center, Office of Award Service, Rm. 2066, 1601 East-West Rd., Honolulu, HI 96848.

9207 ■ University of Hawaii at Manoa Graduate Assistantship Awards *(Graduate/Award)*

Purpose: To assist graduate students with their education. **Focus:** Teaching. **Qualif.:** Applicant must have a strong background in Asian Studies; must have a high scholastic record; must be admitted as a graduate student; must have a high level of English proficiency; must carry at least 6 units of credit each semester and maintain a minimum of 3.0 GPA. **Criteria:** Selection will be based on the academic standing of the applicant.

Funds Avail.: No specific amount. **To Apply:** Applicant must submit a letter of application, resume, and names, addresses and telephone numbers of three references. **Deadline:** March 3. **Contact:** Chair of Asian Studies, Moore Hall 412, University of Hawaii at Manoa, 1890 East-West Rd., Honolulu, HI 96822.

9208 ■ University of Hawaii at Manoa Graduate Student Organization Travel Funds *(Graduate/Grant)*

Purpose: To provide assistance to UH graduate students making scholarly or artistic presentations at conferences and professional meetings on the mainland and elsewhere. **Focus:** General studies. **Qualif.:** Applicant must be a clas-

Awards are arranged alphabetically below their administering organizations

sified graduate student. **Criteria:** Selection of applicant will be based on their application requirements.

Funds Avail.: No specific amount. **Number Awarded:** 3. **To Apply:** Applicants may contact the GSO for the application forms and more detailed information on the amount of stipends. **Deadline:** January 1, June 1, September 1. **Contact:** GSO at 808-956-8776/8018/4832, Hemenway Hall 212.

9209 ■ University of Hawaii at Manoa Japan Travel Bureau Scholarships *(Graduate, Undergraduate/Scholarship)*

Purpose: To promote understanding between peoples and nations of the world through higher education. **Focus:** International affairs and relations, Crosscultural studies. **Qualif.:** Candidate must be a full-time classified UHM graduate student or upper class undergraduate interested in international relations or cross-cultural studies and have demonstrated high scholastic achievement. **Criteria:** Candidates will be selected based on their academic standing.

Funds Avail.: $2,000. **Number Awarded:** 2. **To Apply:** Information and application materials may be obtained from the SPAS Office of Student Academic Services, 315 Moore Hall. **Deadline:** February 21.

9210 ■ University of Louisville Alumni Association
University of Louisville
Malcolm B. Chancey Center
Alumni Office
Louisville, KY 40292
Ph: (502) 852-6186
Fax: (502) 852-6920
Free: 800-813-8635
E-mail: patsy.wynne@louisville.edu
URL: www.uoflalumni.org/s/1157/home.aspx

9211 ■ Beth K. Fields Scholarships
(Undergraduate/Scholarship)

Purpose: To financially support students in their educational pursuit. **Focus:** General studies. **Qualif.:** Applicant must be 25 years old and below; have a minimum of 12 semester hours college credit; have a 3.0 GPA; be a full-time student; and must be supporting at least one dependent. **Criteria:** Applications will be reviewed by the Scholarship Committee of the Board of Directors.

Funds Avail.: No specific amount. **To Apply:** Applicants must submit a completed application form together with their resume orlist of school, community and civic activities; a one-page essay explaining their interest in the award and why they should receive the scholarship; and two letters of recommendation. **Deadline:** March 15. **Contact:** Amanda James, 502-852-8808 or amanda.james@louisville.edu.

9212 ■ Raymond A. Kent-Navy V-12/ROTC Scholarships *(Undergraduate/Scholarship)*

Purpose: To support direct descendants of an individuals who served in the Navy V-12 program or the Naval ROTC program at UofL. **Focus:** General studies. **Qualif.:** Applicant must be a direct descendant of an individual who served the Navy V-12 program or the Naval ROTC program. Applicant must have a 3.0 GPA. **Criteria:** Applications will be reviewed by the Scholarship Committee of the Board of Directors.

Funds Avail.: No specific amount. **To Apply:** Applicants must submit a completed application form together with a copy of official transcripts; a (300-word) essay; and two letters of recommendation. **Deadline:** March 30. **Contact:** Amanda James, 502-852-8808 or amanda.james@louisville.edu.

9213 ■ Kentucky Alumni Club Scholarships - Capital Region Alumni Club *(Undergraduate/Scholarship)*

Purpose: To support students in their educational pursuits. **Focus:** General studies. **Qualif.:** Applicant must reside in the state of Kentucky specifically in Anderson, Franklin, Henry, Owen, Mercer, Shelby and Spencer counties; and must maintain a GPA of 3.0. **Criteria:** Selection is based on the submitted applications.

Funds Avail.: $500 for the first year. **Number Awarded:** 1. **To Apply:** Applicant must complete the application with an essay; official copies of transcripts; test scores; and two letters of recommendation (one from a teacher) submitted to the Scholarship Committee. **Deadline:** March 15. **Contact:** 502-852-6186.

9214 ■ Kentucky Alumni Club Scholarships - Central Kentucky Alumni Club *(Undergraduate/Scholarship)*

Purpose: To support students in their educational pursuits. **Focus:** General studies. **Qualif.:** Applicants must be students pursuing a degree at Uofl; have 3.0 GPA; and must reside in the state of Kentucky specifically in Fayette, Jessamine, Woodford, Clark, Bourbon, Scott, Harrison and Madison counties. **Criteria:** Selection will be based on applicant's leadership ability; academic achievement; breadth of interests; and financial need.

Funds Avail.: No specific amount. **To Apply:** Applicants must complete the application with an essay; official copies of transcripts; test scores; and two letters of recommendation (one from a teacher) submitted to Paul W. Graf, 3367 Ridgecane Rd., Lexington, KY 40513. **Contact:** Amanda James at 502-852-6531 or e-mail at apjame01@louisville.edu.

9215 ■ Kentucky Alumni Club Scholarships - Lake Cumberland Alumni Club *(Undergraduate/Scholarship)*

Purpose: To support students in their educational pursuits. **Focus:** General studies. **Qualif.:** Applicant must reside in the state of Kentucky specifically in Adair, Casey, Clinton, Cumberland, Laurel, McCreary, Pulaski, Rockcastle, Russell and Wayne counties; must be admitted to University of Louisville; have a GPA of 3.5 or above and an ACT/SAT equivalent of 24 or higher. **Criteria:** Selection is based on the submitted applications.

Funds Avail.: $500. **Number Awarded:** 1. **To Apply:** Applicant must complete the application with an essay; official copies of transcripts; test scores; and two letters of recommendation, one of which must come from a teacher. **Deadline:** May 1. **Contact:** Application form and supporting documents must be submitted to Dr. Joe Weigel, 220 Fern Dr., Somerset, KY 4250.

9216 ■ Kentucky Alumni Club Scholarships - Northern Kentucky Alumni Club *(Undergraduate/Scholarship)*

Purpose: To provide financial assistance to students in Northern Kentucky/Greater Cincinnati area. **Focus:** General

Awards are arranged alphabetically below their administering organizations

studies. **Qualif.:** Applicant must reside in the state of Kentucky specifically in Boone, Kenton, Campbelle, Grant, Carroll, Pendleton and Gallatin counties or in Hamilton County in Ohio; must maintain a GPA of 3.0; and an ACT/SAT equivalent of 20 or above. **Criteria:** Selection is based on the submitted applications.

Funds Avail.: No specific amount. **Number Awarded:** 1. **To Apply:** Applicant must complete the application with an essay; official copies of transcripts; test scores; must include a letter of recommendation from either a high school administrative staff or any high school teaching staff. All applications must be submitted to Kathleen Annear Carnes, 332 Forest Hill Dr., Lexington, KY 40509-1970. **Deadline:** April 1. **Contact:** Application form and supporting documents must be submitted to Kathleen Annear Carnes, 839 Pinehurst Dr., Edgewood, KY 41017; Phone: 859-866-6695.

9217 ■ Outstanding Undergraduate Scholarships, Student Organization for Alumni Relations (SOAR) *(Undergraduate/Scholarship)*

Purpose: To support students in their educational pursuits. **Focus:** General studies; to provide funds to an active member of the Student Organization for Alumni Association. **Qualif.:** Applicant must be registered full-time for the semester. **Criteria:** Selection is based on the submitted applications.

Funds Avail.: $1,000. **Number Awarded:** 1. **To Apply:** Complete application includes resume or list of schools, communities and civic activities, a copy of official transcripts; 300-word essay; and two letters of recommendation. **Deadline:** March 15. **Contact:** Amanda James, 502-852-8808 or amanda.james@louisville.edu.

9218 ■ Rodney Williams Legacy Scholarships *(Undergraduate/Grant)*

Purpose: To support the children and grandchildren of UofL alumni. **Focus:** General studies. **Qualif.:** Applicant must be related to a UofL graduate; incoming freshman or transfer student; have a 3.0 GPA; and must be a full-time student for the semester. **Criteria:** Selection is based on the submitted applications.

Funds Avail.: No specific amount. **To Apply:** Applicants must submit a completed application form together with a copy of an official transcript of records; resume or list of school, community and civic activities; a (300-word) essay; and two letters of recommendation. **Deadline:** March 15. **Contact:** Amanda James, 502-852-4956 or amanda.james@louisville.edu.

9219 ■ University of Memphis
101 Wilder Tower
Memphis, TN 38152-3520
Ph: (901) 678-2911
Free: 800-669-2678
URL: www.memphis.edu

9220 ■ Tillie B. Alperin Scholarships *(Undergraduate/Scholarship)*

Purpose: To support the education of female law students at the University of Memphis. **Focus:** Law. **Qualif.:** Applicant must be a female law student who has successfully completed her first year with a B average; has demonstrated a commitment to the legal profession; and demonstrates financial need. **Criteria:** Selection is based on academic performance, leadership, character, personal

achievements and financial need. Preference will be given to applicants who have overcome significant obstacles in pursuit of their education.

Funds Avail.: $1,000 to full in-state tuition. **To Apply:** Applicant must complete the online scholarship application form along with a personal statement; resume; scholarship statement; and recommendation letters. Applicant must also complete the FAFSA Form. **Deadline:** March 15. **Remarks:** Named in honor of the late Tillie Blen Alperin, a 1935 graduate of the old University of Memphis Law School and one of the first women to practice law in Tennessee.

9221 ■ Claude T. Coffman Memorial Scholarships *(Undergraduate/Scholarship)*

Purpose: To support the education of law students at the University of Memphis. **Focus:** Law. **Qualif.:** Applicant must be admitted at the University of Memphis Cecil C. Humphreys School of Law. **Criteria:** Selection is based on academic merit and financial need.

Funds Avail.: $1,000 to full in-state tuition. **To Apply:** Applicants must complete the online scholarship application form along with a personal statement; resume; scholarship statement; and recommendation letters. Applicants must also complete the FAFSA Form. **Deadline:** March 15. **Remarks:** The scholarship is named in honor of the late professor and former interim dean of the Cecil C. Humphreys School of Law.

9222 ■ Cleveland Drennon, Jr. Memorial Scholarships *(Undergraduate/Scholarship)*

Purpose: To support the education of law students at the University of Memphis. **Focus:** Law. **Qualif.:** Applicant must be admitted as full-time student at the University of Memphis Cecil C. Humphreys School of Law. **Criteria:** Selection is based on academic merit and financial need. Special consideration will be given to student-athlete graduates of The University of Memphis or Vanderbilt University.

Funds Avail.: $1,000 to full in-state tuition. **To Apply:** Applicant must complete the online scholarship application form along with a personal statement; resume; scholarship statement; and recommendation letters. Applicants must also complete the FAFSA Form. **Deadline:** March 15. **Remarks:** Funded by Humphrey E. Folk, Jr. and the Drennon family and friends. **Contact:** Ms. DebraAnn Brown, Assistant Director for Student Financial Aid, at 901-678-3737, or dbrown@memphis.edu.

9223 ■ East Tennessee Foundation Scholarships *(Undergraduate/Scholarship)*

Purpose: To support the education of law students at the University of Memphis. **Focus:** Law. **Qualif.:** Applicant must be a second or third year student who demonstrates community involvement or commitment to public service. **Criteria:** Selection is based on academic performance, leadership, character, personal achievements and financial need.

Funds Avail.: $1,000 to full in-state tuition. **Number Awarded:** 1. **To Apply:** Applicant must complete the online scholarship application form along with a personal statement; resume; scholarship statement; and recommendation letters. Applicant must also complete the FAFSA Form. **Remarks:** Scholarship is made possible by a grant from the Tennessee Judicial Conference Foundation. The scholarship is awarded every four years, rotating among the other law schools in the state.

Awards are arranged alphabetically below their administering organizations

9224 ■ Evans and Petree Law Firm Scholarships (Undergraduate/Scholarship)

Purpose: To support the education of law students at the University of Memphis. **Focus:** Law. **Qualif.:** Applicant must be an African American law student. **Criteria:** Selection is based academic performance, leadership, character, personal achievements, and financial need. Preference will be given to a returning African American student with financial need.

Funds Avail.: $1,000 to full in-state tuition. **Number Awarded:** 1. **To Apply:** Applicants must complete the online scholarship application form along with the personal statement; resume; scholarship statement; and recommendation letters. Applicants must also complete the FAFSA Form. **Deadline:** March 15. **Remarks:** Established in Honor of Percy Harvey, Esq. by the Evans and Petree Law Firm. **Contact:** Ms. DebraAnn Brown, Assistant Director for Student Financial Aid, at 901-678-3737, or dbrown@memphis.edu.

9225 ■ Federal Court Bench and Bar Scholarships (Undergraduate/Scholarship)

Purpose: To broaden the Middle District of Tennessee bar through expanded opportunities for law students from all backgrounds. **Focus:** Law. **Qualif.:** Applicants must be economically disadvantaged law students from the Middle District of Tennessee; in good academic standing at the law school or the most recent school attended; have demonstrated financial need; and must have graduated from a high school in, or resided for the previous three years as a non-full time student in one of the following Tennessee Counties: Cannon, Cheatham, Clay, Cumberland, Davidson, DeKalb, Dickson, Fentress, Giles, Hickman, Houston, Humphreys, Jackson, Lawrence, Lewis, Macon, Marshall, Maury, Montgomery, Overton, Pickett, Putnam, Robertson, Rutherford, Smith, Stewart, Sumner, Trousdale, Wayne, White, Williamson, or Wilson. **Criteria:** Recipients will be selected based on financial need.

Funds Avail.: $1,000 to full in-state tuition. **To Apply:** Applicants must complete the online scholarship application form along with a personal statement; resume; scholarship statement; and recommendation letters. Applicants must also complete the FAFSA Form. **Deadline:** March 15.

9226 ■ Wilford Hayes Gowen Scholarships (Undergraduate/Scholarship)

Purpose: To support the education of law students at the University of Memphis. **Focus:** Law. **Qualif.:** Applicant must be a second or third year law student. **Criteria:** Selection is based on academic performance, financial need and personal determination.

Funds Avail.: $1,000 to full in-state tuition. **To Apply:** Applicant must complete the online scholarship application form along with a personal statement; resume; scholarship statement; and recommendation letters. Applicant must also complete the FAFSA Form. **Deadline:** March 15. **Remarks:** Established in memory of Wilford Hayes Gowen, through the Community Foundation of Western North Carolina.

9227 ■ Herbert Herff Presidential Law Scholarships (Undergraduate/Scholarship)

Purpose: To support the education of law students at the University of Memphis. **Focus:** Law. **Qualif.:** Applicants must be admitted at the University of Memphis Cecil C. Humphreys School of Law; have demonstrated high academic or professional achievement; and show potential for an outstanding law career. **Criteria:** Selection is based on academic merit and financial need.

Funds Avail.: $1,000 to full in-state tuition. **To Apply:** Applicants must complete the online scholarship application form along with a personal statement; resume; scholarship statement; and recommendation letters. Applicants must also complete the FAFSA Form. **Deadline:** March 15. **Remarks:** Funded by the Herbert Herff Trust.

9228 ■ Robert and Elaine Hoffman Memorial Scholarships (Undergraduate/Scholarship)

Purpose: To support the education of law students at the University of Memphis. **Focus:** Law. **Qualif.:** Applicants must be admitted at the University of Memphis Cecil C. Humphreys School of Law. **Criteria:** Selection is based on academic merit and financial need.

Funds Avail.: $1,000 to full in-state tuition. **Number Awarded:** 2. **To Apply:** Applicants must complete the online scholarship application form along with a personal statement; resume; scholarship statement; and recommendation letters. Applicants must also complete the FAFSA Form. **Deadline:** March 1. **Remarks:** The scholarship is named in honor of the late Chancellor Robert Hoffman and his sister Elaine. **Contact:** Ms. DebraAnn Brown, Assistant Director for Student Financial Aid, at 901-678-3737, or dbrown@memphis.edu.

9229 ■ Kathryn Hookanson Law Fellowships (Undergraduate/Scholarship)

Purpose: To support the education of law students at the University of Memphis. **Focus:** Law. **Qualif.:** Applicant must be a student at the University of Memphis. **Criteria:** Preference may be given to female students and those in financial need.

Funds Avail.: $1,000 to full in-state tuition. **To Apply:** Applicant must complete the online scholarship application form along with a personal statement; resume; scholarship statement; and recommendation letters. Applicant must also complete the FAFSA Form. **Deadline:** March 15. **Remarks:** Established by Ms. Hookanson, her family, friends and colleagues.

9230 ■ John C. "Jack" Hough Memorial Law Scholarships (Undergraduate/Scholarship)

Purpose: To support the education of law students at the University of Memphis. **Focus:** Law. **Qualif.:** Applicant must be a second or third year law student who demonstrates financial need and is working as a volunteer or in a law school externship in the office of the Shelby County Public Defender. **Criteria:** Selection is based on academic performance, leadership, character, personal achievements and financial need. Preference will be given to applicants who express an interest in a career in government service as a public defender or prosecutor, or in the field of criminal law.

Funds Avail.: $1,000 to full in-state tuition. **To Apply:** Applicant must complete the online scholarship application form along with a personal statement; resume; scholarship statement; and recommendation letters. Applicants must also complete the FAFSA Form. **Deadline:** March 15. **Remarks:** Scholarship is named in honor of the late John C. "Jack" Hough, a former member of the Shelby County Public Defender's Office.

9231 ■ Cecil C. Humphreys Law Fellowships (Undergraduate/Fellowship)

Purpose: To support the education of law students at the University of Memphis. **Focus:** Law. **Qualif.:** Applicant

Awards are arranged alphabetically below their administering organizations

must be a second or third year student. **Criteria:** Selection is based on demonstrated outstanding academic performance, leadership, good citizenship and scholarly achievements.

Funds Avail.: Free waiver for half the cost of in-state tuition. **To Apply:** Applicant must complete the online scholarship application form along with a personal statement; resume; scholarship statement; and recommendation letters. Applicant must also complete the FAFSA Form. **Deadline:** March 15. **Remarks:** Fellowship is funded through a grant from the Plough Foundation. Humphreys Fellows are required to work 15 hours per week as a research assistant to faculty members.

9232 ■ Judge William B. Leffler Scholarships
(Undergraduate/Scholarship)

Purpose: To support the education of law students at the University of Memphis. **Focus:** Law. **Qualif.:** Applicants must be admitted at the University of Memphis Cecil C. Humphreys School of Law. **Criteria:** Selection is based on academic merit and financial need.

Funds Avail.: $1,000 to full in-state tuition. **To Apply:** Applicants must complete the online scholarship application form along with the personal statement; resume; scholarship statement; and recommendation letters. Applicants must also complete the FAFSA Form. **Deadline:** March 15. **Remarks:** The award is funded through the Leffler family, the donations of friends and proceeds from the annual bankruptcy law seminar in Judge Leffler's memory.

9233 ■ H.H. McKnight Memorial Scholarships
(Undergraduate/Scholarship)

Purpose: To support the education of law students at the University of Memphis. **Focus:** Law. **Qualif.:** Applicants must be veterans of the United States Armed Forces interested in pursuing a career in criminal law. **Criteria:** Selection is based on academic merit and financial need.

Funds Avail.: $1,000 to full in-state tuition. **Number Awarded:** 2. **To Apply:** Applicants must complete the online scholarship application form along with a personal statement; resume; scholarship statement; and recommendation letters. Applicants must also complete the FAFSA Form. **Deadline:** March 15. **Contact:** Ms. DebraAnn Brown, Assistant Director for Student Financial Aid, at 901-678-3737, or dbrown@memphis.edu.

9234 ■ Memphis Access and Diversity Law Scholarships *(Undergraduate/Scholarship)*

Purpose: To support the education of law students at the University of Memphis. **Focus:** Law. **Qualif.:** Applicant must be a Tennessee resident. **Criteria:** Selection is based on academic merit and financial need.

Funds Avail.: No specific amount. **To Apply:** Applicants must complete the online scholarship application form along with a personal statement; resume; scholarship statement; and recommendation letters. Applicants must also complete the FAFSA Form. In addition, attach a separate statement explaining in detail the circumstances that qualify the student to be considered for the scholarship. **Deadline:** March 15.

9235 ■ Sam A. Myar Jr. Law Scholarships
(Undergraduate/Scholarship)

Purpose: To support the education of law students at the University of Memphis. **Focus:** Law. **Qualif.:** Applicants must be the Editor-in-Chief and the Managing Editor of the

University of Memphis Law Review. **Criteria:** Selection is based academic performance, leadership, character, personal achievements and financial need.

Funds Avail.: $1,000 to full in-state tuition. **To Apply:** Applicants must complete the online scholarship application form along with a personal statement; resume; scholarship statement; and recommendation letters. Applicants must also complete the FAFSA Form. **Deadline:** March 15. **Remarks:** Established in 1960.

9236 ■ Donald and Susie Polden Dean's Scholarships *(Undergraduate/Scholarship)*

Purpose: To support the education of law students at the University of Memphis. **Focus:** Law. **Qualif.:** Applicants must be law students; must be committed to community or public service; and must express a desire to serve the community during or following law school. **Criteria:** Recipients will be selected based on academic merit and financial need.

Funds Avail.: $1,000 to full in-state tuition. **To Apply:** Applicants must complete the online scholarship application form along with a personal statement; resume; scholarship statement; and recommendation letters. Applicants must also complete the FAFSA Form. **Deadline:** March 15.

9237 ■ Ratner and Sugarmon Scholarships
(Undergraduate/Scholarship)

Purpose: To support the education of law students at the University of Memphis. **Focus:** Law. **Qualif.:** Applicants must be second or third year law students. **Criteria:** Award is given to the student who best exemplifies a commitment to the needs of the underrepresented in society.

Funds Avail.: $1,000 to full in-state tuition. **To Apply:** Applicants must complete the online scholarship application form along with a personal statement; resume; scholarship statement; and recommendation letters. Applicants must also complete the FAFSA Form. **Deadline:** March 15. **Contact:** DebraAnn Brown, Assistant Director for Student Financial Aid, at 901-678-3737, or dbrown@memphis.edu.

9238 ■ Joseph Henry Shepherd Scholarships
(Undergraduate/Scholarship)

Purpose: To support the education of law students at the University of Memphis. **Focus:** Law. **Qualif.:** Applicants must be admitted at the University of Memphis Cecil C. Humphreys School of Law. **Criteria:** Selection is based on academic performance and financial need.

Funds Avail.: $1,000 to full in-state tuition. **Number Awarded:** 3. **To Apply:** Applicants must complete the online scholarship application form along with a personal statement; resume; scholarship statement; and recommendation letters. Applicants must also complete the FAFSA Form. **Deadline:** March 15. **Remarks:** Sponsored by Dorothy S. Shepherd.

9239 ■ Amy E. Spain Memorial Scholarships
(Undergraduate/Scholarship)

Purpose: To support the education of law students at the University of Memphis. **Focus:** Law. **Qualif.:** Applicants must be law students with demonstrated academic merit. **Criteria:** Recipients will be selected based on academic merit; commitment to community/professional service; and personal industriousness.

Funds Avail.: $1,000 to full in-state tuition. **Number Awarded:** 2. **To Apply:** Applicants must complete the online scholarship application form along with a personal

Awards are arranged alphabetically below their administering organizations

statement; resume; scholarship statement; and recommendation letters. Applicants must also complete the FAFSA Form. **Deadline:** March 15. **Remarks:** Established by the family and friends of Amy Elizabeth Spain, who died at age 30 by a car accident in 1997.

9240 ■ James F. and Donna Springfield Scholarships *(Undergraduate/Scholarship)*

Purpose: To support the education of law students at the University of Memphis. **Focus:** Law. **Qualif.:** Applicant must be a graduate of Rhodes College. **Criteria:** Selection is based on academic merit.

Funds Avail.: $1,000 to full in-state tuition. **Number Awarded:** 1. **To Apply:** Applicant must complete the online scholarship application form along with the personal statement; resume; scholarship statement; and recommendation letters. Applicant must also complete the FAFSA Form. **Deadline:** March 15. **Remarks:** Scholarship is made possible by an endowment fund established by Mr. and Mrs. Springfield.

9241 ■ Tennessee Bar Foundation IOLTA Law School Scholarships *(Undergraduate/ Scholarship)*

Purpose: To support the education of law students at the University of Memphis. **Focus:** Law. **Qualif.:** Applicants must be Tennessee residents and rising third year students in good standing. **Criteria:** Selection is based on demonstrated concern for public interest law, financial need and diversity representation.

Funds Avail.: $1,000 to full in-state tuition. **To Apply:** Applicants must complete the online scholarship application form along with a personal statement; resume; scholarship statement; and recommendation letters. Applicants must also complete the FAFSA Form. **Deadline:** March 15. **Remarks:** Scholarship is funded by the Tennessee Bar Foundation.

9242 ■ Wyatt, Tarrant and Combs, LLP Scholarships *(Undergraduate/Scholarship)*

Purpose: To support the education of law students at the University of Memphis. **Focus:** Law. **Qualif.:** Applicant must be admitted as a full-time student at the University of Memphis Cecil C. Humphreys School of Law; and must be a Tennessee or Kentucky resident. **Criteria:** Selection is based on academic merit and financial need. Preference is given to a Tennessee or Kentucky resident.

Funds Avail.: $1,000 to full in-state tuition. **To Apply:** Applicant must complete the online scholarship application form along with a personal statement; resume; scholarship statement; and recommendation letters. Applicant must also complete the FAFSA Form. **Remarks:** Scholarship is made possible by Wyatt, Tarrant & Combs, LLP. The scholarship will be offered every three years.

9243 ■ University of Minnesota

240 Williamson Hall
231 Pillsbury Dr., SE
Minneapolis, MN 55455-0213
Ph: (612) 625-2008
Free: 800-752-1000
E-mail: hrfellow@umn.edu
URL: www1.umn.edu/twincities

9244 ■ Carol E. Macpherson Memorial Scholarship and Alumnae Society Scholarships *(Graduate, Undergraduate/Scholarship)*

Purpose: To provide support for qualified individuals intending to pursue an educational career. **Focus:** General studies. **Qualif.:** Applicant must be a female student who has had a five-year or longer break in their postsecondary education; must demonstrate financial need; must have a admission or pending admission to an undergraduate or graduate/professional degree or credit certificate program at any University of Minnesota campus; must meet half-time enrollment status minimum; must provide academic transcripts of all college/post-secondary enrollment; must have a good academic standing at the University of Minnesota; must submit support letters from two references who have known the applicants and their educational goals. **Criteria:** Applicant selection is weighted by the following characteristics: (1) First generation in family to attend college; (2) First undergraduate degree; (3) Student parent status.

Funds Avail.: $1,000-$4,000. **Number Awarded:** 6-8. **To Apply:** Applicant must submit the complete application, including their personal statement and a copy of their Student Aid Report; must have a transcript of all college/post-secondary enrollment; and two Applicant Appraisal Forms (to be sent directly from references or attached to application in a sealed envelope signed by the writer across the seal). **Deadline:** April 27.

9245 ■ University of Minnesota Women Student Travel Grants *(Graduate, Undergraduate/Grant)*

Purpose: To help the students in University of Minnesota to pursue their education. **Focus:** General studies. **Qualif.:** Applicant must be a University of Minnesota, Twin Cities undergraduate or graduate student in good standing with his/her college; must have a cumulative GPA of 3.00. **Criteria:** Priority will be given to students attending national conferences, their first conference and/or presenting at a conference (conference presentation is a preferred requirement of graduate student applicants).

Funds Avail.: $100-$300. **To Apply:** Application forms are available in the website. Applicant must attach conference program information and proof of registration; must provide the student-issued University transcript, and information about other sources of funding. Application form and other application materials must be sent to: Women's Center, 64 Appleby Hall, 128 Pleasant St. SE, Delivery Code 3503, Minneapolis, MN 55455. **Contact:** Phone: 612-625-9837; Fax: 612-625-9682; email: women@umn.edu.

9246 ■ Upper Midwest Human Rights Fellowship Program *(Professional development/ Fellowship)*

Purpose: To encourage residents of the Upper Midwest to undertake practical experiences/internships in human rights organizations. To promote social justice by providing practical training in the varied aspects of human rights work worldwide. **Focus:** Human rights. **Qualif.:** Applicants must be residents of the Upper Midwest with a particular focus on Minnesota, Montana, North Dakota, South Dakota, and Wisconsin; must have adequate proficiency in the relevant languages. **Criteria:** Primary criterion for selection is a demonstrated interest in, and commitment to, the promotion of international human rights. Subcommittee of the Human Rights Center's Advisory Board will select the grant recipients. Awards will be determined by considering an individual's qualifications and interests together with the

Awards are arranged alphabetically below their administering organizations

needs of the supervising organization.

Funds Avail.: $1,000-$4,500 money will help pay transportation, lodging, and food expenses incurred during the fellowship period. **To Apply:** Applicants must submit a complete application form available online; must provide the confirmation letter from host; transcript (from last ten years only); a resume; and a 2-3-page essay detailing the following: (1) Fellowship placement, (2) Proposed host organization, (3) Significance of the experience for your academic or professional training, (4) Relationship of the fellowship to your future goals, (5) How the host organization will benefit from a fellowship, (6) Description of the key aspects of a current human rights issue in the country/location of your proposed fellowship and how the sponsoring organization addresses it; (7) Description of how you will use your new human rights experiences in your community upon your return home. **Deadline:** February 9. **Contact:** Application form and supporting documents must be submitted to the Human Rights Center,Mondale Hall, Ste. N120, 229 19th Ave. S, Minneapolis. MN 55455 or e-mail hrfellow@umn.edu for additional information.

9247 ■ University of Missouri - St. Louis - Center for International Studies
366 Social Sciences Bldg.
One University Blvd.
Saint Louis, MO 63121
Ph: (314) 516-5753
Fax: (314) 516-6757
E-mail: tmarshall@umsl.edu
URL: www.umsl.edu/services/cis

9248 ■ Post-Doctoral or Sabbatical Fellowships
(Doctorate/Fellowship)

Purpose: To support scholarly research on peace and conflict resolution and violence. **Focus:** Peace Studies. **Qualif.:** Applicants must be Ph.D. students; graduates of university programs in peace studies and conflict resolution. graduates of political science, international relations, and other social science programs who specialized in peace and conflict resolution. **Criteria:** Recipients will be selected based on submitted application and supporting documents. Preference will be given to graduates of university programs in peace studies and conflict resolution.

Funds Avail.: $23,400 for the academic year; $1,000 allowance for research travel and expenses. **To Apply:** Applicants should provide a curriculum vitae, evidence of completion of the Ph.D.; three letters of recommendation; and a research proposal of approximately 750 words. **Deadline:** April 21. **Contact:** Dr. Joel Glassman, Director Center for International Studies; University of Missouri-St. Louis, 366 Social Sciences and Business Building, One University Blvd., St. Louis, MO 63121-4400; Phone: 314-516-5753 Fax: 314-516-6757; jglassman@umsl.edu.

9249 ■ University of New Hampshire (UNH)
Office of Admission
3 Garrison Ave.
Durham, NH 03824
Ph: (603) 862-1360
Fax: (603) 862-0077
E-mail: admission@unh.edu
URL: www.unh.edu

9250 ■ CEPS-Tyco Scholarships
(Undergraduate/Scholarship)

Purpose: To provide financial assistance to students who want to continue their education at UNH. **Focus:** Engineering; Physical sciences. **Qualif.:** Applicants must be high school seniors admitted to the University's College of Engineering and Physical Sciences. **Criteria:** Selection criteria include: (1) Rigorous programs of study including a minimum of five years of mathematics and four years of science, with preference given to Advanced Placement and International Baccalaureate Courses; (2) Grades that indicate excellence; (3) Class rank in the top 10 percent (for students attending schools that provide class rank) or equivalent; (4) SAT Reasoning Test scores of 1310+ (Critical Reading and Math only) or a 30+ composite on the ACT with writing test.

Funds Avail.: $10,000. **Number Awarded:** 2. **To Apply:** Applicants must have an application for admission to a major within the College of Engineering and Physical Sciences at the University of New Hampshire; must have official high school transcripts, including the first marking period of senior year; must have the official test scores for either the SAT Reasoning Test or ACT with writing test; must submit an additional scholarship essay through the online form; must submit a Free Application for Federal Student Aid (FAFSA) form. **Deadline:** February 25. **Contact:** University of New Hampshire, Office of Admission/CEPS-Tyco Scholarship, Grant House, 4 Garrison Ave., Durham, NH 03824.

9251 ■ University of New Hampshire Alumni Association Legacy Scholarships
(Undergraduate/Scholarship)

Purpose: To provide financial assistance to students who want to continue their education at UNH. **Focus:** General studies. **Qualif.:** Applicants must be enrolled or accepted as full-time students in a four-year degree program at UNH, Durham campus; must possess leadership potential as demonstrated through involvement in academic, co-curricular and/or work activities; must have a relative who is an alumnus/a of the University of Hampshire who must have been a dues-paying member at the time of his or her death; and must have a cumulative GPA of 3.2. **Criteria:** The scholarship Committee will judge the applicants based on the following evaluation criteria: (1) Academic record; (2) Leadership potential; (3) Breadth of academic, co-curricular and employment activities; (4) Quality and content of the application, essay, strength of recommendation and interview, if applicable; (5) Length of membership and/or level of service to UNH or the Alumni Association by the related dues-paying member.

Funds Avail.: $3,000. **To Apply:** Applicants must complete the application form available online; and must have a letter of recommendation from a high school teacher, guidance counselor or UNH faculty member. **Deadline:** May.

9252 ■ University of New Hampshire Parent's Association Endowment Scholarship Fund
(Undergraduate/Scholarship)

Purpose: To provide financial assistance to students who want to continue their education at UNH. **Focus:** General studies. **Qualif.:** Applicants must demonstrate academic achievement; must be of good character; must have a minimum cumulative GPA of 2.8; must be involved in community service projects or in the university community; and must be making financial contributions to their education through employment. **Criteria:** Selection of recipients will be based on financial need.

Awards are arranged alphabetically below their administering organizations

Funds Avail.: $5,000-$10,000. **To Apply:** Applicants must submit a University Community and/or Community Service verification letter; an employment verification letter; a background information statement (maximum of one-page double spaced); and must have a faculty recommendation. Application forms are available online and must be sent to University of New Hampshire Parent's Association. **Deadline:** March 1. **Contact:** For more information about scholarship application process, call 603-862-3600 or e-mail at financial.aid@unh.edu.

9253 ■ University of North Carolina School of Journalism and Mass Communication

University of N Carolina, Carol Hall CB 3365
Chapel Hill, NC 27599-3365
Ph: (919) 962-1204
Fax: (919) 962-0620
E-mail: jomc@unc.edu
URL: www.jomc.unc.edu

9254 ■ Floyd S. Alford Jr. Scholarships
(Undergraduate/Scholarship)

Purpose: To educate journalists; to recognize students who demonstrate outstanding journalistic talent and a strong commitment to improve the community through honest and accurate work. **Focus:** Journalism. **Qualif.:** Applicants must be undergraduate students majoring in journalism. **Criteria:** Recipients are selected based on academic performance and financial need.

Funds Avail.: Amount not specified. **To Apply:** Applicants must complete the application form. **Deadline:** February 1. **Contact:** Applications must be e-mailed to jomcscholarships@unc.edu.

9255 ■ Peggy Allen Community Newspaper Internships *(Undergraduate/Internship)*

Purpose: To educate journalists. **Focus:** Journalism; Communication. **Qualif.:** Applicants must be enrolled or plan to enroll in a university and have at least 2.9 GPA. **Criteria:** Recipients are selected based on academic performance, financial need and potential for journalism-mass communication careers.

Funds Avail.: Amount not specified. **To Apply:** Applicants must complete the application form. **Deadline:** February 1. **Contact:** Applications must be e-mailed to jomcscholarships@unc.edu.

9256 ■ Phillip Alston Scholarships
(Undergraduate/Scholarship)

Purpose: To educate journalists. **Focus:** Journalism; Communications. **Qualif.:** Applicants must be undergraduate students in university. **Criteria:** Recipients are selected based on academic performance and financial need.

Funds Avail.: Amount not specified. **To Apply:** Applicants must complete the application form. **Deadline:** February 1. **Remarks:** Established by Joel and Edith Bourne of Tarboro to honor their uncle, a 1932 graduate of the school. **Contact:** Applications must be e-mailed to jomcscholarships@unc.edu.

9257 ■ AT&T Business Internship Awards
(Postgraduate/Internship)

Purpose: To provide financial assistance to undergraduate or graduate students interested in business journalism.

Focus: Journalism. **Qualif.:** Applicants must have arranged a business journalism internship and must be in the Bell-South service area. **Criteria:** Recipients are selected based on academic performance and financial need.

Funds Avail.: Amount not specified. **To Apply:** Applicants must submit a completed application form. **Deadline:** February 1. **Contact:** Applications must be e-mailed to jomcscholarships@unc.edu.

9258 ■ Jim Batten Community Newspaper Internships *(Undergraduate/Internship)*

Purpose: To provide financial assistance to news-editorial journalism and community journalism students. **Focus:** Journalism; Communication. **Qualif.:** Applicants must be enrolled or plan to enroll in a university and have at least 2.9 GPA. **Criteria:** Recipients are selected based on academic performance, financial need and potential for journalism-mass communication careers.

Funds Avail.: Amount not specified. **To Apply:** Applicants must submit a completed application form. Applicants must contact the school's director of graduate studies for other application requirements. **Deadline:** February 1. **Contact:** Applications must be e-mailed to jomcscholarships@unc.edu.

9259 ■ Margaret Blanchard Dissertation Support Fund *(Postgraduate/Grant)*

Purpose: To educate journalists. **Focus:** Communications. **Qualif.:** Applicants must be graduate student who are U.S. citizens. **Criteria:** Recipients are selected based on the academic performance, and financial need.

Funds Avail.: Varies. **To Apply:** Applicants must complete the application form; applicants must contact the school's director of graduate studies. **Deadline:** March 1.

9260 ■ Tom Bost Scholarships *(Undergraduate/ Scholarship)*

Purpose: To educate journalists. **Focus:** Journalism; Communications. **Qualif.:** Applicants must be undergraduate students in university. **Criteria:** Recipients are selected based on academic performance and financial need.

Funds Avail.: $500. **To Apply:** Applicants must complete the application form. **Deadline:** February 1. **Contact:** Applications must be e-mailed to jomcscholarships@unc.edu.

9261 ■ Rick Brewer Scholarships
(Undergraduate/Scholarship)

Purpose: To educate journalists. **Focus:** Broadcasting; Journalism; Public relations. **Qualif.:** Applicants must be undergraduate students with a keen interest in pursuing a career in sports journalism, broadcasting, or public relations. **Criteria:** Recipients are selected based on academic performance and financial need.

Funds Avail.: Amount not specified. **To Apply:** Applicants must complete the application form. **Deadline:** February 1. **Contact:** Applications must be e-mailed to jomcscholarships@unc.edu.

9262 ■ Elton Casey Scholarships
(Undergraduate/Scholarship)

Purpose: To educate journalists. **Focus:** Journalism. **Qualif.:** Applicants must be students who are interested in pursuing a career in sports journalism with a preference given to students from Orange or Durham counties. **Criteria:** Recipients are selected based on academic performance and financial need.

Awards are arranged alphabetically below their administering organizations

Funds Avail.: Amount not specified. **To Apply:** Applicants must complete the application form. **Deadline:** February 1. **Contact:** Applications must be e-mailed to jomcscholarships@unc.edu.

9263 ■ Ardis Cohoon Scholarships
(Undergraduate/Scholarship)

Purpose: To provide educational assistance for journalists who wish to improve their communication skills. **Focus:** Communications; Journalism. **Qualif.:** Applicants must be currently enrolled or have plans to enroll in a university with at least a 2.9 GPA. **Criteria:** Recipients are selected based on academic performance and financial need.

Funds Avail.: $500. **To Apply:** Applicants must complete the application package. **Deadline:** February 1. **Contact:** Applications must be e-mailed to jomcscholarships@unc.edu.

9264 ■ Louis M. Connor Jr. Scholarships
(Undergraduate/Scholarship)

Purpose: To educate journalists. **Focus:** Public relations. **Qualif.:** Applicants must be enrolled or plan to enroll in a university and have at least 2.9 GPA. **Criteria:** Recipients are selected based on academic performance and financial need.

Funds Avail.: $2,500. **To Apply:** Applicants must complete the application form. **Deadline:** February 1. **Contact:** Applications must be e-mailed to jomcscholarships@unc.edu.

9265 ■ Kathryn M. Cronin Scholarships *(Graduate, Undergraduate/Scholarship)*

Purpose: To educate journalists. **Focus:** Journalism; Communications. **Qualif.:** Applicants must be undergraduates or graduate students who have plans to pursue a career in medical journalism. Must have at least 3.0 GPA. **Criteria:** Recipients are selected based on academic performance, financial need and potential for journalism-mass communication careers.

Funds Avail.: Amount not specified. **To Apply:** Applicants must complete the application form; see Professor Tom Linden. **Deadline:** March 1.

9266 ■ Don and Barbara Curtis Excellence Fund for Extracurricular Student Activities
(Undergraduate/Grant)

Purpose: To educate journalists; to support undergraduates who participate in meaningful out-of class activities that will help them in their mass communications careers. **Focus:** Journalism; Communication. **Qualif.:** Applicants must be students who are currently enrolled at the University of North Carolina and/or as a member of a student organization. **Criteria:** Recipients are selected based on the academic performance, financial need, and potential for journalism-mass communication careers.

Funds Avail.: $25,000. **To Apply:** Applicants must complete the application form. **Deadline:** October and February. **Contact:** CB 3365, Chapel Hill, NC 27599.

9267 ■ James Davis Scholarships
(Undergraduate/Scholarship)

Purpose: To educate journalists. **Focus:** Journalism; Communication. **Qualif.:** Applicants must be enrolled or plan to enroll in a university and have at least 2.9 GPA; must be studying North Carolina history and North Carolina natives. **Criteria:** Recipients are selected based on academic performance, financial need and potential for journalism-

mass communication careers.

Funds Avail.: $1,000. **To Apply:** Applicants must complete the application form. **Deadline:** February 1. **Contact:** Applications must be e-mailed to jomcscholarships@unc.edu.

9268 ■ Robert Winchester Dodson Scholarships *(Undergraduate/Scholarship)*

Purpose: To educate journalists. **Focus:** Communication. **Qualif.:** Applicants must be students who are currently enrolled or have plans to enroll in a university. **Criteria:** Recipients are selected based on academic performance and financial need.

Funds Avail.: $1,000. **To Apply:** Applicants must complete the application form. **Deadline:** February 1. **Contact:** Applications must be e-mailed to jomcscholarships@unc.edu.

9269 ■ Vivian Edmonds Scholarships
(Undergraduate/Scholarship)

Purpose: To provide financial assistance to journalism students. **Focus:** Journalism; Communication. **Qualif.:** Applicants must be sophomore students and must have a minimum of 2.9 GPA. **Criteria:** Recipients are selected based on academic performance, financial need and potential for journalism-mass communication careers.

Funds Avail.: Amount not specified. **To Apply:** Applicants must submit a completed application form. **Deadline:** February 1. **Contact:** Applications must be e-mailed to jomcscholarships@unc.edu.

9270 ■ Reese Felts Scholarships
(Undergraduate/Scholarship)

Purpose: To educate journalists. **Focus:** Communication; Journalism. **Qualif.:** Applicants must be currently enrolled or plan to enroll in a university. **Criteria:** Recipients are selected based on academic performance and financial need.

Funds Avail.: $1,500. **To Apply:** Applicants must complete the application form. **Deadline:** February 1. **Contact:** Applications must be e-mailed to jomcscholarships@unc.edu.

9271 ■ Ameel J. Fisher Scholarships
(Undergraduate/Scholarship)

Purpose: To educate journalists. **Focus:** Journalism; Communication. **Qualif.:** Applicants must be enrolled or plan to enroll in a university and have at least 2.9 GPA. **Criteria:** Recipients are selected based on academic performance, financial need and potential for journalism-mass communication careers.

Funds Avail.: $2,500. **To Apply:** Applicants must complete the application form. **Deadline:** February 1. **Contact:** Applications must be e-mailed to jomcscholarships@unc.edu.

9272 ■ Victoria M. Gardner Scholarships
(Undergraduate/Scholarship)

Purpose: To educate journalists so that they can communicate about science and medicine effectively. **Focus:** Education, Medical. **Qualif.:** Applicants must be students interested in families, children and medical issues. **Criteria:** Recipients are selected based on the academic performance, and financial need.

Funds Avail.: $3,000. **To Apply:** Applicants must complete the application form. **Deadline:** February 1. **Contact:** Applications must be e-mailed to jomcscholarships@unc.edu.

9273 ■ Kays Gary Scholarships *(Undergraduate/Scholarship)*

Purpose: To educate journalists. **Focus:** Communications; Journalism. **Qualif.:** Applicants must be currently enrolled

Awards are arranged alphabetically below their administering organizations

or have plans to enroll in a university. Must have at least 2.9 GPA. **Criteria:** Recipients are selected based on academic performance and financial need.

Funds Avail.: $500. **To Apply:** Applicants must complete the application form. **Deadline:** February 1. **Contact:** Applications must be e-mailed to jomcscholarships@unc.edu.

9274 ■ Stephen Gates Scholarships
(Undergraduate/Scholarship)

Purpose: To educate journalists. **Focus:** Communication; Broadcasting. **Qualif.:** Applicants must be student currently enrolled or planning to enroll in a university. **Criteria:** Recipients are selected based on academic performance and financial need.

Funds Avail.: $2,500. **To Apply:** Applicants must complete the application form. **Deadline:** February 1. **Contact:** Applications must be e-mailed to jomcscholarships@unc.edu.

9275 ■ Joy Gibson Scholarships
(Undergraduate/Scholarship)

Purpose: To educate journalists. **Focus:** Journalism; Communications. **Qualif.:** Applicants must be undergraduate students in university. **Criteria:** Recipients are selected based on academic performance and financial need.

Funds Avail.: $1,000. **To Apply:** Applicants must complete the application form. **Deadline:** February 1. **Contact:** Applications must be e-mailed to jomcscholarships@unc.edu.

9276 ■ L.C. Gifford Distinguished Journalism Scholarships *(Undergraduate/Scholarship)*

Purpose: To educate journalists. **Focus:** Communication; Journalism. **Qualif.:** Applicants must be journalism students from the University of North Carolina Chapel Hill. **Criteria:** Recipients are selected based on academic performance and financial need.

Funds Avail.: Amount not specified. **To Apply:** Applicants must complete the application form. **Deadline:** February 1. **Contact:** Applications must be e-mailed to jomcscholarships@unc.edu.

9277 ■ Charles Hauser Scholarships
(Undergraduate/Scholarship)

Purpose: To educate journalists. **Focus:** Communications; Journalism. **Qualif.:** Applicants must be currently enrolled or have plans to enroll in a university. Must have at least 2.9 GPA. **Criteria:** Recipients are selected based on academic performance and financial need.

Funds Avail.: $1,000. **To Apply:** Applicants must complete the application form. **Deadline:** February 1. **Contact:** Applications must be e-mailed to jomcscholarships@unc.edu.

9278 ■ Paul Green Houston Scholarships
(Undergraduate/Scholarship)

Purpose: To educate journalists. **Focus:** Communication; Journalism. **Qualif.:** Applicants must be students majoring in news editorial journalism. **Criteria:** Recipients are selected based on the academic performance, and financial need.

Funds Avail.: $500. **To Apply:** Applicants must complete the application form. **Deadline:** February 1. **Contact:** Applications must be e-mailed to jomcscholarships@unc.edu.

9279 ■ James F. Hurley III Bicentennial Merit Scholarships *(Undergraduate/Scholarship)*

Purpose: To provide financial assistance to journalism students. **Focus:** Journalism; Communication. **Qualif.:** Applicants must be enrolled or plan to enroll in a university and have an at least 2.9 GPA. **Criteria:** Preference is given to students with a newspaper career interest.

Funds Avail.: $5,000. **To Apply:** Applicants must submit a completed application form. Applicants must contact the school's director of graduate studies for other application requirements. **Deadline:** February 1. **Contact:** Applications must be e-mailed to jomcscholarships@unc.edu.

9280 ■ Fred Hutchison Travel Scholarships
(Undergraduate/Scholarship)

Purpose: To educate journalists; to help defray expenses associated with travel to foreign countries for courses. **Focus:** Journalism; Communication. **Qualif.:** Applicants must be students who are currently enrolled or plan to enroll in university. **Criteria:** Recipients are selected based on the academic performance, financial need, and potential for journalism-mass communication careers.

Funds Avail.: No specific amount. **To Apply:** Applicants must complete the application form; see Senior Associate Dean Dulcie Straughan. **Deadline:** March 1. **Contact:** dulcie@email.unc.edu.

9281 ■ Edward Jackson International Scholarships *(Undergraduate/Scholarship)*

Purpose: To educate journalists; to support undergraduate students in traveling to a European country to learn about its politics, culture and mass media by working there. **Focus:** Communication; Journalism. **Qualif.:** Applicants must be news editorial undergraduate students, preferably from North Carolina. **Criteria:** Recipients are selected based on academic performance and journalistic experience.

Funds Avail.: $2,500. **To Apply:** Applicants must complete the application form. **Deadline:** February 1. **Contact:** Questions should be directed to Michael Penny; Phone: 919-843-2753; E-mail: mpenny@email.unc.edu.

9282 ■ Gene Jackson Scholarships
(Undergraduate/Scholarship)

Purpose: To educate journalists. **Focus:** Communication; Journalism. **Qualif.:** Applicants must be graduate students of the school who had a distinguished career in newspaper and worked in the University of North Carolina Chapel Hill Development Office. **Criteria:** Recipients are selected based on academic performance and financial need.

Funds Avail.: Amount not specified. **To Apply:** Applicants must complete the application form. **Deadline:** February 1. **Contact:** Applications must be e-mailed to jomcscholarships@unc.edu.

9283 ■ Peter Lars Jacobson Scholarships
(Undergraduate/Scholarship)

Purpose: To provide educational assistance for journalists to help them achieve effective communication in the fields of science and medicine. **Focus:** Journalism; Communications. **Qualif.:** Applicants must be journalism and mass communication students who are able to write the best medical story. **Criteria:** Recipients are selected based on academic performance and financial need.

Funds Avail.: Amount not specified. **To Apply:** Applicants must submit a completed application form; applicants must submit a story or stories with name, address, telephone number and class year to Professor Tom Linden. **Deadline:** February 1.

Awards are arranged alphabetically below their administering organizations

9284 ■ Glenn Keever Scholarships
(Undergraduate/Scholarship)

Purpose: To educate journalists. **Focus:** Communication; Journalism. **Qualif.:** Applicants must be undergraduate students, preferably in North Carolina. **Criteria:** Recipients are selected based on academic performance and financial need.

Funds Avail.: $2,000. **To Apply:** Applicants must complete the application form. **Deadline:** February 1. **Contact:** Applications must be e-mailed to jomcscholarships@unc.edu.

9285 ■ Charles Kuralt Fellowships in International Broadcasting *(Postgraduate/ Scholarship)*

Purpose: To educate journalists. **Focus:** Broadcasting. **Qualif.:** Applicant must be a recent school graduate, with a bachelor's or master's degree who excelled in electronic communication. **Criteria:** Recipients are selected based on the academic performance, financial need, and potential for journalism-mass communication careers.

Funds Avail.: No specific amount. **To Apply:** Applicants must complete the application form; see Senior Associate Dean Dulcie Straughan. **Deadline:** October 1.

9286 ■ Norval Neil Luxon Prize for Scholarships to Juniors *(Undergraduate/Scholarship)*

Purpose: To educate journalists. **Focus:** Communications. **Qualif.:** Applicant must be junior with the highest grade point of average; applicants must have at least 36 credit hours of graded course work at the University of North Carolina and have completed approximately 90 credit hours by the end of the spring semester. **Criteria:** Recipients are selected based on the academic performance, and financial need.

Funds Avail.: $1,000. **To Apply:** Applicants must complete the application form. **Deadline:** February 1.

9287 ■ Mackey-Byars Scholarships for Communication Excellence *(Undergraduate/ Scholarship)*

Purpose: To educate journalists. **Focus:** Communications. **Qualif.:** Applicants must be minority or disadvantaged students majoring in mass communications. **Criteria:** Recipients are selected based on academic performance and financial need.

Funds Avail.: Amount not specified. **To Apply:** Applicants must complete the application form. **Contact:** Applications must be e-mailed to jomcscholarships@unc.edu.

9288 ■ Raleigh Mann Scholarships
(Undergraduate/Scholarship)

Purpose: To educate journalists. **Focus:** Journalism; Communications. **Qualif.:** Applicants must be undergraduate students in university. **Criteria:** Recipients are selected based on academic performance and financial need.

Funds Avail.: $500. **To Apply:** Applicants must complete the application package. **Deadline:** February 1. **Contact:** Applications must be e-mailed to jomcscholarships@unc.edu.

9289 ■ Donald Mauer Scholarships
(Undergraduate/Scholarship)

Purpose: To educate journalists. **Focus:** Advertising. **Qualif.:** Applicants must be rising juniors in the advertising sequence. **Criteria:** Recipients are selected based on academic performance and financial need.

Funds Avail.: $500. **To Apply:** Applicants must complete the application form. **Deadline:** February 1. **Contact:** Applications must be e-mailed to jomcscholarships@unc.edu.

9290 ■ Maxwell Graduate Scholarships in Medical Journalism *(Postgraduate/Scholarship)*

Purpose: To educate journalists so that they can communicate about science and medicine effectively. **Focus:** Journalism. **Qualif.:** Applicants must be master's students in the medical journalism program. **Criteria:** Recipients are selected based on the academic performance, and financial need.

Funds Avail.: Amount not specified. **To Apply:** Applicants must complete the application form. **Deadline:** February 1.

9291 ■ Molly McKay Scholarships
(Undergraduate/Scholarship)

Purpose: To educate journalists. **Focus:** Religion. **Qualif.:** Applicants must be students interested in religion. **Criteria:** Recipients are selected based on academic performance, and financial need. Preference is given to students interested in religion.

Funds Avail.: $1,000. **To Apply:** Applicants must complete the application form. **Deadline:** February 1. **Contact:** Applications must be e-mailed to jomcscholarships@unc.edu.

9292 ■ C.A. "Pete" McKnight Scholarships
(Undergraduate/Scholarship)

Purpose: To educate journalists. **Focus:** Journalism. **Qualif.:** Applicants must be currently enrolled or have plans to enroll in a university. **Criteria:** Recipients are selected based on academic performance and financial need.

Funds Avail.: Amount not specified. **To Apply:** Applicants must complete the application form. **Deadline:** February 1. **Contact:** Applications must be e-mailed to jomcscholarships@unc.edu.

9293 ■ Edward Heywood Megson Scholarships
(Undergraduate/Scholarship)

Purpose: To educate journalists. **Focus:** Journalism; Communications. **Qualif.:** Applicants must be graduates of University of North Carolina- Chapel Hill. **Criteria:** Recipients are selected based on academic performance and financial need.

Funds Avail.: Amount not specified. **To Apply:** Applicants must complete the application form. **Deadline:** February 1. **Remarks:** Established by Jeanne C. Tucker to honor the memory of her late husband. **Contact:** Applications must be e-mailed to jomcscholarships@unc.edu.

9294 ■ Quincy Sharpe Mills Scholarships
(Undergraduate/Scholarship)

Purpose: To provide financial assistance to minority and disadvantaged students. **Focus:** Journalism; Communication. **Qualif.:** Applicants must be currently enrolled in or planning to attend a university and must have a minimum of 2.9 GPA. **Criteria:** Recipients are selected based on the academic performance, financial need and potential for journalism-mass communication careers. Preference is also given to minority and disadvantaged students.

Funds Avail.: $5,000. **To Apply:** Applicants must submit a completed application form. **Deadline:** February 1. **Contact:** Applications must be e-mailed to jomcscholarships@unc.edu.

Awards are arranged alphabetically below their administering organizations

9295 ■ Minority Presence Grant Program for Doctoral Study (Doctorate, Graduate/Grant)

Purpose: To educate journalists. **Focus:** Law; Medicine, Veterinary. **Qualif.:** Applicants must be African American residents of North Carolina; applicants must be full-time students pursuing doctoral degrees, law degree, or degrees in veterinary medicine at East Carolina University, Carolina State University, University of North Carolina at Chapel Hill, at Greensboro, or at Charlotte Campus. **Criteria:** Recipients are selected based on the academic performance, financial need, and potential for journalism-mass communication careers.

Funds Avail.: $4,000. **To Apply:** Applicants must complete the application form. **Contact:** PO Box 1080, Chapel Hill, NC 27514-1080.

9296 ■ Alexander Morisey Scholarships (Undergraduate/Scholarship)

Purpose: To provide financial assistance to journalism students. **Focus:** Journalism; Communication. **Qualif.:** Applicants must be first year students and must have a minimum of 2.9 GPA. **Criteria:** Recipients are selected based on academic performance, financial need and potential for journalism-mass communication careers.

Funds Avail.: Amount not specified. **To Apply:** Applicants must submit a completed application form. **Deadline:** February 1. **Contact:** Applications must be e-mailed to jomcscholarships@unc.edu.

9297 ■ N.C. Psychoanalytic Foundation Journalism Scholarships (Graduate, Postgraduate/Scholarship)

Purpose: To educate journalists so that they can communicate about science and medicine effectively. **Focus:** Journalism. **Qualif.:** Applicants must be master's students in the medical journalism program. **Criteria:** Recipients are selected based on the academic performance, and financial need.

Funds Avail.: No specific amount. **To Apply:** Applicants must complete the application form; applicants must submit a 200-word proposal for a project in any medium on mental health. **Deadline:** February 1.

9298 ■ Pfizer Minority Medical Journalism Scholarships (Postgraduate/Scholarship)

Purpose: To provide financial assistance to medical journalism students. **Focus:** Journalism; Communication. **Qualif.:** Applicants must be incoming master's students in the medical journalism program. **Criteria:** Recipients are selected based on the academic performance, financial need, and potential for journalism-mass communication careers. Preference is given to minority and disadvantaged students.

Funds Avail.: No stated amount. **To Apply:** Applicants must submit a completed application form. **Contact:** PO Box 1080, Chapel Hill, NC 27514-1080.

9299 ■ Robert Pittman Scholarships (Undergraduate/Scholarship)

Purpose: To provide financial assistance to journalism students. **Focus:** Journalism; Communication. **Qualif.:** Applicants must be enrolled or plan to enroll in university and have at least 2.9 GPA; applicants must have an internship at St. Petersburg Times. **Criteria:** Recipients are selected based on academic performance, financial need and

potential for journalism-mass communication careers. Preference is given to a student with an interest in newspapers.

Funds Avail.: Amount not specified. **To Apply:** Applicants must submit a completed application form and must contact the School's Director of graduate studies for other application requirements. **Deadline:** February 1. **Contact:** Applicants may e-mail their application to jomcscholarships@unc.edu.

9300 ■ Erwin Potts Scholarships (Undergraduate/Scholarship)

Purpose: To provide financial assistance to Latino students studying newspaper journalism. **Focus:** Journalism; Communication. **Qualif.:** Applicants must be currently enrolled or have plans to attend university. Must have a minimum of 2.9 GPA. **Criteria:** Recipients are selected based on academic performance, financial need and potential for journalism-mass communication careers.

Funds Avail.: $1,500. **To Apply:** Applicants must submit a completed application form. **Deadline:** February 1. **Contact:** Applications must be e-mailed to jomcscholarships@unc.edu.

9301 ■ Peter DeWitt Pruden and Phyliss Harrill Pruden Scholarships (Undergraduate/Scholarship)

Purpose: To provide financial assistance to journalism students. **Focus:** Journalism; Communication. **Qualif.:** Applicants must be enrolled or plan to enroll in a university in North Carolina, Tennessee, or Virginia and have an at least 2.9 GPA. **Criteria:** Preference goes to students from Virginia, Tennessee or North Carolina with strong character, excellent academic performance and financial need.

Funds Avail.: $10,000. **To Apply:** Applicants must submit a completed application form. Applicants must contact the school's director of graduate studies for other application requirements. **Deadline:** February 1. **Contact:** Joe Bob Hester at joe.bob.hester@unc.edu.

9302 ■ Bob Quincy Scholarships (Undergraduate/Scholarship)

Purpose: To educate journalists. **Focus:** Communication; Journalism. **Qualif.:** Applicants must be currently enrolled or have plans to enroll in a university. **Criteria:** Recipients are selected based on academic performance and financial need.

Funds Avail.: $1,000. **To Apply:** Applicants must complete the application form. **Deadline:** February 1. **Contact:** Applications must be e-mailed to jomcscholarships@unc.edu.

9303 ■ Marjorie Usher Ragan Scholarships (Undergraduate/Scholarship)

Purpose: To educate journalists. **Focus:** Communication; Journalism. **Qualif.:** Applicants must be women with a career interest in print journalism. **Criteria:** Recipients are selected based on academic performance and financial need. Special consideration will be given to applicants pursuing a news-editorial journalism.

Funds Avail.: $1,000. **To Apply:** Applicants must complete the application form. **Deadline:** February 1. **Contact:** Applications must be e-mailed to jomcscholarships@unc.edu.

9304 ■ Eugene L. Roberts Jr. Prize (Undergraduate/Prize)

Purpose: To educate journalists so that they can communicate effectively. **Focus:** Journalism. **Qualif.:** Applicants

Awards are arranged alphabetically below their administering organizations

must be undergraduate students interested in print journalism who propose the best idea for a Gene Roberts-type story; applicants must be returning to School for at least one semester to research and write a story in JOMC 296. The course is "Independent Study" supervised by a faculty member for three credits. **Criteria:** Recipients are selected based on academic performance and financial need. Special consideration will be given to applicants pursuing a News-Editorial journalism career.

Funds Avail.: $4,000. **To Apply:** Applicants must complete the application form. **Deadline:** February 1. **Contact:** Questions should be directed to Senior Associate Dean Dulcie Straughan; Phone: 919-962-9003; E-mail: dulcie@email.unc.edu.

9305 ■ A.C. Snow Scholarships (Undergraduate/Scholarship)

Purpose: To educate journalists. **Focus:** Journalism. **Qualif.:** Applicants must be news editorial students with an interest in grammar. **Criteria:** Recipients are selected based on academic performance and financial need.

Funds Avail.: $750. **To Apply:** Applicants must complete the application form. **Deadline:** February 1. **Contact:** Applications must be e-mailed to jomcscholarships@unc.edu.

9306 ■ Hal Tanner Jr. Scholarships (Undergraduate/Scholarship)

Purpose: To educate journalists. **Focus:** Communication; Advertising. **Qualif.:** Applicants must be rising senior students majoring in advertising. **Criteria:** Recipients are selected based on academic performance and financial need.

Funds Avail.: Amount not specified. **To Apply:** Applicants must complete the application form. **Deadline:** February 1. **Contact:** Applications must be e-mailed to jomcscholarships@unc.edu.

9307 ■ Jim and Pat Thacker Sports Communication Internships (Undergraduate/Internship)

Purpose: To educate journalists; to pay expenses for a student who has secured a summer internship in sports communication. **Focus:** Communication. **Qualif.:** Applicants must be currently enrolled or plan to enroll in a university. **Criteria:** Recipients are selected based on academic performance and financial need.

Funds Avail.: Amount not specified. **To Apply:** Applicants must complete the application form; must attach a current resume, a one-page essay stating why a chosen career interests and inspires the applicant. **Contact:** Professor John Sweeney, jsweeney@email.unc.edu.

9308 ■ Tucker Family Scholarships (Undergraduate/Scholarship)

Purpose: To provide financial assistance to journalism students. **Focus:** Journalism; Communication. **Qualif.:** Applicants must be enrolled or plan to enroll in a university and have at least 2.9 GPA. **Criteria:** Recipients are selected based on academic performance, financial need and potential for journalism-mass communication careers. Preference is given to students in print or broadcast.

Funds Avail.: $1,000. **To Apply:** Applicants must submit a completed application form. **Deadline:** February 1. **Contact:** Applications must be e-mailed to jomcscholarships@unc.edu.

9309 ■ David Julian Wichard Scholarships (Undergraduate/Scholarship)

Purpose: To educate journalists. **Focus:** Communication; Journalism. **Qualif.:** Applicants must be currently enrolled or planning to enroll in university; applicants must be residents of North Carolina. **Criteria:** Recipients are selected based on the academic performance, and financial need.

Funds Avail.: $2,500. **To Apply:** Applicants must complete the application form. **Deadline:** February 1.

9310 ■ Tom Wicker Scholarships (Undergraduate/Scholarship)

Purpose: To provide financial assistance to news-editorial graduate students. **Focus:** Journalism; Communication. **Qualif.:** Applicants must be enrolled or plan to enroll in university and have an at least 2.9 GPA. **Criteria:** Recipients are selected based on the academic performance, financial need and potential for journalism-mass communication careers. Special consideration will be given to minority and disadvantaged students.

Funds Avail.: $1,250. **To Apply:** Applicants must submit a completed application form. Applicants must contact the school's director of graduate studies for other application requirements. **Deadline:** March 1.

9311 ■ WKIX Alumni Association Scholarships (Undergraduate/Scholarship)

Purpose: To educate journalists. **Focus:** Communications. **Qualif.:** Applicants must be students in electronic communication sequence. **Criteria:** Recipients are selected based on academic performance and financial need.

Funds Avail.: Amount not specified. **To Apply:** Applicants must complete the application form. **Deadline:** February 1. **Contact:** Applications must be e-mailed to jomcscholarships@unc.edu.

9312 ■ WTVD Endowment Scholarships (Undergraduate/Scholarship)

Purpose: To provide financial assistance to journalism students. **Focus:** Journalism; Communication. **Qualif.:** Applicants must be enrolled or have plans to enroll in a university. Must have at least 2.9 GPA and be residents of North Carolina. **Criteria:** Recipients are selected based on academic performance, financial need and potential for journalism-mass communication careers.

Funds Avail.: $500. **To Apply:** Applicants must submit a completed application form. **Deadline:** February 1. **Contact:** Applications must be e-mailed to jomcscholarships@unc.edu.

9313 ■ University of Oregon (UO)

1217 University of Oregon
Eugene, OR 97403
Ph: (541) 346-3201
Fax: (541) 346-5815
Free: 800-BEA-DUCK
E-mail: admissions@uoregon.edu
URL: www.uoregon.edu

9314 ■ Robert W. and Bernice Ingalls Staton Scholarships (Undergraduate/Scholarship)

Purpose: To provide financial support to students who desire to further their education without financial burden.

Awards are arranged alphabetically below their administering organizations

Focus: Humanities; Fine arts; Education; Music. **Qualif.:** Applicants must be Oregon residents and must have an extraordinary financial need. **Criteria:** Recipients are selected based on financial need. Preference is given to students who declare a major in the Humanities, Department of Fine Arts, the College of Education, or the School of Music. Other factors taken into consideration include the student's major and professional objective; academic performance; and family educational history with priority given to first generation students.

Funds Avail.: $5,750. **Number Awarded:** 12. **To Apply:** Applicants must submit the Admission application and Free Application for Federal Student Aid (FAFSA) available online to the Office of Admission. **Deadline:** January 15.

9315 ■ University of Oregon Dean's Scholarships (Undergraduate/Scholarship)

Purpose: To encourage qualified individuals to pursue their studies in the University of Oregon. **Focus:** General studies. **Qualif.:** Applicants must be entering freshmen; must have a minimum cumulative high school GPA of 3.6; must meet all current UO freshman admission requirements; must have not attended another college after graduation from high school. **Criteria:** Recipients will be selected based on high school GPA and coursework.

Funds Avail.: $1,000-$7,000. **To Apply:** Applicants must submit the UO Undergraduate Admission Application available online to the Office of Admission. **Deadline:** January 15.

9316 ■ University of Oregon Diversity Excellence Scholarships (Graduate, Undergraduate/ Scholarship)

Purpose: To encourage the undergraduate and graduate students to enhance their educational experience by sharing diverse cultural experiences. **Focus:** General studies. **Qualif.:** Applicants must be undergraduates and graduate students who enhance the educational experience of all students by sharing diverse cultural experiences; must be U.S citizens or permanent residents; must be currently enrolled as University of Oregon students in good academic standing; must meet the DBS minimum GPA requirements; must have a minimum cumulative GPA of 3.0 for freshmen, and 2.50 for other applicants. **Criteria:** UO Diversity - Building Scholarship Committee gives priority to students who demonstrate the following: (1) Strong academic background as documented by official high school and/or college transcript; (2) Financial need as defined by federal guidelines; (3) Family educational history; (4) Residency status; (5) Commitment to diversity through documented history of community service, leadership, or other activities; (6) Ethnic background; and (7) residency status.

Funds Avail.: No specific amount. **To Apply:** Application forms are available online. Applicants must submit a personal statement, letter of recommendation and official transcripts. Application form and other supporting materials must be submitted to the Office of Student Financial Aid & Scholarships.

9317 ■ University of Oregon General University Scholarships (Undergraduate/Scholarship)

Purpose: To support qualified individuals who wish to pursue their education. **Focus:** General studies. **Qualif.:** Applicants must have a minimum GPA of 3.50. **Criteria:** Selection of applicants will be based on academic performance, SAT or ACT scores (Freshmen), extracurricular involvement, faculty recommendation (junior, senior and graduate students), as well as writing ability and creativity as demonstrated in the career aspirations and scholarship essay.

Funds Avail.: $1,500-$2,700. **To Apply:** Applicants must complete the Scholarship Application Form and submit high school transcripts as well as SAT or ACT scores. **Deadline:** February 15.

9318 ■ University of Oregon Presidential Scholarships (Undergraduate/Scholarship)

Purpose: To provide financial support to the state's brightest students. **Focus:** General studies. **Qualif.:** Applicants must be Oregon residents; must be entering freshmen; must have a minimum GPA of 3.85; have at least 1240 combined math and critical reading SAT score or 28 ACT composite score; and must have significant history of leadership and volunteer service activities. **Criteria:** Applications will be judged by the Scholarship Committee based on academic performance; SAT or ACT scores; extracurricular involvement; writing ability and creativity as demonstrated in the career aspirations and scholarship essay.

Funds Avail.: $8,000. **To Apply:** Applicants must complete the Scholarship Application forms available online; and must submit official high school transcripts and SAT or ACT scores to the Office of Admissions. **Deadline:** January 15.

9319 ■ University of Toronto (U of T)
27 King's College Cir.
Toronto, ON, Canada M5S 1A1
Ph: (416) 978-2011
E-mail: webservices@utoronto.ca
URL: www.utoronto.ca

9320 ■ Dr. Anderson Abbott Awards (Undergraduate/Scholarship)

Purpose: To support students with their educational pursuit. **Focus:** Medicine; Health sciences. **Qualif.:** Applicant must be a black student of UofT. **Criteria:** The selection committee may give preference to student in the medical program or in a related health science program.

Funds Avail.: $4,000. **Number Awarded:** 1. **To Apply:** Applicants must submit a completed Abbot application form along with the required materials and information. **Deadline:** March 30.

9321 ■ Stephanie Ali Memorial Scholarships (Undergraduate/Scholarship)

Purpose: To support students with their educational pursuits. **Focus:** General studies. **Qualif.:** Applicant must be a student of U of T; in financial need; and have demonstrated commitment to community work or participation in charitable activities. **Criteria:** Preference is given to student who are past or present members of the University of Toronto Gospel Choir.

Funds Avail.: Approximately $600. **To Apply:** Applicants must submit a completed Stephanie Ali Memorial Scholarships application form along with the required materials and information. **Deadline:** March 30.

9322 ■ J.P. Bickell Mining Scholarships (Undergraduate/Scholarship)

Purpose: To support students with their educational pursuits. **Focus:** Geology; Geophysics; Earth sciences;

Awards are arranged alphabetically below their administering organizations

Mining; Environmental science. **Qualif.:** Applicant must be a student of U of T; an undergraduate student in second or higher years studying mining (including the geological and geophysical fields as well as environmental sciences, geological sciences, earth science programs and mining engineering); have a minimum GPA of B or better and have demonstrated interest in the mining industry or field. **Criteria:** Selection is based on general proficiency or outstanding achievements.

Funds Avail.: Approximately $2000. **To Apply:** Applicants must submit a letter of application together with a letter outlining the interest in the mining industry. **Deadline:** October 30.

9323 ■ Leon C. Bynoe Memorial Scholarships
(Undergraduate/Scholarship)

Purpose: To support students with their educational pursuits. **Focus:** General studies. **Qualif.:** Applicant must be a student of U of T; an undergraduate student enrolled in an undergraduate degree program; and must demonstrate outstanding service to the Afro-Canadian community. **Criteria:** Selection is based on financial need and outstanding academic achievement. Preference is given to students from the Afro-Canadian community and MTHA residents.

Funds Avail.: Approximately $1300. **To Apply:** Applicants must submit a completed Leon C. Bynoe Memorial Scholarships application form along with the required materials and information. **Deadline:** November 30.

9324 ■ Canadian Federation of University Women Etobicoke Bursary *(Undergraduate/ Scholarship)*

Purpose: To support students with their educational pursuits. **Focus:** General studies. **Qualif.:** Applicant must be a female undergraduate student of U of T; a resident of Etobicoke; and in need of financial assistance for education. **Criteria:** Selection is based on general proficiency or outstanding achievements.

Funds Avail.: $1,200. **Number Awarded:** 2. **To Apply:** Applicants must submit a completed Canadian Federation of University Women Etobicoke Bursary application form along with the required materials and information. **Deadline:** October 26. **Contact:** 172 Saint George St., Toronto, ON M5R 0A3.

9325 ■ City of Toronto Graduate Scholarships for Women in Mathematics *(Graduate/ Scholarship)*

Purpose: To support students with their educational pursuits. **Focus:** Mathematics and mathematical sciences. **Qualif.:** Applicants must be a female student of UofT enrolled in a master's or doctoral program in mathematics. **Criteria:** Selection is based on financial need, academic merit and demonstrated interest in issues related to women in mathematics.

Funds Avail.: Annual income (no less than $9000). **To Apply:** Applicants must submit a completed application form along with the required materials and information. **Deadline:** November 1. **Contact:** osap.staff@utoronto.ca.

9326 ■ City of Toronto Queen Elizabeth II Sesquicentennial Scholarships in Community Health Nursing for Graduates *(Graduate/ Scholarship)*

Purpose: To support students with their educational pursuit. **Focus:** Nursing. **Qualif.:** Applicant must be a graduate student enrolled in the Graduate Department of Nursing Science; have completed courses in community health and demonstrate a commitment to this aspect of nursing. **Criteria:** Selection is based on general proficiency or outstanding achievements.

Funds Avail.: $3000. **Number Awarded:** 1. **To Apply:** Applicants must submit a completed application form along with the required materials and information. **Deadline:** October 5. **Contact:** 172 Saint George St., Toronto, ON M5R 0A3.

9327 ■ City of Toronto Queen Elizabeth II Sesquicentennial Scholarships in Community Health Nursing for Undergraduates
(Undergraduate/Scholarship)

Purpose: To support students with their educational pursuits. **Focus:** Nursing. **Qualif.:** Applicant must be undergraduate student completing the first year of the second-entry two year BScN program. **Criteria:** Preference may be given to students proficient in a language besides English and whose interest is to work with multicultural families.

Funds Avail.: $5000. **Number Awarded:** 1. **To Apply:** Applicants must submit a completed application form along with the required materials and information. **Deadline:** June 30.

9328 ■ City of Toronto Scholarships for Aboriginal Students *(Graduate, Undergraduate/ Scholarship)*

Purpose: To support students with their educational pursuit. **Focus:** Health services administration. **Qualif.:** Applicants must be an undergraduate or graduate aboriginal student studying in any of the health professional programs. **Criteria:** Selection is based on financial need, academic merit and demonstrated community leadership skills.

Funds Avail.: Approximately $4,500. **To Apply:** Applicants must submit a completed application form along with the required materials and information. **Deadline:** October 26. **Contact:** 172 Saint George St., Toronto, ON M5R 0A3.

9329 ■ City of Toronto Women's Studies Scholarships *(Graduate, Undergraduate/ Scholarship)*

Purpose: To support students with their educational pursuits. **Focus:** Women's studies. **Qualif.:** Applicants must be undergraduate or graduate students in Women's Studies. **Criteria:** Selection is based on financial need and academic merit.

Funds Avail.: Undergraduate - $5000; Graduate scholarship valued at the balance of the annual income. **Number Awarded:** 1 undergraduate; and 1 graduate student. **To Apply:** Applicants must submit a completed application form along with the required materials and information. **Deadline:** November 2. **Contact:** 172 Saint George St., Toronto, ON M5R 0A3.

9330 ■ Mary Jane Hendrie Memorial Scholarships *(Graduate, Undergraduate/Scholarship)*

Purpose: To support students with their educational pursuits. **Focus:** Japanese studies. **Qualif.:** Applicant must be a senior undergraduate or graduate student of U of T; interested in relations between Japan and Canada with studies in business, law, economics, international relations, or political science. **Criteria:** Selection is based on general proficiency or outstanding achievements.

Awards are arranged alphabetically below their administering organizations

Funds Avail.: Approximately $3,500. **To Apply:** Applicants must submit a completed application form along with the required materials and information. **Deadline:** November 30. **Remarks:** Faculty members can nominate a student by writing a letter to the Scholarship Selection Committee describing the student's qualifications for the award.

9331 ▪ Irving J. Hoffman Memorial Scholarships *(Undergraduate/Scholarship)*

Purpose: To support students with their educational pursuits. **Focus:** General studies. **Qualif.:** Applicant must be a physically handicapped student, enrolled on either a full-time or part-time basis, demonstrates superior academic achievement; have completed at least five university level courses, or the equivalent. Students registered in OISE are not qualified. **Criteria:** Selection is based on academic achievement and financial need.

Funds Avail.: Approximately $500. **To Apply:** Applicants must submit a completed application form along with the required materials and information. **Deadline:** November 30.

9332 ▪ Hosinec Family Scholarships *(Graduate, Undergraduate/Scholarship)*

Purpose: To support students with their educational pursuits. **Focus:** General studies. **Qualif.:** Applicant must be undergraduate or graduate student of the U of T. **Criteria:** Selection is based on need and academic merit.

Funds Avail.: $3000. **Number Awarded:** 25. **To Apply:** Applicants must submit a completed application form and required materials and information. **Deadline:** November 30. **Remarks:** Funded by the Hosinec Family Endowment Fund.

9333 ▪ In-course Scholarships - Chinese Dance Workshop Scholarships *(Undergraduate/Scholarship)*

Purpose: To support students with their educational pursuits. **Focus:** Dance. **Qualif.:** Applicant must be a student of U of T and have attended a recognized dance institute for at least three years. **Criteria:** Selection is based on academic excellence and demonstrated dance experience.

Funds Avail.: Approximately $2,400. **To Apply:** Applicants must submit a letter of application verifying at least three years of attendance at a recognized dance institute along with a transcript of marks. **Deadline:** October 26.

9334 ▪ Khaki University and Y.M.C.A. Memorial Scholarships *(Undergraduate/Scholarship)*

Purpose: To support students with their educational pursuits. **Focus:** General studies. **Qualif.:** Applicant must be enrolled in the second or higher year of an undergraduate course proceeding to a degree; have at least first class honours standing. **Criteria:** Preference is given to students who are descendent from one who has served in the armed forces.

Funds Avail.: Varies. **To Apply:** Applicants must submit a completed application form along with the required materials and information. **Deadline:** November 30.

9335 ▪ Lo Family Scholarships *(Undergraduate/Scholarship)*

Purpose: To support students with their educational pursuits. **Focus:** General studies. **Qualif.:** Applicant must be a Canadian citizen, permanent resident or protected

person (recognized convention refugee) and will be enrolled full-time; an active leader, respected and considered to be well-rounded citizen in school and community, and have demonstrated financial need. **Criteria:** Selection is based on financial need and academic merit.

Funds Avail.: No specific amount. **To Apply:** Applicants must submit an online UTAPS application and a letter outlining community activity and demonstrated leadership skills; and a letter of support from school. **Deadline:** February 27.

9336 ▪ John Macara, Barrister of Goderich, Scholarships *(Undergraduate/Scholarship)*

Purpose: To support students with their educational pursuits. **Focus:** General studies. **Qualif.:** Applicant must be a Canadian citizen, permanent resident or protected person (recognized convention refugee) and will be enrolled full-time. **Criteria:** Preference is given to applicants who can establish that they are the blood kin of the late Mrs. Jean Glasgow.

Funds Avail.: No specific amount. **To Apply:** Applicants must submit an online UTAPS application and a letter explaining how they are related to the late Mrs. Glasgow. **Deadline:** February 27.

9337 ▪ Joseph McCulley Educational Scholarships *(Graduate, Undergraduate/Scholarship)*

Purpose: To support students with their educational pursuits. **Focus:** Social work. **Qualif.:** Applicant must be a U of T graduate or undergraduate student whose programs of study and career interests lie in the area of public life or social work, emphasizing on penology. **Criteria:** Selection is based on financial need.

Funds Avail.: Variable in value, to the total of the annual income. **To Apply:** Applicants must submit a completed application form together with the required materials and information. **Deadline:** November 30.

9338 ▪ Al Mercury Scholarships *(Undergraduate/Scholarship)*

Purpose: To support students with their educational pursuits. **Focus:** General studies. **Qualif.:** Applicant must be a UofT student demonstrated community involvement, academic excellence, integrity and an appreciation and interest in music. **Criteria:** Selection is based on general proficiency or outstanding achievements.

Funds Avail.: Approximately $700. **To Apply:** Applicants must submit a completed application form along with the required materials and information. **Deadline:** November 30.

9339 ▪ John H. Moss Scholarships *(Undergraduate/Scholarship)*

Purpose: To support students with their educational pursuits. **Focus:** Arts; Science. **Qualif.:** Applicant must be a U of T student having a minimum GPA of 3.3 (B+); demonstrates outstanding academic and extra-curricular leadership; in the graduating year in Arts and Science at the University of Toronto (St. George, Mississauga and Scarborough campuses) and intending to pursue a second degree or studies at the graduate level. **Criteria:** Selection is based on general proficiency or outstanding achievements.

Funds Avail.: Up to $16,650. **To Apply:** Applicants must submit a completed application form together with the required materials and information. **Deadline:** December 7.

Awards are arranged alphabetically below their administering organizations

9340 ■ Nortel Institute Undergraduate Scholarships (Undergraduate/Scholarship)

Purpose: To support students with their educational pursuits. **Focus:** Applied art; Engineering. **Qualif.:** Applicant must be a U of T student and a Canadian citizen or landed immigrant and a resident of Ontario; must be in the second or third year in the Faculty of Applied Science and Engineering, the Faculty of Arts and Science, University of Toronto Mississauga and University of Toronto Scarborough. **Criteria:** Selection is based on financial need, academic merit and on the essay.

Funds Avail.: Approximately $5000. **To Apply:** Applicants must submit a completed application form along with two references and an essay on "The Future of Communications and How Telecommunications Technology Can Benefit Society" (maximum of 500 words). **Deadline:** November 30.

9341 ■ Ontario Hockey Association War Memorial Scholarships (Undergraduate/Scholarship)

Purpose: To support students with their educational pursuits. **Focus:** General studies. **Qualif.:** Applicant must be a Canadian citizen, permanent resident or protected person (recognized convention refugee) and will be enrolled full-time; and a descendent of one who has served with the Canadian forces. **Criteria:** Selection is based on financial need and academic merit.

Funds Avail.: No specific award. **To Apply:** Applicants must submit an online UTAPS application and the proof of service. **Deadline:** January.

9342 ■ Taylor Statten Memorial Fellowships (Graduate/Scholarship)

Purpose: To support students with their educational pursuits. **Focus:** Education, Physical; Psychology; Social work. **Qualif.:** Applicant must be a U of T student in post-baccalaureate study in professional field or career related to youth services (such as physical and health education, psychology, teaching, the ministry and social work). **Criteria:** Consideration is given to academically qualified students with career goals and past interests and experience indicate a serious commitment to working with young people.

Funds Avail.: Approximately $2,000. **To Apply:** Applicants must submit a completed application form together with the required documents and information. **Deadline:** March 30.

9343 ■ Evald Torokvei Foundation Scholarships (Graduate/Scholarship)

Purpose: To support students with their educational pursuits. **Focus:** Chemical engineering. **Qualif.:** Applicant must be a graduate student engaged in research in chemicals and plastics. **Criteria:** Selection is based on academic standing, community and university involvement and financial need.

Funds Avail.: $1,000. **Number Awarded:** 2. **To Apply:** Applicants must submit a letter of application that includes the applicant's name, address, phone number, student number; area of research, name of Research Director; details of the applicant's involvement in the University community; a statement of financial need (if applicable); transcript of marks; and letters of reference. **Deadline:** February 24.

9344 ■ University of Toronto Accenture Scholarships (Undergraduate/Scholarship)

Purpose: To support students with their educational pursuits. **Focus:** Engineering; Computer and information sciences. **Qualif.:** Applicant must be a student of U of T; enrolled in an Engineering, Computer Science or Bachelor of Commerce Degree; a third year student entering the final year of study; have maintained a strong academic background - minimum GPA of 3.0; and actively involved in two or more extracurricular activities. **Criteria:** Selection is based on general proficiency or outstanding achievements.

Funds Avail.: $1,500. **To Apply:** Applicants must submit a completed Accenture Scholarship application form along with the required materials and information. **Deadline:** October 5. **Contact:** 172 Saint George St., Toronto, ON M5R 0A3.

9345 ■ University of Toronto SAC Undergraduate Grants (Undergraduate/Grant)

Purpose: To support students with their educational pursuits. **Focus:** General studies. **Qualif.:** Applicant must be a UofT full-time undergraduate student maintaining a minimum academic standing of "C". **Criteria:** Selection is based on financial need, and extracurricular involvement in the University Community.

Funds Avail.: $1300. **Number Awarded:** One or more. **To Apply:** Applicants must submit a completed application form together with the required materials and information. **Deadline:** November 30.

9346 ■ University of Wisconsin-Madison
716 Langdon St.
Madison, WI 53706-1481
Ph: (608) 263-2400
Fax: (608) 265-3277
E-mail: askbucky@uwmad.wisc.edu
URL: www.wisc.edu

9347 ■ Victor Albright Scholarships-Dane County (Undergraduate/Scholarship)

Purpose: To support Wisconsin students in their education. **Focus:** General studies. **Qualif.:** Applicants must be graduates of a Dane County public high school. **Criteria:** Selection is based on merit.

Funds Avail.: $100. **Number Awarded:** Varies. **To Apply:** Students must be nominated by their high school principals or guidance counselors. Applicants must contact their high school for more information.

9348 ■ Victor Albright Scholarships (Undergraduate/Scholarship)

Purpose: To support Wisconsin students in their education. **Focus:** General studies. **Qualif.:** Applicants must be graduates of public high schools within Wisconsin counties (excluding Dane). **Criteria:** Selection is based on merit.

Funds Avail.: $500-$1,000. **Number Awarded:** 2. **To Apply:** Students must be nominated by their high school principals or guidance counselors.

9349 ■ Bascom Hill Society Scholarships (Undergraduate/Scholarship)

Purpose: To support students in their education. **Focus:** General studies. **Qualif.:** Applicants must be full-time juniors or seniors with outstanding volunteer contributions to the university and/or their community while maintaining a solid academic record; must have a cumulative GPA of at least a 3.2. Wisconsin and Minnesota residents must have an unmet need of at least $1,000 and out-of-state students

Awards are arranged alphabetically below their administering organizations

must have an unmet need of at least $5,000. **Criteria:** Selection is based on merit and financial need.

Funds Avail.: No amount specified. **Number Awarded:** 1. **To Apply:** Applicants must contact the Office of Undergraduate Academic Awards for more information. **Deadline:** April 22. **Contact:** Office of Undergraduate Academic Awards, Julie Stubbs, at 608-890-0370, or stubbs@wisc.edu.

9350 ■ Mary Ann Brichta Scholarships
(Undergraduate/Scholarship)

Purpose: To support UW-Madison students in their education. **Focus:** Education, Secondary. **Qualif.:** Applicants must be UW-Madison sophomore, junior, or senior underrepresented students of color majoring in elementary or secondary education. **Criteria:** Selection is based on academic excellence.

Funds Avail.: No specific amount. **Number Awarded:** Varies. **To Apply:** Scholarship applications are available from the Office of the Dean. **Deadline:** February.

9351 ■ Patricia Buchanan Memorial Scholarships *(Undergraduate/Scholarship)*

Purpose: To support UW-Madison students in their education. **Focus:** Education, Secondary. **Qualif.:** Applicants must be UW-Madison sophomore, junior, or senior underrepresented students of color majoring in elementary or secondary education. **Criteria:** Selection is based on academic excellence.

Funds Avail.: No specific amount. **Number Awarded:** Varies. **To Apply:** Scholarship applications are available from the Office of the Dean. **Deadline:** February.

9352 ■ Engineering Departmental Scholarships
(Undergraduate/Scholarship)

Purpose: To support UW-Madison students in their education. **Focus:** Engineering. **Qualif.:** Applicants must be UW-Madison sophomores, juniors and senior students admitted into a degree-granting department. **Criteria:** Selection is based on academic achievement.

Funds Avail.: Varies. **Number Awarded:** Varies. **To Apply:** Students must contact the specific department office about the application process. **Deadline:** March 15. **Contact:** College of Engineering, Engineering Student Services Office at 608-262-2473, or hansen@engr.wisc.edu.

9353 ■ Engineering Diversity Affairs Scholarships *(All/Scholarship)*

Purpose: To support UW-Madison students in their education. **Focus:** Engineering. **Qualif.:** Applicants must be UW-Madison women and students of color; must be U.S. citizens or permanent residents enrolled in the College of Engineering. **Criteria:** Selection is based on academic achievement.

Funds Avail.: Varies. **Number Awarded:** Varies. **To Apply:** Students must contact the specific department office or the Engineering Student Services office about the application process. **Deadline:** March 15. **Contact:** College of Engineering, Engineering Student Services Office, at 608-262-2473, or hansen@engr.wisc.edu.

9354 ■ Evjue Foundation, Inc./Capital Times Scholarships *(Undergraduate/Scholarship)*

Purpose: To provide financial assistance to students who wish to pursue their education. **Focus:** General studies.

Qualif.: Applicant must be a dependent of a regular full-time employee of The Capital Times. **Criteria:** Recipient selection will be based on academic performance; school participation and leadership; and community service.

Funds Avail.: No amount specified. **Number Awarded:** Varies. **To Apply:** Applicant must contact the Evjue Foundation for more information about the scholarship. **Deadline:** February. **Contact:** The Evjue Foundation, Inc., at 608-252-6401.

9355 ■ Edward R. and Hazel N. Felber Scholarships *(Undergraduate/Scholarship)*

Purpose: To financial assistance to students who wish to pursue their education. **Focus:** General studies. **Qualif.:** Applicant must be a dependent of a Madison Gas and Electric (MG&E) employee. Award is renewable if applicants must: (1) maintain at least 2.5 cumulative GPA; and (2) complete at least 12 credits per semester. **Criteria:** Recipients will be selected based on academic record, leadership, participation in extracurricular activities and work experience. Financial need is not considered.

Funds Avail.: $2,000. **Number Awarded:** Varies. **To Apply:** Applicants must contact MG&E at 608252-7392 to request for an application. **Deadline:** May 1.

9356 ■ Gay, Lesbian, Bisexual, Transgender Alumni Council Scholarships *(Undergraduate/ Scholarship)*

Purpose: To support UW-Madison students in their education. **Focus:** General studies. **Qualif.:** Applicants must be committed to the gay, lesbian, bisexual, and transgender community; and must maintain an outstanding academic achievement. **Criteria:** Priority will be given to students with financial need.

Funds Avail.: Up to $2,000. **Number Awarded:** Varies. **To Apply:** Applicants must contact the Wisconsin Alumni Association for information about the program. **Deadline:** spring. **Contact:** Wisconsin Alumni Association at 608-262-2551, or glbtac@uwalumni.com; visit the website www.uwalumni.com/glbtac.

9357 ■ Barry M. Goldwater Scholarships
(Undergraduate/Scholarship)

Purpose: To provide financial assistance to mathematics, science, and engineering students who wish to pursue their education. **Focus:** Mathematics and mathematical sciences; Science; Engineering. **Qualif.:** Applicants must be full-time juniors or seniors with outstanding potential for a career in mathematics, science, or engineering; have at least a B average; rank in the upper quarter of the high school's class; be U.S. citizens or U.S. nationals; nominated by UW-Madison; have a GPA of 3.75 or above, and previous research experience. **Criteria:** Selection is based on academic achievement, progress toward research goals, research essay, and letters of recommendation.

Funds Avail.: $7,500. **Number Awarded:** 300. **To Apply:** Applicants must contact the Office of Undergraduate Academic Awards for information about the scholarship. **Deadline:** November 15. **Contact:** Office of Undergraduate Academic Awards, Dr. Julie Stubbs, at 608-265-2428, or awards@provost.wisc.edu.

9358 ■ Human Ecology Continuing Undergraduate Student Scholarships
(Undergraduate/Scholarship)

Purpose: To support UW-Madison students in their education. **Focus:** Ecology. **Qualif.:** Applicants must be UW-

Awards are arranged alphabetically below their administering organizations

Madison sophomores, juniors, or seniors enrolled in the School of Human Ecology. **Criteria:** Selection is based on scholastic and extracurricular achievement.

Funds Avail.: $2,000. **Number Awarded:** Up to 35. **To Apply:** Applicants must submit the School of Human Ecology Continuing Undergraduate Student Scholarship Application along with three letters of recommendation, official transcripts and a resume. **Deadline:** February 15. **Contact:** School of Human Ecology, Office of Student Academic Affairs at 608-262-2608.

9359 ■ James Jesinski Scholarships
(Undergraduate/Scholarship)

Purpose: To support students in their education. **Focus:** General studies. **Qualif.:** Applicant must be a dependent of a member of Wisconsin Teamsters Union Locals 43, 56, 75, 200, 344, 354, 446, 563, 579, 662, 695, or 1081. Applicants must also be affiliated with Teamsters Joint Council 39. **Criteria:** Recipient selection will be based on financial need.

Funds Avail.: $2,000. **Number Awarded:** 2. **To Apply:** Applicants must apply for UW-Madison financial aid by March 1. **Deadline:** March 31. **Contact:** Office of Student Financial Services, Scholarship Section, at 608-262-9996, or finaid@finaid.wisc.edu.

9360 ■ Kemper K. Knapp Scholarships
(Undergraduate/Scholarship)

Purpose: To support UW-Madison students in their education. **Focus:** General studies. **Qualif.:** Students must be Wisconsin residents entering UW-Madison as freshmen. **Criteria:** Selection will be based on academic excellence.

Funds Avail.: No specific amount. **Number Awarded:** Varies. **To Apply:** Students will be automatically considered when admitted. **Deadline:** Varies. **Contact:** Office of Student Financial Services, Scholarship Section, at 608-262-9996, or finaid@finaid.wisc.edu.

9361 ■ George Koeppel and Roland W. Zinns Scholarships *(Undergraduate/Scholarship)*

Purpose: To support UW-Madison students in their education. **Focus:** Education, Secondary. **Qualif.:** Applicant must be a full-time undergraduate student in a School of Education who intend to become an elementary school teacher; must be Wisconsin resident with permanent home address in Milwaukee County. **Criteria:** Selection is based on academic excellence.

Funds Avail.: No specific amount. **Number Awarded:** Varies. **To Apply:** Scholarship applications are available from the Office of the Dean. **Deadline:** February. **Contact:** soeinfo@education.wisc.edu.

9362 ■ Lawton Minority Retention Grants
(Undergraduate/Scholarship)

Purpose: To support UW-Madison students in their education. **Focus:** General studies. **Qualif.:** Applicants must be underrepresented students of color; must be Wisconsin or Minnesota residents; must be sophomore, junior, or senior students; must have a minimum cumulative GPA of 2.0; and must be African-American, Hispanic/Latino/Native American, or Southeast Asian (Vietnamese/Cambodian/Laotian born after 1975). **Criteria:** Recipients will be selected based on financial need.

Funds Avail.: Up to $2,500. **Number Awarded:** Varies. **To Apply:** Applicants must file an application at FAFSA in order to be considered. In addition, applicants must contact

the Minority and Disadvantaged Coordinator in the UW-Madison school or college where they are enrolled.

9363 ■ McBurney Disability Scholarships
(Undergraduate/Scholarship)

Purpose: To support UW-Madison students in their education. **Focus:** General studies. **Qualif.:** Applicants must have a documented disability (physical, psychological, sensory, or learning) as verified by the McBurney Disability Resource Center. **Criteria:** Recipients will be selected based on the application materials submitted.

Funds Avail.: $500-$2,500. **Number Awarded:** Up to 20. **To Apply:** Applicants must submit a completed McBurney Scholarship Application along with two letters of recommendation and a current transcript. **Deadline:** April 15.

9364 ■ John P. and Tashia F. Morgridge Scholarships *(Undergraduate/Scholarship)*

Purpose: To support UW-Madison students in their education. **Focus:** Education, Secondary. **Qualif.:** Applicants must be UW-Madison sophomores, juniors, or seniors who are underrepresented students of color. Applicants must be preparing for a teaching career, preferably at the elementary level. **Criteria:** Selection is based on academic achievement and financial need; with preference given to graduates of Wisconsin high schools.

Funds Avail.: Varies. **Number Awarded:** 6. **To Apply:** Scholarship applications are available from the Office of the Dean. **Deadline:** February. **Contact:** School of Education, Office of the Dean, at 608-262-6137, or soeinfo@education.wisc.edu.

9365 ■ Charles S. Pearce Scholarships
(Undergraduate/Prize, Scholarship)

Purpose: To support students in their education. **Focus:** General studies. **Qualif.:** Applicants must be admitted and enrolled at the university; must be Wisconsin residents; and must be winners of the JSEHS research competition. **Criteria:** Selection is made by the symposium committee.

Funds Avail.: No specific amount. **Number Awarded:** 1. **To Apply:** Students must contact the Engineering Learning Center. **Deadline:** December. **Contact:** Engineering Learning Center, Sandy Courter at 608-265-9767, or courter@engr.wisc.edu.

9366 ■ Pi Lambda Theta Scholarships
(Undergraduate/Scholarship)

Purpose: To support UW-Madison students in their education. **Focus:** Education. **Qualif.:** Applicants must be UW-Madison junior students having the highest GPA in the School of Education; and must have completed at least one full semester (12 credits). **Criteria:** Recipient selection is based on academic excellence.

Funds Avail.: $1,000. **Number Awarded:** 2. **To Apply:** Scholarship applications are available from the Office of the Dean. **Deadline:** February. **Contact:** School of Education, Office of the Dean, at 608-262-6137, soeinfo@education.wisc.edu.

9367 ■ Powers-Knapp Scholarships
(Undergraduate/Scholarship)

Purpose: To support UW-Madison students in their education. **Focus:** General studies. **Qualif.:** Applicants must be incoming freshmen, underrepresented, students of color with an outstanding academic achievement. **Criteria:** Recipients will be selected based on academic achievements.

Awards are arranged alphabetically below their administering organizations

Funds Avail.: Wisconsin resident tuition for Wisconsin and Minnesota residents. Non-residents receive the difference between resident and non-resident tuition. **Number Awarded:** Up to 60. **To Apply:** Contact the Chancellor's Scholarships Program for more information. **Deadline:** February 1. **Contact:** 608-262-9315.

9368 ■ Reserve Officers Training Corps Scholarships (ROTC) *(Undergraduate/ Scholarship)*

Purpose: To support UW-Madison students in their education. **Focus:** Military science and education. **Qualif.:** Applicants must be U.S. citizens enrolled in ROTC programs. **Criteria:** Selection is based on merit.

Funds Avail.: Full tuition and fees, book allowance and a monthly tax-free stipend. **Number Awarded:** Varies. **To Apply:** Applicants may contact Air Force Aerospace Studies, Air Force ROTC; Military Science, Army ROTC; Naval Sciences, Navy ROTC for more information about the program. **Deadline:** December 1. **Contact:** Air Force Aerospace Studies, Air Force ROTC at 608-262-3440; Military Science, Army ROTC at 608-262-3411; Naval Sciences, Navy ROTC at 608-262-3794 or 800-443-2672.

9369 ■ School of Education Scholarships for Students from Underrepresented Groups *(Undergraduate/Scholarship)*

Purpose: To support UW-Madison students in their education. **Focus:** Education. **Qualif.:** Applicants must be UW-Madison underrepresented students of color with demonstrated financial need majoring in Education. **Criteria:** Selection is based on academic achievement and financial need.

Funds Avail.: Varies. **Number Awarded:** Varies. **To Apply:** Scholarship applications are available from the Office of the Dean. **Contact:** School of Education, Office of the Dean, at 608-262-6137, soeinfo@education.wisc.edu.

9370 ■ School of Pharmacy Continuing Student Scholarships *(Undergraduate/Scholarship)*

Purpose: To support UW-Madison students in their education. **Focus:** Pharmacology; Toxicology; Pharmacy. **Qualif.:** Applicants must be undergraduates or professional students who are continuing their education in the School of Pharmacy. **Criteria:** Selection is based on academic achievement, extracurricular activities and financial need.

Funds Avail.: Varies. **Number Awarded:** More than 60. **To Apply:** Applicants must contact the Student Services Office for the details and application materials. **Deadline:** Third week of April. **Contact:** School of Pharmacy at 608-262-6234, or pharminfo@pharmacy.wisc.edu.

9371 ■ University of Wisconsin-Madison Academic Excellence Scholarships *(Undergraduate/Scholarship)*

Purpose: To support Wisconsin students in their education. **Focus:** General studies. **Qualif.:** Applicants must be incoming freshmen; must be Wisconsin residents with the highest GPA in high school class; enrolled as first-year students at a post-secondary institution in Wisconsin. **Criteria:** Selection is based on merit.

Funds Avail.: $2,250. **Number Awarded:** 1-6 per high school. **To Apply:** Applicants must contact their high school guidance counselor for information about the scholarship. **Deadline:** February 15.

9372 ■ University of Wisconsin-Madison African American Alumni Scholarships *(Undergraduate/Scholarship)*

Purpose: To support UW-Madison students in their education. **Focus:** General studies. **Qualif.:** Applicants must be African American full-time students. **Criteria:** Recipients will be selected based on financial need.

Funds Avail.: Varies. **Number Awarded:** 1-2. **To Apply:** Applicants must contact Wisconsin Alumni Association for the application materials and procedures. **Deadline:** June 1. **Contact:** Wisconsin Alumni Association at 608-262-2551, or waa@uwalumni.com.

9373 ■ University of Wisconsin-Madison American Indian Alumni Scholarships *(Undergraduate/Scholarship)*

Purpose: To support UW-Madison students in their education. **Focus:** General studies. **Qualif.:** Applicants must be American Indian full-time students. **Criteria:** Recipients will be selected based on financial need.

Funds Avail.: No specific amount. **Number Awarded:** Varies. **To Apply:** Applicants must file the FAFSA. **Deadline:** July 1. **Contact:** Wisconsin Alumni Association at 608-262-2551, or waa@uwalumni.com.

9374 ■ University of Wisconsin-Madison/CALS Continuing Student Scholarships *(Undergraduate/Scholarship)*

Purpose: To support UW-Madison students in their education. **Focus:** Agricultural sciences; Life sciences. **Qualif.:** Applicant must be a UW-Madison sophomore, junior, or senior student enrolled in the College of Agricultural and Life Sciences (CALS). **Criteria:** Selection is based on academic excellence.

Funds Avail.: No specific amount. **Number Awarded:** Up to 200. **To Apply:** Applicants must submit a completed application form together with a letter of recommendation. **Deadline:** February 1.

9375 ■ University of Wisconsin-Madison/CALS Minority Scholarships *(Undergraduate/ Scholarship)*

Purpose: To support UW-Madison students in their education. **Focus:** Agricultural sciences; Life sciences. **Qualif.:** Applicants must be UW-Madison students of color enrolled in the College of Agricultural and Life Sciences (CALS). **Criteria:** Selection is based on academic excellence.

Funds Avail.: $500-$2,000. **Number Awarded:** Varies. **To Apply:** Students must submit a completed CALS Scholarship Application along with the letter of recommendation. **Deadline:** January 15.

9376 ■ University of Wisconsin-Madison Chancellor's Scholarships *(Undergraduate/ Scholarship)*

Purpose: To support UW-Madison students in their education. **Focus:** General studies. **Qualif.:** Applicants must be incoming freshmen, underrepresented, students of color with outstanding academic achievements. **Criteria:** Recipients will be selected based on academic achievements.

Funds Avail.: Full tuition and an annual book stipend of $800. **Number Awarded:** Up to 40. **To Apply:** Contact the Chancellor's Scholarships Program for more information. **Contact:** For application form and other required documents, applicants must contact Mercile Lee, Program and

Awards are arranged alphabetically below their administering organizations

Application Information by calling 608-262-6308.

9377 ■ University of Wisconsin-Madison Hispanic/Latino Alumni Scholarships
(Undergraduate/Scholarship)

Purpose: To support UW-Madison students in their education. **Focus:** General studies. **Qualif.:** Applicants must be Hispanic or Latino full-time students. **Criteria:** Priority will be given to the student with the most financial need.

Funds Avail.: Varies. **Number Awarded:** 1-2. **To Apply:** Applicants must contact the Wisconsin Alumni Association for information about the program. **Deadline:** June 1. **Contact:** Wisconsin Alumni Association, at 608-262-2551, or glbtac@uwalumni.com, visit the website www.uwalumni.com/glbtac.

9378 ■ University of Wisconsin-Madison Minority Teacher Loans *(Professional development, Undergraduate/Loan, Scholarship)*

Purpose: To support UW-Madison students in their education. **Focus:** Education, Secondary. **Qualif.:** Applicants must be UW-Madison juniors or seniors from underrepresented groups enrolled full-time in a teacher preparation program; must be Wisconsin residents planning to teach in selected school districts in Wisconsin; or degree-holders enrolled in a teacher certification program. **Criteria:** Recipients are selected based on academic excellence.

Funds Avail.: $250-$3000. **Number Awarded:** Varies. **To Apply:** Scholarship applications are available from the Office of the Dean. **Deadline:** Varies. **Remarks:** 25 percent of the loan is forgiven for each year the recipient teaches in the selected school district. Teaching for 4 years eliminates 100 percent of the debt. Recipients who do not teach in selected districts must repay the loan at an interest rate of 5 percent.

9379 ■ University of Wisconsin-Madison Music Scholarships *(Undergraduate/Scholarship)*

Purpose: To support UW-Madison students in their education. **Focus:** Music. **Qualif.:** Applicants must be Wisconsin outstanding musicians as demonstrated by a musical background and an audition with the School of Music. Award is renewable up to four years if applicants must: (1) participate in a designated school of music organization; (2) have a cumulative GPA of 3.25; (3) must complete a minimum of 12 credits per semester; and (4) must maintain steady progress towards a music degree. **Criteria:** Consideration is based on musical ability, scholarly accomplishments, or a combination of both.

Funds Avail.: $1,000-$5,000. **Number Awarded:** Varies. **To Apply:** Applicants must fill out the School of Music application and attend the audition. **Deadline:** February. **Contact:** Bonita Brzezinski at 608-263-5986 or admissions@music.wisc.edu.

9380 ■ University of Wisconsin-Madison National Merit Scholarships *(Undergraduate/Scholarship)*

Purpose: To support UW-Madison students in their education. **Focus:** General studies. **Qualif.:** Applicants must be entering UW-Madison as freshman; and must have taken the Preliminary SAT/National Merit Scholarship Qualifying Test (PSAT/NMSQT) during the spring semester of the sophomore year or the fall semester of the junior year. **Criteria:** Recipients will be selected based on a review of all applications.

Funds Avail.: No specific amount. **Number Awarded:** 5. **To Apply:** Students must file a FAFSA to be considered. Applicants must contact their high school councilors for more information. **Contact:** Office of Student Financial Services, Scholarship Section at 608-262-9996, or finaid@finaid.wisc.edu.

9381 ■ University of Wisconsin-Madison Pharmacy New Student Scholarships *(Undergraduate/Scholarship)*

Purpose: To support UW-Madison students in their education. **Focus:** Pharmacology; Toxicology; Pharmacy. **Qualif.:** Applicants must be Wisconsin first year students in the School of Pharmacy. **Criteria:** Recipients will be selected based on academic achievement, extracurricular activities and financial need.

Funds Avail.: Varies. **To Apply:** Applicants must contact the Student Services Office for the details and application materials. **Deadline:** First week of May. **Contact:** School of Pharmacy, at 608-262-6234 or pharminfo@pharmacy.wisc.edu.

9382 ■ University of Wisconsin-Madison Single Parent and Adult Scholarships *(Undergraduate/Scholarship)*

Purpose: To support students in their education. **Focus:** General studies. **Qualif.:** Applicants must be single parents or adults enrolled in at least nine credit units; must be in good academic standing; must be U.S. citizens or permanent residents; must show proof of financial need; and must demonstrate probability for academic success. **Criteria:** Selection is based on merit and need.

Funds Avail.: $1,000-$2,000. **Number Awarded:** Varies. **To Apply:** Applicants must contact the Adult and Student Services Center for more information. **Deadline:** March 1. **Contact:** For more information about the scholarship, call 608-263-6960.

9383 ■ Vilas Equity Scholarships *(Undergraduate/Scholarship)*

Purpose: To support UW-Madison students in their education. **Focus:** General studies. **Qualif.:** Applicants must be entering UW-Madison as freshmen. **Criteria:** Recipient selection is based on academic excellence.

Funds Avail.: $400. **Number Awarded:** Varies. **To Apply:** Students are considered automatically when admitted. **Contact:** Office of Student Financial Services, Scholarship Section, at 608-262-9996, or finaid@finaid.wisc.edu.

9384 ■ William F. Vilas Scholarships *(Undergraduate/Scholarship)*

Purpose: To support UW-Madison students in their education. **Focus:** General studies. **Qualif.:** Students must be entering UW-Madison as freshmen; and must have a strong academic performance based on class rank and GPA. **Criteria:** Selection is based on academic excellence.

Funds Avail.: $400. **Number Awarded:** Varies. **To Apply:** Students will be automatically considered when admitted. **Contact:** Office of Student Financial Services, Scholarship Section at 608-262-9996, or finaid@finaid.wisc.edu.

9385 ■ Wisconsin High School Scholarships *(Undergraduate/Scholarship)*

Purpose: To support Wisconsin students in their education. **Focus:** General studies. **Qualif.:** Applicants must be

Awards are arranged alphabetically below their administering organizations

graduates of participating Wisconsin high schools. **Criteria:** Selection is based on merit.

Funds Avail.: No specific amount. **Number Awarded:** Varies. **To Apply:** Applicants must contact their high school guidance councilors for more information.

9386 ■ Wisconsin-Madison Journalism Scholarships (Undergraduate/Scholarship)

Purpose: To support UW-Madison students in their education. **Focus:** Journalism. **Qualif.:** Applicants must be UW-Madison juniors or senior journalism students who demonstrated academic merit and have gained professional experience. **Criteria:** Consideration is given to underrepresented students of color and students with demonstrated financial need.

Funds Avail.: $500-$1,500. **Number Awarded:** Varies. **To Apply:** Applicants must complete the electronic application available online. **Deadline:** Varies. **Contact:** School of Journalism, Placement Office at 608-263-4858, or salkin@facstaff.wisc.edu.

9387 ■ Wisconsin-Madison Music Clinic Scholarships (Undergraduate/Scholarship)

Purpose: To support UW-Madison students in their education. **Focus:** Music. **Qualif.:** Applicants must be Wisconsin high school graduates with outstanding musical talent who attended the UW-Madison Summer Music Clinic both summers before enrolling at UW-Madison; or must be instrumentalists or vocalists; and must participate in a School of Music major performing group during each semester of enrollment. **Criteria:** Recipients will be selected based on musical ability, scholarly accomplishments, or a combination of both.

Funds Avail.: Wisconsin resident tuition for four years of study. **Number Awarded:** 10. **To Apply:** Applicants must contact the Music Clinic Coordinator for information. **Deadline:** June 1. **Contact:** School of Music, Music Clinic Coordinator at 5538 Humanities Bldg., 455 North Park St., Madison, WI 53706.

9388 ■ Upakar Indian-American Scholarship Foundation
101 Friars Rd.
Bethesda, MD 20817
E-mail: info@upakar.org
URL: www.upakarfoundation.org

9389 ■ Upakar Indian-American Scholarships (Undergraduate/Scholarship)

Purpose: To support the educational and career aspirations of the Indian-American community. **Focus:** Music; Dance. **Qualif.:** Applicants must be students entering a Fine Arts (Music, Dance, Drama, etc.) undergraduate program in the United States; must have either been born or have at least one parent in the Republic of India; must either be U.S. citizens or U.S. Green Card holders; must have latest Family Adjusted Gross Income (AGI) on the IRS form 1040, 1040EZ or 1040A of less than $75,000; and must be graduating high school seniors living in the United States with a cumulative unweighted GPA of 3.6 or higher on a 4.0 scale. **Criteria:** Applicants will be evaluated based on academic achievement.

Funds Avail.: $2,000. **To Apply:** Applicants must submit a completed application form and an essay.

9390 ■ Upsilon Pi Epsilon Association
158 Wetlands Edge Rd.
American Canyon, CA 94503

Ph: (530) 518-8488
Fax: (707) 647-3560
E-mail: upe@acm.org
URL: upe.acm.org

9391 ■ UPE/ACM Scholarship Awards (Graduate, Undergraduate/Award)

Purpose: To encourage academic excellence for students in the computing discipline. To raise the importance of academic achievement and professional commitment in future computer professionals. **Focus:** Computer and information sciences. **Qualif.:** Applicants must be graduate or undergraduate students who are ACM members and members of the ACM student chapter at their academic institution. **Criteria:** Applicants will be selected based on their application form and other supporting documents.

Funds Avail.: $1,000. **Number Awarded:** 4. **To Apply:** Applicant must submit three letters of recommendation (one letter indicating class rank from Department Chair or Advisor); must have a certificate copy of the three years (minimum) official academic transcripts; and must have a statement of participation in the ACM student chapter at their academic institution. Application forms are available in the website. **Contact:** ACM/UPE Scholarship Award, c/o Upsilon Pi Epsilon, 158 Wetlands Edge Rd., American Canyon, CA 94503.

9392 ■ UPE Scholarship Awards (Graduate, Undergraduate/Award)

Purpose: To promote computing sciences and to encourage its contribution to the enhancement of knowledge. **Focus:** Computer and information sciences. **Qualif.:** Applicant must be in graduate or undergraduate student levels. **Criteria:** Application form and other documents will be evaluated by the Executive Council of UPE.

Funds Avail.: $750-$1,500. **To Apply:** Application forms are available in the website address and must be sent to: Upsilon Pi Epsilon, California State University, Chico, 158 Wetlands Edge Rd., American Canyon, CA, 94503. **Deadline:** June 15.

9393 ■ Urban Affairs Association (UAA)
University of Wisconsin-Milwaukee
PO Box 413
Milwaukee, WI 53201-0413
Ph: (414) 229-3025
E-mail: info@uaamail.org
URL: urbanaffairsassociation.org

9394 ■ Alma H. Young Emerging Scholar Awards (Doctorate/Scholarship)

Purpose: To support the development of university education, research, and service programs in urban affairs. **Focus:** General studies. **Qualif.:** Applicants must be pursuing doctoral research in urban affairs, regardless of academic discipline; must have finished the required course work; passed the comprehensive examinations; and have an approved dissertation proposal. **Criteria:** Recipients are selected based on scholarship and commitment to urban issues.

Funds Avail.: $1,000. **To Apply:** Applicants must submit the nomination letter from current UAA members; provide (two-to-three page, double-spaced) personal statement describing urban interests, engagement and career plans; a curriculum vitae; a prospectus for the dissertation of

Awards are arranged alphabetically below their administering organizations

(1,500-2,000 words) that indicate the research questions, argument or hypotheses, literature and data resources, methodology and nature of expected findings. **Deadline:** February 1. **Contact:** Return applications to Shelly Tillinghast at shelviat@udel.edu.

9395 ■ Urban and Land Institute (ULI)
1025 Thomas Jefferson St. NW, Ste. 500 W
Washington, DC 20007
Ph: (202) 624-7000
Fax: (202) 624-7140
Free: 800-321-5011
E-mail: customerservice@uli.org
URL: www.uli.org

9396 ■ Kenneth M. Good Graduate Students Fellowship Program *(Undergraduate/Fellowship)*
Purpose: To promote interdisciplinary education and to encourage excellence in real estate-related studies. **Focus:** Real Estate. **Qualif.:** Applicants must be graduating students who are studying real estate, real estate development, or related subjects at a major North American university. **Criteria:** Recipients are selected based on financial need of the applicant and result of the nomination.
Funds Avail.: $5,000. **Number Awarded:** 8. **To Apply:** Applicants must submit evidence that they are currently attending a real estate degree program.

9397 ■ US-Ireland Alliance
2800 Clarendon Blvd., Ste. 502 W
Arlington, VA 22201
Ph: (202) 643-8742
E-mail: vargo@us-irelandalliance.org
URL: www.us-irelandalliance.org

9398 ■ George J. Mitchell Scholarships *(Undergraduate/Scholarship)*
Purpose: To introduce and connect generations of future American leaders to the island of Ireland, while recognizing and fostering intellectual achievement, leadership, and a commitment to public service and community. **Focus:** Business. **Qualif.:** Applicant must be a U.S. citizen between 18-30 years old; and must hold a bachelor's degree from an accredited college or university. **Criteria:** Applicants will be judged based on academic excellence and intellectual distinction, outstanding record of leadership, sustained commitment to service and community.
Funds Avail.: No specific amount. **Number Awarded:** 12. **To Apply:** Applicants must apply online. **Deadline:** October 2. **Contact:** Anne Glusker, Dir., George Mitchell Scholars Program; Email: glusker@us-irelandalliance.org; Phone: 202-469-9254.

9399 ■ USC Latino Alumni Association
3607 Trousdale Pky., TCC 324
Los Angeles, CA 90089-3104
Ph: (213) 740-4735
Fax: (213) 740-7250
E-mail: latinoalumni@usc.edu
URL: www.usc.edu/maaa

9400 ■ Mexican American Alumni Association Scholarships *(Graduate, Undergraduate/ Scholarship)*
Purpose: To financially support students pursuing Undergraduate and Graduate degrees at University of Southern California. **Focus:** General studies. **Qualif.:** Applicant have a demonstrated commitment to the Latino community; have demonstrated leadership; overall academic and professional promise; current full-time student at USC (potential incoming freshman and incoming transfer student should apply even if not yet admitted into the university); and must have completed 24 or more units with a GPA of 2.7 or better for continuing USC undergraduate student and incoming transfer student, graduate student must have completed 16 units or more with a GPA of 3.0 or better. **Criteria:** Selection is based on: completed application; financial aid need; availability of other financial aid resources; grade point average (2.7 for undergraduate students, 3.0 for graduate students); current student loan obligations; community/ university involvement; and the legibility, completeness, accuracy and quality of information provided in the application.
Funds Avail.: $500-$3500 per academic year for undergraduate students and $1000-$5000 per academic year for graduate students. **To Apply:** Applicants must submit a completed USC MAAA Scholarship application form together with a typed essay of no more than two pages, double spaced; a resume; original letter(s) of recommendation; and unofficial transcripts. Completed applications must be sent to: USC Mexican American Programs, 3601 Trousdale Pkwy., Student Union Building, Rm. 203, Los Angeles, CA 90089-4890. Faxed or emailed applications will not be accepted. **Deadline:** April 2.

9401 ■ USDA Animal and Plant Health Inspection Service (USDA APHIS)
USDA, APHIS, Human Resources/Employment
4700 River Rd., Unit 106
Riverdale, MD 20737
Ph: (301) 734-5596
URL: www.aphis.usda.gov

9402 ■ PPQ William F. Helms Student Scholarships *(Undergraduate/Scholarship)*
Purpose: To provide financial assistance to academically qualified students who are enrolled in college-level programs related to agriculture or the biological sciences. **Focus:** Agricultural sciences. **Qualif.:** Applicants must be: U.S. citizens; enrolled in an accredited college or university within the United States; sophomores or juniors in good academic standing (must maintain at least 2.5 grade point average); enrolled in programs related to agriculture or the biological sciences; must agree to work for the agency during school breaks (both summer and holiday periods) a minimum of 640 hours prior to completion of studies. **Criteria:** Applicants are evaluated based on academic achievement.
Funds Avail.: $5,000. **To Apply:** Applicants must submit a completed application which contains an Optional Application for Federal Employment (OF-612) or resume; a personal letter that describes their interests, goals and chosen career plans, explains how they envision their ability will contribute to the PPQ mission, outlines why they should be selected for this program over other candidates and list of the permanent addresses at which they can be contacted all year. Applicants must also submit transcripts of their college work to date; three letters of recommendation from people not related to them; documentation of service, if they have served in the U.S. Armed Forces. **Deadline:** March 1. **Contact:** Application packets must be submitted to U.S. Department of Agriculture, 1400 Indepen-

Awards are arranged alphabetically below their administering organizations

dence Ave. SW, Rm. 1710, Washington, DC 20250.

9403 ■ Saul T. Wilson, Jr. Scholarships (Graduate, Undergraduate/Scholarship)

Purpose: To provide financial assistance to graduates and undergraduates of veterinary medicine and biomedical sciences. **Focus:** Veterinary science and medicine; Biomedical sciences. **Qualif.:** Applicants must be U.S. citizens enrolled in an accredited college or university within the United States as full-time students in good academic standing; must be undergraduate students who have completed at least two years (60 semester or 90 quarter hours) of a four-year pre-veterinary medicine or other biomedical science curriculum or graduate students who have completed not more than one year (18 semester or 27 quarter hours) of study in veterinary medicine; must be willing to work for the agency during school breaks (both summer and holiday periods). **Criteria:** Applicants are evaluated based on academic achievement.

Funds Avail.: $5,000 up to $10,000. **To Apply:** Applicants must submit a resume, including current and summer addresses and telephone numbers; transcripts of all college courses completed; letter of acceptance, if entering graduate school; three letters of recommendation from college officials; original essay, not exceeding 500 words on the topic: "Why I should receive a Saul T. Wilson, Jr., Scholarship and what contributions I would make to APHIS, Veterinary Services"; documentation of service, if they have served in the U.S. Armed Forces. **Deadline:** March 1.

9404 ■ USS Coral Sea CVA-43 Association
651 E Saginaw Way
Fresno, CA 93704
E-mail: doncolwell@att.net
URL: www.usscoralsea.org

9405 ■ USS Coral Sea Remembrance Scholarships (Undergraduate/Scholarship)

Purpose: To help the beneficiaries of an individual working at USS Coral Sea CVA-43 Association. **Focus:** General studies. **Qualif.:** Applicants must be children, grandchildren, step-children or step-grandchildren of: 1) a member in good standing; 2) a deceased member; 3) a non-member who was killed in the line of duty; 4) an individual who was captured as a prisoner of war; or 5) and individual who was injured while in duty; must be high school seniors with at least a "B" or 3.0 GPA; and must have plans to attend a two or four-year college, university, technical or vocational school. **Criteria:** Essays will be judged based on originality of thought, adherence to topic, completeness, quality, spelling and punctuation. Applicant with the highest GPA will be announced as the winner.

Funds Avail.: $500 and $2,000. **Number Awarded:** 2. **To Apply:** Applicants must submit an original essay; two dated and signed letters of recommendation; and an official transcript of records. Essay must be typed and double-spaced. Reference sources must be listed and footnoted. **Deadline:** April 1. **Contact:** Application form and all supporting documents must be submitted to Bill Williams, 100 Fairway Dr., Camp Hill, PA 17011-2066.

9406 ■ USTA Tennis and Education Foundation (USAT T&EF)
70 W Rd. Oak Ln.
White Plains, NY 10604

Ph: (914) 696-7000
E-mail: foundation@usta.com
URL: www.usta.com

9407 ■ Marian Wood Baird Scholarships (Undergraduate/Scholarship)

Purpose: To provide scholarships to deserving youngsters who have participated in the United States Tennis Association. **Focus:** General studies. **Qualif.:** Applicants must have a strong involvement in extracurricular activities, course work and community service; must exhibit Financial Need; must be involved in an organized community tennis program such as USTA School Tennis, NJTL, USTA Team Tennis, etc.; must be entering first year of undergraduate work as a full-time student in a four-year college or university program; must have minimum of 3.0 GPA on a 4.0 scale. **Criteria:** Scholarship is given based on academic performance.

Funds Avail.: $15,000. **To Apply:** Applicants must submit in one envelope the following required forms and supporting documents: A typed or clearly printed application signed by the applicant and parent or guardian; A typed or clearly printed endorsement from a faculty member from the applicant's high school and from a coach/program director; A typed endorsement from an individual of the applicant's choice; An official high school transcript; ACT/SAT examination scores; The applicant's official financial aid form; and a current photograph of the applicant. **Deadline:** February 10.

9408 ■ Dwight F. Davis Memorial Scholarships (Undergraduate/Scholarship)

Purpose: To provide scholarships to qualified high school seniors. **Focus:** General studies. **Qualif.:** Applicants must be high school seniors with strong involvement in extracurricular activities, coursework and community service; must exhibit financial need; must be actively involved in an organized community tennis program such as USTA School Tennis, NJTL, USTA Team Tennis, etc.; must be entering the first year of undergraduate works as a full-time student in a four-year college/university program; and must have 3.0 GPA on a 4.0 scale. **Criteria:** Scholarship is given based on academic performance.

Funds Avail.: $7,500. **Number Awarded:** 2. **To Apply:** Applicants must submit in one envelope the following required forms and supporting documents: A typed or clearly printed application signed by the applicant and parent or guardian; a typed or clearly printed endorsement from a faculty member from the applicant's high school and from a coach/program director; a typed endorsement from an individual of the applicant's choice; an official high school transcript; ACT/SAT examination scores; applicant's official financial aid form; and a current photograph. **Deadline:** February 4.

9409 ■ Eve Kraft Education and College Scholarships (Undergraduate/Scholarship)

Purpose: To provide scholarships to qualified high school seniors. **Focus:** General studies. **Qualif.:** Applicants must be high school seniors with strong involvement in extracurricular activities, course work and community service; must exhibit financial need; must be actively involved in an organized community tennis program such as USTA School Tennis, NJTL, USTA Team Tennis, etc.; must be entering the first year of undergraduate work as a full-time student in a four-year college/university program. **Criteria:** Scholarship is given based on academic performance.

Awards are arranged alphabetically below their administering organizations

Funds Avail.: $2,500. **Number Awarded:** 2 (one male and one female). **To Apply:** Applicants must submit in one envelope the following required forms and supporting documents: A typed or clearly printed application signed by the applicant and parent or guardian; a typed or clearly printed endorsement from a faculty member from the applicant's high school and from a coach/program director; a typed endorsement from an individual of the applicant's choice; an official high school transcript; ACT/SAT examination scores; applicant's official financial aid form; and a current photograph. **Deadline:** February 12. **Remarks:** The scholarship is partially supported by Robert Kraft and family.

9410 ■ Dwight Mosley Scholarships
(Undergraduate/Scholarship)

Purpose: To provide scholarship to high school seniors of ethnically diverse heritage. **Focus:** General studies. **Qualif.:** Applicants must be high school seniors with strong involvement in extracurricular activities, course work and community service; must exhibit financial need; must be actively involved in an organized community tennis program such as USTA School Tennis, NJTL, USTA Team Tennis, etc.; must be entering the first year of undergraduate work as a full-time student in a four-year college/university program. **Criteria:** Scholarship is given based on academic performance.

Funds Avail.: $10,000. **Number Awarded:** 2 (1 male and 1 female). **To Apply:** Applicants must submit in one envelope the following required forms and supporting documents: A typed or clearly printed application signed by the applicant and parent or guardian; a typed or clearly printed endorsement from a faculty member from the applicant's high school and from a coach/program director; a typed endorsement from an individual of the applicant's choice; an official high school transcript; ACT/SAT examination scores; applicant's official financial aid form; and a current photograph. **Deadline:** February 10.

9411 ■ USTA Serves College Education
Scholarships *(Undergraduate/Scholarship)*

Purpose: To provide scholarships to qualified high schools. **Focus:** General Studies. **Qualif.:** Applicants must be high school seniors with strong involvement in extracurricular activities, course work and community service; must exhibit financial need; must be actively involved in an organized community tennis program such as USTA School Tennis, NJTL, USTA Team Tennis, etc.; must be entering the first year of undergraduate work as a full-time student in a four-year college/university program; and must have 3.0 GPA on a 4.0 scale. **Criteria:** Scholarship is given based on academic performance.

Funds Avail.: $6,000. **To Apply:** Applicants must submit in one envelope the following required forms and supporting documents: A typed or clearly printed application signed by the applicant and parent or guardian; a typed or clearly printed endorsement from a faculty member from the applicant's high school and from a coach/program director; a typed endorsement from an individual of the applicant's choice; an official high school transcript; ACT/SAT examination scores; applicant's official financial aid form; and a current photograph. **Deadline:** February 10.

9412 ■ USTA Tennis and Education Foundation
College Textbook Scholarships *(Undergraduate/ Scholarship)*

Purpose: To provide a one-time award to assist students in purchasing textbooks or supplies. **Focus:** General stud-

ies. **Qualif.:** Applicants must be high school seniors with strong involvement in extracurricular activities, course work and community service; must exhibit financial need; must be actively involved in an organized community tennis program such as USTA School Tennis, NJTL, USTA Team Tennis, etc.; must be entering the first year of undergraduate work as full-time students in a four-year college/ university program. **Criteria:** Scholarship is given based on academic performance.

Funds Avail.: $1,000. **To Apply:** Applicants must submit in one envelope the following required forms and supporting documents: A typed or clearly printed application signed by the applicant and parent or guardian; a typed or clearly printed endorsement from a faculty member from the applicant's high school and from a coach/program director; a typed endorsement from an individual of the applicant's choice; an official high school transcript; ACT/SAT examination scores; applicant's official financial aid form; and a current photograph. **Deadline:** February 10.

9413 ■ Vanderbilt Center for Environmental Management Studies (VCEMS)
Vanderbilt University
2301 Vanderbilt Pl.
Nashville, TN 37235
Ph: (615) 322-2697
Fax: (615) 343-7177
E-mail: james.h.clarke@vanderbilt.edu
URL: www.vanderbilt.edu/vcems

9414 ■ Bridgestone Americas Fellowships
(Graduate/Fellowship)

Purpose: To support students with research interests in Environmental Management who are pursuing a PhD at Vanderbilt University in an appropriate related discipline. **Focus:** Environmental science. **Qualif.:** Applicant must be a current or former student involved with VCEMS and have backgrounds in engineering, economics, divinity, technology, business administration and law. **Criteria:** Selection is based on the application materials submitted for review.

Funds Avail.: No specific amount. **To Apply:** Applicants may apply online, or may send a request for a hard copy application to the Graduate School (must be accompanied by a non-refundable fee of $40). Application packet includes: two copies of the application form and all supporting materials; statement and purpose; two official transcripts of all post-secondary work; Graduate Record Examination scores; acknowledgment of Application Card (self-addressed). In addition, applicants must send a resume/ CV; a business writing sample; three letters of recommendation in duplicate; and a photocopy of standardized test scores. Submit application packet to: Vanderbilt University Graduate School, 411 Kirkland Hall, Nashville, TN 37240.

9415 ■ Vector Marketing Corporation
5301 Limestone Rd., Ste. 105
Wilmington, DE 19808
Ph: (302) 372-8020
E-mail: campus@cutco.com
URL: www.vectorscholarships.com

9416 ■ All-American Vector Marketing Scholarship Program *(Undergraduate/Scholarship)*

Purpose: To recognize students who have excelled in their roles as sales representatives. **Focus:** Marketing and

Awards are arranged alphabetically below their administering organizations

distribution. **Qualif.:** Applicants must be full-time students at an accredited college or university; active in the business at the conclusion of the Scholarship Race. **Criteria:** Selection will be based on sales performance. Scholastic achievement and financial need are not taken into consideration.

Funds Avail.: A total of $50,000. **To Apply:** Applicants must provide current official transcript as well as a copy of current semester registration. Applicants may contact Vector Marketing Corporation for other requirements. **Contact:** Vector Marketing Corporation at the above address.

9417 ■ Vector Marketing Canadian Scholarship Awards *(Undergraduate/Scholarship)*

Purpose: To provide financial assistance to student sales representatives and the institutions of higher education they attend. **Focus:** Marketing and distribution. **Qualif.:** Applicants must be full-time university or college students working with Vector; and must be currently active on Vector Marketing All-American program tracking system. **Criteria:** Scholarship recipients are selected based on the committee's review of the application materials.

Funds Avail.: No specific amount. **To Apply:** Applicants must provide current official transcript as well as a copy of current semester registration. Applicants may contact Vector Marketing Corporation for other requirements. **Contact:** Vector Marketing Corporation at the above address.

9418 ■ Vermont Paralegal Organization (VPO)
PO Box 5755
Burlington, VT 05402-5755
Ph: (802) 864-9891
Fax: (802) 864-6815
E-mail: vermont@paralegals.org
URL: www.vtparalegal.org/index.html

9419 ■ Vermont Paralegal Organization Scholarships *(Undergraduate/Scholarship)*

Purpose: To promote excellence in the paralegal profession. **Focus:** Paralegal studies. **Qualif.:** Applicants must be attending, at least part-time, accredited paralegal/legal studies program. **Criteria:** Selection will be based on the quality of submitted essays, individual's academic achievement and financial need.

Funds Avail.: $500. **To Apply:** Applicants must submit a completed application, including their essays. **Deadline:** March 9. **Contact:** Carie Tarte, Scholarship Committee Chair at the above address.

9420 ■ Vesalius Trust (VT)
c/o Lisa Warren, Exec. Dir.
20751 W Chartwell Dr.
Kildeer, IL 60047
Ph: (847) 540-8671
Fax: (847) 540-8681
E-mail: vesaliustrust@aol.com
URL: www.vesaliustrust.org

9421 ■ Inez Demonet Scholarships *(Graduate/Scholarship)*

Purpose: To support students with promising contributions to the profession of medical illustration. **Focus:** Illustrators and illustrations. **Qualif.:** Applicant must be a second year graduate student enrolled in a medical illustration accredited by the Accreditation Review Committee for the Medical Illustrators (ARC-MI) and Commission on Accreditation of the Allied Health Education Program (CAA-HEP). **Criteria:** Applicants are evaluated based on past performances and potential for significant contributions to the field.

Funds Avail.: $2,000. **To Apply:** Application form is available at the website. Applicants must prepare a resume (one page); transcripts; references; portfolio of five portfolio pieces; and an essay. **Deadline:** February 10. **Contact:** Original application form and three photocopies of supporting documents must be sent to: Tami Tolpa, VT Student Grants and Scholarships, Tolpa Studios Inc., 6523 California Ave. SW, No. 110, Seattle, WA 98136; Phone: 206-420-1754; E-mail: tami@tolpa.com.

9422 ■ Vesalius Trust Student Scholarships *(Graduate, Undergraduate/Scholarship)*

Purpose: To support students enrolled in medical illustration programs. **Focus:** Illustrators and illustrations. **Qualif.:** Applicants must be enrolled in a medical illustration program and must have completed one year of the curriculum. **Criteria:** Applicants are judged based on background, education and project concept, design and production plan.

Funds Avail.: No specific amount. **To Apply:** Applicants must submit an application form; a resume; graduate project description; budget and timeline; transcripts; preceptor form and faculty advisor form. **Contact:** Tami Tolpa, VT Student Grants and Scholarships, 206-436-9214 or tami@tolpa.com.

9423 ■ Vietnam Education Foundation (VEF)
2111 Wilson Blvd., Ste. 700
Arlington, VA 22201
Ph: (703) 351-5053
Fax: (703) 351-1423
E-mail: information@vef.gov
URL: home.vef.gov

9424 ■ VEF Fellowship Program *(Doctorate, Master's/Fellowship)*

Purpose: To financially assist Vietnamese to pursue their graduate education in the United States. **Focus:** Science; Mathematics and mathematical sciences; Medicine; Engineering; Technology. **Qualif.:** Applicants must be Vietnamese nationals to begin graduate studies in the United States; must be interested in pursuing a PhD or Master's degree in the major disciplines of Sciences, Mathematics, Medicine, Engineering and Technology; must have GPA of 7.0-10.0; must demonstrate sufficient proficiency in the English language. **Criteria:** Winners will be chosen based on individual merit, including academic performance and preparation, intellectual capabilities, English proficiency, potential contribution to scientific education and research in Vietnam.

Funds Avail.: No specific amount. **Number Awarded:** 45. **To Apply:** Applicants must submit a completed application form; must submit their undergraduate/graduate certificate and transcripts, evidence of English language proficiency, GRE score, one-page academic statement and one-page personal statement, three letters of recommendation/reference, U.S. universities. **Contact:** vef2013@vef.org.

Awards are arranged alphabetically below their administering organizations

9425 ■ VEF Visiting Scholars Program
(Doctorate/Scholarship)

Purpose: To support professional development training for doctorate students. **Focus:** Science; Engineering; Mathematics and mathematical sciences; Medicine; Technology. **Qualif.:** Applicants must be Vietnamese nationals who already hold a doctoral degree in a field supported by VEF; must demonstrate a high level of English proficiency. **Criteria:** Recipients will be chosen based on the following categories: a) evidence of superior academic achievement; b) quality and value of visiting scholar professional development plan; c) demonstrated commitment to the educational and scientific development of Vietnam; d) demonstrated commitment of support from the U.S. host institution; e) demonstrated commitment of support from the Vietnamese institution(s).

Funds Avail.: $2,300 per month. **Number Awarded:** 15. **To Apply:** Applicants must submit a completed application form. **Deadline:** May 2.

9426 ■ Vietnam Veterans of America (VVA)
8719 Colesville Rd., Ste. 100
Silver Spring, MD 20910
Ph: (301) 585-4000
Fax: (301) 585-0519
Free: 800-882-1316
E-mail: communications@vva.org
URL: www.vva.org

9427 ■ Mike Nash Memorial Scholarships
(Undergraduate/Scholarship)

Purpose: To provide support and assistance to veterans in securing earned benefits from the Department of Veterans Affairs. **Focus:** General studies. **Qualif.:** Applicants must be dependent children, grandchildren, orphans, and widows of deceased Vietnam Veterans. **Criteria:** Recipients are selected based on the completeness of the application, demonstrated need, and grade point average.

Funds Avail.: No amount specified. **Number Awarded:** 1. **To Apply:** Applicants must submit a completed application form; a high school or college transcript; photocopy of SAT, ACT, or other acknowledged testing source results; a letter of acceptance from a college, university or post-secondary training institution; a copy of form DD-214 and death certificate from the related Vietnam era veteran, if the veteran is deceased. Applicants must provide a statement describing financial need; include a copy of the applicant's parent and the applicant's most current personal income tax form; two letters of reference from current or former teachers, academic advisors, employers, or ministers attesting the applicant's character; and a letter in the applicant's own words, expressing current educational goals and objectives, individual accomplishments and any other personal information that may assist in the selection process. **Deadline:** May 31. **Contact:** finance@wa.org.

9428 ■ Vietnamese American Bar Association of Northern California (VABANC)
1570 The Alameda Ste. 212
San Jose, CA 95126
Ph: (408) 512-3818
E-mail: president@vabanc.org
URL: www.vabanc.org

9429 ■ VABANC Scholarships *(Graduate, Undergraduate/Scholarship)*

Purpose: To support law students committed to serving the Vietnamese American community. **Focus:** Law. **Qualif.:** Applicant must be a law student who is committed to serving the Vietnamese American community and is in need of funding for the upcoming school year. **Criteria:** Selection is based on merit.

Funds Avail.: $1,000. **Number Awarded:** 3. **To Apply:** Applicants must submit a completed application form along with a resume; three references; and a personal statement of no more than 800 words. Submit application materials to scholarships@vabanc.org. **Deadline:** August 26. **Contact:** scholarships@vabanc.org.

9430 ■ Vietnamese American Scholarship Foundation
PO Box 429
Stafford, TX 77497
E-mail: scholarships@vietscholarships.org
URL: www.vietscholarships.org

9431 ■ Danny T. Le Memorial Scholarships
(High School, Undergraduate/Scholarship)

Purpose: To provide financial assistance to students of Vietnamese descent from the Greater Houston area for pursuing further education. **Focus:** General studies. **Qualif.:** Applicants must be of Vietnamese descent; must be graduated or graduating from a high school in the Greater Houston Area and pursuing degree at an accredited four-year college or university. **Criteria:** Applicants are evaluated based on academic excellence; compassion and desire to help others; strong will and determination to achieve their goals.

Funds Avail.: $2,000. **To Apply:** Applicants must download and complete the application form and submit it with their resume, an essay and a letter of recommendation. **Deadline:** May 6. **Contact:** Questions can be addressed to dannylescholarship@vietscholarships.org.

9432 ■ Le Hoang Nguyen College Scholarships (LHN) *(High School/Scholarship)*

Purpose: To provide financial assistance to outstanding graduating high school seniors attending college in the upcoming fall semester. **Focus:** General studies. **Qualif.:** Applicants must be Vietnamese descendants and residents of the state of Texas; must be graduating high school seniors with a GPA of 3.0 or higher; must be ranked in the top 10% of graduating high school class; must attend the first semester at an accredited college or university immediately following notification of the scholarship award. **Criteria:** Applicants are evaluated based on academic achievement and financial need.

Funds Avail.: $500. **Number Awarded:** 1. **To Apply:** Applicants must complete the online application form with uploaded resume, essay and recommendation; and must submit a transcript of records. **Deadline:** May 6. **Contact:** Questions can be addressed to scholarship@vietscholarships.org.

9433 ■ The Thuy Nguyen Scholarships *(High School/Scholarship)*

Purpose: To provide financial assistance to high school senior students for furthering their education. **Focus:** Gen-

Awards are arranged alphabetically below their administering organizations

eral studies. **Qualif.:** Applicants must be graduating high school seniors from Houston or the surrounding area; must have a cumulative GPA of 3.5 or higher; must be descendants of at least one Vietnamese parent; and must have a family annual income of less than $50,000. **Criteria:** Applicants are evaluated based on financial need.

Funds Avail.: $2,000. **To Apply:** Applicants must complete the online application with resume, essay with a cover letter; must submit a transcript of records, recommendation and a copy of their parent's W-2 forms and a photo. **Deadline:** May 6. **Contact:** Completed application form and supporting documents must be submitted to Kaitlin Trinh, Guggenheim Partners, 135 E 57th St., 7th Fl., New York, NY 10022. Questions can be directed to katielyntrinh@hotmail.com.

9434 ■ Vera Tran Memorial Scholarships
(Undergraduate/Scholarship)

Purpose: To provide financial assistance to graduating high school seniors of Vietnamese descent wishing to pursue further education. **Focus:** General studies. **Qualif.:** Applicants must be of Vietnamese descent, graduating high school seniors from Houston or the surrounding area who are planning to pursue an education at an accredited four-year college or university. **Criteria:** Applicants are evaluated based on demonstrated dedication to academic excellence; passion for learning; compassion and desire to help others; pursuit of their dreams; and proven leadership.

Funds Avail.: $2,000. **To Apply:** Applicants must complete the online application and submit it with their resume; must also send one transcript and recommendation. **Deadline:** May 6.

9435 ■ Violin Society of America (VSA)
341 N Maitland Ave., Ste. 130
Maitland, FL 32751
Ph: (407) 647-8839
Fax: (407) 629-2502
Free: 407-629-2502
E-mail: info@vsaweb.org
URL: www.vsa.to

9436 ■ Violin Society of America Scholarships
(Undergraduate/Scholarship)

Purpose: To provide financial assistance for needy and deserving students of the art of violin and bow-making and restoration. **Focus:** Music. **Qualif.:** Applicant must be a U.S. citizen; a student who has satisfactorily completed at least one full year of study in the program and has shown serious effort, talent and future promise and has financial need. **Criteria:** Applicants will be evaluated by the administrator of the program and will be recommended to the VSA.

Funds Avail.: No amount mentioned. **To Apply:** Teachers and faculty of leading American-violin making schools annually submit the names of those students most worthy of scholarship aid.

9437 ■ Virgin Islands Bar Association
PO Box 4108
Christiansted, VI 00822
Ph: (340) 778-7497
Fax: (340) 773-5060
E-mail: executivedirector@vibar.org
URL: www.vibar.org

9438 ■ Almeric Christian Memorial Scholarships *(Graduate/Scholarship)*

Purpose: To support the education of law students. **Focus:** Law. **Qualif.:** Applicant must be a college graduate who has been accepted to or is attending a law school accredited by the American Bar Association; must be a permanent resident of the United States Virgin Islands and plan to engage in the practice of law in the United States Virgin Islands within three years of graduation from law school. Applicants who are already attending the law school must have a 2.75 GPA and those who have not yet started a law study must have at least 3.0 GPA. **Criteria:** Selection is based on the application.

Funds Avail.: No specific amount. **To Apply:** Applicants must submit a completed application form along with a letter of acceptance to a law school or most recent transcript if already enrolled in a law school; three letters of recommendation, one from a former college or law school professor and the rest from individuals that are not related to the applicant by blood or marriage; an essay on career objectives and how the schooling plan will prepare the applicant to attain these goals (typewritten); official copy of undergraduate college transcript (if entering the first year of law school) or a copy of latest official transcript (if presently attending law school); and a copy of Student Financial Aid form (FAF), or the equivalent thereof. **Deadline:** June 30. **Contact:** Micol Morgan, Chair at the above address.

9439 ■ Virginia Business and Professional Women's Foundation
PO Box 4842
McLean, VA 22103-4842
Free: 800-525-3729
E-mail: bpwfoundation@act.org
URL: www.vabpwfoundation.org

9440 ■ Buena M. Chesshir Memorial Women's Educational Scholarships *(Graduate, Master's, Undergraduate/Scholarship)*

Purpose: To provide financial assistance to increase the skill of mature women who are employed or seeking employment; to increase the number of women qualified for higher-level positions; and to help women achieve economic self-sufficiency. **Focus:** General studies. **Qualif.:** Applicant must be a woman 25 years of age or older; not a Virginia BPW Foundation Trustee, or related to a Trustee; a citizen of the United States; a resident of Virginia; be officially accepted to an accredited program or course of study at a Virginia-based institution; must complete course of study to obtain a bachelor's or higher degree within two years following the application deadline; demonstrate need for financial assistance to upgrade skills or education; and have a definite plan to use the desired training to improve chances for upward mobility in the workforce. **Criteria:** Selection is based on financial need, scholastic record and educational goals.

Funds Avail.: $500-$1,000. **To Apply:** Applicants must submit a completed application form along with three letters of recommendation from non-relatives, including at least one work related and one scholastic; transcripts of all schooling within the last 10 year (but no further back than high school); proof of Virginia Residence (copy of driver's license, voter registration card, a Virginia Tax Return or DMV identification card); and a proof of US citizenship (copy of birth certificate, US passport, certificate of citizenship or naturalization, voter's registration card). **Deadline:** April 1.

Awards are arranged alphabetically below their administering organizations

9441 ■ Karen B. Lewis Career Education Scholarships (Undergraduate/Scholarship)

Purpose: To provide financial assistance to girls and women pursuing post-secondary job-oriented career education. **Focus:** Business; Industry and trade. **Qualif.:** Applicant must be a woman 18 years of age or older; not a Virginia BPW Foundation Trustee, or related to a Trustee; a citizen of the United States; a resident of Virginia; be officially accepted into an accredited training program or course of study in Virginia; must complete training program or obtain an associate's degree within 2 years following the application deadline; demonstrate need for financial assistance to upgrade skills; and have a definite plan to use the training in a business, trade or industrial occupation. **Criteria:** Selection is based on financial need, scholastic record and educational goals.

Funds Avail.: $500-$1,000. **To Apply:** Applicants must submit a completed application form along with three letters of recommendation from non-relatives, including at least one work related and one scholastic; transcripts of all schooling within the last 10 year (but no further back than high school); proof of Virginia Residence (copy of driver's license, voter registration card, a Virginia Tax Return or DMV identification card); and a proof of U.S. citizenship (copy of birth certificate, US passport, certificate of citizenship or naturalization, voter's registration card). **Deadline:** April 1.

9442 ■ Women in Science and Technology Scholarships (Doctorate, Graduate, Master's, Undergraduate/Scholarship)

Purpose: To provide financial assistance to girls and women who are striving to enter or achieve higher-level positions in scientific and technical fields. **Focus:** Actuarial science; Biology; Bioengineering; Chemistry; Computer and information sciences; Dentistry; Engineering; Mathematics and mathematical sciences; Medicine; Physics. **Qualif.:** Applicant must be a woman 18 years of age or older; not a Virginia BPW Foundation Trustee, or related to a Trustee; a citizen of the United States; a resident of Virginia; officially accepted to an accredited course of study at a Virginia-based college or university; majoring in one of the following fields: actuarial science, biology, bioengineering, chemistry, computer science, dentistry, engineering, mathematics, medicine, physics or similar scientific and technical fields; must complete course of study and earn a bachelor's, master's or doctoral degree within two years following the application deadline; demonstrate need for financial assistance to further her education; and have a definite plan to use the education in a scientific or technical profession. **Criteria:** Selection is based on financial need, scholastic record and educational goals.

Funds Avail.: $500-$1,000. **To Apply:** Applicants must submit a completed application form along with three letters of recommendation from non-relatives, including at least one work related and one scholastic; transcripts of all schooling within the last 10 year (but no further back than high school); proof of Virginia Residence (copy of driver's license, voter registration card, a Virginia Tax Return or DMV identification card); and a proof of U.S. citizenship (copy of birth certificate, US passport, certificate of citizenship or naturalization, voter's registration card). **Deadline:** April 1.

9443 ■ Nettie Tucker Yowell Scholarships (Undergraduate/Scholarship)

Purpose: To provide financial aid to Virginia young people pursuing a baccalaureate degree at a Virginia-based college or university. **Focus:** General studies. **Qualif.:** Applicant must be a high school senior; not a Virginia BPW Foundation Trustee, or related to a Trustee; a citizen of the United States; a resident of Virginia; have a 3.0 or better GPA; have pass all SOL tests; scored 1000 or above on the Scholastic Assessment Test (SAT) or a comparable score on another college board exam; and pursuing a baccalaureate degree at a Virginia-based college/university. **Criteria:** Selection is based on financial need; scholastic record; educational goals; and commitment to Virginia BPW Foundation's Vision which is "Empowered Workingwomen" and its Mission which is "Dedicated to providing information, resources and educational opportunities to current and future workingwomen in Virginia".

Funds Avail.: $500-$1,000. **Number Awarded:** At least one. **To Apply:** Applicants must submit a completed application form along with a proof of Virginia residency (copy of driver's license, voter registration card, a Virginia Tax Return or DMV identification card), and a proof of U.S. citizenship (copy of birth certificate, US passport, certificate of citizenship or naturalization, voter's registration card). In addition, applicant's guidance counselor must provide the applicant's complete secondary record of grades; GPA; standardized test scores; statement that all SOL tests were passed; type of diploma the applicant will receive; and a letter of recommendation (from guidance counselor or principal). **Deadline:** April 1.

9444 ■ Virginia Dental Hygienist's Association Foundation

c/o Marge Green, Treas.
1919 Old York Hampton Hwy.
Yorktown, VA 23692-4143
URL: vdhafoundation.org

9445 ■ Alice Hinchcliffe Williams, RDH, MS Graduate Scholarships (Graduate/Scholarship)

Purpose: To provide support and serve as the primary provider of lifelong learning for dental hygienists throughout Virginia. **Focus:** Dental hygiene. **Qualif.:** Applicants must be ADHA members who are Virginia residents; must be enrolled in a graduate degree program in dental hygiene or any fields of study directly related to the professional roles of dental hygienist; must demonstrate a minimum GPA of at least 3.0 on a 4.0 scale. **Criteria:** Applicants will be evaluated based on merit, fulfillment of the required criteria and approval of the written narrative.

Funds Avail.: Amount not specified. **To Apply:** Applicants must complete the application form and must submit a narrative. **Deadline:** February 1. **Remarks:** Administered by ADHA Institute for Oral Health.

9446 ■ Virginia Federation of Republican Women (VFRW)

c/o Denise Bailey, Scholarship Co-Chairman
7516 Deer Branch Rd.
Roanoke, VA 24019
URL: www.vfrw.org

9447 ■ Political Studies Scholarships (Undergraduate, Graduate/Scholarship)

Purpose: To reflect on the cause of good government and to promote political activism and savvy. **Focus:** Govern-

Awards are arranged alphabetically below their administering organizations

ment; Political science; Law. **Qualif.:** Applicants must be undergraduate or graduate students enrolled in an accredited Virginia college or university, studying government, political science or law. **Criteria:** Selection will be based on the committee's criteria.

Funds Avail.: $1,000. **Number Awarded:** Three. **To Apply:** Applicants must submit a completed application form and a 500-word typed essay entitled: "Political Activism and the Roll of the Republican Woman". Applicants must also submit a copy of their resume, list of their educational and professional interests and achievements. **Deadline:** March 22.

9448 ■ Virginia Foundation for Independent Colleges (VFIC)

8010 Ridge Rd., Ste. B
Richmond, VA 23229-7288
Ph: (804) 288-6609
Fax: (804) 282-4635
Free: 800-230-6757
E-mail: info@vfic.org
URL: www.vfic.org

9449 ■ Hilb, Rogal and Hobbs Scholarships
(Undergraduate/Scholarship)

Purpose: To provide financial assistance to students who will be juniors at a VFIC member college. **Focus:** Marketing and distribution; Business; Economics; Finance; Mathematics and Mathematical sciences. **Qualif.:** Applicants must be full-time students at one of the fifteen private colleges/universities associated with the Virginia Foundation for Independent Colleges; must be first-semester juniors at the time of application with a cumulative grade point average of at least 3.0 on a 4.0 scale, who have declared, or intend to declare a major in one of the following disciplines: marketing, business, economics, finance, mathematics or related fields; must be U.S. citizens. **Criteria:** Applicants will be evaluated based on demonstrated financial need and academic achievement.

Funds Avail.: $2,500. **To Apply:** Applicants must submit all the required application information. **Deadline:** October 31.

9450 ■ Norfolk Southern Scholarships
(Undergraduate/Scholarship)

Purpose: To provide financial assistance to students who will be juniors at a VFIC member college to defray educational expenses. **Focus:** Economics; Business; Finance; Accounting. **Qualif.:** Applicants must be full-time students at one of the fifteen private colleges/universities associated with the VFIC; first semester juniors at the time of application with a cumulative GPA of at least 3.0 on a 4.0 scale and declared major in economics, business, finance, accounting or related fields, and interested in a career in a Fortune 500 corporate setting; must be United States citizens. **Criteria:** Applicants will be evaluated based on academic achievement and financial need.

Funds Avail.: $5,000. **Number Awarded:** 3. **To Apply:** Applicants must submit resume, college transcript, two letters of recommendation and the completed application form. **Deadline:** October 14.

9451 ■ Witt Mares Scholarships *(Undergraduate/Scholarship)*

Purpose: To provide financial assistance for students who are current juniors of VFIC institutions. **Focus:** Accounting.

Qualif.: Applicants must be full-time students at one of the five pre-selected private colleges/universities associated with the Virginia Foundation for Independent Colleges: Lynchburg College, Shenandoah University, Marymount University, Virginia Wesleyan College, Randolph-Macon College; must have a cumulative grade point average of at least a 3.0 on a 4.0 scale; be a junior at the time of application; be an accounting major, or have a related major or minor with coursework which includes completion of the Introductory Accounting sequence (sophomore year) and planning to complete the Intermediate Accounting sequence in their junior year; must be citizens of the United States of America. **Criteria:** Recipients will be selected by the staff of the Virginia Foundation for Independent Colleges with consultation from the Witt Mares Human Resources Manager.

Funds Avail.: $2,500. **Number Awarded:** 5. **To Apply:** Applicants must submit online application, resume and two (2) letters of recommendation. **Deadline:** October 31.

9452 ■ Virginia Historical Society (VHS)

PO Box 7311
Richmond, VA 23221-0311
Ph: (804) 358-4901
Fax: (804) 355-2399
E-mail: plevengood@vahistorical.org
URL: www.vahistorical.org/

9453 ■ Virginia Historical Society Research Fellowships *(Doctorate/Fellowship)*

Purpose: To promote the interpretation of Virginia history. **Focus:** History, American. **Qualif.:** Applicants must be doctoral candidates. **Criteria:** Selection is based on applicants' scholarly qualifications, the merits of the proposals and the appropriateness of the topics as demonstrated by citation to specific sources in the collections.

Funds Avail.: $150-$500/week. **To Apply:** Applicants must submit an original and three copies of a cover letter; a resume; two letters of recommendation (may be sent separately); and a description of the research project (no longer than two double-spaced pages). **Deadline:** February 1. **Contact:** Dr. Nelson D. Lankford at 804-342-9672, 804-355-2399 (fax) or nlankford@vahistorical.org.

9454 ■ Virginia Lakes and Watershed Association (VLWA)

c/o Shelly Frie
5700 Cleveland St., Ste. 101
Virginia Beach, VA 23462
Ph: (757) 671-6222
URL: www.vlwa.org

9455 ■ Leo Bourassa Scholarships
(Undergraduate, Graduate/Scholarship)

Purpose: To support and acknowledge students for academic and personal accomplishments in the field of water resources. **Focus:** Water resources. **Qualif.:** Applicants must be full-time undergraduate and full- or part-time graduate students enrolled in a curriculum related to water resources; must be students in good standing at any Virginia accredited college or university; must be residents of Virginia at the time of application and at the time of award. Undergraduate students must have successfully completed at least two semesters. **Criteria:** Recipients will

Awards are arranged alphabetically below their administering organizations

be evaluated based on academic performance, educational plans and contribution to the field of water resources.

Funds Avail.: $2,500. **Number Awarded:** 2. **To Apply:** Applicants must complete the application form; must attach a copy of current college transcripts, list of clubs and organizations related to water resources as proof of being a member, description of experience(s) to water resources and watershed management, no more than one-page explaining why you deserves to get the scholarship. **Deadline:** May 31. **Contact:** Shelly Frie at scholarship@vlwa.org.

9456 ■ Virginia Museum of Fine Arts
200 N Blvd.
Richmond, VA 23220-4007
Ph: (804) 340-1400
Fax: (804) 340-1548

9457 ■ Virginia Museum of Fine Arts Visual Arts Fellowships *(Graduate, Professional development, Undergraduate/Fellowship)*

Purpose: To support Virginia's professional artists and art students who demonstrate exceptional creative ability in their chosen field. **Focus:** Visual arts; Art history. **Qualif.:** Applicants must be undergraduate or graduate students enrolled full-time in a degree-seeking program at an accredited university, college, or school of the arts. Professional applicants must not be enrolled in a degree-seeking program. College-bound high school seniors are also eligible to apply. All applicants must be legal residents of Virginia. **Criteria:** Awards will be given to those applicants of the highest artistic merit.

Funds Avail.: $4,000 (undergraduates); $6,000 (graduates); $8,000 (professionals). **Number Awarded:** 43. **To Apply:** Applicants must complete the required fields on the application form. Crafts, Drawing, Painting, Photography and Sculpture applicants must submit a work sample consists of eight digital images, at least six must represent individual works and two images for details. Professional applicants must submit all works that have been completed in the past three years. Students must submit at least four sample works. Submit images on a PC-formatted CD-R, labeled with the applicant's name. Format digital images as JPEGs, no larger than 2 MB and 1000 pixels on the longest side. Mixed Media applicants must submit six images representing individual works plus two images for details. Film/Video applicants must submit a 15-minute (maximum) DVD sample of three works. These should be on a PC-formatted DVD, labeled with applicant's name and must include a menu on a DVD with links to each work and running times. Format submissions as files that are compatible with both QuickTime and RealPlayer. Art History applicants must submit two hard copies of the three research papers or published articles. Applicants are also required to submit a current resume, one-page artistic statement for professionals and transcript of records for students. SASE envelope and confirmation postcard are optional. **Deadline:** November 10. **Remarks:** The Fellowship Program was established in 1940 through a generous contribution made by the late John Lee Pratt of Fredericksburg.

9458 ■ Virginia Society of Certified Public Accountants (VSCPA)
4309 Cox Rd.
Glen Allen, VA 23060

Ph: (804) 270-5344
Fax: (804) 273-1741
Free: 800-733-8272
E-mail: vscpa@vscpa.com
URL: www.vscpa.com

9459 ■ H. Burton Bates Jr. Scholarships *(Graduate, Undergraduate/Scholarship)*

Purpose: To provide financial support to students pursuing a degree in accounting. **Focus:** Accounting. **Qualif.:** Applicant must be a U.S. citizen; a junior or senior accounting major currently enrolled full time at an accredited Virginia college/university, or have earned an undergraduate degree from an accredited Virginia college/university and enrolled at least part-time (as defined by the institution) during the term of application and throughout the term of scholarship in coursework required to qualify to take the Uniform CPA Examination; must be in good academic standing during the term of application and remain in good academic standing throughout the term of the scholarship. **Criteria:** Selection is based on the application materials submitted.

Funds Avail.: $1,750. **Number Awarded:** 1. **To Apply:** Applicants must submit a completed application together with a faculty letter of recommendation (may be mailed separately); an essay (500-word maximum); a current resume; and official transcript reflecting GPA (may be mailed separately). Submit finalized materials to: VSCPA Educational Foundation, Inc. PO Box 4620 Glen Allen, VA 23058-4620. **Deadline:** April 1.

9460 ■ Thomas M. Berry Jr. Scholarships *(Graduate, Undergraduate/Scholarship)*

Purpose: To provide financial support to students pursuing a degree in accounting. **Focus:** Accounting. **Qualif.:** Applicant must be a U.S. citizen; currently enrolled in an accredited Virginia college/university undergraduate or graduate program with the intent to pursue a degree in accounting; must have completed at least three hours of accounting and be currently registered for at least three more accounting credit hours (supporting documentation required). **Criteria:** Selection is based on demonstrated academic excellence, financial need and exemplary leadership skills.

Funds Avail.: $3,000. **Number Awarded:** 1. **To Apply:** Applicants must submit a completed application form along with a faculty letter of recommendation (may be mailed separately); leadership essay (500-word maximum); a current resume; and official transcript reflecting GPA (may be mailed separately). Submit finalized materials to: VSCPA Educational Foundation, Inc. PO Box 4620 Glen Allen, VA 23058-4620. **Deadline:** April 1. **Contact:** Tracey Zink at 804-612-9427 or tzink@vscpa.com.

9461 ■ Austin M. Cloyd, Matthew G. Gwaltney and Maxine S. Turner Doctoral Scholarships *(Doctorate/Scholarship)*

Purpose: To provide financial support to students pursuing a doctoral degree in accounting. **Focus:** Accounting. **Qualif.:** Applicant must be a U.S. citizen; accepted or currently enrolled in the doctoral accounting program at Virginia Tech; demonstrate a minimum overall and accounting GPA of 3.0 or higher; and a full-time doctoral student at Virginia Tech. **Criteria:** Selection is based on the application materials submitted.

Funds Avail.: $2,500. **Number Awarded:** 1. **To Apply:** Applicants must contact Robert M. Brown to be considered

Awards are arranged alphabetically below their administering organizations

for the scholarship. **Deadline:** December 31. **Remarks:** The scholarship was developed to honor and remember the lives of students of Virginia accounting families who were lost in the tragic events at Virginia Tech on April 16, 2007. **Contact:** Robert M. Brown at moren@vt.edu.

9462 ■ Cocke, Szpanka and Taylor Scholarships (Undergraduate/Scholarship)

Purpose: To financially support undergraduate accounting students. **Focus:** Accounting. **Qualif.:** Applicant must be a U.S. citizen; a junior or senior accounting major at the University of Virginia or George Mason University with the intent to take the CPA Exam; from the Washington, D.C. metro area; must demonstrate a minimum overall and accounting GPA of 3.0. **Criteria:** Selection is based on academic excellence, financial need and plans to pursue a career in public accounting.

Funds Avail.: $2,500. **Number Awarded:** 1. **To Apply:** Applicants must submit a completed application together with a faculty letter of recommendation (may be mailed separately); an essay (500-word maximum); a current resume; and official transcript reflecting GPA (may be mailed separately). Submit finalized materials to: VSCPA Educational Foundation, Inc. PO Box 4620 Glen Allen, VA 23058-4620. **Deadline:** January 10. **Contact:** For further information, applicants may email info@vscpafoundation.com.

9463 ■ Goodman & Company Scholarships (Undergraduate/Scholarship)

Purpose: To financially support undergraduate accounting students. **Focus:** Accounting. **Qualif.:** Applicant must be a U.S. citizen; a junior or senior accounting major currently enrolled at an accredited Virginia college/university with the intent to take the CPA exam; must demonstrate a minimum overall and accounting GPA of 3.0. **Criteria:** Selection is based on academic excellence, financial need and plans to pursue a career in public accounting.

Funds Avail.: $2,500. **Number Awarded:** 1. **To Apply:** Applicants must submit a completed application together with a faculty letter of recommendation (may be mailed separately); an essay (500-word maximum); a current resume; and official transcript reflecting GPA (may be mailed separately). Submit finalized materials to: VSCPA Educational Foundation, Inc. PO Box 4620 Glen Allen, VA 23058-4620. **Deadline:** January 10. **Contact:** Tracey Zink at 804-612-9427 or tzink@vscpa.com.

9464 ■ VSCPA Educational Foundation Graduate Scholarships (Graduate/Scholarship)

Purpose: To financially support graduate accounting students. **Focus:** Accounting. **Qualif.:** Applicant must be a U.S. citizen; accepted or currently enrolled in a graduate accounting program at an accredited Virginia college/university; and must demonstrate a minimum overall and accounting undergraduate GPA of 3.0 or higher. **Criteria:** Selection is based on demonstrated academic excellence and financial need.

Funds Avail.: $1,000. **Number Awarded:** 4. **To Apply:** Applicants must submit a completed application together with a faculty letter of recommendation (may be mailed separately); an essay (500-word maximum); a current resume; and official transcript reflecting GPA (may be mailed separately). Submit finalized materials to: VSCPA Educational Foundation, Inc. PO Box 4620 Glen Allen, VA 23058-4620. **Deadline:** April 1.

9465 ■ VSCPA Educational Foundation Minority Scholarships (Graduate, Undergraduate/Scholarship)

Purpose: To financially support minority accounting students. **Focus:** Accounting. **Qualif.:** Applicant must be a U.S. citizen; a member of one of the race/ethnic groups (American Indian or Alaskan Native, Asian, Black or African American, Hispanic or Latino, Native Hawaiian or other Pacific Islander); currently enrolled in an accredited Virginia college/university undergraduate or graduate program with the intent to pursue a bachelor's degree in accounting; must have completed at least three hours of accounting and be currently registered for at least three more accounting credit hours (supporting documentation required); must demonstrate a minimum overall and accounting GPA of 3.0. **Criteria:** Selection is based on demonstrated academic excellence and financial need.

Funds Avail.: $1,000. **Number Awarded:** 4. **To Apply:** Applicants must submit a completed application including the ethnicity section together with a faculty letter of recommendation (may be mailed separately); an essay (500-word maximum); current resume; and an official transcript reflecting GPA (may be mailed separately). Submit finalized materials to: VSCPA Educational Foundation, Inc. PO Box 4620 Glen Allen, VA 23058-4620. **Deadline:** April 1.

9466 ■ VSCPA Educational Foundation Undergraduate Scholarships (Undergraduate/Scholarship)

Purpose: To financially support undergraduate accounting students. **Focus:** Accounting. **Qualif.:** Applicant must be a U.S. citizen; currently enrolled in an accredited Virginia college/university undergraduate program with the intent to pursue a bachelor's degree in accounting; must have completed at least three hours of accounting and be currently registered for at least three more accounting credit hours (supporting documentation required); and must demonstrate a minimum overall and accounting GPA of 3.0. **Criteria:** Selection is based on demonstrated academic excellence and financial need.

Funds Avail.: $1,000. **Number Awarded:** 4. **To Apply:** Applicants must submit a completed application together with a faculty letter of recommendation (may be mailed separately); an essay (500-word maximum); current resume; and official transcript reflecting GPA (may be mailed separately). Submit finalized materials to: VSCPA Educational Foundation, Inc. PO Box 4620 Glen Allen, VA 23058-4620. **Deadline:** April 1.

9467 ■ VSCPA PhD Accounting Scholarships (Doctorate, Graduate/Scholarship)

Purpose: To financially support graduate students pursuing a PhD in accounting. **Focus:** Accounting. **Qualif.:** Applicant must be a U.S. citizen; accepted or currently enrolled in a doctoral accounting program at an accredited Virginia college/university; must demonstrate a minimum overall and accounting GPA of 3.0 or higher; and must be a full-time doctoral student. **Criteria:** Selection is based on demonstrated academic excellence and financial need.

Funds Avail.: $2,500. **Number Awarded:** 1. **To Apply:** Applicants must submit a completed application along with a faculty letter of recommendation (may be mailed separately); an essay (500-word maximum); a current resume; and official undergraduate and graduate (if applicable) transcripts to date (may be mailed separately). **Deadline:** April 1. **Contact:** Questions can be addressed to Tracey

Awards are arranged alphabetically below their administering organizations

Zink at the above address; E-mail: tzink@vscpa.com.

9468 ■ Yount, Hyde & Barbour Scholarships
(Undergraduate/Scholarship)

Purpose: To provide financial support to students pursuing a degree in accounting. **Focus:** Accounting. **Qualif.:** Applicant must be a U.S. citizen; a junior or senior accounting major currently enrolled at an accredited Virginia college/university with the intent of taking the CPA exam; and must demonstrate a minimum overall and accounting GPA of 3.0. **Criteria:** Selection is based on academic excellence and financial need, and intent to pursue a career in public accounting.

Funds Avail.: $2,500. **Number Awarded:** 1. **To Apply:** Applicants must submit a completed application form together with a faculty letter of recommendation (may be mailed separately); an essay (500-word maximum); a current resume; and official transcript reflecting GPA (may be mailed separately). Submit finalized materials to: VSCPA Educational Foundation, Inc. PO Box 4620 Glen Allen, VA 23058-4620. **Deadline:** April 1.

9469 ■ John D. Voelker Foundation
PO Box 15222
Lansing, MI 48901-5222
Ph: (616) 897-1304
URL: www.voelkerfdn.org

9470 ■ John D. Voelker Foundation Native American Scholarships *(Undergraduate/Scholarship)*

Purpose: To assist Native American students to pursue the dream of a legal education. **Focus:** Paralegal studies; Law. **Qualif.:** Applicants must have a sincere interest in studying law and using a legal education to benefit Native American people; must be enrolled member of a federal recognized Michigan or Wisconsin tribe; must have the academic potential to succeed in school, as evidenced by past academic success or admission to an accredited law school; must have a greatest financial need; must be willing to provide an annual report to the Foundation on the progress of their studies for each academic year in which a grant is received. **Criteria:** Selection will be based on the committee's criteria.

Funds Avail.: No specific amount. **To Apply:** Applicants must submit a simple letter addressing each of the eligibility criteria applicable to the applicants. Letters of reference from teachers or employers, transcripts and documentation confirming tribal membership are encouraged.

9471 ■ The Voice Foundation (VF)
1721 Pine St.
Philadelphia, PA 19103
Ph: (215) 735-7999
Fax: (215) 735-9293
E-mail: office@voicefoundation.org
URL: www.voicefoundation.org

9472 ■ Institutional Grants: Educational and Research Projects *(All/Grant)*

Purpose: To support voice research and care. **Focus:** Music, Vocal. **Qualif.:** Applicants must be conducting research or projects about human voice. **Criteria:** Proposals are reviewed by a panel selected by the Chairman of the Scientific Advisory Board.

Funds Avail.: No specific amount. **To Apply:** Applicants must visit the website for the online application process.

9473 ■ Voluntary Protection Programs Participants' Association (VPPPA)
7600-E Leesburg Pke., Ste. 100
Falls Church, VA 22043-2004
Ph: (703) 761-1146
Fax: (703) 761-1148
E-mail: administration@vpppa.org
URL: www.vpppa.org

9474 ■ VPPPA Stephen Brown Scholarships
(Graduate, Undergraduate/Scholarship)

Purpose: To encourage careers in the areas of safety, health and environment by providing educational support. **Focus:** Environmental conservation; Occupational safety and health. **Qualif.:** Applicants must be students who either work at a current VPP site or the children/grandchildren of an employee of a VPP site (the site must be a VPPPA full member in good standing); must be pursuing a degree (undergraduate or graduate) in the environmental, safety and health areas (either part-time or full-time); must have at least a 2.5 GPA on a scale of 4.0. **Criteria:** Recipients are chosen on the basis of demonstrated occupational safety, health and/or environmental outreach efforts in their schools, communities and/or workplace, leadership skills, extracurricular activities, involvement in professional organizations, communication skills and other awards and honors earned at educational institutions or at their place of employment.

Funds Avail.: No specific amount. **Number Awarded:** 1. **To Apply:** Applicants must submit a completed application form available in the website; a typewritten biography of at least 300 words describing interests and accomplishments; copy of current transcript; reference letters from the VPPPA site employee and from high school teacher, university's department head, professor or supervisor at current job. Forward all requirements to: VPPPA, Inc., Attn: Awards Committee. **Deadline:** May 7.

9475 ■ Delta/VPPPA Safety, Health and Environmental Scholarships *(Undergraduate, Vocational/Occupational, Graduate/Scholarship)*

Purpose: To encourage students' active participation in occupational safety, health and/or environmental outreach programs in their schools, community and/or workplace. **Focus:** Environmental conservation; Occupational safety and health. **Qualif.:** Applicants must be students who are enrolled or enrolling in a college or university (graduate or undergraduate level) or a vocational school pursuing a degree in the environmental, occupational safety and/or health field; they must be either employed at a VPPPA Full, Corporate or Associate member company or the child or grandchild of an employee; and must have had or have at least a 2.5 GPA on a scale of 4.0. **Criteria:** Recipients are chosen on the basis of demonstrated occupational safety, health and/or environmental outreach efforts in their schools, communities and/or workplace, leadership skills, extracurricular activities, involvement in professional organizations, communication skills and other awards and honors earned at educational institutions or at their place of employment; Preference is given to applicants from airline and associated aviation industries.

Funds Avail.: No specific amount. **To Apply:** Applicants

Awards are arranged alphabetically below their administering organizations

must submit a completed application form; official transcript; reference letter relating to safety, health and environmental outreach activities from a VPP coordinator, operations manager, EHS staff , OSHA, regional VPPPA Chapter Chairperson, community contact and must submit a typed biography or current resume. **Deadline:** May 7. **Remarks:** The scholarship supports Delta's "Force for Global Good" initiative that focuses on Breast Cancer Awareness, The Red Cross, Habitat for Humanity and environmental responsibility.

9476 ■ VPPPA William Sullivan Scholarships
(Graduate, Undergraduate/Scholarship)

Purpose: To recognize an employee at a VPPPA full member site who has made significant contributions to the VPP program at his or her site. **Focus:** Environmental conservation; Occupational safety and health. **Qualif.:** Applicant must be a current employee at a VPP site (the site must be a VPPPA full member in good standing); must demonstrate their contributions to the VPP site; must be pursuing a degree (undergraduate or graduate) either part-time or full-time; and must have at least a 2.5 GPA on a scale of 4.0. **Criteria:** Recipient is chosen based on merit.

Funds Avail.: No specific amount. **To Apply:** Applicants must submit a completed application form, an official transcript and a reference letter relating to your VPP involvement at your site from a site VPP coordinator, operations manager, site EHS staff, OSHA, Regional VPPPA Chapter Chairperson, and others. Forward to: VPPPA, Inc., Attn: Awards Committee. **Deadline:** May 7.

9477 ■ VPPPA June Brothers Scholarships
(Graduate, Undergraduate/Scholarship)

Purpose: To encourage careers in the areas of safety, health and environment by providing educational support. **Focus:** Environmental conservation; Occupational safety and health. **Qualif.:** Applicants must be students who either work at a current VPP site or the children/grandchildren of an employee of a VPP site (the site must be a VPPPA full member in good standing); must be pursuing a degree (undergraduate or graduate) in the environmental, safety and health areas (either part-time or full-time); must have at least a 2.5 GPA on a scale of 4.0. **Criteria:** Recipients are chosen on the basis of demonstrated occupational safety, health and/or environmental outreach efforts in their schools, communities and/or workplace, leadership skills, extracurricular activities, involvement in professional organizations, communication skills and other awards and honors earned at educational institutions or at their place of employment.

Funds Avail.: No specific amount. **Number Awarded:** Varies. **To Apply:** Applicants must submit completed application form available in the website; a typewritten biography of at least 300 words describing interests and accomplishments or current resume; copy of current transcript; reference letters from the VPPPA site employee and from a high school teacher, university's department head, professor or supervisor at current job. Forward all requirements to: VPPPA, Inc., Attn: Awards Committee. **Deadline:** May 7.

9478 ■ Walmart Foundation
702 SW 8th St.
Bentonville, AR 72716-8611
Free: 800-925-6278
URL: walmartstores.com/CommunityGiving/
8736.aspx?p=236

9479 ■ Walmart Associate Scholarships
(Undergraduate/Scholarship)

Purpose: To provide educational grants to deserving students who want to pursue their studies. **Focus:** General studies. **Qualif.:** Applicant must be a U.S. citizen or permanent Legal Resident of the United States; must be a active employee of Walmart Stores, Inc. or dependent of an actively employed associate with Walmart Stores, Inc. for at least six consecutive months; must be a graduating high school senior; must have a high school diplomas and GED equivalent certificates; must have a cumulative high school GPA of at least 2.5 on a 4-point scale; must plan to enroll as a freshman at a two-year college or university that is located in the U.S. and is accredited and listed on the official website of the U.S. Department of Education. **Criteria:** Awards are given based on merit and need.

Funds Avail.: $3,000. **To Apply:** Applicants must submit a completed scholarship application available online and must be sent to Walmart Associate Scholarship, PO Box 4030, Iowa City, IA 52243. **Deadline:** January 29.

9480 ■ Sam Walton Community Scholarships
(Undergraduate/Scholarship)

Purpose: To provide financial assistance to deserving students who want to pursue their studies. **Focus:** General studies. **Qualif.:** Applicant must be a U.S. citizen or permanent Legal Resident of the United States; must not be a Walmart Stores, Inc. Associate; must be a graduating high school senior; must have a cumulative high school grade point average of at least 2.5; must have taken either the ACT or SAT test; must have plan to enroll as a freshman at a two-year or four-year college or university that is located in the U.S. and is accredited and listed on the official website of the U.S. Department of Education; must have financial need and be able to demonstrate the need with required documents. **Criteria:** Awards are given based on merit and need.

Funds Avail.: $3,000. **To Apply:** Applicants must submit a completed scholarship application available online. **Deadline:** January 31.

9481 ■ Walton Family Foundation Scholarships
(Undergraduate/Scholarship)

Purpose: To provide educational grants to deserving individuals who want to pursue their studies. **Focus:** General studies. **Qualif.:** Applicant must be a U.S. citizen or permanent Legal Resident of the United States; must be the dependent of an actively employed, full-time Walmart Stores, Inc. Associate who has been employed for at least twelve consecutive months; must be a graduating high school senior; must have achieved an ACT composite score of 22 or a combined SAT score of 1030; must have plan to enroll as a freshman at a two-year or four-year college or university that is located in the U.S. and is accredited and listed on the official website of the U.S. Department of Education; must have a financial need and be able to demonstrate the need with required documents. **Criteria:** Award is given based on the application materials.

Funds Avail.: $13,000. **To Apply:** Applicants must submit a completed scholarship application available online. **Deadline:** January 31.

9482 ■ Warner Norcross & Judd LLP (WNJ)
900 Fifth Third Ctr.
111 Lyon St. NW
Grand Rapids, MI 49503-2487

Awards are arranged alphabetically below their administering organizations

Ph: (616) 752-2000
Fax: (616) 752-2500
Free: 866-533-3018
E-mail: contactwnj@wnj.com
URL: www.wnj.com

9483 ■ Warner Norcross & Judd LLP Minorty Scholarships *(Undergraduate/Scholarship)*

Purpose: To provide encouragement and financial assistance to students of racial and ethnic minority heritage pursuing a career in law. **Focus:** Law; Paralegal studies. **Qualif.:** Applicants must be former or current residents of Michigan or attending a Michigan law school. **Criteria:** Applicants will be selected based on academic standing and financial need.

Funds Avail.: $5,000, $2,000 and $1,000. **Number Awarded:** 1. **To Apply:** Applicants must submit completed application forms; a statement of goals and aspirations related to their studies in the legal profession, and must indicate the reason why they choose the legal profession/field as their area of study; and two letters of reference. **Deadline:** April 1. **Contact:** Ruth Bishop, Grand Rapids Community Foundation, at rbishop@grfoundation.org or to Rodney Martin, Warner Norcross & Judd LLP, at rmartin@wnj.com.

9484 ■ Washburn University School of Law

1700 SW College Ave.
Topeka, KS 66621
Ph: (785) 670-1060
Fax: (785) 670-3249
URL: washburnlaw.edu

9485 ■ Business and Transactional Law Center Scholarships *(Undergraduate/Scholarship)*

Purpose: To financially assist Washburn University students with their education. **Focus:** Law. **Qualif.:** Applicants must be admitted to Washburn Law; and must have an interest in business law or transactional law. **Criteria:** Recipients are selected based on the quality of all application materials submitted.

Funds Avail.: Maximum of $20,000 per year. **To Apply:** Applicants must attach a 1-2 paragraph description of interest, background or qualifications related to the scholarship specific area.

9486 ■ Child and Family Advocacy Fellowships *(Undergraduate/Scholarship)*

Purpose: To financially assist Washburn University students with their education. **Focus:** Law. **Qualif.:** Applicants must be admitted to Washburn Law and must pursue careers in child and family advocacy. **Criteria:** Award is given based on the application materials.

Funds Avail.: Maximum of $19,000 per year. **To Apply:** Applicants must attach a 1-2 paragraph description of interest, background or qualifications related to the scholarship specific area.

9487 ■ Judge Delmas C. Hill Scholarships *(Undergraduate/Scholarship)*

Purpose: To financially assist Washburn University students with their education. **Focus:** Law. **Qualif.:** Applicants must be admitted as full-time students in Washburn Law; must be in the top ten percent of the class; and

must have a 2.5 GPA. **Criteria:** Award is given based on the application materials.

Funds Avail.: Full-tuition and a stipend of $4,000 per year. **Number Awarded:** 1. **To Apply:** Applicants must submit a statement showing: the reason for interest in the law as a profession; public and community service activities; leadership activities; and potential for leadership.

9488 ■ Koch Scholarships *(Undergraduate/Scholarship)*

Purpose: To financially assist Washburn University students with their education. **Focus:** Law. **Qualif.:** Applicants must be admitted as full-time students in Washburn Law; must be in the top ten percent of the class; and must have a 3.0 GPA. **Criteria:** Award is given based on the application materials.

Funds Avail.: Full-tuition for three years of law school; student fees; and a stipend of $6,000 for the first year of law school, $3,000 per year in the second and $3,000 per year in the third years. **Number Awarded:** 1. **To Apply:** Applicants must submit a statement showing: the reason for interest in the law as a profession; public and community service activities; leadership activities; and potential for leadership.

9489 ■ Pittsburg State University Distinguished Graduate Scholarships *(Undergraduate/Scholarship)*

Purpose: To help defray some of the costs of a legal education for a Pittsburg State University student elected to attend Washburn Law. **Focus:** Law. **Qualif.:** Applicants must be PSU students admitted to Washburn Law. **Criteria:** Award is given based on merit.

Funds Avail.: No specific amount. **To Apply:** PSU applicants admitted to Washburn Law will be automatically considered. **Remarks:** Established by David Pierce, Washburn Law Professor and Pittsburg State University graduate.

9490 ■ Polsinelli Diversity Scholarships *(Undergraduate/Scholarship)*

Purpose: To financially assist Washburn University minority students with their education. **Focus:** Law. **Qualif.:** Applicants must be incoming first-year minority law students. **Criteria:** Award is given based on merit.

Funds Avail.: $15,000 each year. **Number Awarded:** 1. **To Apply:** Applicants admitted to Washburn Law will be automatically considered. **Remarks:** Created through the contributions of the Polsinelli Shalton Flanigan Suelthause PC law firm.

9491 ■ Shamberg Scholarships *(Undergraduate/Scholarship)*

Purpose: To financially assist Washburn University students with their education. **Focus:** Law. **Qualif.:** Applicants must be admitted to Washburn Law. **Criteria:** Selection is based on academic achievements and leadership potential.

Funds Avail.: Full-tuition for all three years of law school and a $4,000 stipend. **Number Awarded:** 3. **To Apply:** Admitted students who qualify will be automatically considered.

9492 ■ J.L. Weigand, Jr. Legal Education Trust Scholarships *(Undergraduate/Scholarship)*

Purpose: To promote excellence in legal education and to encourage the most scholastically qualified students who are long-term Kansas residents to remain in or return to Kansas to practice law. **Focus:** Law. **Qualif.:** Applicants must be admitted full-time to Washburn Law; must be in the top ten percent of the class and have been a legal resident of Kansas for at least ten years prior to their admission to law school. **Criteria:** Selection is based on merit.

Funds Avail.: No specific amount. **To Apply:** Applicants admitted to Washburn Law will be automatically considered. **Deadline:** February 1. **Remarks:** Established by John L. Weigand, Jr. **Contact:** Karla Whitaker at the above address.

9493 ■ Washington City/County Management Association (WCMA)

c/o Davis Ramsey
11405 NE 104th St.
Kirkland, WA 98033
Ph: (425) 827-9150
Fax: (425) 941-8630
E-mail: dhramsey@aol.com
URL: www.wccma.org

9494 ■ Washington City/County Management Association Scholarships *(Graduate/ Scholarship)*

Purpose: To provide financial assistance to students who have chosen to pursue a graduate degree in public administration and who have a desire to work in city or county management. **Focus:** Public administration. **Qualif.:** Applicant must reside in Washington State; have a bachelor's degree; enrolled in or accepted for admission to a graduate school in Washington, Oregon or Idaho; and demonstrate a serious commitment to pursue a career in local government. **Criteria:** Preference will be given to graduate students pursuing a degree in public administration, public affairs, or public policy.

Funds Avail.: $2,500. **Number Awarded:** 1. **To Apply:** Applicants must submit a completed application form along with one official copy of undergraduate transcripts; one official copy of graduate transcripts (if applicable); two letters of reference, one from a previous or current undergraduate or graduate academic instructor and the other from a previous or current work supervisor; and a letter of application (no more than two pages). An initial unofficial copy of transcripts is sufficient to meet the deadline but must be followed by an official copy of them. **Deadline:** June 30. **Contact:** Cathleen Koch at ckoch@cityofprosser.com.

9495 ■ The Washington Group (TWG)

PO Box 11248
Washington, DC 20008
Ph: (202) 586-7227
Fax: (202) 586-3617
E-mail: president@thewashingtongroup.org
URL: www.thewashingtongroup.org

9496 ■ Alberta Ukrainian Centennial Commemorative Scholarships *(Graduate/Scholarship)*

Purpose: To encourage active participation in the Ukrainian community. **Focus:** General studies. **Qualif.:** Applicants must be graduate students intending to study in Alberta or Canadian graduate students from Alberta intending to study in Ukraine. **Criteria:** Recipients are selected based on academic records.

Funds Avail.: No specific amount. **Number Awarded:** 2. **To Apply:** Applicants must fill out the application and must submit supporting materials. **Deadline:** February 1. **Contact:** Alberta Heritage Scholarship Fund at 9940 106th Street, Edmonton, Alberta, T5K 2V1, Canada; 1403-427-5538; 1403-422-4516.

9497 ■ Canada-Ukraine Parliamentary Program Internship Scholarships (CUPP) *(Undergraduate/ Scholarship)*

Purpose: To encourage active participation in the Ukrainian community. **Focus:** General studies. **Qualif.:** Program is open for individuals seeking scholarships for a three-month internship for Ukrainian undergraduates with a Member of Parliament of the House of Commons in Ottawa, Canada. This internship is open only to citizens of Ukraine. Proficiency in English or French as well as in Ukrainian is a requirement. **Criteria:** Recipients are selected based on academic records.

Funds Avail.: No specific amount. **To Apply:** Application is available online. **Deadline:** February 1. **Contact:** Ukrainian Studies Foundation, 620 Spadina Avenue, Toronto, Ontario, Canada M5S 2H4; 416-234-9114; cupp@infoukes.com.

9498 ■ Chopivsky Fellowships *(Graduate/ Scholarship)*

Purpose: To encourage active participation in the Ukrainian community. **Focus:** Forestry; Environmental Science; Economics. **Qualif.:** Applicants must be Ukrainian citizens and must be first admitted to the appropriate faculties at Yale; must be in a graduate degree program leading to a master's degree at the Yale School of Management at the Yale School of Forestry and Environmental Studies, and in the Departments of International Relations, International Economics and Developmental Studies. **Criteria:** Recipients are selected based on academic records.

Funds Avail.: No specific amount. **Number Awarded:** 2. **To Apply:** Applicants must fill out the application form and supporting materials. **Deadline:** January 1. **Contact:** PO Box 208206, New Haven, CT 06520-8606; 1203-432-3423; 12034325963; Email: rees@yale.edu.

9499 ■ Eugene & Elinor Kotur Scholarship Trust Fund *(Undergraduate, Graduate/ Scholarship)*

Purpose: To encourage active participation in the Ukrainian community. **Focus:** General studies. **Qualif.:** Applicants must be enrolled in the sophomore or higher year or graduate school of about thirty leading colleges and universities in the USA listed on the application form. Applicants may have to be members of the Ukrainian Fraternal Association for two years. **Criteria:** Recipients are selected based on academic records.

Funds Avail.: $1,000. **To Apply:** Applicants must write for application. **Contact:** Ukrainian Fraternal Association Scholarship Program, PO Box 350, Scranton, PA 18501-0350; 1717-342-0937.

9500 ■ The Ivan Shandor Memorial Ukrainian American Bar Association Scholarships *(Master's/Scholarship)*

Purpose: To encourage active participation in the Ukrainian community. **Focus:** Law. **Qualif.:** Applicants must be enrolled in the Masters of Law degree program at Georgetown University Law center; must be residents or resided in

---

Awards are arranged alphabetically below their administering organizations

Ukraine; must be fluent in Ukrainian language; and must demonstrate a desire to promote democracy and uphold the rule of law in Ukraine. **Criteria:** Recipients are selected based on academic records.

Funds Avail.: No specific amount. **To Apply:** Applicants must fill out the application form. **Contact:** Scholarships for International Students, Georgetown university Law Center, Office of development, 600 New Jersey Avenue, N.W., Washington, DC 20001; 202-662-9000.

9501 ■ Marusia Yaworska Entrance Scholarships (Graduate/Scholarship)

Purpose: To encourage active participation in the Ukrainian community. **Focus:** Music. **Qualif.:** Applicants must be graduate level students from Ukraine or Canada willing to study anywhere in the world; must be enrolled in the field of music. **Criteria:** Recipients are selected based on academic records.

Funds Avail.: $5,000. **Number Awarded:** 2. **To Apply:** Applicants must fill out the application and supporting materials. **Deadline:** March 31. **Contact:** Department of Music, Faculty of Arts, University of Ottawa, 50 University Private, Ottawa, Ontario, K1N 6N5, Canada.

9502 ■ Washington Higher Education Coordinating Board

917 Lakeridge Way
Olympia, WA 98502
Ph: (360) 753-7800
E-mail: info@hecb.wa.gov
URL: www.hecb.wa.gov

9503 ■ American Indian Endowed Scholarships (Graduate, Undergraduate/Scholarship)

Purpose: To help financially needy students with close social and cultural ties to a Native American community to pursue undergraduate and graduate studies. **Focus:** General studies. **Qualif.:** Applicant must have demonstrated financial need based on a completed FAFSA; a Washington state resident; enrolled full-time as an undergraduate or graduate student in an eligible program; and not pursuing a degree in theology. **Criteria:** Selection is based on academic merit and commitment to serve the American Indian community.

Funds Avail.: $500-$2000. **Number Awarded:** 15. **To Apply:** Applicants must submit an American Indian Endowed Scholarship application form together with the required materials and information. **Deadline:** February 1. **Remarks:** Students can use the scholarships at public colleges and universities and accredited independent colleges, universities and career schools in Washington.

9504 ■ Washington College Bound Scholarships (Undergraduate/Scholarship)

Purpose: To provide hope and incentive for students and families who otherwise might not consider college as an option because of its cost. **Focus:** General studies. **Qualif.:** Applicants must be seventh-grade students from families eligible for free or reduced-price lunches who sign the pledge. Their family income must remain at 65 percent or less of the state's median income by the time of high school graduation. **Criteria:** Student must have signed a pledge in 7th and 8th grade promising to graduate from high school and demonstrate good citizenship.

Funds Avail.: Covers the cost of college tuition, fees and books. **To Apply:** The online application and brochure are being finalized. Materials will be sent to all middle schools, including a link to the online application. **Deadline:** June 30.

9505 ■ Washington Higher Education Coordinating Board Educational Opportunity Grants (Undergraduate/Grant)

Purpose: To encourage financially needy students to complete a bachelor's degree. **Focus:** General studies. **Qualif.:** Applicants must have placebound circumstances (having personal barriers which unable the student to continue education); a Washington resident; have at least junior standing before the first term of enrollment at an eligible four-year college; have financial need; and a junior or senior transfer student (student cannot receive EOG to continue at the current college). **Criteria:** Selection is based on the student's placebound circumstances and financial need.

Funds Avail.: $5000. **To Apply:** Applicants must submit a completed application form along with the required materials and information. **Deadline:** July 15.

9506 ■ Washington Higher Education Coordinating Board Health Professional Scholarships (Graduate/Scholarship)

Purpose: To attract and retain health professionals to serve in critical shortage areas in Washington state. **Focus:** Physics; Nursing; Midwifery; Pharmacy; Dentistry. **Qualif.:** Applicant must be a student training to become a primary care health professional in an eligible profession; a U.S. citizen; have completed all prerequisite course work; not be in default on any educational loans; and must sign a Promissory Note agreeing to serve for a minimum of three years in a designated shortage area in Washington state or pay back funds with double penalty plus interest. **Criteria:** Priority is given to those applicants enrolled in Undergraduate Nursing, Nursing Faculty, Dental, Dental Hygienist, and Pharmacist programs who demonstrate a commitment to rural communities and underserved populations as outlined in the narrative portion of the application.

Funds Avail.: Varies by educational program. **To Apply:** Applicants must submit a completed application form along with the required materials and information. **Deadline:** April 30. **Remarks:** Participants must agree, in return for the assistance, to provide primary healthcare in rural or underserved urban areas with designated shortages for a minimum of three years. **Contact:** Chris Wilkins, healthprof@hecb.wa.gov.

9507 ■ Washington Higher Education Coordinating Board - State Need Grants (SNG) (Undergraduate/Grant)

Purpose: To help state's lowest-income undergraduate students pursue degrees, hone skills, or retrain for new careers. **Focus:** General studies. **Qualif.:** Applicant must have a family income of equal to or less than 70 percent of the state median; a Washington State resident; enrolled as an undergraduate student in an eligible program, at a minimum of 3 credits; pursuing a certificate, bachelor's degree, or first associate degree; and not pursuing a degree in theology. **Criteria:** Selection is based on the applicant's family income.

Funds Avail.: Amounts vary by the type of school the applicant is attending. **To Apply:** Applicants must file a FAFSA (Free Application for Federal Student Aid) to be considered.

Awards are arranged alphabetically below their administering organizations

Contact: finaid@hecb.wa.gov.

9508 ■ Washington Hospital Healthcare System (WHHS)
2000 Mowry Ave.
Fremont, CA 94538-1716
Ph: (510) 797-1111
E-mail: feedback@whhs.com
URL: www.whhs.com

9509 ■ Medical Staff Scholarships
(Undergraduate/Scholarship)

Purpose: To meet the healthcare needs of the district residents through medical services, education and research. **Focus:** Health sciences. **Qualif.:** Applicants must be students residing within the Washington Township Health Care District who are pursuing careers in the health sciences field; must be students enrolled in the nursing program at San Jose State University or Ohlone College. **Criteria:** Recipients are selected based on academic performance and demonstrated interest in a health-related field.

Funds Avail.: $1,500. **Number Awarded:** 1. **To Apply:** Applicants must submit a completed application form. **Deadline:** March 16. **Contact:** 510-791-3446.

9510 ■ Service League Volunteer Scholarships
(Undergraduate/Scholarship)

Purpose: To meet the healthcare needs of district residents through medical services, education and research. **Focus:** Health care services. **Qualif.:** Applicants must be graduating high school seniors or college students who are pursuing studies in a health-related field; must have 2.50 GPA or higher; must be U.S. citizens and residents of Washington Hospital District; must have been accepted by an accredited school, college or university offering a bachelor or higher degree program in a health-related field; must be full-time students and must have completed 100 hours of volunteer service or employment in a health-related field. **Criteria:** Recipients are selected based on academic performance.

Funds Avail.: $1,000. **Number Awarded:** 2. **To Apply:** Applicants must submit: completed application form; current letters of recommendation from a Director of Volunteer Services, employer, counselor, advisor or teacher; high school or college transcript and proof of citizenship. **Deadline:** April 1. **Contact:** 510-791-3465.

9511 ■ Washington Indian Gaming Association (WIGA)
1110 Capitol Way S, Ste. 404
Olympia, WA 98501
Ph: (360) 352-3248
Fax: (360) 352-4819
E-mail: estebbins@reachone.com
URL: www.washingtonindiangaming.org

9512 ■ WIGA Scholarships *(Postgraduate, Professional development, Undergraduate/ Scholarship)*

Purpose: To promote tribal economic development and self-sufficiency. **Focus:** General studies. **Qualif.:** Applicant must be a Native American/Alaska Native student who is an enrolled member of a Washington tribe or a Washington state resident; or a Native American student from Washington attending college in another state, as well as a Native American student from outside of Washington who attends college in Washington. Applicant must be pursuing a degree at a community/technical college, four-year college, postgraduate or professional school. **Criteria:** Selection is based on the application materials submitted for review.

Funds Avail.: $1,000-$1,500. **Number Awarded:** Varies. **To Apply:** Applicants must submit a completed WIGA Scholarship application along with a personal essay; two letters of recommendation; verification of tribal enrollment; copy of Tribe's Educational Assistance Policy (if any); and high school or most recent College Transcript of GED certificate. **Deadline:** March 13.

9513 ■ Washington Society of Certified Public Accountants (WSCPA)
902 140th Ave. NE
Bellevue, WA 98005-3480
Ph: (425) 644-4800
Fax: (425) 562-8853
Free: 800-272-8273
E-mail: memberservices@wscpa.org
URL: www.wscpa.org/content/home.aspx

9514 ■ Washington CPA Foundation Scholarships *(Graduate, Undergraduate/Scholarship)*

Purpose: To financially support accounting students. **Focus:** Accounting. **Qualif.:** Applicant must have a minimum of 3.0 GPA overall and in accounting courses; have on-campus and community activities; probability of earning a CPA License; at least in Junior status; have work history; and be accepted into Accounting Department. **Criteria:** Selection is based on the application materials submitted for review.

Funds Avail.: $500-$3,000. **Number Awarded:** Varies. **To Apply:** Applicants must submit a completed application together with a current resume; unofficial transcript from all schools attended; copy of most recent quarter/semester grades (if available); documentation of Accounting Major; and two letters of recommendation (one from a current college advisor and one from current/former employer). Mail three copies of completed application and three copies of required materials by deadline to WSCPA. **Deadline:** February 15.

9515 ■ George Waterman Memorial Scholarships *(Graduate, Undergraduate/Scholarship)*

Purpose: To financially support accounting students. **Focus:** Accounting. **Qualif.:** Applicant must have a minimum of 3.0 GPA overall and in accounting courses; have on-campus and community activities; probability of earning a CPA License; at least in Junior status; have work history; and be accepted into Accounting Department. **Criteria:** Selection is based on the application materials submitted for review.

Funds Avail.: $500-$3,000. **Number Awarded:** Varies. **To Apply:** Applicants must submit a completed application together with a current resume; unofficial transcript from all schools attended; copy of most recent quarter/semester grades (if available); documentation of Accounting Major; and two letters of recommendation (one from a current college advisor and one from current/former employer). Mail three copies of completed application and three copies of required materials by deadline to WSCPA. **Deadline:** February 15.

Awards are arranged alphabetically below their administering organizations

9516 ■ WSCPA Chapter Scholarships *(Graduate, Undergraduate/Scholarship)*

Purpose: To financially support accounting students. **Focus:** Accounting. **Qualif.:** Applicant must have a minimum of 3.0 GPA overall and in accounting courses; have on-campus and community activities; probability of earning a CPA License; at least in Junior status; have work history; and be accepted into Accounting Department. **Criteria:** Selection is based on the application materials submitted for review.

Funds Avail.: $500-$3,000. **Number Awarded:** Varies. **To Apply:** Applicants must submit a completed application together with a current resume; unofficial transcript from all schools attended; copy of most recent quarter/semester grades (if available); documentation of Accounting Major; and two letters of recommendation (one from a current college advisor and one from current/former employer). Mail three copies of completed application and three copies of required materials by deadline to WSCPA. **Deadline:** February 15.

9517 ■ Washington State Association for Justice (WSAJ)

1809 7th Ave., Ste. 1500
Seattle, WA 98101-1328
Ph: (206) 464-1011
Fax: (206) 464-0703
E-mail: wsaj@washingtonjustice.org
URL: www.washingtonjustice.org

9518 ■ Women of WSAJ Bar Preparation Scholarships *(Undergraduate/Scholarship)*

Purpose: To help defray the cost of bar review courses. **Focus:** Law. **Qualif.:** Applicants must be female individuals who will take the Washington State bar exam in July 2011 or February 2012. **Criteria:** Recipients will be selected based on financial need, demonstrated interest and intent to practice in the plaintiff's bar.

Funds Avail.: No specific amount. **Number Awarded:** Varies. **To Apply:** Applicants must submit a resume and an essay (not to exceed two pages, typed and double-spaced). Additional documents that will support the application are acceptable. **Deadline:** March. **Contact:** For further information, applicants must contact Shannon Kilpatrick at 425-453-8161 or may e-mail Denise Diskin at ddiskinwsaj@gmail.com.

9519 ■ WSAJ American Justice Essay Scholarships *(Undergraduate/Scholarship)*

Purpose: To help students pursue a post-secondary education. **Focus:** General studies. **Qualif.:** Applicants must be high school seniors who are currently attending high school in Washington and also residents of the state of Washington. **Criteria:** Recipients will be chosen based on excellence in writing and eloquence in addressing the essay topic.

Funds Avail.: $1,000 to $3,000. **Number Awarded:** 3. **To Apply:** Applicants must submit an essay. It should be four-to-five pages, typewritten and double-spaced, original and should pertain to any subject within the scope of the topic. Applicants must also provide a cover sheet with the name and contact information. **Deadline:** March. **Contact:** Applications should be submitted to Cathy Nordstrom, 1511 State Ave. NE, Olympia, WA 98506.

9520 ■ WSAJ Diversity Bar Preparation Scholarships *(Undergraduate/Scholarship)*

Purpose: To assist diverse individuals in covering the tuition cost of a bar preparation course. **Focus:** Law. **Qualif.:** Applicants must be individuals who are underrepresented in the legal profession based on disability, gender identity and expression, race, ethnicity, religion and sexual orientation who will take the Washington State bar exam in July 2011 or February 2012. **Criteria:** Applicants will be chosen based on qualifications and submitted materials.

Funds Avail.: No specific amount. **Number Awarded:** Varies. **To Apply:** Applicants must submit a resume and a brief essay (not to exceed two pages, typed and double-spaced). Additional documents that will support the application are accepted. **Deadline:** March. **Contact:** Questions can be forwarded to brandi@washingtonjustice.org.

9521 ■ WSAJ Presidents' Scholarships *(Undergraduate/Scholarship)*

Purpose: To support and encourage the efforts of high school students who have overcome obstacles to pursue their education. **Focus:** General studies. **Qualif.:** Applicants must be high school senior students who are residents of the state of Washington. **Criteria:** Winners will be selected based on the following criteria: 1) demonstrated academic achievements and planned advancement toward a degree in an institution of higher learning; 2) documented need for financial assistance; 3) history of achievement despite disability; 4) record of commitment in helping needy people or protecting the rights of injured persons; 5) plan or commitment to apply the education in helping people; and 6) residency.

Funds Avail.: Amount not specified. **To Apply:** Applicants must submit all high school and community college academic transcripts; name, address and telephone numbers of two references, at least one of which must be outside the school environment; a brief written financial statement; and any other documentation that will support the application. Applicants are also required to send a letter to the scholarship committee describing the qualifications and explaining the reasons why they deserve the scholarship. **Deadline:** March. **Contact:** Applications should be submitted to Cathy Nordstrom, 1511 State Ave. NE, Olympia, WA 98506.

9522 ■ Washington State Business Education Association

c/o Jackie Floetke
Wilson Creek, WA 98860
E-mail: lfinn@wwps.org
URL: www.wsbea.org

9523 ■ Dr. F. Ross Byrd Scholarships *(Graduate, Vocational/Occupational/Scholarship)*

Purpose: To provide financial support to those students who are in need. **Focus:** Business. **Qualif.:** Applicants must be graduate students with a minimum of one quarter or one semester of graduate classes to complete. Applicants must be pursuing an advanced degree in business education or a related education field (Vocational Administration, Business & Marketing, Curriculum, etc.). **Criteria:** Preference will be given to those who meet the criteria.

Funds Avail.: No specific amount. **To Apply:** Applicants must submit a completed application form and 3 letters of recommendation, one of which must be from a member of

Awards are arranged alphabetically below their administering organizations

the student's graduate advisory committee, another one from a local vocational director/vocational administrator/administrator, and one from a member of WSBEA. **Deadline:** May 1. **Contact:** Jackie Floetke, WSBEA Scholarship Committee at PO Box 138 Wilson Creek, WA 98860.

9524 ■ Doris Y. and John J. Gerber Scholarships *(Undergraduate/Scholarship)*

Purpose: To provide financial assistance to those students who are in need. **Focus:** Business. **Qualif.:** Applicants must be junior or senior students majoring in Business Education. Applicants must be nominated by their advisor who is a current dues-paying member of WSBEA. **Criteria:** Preference will be given to those who meet the criteria.

Funds Avail.: No specific amount. **To Apply:** Applicants must inquire online for the application process. **Deadline:** December 1. **Contact:** Jackie Floetke, WSBEA Scholarship Committee at PO Box 138 Wilson Creek, WA 98860.

9525 ■ Washington State Lake Protection Association (WALPA)
PO Box 4245
Seattle, WA 98194
Ph: (206) 263-6242
E-mail: info@walpa.org
URL: www.walpa.org

9526 ■ WALPA Lake Scholarships *(Graduate, Undergraduate/Scholarship)*

Purpose: To support undergraduate and graduate students in their pursuit of degrees specializing in the fields of Environmental Science. **Focus:** Environmental Science. **Qualif.:** Applicants must be enrolled as part or full time undergraduate or graduate students in an accredited college or university in Washington or Idaho and be completing course work or research related to biology, hydrology, ecology and management or restoration of lakes and watersheds in Washington and Idaho. **Criteria:** Selection will be based on the quality of research topic, its significance to the fields of Environmental Science, particularly limnology and hydrology, and relevance to the applicant's interests and career goals.

Funds Avail.: $750-$1,000. **Number Awarded:** 2. **To Apply:** Applicants must provide a statement of interests, including: research interests and explain why their research is of importance to the field of limnology and/or watershed management, career goals, and intended use of scholarship funds (one-page limit); a one-page resume; and recent transcripts of all college/university course work. A recommendation from someone in the applicant's field of study is encouraged, but not required. Completed application packet must be sent to: Frank M. Wilhelm, Department of Fish and Wildlife Resources, University of Idaho, PO Box 441136, Moscow ID 83844-1136. **Deadline:** April 27. **Contact:** Frank M. Wilhelm, fwilhelm@uidaho.edu.

9527 ■ Washington State Nurses Association
575 Andover Pk. W, Ste. 101
Seattle, WA 98188
Ph: (206) 575-7979
Fax: (206) 575-1908
E-mail: wsna@wsna.org
URL: www.wsna.org

9528 ■ Washington State Nurses Association Foundation Scholarships (WSNF) *(Graduate, Undergraduate/Scholarship)*

Purpose: To support the education of students preparing for a career as registered nurses in Washington State. **Focus:** Nursing. **Qualif.:** Applicant must be an undergraduate student enrolled in an approved program leading to an associate or baccalaureate nursing degree, and must have completed at least 12 nursing credits (Credits from LPN programs do not apply towards the 12 completed credits); or a graduate student enrolled in an approved graduate nursing program. Applicant must be either a resident of Washington State or enrolled in an approved RN program in Washington State. Licensed RN applicant must be a WSNA member. **Criteria:** Selection is based on academic performance, nursing leadership, school and community involvement, professional activities and commitment to WSNA.

Funds Avail.: $1,000. **Number Awarded:** 4. **To Apply:** Applicant must submit a completed WSNF Scholarship application form along with the official transcript and two completed Applicant Recommendation forms from two current nursing instructors. **Deadline:** February 11.

9529 ■ Washington University Law School
Campus Box 1120
One Brookings Dr.
Saint Louis, MO 63130-4899
Ph: (314) 935-6400
Fax: (314) 935-8778
E-mail: eckricheckrich@wulaw.wustl.edu
URL: www.law.wustl.edu

9530 ■ Buder Scholarships for American Indian Law Students *(Undergraduate/Scholarship)*

Purpose: To provide financial assistance to law students. **Focus:** Law. **Qualif.:** Applicants must be American Indian Law students. **Criteria:** Recipient selection will be based on demonstrated potential for success in law school as evidenced by undergraduate academic performance.

Funds Avail.: No specific amount. **To Apply:** Applicants must submit an application letter and other requirements to the office.

9531 ■ Walter Moran Farmer Scholarships *(Undergraduate/Scholarship)*

Purpose: To provide financial assistance to public service students who wish to continue their education. **Focus:** Public service. **Qualif.:** Applicants must be the first generation of their families to attend college or graduate school. **Criteria:** Recipient selection will be based on intellectual, leadership and community service achievement; demonstrated commitment of bringing diverse people together; and demonstrated achievement in the face of personal challenges.

Funds Avail.: No specific amount. **To Apply:** Applicants must submit the application letter and other requirements.

9532 ■ Washington University Law School Chancellor's Graduate Fellowships *(Graduate/Fellowship)*

Purpose: To provide encouragement as well as financial support to students interested in careers as college or university professors. **Focus:** Arts; Business; Social Work;

Awards are arranged alphabetically below their administering organizations

Engineering; Law. **Qualif.:** Applicants must be graduate students who are interested in becoming college or university professors. **Criteria:** Recipients will be selected based on potential contributions to the diversity of graduate education at Washington University.

Funds Avail.: $27,500. **To Apply:** Applicants may download an application form from the website. **Deadline:** January 15.

9533 ■ Washington University Law School Olin Fellowships for Women *(Graduate/Fellowship)*

Purpose: To provide financial assistance to women who wish to have careers in higher education. **Focus:** Architecture; Art; Business; Engineering; Medicine; Social Work. **Qualif.:** Applicants must be women. **Criteria:** Recipients will be selected based on the committee's review of all applications.

Funds Avail.: No specific amount. **To Apply:** Applicants must submit a completed application form; a one-page information form; a curriculum vitae; an essay; three letters of recommendation; a transcript; and test scores. **Deadline:** February 1. **Contact:** Office of Admissions, Campus Box 1120, One Brookings Dr., St. Louis, MO 63130-4899; 314-935-4525.

9534 ■ Webster Society Scholarships *(Undergraduate/Scholarship)*

Purpose: To provide financial assistance to public service students who wish to continue their education. **Focus:** Public service. **Qualif.:** Applicants must be entering first-year JD students with exemplary academic credentials and an established commitment to public service. **Criteria:** Selection will be based on academic merit.

Funds Avail.: $5,000. **To Apply:** Interested applicants should write a short statement summarizing their involvement in public service activities. **Deadline:** February 1.

9535 ■ Water Environment Federation (WEF)
601 Wythe St.
Alexandria, VA 22314-1994
Ph: (703) 684-2400
Fax: (703) 684-2492
Free: 800-666-0206
E-mail: jeger@wef.org
URL: www.wef.org

9536 ■ WEF Canham Graduate Studies Scholarships *(Graduate/Scholarship)*

Purpose: To provide financial assistance to post-baccalaureate students in the water environment field. **Focus:** Water resources. **Qualif.:** Applicants must be members of the Water Environment Federation; must be pursuing post-baccalaureate degrees in the water environment field; must have practical experience. Recipients are expected to make a commitment to work in the water environment field for two years following the completion of the degree. **Criteria:** Selection will be based on evaluation of submitted documents and specific criteria.

Funds Avail.: $25,000. **To Apply:** Applicants must submit a completed application form providing a summary of academic and practical experience in the environmental field; official college/university transcripts; letter of acceptance to a graduate program in the water environment field; recommendations from three persons; detailed state-

ment of degree objectives as related to career goals and intent to work in the water environment field (750-1000 words). **Deadline:** March 1. **Remarks:** The scholarship is for education related expenses such as room and board, tuition and books. The scholarship may not be used to cover stipends or wages. **Contact:** Materials should be submitted to awards@wef.org.

9537 ■ Water and Sewer Distributors of America (WASDA)
100 N 20th St., 4th Fl.
Philadelphia, PA 19103-1443
Ph: (215) 320-3882
Fax: (215) 564-2175
E-mail: wasda@fernley.com
URL: www.wasda.com

9538 ■ Matt Stager Memorial Scholarship Fund *(Undergraduate/Scholarship)*

Purpose: To promote the waterworks/wastewater products distribution industry; to improve the image of WASDA and the industry. **Focus:** General studies. **Qualif.:** Applicant must have been employed by a company which was or is a regular Member of WASDA; must have an office in Canada, United States or Puerto Rico; must have knowledge in distribution selling in waterworks, and sewer or storm drainage pipes. **Criteria:** Recipients will be selected based on the review of all application materials submitted.

Funds Avail.: No specific amount. **To Apply:** Applicants must prepare a one-page detailed narrative description of the academic plans for the future and the career goals; must attach two letters of recommendation from teachers who are not related or members of the Matt Stager Scholarship Section Committee who have knowledge in academic achievements and who are able to comment on the academic motivation and character; must have a WASDA member contact verify parent's employment; have the Counselor fill out the counselor's report; submit the required scores and forward all requirements to the WASDA Headquarters. **Deadline:** April 2.

9539 ■ Watson-Brown Foundation
310 Tom Watson Way
Thomson, GA 30824
Ph: (706) 595-8886
Fax: (706) 595-3948
E-mail: tbrown@watson-brown.org
URL: www.watson-brown.org

9540 ■ Watson-Brown Scholarships *(Undergraduate/Scholarship)*

Purpose: To assist Georgia and South Carolina students with their educational pursuits. **Focus:** General studies. **Qualif.:** Applicants must be students from Georgia or South Carolina; must be high school seniors or current undergraduate students. **Criteria:** Scholarship recipients are selected based on merit and need.

Funds Avail.: $3,000 and $5,000. **Number Awarded:** Approximately 200. **To Apply:** Applicants must complete the online scholarship application and submit supporting documents (essay, financial need statement, letters of recommendation, high school/college transcript, IRS Form 1040 or 1040 EZ) which must be mailed separately. **Deadline:** February 15. **Contact:** Sarah Katherine McNeil, Director of

Awards are arranged alphabetically below their administering organizations

Scholarships and Alumni Relations, at skmcneil@watson-brown.org.

9541 ■ Jeannette K. Watson Fellowships (JKW)

11 Park Pl., Ste. 1503
New York, NY 10007
Ph: (212) 655-0201
Fax: (212) 843-0370
URL: www.jkwatson.org

9542 ■ Jeannette K. Watson Fellowships
(Undergraduate/Fellowship)

Purpose: To provide internships, mentoring, and enriched educational opportunities to promising New York City undergraduates with the goal of increasing their life choices and developing their capacity to make a difference in their own and other people's lives. **Focus:** Liberal arts. **Qualif.:** Applicant must be a second semester freshman or sophomore at one of the ten invited colleges namely: Baruch College; Brooklyn College; College of Staten Island; Hunter College; John Jay College; Lehman College; Long Island University, Brooklyn Campus; Marymount Manhattan College; Pace University, Manhattan Campus; Queens College; St. John's University; The City College of New York. Applicant must also have at least four semesters of full-time academic work remaining; be registered in a liberal arts track; demonstrate competence in college level work; below 25 years old on March; be an American citizen or "green card" holder. **Criteria:** Selection is based on the application materials submitted.

Funds Avail.: $5,000 for the first summer, $6000 for the second summer and $6000 for the third summer. **Number Awarded:** 15. **To Apply:** Applicants must submit a completed application form along with two letters of recommendation (sent directly to the Campus Representatives). **Deadline:** Applicants must consult the Watson Campus Representative at their college to find out the application deadline on their campus.

9543 ■ Thomas J. Watson Foundation (TJW)

11 Park Pl., Ste. 1503
New York, NY 10007
Ph: (212) 245-8859
Fax: (212) 245-8860
E-mail: tjw@watsonfellowship.org
URL: www.watsonfellowship.org

9544 ■ Thomas J. Watson Fellowships
(Graduate/Fellowship)

Purpose: To enhance the capacity of college graduates for resourcefulness, imagination, openness and leadership and to foster their humane and effective participation in the world community. **Focus:** General studies. **Qualif.:** Applicant must be eligible to graduate with a bachelor's degree from a participating institution by the end of the academic year; and must be nominated by that participating institution. Applicant must contact his/her college liaison for details. **Criteria:** Selection is based on submitted materials and the interview.

Funds Avail.: $25,000. **Number Awarded:** 50. **To Apply:** Applicants nominated by a participating college must submit a proposal for a project that is creative, feasible and personally significant; a personal statement; an application form; personal photo; a copy of transcript; and letters of recom-

mendation. All materials must be submitted electronically. **Deadline:** November 7. **Remarks:** Stipend will be $35,000 if accompanied by a spouse or dependent child.

9545 ■ Wayne County Foundation, Inc.

33 S 7th St.
Richmond, IN 47374
Ph: (765) 962-1638
Fax: (765) 966-0882
E-mail: steve@waynecountyfoundation.org
URL: www.waynecountyfoundation.org

9546 ■ Jonathan Alan Scholarship Fund
(Undergraduate/Scholarship)

Purpose: To promote various medical related purposes. **Focus:** Medical education. **Qualif.:** Applicants must be Richmond high school graduates who have plans to enter a medical field and must demonstrate financial need. **Criteria:** Recipients are selected based on academic standing and financial need.

Funds Avail.: No specific amount. **To Apply:** For further information about the application form and materials, applicants are advised to contact the Wayne County Foundation at the above address or visit the website.

9547 ■ Anonymous Scholarship Fund
(Graduate/Scholarship)

Purpose: To enhance education and careers in the music product industry. **Focus:** Music. **Qualif.:** Applicants must be graduates of Lincoln, Hagerstown, Northeastern, Seton, or Centerville high schools who are pursuing a degree in music. **Criteria:** Selection is based on submitted application and supporting documents.

Funds Avail.: No specific amount. **To Apply:** For further information about the application form and materials, applicants are advised to contact the Wayne County Foundation at the above address or visit the website.

9548 ■ Erika A. and George E. Brattain Sr. Scholarship Fund *(Undergraduate/Scholarship)*

Purpose: To financially support students in pursuing their education. **Focus:** Music. **Qualif.:** Applicants must be Lincoln High School graduating seniors who are pursuing an education in music. **Criteria:** Applicants are selected based on the criteria.

Funds Avail.: No specific amount. **To Apply:** For further information about the application form and materials, applicants are advised to contact the Wayne County Foundation at the above address or visit the website.

9549 ■ Ralph Burkhardt Scholarship Fund
(Undergraduate/Scholarship)

Purpose: To support orchestra students in pursuing their career in the music industry. **Focus:** Music. **Qualif.:** Applicants must be graduating Richmond High School seniors who have been outstanding orchestra students and intend to study music in college. **Criteria:** Selection will be based on the committee's criteria.

Funds Avail.: No specific amount. **To Apply:** For further information about the application form and materials, applicants are advised to contact teh Wayne County Foundation at the above address or visit the website.

9550 ■ Lucille Campbell Scholarship Fund
(Undergraduate/Scholarship)

Purpose: To assist graduating high school seniors of Wayne County obtain a higher education. **Focus:** General

Awards are arranged alphabetically below their administering organizations

studies. **Qualif.:** Applicants must be Wayne County high school graduating seniors. **Criteria:** Applicants are selected based on proof of eligibility and relative financial need.

Funds Avail.: No specific amount. **To Apply:** For further information about the application form and materials, applicants are advised to contact the Wayne County Foundation at the above address or visit the website.

9551 ■ Betty J. Cecere Memorial Scholarship Endowment Fund *(Undergraduate/Scholarship)*

Purpose: To provide opportunities for deserving young people to achieve a higher education. **Focus:** General studies. **Qualif.:** Applicants must be Richmond High School graduating female seniors. **Criteria:** Selection will be based on the committee's criteria.

Funds Avail.: No specific amount. **To Apply:** For further information about the application form and materials, applicants are advised to contact the Wayne County Foundation at the above address or visit the website.

9552 ■ Centerville-Abington Dollars for Scholars *(Undergraduate/Scholarship)*

Purpose: To provide financial assistance to those students who are in need. **Focus:** General studies. **Qualif.:** Applicants must be students who want to pursue their education beyond high school. **Criteria:** Preference will be given to those who meet the criteria.

Funds Avail.: No specific amount. **To Apply:** For further information about the application form and materials, applicants are advised to contact the Wayne County Foundation at the above address or visit the website.

9553 ■ Jason Chaney Memorial Scholarship Fund *(Undergraduate/Scholarship)*

Purpose: To provide scholarship assistance to male student who wants to pursue his education. **Focus:** General studies. **Qualif.:** Applicants must be Hagerstown High School graduating male seniors. **Criteria:** Scholarship recipient will be selected based on scholastic ability.

Funds Avail.: No specific amount. **To Apply:** For further information about the application form and materials, applicants are advised to contact the Wayne County Foundation at the above address or visit the website.

9554 ■ Melba Dawn Chiarenza Scholarship Fund *(Undergraduate/Scholarship)*

Purpose: To provide financial assistance for Lincoln High School graduates. **Focus:** Business; Nursing; Drama criticism. **Qualif.:** Applicants must be Lincoln High School graduates who plan to obtain a degree in business, nursing, or drama. **Criteria:** Applicants will be evaluated based on criteria designed by the Scholarship Selection Committee.

Funds Avail.: No specific amount. **To Apply:** For further information about the application form and materials, applicants are advised to contact the Wayne County Foundation at the above address or visit the website.

9555 ■ Niqui McCown Honor and Memorial Scholarship Fund *(Undergraduate/Scholarship)*

Purpose: To support the needy student who is deeply committed to the law and criminal justice. **Focus:** Law; Criminal justice. **Qualif.:** Applicants must be graduating seniors of Richmond High School who intend to pursue careers relating to the law or criminal justice. **Criteria:** Selection of applicants will be based on the moral character and academic achievements.

Funds Avail.: No specific amount. **To Apply:** For further information about the application form and materials, applicants are advised to contact the Wayne County Foundation at the above address or visit the website.

9556 ■ Nixon Family Scholarship Fund *(Undergraduate/Scholarship)*

Purpose: To assist students pursuing a degree in engineering, technology or related fields. **Focus:** Engineering; Technology. **Qualif.:** Applicants must be graduating seniors of Centerville High School; must have completed a two-year course of vocational study at the Whitewater Technical Career in Computer Assisted Design, Precision Machining, Welding, Electricity, Construction, or Project Lead the Way Programs. **Criteria:** Applicants are judged based on financial need.

Funds Avail.: $500. **Number Awarded:** 4. **To Apply:** For further information about the application form and materials, applicants are advised to contact teh Wayne County Foundation at the above address or visit the website.

9557 ■ Reid Hospital Graduate Student Scholarships *(Graduate/Scholarship)*

Purpose: To provide scholarship opportunities and assistance for students engaged in practical nursing, pharmacy, physical therapy, occupational therapy, speech and language pathology, and medicine. **Focus:** Health care services. **Qualif.:** Applicants must be pursuing a graduate degree at an accredited university or college; must be enrolled full-time and must be fifth year or greater graduate students; must be residents of one of the following Indiana counties: Wayne, Fayette, Henry, Randolph, or Union or residents of one of the following Ohio counties: Darke or Preble. **Criteria:** Preference will be given to those who meet the criteria.

Funds Avail.: $2,500. **To Apply:** Applicants must complete the application form available online; must provide an official transcript of grades and letter of recommendation from a professor, guidance counselor, or dean of program that they have known for at least one year; must submit a two-page maximum statement including: their future plans, why they should be selected for the scholarship, and what inspired them to the health care profession. **Deadline:** March 31. **Contact:** Andrea Stuckey at the above address.

9558 ■ Rob and Bessie Welder Wildlife Foundation

c/o Dr. D. Lynn Drawe, Dir.
Sinton, TX 78387
Ph: (361) 364-2643
Fax: (361) 364-2650
E-mail: welderfoundation@welderwildlife.org
URL: www.welderwildlife.org

9559 ■ Welder Wildlife Foundation Fellowships *(Doctorate, Graduate/Fellowship)*

Purpose: To promote the education of exceptionally qualified students and provide research information to manage wildlife populations. **Focus:** Animal science and behavior; Biology; Botany; Conservation of natural resources; Ecology; Genetics; Ornithology; Veterinary science and medicine; Wildlife conservation, management, and science. **Qualif.:** Applicant must be a graduate student having a

Awards are arranged alphabetically below their administering organizations

research interest related to wildlife management and conservation or a closely related area. To be eligible for financial support, a student must have a minimum GRE score of 1100 (verbal plus quantitative) and a "B" average in the last two years of undergraduate or graduate work. **Criteria:** Selection is based on the submitted proposals.

Funds Avail.: 1,400/month for MS candidates, and $1,600/month for PhD candidates; travel allowance of $1,200/year or $100/month. **To Apply:** Applicants must submit a completed proposal which includes: objectives, background and relevance, study site, methods, analytical procedures, itemized budget, timetable, and a biographical data and degree sought by the application. Materials concerning the proposed Scholarship recipient should include: Biographical data, degree sought, three letters of recommendation, complete academic record, GRE score (verbal and quantitative). **Deadline:** September 1.

9560 ■ Wenner-Gren Foundation

470 Park Ave. S
New York, NY 10016
Ph: (212) 683-5000
Fax: (212) 683-9151
E-mail: inquiries@wennergren.org
URL: www.wennergren.org

9561 ■ Hunt Postdoctoral Fellowships
(Doctorate/Fellowship)

Purpose: To support basic research in anthropology. **Focus:** Anthropology. **Qualif.:** Applicants must have received a PhD or equivalent within ten years of the application deadline. Qualified scholars are eligible without regard to nationality or institutional or departmental affiliation. **Criteria:** The main criteria of evaluation are the quality of the research and its potential contribution to anthropological knowledge, theory and debate.

Funds Avail.: $40,000. **Number Awarded:** 8. **To Apply:** The Foundation operates an online application submission procedure. All application forms and other required application materials must be submitted online. If it is not possible to submit an application online because of inadequate internet access in applicant's country of origin, applicant must notify the Foundation at least one week before the deadline to arrange a submission of application by conventional mail. In addition to online submission, five printed copies of the application form and other required materials must be sent to the Foundation. **Deadline:** May 1 and November 1.

9562 ■ Wadsworth International Fellowships
(Graduate/Fellowship)

Purpose: To support basic anthropological research into humanity's biological and cultural origins, development and variation. **Focus:** Anthropology. **Qualif.:** Applicants must be from countries where anthropology is underrepresented and where there are limited resources to send students overseas for training; must be under 35 years of age at the time they begin their fellowship; must have a Host Sponsor who holds an academic position at the Host Institution and in the department where the applicant will be registered. **Criteria:** Priority is given to applicants who have not already earned a prior degree from an institution outside of their home country and have not already begun their graduate training outside of their home country.

Funds Avail.: $17,500. **To Apply:** The Foundation operates an online application submission procedure. All ap-

plication forms and other required application materials must be submitted online. If it is not possible to submit an application online because of inadequate internet access in applicant's country of origin, applicant must notify the Foundation at least one week before the deadline to arrange a submission of application by conventional mail. In addition to online submission, two printed copies of the application materials must also be mailed to the Foundation. **Deadline:** March 1. **Contact:** Questions can be emailed to internationalprograms@wennergren.org.

9563 ■ Wenner-Gren Foundation Dissertation Fieldwork Grants *(Doctorate/Grant)*

Purpose: To support basic research in anthropology. **Focus:** Anthropology. **Qualif.:** Applicants must be students enrolled in a doctoral program (or equivalent, if applying from outside the United States) at the time of application. Qualified doctoral students are eligible without regard to nationality or institutional or departmental affiliation. **Criteria:** The main criteria of evaluation are the quality of the research and its potential contribution to anthropological knowledge, theory and debate.

Funds Avail.: $20,000. **To Apply:** The Foundation operates an online application submission procedure. All application forms and other required application materials must be submitted online. If it is not possible to submit an application online because of inadequate internet access in applicant's country of origin, applicant must notify the Foundation at least one week before the deadline to arrange a submission of application by conventional mail. **Deadline:** May 1 and November 1.

9564 ■ Wenner-Gren Foundation Post-PhD Research Grants *(Doctorate/Grant)*

Purpose: To support basic research in anthropology. **Focus:** Anthropology. **Qualif.:** Applicants must be individuals holding a PhD or equivalent degree. Qualified scholars are eligible without regard to nationality or institutional or departmental affiliation. **Criteria:** The main criteria of evaluation are the quality of the research and its potential contribution to anthropological knowledge, theory, and debate.

Funds Avail.: $20,000. **To Apply:** The Foundation operates an online application submission procedure. All application forms and other required application materials must be submitted online. If it is not possible to submit an application online because of inadequate internet access in applicant's country of origin, applicant must notify the Foundation at least one week before the deadline to arrange a submission of application by conventional mail. In addition to online submission, five printed copies of the application form and other required materials must be sent to the Foundation. **Deadline:** May 1 and November 1. **Contact:** Application form and supporting documents can be submitted electronically to applications@wennergren.org.

9565 ■ West Virginia Coal Association

PO Box 3923
Charleston, WV 25339
Ph: (304) 342-4153
E-mail: braney@wvcoal.com
URL: www.wvcoal.com

9566 ■ Friends of Coal Scholarships
(Undergraduate/Scholarship)

Purpose: To provide a strong and dependable infrastructure for the continued mining of West Virginia coal. **Focus:**

Awards are arranged alphabetically below their administering organizations

General studies. **Qualif.:** Applicants must be high school honor graduates; must have high GPA's in high school; must be living in West Virginia. **Criteria:** Recipients are selected based on academic performance and financial need.

Funds Avail.: $2,500. **To Apply:** Applicants must submit a filled-out application form.

9567 ■ West Virginia Congress of Parents and Teachers (WV PTA)

PO Box 3557
Parkersburg, WV 26103
Ph: (304) 420-9576
Fax: (304) 420-9577
E-mail: wv_office@pta.org
URL: www.wvpta.net

9568 ■ West Virginia PTA Scholarships
(Undergraduate/Scholarship)

Purpose: To support the education of WV students. **Focus:** General studies. **Qualif.:** Applicants must be high school seniors in a WV school; and have at least 2.0 grade point average. **Criteria:** Selection is based on the overall presence of the essay and application; volunteer service; honors received; extracurricular activities; GPA, ACT and SAT scores.

Funds Avail.: $500. **To Apply:** Applicant's must submit five sets (one original, four copies) of high school transcripts; (one-page) three letters of recommendation; ACT and SAT scores; and (one-page, double-spaced) essay reflecting long-term goals. Applications must have notarized signatures of parents, guardians and students. **Deadline:** February 15. **Contact:** Leigh Temple, Committee Chair at 304-229-3687, or 304-420-9576.

9569 ■ West Virginia Hospitality and Travel Association (WVHTA)

PO Box 2391
Charleston, WV 25328
Ph: (304) 342-6511
Fax: (304) 345-1538
E-mail: carol@wvhta.com
URL: www.wvhta.com

9570 ■ West Virginia Educational Foundation Hospitality Business Alliance Scholarships
(Undergraduate/Scholarship)

Purpose: To complete the educational pathway already underway in West Virginia. **Focus:** Travel and tourism. **Qualif.:** Applicants must be prostart and lodging management program high school senior students who plan to enroll in a hospitality degree program. Applicants must be West Virginia residents and may be planning to attend out-of-state schools. **Criteria:** Recipients are selected based on academic performance and financial need.

Funds Avail.: $2,000. **To Apply:** Applicants must submit a completed application form.

9571 ■ West Virginia Hospitality and Travel Association General Scholarships *(Undergraduate/Scholarship)*

Purpose: To complete the educational pathway already underway in West Virginia. **Focus:** Travel and tourism.

Qualif.: Applicants must be graduating seniors in a West Virginia High School; must have a minimum grade point of average of 2.75 on a 4.0 scale; must have performed a minimum of 250 hours of hospitality and travel industry related work experience; must have applied to a hospitality, travel, or recreation management program in a post-secondary institution, either full-time or substantial part-time with the intent to enroll in a minimum of 2 terms. **Criteria:** Recipients are selected based on academic performance, industry-related work experience, strength of letters of recommendation, content, style, and required essay question and presentation of application.

Funds Avail.: $1,000. **To Apply:** Applicants must submit a typed or neatly printed application; an official transcript from high school attended; proof of hospitality and travel-related work experience with a minimum of 250 hours verified by copies of paycheck stubs or letters from employer stipulating number of hours worked; one letter of recommendation on letterhead from a current/previous employer; and acceptance letter from the post-secondary institution. **Deadline:** March 31. **Contact:** To request a hard copy of the application, applicants must call 304-345-1588.

9572 ■ Western Aquatic Plant Management Society (WAPMS)

Cygnet Enterprises, Inc.
5040 Commercial Cir., Ste. E
Concord, CA 94520
Free: 800-530-0885
E-mail: aaustel@cygnetenterprises.com
URL: www.wapms.org

9573 ■ Barbara H. Mullin Memorial Scholarships *(Graduate, Undergraduate/Scholarship)*

Purpose: To support students in the pursuit of a degree in aquatic sciences. **Focus:** Biology; Ecology; Fisheries sciences/management **Qualif.:** Applicants must be current undergraduate or graduate students in an accredited college or university in the western United States; must be engaged in coursework or research related to the biology, ecology, management, or education of aquatic plants. **Criteria:** Recipients will be selected based on submitted materials.

Funds Avail.: $2,000. **To Apply:** Applicants must provide a short resume/curriculum vitae, transcripts of college/university coursework (unofficial is acceptable), statement that describes the intended use of scholarship funds, applicable collaborators and career goals and two letters of support. **Deadline:** March. **Contact:** Application materials should be submitted electronically to Dr. Scott Nissen at snissen@lamar.colostate.edu.

9574 ■ Western Golf Association (WGA)

1 Briar Rd.
Golf, IL 60029-0301
Ph: (847) 724-4600
Fax: (847) 724-7133
URL: www.westerngolfassociation.com

9575 ■ Chick Evans Caddie Scholarships
(Undergraduate/Scholarship)

Purpose: To help caddies to pursue education. **Focus:** General studies. **Qualif.:** Applicant must be caddies nominated by their club and have caddied, successfully

Awards are arranged alphabetically below their administering organizations

and regularly, for a minimum of two years and also expected to caddie or work at their sponsoring club during the summer prior to the application; have completed junior year of high school with above B average in college preparatory courses and are required to take the ACT; have clearly established their need for financial assistance; and have an outstanding character. **Criteria:** Scholarship Committee will select finalist and will conduct an interview.

Funds Avail.: Full-tuition. **To Apply:** Caddies must be nominated by their respective clubs. **Deadline:** September 30.

9576 ■ Western Michigan Society of Health-System Pharmacists (WMSHP)

Brad Miller, Sec.
8835 Summerset Woods Ct. SE
Alto, MI 49302
Ph: (616) 881-3061
E-mail: webmaster@wmshp.net
URL: www.wmshp.net

9577 ■ Western Michigan Society of Health-System Pharmacists Scholarships
(Undergraduate/Scholarship)

Purpose: To develop community and health-system pharmacists, technicians and students. **Focus:** Pharmacy. **Qualif.:** Applicants must be in good standing with the College of Pharmacy; must be natives or current residents of the Western Michigan area. **Criteria:** Recipients are selected based on demonstrated interest in health-system pharmacy and involvement in or leadership positions with professional organizations.

Funds Avail.: $1,000. **Number Awarded:** 1. **To Apply:** Applicants must complete the application form. **Deadline:** March 31. **Contact:** Applications must be submitted to Kali Schulz, 200 Jefferson Ave. SE, Grand Rapids, MI 49503.

9578 ■ Western Social Science Association (WSSA)

Yuma Branch Campus - NAU
Yuma, AZ 85366-6236
Ph: (928) 317-6475
Fax: (928) 317-6419
E-mail: larry.gould@nau.edu
URL: wssa.asu.edu

9579 ■ WSSA Students Paper Competition
(Undergraduate/Award)

Purpose: To encourage undergraduate and graduate students to present their research papers. **Focus:** General studies. **Qualif.:** Both undergraduate and graduate students are eligible for the award. **Criteria:** Submitted papers will be judged based on 1) advancement of knowledge; 2) appropriateness for a broad social science audience; 3) quality and implementation of the research design; 4) definition and significance of topic; 5) analysis of findings and discussion of their implications; and, 6) clarity and cogency of writing.

Funds Avail.: $500 and a plaque. **To Apply:** Paper should not exceed 25 pages and must be double-spaced in 12 pt. Arial font. Applicants must provide an abstract (not to exceed 200 words) with the title of the paper but not the author(s)/affiliation(s). **Deadline:** January. **Contact:** Papers

must be submitted to Thomas Isern, Professor, Dakota State University, Department of History, Putnam 20, Fargo ND 58102, 701-799-2942 or e-mail at thomas.isern@ndsu.edu.

9580 ■ Western Society of Criminology (WSC)

c/o California State University
Department of Criminal Justice
1250 Bellflower Blvd.
Long Beach, CA 90840
E-mail: secretary-treasurer@westerncriminology.org
URL: westerncriminology.org

9581 ■ Libby Deschenes Prize for Applied Research *(Undergraduate/Prize)*

Purpose: To recognize criminology or criminal justice students. **Focus:** Criminal justice; Criminology. **Qualif.:** Applicants must be students interested in criminal justice or criminology field of study. **Criteria:** Award will be given to students who have demonstrated commitment in improving policy, practice, or programs in criminal justice through research or the application of research.

Funds Avail.: Amount not specified. **To Apply:** Applicants must contact WSC office for further information and other required documents.

9582 ■ June Morrison Scholarship Fund
(Undergraduate/Scholarship)

Purpose: To financially assist undergraduate students and help defray the cost of attending the annual meeting. **Focus:** Criminal justice; Criminology. **Qualif.:** Applicants must be criminal justice students or individuals who are interested in criminology field. **Criteria:** Recipients will be selected based on submitted materials.

Funds Avail.: Amount not specified. **To Apply:** Applicants must submit a paper and must contact WSC office for further information and other required documents.

9583 ■ Miki Vohryzek-Bolden Student Paper Awards *(Undergraduate/Award)*

Purpose: To recognize undergraduate students who are involved in criminal justice or criminology field. **Focus:** Criminal justice; Criminology. **Qualif.:** Applicants must be criminal justice students or individuals who are interested in criminology field. **Criteria:** Recipients will be selected based on submitted materials.

Funds Avail.: Amount not specified. **To Apply:** Applicants must submit an original manuscript and must contact WSC office for further information and other required documents.

9584 ■ Western Society of Weed Science

205 W Boutz, Bldg. 4, Ste. 5
Las Cruces, NM 88005
Ph: (575) 527-1888
E-mail: wsws@marathonag.com
URL: www.wsweedscience.org

9585 ■ Western Society of Weed Science Outstanding Student Scholarship Program
(Doctorate, Graduate, Undergraduate/Scholarship)

Purpose: To encourage new weed science research and future weed science careers. **Focus:** General studies; Agricultural sciences. **Qualif.:** Applicants must be under-

Awards are arranged alphabetically below their administering organizations

graduate or graduate students enrolled in a degree program (B.S., M.S., or PhD) at an accredited college or university in the western region. Applicants must be current WSWS members at the time of application. **Criteria:** Applicants will be evaluated based on contribution of research to the discipline of weed science and to the WSWS objectives, academic record and scholarly achievements, potential contributions to the future of weed science, and participation in extracurricular pursuits contributing to the advancement on any of the following: weed science, natural resource management, and/or education and mentoring

Funds Avail.: A total of $3,000. **Number Awarded:** 3. **To Apply:** Applicants must submit a completed and signed Application Form; one-page cover letter describing how applicant became interested in weed science, how applicant's research will contribute to the field of weed science and the WSWS objectives, and what future contributions applicant hopes to make to the field of weed science including career goals; 1 or 2-page resume highlighting recent relevant experience through school, work and/or internships; abstract submitted for paper or poster presentation at WSWS annual meeting; two letters of support, at least one of which must be from a college/university faculty member (preferably major advisor) familiar with the applicant's abilities, interests, and career goals; academic transcripts (unofficial copy is acceptable). Completed application must be submitted to: Dr. Frank Young, USDA-ARS, Rm. 161 Johnson Hall, Washington State University, Pullman, WA 99164. **Deadline:** November 1. **Contact:** Dr. Joe DiTomaso, Email: jmditomaso@ucdavis.edu.

9586 ■ Western Washington University Alumni Association

516 High St.
Bellingham, WA 98225
Ph: (360) 650-3353
Fax: (360) 650-6555
Free: 800-676-6885
E-mail: alumni@wwu.edu
URL: www.alumniconnections.com/olc/pub/WWH

9587 ■ Why Get Your Blue On? Video Scholarships *(Graduate, Undergraduate/Award, Scholarship)*

Purpose: To support current, full-time students enrolled at Western Washington University. **Focus:** General studies. **Qualif.:** Contestant must be a current, full-time student at Western Washington University, and must have a valid user account with YouTube. **Criteria:** Scholarship Committee will take into consideration the following factors when evaluating the video submission: Creativity: Originality, uniqueness, and ingenuity demonstrated in the video; Relevance: How well the video related to wearing the blue and WWU.

Funds Avail.: One Grand Prize: $1,000 non-renewable scholarship award; One Second Place Prize: $500 non-renewable scholarship award; One Third Place Prize: $250 non-renewable scholarship award. **To Apply:** Contestants must create a 5 minute (or less) video response to the question, "Why Get Your Blue On?". Submit a completed Official Entry Form, after successfully uploaded the video on YouTube. **Deadline:** December 10.

9588 ■ Wexner Foundation

8000 Walton Pkwy., Ste. 110
New Albany, OH 43054

Ph: (614) 939-6060
E-mail: info@wexnerfoundation.org
URL: www.wexnerfoundation.org

9589 ■ Wexner Graduate Fellowships/Davidson Scholars *(Graduate/Fellowship)*

Purpose: To encourage promising candidates to successfully meet the challenges of professional Jewish leadership in the North American Jewish community. **Focus:** Jewish studies; Religion. **Qualif.:** Applicant must be entering (and not already matriculated in) a degree granting graduate program, based in North America, that will allow him/her to pursue a career as a professional Jewish leader in North America and commit to doing so, and must be between the ages of 21 and 40 upon entering the graduate program. Applicant who is not a citizen of a North American country must have documentation that allows him/her to study and to work in that country. **Criteria:** Selection is based on applicant's strong personal commitment to the Jewish community; demonstrated excellence in academic achievement; and possess the potential to provide outstanding professional leadership that will shape the future of Jewish communal life in North America.

Funds Avail.: $20,000. **To Apply:** Applicants must complete the application online. In addition, applicants must submit academic transcripts (undergraduate and, if applicable, graduate); scores from the General Test of the Graduate Record Examination (Institution No. 3134); three letters of recommendation; and confirmation letter or acceptance letter. **Deadline:** February 11. **Remarks:** Established in 1988. **Contact:** Or Mars at omars@wexner.net or Linda Smith at lsmith@wexner.net.

9590 ■ Weyburn Credit Union

PO Box 1117
Weyburn, SK, Canada S4H 2L3
Ph: (306) 842-6641
Free: 800-567-8111
E-mail: info@weyburn.cu.sk.ca
URL: www.weyburncu.ca

9591 ■ C.H.(Chuck) Hodgson Scholarships *(Undergraduate/Scholarship)*

Purpose: To provide financial assistance to graduated high school students who want to pursue their college education. **Focus:** General studies. **Qualif.:** Applicants must be recently graduated grade 12 students under age 21 who have been out of High School for at least one year; must be member of Weyburn Credit Union; must be enrolled full time (3 or more classes) at the Southeast Regional College. **Criteria:** Scholarships will be awarded on the basis of academic excellence, good citizenship and effort.

Funds Avail.: $500. **To Apply:** Applicants must submit the following: application form; resume; a brief description of any clubs, groups, organizations, etc. in which they are involved, what the group achieved and, most important, what part they played, time which they invested in working with the group and what they contributed to the group's success. On an individual level, applicants should include: any individual achievements over the past years and how they achieved them; how and why they chose their particular area of post-secondary study; applicants' future goals and ambitions. Applicants must also include letters of reference. These letters should come from people who can give a good evaluation and recommendation of the ap-

Awards are arranged alphabetically below their administering organizations

plicants' character (i.e. school counsellors, principals, homeroom teachers, youth leaders, part-time employer; or any other individual). The application may include as many letters of reference as applicants wish. **Deadline:** December 15.

9592 ■ Q.O.(Quint) Patrick Scholarships
(Undergraduate/Scholarship)

Purpose: To provide financial assistance to graduated high school students who want to pursue their college education. **Focus:** General studies. **Qualif.:** Applicants must be mature students, defined as someone age 21 or older; must be member of Weyburn Credit Union; must be enrolled full time (3 or more classes) at the Southeast Regional College. **Criteria:** Scholarship will be awarded on the basis of academic excellence, good citizenship and effort.

Funds Avail.: $500. **To Apply:** Applicants must submit the following: application form; resume; a brief description of any clubs, groups, organizations, etc. in which they are involved, what the group achieved and, most important, what part they played, time which they invested in working with the group and what they contributed to the group's success. On an individual level, applicants should include: any individual achievements over the past years and how they achieved them; how and why they chose their particular area of post-secondary study; applicants' future goals and ambitions. Applicants must also include letters of reference. These letters should come from people who can give a good evaluation and recommendation of the applicants' character (i.e. school counsellors, principals, homeroom teachers, youth leaders, part-time employer; or any other individual). The application may include as many letters of reference as applicants wish. **Deadline:** December 15.

9593 ■ RS Williamson and Eliford Mott Memorial Scholarships *(Undergraduate/Scholarship)*

Purpose: To provide financial assistance to graduating high school students. **Focus:** General studies. **Qualif.:** Applicants must be graduating students from a high school within the Weyburn Credit Union defined trade area; applicants or the parents of the applicants must be members of Weyburn Credit Union. **Criteria:** Scholarships will be awarded on the basis of academic excellence, good citizenship and effort.

Funds Avail.: $1,000. **Number Awarded:** Three. **To Apply:** Applicants must submit the following: application form; resume; a brief description of any clubs, groups, organizations, etc. in which they are involved, what the group achieved and, most important, what part they played, time which they invested in working with the group and what they contributed to the group's success. On an individual level, applicants should include: any individual achievements over the past years and how they achieved them; how and why they chose their particular area of post-secondary study; applicants' future goals and ambitions. Applicants must also include letters of reference. These letters should come from people who can give a good evaluation and recommendation of the applicants' character (i.e. school counsellors, principals, homeroom teachers, youth leaders, part-time employer; or any other individual). The application may include as many letters of reference as applicants wish. **Deadline:** June 1.

9594 ■ Helen Hay Whitney Foundation
20 Squadron Blvd., Ste. 630
New City, NY 10956
Ph: (845) 639-6799
Fax: (845) 639-6798
E-mail: hhwf@earthlink.net
URL: www.hhwf.org

9595 ■ Helen Hay Whitney Foundation Fellowships *(Doctorate, Graduate/Fellowship)*

Purpose: To increase the number of imaginative, well-trained and dedicated medical scientists. **Focus:** Biomedical research. **Qualif.:** Applicants must hold, or are in the final stages of obtaining a PhD, MD, or equivalent degree and are seeking beginning postdoctoral training in basic biomedical research. Applicants must have no more than one year of postdoctoral research experience at the time of the deadline; or should have received a PhD (or D.Phil. or equivalent) degree no more than two years before the deadline, or an M.D. degree no more than three years before the deadline. **Criteria:** Selection is based on the quality of the application materials submitted.

Funds Avail.: $49,000-$51,000/year, and a research allowance of $2,500/year. **To Apply:** Applicants are required to fill out and submit applications online. **Deadline:** July 16. **Remarks:** There is a Dependent Child Allowance of $1,000/year for each child.

9596 ■ Elie Wiesel Foundation for Humanity
555 Madison Ave., 20th Fl.
New York, NY 10022
Fax: (212) 490-6006
URL: www.eliewieselfoundation.org

9597 ■ Elie Wiesel Prize in Ethics
(Undergraduate/Prize)

Purpose: To allow students to, through their writing, explore their concerns, beliefs, fears and hopes. **Focus:** General studies. **Qualif.:** Applicants must be full-time undergraduate juniors and seniors at accredited four-year colleges and universities in the United States. **Criteria:** Selection will be based on the committee's criteria.

Funds Avail.: 1st Prize-$5,000; 2nd Prize-$2,500; 3rd Prize-$1,500; Two Honorable Mentions-$500 each. **To Apply:** Applicants must submit the essays following the suggested essay topics. Essay format must be in 3,000 to 4,000 words, may be written in the formal or informal voice, but an individual voice should be evident. Essay should be developed from the applicant's point of view and may take the form of an analysis that is biographical, historical, literary, philosophical, sociological or theological. Essay must be the original, unpublished work of one student, have a title, and typed in 12-point font in English, double-spaced with 1″ margins and numbered pages. Applicants must submit the following: three copies of essay (one copy paper-clipped and two stapled); completed Entry Form (signed by both the student and faculty sponsor); and a letter on school stationery from the Registrar's Office, verifying the applicant's eligibility. **Deadline:** December 6.

9598 ■ Wild Felid Research and Management Association (WFA)
PO Box 3335
Montrose, CO 81402
Ph: (970) 252-1928
E-mail: lsweanor@gmail.com
URL: www.wildfelid.com

Awards are arranged alphabetically below their administering organizations

9599 ■ Wild Felid Legacy Scholarships
(Graduate/Scholarship)

Purpose: To encourage and support graduate students involved in wild felid research. **Focus:** Wildlife conservation, management, and science. **Qualif.:** Applicants must be student members of the Wild Felid Research and Management Association; must have completed a Bachelor of Science or Arts Degree and be enrolled in a graduate program in wildlife biology; wildlife management or any related natural resource field. **Criteria:** Applicants will be evaluated based on demonstrated need for financial aid; participation in a research project that aims to improve our understanding of wild felid biology, management and/or conservation; undergraduate and graduate GPA.

Funds Avail.: $1,000. **To Apply:** Applicants must submit a completed application form; current resume; Bachelor's Degree transcript; graduate studies transcript or copy of acceptance letter into a graduate program in wildlife biology, wildlife management or any related natural resource fields; two reference letters from professor and supervisor; short essay (500-750 words) describing interests in wild felid research, career goals and usage of award to further professional development, demonstration of financial need. **Deadline:** May. **Contact:** Dr. Marcella Kelly, Associate Professor, Department of Fisheries and Wildlife, Virginia Tech, 146 Cheatham Hall, Blacksburg, VA 24061-0321 or e-mail at makelly2@vt.edu.

9600 ■ The Wilderness Society (TWS)
1615 M St. NW
Washington, DC 20036
Ph: (202) 833-2300
Fax: (202) 429-8443
Free: 800-843-9453
E-mail: action@tws.org
URL: www.wilderness.org

9601 ■ Gloria Barron Wilderness Society Scholarships *(Graduate/Scholarship)*

Purpose: To encourage individuals who have the potential to make a significant positive difference in the long term protection of wilderness in North America. **Focus:** Conservation of natural resources. **Qualif.:** Applicant must be enrolled in an accredited graduate institution in North America; have strong academic qualifications; and have academic and/or career goals focused on making a significant positive difference in the long-term protection of wilderness in North America. **Criteria:** Selection is based on submitted application materials.

Funds Avail.: $10,000. **To Apply:** Applicants must submit a two-page double-spaced cover letter; a 3-5 page double-spaced proposal; a current resume or curriculum vitae; two letters of recommendation describing the applicant's ability to meet the objectives of the scholarship and proposed work; and undergraduate and graduate transcripts (official or unofficial). **Deadline:** March 31. **Contact:** Christine Soliva at barron_scholarship@tws.org.

9602 ■ Wilkinson & Company LLP
PO Box 757
Belleville, ON, Canada K8N 5B5
Ph: (613) 966-5105
Fax: (613) 962-7072
Free: 888-728-3890

URL: www.wilkinson.net

9603 ■ Wilkinson & Company LLP Secondary School Scholarships *(Undergraduate/Scholarship)*

Purpose: To provide financial support for students. **Focus:** Business-related course. **Qualif.:** Applicants must have highest mark in business-related course. **Criteria:** Priority will be based on scholastic records.

Funds Avail.: $300. **To Apply:** Applicants must submit a completed application form. **Contact:** hrdept@wilkinson.net.

9604 ■ Willamette University
900 State St.
Salem, OR 97301
Ph: (503) 370-6300
URL: www.willamette.edu

9605 ■ Melvin Henderson-Rubio Scholarships
(Undergraduate/Scholarship)

Purpose: To provide financial support to individuals who wish to pursue their studies. **Focus:** General studies. **Qualif.:** Applicants must be minority students who have plans to enroll from a home address in the greater Los Angeles area. **Criteria:** Applicants will be selected based on academic credentials and financial need.

Funds Avail.: $5,000. **Number Awarded:** 1. **To Apply:** For more information about the scholarship, applicants must contact the Office of Financial Aid. **Contact:** E-mail at gradaid@willamette.edu.

9606 ■ Mary Stuart Rogers Scholarships
(Undergraduate/Scholarship)

Purpose: To provide financial support to individuals who wish to pursue their studies. **Focus:** General studies. **Qualif.:** Applicants must be enrolled as full-time students and have 3.0 GPA to be considered. **Criteria:** Applicants will be selected based on academic credentials; strength in service; leadership and financial need.

Funds Avail.: $4,000. **Number Awarded:** 14. **To Apply:** For more information about the scholarship, applicants must contact the Office of Financial Aid.

9607 ■ The Williams Chorale
c/o Herb Ellison
27 S Lakeview Rd.
Norton, MA 02766
Ph: (508) 285-4661
E-mail: thewilliamschorale@verizon.net
URL: www.thewilliamschorale.org

9608 ■ Williams Chorale Bacardi Fallon Performing Arts Scholarships *(Undergraduate/ Award, Scholarship)*

Purpose: To help area high school juniors or seniors in their pursuit of a musical education. **Focus:** Education, Music. **Qualif.:** Applicant must be a high school junior or senior pursuing musical education. **Criteria:** Selection is based on the application recording.

Funds Avail.: 1st Prize: $5000; 2nd prize: $2000; 3rd prize: $1000; Director's Choice: $500; All other finalists: $300. **To Apply:** Application recording must include at least 5

Awards are arranged alphabetically below their administering organizations

minutes of total playing time and must include at least two movements of contrasting style. All recording submissions must be on compact discs. **Deadline:** March 15. **Contact:** Peter J. Williams at the above address.

9609 ■ John G. Williams Foundation

PO Box 1229
Camp Hill, PA 17001-1229
Ph: (717) 795-9880
Fax: (717) 795-1002
E-mail: amgrpmld@aol.com
URL: www.jgwfoundation.org

9610 ■ John G. Williams Scholarship Fund
(Undergraduate/Scholarship)

Purpose: To provide financial assistance to Pennsylvania residents for their pursuit of college, post-graduate, and/or professional education opportunities, in courses and at educational institutions that they select and that are acceptable to the Board of Trustees. **Focus:** General studies. **Qualif.:** Applicants must be residents of Pennsylvania; must be high school graduates and enrolled full-time; must have a minimum GPA of 3.0 or its equivalent. Applicants must have been accepted by an institution of higher learning before making application for assistance. Application may be made at any time during a student's undergraduate or graduate career. **Criteria:** Recipients are selected based on demonstrated financial need, personal initiative and civic responsibility.

Funds Avail.: No specific amount. **To Apply:** Applicants must complete the standard financial need and financial aid form; must submit a transcript of grades for the most recent academic year; must provide evidence of acceptance and attendance by a college or graduate school and two character recommendations. **Deadline:** June 15.

9611 ■ Woodrow Wilson International Center for Scholars

1 Woodrow Wilson Plz.
1300 Pennsylvania Ave. NW
Washington, DC 20004-3027
Ph: (202) 691-4000
E-mail: wwics@wilsoncenter.org
URL: www.wilsoncenter.org

9612 ■ Woodrow Wilson International Center for Scholars Fellowships *(Doctorate/Fellowship)*

Purpose: To support individuals conduct an independent research on national and/or international issues addressing key public policy challenges. **Focus:** General studies. **Qualif.:** Applicants must be citizens or permanent residents from any country. Foreign nationals must be able to hold a valid passport and obtain a J1 Visa; men and women with outstanding capabilities and experience from a wide variety of backgrounds, including government, the corporate world, professions and academia; academic candidates holding a PhD; academic candidates demonstrating scholarly achievement by publications beyond their doctoral dissertations; practitioners or policymakers with an equivalent level of professional achievement; be English proficiency as the Center is designed to encourage the exchange of ideas among its fellows. **Criteria:** Fellowships will be awarded on a competitive basis. Selection will be based on the following criteria: significance of the proposed research, including

the importance and originality of the project; quality of the proposal in definition, organization, clarity and scope; capabilities and achievements of the applicants and the likelihood that they will accomplish the proposed project; the relevance of the project to contemporary policy issues; potential as a fellow, including what is the applicant's potential for participating in the life and priorities of the Center and its outreach in fulfilling its mission.

Funds Avail.: No specific amount. **To Apply:** Applicants may submit their applications online. If submitted by mail, a complete application must include the following: a two-page, single-sided Fellowship application form; not to exceed three page list of applicant's publications that include exact titles, names of the publishers, dates of publication and status of forthcoming publications; not to exceed five single-spaced typed pages, using 12-point, typed project proposal; maximum of three pages of bibliography for the project that includes primary sources and relevant secondary sources; and a one-page Financial Information Form. All application materials must be submitted in English. Two reference letters must be submitted directly to the Center by the referees or mailed with the application. **Deadline:** October 1. **Contact:** fellowships@wilsoncenter.org.

9613 ■ Woodrow Wilson National Fellowship Foundation (WWNFF)

PO Box 5281
Princeton, NJ 08543-5281
Ph: (609) 452-7007
Fax: (609) 452-0066
E-mail: communications@woodrow.org
URL: www.woodrow.org

9614 ■ Leonore Annenberg Teaching Fellowships *(Graduate/Fellowship)*

Purpose: To support the development of future leaders at a variety of career stages in several critical fields. **Focus:** Education, Secondary. **Qualif.:** Applicants must be recent college graduates and career-changers who agree to work in urban and rural secondary schools serving high proportions of disadvantaged students. **Criteria:** Selection will be based on the committee's criteria.

Funds Avail.: $30,000. **To Apply:** Applicants may visit the website for further details and application information. **Contact:** Debbie Lynch, wwteachingfellowships@woodrow.org.

9615 ■ Doris Duke Conservation Fellows Program *(Graduate/Fellowship)*

Purpose: To support future conservation leaders. **Focus:** General studies; Conservation of natural resources. **Qualif.:** Applicants must be students enrolled in master's program at eight universities - Yale, Duke, Cornell, Florida A&M University, Northern Arizona University and the universities of Michigan, Wisconsin, and California at Santa Barbara. **Criteria:** Selection will be based on the committee's criteria.

Funds Avail.: No specific amount. **To Apply:** Interested applicants may contact Nolan Yamashiro for application process. **Contact:** Nolan Yamashiro, 609-452-7007; yamashiro@woodrow.org.

9616 ■ MMUF Dissertation Grants *(Doctorate/Grant)*

Purpose: To provide graduate students at the critical juncture of completing their graduate degrees with support

Awards are arranged alphabetically below their administering organizations

to spend a year finishing the writing of the dissertation. **Focus:** General studies. **Qualif.:** Applicants must be Mellon Mays Undergraduate Fellows and candidates for the PhD degree in the fields recognized under the terms of the Mellon Mays Undergraduate Fellowship Program. Candidates must have completed all pre-dissertation requirements preceding the application deadline. Specifically, each applicant must have passed all comprehensive examination, completed all coursework for the degree, received approval of the dissertation topic, and completed most or all of the fieldwork and/or research necessary to begin writing. **Criteria:** Selection will be based on the committee's criteria.

Funds Avail.: $20,000. **To Apply:** Applications must include the following: a three-page prospectus; a draft dissertation chapter; a three-page personal statement; an official graduate transcript; two letters of recommendation - one from the dissertation director and one from another academic knowledgeable about the Fellow's academic performance and/or familiar with the Fellow's dissertation project and its contribution to the field of scholarship; official budget form; a declaration of previous fellowship awards. **Contact:** Caryl McFarlane, Asst. Dir., mmufdis@woodrow.org.

9617 ■ MMUF Travel and Research Grants
(Doctorate/Grant)

Purpose: To provide eligible graduate students with the financial means to complete their research prior to the start of dissertation writing. **Focus:** General studies. **Qualif.:** Applicants must be Mellon Mays Undergraduate Fellows and candidates for the PhD degree in the fields recognized under the terms of the Mellon Mays Undergraduate Fellowship Program. All candidates must have passed all comprehensive examinations, completed all course work for the degree, and selected a dissertation topic that has been approved by the dissertation advisor. **Criteria:** Selection will be based on the committee's criteria.

Funds Avail.: $5,000. **To Apply:** Applications must include the following: official application form; a resume; a personal statement as outlined in the application; an official budget form (funding may be applied to travel to research sites, cost of meals and lodging at research sites, photocopying or microfilming of documents, purchase of access to research databases, fees for use of research facilities, and other research-related expenses); an official graduate transcript; and a brief letter of recommendation (two-page maximum) from the dissertation advisor endorsing the request for funding. **Deadline:** March 22. **Contact:** Caryl McFarlane, Asst. Dir., mmufdis@woodrow.org.

9618 ■ Charlotte W. Newcombe Doctoral Dissertation Fellowships *(Doctorate/Fellowship)*

Purpose: To encourage original and significant study of ethical or religious values in all fields of the humanities and social sciences. **Focus:** Humanities; Social sciences. **Qualif.:** Applicants must be candidates of PhD or ThD degrees in doctoral programs at graduate schools in the US; must be able to fulfill all pre-dissertation requirements by the application deadline, including approval of the dissertation proposal; be in the writing stage of the dissertation. Usually, this means that fieldwork or other research is complete and writing has begun by the time of the award; have never held a similar national award for the final year of dissertation writing; plan to write on topics where ethical or religious values are a central concern; have never applied for the Fellowship before. **Criteria:** Selection will be based on the committee's criteria.

Funds Avail.: $25,000. **Number Awarded:** 20. **To Apply:**

Applications must be filed using the online form. A completed application comprises the online application from , two letters of recommendation, and a current transcript. Included in the online application are these five required narrative components: an abstract, a full proposal, a selected bibliography, a timetable for completion, three letters of recommendation, and transcript. **Deadline:** November 15. **Contact:** Susan Billmaier, 609-452-7007 or e-mail at billmaier@woodrow.org.

9619 ■ Thomas R. Pickering Graduate Foreign Affairs Fellowships *(Graduate/Fellowship)*

Purpose: To provide funding to participants as they are prepared academically and professionally to enter the United States Department of State Foreign Service. **Focus:** International affairs and relations; Public administration; Business; Economics; Political science; Sociology; Foreign languages. **Qualif.:** Applicants must be US citizens at the time of application; must have a minimum undergraduate GPA of 3.2 or higher on a 4.0 scale; must be seeking admission to graduate school for the following year; demonstrate financial need. Winners are expected to enroll in a two-year, full-time master's degree program in either public policy, international affairs, or public administration, or in an academic field such as business, economics, political science, sociology, or foreign languages (US graduate institutions only). **Criteria:** Selection will be based on the committee's criteria.

Funds Avail.: $40,000. **To Apply:** Completed application includes both an online application form, which requires secure registration at the Woodrow Wilson Foundation Web site, and a series of hard-copy supporting documents, as follows: Certification of US citizenship (copy of US passport, birth certificate, or US citizen naturalization papers); copy of GRE scores; two letters of recommendation; official academic transcripts from every undergraduate school attended; two page resume. In addition, all applicants who received financial aid must also provide a copy of their most recent financial aid letter that list grants or loans. Applicants must also provide a copy of the Student Aid Report (SAR), which indicates the Estimated Family Contribution number. **Deadline:** February 7. **Contact:** Dr. Richard O. Hope, PO Box 2437 Princeton, NJ 08543-2437; pickeringgfaf@woodrow.org.

9620 ■ Woodrow Wilson Dissertation Fellowships in Women's Studies *(Graduate/Fellowship)*

Purpose: To support original, significant, interdisciplinary doctoral dissertations on women's issues. **Focus:** Women's studies. **Qualif.:** Candidates must have completed all pre-dissertation requirements; must be writing on issues related to women, gender, women's studies or feminist/gender/LGBTQ theory; must be enrolled in a graduate school in the United States; expected to complete the PhD by summer 2011. **Criteria:** Applications will be judged on originality and significance to women's studies, scholarly validity, the applicant's academic preparation and ability to accomplish the work, and whether the dissertation will be completed within a reasonable time period.

Funds Avail.: $2,000. **To Apply:** Applications must be filed using the online form. A completed application comprises the online application from , two letters of recommendation, and a current transcript. Included in the online application are these five required narrative components: an abstract, a full proposal, a selected bibliography, a timetable for completion, and a statement of commitment to women's studies. **Deadline:** October 11. **Contact:** Susan Billmaier, 609-452-7007 or e-mail at billmaier@woodrow.org.

Awards are arranged alphabetically below their administering organizations

9621 ■ Woodrow Wilson-Rockefeller Brothers Fund Fellowships for Aspiring Teachers of Color *(Graduate/Fellowship)*

Purpose: To support the development of future leaders at a variety of career stages in several critical fields. **Focus:** Education, Secondary. **Qualif.:** Applicant must: be a person of color (African American/Black, Asian, Hispanic, Latino(a), Native American) in his/her senior year of undergraduate preparation; be nominated by an eligible nominating institution; demonstrate a commitment to the program and its goals; have US citizenship or permanent residency; expect to attain a bachelor's degree by June 30, 2011; have substantial background in the arts and sciences and high academic performance with a cumulative undergraduate GPA of 3.0 or better on a 4.0 scale (negotiable for applicants from institutions that do not employ a 4.0 GPA scale); not currently in a teacher preparation program which leads to initial teacher certification. **Criteria:** Selection will be based on the committee's criteria.

Funds Avail.: $30,000. **To Apply:** Applicants must visit the website for application and registration. Information required on the application includes: educational background; preference(s) of master's program(s); two 500-word essays; contact information for the two recommenders you've asked to write letters for you; personal information; additional information. In addition to online application, applicants must submit a resume, two recommendations, and official transcripts. **Deadline:** October 15.

9622 ■ Winston-Salem Foundation
860 W Fifth St.
Winston-Salem, NC 27101-2506
Ph: (336) 725-2382
Fax: (336) 727-0581
E-mail: info@wsfoundation.org
URL: www.wsfoundation.org

9623 ■ William H. Andrews/HAWS Scholarships
(Undergraduate/Scholarship)

Purpose: To assist graduating high school seniors and adults in their studies. **Focus:** General studies. **Qualif.:** Applicants must be graduating high school seniors or adults wishing to continue in post-secondary education; must be residents living in a property owned or managed by HAWS; must have cumulative GPA of 2.0 at the time of initial application; and must demonstrate evidence of community involvement or school activities including any awards or leadership roles. **Criteria:** Recipients are selected based on the committee's review of applications.

Funds Avail.: $500-$1,000. **To Apply:** Applicants must download and complete the online application form; must submit a signed certification signature page; graduating high school seniors must provide a grade transcript through first semester of 12th grade. **Deadline:** April 15. **Contact:** Questions regarding this scholarship should be directed to WSF Student Aid Department by calling 336-714-3445 or e-mail at studentaid@wsfoundation.org.

9624 ■ Chester Arzell and Helen Miller Montgomery Scholarships *(Undergraduate/ Scholarship)*

Purpose: To graduating high school seniors from Stokes County public high schools. **Focus:** General studies. **Qualif.:** Applicants must have a minimum, cumulative, unweighted GPA of 2.0; participate in community service;

demonstrate good character; participate in extracurricular activities; demonstrate financial need. **Criteria:** Selection will be based on the committee's criteria.

Funds Avail.: $1,000. **To Apply:** Scholarship applications are available online or in the guidance offices of the three Stokes county high schools. **Deadline:** April 1. **Contact:** Questions regarding this scholarship should be directed to WSF Student Aid Department by calling 336-714-3445 or e-mail at studentaid@wsfoundation.org.

9625 ■ F.A. and Charlotte Blount Scholarships
(Undergraduate/Scholarship)

Purpose: To assist graduating high school students of Forsyth County. **Focus:** General studies. **Qualif.:** Applicants must be graduating Forsyth County high school students who will pursue a baccalaureate degree at an accredited college or university; must be African American or Hispanic; must demonstrate a minimum cumulative unweighted GPA of 3.0; must demonstrate financial need, however, the scholarship is not restricted to lowest family incomes. **Criteria:** Preference will be given to minority students.

Funds Avail.: $750. **To Apply:** Applicants must submit a completed application form; grade transcript through first semester of the 12th grade; and one recommendation. **Deadline:** March 31. **Contact:** Winston-Salem Foundation at the above address.

9626 ■ Sam L. Booke, Sr. Scholarships
(Undergraduate/Scholarship)

Purpose: To encourage students to pursue careers in the Mathematics field. **Focus:** Mathematics and mathematical sciences. **Qualif.:** Applicants must be graduating seniors from public high schools in the Winston-Salem/Forsyth County School; must demonstrate interest in Mathematics. **Criteria:** Recipients are selected based on: evidence of excellence in Mathematics through both course selection and grades; intent to pursue a career in Mathematics; potential to achieve career goal; evidence of scholarship including appropriate selection of high school curriculum and academic standing; evidence that students have shown interest and concern for being members of the society.

Funds Avail.: $1,000. **To Apply:** Applicants must complete online application form. Applicants must also submit one teacher recommendation from math teacher; and official high school grade transcript (through at least first semester of the 12th grade and including SAT scores and class rank). **Deadline:** April 15. **Contact:** Questions regarding this scholarship should be directed to WSF Student Aid Department by calling 336-714-3445 or e-mail at studentaid@ wsfoundation.org.

9627 ■ Tien Bui Memorial Scholarships
(Undergraduate/Scholarship)

Purpose: To assist graduating high school seniors who have attended the Winston-Salem/Forsyth County Schools' Career Center. **Focus:** General studies. **Qualif.:** Applicants must: demonstrate a minimum cumulative GPA of 3.5; must have strong SAT scores and challenging academic course selection as graduating high school seniors; must demonstrate financial need (award not restricted to lowest family income); have attended the Winston-Salem/Forsyth County Schools' Career Center during their high school and successfully completed either advanced placement in Math or Science. **Criteria:** Recipients are selected based on the committee's review of application materials.

Funds Avail.: $1,000. **To Apply:** Scholarship applications

Awards are arranged alphabetically below their administering organizations

are available online. Applicants must complete the Tien Bui Memorial Scholarship application; must submit grade transcript through 1st semester of 12th grade; submit letter of acceptance from NCSU that specifies enrollment in the College of Engineering; and must submit a signed certification signature page. **Deadline:** April 15. **Contact:** Questions regarding this scholarship should be directed to WSF Student Aid Department by calling 336-714-3445 or e-mail at studentaid@wsfoundation.org.

9628 ■ Wes Burton Memorial Scholarships
(Undergraduate/Scholarship)

Purpose: To assist graduating high school seniors of Mt. Tabor High School. **Focus:** Mathematics and mathematical science; Computer and information sciences; Business administration; Engineering. **Qualif.:** Applicants must have a minimum GPA of 3.5; must demonstrate community and school service; must have an intent to pursue a career in Mathematics, Computer Science, Business Administration, or Engineering; demonstrate financial need (award is not restricted to lowest family incomes). **Criteria:** Award is given based on the committee's criteria.

Funds Avail.: $500. **To Apply:** Student must complete the application in its entirety and include supplemental items and information requested in the various sections of the application. The supplemental items include: an interview with the Foundation; a grade transcript; a resume or list of student activities; one letter of recommendation from a math teacher, business teacher, or computer science teacher. **Deadline:** April 15. **Contact:** Questions regarding this scholarship should be directed to WSF Student Aid Department by calling 336-714-3445 or e-mail at studentaid@wsfoundation.org.

9629 ■ Andrew Blake Clark Memorial Scholarships *(Undergraduate/Scholarship)*

Purpose: To provide college scholarships to worthy graduating high school seniors at Mt. Tabor High School. **Focus:** General studies. **Qualif.:** Applicants must be graduating seniors at Mt. Tabor High School. **Criteria:** Selection will be based on the academic promise, financial need, and school and/or community leadership.

Funds Avail.: $1,000. **To Apply:** Students interested in being considered for the scholarship award should submit the following to Stan Huck in the Mt. Tabor Guidance Office: transcript of high school courses through 1st semester 12th grade; high school resume; personal statement describing accomplishments and future plans. **Deadline:** April 4. **Contact:** WSF Student Aid Department, 336-714-3445.

9630 ■ Elmer and Rosa Lee Collins Scholarships *(Undergraduate/Scholarship)*

Purpose: To provide a college scholarship to a worthy graduating high school senior from a Forsyth County high school. **Focus:** General studies. **Qualif.:** Applicants must demonstrate character and purpose as evidenced in school, community, church, and work activities; academic success by achieving a minimum, unweighted, cumulative GPA of 3.5 with strong course selection; financial need (however, the scholarship is not restricted to lower family incomes); and must be US citizens. **Criteria:** Selection will be based on the committee's criteria.

Funds Avail.: $2,500. **To Apply:** Eligible high school seniors may complete an application online. Applicants are responsible for submitting the completed application and all supplemental items to the Foundation. Supplemental items include: grade transcript through the 1st semester of the

12th grade; one recommendation from a teacher, guidance counselor, coach, principal, employer, clergy, or other community leader who has supervised, counseled or coached applicant in some capacity. **Deadline:** April 15. **Contact:** WSF Student Aid Department, 336-714-3445.

9631 ■ Lloyd E. and Rachel S. Collins Scholarships *(Undergraduate/Scholarship)*

Purpose: To award scholarships to worthy graduating high school seniors from North, South, and West Stokes High Schools who will attend an accredited two or four-year college or university. **Focus:** General studies. **Qualif.:** Applicants must demonstrate academic achievement, participate in community service, demonstrate good character, participate in extracurricular activities, demonstrate financial need. **Criteria:** Selection will be based on the committee's criteria.

Funds Avail.: $1,000. **To Apply:** Applications for the scholarship are available in the guidance offices of the three Stokes County high schools. **Deadline:** April 1. **Remarks:** Established in 1991. **Contact:** WSF Student Aid Department, 336-714-3445.

9632 ■ D.C. Cornelius Memorial Scholarships *(Undergraduate/Scholarship)*

Purpose: To award scholarship to a graduating high school senior from Forbush High School. **Focus:** General studies. **Qualif.:** Applicants must demonstrate, character, leadership, compassion for all people and dedication to service of community and school. Applicants must have a minimum GPA of 2.8. Demonstration of financial need is preferred. Applicants must be U.S. citizens. **Criteria:** Award is given based on the committee's criteria.

Funds Avail.: $1,000. **To Apply:** Scholarship applications will be available in the guidance office at Forbush High School and also online. Students must complete the application in its entirety; include grade transcripts with the application at time of submittal; and include recommendations with the application. **Deadline:** April 15. **Contact:** Contact Forbush High School guidance office at 336-961-4644.

9633 ■ Serena D. Dalton Scholarships *(Undergraduate/Scholarship)*

Purpose: To provide financial aid for needy students. **Focus:** General studies. **Qualif.:** Applicants must have adjusted gross income within the table guidelines (table is based on up to 300% above the federal poverty level); be a resident of Forsyth County; must have achieved a current cumulative GPA of at least 2.0; must be enrolled a minimum of six credit hours/semester during the academic year in a program leading to a first time two or four year degree, certificate, or diploma from an accredited institution which participates in the federal student aid program; must be a US citizen. **Criteria:** Selection will be based on the committee's criteria.

Funds Avail.: No specific amount. **To Apply:** The following items are required to complete the application process: Submittal of completed application and signed signature page; Signed copy of parents'/guardians'/family's previous year's 1040, 1040A, or 1040EZ income tax return (for dependent students); Signed copy of applicant's previous year's tax return; Official high school grade transcript through at least 1st semester of the 12th grade or year-end college grade transcript, whichever is the most recent (request from the school's Registrar and forward to the Foundation); Copy of the Student Aid Report if applicant

Awards are arranged alphabetically below their administering organizations

has applied for federal aid; Copy of the financial aid award letter. Please submit the application on-line and follow with additional items as soon as you receive them. **Deadline:** August 15. **Contact:** WSF Student Aid Department, 336-714-3445.

9634 ■ Dean Prim Scholarships (Undergraduate/ Scholarship)

Purpose: To provide travel and college scholarships to high school juniors and seniors. **Focus:** General studies. **Qualif.:** Qualified candidates must be: at least 16 years of age; a high school junior or high school senior; must demonstrate excellence in schoolwork as evidenced by course selection and grades (minimum unweighted GPA of 3.0); must participate in extracurricular school activities, community and/or church activities, and school or community athletics; must demonstrate good character and show interest in and concern for being an active member of society; must be committed to traveling and studying in China and have the full support of parent(s) to participate. The scholarship is available to students regardless of race, sex, national, origin, or religion. **Criteria:** Selection will be based on the committee's criteria.

Funds Avail.: $500. **To Apply:** The Prim scholarship application is on The Winston-Salem Foundation's web site. It is the student's responsibility to make sure that, along with submittal for the electronic application completed in its entirety, all supplemental materials are in the office of The Winston-Salem Foundation by the deadline. Supplemental materials include: a grade transcript, through 10th grade for juniors and 11th grade for seniors; two recommendations as described in the application; a recent photograph (include student's name on back of photo); **Deadline:** October 31. **Contact:** WSF Student Aid Department, 336-714-3445.

9635 ■ Wade and Marcelene Duncan Scholarships (Undergraduate/Scholarship)

Purpose: to provide scholarships to worthy high school seniors graduating from either North Stokes or South Stokes High schools. **Focus:** General studies. **Qualif.:** Applicant must be a graduating senior from either North Stokes or South Stokes High School who will attend an accredited four-year educational institution. Applicants must demonstrate leadership, participate in community service, participate in athletics and be generally well-rounded. **Criteria:** The applications will be reviewed by the Wade and Marcelene Duncan Scholarship Fund Committee at each high school. Upon determination of the scholarship recipient each year, the selection committee will notify The Winston-Salem Foundation of that individual's name, address, college of choice, social security number, and telephone number.

Funds Avail.: $250. **To Apply:** Applications and all required materials must be delivered to your high school guidance office. Students should contact the guidance office at North Stokes High School or South Stokes High School to request applications. Applications are also available online. **Deadline:** March 31. **Contact:** North Stokes High School, 336-593-8134; South Stokes High School, 336-994-2995.

9636 ■ Forsyth County Nursing Scholarships (Undergraduate/Scholarship)

Purpose: To provide educational need-based scholarships for Forsyth County residents seeking nursing degrees at accredited two year and four year colleges and who will,

upon completing a degree, practice nursing in Forsyth County, N.C. Preference will be given to those seeking first-time associate or baccalaureate nursing degree. **Focus:** Nursing. **Qualif.:** Applicants must have a family adjusted gross income within the table guidelines (table is based on up to 330% above the federal poverty level); have achieved a current cumulative grade point average of at least 2.0; be a US citizen; be a child of a living or deceased Vietnam veteran; be a Forsyth County N.C. resident; and provide a letter of acceptance into a nursing program. **Criteria:** Selection will be based on the committee's criteria.

Funds Avail.: No specific amount. **To Apply:** The following items are required to complete the application process: Submittal of completed application and signed signature page; Signed copy of parents'/guardians'/family's previous year's 1040, 1040A, or 1040EZ income tax return (for dependent students); Signed copy of applicant's previous year's tax return; Official high school grade transcript through at least 1st semester of the 12th grade or college grade transcript, whichever is the most recent (request from the school's Registrar and forward to the Foundation); Copy of the Student Aid Report if applicant has applied for federal aid; Copy of the financial aid award letter. Please submit the application on-line and follow with additional items as soon as you receive them. **Deadline:** April 15. **Contact:** WSF Student Aid Department, 336-714-3445.

9637 ■ Denise Franklin Journalism Scholarships (Undergraduate/Scholarship)

Purpose: To provide a merit scholarship to a high school senior planning to pursue a career in journalism. **Focus:** Journalism. **Qualif.:** Students must have a minimum, unweighted, grade point average of 3.0. Applicants should have a minimum of two years involvement in a journalism project or involvement in two different types of journalistic media. Students of color with a strong academic record and desire to pursue a career in journalism are encouraged to apply. Applicant must be a US citizen. **Criteria:** Selection will be based on the committee's criteria.

Funds Avail.: $500. **To Apply:** Applicants must complete and submit an application online at the Foundation's Web site. In addition to submittal of the application, applicants must also provide the following to be considered: Provide a letter of recommendation from a current journalism instructor; Submit up to three samples of journalism work such as published newspaper articles, audio or videotapes, a website or a photo essay (samples will not be returned); High school grade transcript through first semester, 12th grade. **Deadline:** April 15. **Remarks:** Established in 2004. **Contact:** Edna Barker, 336-714-3445; Kay Dillon, 336-714-3446.

9638 ■ Gaddy Student Scholarships (Undergraduate/Scholarship)

Purpose: To give priority consideration to those students who will attend Davidson College or Wake Forest University. **Focus:** General studies. **Qualif.:** This renewable scholarship seeks to identify those students: who are graduating high school seniors from R.J. Reynolds High School; who demonstrate academic promise; who are US citizens; who have participated as athletes or in support positions in high school athletics (broad consideration); who have financial need (broad consideration given - not restricted to lower family incomes). **Criteria:** Selection will be based on the committee's criteria.

Funds Avail.: $1,000. **To Apply:** Students must provide

Awards are arranged alphabetically below their administering organizations

the following: A completed application; grade transcript through 1st semester, 12th grade; one recommendation as described in the application guidelines. Schedule an interview, if so advised. **Deadline:** April 15. **Remarks:** Established in 1997. **Contact:** WSF Student Aid Department, 336-714-3445.

9639 ■ Garden Club Council of Winston-Salem and Forsyth County Council (Undergraduate/Scholarship)

Purpose: To provide financial support for educational opportunities to legal residents of North Carolina who will attend a two and/or four year college and have been accepted into the Horticulture Technology or Landscape Architecture curriculums at Forsyth Technical Community College or other accredited post-secondary schools in North Carolina. **Focus:** Horticulture; Landscape architecture and design. **Qualif.:** Applicants must demonstrate academic potential; financial need; full-time attendance (minimum of 12 credit hours/semester); pursuit of undergraduate associate or baccalaureate degree (first-time degrees preferred); must be US citizens. The scholarship is renewable for a second consecutive year if student maintains a cumulative college GPA of 2.0, continues full-time enrollment and continues in horticulture or landscape architecture; otherwise, scholarship is forfeited. Available to traditional and non-traditional age students. **Criteria:** Applicants will be evaluated based on qualifications, academic standing and demonstrated financial need.

Funds Avail.: No specific amount. **To Apply:** Application must be completed and submitted with all required materials to the Student Aid Department at The Winston-Salem Foundation. Supplemental materials listed on the last page of the application include previous year's federal tax return for student and parent, if student is a dependent; academic year-end grade transcript; Federal Student Aid Report; federal award notice and interview with student aid staff. **Deadline:** August 15. **Contact:** Edna Barker, 336-714-3445; Kay Dillon, 336-714-3446; E-mail: studentaid@wsfoundation.org.

9640 ■ L. Gordon, Jr. and June D. Pfefferkorn Scholarships (Undergraduate/Scholarship)

Purpose: To award worthy graduating high school seniors in Forsyth County. **Focus:** General studies. **Qualif.:** Applicants must: attend an accredited four-year college or university in North Carolina; be a resident of Forsyth County; have achieved a current cumulative, unweighted GPA of at least 3.5; demonstrate significant promise in leadership, community service, and school service; be US citizens; demonstrate financial need, (award not restricted to lowest family incomes); be graduating high school seniors. **Criteria:** Selection will be based on the committee's criteria.

Funds Avail.: No specific amount. **To Apply:** The following items are required to complete the application process: submittal of completed application and signed signature page; signed copy of parents'/guardians'/ family's previous year's 1040, 1040A, 1040EZ income tax return; signed copy of applicant's previous year's tax return; official high school grade transcript through at least 1st semester of the 12th grade; one recommendation from a teacher, guidance, coach, principal, employer, clergy, or other community leader who has supervised, counseled or coached applicant in some capacity. **Deadline:** April 15. **Contact:** WSF Student Aid Department, 336-714-3445.

9641 ■ Claude B. Hart Memorial Scholarships (Undergraduate/Scholarship)

Purpose: To award scholarship to worthy graduating high school seniors from Elkin High School who are US citizens. **Focus:** Mathematics and mathematical sciences; Engineering. **Qualif.:** Applicants must demonstrate significant promise in academics, leadership, community service and school service and intend to major in mathematics (accounting, computer science, business administration) and/or engineering (mechanical, civil, chemical, etc.) in college. Demonstration of financial need is preferred, but award is not restricted to lowest family incomes. Renewal of the award after the first year will require that the student be a full-time undergraduate student at an accredited four-year institution, maintain a minimum cumulative grade point average of 2.5, and continue to major in mathematics or engineering. **Criteria:** Selection will be based on the committee's criteria.

Funds Avail.: No specific amount. **To Apply:** Scholarship applications will be provided in the guidance office at Elkin High School. Student must complete the application, requested transcripts, and financial information before being considered by the Elkin High School Scholarship Committee. The Scholarship Committee will submit up to 5 candidates to The Winston-Salem Foundation for review by the Elkin Advisory Committee or its appointed subcommittee. **Deadline:** April 1. **Contact:** WSF Student Aid Department by calling 336-714-3445 or e-mail at studentaid@wsfoundation.org.

9642 ■ Oliver Joel and Ellen Pell Denny Healthcare Scholarship Fund (Undergraduate/Scholarship)

Purpose: To provide grants to the North Carolina residents pursuing education in the allied health fields. **Focus:** Health care services. **Qualif.:** Applicants must be seeking a two or four year degree or be enrolled in a program leading to a certificate or diploma; be attending an accredited North Carolina school pursuing healthcare education such as, but not limited, registered nursing, licensed practical nursing, nuclear medicine, radiography, and respiratory therapy; provide an acceptance letter for all programs; have a high school/college cumulative GPA of at least 2.5 for all healthcare programs, including nursing. Students must be North Carolina residents and US citizens. Preference will be given to those living in Forsyth, Davidson, Davie, Stokes, Surry, and Yadkin counties. **Criteria:** Selection will be based on the committee's criteria.

Funds Avail.: $1,200. **To Apply:** The Winston-Salem Foundation's General Financial Aid Application will be used to apply for this scholarship. The General Financial Aid Applications are available in high school guidance office and on the website. **Deadline:** August 15. **Contact:** WSF Student Aid Department, 336-714-3445.

9643 ■ Stella B. Johnson Scholarships (Undergraduate/Scholarship)

Purpose: To provide educational aid for college to qualified traditional and non-traditional age applicants from charitable funds established by generous supporters of the community. **Focus:** General studies. **Qualif.:** Applicants must: have a family adjusted gross income within the table guidelines (table is based on up to 330% above the federal poverty level); be residents of Forsyth County; have achieved a current cumulative grade point average of at least 2.0; must be enrolled a minimum of six credit hours/semester during the academic year in a program leading to

Awards are arranged alphabetically below their administering organizations

a first time two or four year degree, certificate, or diploma from an accredited institution which participates in the federal student aid program; must be US citizens. **Criteria:** Selection will be based on the committee's criteria.

Funds Avail.: No specific amount. **To Apply:** The following items are required to complete the application process: submittal of completed application and signed signature page; signed copy of parents'/guardians'/family's previous year's 1040, 1040A, or 1040EZ income tax return (for dependent students); signed copy of applicant's previous year's tax return; official high school grade transcript through at least 1st semester of the 12th grade or year-end college grade transcript, whichever is the most recent (request from the school's Registrar and forward to the Foundation); copy of the Student Aid Report if applicant has applied for federal aid; copy of the financial aid award letter; interview if so advised. Please submit the application on-line **Deadline:** August 15. **Contact:** WSF Student Aid Department, 336-725-2382.

9644 ■ Douglas Gray Kimel Scholarships
(Undergraduate/Scholarship)

Purpose: To award freshman who will pursue a degree in music from one of the following institutions: North Carolina School of the Arts, Salem College, Wake Forest University, or Winston-Salem State University. **Focus:** Music. **Qualif.:** This scholarship seeks to identify those students who: will pursue a degree in music; demonstrate a minimum, cumulative, unweighted GPA of 3.5; have financial need (scholarship is not restricted to lowest family incomes); are residents of Forsyth County; are Moravian, preferably; are studying to enter a church-related vocation, preferably. **Criteria:** Selection will be based on the committee's criteria.

Funds Avail.: $500. **To Apply:** Scholarship applications will be available online. Students must: complete the scholarship application; provide grade transcript through the 1st semester of 12th grade; submit one recommendation as outlined on the application; attend an interview if so advised. **Deadline:** April 15. **Contact:** WSF Student Aid Department, 336-714-3445.

9645 ■ Johnny Lineberry Memorial Scholarships *(Undergraduate, Vocational/Occupational/ Scholarship)*

Purpose: To award a worthy Forbush High School senior who will go directly to an accredited vocational/technical school, community college, or college/university in pursuit of a certificate, diploma or baccalaureate degree. **Focus:** General science. **Qualif.:** Applicants must be graduating high school seniors from Forsbush High School in East Bend, N.C.; demonstrate a minimum, cumulative, unweighted GPA of at least 2.5; demonstrate strong character and community involvement; intend to study the field of electronics, preferably. **Criteria:** Selection will be based on the committee's criteria.

Funds Avail.: $500. **To Apply:** Applications for the scholarship are available in the guidance office at Forbush High School and from The Winston-Salem Foundation's web site. Completed applications should be submitted to the guidance office. **Deadline:** March 31. **Contact:** WSF Student Aid Department, 336-714-3445.

9646 ■ L.D. and Elsie Long Memorial Scholarships *(Graduate/Scholarship)*

Purpose: To provide educational scholarships for residents of Forsyth County to attend Wake Forest University pursuing graduate degrees. **Focus:** General studies. **Qualif.:**

Applicant must have a family adjusted gross income within the table guidelines (table is based on up to 330% above the federal poverty level); be a resident of Forsyth County; have achieved a current cumulative GPA of at least 2.0; must be enrolled a minimum of six credits hours/semester during the academic year in a program leading to a graduate degree from Wake Forest University. **Criteria:** Selection will be based on the committee's criteria.

Funds Avail.: No specific amount. **To Apply:** The following items are required to complete the application process: submittal of completed application and signed signature page; signed copy of applicant's previous year's tax return; official high school grade transcript through at least 1st semester of the 12th grade or year-end college grade transcript, whichever is the most recent (request from the school's Registrar and forward to the Foundation); copy of the Student Aid Report (SAR) if applicant has applied for federal aid; copy of the financial award letter; interview if so advised. **Deadline:** August 15. **Contact:** Director of Financial Aid at Wake Forest University at 336-758-5154.

9647 ■ N.W. Mitchell-Piedmont Federal Savings and Loans Endowed Scholarships
(Undergraduate/Scholarship)

Purpose: To provide merit-based scholarships for worthy students attending Forsyth Technical Community College. **Focus:** General studies. **Qualif.:** The renewable scholarship seeks to identify those students who: demonstrate academic success; are residents of Forsyth, Davie, Davidson, Stokes, Surry, Watauge, or Yadkin counties; are first semester students enrolled in a minimum of 12 course hours per semester; are US citizens or eligible noncitizens (as verified by the Student Aid Report); show interest and concern for being an active member of society. **Criteria:** Selection will be based on the committee's criteria.

Funds Avail.: $1,000. **Number Awarded:** 2. **To Apply:** Students should complete the application in its entirety and submit it by the deadline. In addition, the following supplemental items must also be submitted by the deadline: official year-end grade transcript; one recommendation; and student aid report. **Deadline:** April 15. **Contact:** Forsyth Technical Community College Student Financial Services at 336-734-7235.

9648 ■ Orthopaedic Specialists Nursing Scholarships *(Undergraduate/Scholarship)*

Purpose: To provide educational need-based scholarships for Forsyth County residents seeking nursing degrees at Forsyth Technical Community College or Winston-Salem State University. **Focus:** Nursing. **Qualif.:** Applicants must be pursuing a first-time associate degree or a bachelors degree in nursing. Must provide a copy of letter of admission to the nursing program at FTCC or WSSU (students ineligible until accepted into nursing program); demonstration of academic promise. Must have achieved 3.0 cumulative, unweighted GPA for graduating high school senior or 2.6 cumulative GPA as a college student; demonstrate financial need based on 300% of federal poverty guidelines. Scholarship recipients are expected to make themselves available for scholarship presentation events. **Criteria:** Selection will be based on the committee's criteria.

Funds Avail.: $1,000. **To Apply:** Scholarship application may be obtained online and submitted after January 1 each year for the next academic year. In addition to the application, the following items are required for first-time applicants: signed copy of parent/guardian federal income tax return (for dependent students); signed copy of applicant's

Awards are arranged alphabetically below their administering organizations

federal income tax return; current official transcript of academic records (obtain from school Registrar); copy of Student Aid Report if student applied for federal aid; copy of financial aid notice from college if student applied for federal aid; and a letter of acceptance into a nursing program. **Deadline:** August 15. **Contact:** Questions regarding this scholarship should be directed to WSF Student Aid Department by calling 336-714-3445 or e-mail at studentaid@wsfoundation.org.

9649 ■ Alice Conger Patterson Scholarships
(Undergraduate/Scholarship)

Purpose: To help deserving adult women achieve their educational goals. **Focus:** General studies. **Qualif.:** Scholarship seeks to identify those: who demonstrate financial need; who are female students, 23 years of age or older; who have earned a high school diploma or equivalent certificate (GED, home school completion, adult high school diploma); who are applying to or are currently enrolled in a four-year college or university in the Piedmont Triad of North Carolina in pursuit of an undergraduate degree. Preference will be given to students at Salem College who demonstrate a strong purpose in pursuing a liberal arts degree; and must have a minimum cumulative GPA of 2.6. **Criteria:** Selection will be based on the committee's criteria.

Funds Avail.: $500. **To Apply:** Scholarship applications will be available online. Students must submit: completed application and signed signature page; copy of federal tax return for previous year; copy of the financial aid award letter for upcoming year; grade transcripts with class ranking in high school and transcripts for all college or university work to date; one recommendation. **Deadline:** August 15. **Contact:** WSF Student Aid Department, 336-714-3445 or e-mail studentaid@esfoundation.org.

9650 ■ William H. and Lena M. Petree Scholarships *(Undergraduate/Scholarship)*

Purpose: To provide college scholarships for worthy Forsyth County residents. **Focus:** General studies. **Qualif.:** Applicants must be graduating high-school seniors; demonstrate academic promise during high-school; have a minimum, cumulative, unweighted GPA of 3.5 through 1st semester, 12th grade; demonstrate a willingness for self-help during high school; demonstrate leadership, school service, and community service during high school; demonstrate financial need for upcoming college expenses (award not restricted to lowest family incomes); be US citizens. **Criteria:** Selection will be based on the committee's criteria.

Funds Avail.: $5,000. **To Apply:** Application may be downloaded from the Foundation's web site. In addition to completing the application, students must: submit one recommendation; submit a grade transcript through first semester, 12th grade; be present for an interview; and a signed copy of student's and parent's federal tax return from previous year. **Deadline:** April 15. **Contact:** Questions regarding this scholarship should be directed to WSF Student Aid Department by calling 336-714-3445 or e-mail at studentaid@wsfoundation.org.

9651 ■ Pfafftown Jaycees/Lynn Canada Memorial Scholarships *(Undergraduate/Scholarship)*

Purpose: To provide scholarships for Forsyth County residents seeking nursing degrees at Forsyth Technical Community College. **Focus:** General studies. **Qualif.:** Applicants must be enrolled on a full-time basis in the pursuit of a first associate or a first baccalaureate degree; provide

a copy of letter of admission into the nursing program at FTCC (ineligible until accepted into nursing program); maintain an unweighted high school or college cumulative GPA of 2.5; not exceed annual adjusted gross family income of $80,000; be US citizens. **Criteria:** Selection will be based on the committee's criteria.

Funds Avail.: $1,000. **To Apply:** Eligible applicants may obtain a scholarship application from The Winston-Salem Foundation's website. In addition to the completed/signed application, applicants are responsible for providing the following required supplemental items: signed copy of parent/guardian's federal income tax return; signed copy of student's federal income tax return, if applicable; applicant's official high school (as of 1st semester, 12th grade) or official college grade transcript (as of academic year-end); copy of Student Aid Report and financial aid notice if student applied for federal aid; and must provide a letter of acceptance into a nursing program. **Deadline:** August 15. **Contact:** Questions regarding this scholarship should be directed to WSF Student Aid Department by calling 336-714-3445 or e-mail at studentaid@wsfoundation.org.

9652 ■ John S. and Jacqueline P. Rider Scholarships *(Undergraduate/Scholarship)*

Purpose: To provide an award to a graduating high school senior in Forsyth County N.C. **Focus:** General studies. **Qualif.:** Applicants must: demonstrate financial need (not restricted to lower family incomes); be a resident of Forsyth County; have achieved a current cumulative grade point average of at least 3.5; must be enrolled full-time in a program leading to a two or four year degree, certificate, or diploma from an accredited institution which participates in the federal student aid program; be a graduating high school senior. **Criteria:** Selection will be based on merit and financial need though need is not restricted to lower incomes.

Funds Avail.: $500. **To Apply:** The following items are required to complete the application process: submittal of completed application and signed signature page; signed copy of parent's/guardians'/family's previous year's 1040, 1040A, or 1040EZ income tax return; signed copy of applicant's previous year's tax return; official high school grade transcript through at least 1st semester of the 12th grade (request from the school's registrar and forward to the Foundation); one recommendation from a teacher, guidance counselor, coach, principal, employer, clergy, or other community leader who has supervised, counseled or coached applicant in some capacity. **Deadline:** April 15. **Contact:** WSF Student Aid Department, 336-714-3445.

9653 ■ Ray and Pearl Sams Scholarships *(Undergraduate/Scholarship)*

Purpose: To provide financial assistance for college tuition, fees and room and board for worthy graduating high school seniors in Forsyth County. **Focus:** General studies. **Qualif.:** This fund seeks to identify the well-rounded graduating high-school senior who: has achieved excellence in school work as evidence by course selection and grades (minimum cumulative unweighted GPA of 3.5 on a 4.0 scale, or equivalent) through 1st semester of the 12th grade; has participated in school service clubs and/or other school activities; has participated in non-school community service activities; demonstrates good moral character; demonstrates evidence of financial need, although award is not restricted to lower incomes; is a United States citizen. **Criteria:** Selection will be based on the committee's criteria.

Funds Avail.: $2,500. **To Apply:** High school seniors may

Awards are arranged alphabetically below their administering organizations

complete and submit the application online. The application and the following items must be received in the foundation's office by the deadline: official grade transcript through the 1st semester of the 12 grade; one recommendation from a teacher, guidance counselor, coach, principal, employer, clergy, or other community leader who has supervised, counseled or coached applicant in some capacity; an interview with the Foundation's Director of Student Aid, if so advised **Deadline:** April 15. **Contact:** WSF Student Aid Department, 336-714-3445 or studentaid@ wsfoundation.org.

9654 ■ Bruce Shelton Scholarships
(Undergraduate/Scholarship)

Purpose: To provide an award to a graduating high school student from a Forsyth County school who displays the traits of athletic excellence, academic achievement, leadership, and social responsibility. **Focus:** General studies. **Qualif.:** The renewable scholarship seeks to identify students who exhibit the following qualities in equal measure: athletic excellence the student must have excelled in at least one varsity sport; social responsibility - the student must have participated in at least one extra-curricular or community activity; academic success - the student must have a minimum, unweighted high school cumulative grade point average of at least 3.0, as of the 1st semester of the 12th grade and be ranked in the top 25% of the senior class; leadership - the student must possess qualities that exhibit a willingness to "go the extra mile". Recipients receiving renewal awards must maintain a minimum cumulative GPA of 2.5 and full time enrollment of at least 12 hours each semester at accredited four-year institutions. Official grade transcripts must be submitted each summer by July 1 for verification of acceptable academic pace and GPA. Recipients should request grade transcripts from the Registrar for themselves and forward to the Foundation. **Criteria:** Selection will be based on the committee's criteria.

Funds Avail.: $1,000. **To Apply:** Students should complete the application in its entirety and submit it by the deadline. In addition, the following supplemental items must be submitted: a grade transcript through the first semester of the 12th grade; one recommendation as described in the application. **Deadline:** April 15. **Contact:** WSF Student Aid Department, 336-714-3445.

9655 ■ Tom Shown Scholarships
(Undergraduate/Scholarship)

Purpose: To award worthy students from the counties of Forsyth, Wikes, Surry, Yahkin, and Davie who plan to attend an accredited two or four year college or university, preferably in North Carolina. **Focus:** General studies. **Qualif.:** Applicants must: demonstrate financial need (award not restricted to lower incomes); have a cumulative, minimum high school GPA of 3.0 or college GPA of 2.5; must be employed a minimum of 20 hours, monthly (including college work study); be US citizens. **Criteria:** Selection will be based on the committee's criteria.

Funds Avail.: $1,000. **To Apply:** The General Financial Aid Application should be completed for this scholarship and is available online. Applicants are responsible for submitting the completed application and all supplemental items. Supplemental items include: Parent/guardian's tax return (for dependent students); applicant's tax return; official high school grade transcript through at least the first semester of the 12th grade or year-end college grade transcript; a copy of your Student Aid Report and financial aid notice if student applied for federal aid; an interview at

The Winston-Salem Foundation. **Deadline:** April 15. **Contact:** Application form and supporting materials should be submitted to Shown Scholarship Selection Committee 2625 Evans Rd., Winston-Salem, NC 27127.

9656 ■ Stultz Scholarships *(Undergraduate/Scholarship)*

Purpose: To provide educational aid to qualified traditional and non-traditional age applicants from charitable funds established by generous supporters of the community. **Focus:** General studies. **Qualif.:** Applicant must: have a family adjusted gross income within the table guidelines (table is based on up to 330% above the federal poverty level); be a resident of Forsyth County; have achieved a current cumulative grade point of at least 2.0; be enrolled a minimum of six credit hours/semester during the academic year, in a program leading to a first time two or four year degree, certificate, or diploma from an accredited institution which participates in the federal student aid program; be a US citizen. **Criteria:** Selection will be based on the committee's criteria.

Funds Avail.: No specific amount. **To Apply:** The following items are required to complete the application process: submittal of completed application and signed signature page; signed copy of parent's/guardians'/family's previous year's 1040, 1040A, or 1040EZ income tax return; signed copy of applicant's previous year's tax return; official high school grade transcript through at least 1st semester of the 12th grade or year-end college grade transcript, whichever is the most recent, (request from the school's Registrar and forward to the Foundation); copy of the Student Aid Report (SAR) and financial aid award letter if applicant has applied for federal aid; interview if so advised. **Deadline:** August 15. **Contact:** WSF Student Aid Department, 336-714-3445 or edna.barker@wsfoundation.org.

9657 ■ Virginia Elizabeth and Alma Vane Taylor Student Nurse Scholarships *(Undergraduate/Scholarship)*

Purpose: Provides scholarships for N.C. residents pursuing two and four-year Nursing degrees at accredited N.C. colleges. **Focus:** Nursing. **Qualif.:** Applicants must: be accepted into an accredited North Carolina school of nursing program, as verified by an acceptance letter; have a family adjusted gross income that does not exceed $80,000; have a high school/college cumulative GPA of at least 2.5. Preference will be given to those seeking first time associate or baccalaureate degrees; those with masters degrees in any area will be ineligible to apply. **Criteria:** Selection will be based on the committee's criteria.

Funds Avail.: $1,200. **To Apply:** The Winston-Salem Foundation's General Financial Aid Application will be used to apply for this scholarship. The General Financial Aid Application is available online or you may request an application to the Foundation's Student Aid Committee. **Deadline:** August 15. **Contact:** WSF Student Aid Department, 336-714-3445.

9658 ■ Jeff Turner-Forsyth Audubon Society Scholarships *(Undergraduate/Scholarship)*

Purpose: To support worthy graduating high school seniors from a Forsyth County High School and admitted to a four year accredited college or university. **Focus:** General studies. **Qualif.:** Applicants must demonstrate character, leadership, and solid academic skills (minimum unweighted GPA of 3.0). Demonstration of financial need will be considered but is not required. US citizenship is required. **Criteria:**

Awards are arranged alphabetically below their administering organizations

Recipients will be evaluated on submitted materials and result of the interview.

Funds Avail.: $1,000. **To Apply:** Scholarship Applications will be available online. Student must: complete the Winston-Salem Foundation application in its entirety, including an attached listing of student activities as well as personal statement; provide grade transcript through 1st semester of 12th grade with the application, at time of submittal; include at least one letter of reference (3 maximum) which addresses the applicant's character as well as environmental interest/experiences. **Deadline:** April 15. **Remarks:** Established in May of 2005. **Contact:** WSF Student Aid Department, Phone: 336-714-3445; E-mail: studentaid@wsfoundation.org.

9659 ■ Nell and Spencer Waggoner Scholarships (Undergraduate/Scholarship)

Purpose: To award merit-based scholarships to worthy graduating high school seniors in Forsyth County who intend to pursue baccalaureate degrees at accredited universities and colleges. **Focus:** General studies. **Qualif.:** Preference is given to students who: demonstrate evidence of excellence through course selection and academic achievement with a minimum cumulative GPA of 3.5 (D's are undesirable in any coursework in grades 9-12); outstanding community and school leadership; demonstrate community service and/or school service and concern for being a contributing member of society (work experience recognized for those who have less community involvement due to work obligations). The scholarships are for four consecutive years, provided requirements for renewal are met. Renewing recipients must provide an official academic year-end grade transcript to the Foundation each year. Students must request grade transcripts for themselves from the college registrar and then forward the transcript to the Foundation. **Criteria:** Selection will be based on the committee's criteria.

Funds Avail.: $3,000. **To Apply:** In addition to a completed application, the following items are required: a high school grade transcript through at least the first semester of the 12th grade; an interview if so advised; one recommendation; and signed certification signature page. **Deadline:** April 15. **Contact:** For further information, applicants may call 336-714-3445 or by e-mail at studentaid@wsfoundation.org.

9660 ■ Art and Dannie Weber Scholarships (Undergraduate/Scholarship)

Purpose: To provide a consecutive four-year renewable award to a graduating high school senior form a Forsyth County high school who will pursue post-secondary education. **Focus:** General studies. **Qualif.:** Applicants must: have demonstrated character and purpose as evidenced in school, community, church, and work activities; have financial need (however, the scholarship is not restricted to lower family incomes); demonstrate academic success by having achieved minimum, unweighted high school cumulative grade point average (GPA) between 2.5-3.5. **Criteria:** Selection will be based on the committee's criteria.

Funds Avail.: $750. **To Apply:** Students who are interested in applying for this scholarship should complete the application in its entirety and submit it by the deadline. In addition, the following supplemental items must be submitted: a grade transcript through the first semester of the 12th grade; family federal tax return for last year; one recommendation from a teacher, guidance counselor, coach, principal, employer, clergy, or other community leader who

has supervised, counseled or coached applicant in some capacity. **Deadline:** April 15. **Contact:** Questions regarding this scholarship should be directed to WSF Student Aid Department by calling 336-714-3445 or e-mail at studentaid@wsfoundation.org.

9661 ■ Edward Kent Welch Memorial Scholarships (Undergraduate/Scholarship)

Purpose: To provide college scholarships to graduating high school seniors at Mt. Tabor High School who will attend the University of North Carolina at Chapel Hill. **Focus:** General studies. **Qualif.:** Students must: have academic promise; evidence of strong moral character; have a genuine concern for others; have school and/or community leadership. The scholarship is available to students regardless of race, sex, national origin, religion, or handicap. **Criteria:** Selection will be based on the committee's criteria.

Funds Avail.: $1,500. **To Apply:** The Mt. Tabor Guidance Office will select the recipient of this award from its pool of students admitted by and planning to attend UNC-Chapel Hill. **Contact:** WSF Student Aid Department, 336-714-3445.

9662 ■ Elizabeth T. Williams Scholarships (Undergraduate/Scholarship)

Purpose: To award worthy graduating high school seniors who plan to attend the University of North Carolina at Chapel Hill. **Focus:** General studies. **Qualif.:** This fund seeks to identify the well-rounded individual who: has achieved academic success (minimum, cumulative, unweighted GPA of 3.0 on a 4.0 scale, or equivalent through first semester, 12th grade with appropriate course selection); has participated in student service clubs and/or other school activities; has participated in non-school community service activities; has participated directly in athletics or in support positions for athletics; may or may not have part-time work experience; demonstrates good moral character; shows evidence of financial need (not restricted to lowest incomes); and is a United States citizen. **Criteria:** Selection will be based on the committee's criteria.

Funds Avail.: No specific amount. **To Apply:** Applications may be submitted by accessing the Foundation's web site. Applicants are responsible for submitting the application and getting the supplemental items to The Winston-Salem Foundation on or before the deadline. The application packet will contain the following components: the completed application; grade transcript; two recommendations; list of student activities. **Deadline:** April 15. **Contact:** WSF Student Aid Department, 336-714-3445.

9663 ■ Edwin H. and Louise N. Williamson Endowed Scholarships (Undergraduate/Scholarship)

Purpose: To provide scholarships to a graduating high school senior who will pursue a bachelor's degree at the University of North Carolina-Greensboro. **Focus:** General studies. **Qualif.:** This scholarship seeks to identify those students who: demonstrate a minimum, cumulative, unweighted GPA of 3.0; have a financial need, however, the scholarship is not restricted to lowest family incomes; will attend the University of North Carolina-Greensboro; are graduating from a Forsyth County high school. **Criteria:** Selection will be based on the committee's criteria.

Funds Avail.: $1,500. **To Apply:** Scholarship applications are available online. Students must: complete application in its entirety; provide grade transcript through the 1st semester of 12th grade; provide one recommendation, as described in the application; attend an interview, if so

Awards are arranged alphabetically below their administering organizations

advised. **Deadline:** April 15. **Contact:** WSF Student Aid Department, 336-714-3445.

9664 ■ Winston-Salem Foundation Scholarships *(Undergraduate/Scholarship)*

Purpose: To provide scholarships to Forsyth County graduating seniors who will pursue post-secondary education at accredited institutions. **Focus:** General studies. **Qualif.:** Applicants must be residents of Forsyth County; must be graduating high school seniors; have a minimum unweighted cumulative GPA between 3.0 and 3.5; must demonstrate community service; exemplify Foundation's core values of generosity, integrity, inclusion and excellence; must demonstrate financial need. **Criteria:** Selection will be based on the committee's criteria.

Funds Avail.: $1,000. **To Apply:** Scholarship application will be available online. Students must: complete the scholarship application in its entirety; provide grade transcript through the 1st semester of the 12th grade; must submit a signed certification signature page; and last year's family federal tax return. **Deadline:** April 15. **Contact:** WSF Student Aid Department by calling 336-714-3445 or e-mail at studentaid@wsfoundation.org.

9665 ■ Blanche Raper Zimmerman Scholarships *(Professional development/Scholarship)*

Purpose: To assist public or private teachers specializing in social science studies or history. **Focus:** History. **Qualif.:** Applicants must be history or social studies teachers of any grade, kindergarten through twelfth; must have a minimum of three years full-time teaching experience in Forsyth County. **Criteria:** Recipients are selected based on committee's review of application materials.

Funds Avail.: No specific amount. **To Apply:** Applicants should write a letter of application (no more than two pages single-spaced, typewritten) to Kay Dillon, describing the proposed participation in a conference, workshop or foreign travel, as specified in the purpose and requirements; should prepare an itemized statement of all costs associated with a conference, workshop, or travel, including costs of registration, transportation, housing, and meals; and should provide letter of recommendation from his or her principal which includes a verification of the number of years of teaching experience. **Deadline:** April 15. **Contact:** Kay Dillon, 336-714-3446; Edna Barker, 336-714-3445.

9666 ■ Winterthur Museum, Garden, and Library
5105 Kennett Pke.
Wilmington, DE 19735
Ph: (302) 888-4600
Fax: (302) 888-4890
Free: 800-448-3883
E-mail: tourinfo@winterthur.org
URL: www.winterthur.org

9667 ■ McNeil Dissertation Fellowships *(All/Fellowship)*

Purpose: To provide financial assistance to humanities students who wish to pursue advanced research. **Focus:** Humanities. **Qualif.:** Applicants must be pursuing doctoral degree program conducting a dissertation research. **Criteria:** Recipients are selected based on the significance of the research.

Funds Avail.: $7,000. **To Apply:** Applicants must submit the application cover sheet; prepare an application essay

of no more than 1500 words that opens a concise overview of the project; a copy of the curriculum vitae; maximum of two pages bibliography; and two letters of reference addressing the previous scholarly record and current project. Applicants must mail six copies of the completed application package. **Deadline:** January 15. **Contact:** Return application and materials to Kay Collins, Administrative Assistant, Research Fellowship Program Academic Programs, Winterthur Museum & Country Estate, Winterthur, DE 19735, or e-mail at researchapplication@winterthur.org.

9668 ■ Winterthur Research Fellowships *(All/Fellowship)*

Purpose: To provide financial assistance to humanities students who wish to pursue advanced research. **Focus:** Humanities. **Qualif.:** Applicants must be academic, independent or museum scholars and graduate students conducting a research in the areas of social and cultural history. **Criteria:** Recipients are selected based on the significance of the research.

Funds Avail.: $1,500. **To Apply:** Applicants must submit the application cover sheet; an application essay of no more than 1500 words which opens a concise overview of the project; a copy of the curriculum vitae; maximum of two pages bibliography; and two letters of reference addressing the previous scholarly record and current project. Applicants must mail six copies of the completed application package. **Deadline:** January 15. **Contact:** Return application and materials to Kay Collins, Administrative Assistant, Research Fellowship Program Academic Programs, Winterthur Museum & Country Estate, Winterthur, DE 19735, or e-mail at researchapplication@winterthur.org.

9669 ■ Wire Reinforcement Institute (WRI)
942 Main St., Ste. 300
Hartford, CT 06103
Ph: (860) 240-9545
Fax: (860) 808-3009
E-mail: admin@wirereinforcementinstitute.org
URL: www.wirereinforcementinstitute.org

9670 ■ WRI Education Foundation Scholarships - Graduate *(Graduate/Scholarship)*

Purpose: To financially support students pursuing graduate level degrees in structural and/or civil engineering. **Focus:** Civil engineering. **Qualif.:** Applicant must be enrolled/registered graduate level student presently pursuing a graduate level degree in structural and/or civil engineering, and enrolled full-time in an accredited four year university program in the United States or Canada. **Criteria:** Selection is based on submitted application.

Funds Avail.: $2,500-$5,000. **To Apply:** Applicants must submit a completed application form along with an up-to-date transcript of university grades; two letters of recommendation from engineering department faculty members; a letter of recommendation from applicant's past or current employer (if presently working in the areas of construction, engineering or architectural design); a signed and notarized statement confirming the enrollment/registration in an accredited four year United States or Canadian university in pursuit of a graduate degree in structural and/or civil engineering. **Deadline:** April 15. **Contact:** Questions can be addressed by email at admin@wirereinforcementinstitute.org or applicants outside the United States may call 800-552-4974.

Awards are arranged alphabetically below their administering organizations

9671 ■ WRI Education Foundation Scholarships - High School Seniors *(Undergraduate/Scholarship)*

Purpose: To support students pursuing undergraduate degrees in structural and/or civil engineering. **Focus:** Civil engineering. **Qualif.:** Applicant must be a high school senior intending to pursue a four year undergraduate degree in structural and/or civil engineering that has been accepted to and will be registered/enrolled in a four year accredited university/college program in the United States or Canada. **Criteria:** Selection is based on the application materials submitted for review.

Funds Avail.: $2,500-$5,000. **To Apply:** Applicants must submit a completed application form along with the most recent transcript of high school grades (including ACT/SAT scores and high school class ranking); two letters of recommendation from faculty of math and science departments; and a proof of acceptance to a four year accredited university/college located in the United States or Canada accompanied; a signed statement of intent to enroll in the university/college and to major in structural and/or civil engineering (statement of intent must be signed by the applicant before a Notary Public). **Deadline:** April 15. **Contact:** Questions can be addressed by email at admin@wirereinforcementinstitute.org or applicants outside the United States may call 800-552-4974.

9672 ■ WRI Education Foundation Scholarships - Undergraduate *(Undergraduate/Scholarship)*

Purpose: To financially support undergraduate students in structural and/or civil engineering. **Focus:** Civil engineering. **Qualif.:** Applicant must be currently enrolled/registered undergraduate level student presently pursuing a four year undergraduate level degree in structural and/or civil engineering; or either be enrolled full-time in a four year accredited university/college program in the United States or Canada. **Criteria:** Selection is based on submitted application.

Funds Avail.: $2,500-$5,000. **To Apply:** Applicants must submit a completed application form along with an up-to-date transcript of university/college grades; two letters of recommendation from engineering department faculty members; a letter of recommendation from applicant's past or current employer (if presently working in the areas of construction, engineering or architectural design); a signed and notarized statement confirming the registration or enrollment and intent to pursue an undergraduate degree in structural and/or civil engineering from a four year university/college in the United States or Canada. **Deadline:** April 15. **Contact:** Questions can be addressed by email at admin@wirereinforcementinstitute.org or applicants outside the United States may call 800-552-4974.

9673 ■ Wisconsin Association for Food Protection (WAFP)
PO Box 620705
Middleton, WI 53562
E-mail: steve.stoner@wisconsin.gov
URL: www.wafp-wi.org

9674 ■ E.H. Marth Food and Environmental Scholarships *(Undergraduate/Scholarship)*

Purpose: To promote and sustain interest in fields of study that may lead to a career in dairy, food, or environmental

sanitation. **Focus:** Food science and technology. **Qualif.:** Applicants must be accepted or enrolled in an accredited post high school undergraduate degree or diploma program (university, college, or technical college) in Wisconsin or an out-of-state school with a reciprocal enrollment agreement with Wisconsin. They must be full-time students enrolled in a dairy science, food science, environmental sanitation or closely related major who are residents of Wisconsin. **Criteria:** Recipients are selected based on academic performance, professional potential, activities and financial need.

Funds Avail.: No specific amount. **To Apply:** Applicants must submit a complete application form; a copy of official transcript; recommendation of advisor or instructor which should address scholastic ability, professional potential, applicable work experience, extra-curricular activities, financial need and other relevant information. **Deadline:** July 1. **Contact:** George Nelsonnel, song@uwstout.edu.

9675 ■ Wisconsin Athletic Trainers' Association (WATA)
c/o Heidi Gutschow, Treas.
3955 Rileys Point Rd.
Sturgeon Bay, WI 54235
E-mail: heidig@prevea.com
URL: www.watainc.org

9676 ■ Founding Fathers Leadership Scholarships *(Undergraduate/Scholarship)*

Purpose: To provide support for future athletic training professionals. **Focus:** Athletics. **Qualif.:** Applicants must be members of the NATA and WATA; currently enrolled in the first year of an athletic training curriculum program at a college or university in Wisconsin; distinguished academically with an overall minimum accumulative GPA of 3.0 on a 4.0 scale or its equivalent; demonstrated qualities of leadership as members of the Athletic Training Student program. **Criteria:** Selection will be based on application.

Funds Avail.: $500. **To Apply:** Applicants must be nominated by a Licensed/Certified Athletic Trainer. Submit the following with the application: (signed by the nominating Licensed/Certified Athletic Trainer) Embossed undergraduate transcript at completion of the semester preceding the filing of the application; Letter of recommendation completed by the nominating Licensed/Certified Athletic Trainer (Section II); A second letter of recommendation completed by a nominating physician or coach. **Deadline:** March 1. **Contact:** Send complete application to: David F. Kroll at HWC No. 1246, 1810 Catlin Ave., Superior, WI 54880, E-mail: dkroll@uwsuper.edu, Fax: 715-395-4607.

9677 ■ Mueller Undergraduate Scholarships *(Undergraduate/Scholarship)*

Purpose: To provide support for future athletic training professionals. **Focus:** Athletics. **Qualif.:** Applicants must be members of NATA and WATA; distinguished academically with an overall minimum accumulative GPA of 3.0 on a 4.0 scale or its equivalent; performed with distinction as members of the Athletic Training Student program in the declared major. **Criteria:** Consideration will be given to students who will demonstrate qualities of leadership.

Funds Avail.: $1,000. **Number Awarded:** 2. **To Apply:** Applicants must be nominated by a Licensed/Certified Athletic Trainer. Nominee must submit a completed and signed application form together with the essay and embossed transcript. Evaluation form must be completed

Awards are arranged alphabetically below their administering organizations

and signed by the Licensed/Certified Athletic Trainer supervisor. **Deadline:** March 1. **Contact:** Send complete application to: David F. Kroll at HWC No. 1246, 1810 Catlin Ave., Superior, WI 54880, E-mail: dkroll@uwsuper.edu, Fax: 715-395-4607.

9678 ■ Jeff Oliphant Memorial Post-Graduate Scholarships (Postgraduate/Scholarship)

Purpose: To provide support for future athletic training professionals. **Focus:** Athletics. **Qualif.:** Applicants must be current members of WATA; must demonstrate enrollment in post-graduate program at an accredited institution of higher learning; distinguished academically with an overall minimum accumulative GPA of 3.0 on a 4.0 scale or its equivalent; have performed with distinction as participants with their athletic training program, academic major and institution; and have the intention to pursue certification by NATA, and confirm intent to pursue the athletic training profession as their primary means of livelihood. **Criteria:** Consideration will be given to students who will demonstrate qualities of leadership.

Funds Avail.: $1,000. **Number Awarded:** 1. **To Apply:** Applicants must complete all required sections in the application form. Section I General Information (to be completed and signed by the applicant); Section II Nomination Form (to be completed and signed by a BOC certified athletic trainer, who can attest to the applicant's skills, abilities and scholarly activities as they relate to the application); Section III Institutional Endorsement (to be completed and signed by the dean of the college or the department head responsible for the applicant's academic program); Section IV Applicant's Essay (to be written and signed by the applicant). **Deadline:** March 1. **Remarks:** Established in 2006. **Contact:** Materials should be submitted to David F. Kroll at HWC No. 1246, 1810 Catlin Ave., Superior, WI 54880, E-mail: dkroll@uwsuper.edu, Fax: 715-395-4607.

9679 ■ Wisconsin Black Law Alumni Association (WBLAA)

544 E Ogden Ave., Ste. 700-309
Milwaukee, WI 53202
Ph: (414) 369-2522
E-mail: give@wblaa.org
URL: wblaa.com

9680 ■ Dean James Thomas Memorial Scholarships (Undergraduate/Scholarship)

Purpose: To financially assist students enrolled at the University of Wisconsin Law School. **Focus:** Law. **Qualif.:** Applicants must be first year students currently enrolled at the University of Wisconsin Law School. **Criteria:** Applicants will be evaluated based on academic accomplishments, demonstrated community service and leadership ability.

Funds Avail.: $25,000. **To Apply:** Applicants must attach a resume; must write an essay explaining the reason(s) why they want to become an attorney. **Deadline:** March 21. **Contact:** info@wblaa.org.

9681 ■ Wisconsin Broadcasters Association (WBA)

44 E Mifflin St., Ste. 900
Madison, WI 53703
Ph: (608) 255-2600
Fax: (608) 256-3986

Free: 800-236-1922
E-mail: mendicott@wi-broadcasters.org
URL: www.wi-broadcasters.org

9682 ■ Wisconsin Broadcasters Association Scholarships (Undergraduate/Scholarship)

Purpose: To assist students enrolled in broadcasting-related educational programs at four-year public or private colleges and universities. **Focus:** Broadcasting. **Qualif.:** Applicants must have completed 60 credits and must be majoring in broadcasting, communications, or related field at a four-year public or private college or university; must have a Wisconsin connection in that they must have either graduated from a Wisconsin high school or be attending a Wisconsin college or university; and must be planning a career in radio or television broadcasting. **Criteria:** Recipients are selected based on academic performance and quality of the essay.

Funds Avail.: $1,000-$2,000. **Number Awarded:** 4. **To Apply:** Applicants must submit a completed application form; a current official transcript of college/university grades; two brief letters of recommendation supporting the application; an original, typed, double-spaced essay (3 pages maximum) written by the applicant forecasting what the broadcasting industry will be like in five years and how the applicant believes he or she will contribute to radio or television during that time. **Deadline:** October 15. **Contact:** Mr. John Laabs at the above address.

9683 ■ Wisconsin Dietetic Association (WDA)

Badger Bay Management Company
563 Carter Ct., Ste. B
Kimberly, WI 54136
Ph: (920) 560-5619
Free: 888-232-8631
E-mail: eatrightwisc@gmail.com
URL: www.eatrightwisc.org

9684 ■ WDA Full-Time Graduate Scholarships (Graduate/Scholarship)

Purpose: To provide financial assistance to dietetic students. **Focus:** Dietetics. **Qualif.:** Applicants must be Wisconsin residents or must be qualified for in-state tuition; have completed minimum of 12 credits a year; must intend to complete an ADA approved internship; coordinated undergraduate program, graduate program or dietetic technician program. **Criteria:** Selection will be based on evaluation of submitted documents and specific criteria.

Funds Avail.: $1,000. **To Apply:** Applicants must submit a completed application form; official transcripts from all universities/institutions attended where five or more hours have been earned; three reference letters; resume. Include additional sheets to answer questions as needed and also include the original along with three copies of completed applications. **Deadline:** February. **Contact:** 1411 W Montgomery St., Sparta, WI 54656-1003; E-mail: wda@centurytel.net.

9685 ■ WDA Part-Time Graduate Scholarships (Graduate/Scholarship)

Purpose: To provide financial assistance to dietetic students. **Focus:** Dietetics. **Qualif.:** Applicants must be Wisconsin residents or must be qualified for in-state tuition; have completed minimum of six credits a year; must intend to complete an ADA approved internship; coordinated

Awards are arranged alphabetically below their administering organizations

undergraduate program, graduate program or dietetic technician program. **Criteria:** Selection will be based on evaluation of submitted documents and specific criteria.

Funds Avail.: $500. **To Apply:** Applicants must submit a completed application form; official transcripts from all universities/institutions attended where five or more hours have been earned; three reference letters; resume. Include additional sheets to answer questions as needed and also include the original along with three copies of completed applications. **Deadline:** February. **Contact:** 1411 W Montgomery St., Sparta, WI 54656-1003; E-mail: wda@centurytel.net.

9686 ■ Wisconsin Indian Education Association (WIEA)
PO Box 910
Keshena, WI 54135
Ph: (715) 799-5110
URL: www.wiea.org

9687 ■ WIEA Scholarships *(Doctorate, Graduate, Undergraduate, Vocational/Occupational/ Scholarship)*

Purpose: To provide financial assistance to American Indian students attending institutes of higher education. **Focus:** General studies. **Qualif.:** Applicant must be an American Indian and a Wisconsin resident. **Criteria:** Awards will be given on a merit basis.

Funds Avail.: $1,000 ($500/semester). **Number Awarded:** 4 (graduating high school senior, undergraduate college student, technical college student and Graduate or PhD student). **To Apply:** Applicants must submit a completed application form together with a copy of current or most recent school transcript; two sealed letters of recommendation (one from a teacher, employer or other professional familiar with student's academic potential); a one-page typed personal essay. Faxed applications will not be considered. **Deadline:** March 19.

9688 ■ Wisconsin Laboratory Association (WLA)
PO Box 154
De Pere, WI 54115
Ph: (920) 406-8300
URL: www.wisconsinlabassociation.org

9689 ■ Wisconsin Laboratory Association Graduate Student Scholarships *(Graduate/ Scholarship)*

Purpose: To financially support students to pursue a career in a non-medical laboratory related field. **Focus:** Laboratory technology. **Qualif.:** Applicant must be a graduate student enrolled in a curriculum that will enable him/her to pursue a career in a non-medical laboratory related field and has at least a 3.0 or higher GPA. **Criteria:** Selection is based on submitted application.

Funds Avail.: $1,000. **Number Awarded:** 1. **To Apply:** Applicants must submit a completed application form along with the supporting documents. **Deadline:** October 1. **Contact:** Gina Steiner, PO Box 808, Fort Atkinson, WI 53538, email: ginas@jonesdairyfarm.com.

9690 ■ Wisconsin Laboratory Association Technical Student Scholarships *(Undergraduate/ Scholarship)*

Purpose: To financially support students who plan to pursue a career in a non-medical laboratory related field.

Focus: Laboratory technology. **Qualif.:** Applicant must be a technical student (second year) enrolled in a curriculum that enables him/her to pursue a career in a non-medical laboratory related field and has at least a 3.0 or higher GPA. **Criteria:** Selection is based on application materials.

Funds Avail.: $1,000. **Number Awarded:** 1. **To Apply:** Applicants must submit a completed application form along with the supporting documents. **Deadline:** September 1. **Contact:** Gina Steiner, PO Box 808, Fort Atkinson, WI 53538, email: ginas@jonesdairyfarm.com.

9691 ■ Wisconsin Laboratory Association Undergraduate University Student Scholarships *(Undergraduate/Scholarship)*

Purpose: To financially support students who plan to pursue a career in a non-medical laboratory related field. **Focus:** Laboratory technology. **Qualif.:** Applicant must be an undergraduate university student entering 3rd, 4th or 5th year of college; enrolled in a curriculum that will enable him/her to pursue a career in a non-medical laboratory related field and has at least a 3.0 or higher GPA. **Criteria:** Selection is based on application.

Funds Avail.: $1,000. **Number Awarded:** 1. **To Apply:** Applicants must submit a completed application form along with the supporting documents. **Deadline:** September 1. **Contact:** Gina Steiner, PO Box 808, Fort Atkinson, WI 53538, email: ginas@jonesdairyfarm.com.

9692 ■ Wolf Trap Foundation for the Performing Arts (WTFPA)
1645 Trap Rd.
Vienna, VA 22182
Ph: (703) 255-1900
Free: 877-965-3872
E-mail: wolftrap@wolftrap.org
URL: www.wolftrap.org

9693 ■ Wolf Trap Foundation Scholarship Program for Performing Arts Teachers *(Professional development/Scholarship)*

Purpose: To enhance the strategies of teachers in teaching arts education. **Focus:** Performing arts. **Qualif.:** Applicants must be performing arts public high school teachers in Washington , DC; Montgomery County, MD; Prince George's County, MD; and Fairfax County, VA. **Criteria:** Selection is based on proposals.

Funds Avail.: $2,500. **To Apply:** Proposals by invitation only. **Contact:** Wolf Trap's Education Department at 703-255-1933, education@wolftrap.org.

9694 ■ The Wolf Trap Internship Program *(Graduate, Professional development, Undergraduate/Internship)*

Purpose: To provide training program for the performing arts. **Focus:** Performing arts. **Qualif.:** Applicants must be undergraduate students (completed one year of study or equivalent), graduate students, or recent graduates (up to two years of school); career-changers enrolled in a degree program; and international students (J-1 or F-1 Visa required). **Criteria:** Committee will review submitted materials.

Funds Avail.: No specific amount. **To Apply:** Applicants must submit a cover letter with a brief personal statement and an outline of career goals; a resume; two academic or

Awards are arranged alphabetically below their administering organizations

professional recommendations; two contrasting writing samples, (maximum of 3 pages each). Applicants must send the requirements to Internship Program Wolf Trap Foundation for the Performing Arts, 1645 Trap Road, Vienna, VA 22182, 703-255-1924 (fax), internships@wolftrap.org (e-mail). **Deadline:** March 1, July 1 and November 1. **Contact:** 703-937-6304, 800-404-8461, or e-mail internships@wolftrap.org.

9695 ■ Women in Defense, a National Security Organization (WID)

2111 Wilson Blvd., Ste. 400
Arlington, VA 22201-3001
Ph: (703) 522-1820
Fax: (703) 522-1885
E-mail: wid@ndia.org
URL: wid.ndia.org/Pages/default.aspx

9696 ■ Women In Defense HORIZONS Scholarships *(Graduate, Undergraduate/Scholarship)*

Purpose: To provide financial assistance to further educational objectives of women either employed or planning careers in defense or national security areas. **Focus:** National security; Military history; Government; Engineering; Computer and information sciences; Physics; Mathematics and mathematical sciences; Business; Law; International affairs and relations; Political science; Economics. **Qualif.:** Applicant must be currently enrolled at an accredited university/college, either full-time or part-time; must have junior, senior or graduate status; demonstrate interest in pursuing a career related to national security or defense; demonstrate financial need; have a minimum GPA of 3.25. Applicant must be a female citizen of the United States. **Criteria:** Awards are given based on academic achievement, participation in defense and national security activities, field of study, work experience, statements of objectives, recommendations, and financial need.

Funds Avail.: No specific amount. **To Apply:** Applicants must submit a completed scholarship application form with the essays, recommendations, and transcripts. **Deadline:** July 1. **Remarks:** Established in 1988.

9697 ■ Women Divers Hall of Fame (WDHOF)

2753 Broadway, Box 206
New York, NY 10025
E-mail: info@wdhof.org
URL: www.wdhof.org

9698 ■ Cecilia Connelly Memorial Scholarships in Underwater Archaeology *(Graduate, Undergraduate/Scholarship)*

Purpose: To provide financial and educational support to individuals of all ages, particularly those who are preparing for professional careers that involve scuba diving. **Focus:** Aquaculture; Archeology. **Qualif.:** Applicant must be an undergraduate or graduate student enrolled in an accredited course of study in the field of Underwater Archaeology; have an overall GPA of 2.5 or better (undergraduate) or 3.0 or better (graduate); and must be in good standing. First year graduate student may submit verification of a minimum overall GPA of 2.5 from the final year as an undergraduate. **Criteria:** Selection is based on submitted application.

Funds Avail.: $1,500. **Number Awarded:** 1. **To Apply:** Applicant must submit a completed application form along with a personal biography, resume or CV detailing relevant activities (maximum of 2 pages) including reasons for being interested in underwater archaeology, the high points of experience in underwater archaeology to date, future goals and how the applicant would use the scholarship; an essay on professional goals and how the scholarship will help in achieving the goals (approximately 750-1000 words); and two letters of recommendation from either faculty or field study supervisors (one letter should contain a statement verifying GPA and good standing at the institution, including the referee's contact information) mailed directly to spomponi@hboi.fau.edu. Application and supporting materials must be sent electronically to spomponi@hboi.fau.edu with a subject line WDHOF AWARD APPLICATION and (applicant's name). **Deadline:** November 15. **Contact:** scholarships@wdhof.org.

9699 ■ Elizabeth Greenhalgh Memorial Scholarships in Journalism, Graphic Arts, or Photography *(Graduate, Undergraduate/Scholarship)*

Purpose: To provide financial and educational support to individuals of all ages, particularly those who are preparing for professional careers that involve scuba diving. **Focus:** Journalism; Graphic art and design; Photography. **Qualif.:** Applicant must be a woman diver who is furthering her education beyond high school in the field of journalism, graphic arts, or photography to better serve the ocean environment or ocean community. **Criteria:** Selection is based on the application materials submitted for review.

Funds Avail.: $1,500. **Number Awarded:** 1. **To Apply:** Applicant must submit a completed application form along with a personal biography, resume or CV detailing relevant activities (maximum of 2 pages); an essay on professional goals and how the scholarship will help in achieving the goals (approximately 750-1000 words); and two letters of recommendation from persons in the community, scuba instructor, teachers, or professors who can assess applicants' likelihood of success with the scholarship or training grant to be e-mailed from the referee directly to spomponi@hboi.fau.edu. Application and supporting materials must be sent electronically to spomponi@hboi.fau.edu with a subject line WDHOF AWARD APPLICATION and (applicant's name). **Deadline:** November 15. **Contact:** scholarships@wdhof.org.

9700 ■ WDHOF Scholarships in Marine Conservation *(Graduate, Undergraduate/Scholarship)*

Purpose: To provide financial and educational support to individuals of all ages, particularly those who are preparing for professional careers that involve scuba diving. **Focus:** Conservation of natural resources. **Qualif.:** Applicant must be a woman of any age; enrolled in an accredited academic or research program in the field of marine conservation. **Criteria:** Selection is based on the application materials submitted for review.

Funds Avail.: $2,500. **Number Awarded:** 1. **To Apply:** Applicant must submit a completed application form along with a personal biography, resume or CV detailing relevant activities (maximum of 2 pages); an essay on professional goals and how the scholarship will help in achieving the goals (approximately 750-1000 words); and two letters of recommendation from persons in the community, scuba instructor, teachers, or professors who can assess ap-

Awards are arranged alphabetically below their administering organizations

plicants' likelihood of success with the scholarship or training grant to be e-mailed from the referee directly to spomponi@hboi.fau.edu. Application and supporting materials must be sent electronically to spomponi@hboi.fau.edu with a subject line WDHOF AWARD APPLICATION and (applicant's name). **Deadline:** November 15. **Contact:** scholarships@wdhof.org.

9701 ■ Women in Federal Law Enforcement (WIFLE)

2200 Wilson Blvd., Ste. 102
PMB 204
Arlington, VA 22201-3324
Ph: (301) 805-2180
Fax: (301) 560-8836
Free: 877-850-8302
E-mail: wifle@comcast.net
URL: www.wifle.org

9702 ■ The WIFLE Scholarship Fund *(Graduate, Postdoctorate, Undergraduate/Scholarship)*

Purpose: To provide financial assistance to women interested in law enforcement careers. **Focus:** Law enforcement. **Qualif.:** Applicants must be U.S. citizens; must be full-time students at an accredited four-year college or university, or a fully accredited community college with the intention of transferring to a four-year degree; must have completed at least one full academic year of college work; must major in Criminal Justice or a related discipline such as social sciences, public administration, computer science, finance, linguistic arts, chemistry, or physics leading to a four-year degree; have a minimum 3.0 overall grade point average (GPA). **Criteria:** Recipients will be selected based on academic potential, achievement and commitment to serving communities in the field of law enforcement.

Funds Avail.: $1,500. **To Apply:** Applicants must complete the application with a 500-word essay describing the applicant's involvement in a community project and the results or impact of that involvement to the community. If the applicant is currently serving or has served an internship with a law enforcement agency, preferably a federal law enforcement agency, the applicant must provide details including the name of the agency, the dates served and the value of the experience and the accomplishment through the internship in a 500-word essay. Applicants must have at least one community leader or member of a community or police official sponsor their applications with a written statement of support. **Deadline:** February 1.

9703 ■ Women Lawyers Association of Greater St. Louis

PO Box 775512
Saint Louis, MO 63177
E-mail: wla@wlastl.org
URL: www.wlastl.org

9704 ■ Linda J. Murphy Scholarships
(Undergraduate/Scholarship)

Purpose: To support law students in their pursuit of legal education. **Focus:** Law. **Qualif.:** Applicants must be part-time or full-time female law students, must be currently enrolled in a Missouri law school and must be committed to continue law school enrollment in the fall semester follow-

ing the award. **Criteria:** Selection of recipients is based on demonstrated commitment to causes that are consistent with the Mission of the WLA. Academic achievement and financial need are taken into account to a lesser extent.

Funds Avail.: $1000-$6000 depending on the amount of funds available. **To Apply:** Applicants must submit a completed application form along with the personal statement and official or unofficial law school transcripts. Applications and all accompanying materials must be submitted via e-mail to: jboyer@stinson.com. **Deadline:** April 6. **Remarks:** The scholarship fund was named after Linda J. Murphy after her death in 1999. **Contact:** Anne Kerns at akerns@lewisrice.com or Jennifer Gustafson at jgustafson@lewisrice.com.

9705 ■ Women Marines Association

PO Box 377
Oaks, PA 19456
Free: 888-525-1943
E-mail: wma@womenmarines.org
URL: www.womenmarines.org

9706 ■ LaRue A. Ditmore Music Scholarships
(Undergraduate/Scholarship)

Purpose: To financially assist students with their educational pursuits. **Focus:** Maritime studies. **Qualif.:** Applicant must have served, or be serving in the U.S. Marine Corps or Reserve; or a direct descendant by blood, or legal adoption or stepchild of a Marine on active duty, or who has served in the U.S. Marine Corps, Regular or Reserve; or a sibling or a descendant of a sibling by blood, or legal adoption or stepchild of a Marine on active duty, or who has served in the U.S. Marine Corps, Regular or Reserve; or have completed two years in a Marine Corps JROTC program. High school applicant must have maintained a B+ average for the sophomore or junior years; have a SAT score of 1100 (combined Math/Verbal); have an ACT score of 25 (combined Math/Verbal). College students must have a GPA of 3.5. Applicant must have a WMA member sponsor. **Criteria:** A selection board of five members will review qualified applications.

Funds Avail.: $1500. **To Apply:** Applicants must submit a completed application form together with a copy of Sponsor's National Membership Card; a wallet-size photo (name written on lower back); three letters of reference from a school personnel (on official letterhead signed and sealed envelope); proof of relationship to a U.S. Marine; and a permanent and an alternate email address. High school students must also send official transcripts (mailed directly from the school) and a letter of acceptance for the following year. College freshmen students must send an additional official final high school transcript (including SAT/ACT scores) and current college transcript. **Deadline:** January 31. **Remarks:** Male applicants must submit a proof of draft registration when applying on or after their eighteenth birthday. **Contact:** Dottie Stover-Kendrick at PO Box 134, Stilwell, KS 66085; E-mail at scholarship@womenmarines.org; Luann Weeks, 251 SW 1300th Road, Chilhowee, MO 64733-8133, ldweeks@pocketmail.com.

9707 ■ Lily H. Gridley Memorial Scholarships
(Undergraduate/Scholarship)

Purpose: To financially assist students with their educational pursuits. **Focus:** Maritime studies. **Qualif.:** Applicant must have served, or be serving in the U.S. Marine Corps or Reserve; or a direct descendant by blood, or legal adop-

Awards are arranged alphabetically below their administering organizations

tion or stepchild of a Marine on active duty, or has served in the U.S. Marine Corps, Regular or Reserve; or a sibling or a descendant of a sibling by blood, or legal adoption or stepchild of a Marine on active duty, or who has served in the U.S. Marine Corps, Regular or Reserve; or have completed two years in a Marine Corps JROTC program. High school applicant must have maintained a B+ average for the sophomore or junior years; have a SAT score of 1100 (combined Math/Verbal); have an ACT score of 25 (combined Math/Verbal). College students must have a GPA of 3.5. Applicant must have a WMA member sponsor. **Criteria:** A selection board of five members will review qualified applications.

Funds Avail.: $1500. **To Apply:** Applicants must submit a completed application form together with a copy of Sponsor's National Membership Card; a wallet-size photo (name written on lower back); three letters of reference from a school personnel (on official letterhead signed and sealed envelope); proof of relationship to a U.S. Marine; and a permanent and an alternate email address. High school students must also send official transcripts (mailed directly from the school) and a letter of acceptance for the following year. College freshmen students must send an additional official final high school transcript (including SAT/ACT scores) and current college transcript. **Deadline:** January 31. **Remarks:** Male applicants must submit a proof of draft registration when applying on or after their eighteenth birthday. **Contact:** Dottie Stover-Kendrick at PO Box 134, Stilwell, KS 66085; E-mail at scholarship@womenmarines.org; Luann Weeks, 251 SW 1300th Road, Chilhowee, MO 64733-8133, ldweeks@pocketmail.com.

9708 ■ Ethyl and Armin Wiebke Memorial Scholarships *(Undergraduate/Scholarship)*

Purpose: To financially assist students with their educational pursuits. **Focus:** Maritime studies. **Qualif.:** Applicant must have served, or be serving in the U.S. Marine Corps or Reserve; or a direct descendant by blood, or legal adoption or stepchild of a Marine on active duty, or who has served in the U.S. Marine Corps, Regular or Reserve; or a sibling or a descendant of a sibling by blood, or legal adoption or stepchild of a Marine on active duty, or who has served in the U.S. Marine Corps, Regular or Reserve; or have completed two years in a Marine Corps JROTC program. High school applicant must have maintained a B+ average for the sophomore or junior years; have a SAT score of 1100 (combined Math/Verbal); have an ACT score of 25 (combined Math/Verbal). College students must have a GPA of 3.5. Applicant must have a WMA member sponsor. **Criteria:** A selection board of five members will review qualified applications.

Funds Avail.: $1500. **Number Awarded:** 1. **To Apply:** Applicants must submit a completed application form together with a copy of Sponsor's National Membership Card; a wallet-size photo (name written on lower back); three letters of reference from a school personnel (on official letterhead signed and sealed envelope); proof of relationship to a U.S. Marine; and a permanent and an alternate Email address. High school students must also send official transcripts (mailed directly from the school) and a letter of acceptance for the following year. College freshmen students must send an additional official final high school transcript (including SAT/ACT scores) and current college transcript. **Deadline:** January 31. **Remarks:** Male applicants must submit a proof of draft registration when applying on or after their eighteenth birthday. **Contact:** Dottie Stover-Kendrick at PO Box 134, Stilwell, KS 66085; E-mail at scholarship@womenmarines.org; Luann Weeks, 251

SW 1300th Road, Chilhowee, MO 64733-8133, ldweeks@pocketmail.com.

9709 ■ WMA Memorial Scholarships *(Undergraduate/Scholarship)*

Purpose: To financially assist students with their educational pursuits. **Focus:** Maritime studies. **Qualif.:** Applicant must have served, or be serving in the U.S. Marine Corps or Reserve; or a direct descendant by blood, or legal adoption or stepchild of a Marine on active duty, or who has served in the U.S. Marine Corps, Regular or Reserve; or a sibling or a descendant of a sibling by blood, or legal adoption or stepchild of a Marine on active duty, or who has served in the U.S. Marine Corps, Regular or Reserve; or have completed two years in a Marine Corps JROTC program. High school applicant must have maintained a B+ average for the sophomore or junior years; have a SAT score of 1100 (combined Math/Verbal); have an ACT score of 25 (combined Math/Verbal). College students must have a GPA of 3.5. Applicant must have a WMA member sponsor. **Criteria:** A selection board of five members will review qualified applications.

Funds Avail.: $1500. **To Apply:** Applicants must submit a completed application form together with a copy of Sponsor's National Membership Card; a wallet-size photo (name written on lower back); three letters of reference from a school personnel (on official letterhead signed and sealed envelope); proof of relationship to a U.S. Marine; and a permanent and an alternate email address. High school students must also send official transcripts (mailed directly from the school) and a letter of acceptance for the following year. College freshmen students must send an additional official final high school transcript (including SAT/ACT scores) and current college transcript. **Deadline:** January 31. **Remarks:** Male applicants must submit a proof of draft registration when applying on or after their eighteenth birthday. **Contact:** Dottie Stover-Kendrick at PO Box 134, Stilwell, KS 66085; E-mail at scholarship@womenmarines.org; Luann Weeks, 251 SW 1300th Road, Chilhowee, MO 64733-8133, ldweeks@pocketmail.com.

9710 ■ Women's Army Corps Veterans' Association (WACVA)
PO Box 5577
Fort McClellan, AL 36205-0577
Ph: (256) 820-6824
E-mail: info@armywomen.org
URL: www.armywomen.org

9711 ■ Women's Army Corps Veterans Association Scholarships *(Undergraduate/Scholarship)*

Purpose: To provide educational assistance to relatives of Army Service Women. **Focus:** General studies. **Qualif.:** Applicants must be relatives of Army Service Women who are U.S. citizens; must be high school graduating seniors or planning to enroll as full-time students at an accredited college or university; and have 3.5 GPA on a 4.0 scale. **Criteria:** Selection is based on academic achievement; leadership as expressed through co-curricular activities and community involvement; biographical sketch; and recommendations.

Funds Avail.: $1,500. **To Apply:** Applicants must submit the completed application form available from the website, an official 7-semester high school transcript, three letters of recommendation (one of which must be written by a teacher, counselor or principal); biographical sketch; and

Awards are arranged alphabetically below their administering organizations

documentation of sponsor's military service. Forward materials to: Women's Army Corps Veteran's Association, Women's Army Corps Veterans Scholarship, PO Box 5577, Fort McClellan, Alabama 36205-5577. **Deadline:** May 1.

9712 ■ Women's Association of the Mining Industry of Canada Foundation (WAMICF)
Postal Sta. A
Toronto, ON, Canada M5W 1B2
E-mail: scholarships@cogeco.ca
URL: www.pdac.ca/wamic

9713 ■ Women's Association of the Mining Industry of Canada Foundation National Geophysics Scholarships *(Undergraduate/Scholarship)*

Purpose: To support undergraduate students enrolled in mining related or earth science programs in Canadian universities. **Focus:** Earth sciences, Mining. **Qualif.:** Applicants must be currently registered in third year geophysics; must be undergraduate students who have attained the highest academic average on completion of their year in an accredited geophysics program at a qualified Canadian university. **Criteria:** Applicants are selected based on academic standing and financial need.

Funds Avail.: $1,000. **To Apply:** Application must include: student's name; official transcript of the student's marks (including his/her third year marks); student's sessional and permanent home addresses; student's social insurance number; professor's recommendations; and other scholarships, bursaries or awards that the student has applied for and received. **Deadline:** June 4. **Contact:** Application form and supporting documents must be forwarded to WAMIC Foundation office or may send electronically to scholarships@cogeco.ca.

9714 ■ Women's Association of the Mining Industry of Canada Foundation National Scholarships *(Undergraduate/Scholarship)*

Purpose: To support undergraduate students enrolled in mining related or earth science programs in Canadian universities. **Focus:** Earth sciences; Mining. **Qualif.:** Applicants must be currently registered in third year geophysics; must be undergraduate students who have attained the highest academic average on completion of their year in an accredited geophysics program at a qualified Canadian University. **Criteria:** Applicants are selected based on academic standing and financial need.

Funds Avail.: $1,000. **To Apply:** Application must include: student's name and curriculum vitae; official transcript of the student's marks (including his/her third year marks); student's sessional and permanent home addresses; student's social insurance number; professor's recommendations; and other scholarships, bursaries or awards that the student has applied for and received. **Deadline:** June 4. **Contact:** Application form and supporting documents must be forwarded to WAMIC Foundation office or may send electronically to scholarships@cogeco.ca.

9715 ■ Women's Association of the Mining Industry of Canada Foundation Wood Bursary Awards *(Undergraduate/Award)*

Purpose: To support undergraduate students enrolled in mining related or earth science programs in Canadian universities. **Focus:** Earth sciences; Mining. **Qualif.:** Ap-

plicants must be third or fourth year undergraduate students who are enrolled in an accredited mining related program in a Canadian university. **Criteria:** Applicants will be evaluated based on academic standing and financial need.

Funds Avail.: $6,000. **To Apply:** Application forms and other documents must be submitted to the chairperson of the Awards Committee, Women's Association of the Mining Industry of Canada Foundation, PO Box 207, Postal Station A, Toronto, ON M5W 1B2. **Deadline:** June 4. **Contact:** Applicants may e-mail their applications to scholarships@cogeco.ca.

9716 ■ Women's Business Enterprise National Council (WBENC)
1120 Connecticut Ave. NW, Ste. 1000
Washington, DC 20036
Ph: (202) 872-5515
Fax: (202) 872-5505
E-mail: kjones@wbenc.org
URL: www.wbenc.org

9717 ■ Dorothy B. Brothers Executive Scholarship Program *(High School/Scholarship)*

Purpose: To provide financial assistance and opportunities for women to attend an executive level course. **Focus:** General Studies. **Qualif.:** Applicants must be currently certified as a woman business enterprise by WBENC; must have at least three-to-five years experience running a business; must employ at least three full-time employees; must maintain a minimum annual sales volume of $500,000 (the range is $500,000-$50,000); must not have previously attended a comparable executive management program (TUK-WBENC Executive Program). **Criteria:** Recipients are selected based on the quality of the essay.

Funds Avail.: $2,500 or $11,000. **To Apply:** Applicants must fill out the application form and submit an essay stating the applicant's career goals related to business. **Deadline:** July 2.

9718 ■ Women's Business Support Network (WBSN)
PO Box 572563
Houston, TX 77257-2563
Ph: (713) 752-WBSN
E-mail: wbsn@wbsnonline.org
URL: www.wbsnonline.org

9719 ■ WBSN Foundation Scholarships *(Graduate, Professional development/Scholarship)*

Purpose: To further the education of women re-entering the work force. **Focus:** General studies. **Qualif.:** Applicant must be a female and Houston resident; pursuing to further career opportunities through additional education and must have at least five years of work experience. **Criteria:** Selection is based on the application.

Funds Avail.: $500, $1,000 and $2,000. **Number Awarded:** Varies. **To Apply:** Applicants must submit a completed application form together with scholarship objectives and financial need; educational information; community activities; official transcripts; and a copy of latest income tax return with W-2 and/or 1099 forms. **Deadline:** May 19. **Contact:** For questions, applicants may email at rebeccamaddux@netzero.com.

Awards are arranged alphabetically below their administering organizations

9720 ■ Women's Health Research Foundation of Canada (WHRFC)

RPO Grant Park
Winnipeg, MB, Canada R3M 3X8
E-mail: whrfc_inc@yahoo.ca
URL: www.whrfcinc.com

9721 ■ Women's Health Research Foundation of Canada Scholarship Program *(Graduate/Scholarship)*

Purpose: To support research in women's health through financial assistance. **Focus:** Women's studies. **Qualif.:** Applicants must be registered in a graduate program at the University of Manitoba; must have research concentration in some area of women's health. **Criteria:** Selection of applicants will be based on their research studies and application requirements.

Funds Avail.: 3,000. **To Apply:** Applicants must complete the application form available online; must submit an official transcript or student history; must have an official transcript from all other universities attended; must have two letters of reference. **Deadline:** April 15. **Contact:** For further information, applicants must contact Enza Pohl at enza_pohl@umanitoa.ca or 204-474-6827.

9722 ■ Women's International Network of Utility Professionals (WiNUP)

PO Box 64
Grove City, OH 43123-0064
Ph: (614) 738-0603
E-mail: winup@att.net
URL: winup.info

9723 ■ Julia Kiene Fellowships in Electrical Energy *(Graduate/Fellowship)*

Purpose: To support students engaging in graduate work toward an advanced degree in any phase of electrical energy. **Focus:** Electrical engineering. **Qualif.:** Applicant must be a graduate student in an advanced degree in electrical energy. **Criteria:** Selection is based on the application.

Funds Avail.: $2000. **To Apply:** Applicants must submit a completed application form along with the required materials. **Deadline:** March 31. **Remarks:** Established in memory of Julia Kiene, past president of the organization.

9724 ■ Lyle Mamer Fellowships *(Graduate/Fellowship)*

Purpose: To support students engaging in graduate work toward an advanced degree in any phase of electrical energy. **Focus:** Electrical engineering. **Qualif.:** Applicant must be a graduate student earning an advanced degree in electrical energy. **Criteria:** Selection is based on the application.

Funds Avail.: $1000. **To Apply:** Applicants must submit a completed application form along with the required materials. **Deadline:** March 31. **Remarks:** Established in memory of Lyle Mamer who served as an Associate Professor at the University of Tennessee College of Home Economics for 35 years.

9725 ■ Women's Jewelry Association (WJA)

52 Vanderbilt Ave., 19th Fl.
New York, NY 10017-3827
Ph: (212) 687-2722
Fax: (646) 355-0219
E-mail: info@womensjewelry.org
URL: wjamarion.memberlodge.com

9726 ■ Women's Jewelry Association Member Grants *(All/Grant)*

Purpose: To provide educational financial assistance for students in the international jewelry, watch and related industries. **Focus:** Fashion design; Design. **Qualif.:** Applicants must be WJA members. **Criteria:** Applicants are selected through a random drawing of the WJA Member Grant Committee.

Funds Avail.: $500. **To Apply:** Applicants must provide in a printed text limited to one 8 1/2 x 11 page: a short statement about applicant's personal information, work, the course and how the grant will benefit the applicant (mandatory); applicant's signature to accept all terms and conditions of the WJA Grants (mandatory); a brief description of the applicant's contributions to the jewelry and/or related industries (optional). Applicants must submit a completed application form and all supporting documents to WJA Member Grant Committee. **Deadline:** January 31. **Contact:** Alexandra Hart, Chair - Member Grants at the above address.

9727 ■ Women's Missionary Council of the Christian Methodist Episcopal Church

c/o Princess A. Pegues, Pres.
2309 Bonnie Ave.
Bastrop, LA 71220
Ph: (318) 281-3044
Fax: (318) 283-9084
E-mail: annpegues@bellsouth.net
URL: www.womensmissionarycouncilcme.org

9728 ■ The Helena B. Cobb Annual Scholarships *(Undergraduate, Vocational/Occupational/Scholarship)*

Purpose: To emphasize the importance of educational training beyond the high school level. **Focus:** General studies. **Qualif.:** Applicant must be a member of the Christian Methodist Episcopal Church; a high school graduate; and enrolled in a college, university, or vocational-technical school. **Criteria:** Selection is based on the application.

Funds Avail.: $100. **To Apply:** Applicants must submit a completed application form. **Deadline:** December 31. **Remarks:** The program was named for the first Vice President of the Council, Helena B. Cobb.

9729 ■ The Helena B. Cobb Four-Year Higher Education Grants *(Undergraduate, Vocational/Occupational/Scholarship)*

Purpose: To emphasize the importance of educational training beyond the high school level. **Focus:** General studies. **Qualif.:** Applicant must be a member of the Christian Methodist Episcopal Church; a high school graduate; and enrolled in a college, university, or vocational-technical school. **Criteria:** Applicants are chosen through a four-year progressive competitive system from the local to Episcopal levels.

Funds Avail.: $1000-$4000. **Number Awarded:** 10. **To Apply:** Applicants must submit a completed application form. **Deadline:** December 31. **Remarks:** The program

Awards are arranged alphabetically below their administering organizations

was named for the first Vice President of the Council, Helena B. Cobb.

9730 ■ Women's National Book Association (WNBA)
PO Box 237
New York, NY 10150
Ph: (615) 386-6760
Fax: (212) 208-4629
E-mail: info@wnba-books.org
URL: www.wnba-books.org

9731 ■ WNBA Eastman Grants *(Professional development/Grant)*

Purpose: To provide funds for librarians who are interested in learning about the publishing process. **Focus:** Publishing. **Qualif.:** Applicant must be an MLS or its equivalent and must have at least two years of post-master's work experience in a library. **Criteria:** Recipients are selected based on the likelihood of career benefit to the person taking the course.

Funds Avail.: $500. **Number Awarded:** 1. **To Apply:** Applicants must provide a current resume; a personal statement of not more than 300 words concerning an ongoing interest in the publishing process and how a better understanding of this process would enhance the applicant's library career; a list of publishing courses to which the applicant would apply; and a signed acknowledgement of intent to submit to ALA and WNBA a simple report and verification of attendance at the chosen publishing course. **Remarks:** Established in 1997 in honor of Ann Heidbreder Eastman, a prominent member of both the publishing and library communities and a member of both WNBA and ALA until her death in 1993.

9732 ■ Women's Overseas and Service League
319 Wickes St.
San Antonio, TX 78210
E-mail: carolhabgood@sbcglobal.net
URL: www.wosl.org

9733 ■ Women's Overseas and Service League Scholarships for Women *(Undergraduate/ Scholarship)*

Purpose: To assist women who have served overseas in or with the Armed Forces. **Focus:** General studies. **Qualif.:** Applicants must be women who are committed to the advancement in military or other public service careers; must have demonstrated such commitment through life experiences; have successfully completed a minimum of 12 semester (18 quarter) hours of study in any institution of higher Education with a minimum of 2.5 grade point average; must be admitted for study in an institution of higher learning program leading to an academic degree (Associate Degree or higher). The program must be professional or technical in nature; must agree to enroll for a minimum of six semester (nine quarter) hours of study each academic period; and she must agree to maintain academic standards. **Criteria:** Scholarship Committee of the Women's Overseas Service League Board of Directors will evaluate the student's application based on academic records.

Funds Avail.: $500-$1,000.00. **To Apply:** Applicants must fill out the application form; must include all needed documents such as resume, transcripts, essays and references.

Deadline: March 1. **Contact:** kelsey@openix.com.

9734 ■ Women's Research and Education Institute (WREI)
1828 L St., NW Ste. 801
Washington, DC 20003
Ph: (202) 280-2720
E-mail: wrei@wrei.org
URL: www.wrei.org

9735 ■ WREI Congressional Fellows on Women and Public Policy *(Doctorate, Graduate, Master's/ Fellowship)*

Purpose: To encourage more effective participation by women in the formulation of policy options. **Focus:** General studies. **Qualif.:** Applicant must be currently enrolled in a master's or doctoral program at an accredited institution in the United States or have completed such a program within the past 18 months; have completed at least nine hours of graduate coursework; and have a demonstrated interest in research or political activity related to women's social and political status. **Criteria:** Fellows are selected on the basis of academic competence as well as their demonstrated interest in the public policy process.

Funds Avail.: $1,450 per month plus an additional sum of $500 for health insurance. **To Apply:** Applicants must submit a completed application via regular mail or by email. Applicants must also present transcripts of previous academic work (college and graduate level) and three letters of reference sent directly to WREI. **Deadline:** May 21. **Remarks:** Established in 1980.

9736 ■ Women's Sports Foundation (WSF)
424 W 33rd St., Ste. 150
New York, NY 10001-2619
Ph: (646) 845-0273
E-mail: info@womenssportsfoundation.org
URL: www.womenssportsfoundation.org

9737 ■ Dorothy Harris Endowed Scholarships *(Graduate/Scholarship)*

Purpose: To provide female graduate students in Physical Education, Sport Management, Sport Psychology or Sport Sociology with a means to attend graduate school. **Focus:** Physical education; Sports studies. **Qualif.:** Applicant must be a female American citizen or legal resident; and a graduate student pursuing a full-time course of study at an accredited postgraduate institution. **Criteria:** Applicants will be evaluated based on career goals, GPA, financial need, research studies and sports participation and/or influence.

Funds Avail.: $1,500. **Number Awarded:** 2. **To Apply:** Applicants must submit a completed scholarship application form together with a copy of official transcripts from all colleges/universities attended and two letters of recommendation. Submit four complete stapled copies of the application package. **Deadline:** December 31. **Remarks:** Established in September 1990 in honor of Dr. Dorothy Harris, pioneer and advocate for women in sports.

9738 ■ Women's Transportation Seminar (WTS)
1701 K St. NW, Ste. 800
Washington, DC 20006
Ph: (202) 955-5085

Awards are arranged alphabetically below their administering organizations

Fax: (202) 955-5088
E-mail: membership@wtsinternational.org
URL: wtsinternational.org

9739 ■ Sharon D. Banks Undergraduate Memorial Scholarships *(Undergraduate/Scholarship)*

Purpose: To introduce cultural and organizational changes aimed at motivating the public transit work force. **Focus:** Transportation; Finance; Logistics. **Qualif.:** Applicants must be women pursuing undergraduate studies in transportation engineering, planning, finance or logistics, or related fields. Applicants must have at least a GPA of 3.0 or higher. **Criteria:** Recipients are selected based on specific transportation goals, academic record, transportation-related activities, or job skills.

Funds Avail.: $3,000. **To Apply:** Applicants must fill out and submit the scholarship application form.

9740 ■ Ann Koby Legacy Scholarships *(Undergraduate/Scholarship)*

Purpose: To provide financial assistance to women who wish to further their careers as leaders in the transportation industry. **Focus:** Transportation; Finance; Logistics. **Qualif.:** Applicants must be women pursuing undergraduate studies in transportation engineering, planning, finance or logistics, or related fields; and must have a GPA of at least 3.0 or higher. **Criteria:** Recipients are selected based on specific transportation goals, academic record, transportation-related activities or job skills.

Funds Avail.: $3,000. **To Apply:** Applicants must fill out the scholarship application form and submit them to local WTS Chapters. **Deadline:** November 17. **Contact:** Hayes Morrison at hayesm@ctps.com.

9741 ■ Helene M. Overly Memorial Scholarships *(Undergraduate/Scholarship)*

Purpose: To introduce cultural and organizational changes aimed at motivating the public transit work force. **Focus:** Transportation; Finance; Logistics. **Qualif.:** Applicants must be women pursuing undergraduate studies in transportation engineering, planning, finance or logistics, or related fields. Applicants must have at least a GPA of 3.0 or higher. **Criteria:** Recipients are selected based on specific transportation goals, academic record, transportation-related activities, or job skills.

Funds Avail.: $6,000. **To Apply:** Applicants must fill out the scholarship application form **Deadline:** November 7.

9742 ■ Carter G. Woodson Institute for African-American and African Studies

University of Virginia
108 Minor Hall
108 Minor Hall
Charlottesville, VA 22904-4162
Ph: (434) 924-3109
Fax: (434) 924-8820
E-mail: woodson@virginia.edu
URL: artsandsciences.virginia.edu/woodson

9743 ■ Post-doctoral Residential Research and Teaching Fellowships *(Postdoctorate/Fellowship)*

Purpose: To facilitate the writing of dissertations or manuscripts and provide successful applicants the opportunity to discuss and exchange works-in-progress both with each other and the larger intellectual community of the University. **Focus:** Humanities; Social Sciences. **Qualif.:** Applicants for the post-doctoral fellowship must have been awarded their Ph.D. by the time of application or furnish proof from the relevant registrar that all documentation required for the Ph.D. has been submitted. **Criteria:** Selection will be based on the following criteria: significance of the proposed work; qualifications of the applicant; familiarity with existing relevant research literature; research design of the project; promise of completion within the award period. Preference will be given to applicants whose field research is already substantially completed.

Funds Avail.: $45,000 plus benefits. **To Apply:** Applicants must submit a Candidate Profile on-line through Jobs@UVA and must attach the following: a maximum of 250-word letter of application stating interest in the program; a curriculum vitae which must include the personal information, date(s) and location(s) of degree(s) earned, honors and awards, lectures and conference presentations, publications and the names of three referees. Applicants must also submit the following: a project abstract, including title, not to exceed 50 words as well as a project description, including title, not to exceed seven double-spaced pages (1,750 words). It must indicate the nature of the research to be completed during the period of the fellowship award, as well as the significance of this work. The project description must include a detailed research plan giving concrete objectives to be achieved during the award period. Project descriptions must be attached through Jobs@ under Writing Sample 1; a working bibliography not to exceed four double-spaced pages. The bibliography must list those scholarly works that the applicant considers most important to the intellectual development of the project. The working bibliography must be attached through Jobs@ under Writing Sample 2; an original, signed three confidential letters of reference sent directly to the Woodson Institute by persons qualified to evaluate the proposals for which support is being sought. **Deadline:** December 1. **Contact:** Lawrie Balfour at dem8z@virginia.edu; Cheryll Lewis at 434-924-6255, cll2d@virginia.edu.

9744 ■ Pre-doctoral Residential Research Fellowships *(Doctorate/Fellowship)*

Purpose: To facilitate the writing of dissertations or manuscripts and provide successful applicants the opportunity to discuss and exchange works-in-progress both with each other and the larger intellectual community of the University. **Focus:** Humanities; Social Sciences. **Qualif.:** Open to all qualified candidates without restriction as to citizenship or current residence whose work focused on Africa and/or African Diaspora. **Criteria:** Selection will be based on the following criteria: significance of the proposed work; qualifications of the applicant; familiarity with existing relevant research literature; research design of the project; promise of completion within the award period. Preference will be given to applicants whose field research is already substantially completed.

Funds Avail.: $20,000 plus health insurance. **To Apply:** Applicants must submit a Candidate Profile on-line through Jobs@UVA and must attach the following: a maximum of 250-word letter of application stating interest in the program; a curriculum vitae which must include the personal information, date(s) and location(s) of degree(s) earned, honors and awards, lectures and conference presentations, publications and the names of three referees. Applicants must also submit the following: a project abstract, including title, not to exceed 50 words as well as a project description, including title, not to exceed seven

Awards are arranged alphabetically below their administering organizations

double-spaced pages (1,750 words). It must indicate the nature of the research to be completed during the period of the fellowship award, as well as the significance of this work. The project description must include a detailed research plan giving concrete objectives to be achieved during the award period. Project descriptions must be attached through Jobs@ under Writing Sample 1; a working bibliography not to exceed four double-spaced pages. The bibliography must list those scholarly works that the applicant considers most important to the intellectual development of the project. The working bibliography must be attached through Jobs@ under Writing Sample 2; an original, signed three confidential letters of reference sent directly to the Woodson Institute by persons qualified to evaluate the proposals for which support is being sought. **Deadline:** December 1. **Contact:** Lawrie Balfour at dem8z@virginia.edu; Cheryll Lewis at 434-924-6255, cll2d@virginia.edu.

9745 ■ Worcester District Medical Society (WDMS)

Mechanics Hall, 321 Main St.
Worcester, MA 01608
Ph: (508) 753-1579
Fax: (508) 754-6246
E-mail: info@wdms.org
URL: www.wdms.org

9746 ■ Worcester District Medical Society Scholarship Fund *(Undergraduate/Scholarship)*

Purpose: To provide educational assistance to medical students. **Focus:** Medicine. **Qualif.:** Applicants must be second, third or fourth year students enrolled (with tuition obligation) in an accredited medical or osteopathic school; and must be legal residents of Central Massachusetts at the time of applying to medical school. **Criteria:** Recipients are selected based on academic achievement; community service; and financial need.

Funds Avail.: No specific amount. **To Apply:** Applicants must submit a completed application form; current transcript; two letters of recommendation; and an essay stating the reasons for selecting a career in medicine and why they deserve the award. **Deadline:** July 27.

9747 ■ Working for Farmers' Success (WFS)

PO Box 68
Truman, MN 56088
Ph: (507) 776-1234
Fax: (507) 776-2871
Free: 800-657-3282
E-mail: wfsinfo@wfsag.com
URL: www.wfsag.com

9748 ■ Working for Farmers' Success Scholarships *(Undergraduate/Scholarship)*

Purpose: To encourage young people to pursue an agricultural career. **Focus:** Agricultural economics. **Qualif.:** Applicants must be senior students who are graduating from the WFS trade territory. **Criteria:** Recipients will be selected based on academic performance, qualities of leadership, integrity and good community citizenship. Financial need is also given consideration.

Funds Avail.: $500. **Number Awarded:** 20. **To Apply:** Applicants must submit a completed application form. **Dead-**

line: March 31. **Contact:** Jo Ann Gumto at the above address.

9749 ■ World Association for Cooperative Education (WACE)

600 Suffolk St.
Wannalancit Business Ctr., 1st Fl.
Lowell, MA 01854
Ph: (978) 934-1867
Fax: (978) 934-4084
E-mail: paul_stonely@uml.edu
URL: www.waceinc.org

9750 ■ National Co-op Scholarship Program *(Undergraduate/Scholarship)*

Purpose: To assist students pursuing education in science, mathematics, engineering and technology. **Focus:** Mathematics and mathematical sciences; Science; Engineering. **Qualif.:** Applicants must have GPA of 3.5 equivalent to "B" or better. **Criteria:** Selection is based on the application.

Funds Avail.: $6,000. **Number Awarded:** 170. **To Apply:** Applicants must submit a complete National Co-op Scholarship program Application including a typed, one-page essay (500 words). **Deadline:** February 15. **Contact:** Questions should be directed to Frank Schettino; Phone: 617-373-3406; E-mail: f.schettino@neu.edu.

9751 ■ World Council of Credit Unions (WOCCU)

601 Pennsylvania Ave. NW
S Bldg., Ste. 600
Washington, DC 20004-2601
Ph: (202) 638-0205
Fax: (202) 638-3410
E-mail: mail@woccu.org
URL: www.woccu.org

9752 ■ WYCUP Scholarships *(Professional development/Scholarship)*

Purpose: To engage and promote the next generation of credit union professionals and volunteers in the international credit union movement. **Focus:** General studies. **Qualif.:** Applicant must be 35 years of age or younger; must be actively involved either as an employee or volunteer with a credit union or credit organization affiliated with the international credit union movement; must demonstrate personal commitment and the ability to significantly influence credit unions in his/her country; must exhibit the potential to advance the international credit union system; must not have been a previous WYCUP Scholarship recipient. **Criteria:** Individual selected for the scholarship are those the committee believes have the greatest potential to contribute to the international credit union system.

Funds Avail.: Scholarship covers all costs associated with the event, including conference registration fee, travel costs, hotel accommodation and metals. **Number Awarded:** 5. **To Apply:** Applicant must have two Nomination Forms (attached) completed by the nominee and the sponsor; must provide the proof of age (photocopy of passport, driver's license, birth certificate or other official document); must prepare a brief 500-word essay describing the contribution made to the development of the candidate's credit union or credit union organization. **Deadline:** June 1. **Contact:** Liliana Tangwall, Credit Union Analyst, at 608-395-2043, or ltangwall@woccu.org.

Awards are arranged alphabetically below their administering organizations

9753 ■ World Forest Institute (WFI)
c/o World Forestry Center
4033 SW Canyon Rd.
Portland, OR 97221
Ph: (503) 228-1367
E-mail: swu@worldforestry.org
URL: wfi.worldforestry.org

9754 ■ WFI International Fellowships
(Undergraduate/Fellowship)

Purpose: To provide assistance to students interested in the forestry field. **Focus:** Forestry. **Qualif.:** Applicants must obtain a bachelor's degree or equivalent in the field of forestry, natural resources, or other related degree; must have written and oral proficiency in English; 21 years of age; must have an initial research proposal on a topic relevant to forestry; should be self-motivated, be able to work independently towards a clear research goal or output, be able to work with colleagues from diverse backgrounds; and should obtain funding from the fellowship. **Criteria:** Selection will be based on submitted documents and specific criteria.

Funds Avail.: $10,000 for six month fellowship and $12,000 for twelve month fellowship. **To Apply:** Applicants should submit a completed application form; project proposal; and curriculum vitae. The project should take advantage of being located in the Pacific Northwest which involves collaboration with forest industry, local organizations, researchers, or communities. **Contact:** Sara Wu at the above address.

9755 ■ World Leisure Organization (WLO)
University of Northern Iowa
03 Wellness/Recreation Ctr.
Cedar Falls, IA 50614
Ph: (319) 273-6279
Fax: (319) 273-5958
URL: www.worldleisure.org

9756 ■ Thomas and Ruth River International Scholarships *(Undergraduate, Graduate/ Scholarship)*

Purpose: To provide opportunities for seniors or graduate students who are studying recreation or tourism studies related fields. **Focus:** Travel and Tourism; Parks and recreation. **Qualif.:** Applicants must be undergraduate or be final year graduate students majoring in recreation, leisure studies, leisure services and resources, or tourism studies; must have a GPA of 3.5 on a 4.0 scale for undergraduates and 3.8 on a 4.0 scale if graduate students; must be recommended by two faculty members; must have demonstrated interest in recreation, leisure and/or tourism internationally; must have had either volunteer or paid work experience in the recreation, leisure services or tourism fields. **Criteria:** Applicants will be selected based on submitted application and supporting documents.

Funds Avail.: No specific amount. **To Apply:** Applicants must complete the application form; must submit the Faculty Validation of Student Applicant form and a copy of the abstract submitted to the World Congress Program Committee. If the college or university does not have a major in required fields, applicants must obtain a letter from their major professor indicating the area of study. If the college or university does not require coursework, applicants must obtain a letter indicating the required learning/

research activities and performance evaluation. **Deadline:** May 1. **Contact:** Prof. Stephen Anderson; Barry University, 11300 NE, 2nd Ave., Miami Shores, FL 33161; Phone: 305-899-3447; Fax: 305-899-4809; E-mail: sanderson@mail.barry.edu.

9757 ■ George Torkildsen Literary Awards
(Professional development/Award)

Purpose: To recognize individuals who made a significant contribution to the recreation, parks and leisure service literature by advancing innovative ideas, thoughts and/or philosophical perspectives. **Focus:** Parks and recreation. **Qualif.:** Applicants must be individuals who made contributions in recreation, parks and leisure service literatures. **Criteria:** Applicants will be evaluated based on literary contributions to advance leisure concerns worldwide; impact of the contributions to influence the general public and/or profession; clarity, solutions and insights brought to emerging trends, issues and concepts.

Funds Avail.: Amount not specified. **To Apply:** Applicants must be include their full name, title, organizational affiliation and full contact details; must submit a written statement of no more than 1000 words that addresses the nominees scholarly efforts and other professional contributions, referencing the impact that the nominees contributions have made to the literature; and must submit a curriculum vitae.

9758 ■ World Wildlife Fund (WWF)
PO Box 97180
Washington, DC 20090-7180
Ph: (202) 293-4800
Fax: (202) 293-9211
Free: 800-960-0993
E-mail: membership@wwfus.org
URL: www.worldwildlife.org

9759 ■ Kathryn Fuller Science for Nature Post-Doctoral Fellowships *(Graduate, Postdoctorate/ Fellowship)*

Purpose: To support early-career scientists working on issues of exceptional importance and relevance to conservation. **Focus:** Conservation of natural resources. **Qualif.:** Applicant must have earned the doctoral degree between June 1, 2006 and June 1, 2011; proposing a research plan that addresses the following topics: 1) ecosystem services; 2) measuring and monitoring carbon stocks in forests; 3) climate change impacts on/and adaptation of freshwater resources. Staff, directors and immediate family members are not eligible for the fellowship. **Criteria:** Selection is based on applicants' ability, accomplishments and potential to become a leader in the field; scientific merit, feasibility and significance of the research proposal; and relevance of the research to conservation practice in general, WWF's mission and programs. Preference will be given to those applicants whose research proposes their country of origin.

Funds Avail.: $140,000 stipend and up to 17,500 to cover indirect costs at host institution. **To Apply:** Applicants are required to apply online. In addition, applicants must submit two letters of recommendation, proof of PhD, curriculum vitae and an indirect cost waiver **Contact:** Applicants may mail or email their application form and supporting documents to fullerfund@wwfus.org.

9760 ■ Worldstudio Foundation
200 Varick St., Ste. 507
New York, NY 10014

Awards are arranged alphabetically below their administering organizations

Ph: (212) 366-1317
Fax: (212) 807-0024
E-mail: info@worldstudio.org
URL: scholarships.worldstudioinc.com/worldstudio-foundation

9761 ■ Worldstudio AIGA Scholarships *(Graduate, Undergraduate/Scholarship)*

Purpose: To help the next generation of artists, architects and designers realize their dreams while being pro-actively involved in their communities. **Focus:** Advertising; Architecture; Cartooning; Crafts; Environmental design; Fashion design; Filmmaking; Fine arts; Graphic art and design; Illustrators and illustrations; Industrial design; Interior design; Landscape architecture and design; Photography; Urban affairs/design/planning. **Qualif.:** Applicants must be U.S. citizens or in possession of a Green Card; pursuing an undergraduate or graduate degree in the fine or commercial arts, design or architecture and planning to enter a career in the creative professions; planning or matriculated at an accredited college/university in the United States; maintaining a full-time status; have at least 2.0 GPA; and must demonstrate financial need. Minority students are encouraged to apply. **Criteria:** Selection is based on the quality of submitted work, financial need, minority status, academic record, recommendations and strength of written statement.

Funds Avail.: Basic: $2,000 to $5,000 and $500 cash for honorable mention prizes. **To Apply:** Applicants must submit up to ten examples of their work and must follow the format indicated at the website. Applicants must mail the disks with film, motion graphics or interactive; transcript(s); and letters of recommendation. **Deadline:** March 30. **Remarks:** In partnership with AIGA. **Contact:** Worldstudio AIGA Scholarships 164 Fifth Ave. New York, NY 10010, email: scholarship@aiga.org.

9762 ■ Worldwide Assurance for Employees of Public Agencies (WAEPA)

433 Park Ave.
Falls Church, VA 22046
Ph: (703) 790-8010
Fax: (703) 790-4606
Free: 800-368-3484
E-mail: info@waepa.org
URL: www.waepa.org

9763 ■ WAEPA Scholarship Program
(Undergraduate, Vocational/Occupational/Scholarship)

Purpose: To assist policy holders' children who plan to continue education in college or vocational school programs. **Focus:** General studies. **Qualif.:** Applicants must be children, under the age of 23, of WAEPA life insurance policy holders; must be high school seniors or graduates who plan to enroll or accepted as full-time in an accredited two-year or four-year college, university or vocational-technical school; must have minimum grade point average of 3.0 on a 4.0 scale or its equivalent. **Criteria:** Recipients are selected based on academic record, demonstrated leadership and participation in school, community and volunteer activities, honors, work experience, statement of goals and aspirations, unusual personal or family circumstances and an outside appraisal.

Funds Avail.: $1,000 to $4,000. **Number Awarded:** 65. **To**

Apply: Applicants must complete the application and mail it along with a current and complete transcript of grades to Scholarship America. **Deadline:** February 1. **Contact:** WAEPA Scholarship Program; Scholarship America; One Scholarship Way, PO Box 297, Saint Peter, MN 56082; Telephone: 507-931-1682.

9764 ■ Wound, Ostomy and Continence Nurses Society (WOCN)

15000 Commerce Pkwy., Ste. C
Mount Laurel, NJ 08054
Fax: (856) 439-0525
Free: 888-224-9626
E-mail: wocn_info@wocn.org
URL: www.wocn.org

9765 ■ WOCN Accredited Nursing Education Scholarships *(Graduate, Undergraduate/Scholarship)*

Purpose: To support individuals seeking education in wound, ostomy and continence nursing specialties. **Focus:** Nursing. **Qualif.:** Applicants must be pursuing an education in wound, ostomy and continence nursing care; accepted in a WOCN-accredited WOC Educational Program; currently enrolled in a WOCN-accredited WOC Education Program. **Criteria:** WOCN Scholarship Committee will review completed applications.

Funds Avail.: No specific amount. **To Apply:** Application form is available at the website. Applicants must submit completed, legible application; signed consent forms; acceptance letter, proof of current enrollment or certificate of completion from a WOCN accredited WOC Education Program; and three letters of recommendation.

9766 ■ WOCN Advanced Education Scholarships *(Doctorate, Graduate, Undergraduate/Scholarship)*

Purpose: To support individual seeking education in wound, ostomy and continence nursing specialties. **Focus:** Nursing. **Qualif.:** Applicant must be seeking a baccalaureate, master's or doctoral degree or NP certificate; a member of WOCN; employed (for at least three years) as a wound, ostomy or continence nurse; accepted in an NLN-accredited nursing program or other accredited college/university program for non-nursing degree. **Criteria:** WOCN Scholarship Committee will review completed applications.

Funds Avail.: No specific amount. **To Apply:** Application form is available at the website. Applicants must provide three letters of recommendation; signed consent forms; proof of current enrollment or acceptance into an NLN accredited nursing program or other accredited college/university program for non-nursing degree; proof of current or previous employment as a wound, ostomy and/or continence nurse during the last 3 years; proof of current, unrestricted RN license; copy of WOCN member card; and copy of WOCNCB certification certificate. **Deadline:** November 1 and May 1.

9767 ■ Xavier University

3800 Victory Pky.
Cincinnati, OH 45207-7750
Ph: (513) 745-3000
Free: 800-344-4698
URL: www.xavier.edu

Awards are arranged alphabetically below their administering organizations

9768 ■ Edgecliff Alumni Awards (Undergraduate/Scholarship)

Purpose: To financially support students with their education. **Focus:** General studies. **Qualif.:** Applicants must be incoming freshmen and the children, grandchildren, nieces or nephews of Edgecliff College alumni. **Criteria:** Selection is based on academic merit and financial need.

Funds Avail.: No specific amount. **To Apply:** Applicants admitted at the Xavier University are automatically considered. **Deadline:** February 1.

9769 ■ Edgecliff McAuley Art Scholarships (Undergraduate/Scholarship)

Purpose: To financially support students with their education. **Focus:** Arts. **Qualif.:** Applicant must be an incoming first year student with good academic achievement and outstanding artistic talent, and has declared a major in the Arts. **Criteria:** Selection is based on the submitted portfolio.

Funds Avail.: One full-tuition, and two half-tuition. **Number Awarded:** 3. **To Apply:** Students admitted at the Xavier University are automatically considered. Applicants must submit a portfolio (minimum of eight or maximum of twelve examples of applicant's best work). Portfolios must be clearly labeled with the applicant's name, home phone number, school, and must include an inventory list and a one page personal resume. All pieces must be matted (white mats are mandatory) unless in slide/digital format. All work must be original. **Deadline:** February 4.

9770 ■ Edgecliff McAuley Music Scholarships (Undergraduate/Scholarship)

Purpose: To financially support students with their education. **Focus:** Music. **Qualif.:** Applicant must be an incoming student. **Criteria:** Selection is based on musical talent and achievement.

Funds Avail.: Full-tuition (up to $5,000). **Number Awarded:** 1. **To Apply:** Students admitted at the Xavier University are automatically considered. Applicants must pass the audition held on January 29, February 12, February 26. **Contact:** Ms. Scarpaci at 513-745-3801, fax at 513-745-3343 or scarpaci@xavier.edu.

9771 ■ James E. Hoff, S.J. Scholars (Undergraduate/Scholarship)

Purpose: To financially support students with their education. **Focus:** General studies. **Qualif.:** Applicants must be the children, grandchildren, nieces or nephews of Edgecliff College alumni; must demonstrate exceptional leadership, vision, courage, service and compassion in academic and personal life. **Criteria:** Selection is based on academic merit and financial need.

Funds Avail.: Varies. **To Apply:** Applicants admitted at the Xavier University are automatically considered. **Remarks:** Award may be given to Edgecliff alumni award recipients.

9772 ■ Indiana Alumni Scholarships (Undergraduate/Scholarship)

Purpose: To financially support students with their education. **Focus:** General studies. **Qualif.:** Applicant must be an incoming freshman from Indiana. **Criteria:** Selection is based on need.

Funds Avail.: $2000. **Number Awarded:** 2. **To Apply:** Applicants must apply for financial aid by completing the FAFSA. **Deadline:** FAFSA deadline: February 15; Application deadline: March 1.

9773 ■ Ohio War Orphan Scholarships (Undergraduate/Scholarship)

Purpose: To financially support students with their education. **Focus:** General studies. **Qualif.:** Applicant must be student with a parent who served at least 90 days of active duty during wartime and is disabled or deceased as a result of service. **Criteria:** Qualified students are automatically considered.

Funds Avail.: $660. **To Apply:** Applications available from high school guidance counselors or veterans offices.

9774 ■ Miguel Pro Scholarships (Undergraduate/Scholarship)

Purpose: To financially support students with their education. **Focus:** General studies. **Qualif.:** Applicant must be a Hispanic/Latino first-year student with excellent academic achievement. **Criteria:** Selection is based on merit.

Funds Avail.: Up to full-tuition. **To Apply:** Applicants admitted at the Xavier University are automatically considered. **Deadline:** February 1. **Remarks:** Selected students will be interviewed on the campus. The scholarship is named in honor of Miguel Pro, S.J., a Mexican priest who was martyred by the Mexican government in 1927 for his practice and teaching of the Catholic faith.

9775 ■ St. Francis Xavier Scholarships (Undergraduate/Scholarship)

Purpose: To financially support students with their education. **Focus:** General studies. **Qualif.:** Applicant must be an incoming first-year student with exceptional academic achievement and outstanding leadership involvement in the community or school. **Criteria:** Selection is based on merit.

Funds Avail.: Full-tuition. **Number Awarded:** 10. **To Apply:** Applicants admitted at the Xavier University are automatically considered. **Deadline:** December 1. **Remarks:** Selected students will be interviewed in the campus.

9776 ■ Trustee, Schawe, and Presidential Scholarships (Undergraduate/Scholarship)

Purpose: To financially support students with their education. **Focus:** General studies. **Qualif.:** Applicant must be an incoming first-year student with excellent academic achievement (rank at least in the top 25 percent of high school class, have appropriately high grades, and have a minimum SAT of 1130, 25 ACT). **Criteria:** Selection is based on merit.

Funds Avail.: $13,000-$15,000. **To Apply:** Applicants admitted at the Xavier University are automatically considered.

9777 ■ Francis X. Weninger Scholarships (Undergraduate/Scholarship)

Purpose: To financially support students with their education. **Focus:** General studies. **Qualif.:** Applicant must be an African American first-year student with excellent academic achievement. **Criteria:** Selection is based on merit.

Funds Avail.: Up to full-tuition. **To Apply:** Applicants admitted at the Xavier University are automatically considered. **Deadline:** February 1. **Remarks:** Selected students will be interviewed on the campus. The Scholarship is named in honor of Francis Xavier Weninger, S.J., founder of St. Ann Parish in 1865.

9778 ■ Xavier Community-Engaged Fellowships (Undergraduate/Fellowship)

Purpose: To financially support students with their education. **Focus:** General studies. **Qualif.:** Applicant must be

Awards are arranged alphabetically below their administering organizations

incoming first-year student who have demonstrated high academic achievement, outstanding service to community, school, or church, and leadership in encouraging others to serve. **Criteria:** Preference is given to students demonstrating exemplary involvement in volunteer service; have shown potential for leading other students in service; have attained a minimum score of 29 on the ACT composite or 1280 on the SAT; and in the top ten percent of the high school senior class.

Funds Avail.: $22,000 annually. **Number Awarded:** 8. **To Apply:** Applicants admitted at the Xavier University are automatically considered. **Deadline:** December 1. **Remarks:** Selected students will be interviewed on the campus.

9779 ■ Xavier University Chancellor Scholarships (Undergraduate/Scholarship)

Purpose: To financially support students with their education. **Focus:** General studies. **Qualif.:** Applicant must be an incoming first-year student with excellent academic achievement. **Criteria:** Selection is based on merit.

Funds Avail.: $17,000. **Number Awarded:** 15. **To Apply:** Applicants admitted at the Xavier University are automatically considered. **Deadline:** December 1. **Remarks:** Selected students will be interviewed in the campus. Named in honor of Xavier's late Chancellor James E. Hoff, S.J.

9780 ■ Xavier University Departmental Scholarships (Undergraduate/Scholarship)

Purpose: To financially support students with their education. **Focus:** Chemistry; Classical studies; History; Mathematics and mathematical sciences; Modern languages; Physics. **Qualif.:** Applicant must top the score in either of the six departmental exams (chemistry, classics (Latin), history, mathematics, modern languages (French, German or Spanish) and physics). Student must major in the area for which the scholarship is awarded. **Criteria:** Scholarship is given to the highest scorer on the exams.

Funds Avail.: $2,500. **To Apply:** Participants will take an exam in the appropriate subject area and have an opportunity to speak with faculty and learn more about the department. **Deadline:** January 30.

9781 ■ Xavier University Honors Bachelor of Arts Scholarships (Undergraduate/Scholarship)

Purpose: To financially support students with their education. **Focus:** Arts. **Qualif.:** Applicant must be a student enrolled in the honor bachelor of arts program. **Criteria:** Selection is based on merit.

Funds Avail.: One-quarter tuition. **To Apply:** Applicants admitted at the Xavier University are automatically considered.

9782 ■ Xavier University Legacy Scholarships (Undergraduate/Scholarship)

Purpose: To financially support students with their education. **Focus:** General studies. **Qualif.:** Applicants must be full-time undergraduate student who are children or grandchildren of Xavier alumni. **Criteria:** Selection is based on academic merit, leadership and service activities.

Funds Avail.: $3000. **Number Awarded:** 2. **To Apply:** Applicants must submit a completed Legacy Scholarship Application along with the required supporting materials. **Deadline:** February 1.

9783 ■ Xavier University ROTC Scholarships - Air Force ROTC (Undergraduate/Scholarship)

Purpose: To financially support students with their education. **Focus:** Aerospace sciences. **Qualif.:** Applicants must be high school students pursuing an Air Force ROTC or college freshmen and sophomores pursuing an in-college Air Force ROTC. **Criteria:** Selection is based on merit.

Funds Avail.: Covers the cost of remaining tuition, room and board. **To Apply:** Applicants must contact the Detachment 665 Unit Admission Officer for the application process. **Contact:** 513-556-2237.

9784 ■ Xavier University ROTC Scholarships - Army ROTC (Undergraduate/Scholarship)

Purpose: To financially support students with their education. **Focus:** Military science and education. **Qualif.:** Applicant may be a freshman, sophomore, junior, or senior student pursuing military science at Xavier University. Nursing students can also compete for an Army ROTC nursing scholarship and upon graduation become an Army Nurse. **Criteria:** Selection is based on a student's merit and grades, not financial need.

Funds Avail.: Full-tuition, $1,200 yearly book allowance and a monthly stipend starting at $300/month during the academic school year. **To Apply:** High School students may apply online for an Army ROTC Scholarship at www.goarmy.com/rotc. **Deadline:** March 1. **Contact:** Capt. Hayes, at 513-745-1066.

9785 ■ Xavier University Williams Scholarships (Undergraduate/Scholarship)

Purpose: To financially support students with their education. **Focus:** Business. **Qualif.:** Applicant must be a first year student declared a major in the Williams College of Business. **Criteria:** Selection is based on merit.

Funds Avail.: $3000. **Number Awarded:** 4. **To Apply:** Applicants must complete the online application. **Deadline:** February 15.

9786 ■ Xerox
PO Box 4505
Norwalk, CT 06856-4505
Ph: (203) 968-3000
Free: 800-334-6200
E-mail: info@xerox.com
URL: www.xerox.com

9787 ■ Xerox Technical Minority Scholarships (Graduate, Undergraduate/Scholarship)

Purpose: To provide financial support and experiences for minorities enrolled in a technical degree program. **Focus:** Chemistry; Computer and information sciences; Materials research/science; Printing trades and industries; Optics; Physics; Engineering, Chemical; Engineering, Computer; Engineering, Electrical; Engineering, Mechanical; Engineering, Optical. **Qualif.:** Applicant must be an academic high-achiever (3.0 or better GPA); a U.S. citizen or visa-holding Permanent Resident of African American, Asian, Pacific Island, Native American, Native Alaskan, or Hispanic descent; enrolled as a full-time undergraduate or graduate student in any technical fields (Chemistry, Information Management, Computing & Software Systems, Material Science, Printing Management Science, Laser Optics, Physics, Material Science, Engineering: Chemical, Computer, Electrical, Imaging, Manufacturing, Mechanical, Optical, or Software). **Criteria:** Selection is based on the application materials submitted for review.

Funds Avail.: $1,000-$10,000. **To Apply:** Applicants must complete the scholarship application form, attach a resume

---

Awards are arranged alphabetically below their administering organizations

and have the Financial Aid Office complete the bottom portion of the application. Submit application package to: Xerox Technical Minority Scholarship Program 150 State St., 4th Fl. Rochester, NY 14614, email: xtmsp@rballiance.com. **Deadline:** September 30. **Contact:** Nancy Dempsey at nancy.dempsey@xerox.com, or Garvin Byrd at garvin.byrd@xerox.com.

9788 ■ York Art Association (YAA)
PO Box 74
York, ME 03909
Ph: (207) 363-4049
URL: www.yorkartassociation.com

9789 ■ Letitia Moore Art Scholarships
(Undergraduate/Scholarship)

Purpose: To financially assist students majoring in art or art history. **Focus:** Art history; Art. **Qualif.:** Applicants must be enrolled in an accredited college or university; must be majoring in art or art history; must have completed their first year of study with a GPA of at least 3.0 or greater. **Criteria:** Recipients will be selected based on submitted materials.

Funds Avail.: Amount not specified. **To Apply:** Applicants must submit a letter of application and provide proof of their eligibility. The letter should describe the applicant's educational and career goals and should identify the names and telephone numbers of two or three references familiar with their ability and aspirations. **Deadline:** September 1.

9790 ■ Young Musicians Foundation (YMF)
195 S Beverly Dr., Ste. 414
Beverly Hills, CA 90212
Ph: (310) 859-7668
Fax: (310) 859-1365
E-mail: info@ymf.org
URL: www.ymf.org

9791 ■ YMF Scholarships *(All/Scholarship)*

Purpose: To provide financial assistance to young musicians for their private music instruction. **Focus:** Music. **Qualif.:** Applicant must demonstrate exceptional talent and financial need; be a resident of Southern California. Instrumentalist or pianist may apply through the completion of their senior year of high school. Vocalists must be between the ages of 12-26. Applicant who is not a U.S. citizen and is under age 18, applicant's parents must live in the state of California. **Criteria:** Recipients will be selected at the four days countrywide auditions. Selection is based on outstanding talent and financial need.

Funds Avail.: $250-$10,000. **Number Awarded:** 40. **To Apply:** Applicant must submit a completed application. **Contact:** Questions can be addressed to Rachel Francis at the above address; E-mail: rachel@ymf.org or Jake Wenger at jake@ymf.org.

9792 ■ Young Women's Alliance (YWA)
PO Box 684612
Austin, TX 78768
E-mail: administrator@youngwomensalliance.org
URL: www.youngwomensalliance.org

9793 ■ YWA Foundation Scholarships *(Graduate, Undergraduate/Scholarship)*

Purpose: To financially support female students with their educational pursuit. **Focus:** General studies. **Qualif.:** Applicant must be a female U.S. resident under the age of 40, and be a junior or senior in college or pursuing a graduate degree at a university or accredited institution of higher learning within Central Texas. **Criteria:** Selection is based on demonstrated financial need, commitment to community service, academic achievement and leadership potential.

Funds Avail.: $2,500. **Number Awarded:** 1. **To Apply:** Applicants must submit a completed application form along with an official copy of college transcript; a personal statement; copy of Federal Tax Return (or parents') for the previous year; proof of current income (copy of recent paycheck or stub); and two letters of recommendation (from persons outside the family). **Contact:** Application form and supporting documents must be submitted to YWA Foundation Scholarship, PO Box 1503, Austin, TX 78767 or may send via email to foundationpresident@youngwomensalliance.org.

9794 ■ Youth Maritime Training Association (YMTA)
PO Box 70425
Seattle, WA 98127-0425
Ph: (206) 300-5559
E-mail: garystauffer47@msn.com
URL: www.ymta.net

9795 ■ Norm Manly - YMTA Maritime Educational Scholarships *(Undergraduate/Scholarship)*

Purpose: To support students pursuing maritime training and education. **Focus:** Maritime studies. **Qualif.:** Applicants must be planning to pursue a post-secondary training or educational program leading to maritime or marine-related career; must be under 21 at time of application; must be high school seniors enrolled in the State of Washington; and have GPA of at least 2.5. Relatives of YMTA Executives, Honorary and Advisory Board members are not eligible for YMTA Scholarships. **Criteria:** Recipients will be selected based on a review of all the application materials submitted.

Funds Avail.: $1,000, $3,000, and $5,000. **Number Awarded:** 4. **To Apply:** Applicants are required to complete the application form; must submit the high school transcripts; a 300-500 words essay; and letter of support from teacher. Application must have signature and date. **Deadline:** February 22 and April 2. **Contact:** Carleen See at the above address or e-mail at carleeninballard@yahoo.com.

9796 ■ Youth for Understanding (YFU)
6400 Goldsboro Rd., Ste. 100
Bethesda, MD 20817
Ph: (240) 235-2100
Fax: (240) 235-2104
Free: 866-4YFU-USA
E-mail: admission@yfu.org
URL: www.yfu-usa.org

9797 ■ Youth for Understanding Scholarships *(Undergraduate/Scholarship)*

Purpose: To provide deserving individuals with the best international exchange experience. **Focus:** Travel and tourism. **Qualif.:** Applicants must be between the ages of 15 and 18 and have maintained a minimum 3.0 GPA for a year or semester program or 2.0 GPA for a summer program,

Awards are arranged alphabetically below their administering organizations

and be in good health. **Criteria:** Recipient will be selected based on a comprehensive evaluation process done by the Selection Committee at the YFU USA national office.

Funds Avail.: No specific amount. **To Apply:** Applicant must file an application online at the website of YFU.

9798 ■ Yukon Law Foundation
Box 31789
Whitehorse, YT, Canada T1A 6L3
Ph: (867) 667-7500
Fax: (867) 393-3904
E-mail: info@yukonlawfoundation.com
URL: www.yukonlawfoundation.com

9799 ■ Yukon Law Foundation Scholarships
(Undergraduate/Scholarship)

Purpose: To provide financial assistance to qualified students who want to pursue their studies. **Focus:** Law. **Qualif.:** Applicants must be students attending law or law related studies. **Criteria:** Recipients will be selected based on academic achievement, residency, community involvement, and financial need.

Funds Avail.: $15,000. **To Apply:** Applicants must complete the application form available online; submit a transcript of record and two letters of recommendation. Application form and other supporting documents must be sent to Yukon Law Foundation or dropped off at No. 202-302 Steel St., Whitehorse, YT CA Y1A 2C5. **Deadline:** August 31.

9800 ■ Zeta Phi Beta Sorority
1734 New Hampshire Ave. NW
Washington, DC 20009
Ph: (202) 387-3103
Fax: (202) 232-4593
E-mail: ihq@zphib1920.org
URL: www.zphib1920.org

9801 ■ Mildred Cater Bradham Social Work Fellowships *(Graduate/Fellowship)*

Purpose: To support students in pursuit of higher education. **Focus:** Social work. **Qualif.:** Applicant must be a Zeta Phi Beta Sorority, Inc. member; pursuing a full-time graduate or professional degree in social work in an accredited college or university program. **Criteria:** Selection is based on the application and supporting documents.

Funds Avail.: $500-$1000. **Number Awarded:** 1. **To Apply:** Applicants must submit completed application forms along with the required materials. **Deadline:** February 1.

9802 ■ Lullelia W. Harrison Scholarships in Counseling *(Graduate, Undergraduate/ Scholarship)*

Purpose: To support students in pursuit of higher education. **Focus:** Counseling/Guidance. **Qualif.:** Applicant must be a full-time graduate or undergraduate level student enrolled in a degree program in counseling. **Criteria:** Selection is based on the application and supporting documents.

Funds Avail.: $500-$1000. **Number Awarded:** 1. **To Apply:** Applicants must submit completed application forms along with the required materials.

9803 ■ Isabel M. Herson Scholarships in Education *(Graduate, Undergraduate/Scholarship)*

Purpose: To support students in pursuit of higher education. **Focus:** Education, Elementary; Education-Curricula.

Qualif.: Applicant must be a graduate or undergraduate level student enrolled full-time in a degree program in either elementary or secondary education. **Criteria:** Selection is based on the application and supporting documents.

Funds Avail.: $500-$1000. **Number Awarded:** 1. **To Apply:** Applicants must submit completed application forms along with the required materials.

9804 ■ Zora Neale Hurston Scholarships
(Graduate/Scholarship)

Purpose: To support students in pursuit of higher education. **Focus:** Anthropology. **Qualif.:** Applicant must be a graduate student enrolled full-time and pursuing a degree in anthropology. **Criteria:** Selection is based on the application and supporting documents.

Funds Avail.: $500-$1000. **Number Awarded:** 1. **To Apply:** Applicants must submit completed application forms along with the required materials.

9805 ■ S. Evelyn Lewis Memorial Scholarships in Medical Health Sciences *(Graduate, Undergraduate/Scholarship)*

Purpose: To support students in pursuit of higher education. **Focus:** Medicine; Health sciences. **Qualif.:** Applicant must be a female full-time graduate or undergraduate enrolled in a program leading to a degree in medicine or health sciences. **Criteria:** Selection is based on the application and supporting documents.

Funds Avail.: $500-$1000. **Number Awarded:** 1. **To Apply:** Applicants must submit completed application forms along with the required materials. **Deadline:** February 1.

9806 ■ Nancy B. Woolridge McGee Graduate Fellowships *(Graduate/Fellowship)*

Purpose: To support students in pursuit of higher education. **Focus:** General studies. **Qualif.:** Applicant must be a Zeta Phi Beta Sorority, Inc. member; pursuing a full-time graduate or professional degree in an accredited college or university program. **Criteria:** Selection is based on the application and supporting documents.

Funds Avail.: $500-$1000. **Number Awarded:** 1. **To Apply:** Applicants must submit completed application forms along with the required materials. **Deadline:** February 1.

9807 ■ Deborah Partridge Wolfe International Fellowships *(Graduate, Undergraduate/ Fellowship)*

Purpose: To support students in pursuit of higher education. **Focus:** General studies. **Qualif.:** Applicant must be a full-time graduate or undergraduate U.S. student studying abroad; or full-time graduate or undergraduate foreign student studying in the U.S. **Criteria:** Selection is based on the application and supporting documents.

Funds Avail.: $500-$1000. **To Apply:** Applicants must submit a completed application form and documented proof of academic study and plan of program to the Scholarship Chairperson with signature of school administrator or Program Director.

9808 ■ Zeta Phi Beta Sorority General Graduate Scholarships *(Graduate, Postdoctorate/ Scholarship)*

Purpose: To support students for the pursuit of higher education. **Focus:** General studies. **Qualif.:** Applicant must be a female full-time graduate on a professional degree,

Awards are arranged alphabetically below their administering organizations

masters, doctoral or enrolled in post-doctoral study. **Criteria:** Selection is based on the application.

Funds Avail.: $2,500 per year. **Number Awarded:** 1. **To Apply:** Applicants must submit a completed application form along with the required materials. **Deadline:** February 1.

9809 ■ Zeta Phi Beta Sorority General Undergraduate Scholarships *(Undergraduate/ Scholarship)*

Purpose: To support students for the pursuit of higher education. **Focus:** General studies. **Qualif.:** Applicant must be a full-time undergraduate freshman, sophomore, junior, senior or graduating high school planning to enter college. **Criteria:** Selection is based on the application and supporting documents.

Funds Avail.: $500-$1000. **Number Awarded:** 1. **To Apply:** Applicants must submit a completed application form along with the required materials. Applicants must submit a proof of enrollment or university acceptance.

9810 ■ Zonta Club of Hilo
PO Box 1915
Hilo, HI 96721-1915
Ph: (808) 959-2711
E-mail: info@zontahilo.org
URL: zontahilo.org

9811 ■ Amelia Earhart Fellowship Program *(Postdoctorate/Fellowship)*

Purpose: To provide financial support for qualified females intending to pursue their graduate Ph.D./doctoral degrees in aerospace-related science and aerospace-related engineering. **Focus:** Engineering, Aerospace; Aerospace sciences. **Qualif.:** Applicants must be registered in an accredited Ph.D/doctoral program in a qualifying area of science or engineering closely related to advanced studies in aerospace-related engineering; must demonstrate a superior academic record at a recognized university or college with accredited courses in aerospace-related studies as verified by transcripts and recommendation; must provide evidence of a well-defined research program in aerospace-related science or aerospace-related engineering as described in the application essay, research and

publication; must clearly demonstrate the relationship of the research to aerospace and furnish verification of the research program through at least one of the reference letters required with the application; and must be registered in a Ph.D/ doctorate program by the time the fellowship is awarded. **Criteria:** Selection of applicants will be based on the application requirements.

Funds Avail.: $10,000. **Number Awarded:** 35. **To Apply:** Applicants must submit transcripts of grades and school verification form; must have the list of schools attended and degrees received, employment history, plans for intended study, essay on academic and professional goals, and three recommendations from teachers or supervisors. **Deadline:** November 15.

9812 ■ Zonta International Foundation (ZIF)
1211 W 22nd St., Ste. 900
Oak Brook, IL 60523
Ph: (630) 928-1400
Fax: (630) 928-1559
E-mail: zontaintl@zonta.org
URL: www.zonta.org

9813 ■ Jane M. Klausman Women in Business Scholarships *(Graduate, Undergraduate/ Scholarship)*

Purpose: To help women pursue their undergraduate and Master's degree in business management. **Focus:** Business. **Qualif.:** Applicants must be women pursuing a business or business-related degree who demonstrate outstanding potential in the chosen field; must be enrolled in the second year of an undergraduate program through the final year of a Master's program at the time of the application; must have achieved an outstanding academic record; and living or studying in a Zonta region/district. Online students are also eligible. **Criteria:** Recipients will be selected based on submitted applications.

Funds Avail.: Maximum amount of $5,000. **To Apply:** Applicants must complete an application form; must submit one recommendation from a faculty member and from an employer, volunteer supervisor, or academic advisor; must submit a 500-word essay that describes academic and professional goals; verification of enrollment; and transcript of grades. All non-English documents must be translated in English. **Deadline:** July.

Awards are arranged alphabetically below their administering organizations

This index classifies awards by one or more of some 400 specific subject categories. Citations are arranged alphabetically under all appropriate subject categories. Each citation is followed by the study level and award type, which appear in parentheses. The number following the parenthetical information indicates the book entry number for a particular award, not a page number.

Abortion (See Family planning)

Academic medicine (See Medicine)

Accounting

African American Network - Carolinas Scholarship Fund *(Undergraduate/Scholarship)* [3882]
ALPFA Scholarship Programs *(Postgraduate, Undergraduate/Scholarship)* [1824]
American Society of Military Comptrollers National Scholarship Program *(Undergraduate/Scholarship)* [1305]
APS/ASU Scholarships *(Undergraduate/Scholarship)* [7332]
APS/Maricopa County Community Colleges Scholarships *(Undergraduate/Scholarship)* [7333]
ASCEND/ING Scholarships *(Undergraduate/Scholarship)* [1635]
ASCPA High School Scholarships *(Undergraduate/Scholarship)* [1528]
Association of College and University Auditors Scholarships *(Graduate, Undergraduate/Scholarship)* [1742]
Association of Government Accountants Undergraduate/Graduate Scholarships for Community Service Accomplishments *(Graduate, Undergraduate/Fellowship, Scholarship)* [1789]
Association of Government Accountants Undergraduate/Graduate Scholarships for Full-time study *(Graduate, Undergraduate/Fellowship, Scholarship)* [1790]
Association of Government Accountants Undergraduate/Graduate Scholarships for Part-time study *(Graduate, Undergraduate/Fellowship, Scholarship)* [1791]
ASWA 2-Year College Scholarships *(Undergraduate/Scholarship)* [1374]
ASWA Undergraduate Scholarships *(Undergraduate/Scholarship)* [1375]
Frank H. Ault Scholarships *(Undergraduate/Scholarship)* [7908]
Avista Corporation Minds in Motion Scholarships *(Undergraduate/Scholarship)* [5412]
AWSCPA National Scholarships *(Graduate/Scholarship)* [1452]
H. Burton Bates Jr. Scholarships *(Graduate, Undergraduate/Scholarship)* [9459]
Thomas M. Berry Jr. Scholarships *(Graduate, Undergraduate/Scholarship)* [9460]
Bill & Nell Biggs Scholarships *(Undergraduate/Scholarship)* [9140]
T. Frank Booth Memorial Scholarship Fund *(Undergraduate/Scholarship)* [3888]
Stuart Cameron and Margaret McLeod Memorial Scholarships (SCMS) *(Graduate, Undergraduate/Scholarship loan)* [4814]
Chrysler Foundation Scholarship Awards *(Undergraduate/Scholarship)* [4546]
Austin M. Cloyd, Matthew G. Gwaltney and Maxine S. Turner Doctoral Scholarships *(Doctorate/Scholarship)* [9461]

Cocke, Szpanka and Taylor Scholarships *(Undergraduate/Scholarship)* [9462]
Mable B. Crawford Memorial Scholarships *(Undergraduate/Scholarship)* [9146]
CSCPA College Scholarships *(Graduate, Undergraduate/Scholarship)* [3005]
CSCPA High School Scholarships *(Undergraduate/Scholarship)* [3006]
CSCPA Sophomore Scholarships *(Undergraduate/Scholarship)* [3007]
DBPR Division of CPA - BOA Minority Scholarships *(Undergraduate/Scholarship)* [3430]
Dixon Hughes Goodman LLP Annual Scholarship *(Undergraduate/Scholarship)* [3465]
EFWA Moss Adams Foundation Scholarships *(Graduate, Undergraduate/Scholarship)* [3598]
Ernst and Young/Ascend Leadership Scholarship Program *(Undergraduate/Scholarship)* [1636]
FICPA Educational Foundation 1040K Race Scholarships *(Undergraduate/Scholarship)* [3836]
Future CPA Scholarships *(Community College, Graduate, Undergraduate/Scholarship)* [1529]
Sam Gallant Memorial Scholarships *(Graduate, Undergraduate/Scholarship)* [1530]
Max Godwin Endowed Scholarships *(Undergraduate/Scholarship)* [8880]
Goodman & Company Scholarships *(Undergraduate/Scholarship)* [9463]
Community Bank - Lee Guggisberg Foundation Memorial Scholarships *(Undergraduate/Scholarship)* [7651]
GWSCPA Scholarships *(Undergraduate/Scholarship)* [4343]
Lenore & George Hedla Accounting Scholarships *(Undergraduate/Scholarship)* [9099]
HSBC-North America Scholarship Program *(Undergraduate/Scholarship)* [4571]
HSF/General Motors Scholarship Program *(Undergraduate/Scholarship)* [4574]
HSF/Wal-Mart Stores Inc. Scholarship Program *(Graduate, Undergraduate/Scholarship)* [4577]
Idaho Society of CPA's Scholarships *(Undergraduate/Scholarship)* [4671]
IMA Memorial Education Fund Scholarships (MEF) *(Graduate, Undergraduate/Scholarship loan)* [4815]
Institute of Management Accountants FAR Doctoral Student Grants Program *(Doctorate/Grant)* [4816]
Journyx Scholarships *(Graduate, Undergraduate/Scholarship)* [5171]
Robert A. Kleckner Scholarships *(Undergraduate/Scholarship)* [8612]
KPMG Foundation Minority Accounting Doctoral Scholarships *(Postdoctorate/Scholarship)* [5304]
Michael B. Kruse Scholarships *(Graduate, Undergraduate/Scholarship)* [3115]
KYCPA Scholarships *(Undergraduate/Scholarship)* [5253]
Paul J. Laninga Memorial Scholarship Fund *(Undergraduate/Scholarship)* [4226]
Lewis-Clark State College/Idaho Society of CPAs Scholarships Fund *(Undergraduate/Scholarship)* [5444]
MACPA Scholarships *(Graduate, Undergraduate/Scholarship)* [5652]

Marathon Oil Corporation College Scholarship Program *(Graduate, Undergraduate/Scholarship)* [4578]
Michele L. McDonald Scholarships *(Undergraduate/Scholarship)* [3599]
Harry Mestel Memorial Accounting Scholarship Fund *(Undergraduate/Scholarship)* [8690]
Michigan Accountancy Foundation Fifth/Graduate Year Scholarships (MAF) *(Graduate/Scholarship)* [5808]
MillerCoors National Scholarships *(Undergraduate/Scholarship)* [48]
Minnesota Association of Public Accountant Scholarships *(Undergraduate/Scholarship)* [5892]
MSCPA Undergraduate Scholarships *(Undergraduate/Scholarship)* [5910]
NABA National Scholarship Program *(Graduate, Undergraduate/Scholarship)* [6037]
National Society of Accountants Scholarship Program *(Undergraduate/Scholarship)* [6481]
NCCPAP and AICPA Scholarships for Graduating High School Seniors *(Undergraduate/Scholarship)* [6206]
Hubert A. Nelson Scholarships *(Undergraduate/Scholarship)* [3539]
NESCPA Fifth-Year Scholarships *(Graduate/Scholarship)* [6612]
NESCPA General Scholarships *(Graduate, Undergraduate/Scholarship)* [6613]
NHSCPA Scholarships *(Graduate, Undergraduate/Scholarship)* [6635]
NJSCPA College Scholarships *(Graduate, Undergraduate/Scholarship)* [6657]
NJSCPA High School Scholarships *(Undergraduate/Scholarship)* [6658]
Norfolk Southern Scholarships *(Undergraduate/Scholarship)* [9450]
North Carolina CPA Foundation Scholarships *(Undergraduate/Scholarship)* [6752]
NYSSCPA - FAE Excellence in Accounting Scholarships *(Undergraduate/Scholarship)* [6683]
OAIA Scholarships *(Graduate, Undergraduate/Scholarship)* [6931]
OSCPA Educational Foundation College Scholarships *(Community College, Graduate, Undergraduate/Scholarship)* [6954]
OSCPA Educational Foundation High School Scholarships *(Community College, Undergraduate/Scholarship)* [6955]
Outstanding Minority Accounting Student Scholarships *(All/Scholarship)* [6753]
Chet and Jannett Perry Scholarships *(Undergraduate/Scholarship)* [8617]
Ritchie-Jennings Memorial Scholarships *(Graduate, Undergraduate/Scholarship)* [1738]
SCACPA Educational Foundation Scholarships *(Graduate, Undergraduate/Scholarship)* [8542]
Seattle Chapter ASWA Scholarships *(Undergraduate/Scholarship)* [3600]
John M. and Mary A. Shanley Memorial Scholarships *(Undergraduate/Scholarship)* [8622]
Snodgrass Scholarships *(Undergraduate/Scholarship)* [9175]
Society of Louisiana Certified Public Accountants Scholarships *(Undergraduate/Scholarship)* [8367]

The Stanley H. Stearman Awards *(Undergraduate/ Scholarship)* [6482]

Surety Industry Scholarship Program for Minority Students *(Undergraduate/Scholarship)* [8778]

Talbert Family Memorial Accounting and Financial Management Scholarships *(Undergraduate/Scholarship)* [2961]

Ross/Nickey Scholarships and Gary E. Thornton Memorial Scholarships *(Graduate/Scholarship)* [5911]

Toyota High School Scholarship Program *(Undergraduate/Scholarship)* [4581]

UAA Accounting Club Scholarships *(Undergraduate/ Scholarship)* [9114]

University Junior Standing Scholarships *(Undergraduate/Scholarship)* [1531]

University Senior and Master's Program Scholarships *(Graduate/Scholarship)* [1532]

VSCPA Educational Foundation Graduate Scholarships *(Graduate/Scholarship)* [9464]

VSCPA Educational Foundation Minority Scholarships *(Graduate, Undergraduate/Scholarship)* [9465]

VSCPA Educational Foundation Undergraduate Scholarships *(Undergraduate/Scholarship)* [9466]

VSCPA PhD Accounting Scholarships *(Doctorate, Graduate/Scholarship)* [9467]

Wachovia Scholars Program *(Undergraduate/Scholarship)* [4551]

Washington CPA Foundation Scholarships *(Graduate, Undergraduate/Scholarship)* [9514]

George Waterman Memorial Scholarships *(Graduate, Undergraduate/Scholarship)* [9515]

Wells Fargo American Indian Scholarships - Graduate *(Graduate/Scholarship)* [828]

Witt Mares Scholarships *(Undergraduate/Scholarship)* [9451]

UAA Melissa J. Wolf Scholarships *(Undergraduate/ Scholarship)* [9128]

Women In Need Scholarships *(Undergraduate/ Scholarship)* [3601]

Women In Transition Scholarships *(Undergraduate/ Scholarship)* [3602]

WSCPA Chapter Scholarships *(Graduate, Undergraduate/Scholarship)* [9516]

Yount, Hyde & Barbour Scholarships *(Undergraduate/Scholarship)* [9468]

Harry and Angel Zerigian Scholarships *(Undergraduate/Scholarship)* [1609]

Acquired immune deficiency syndrome

Elizabeth Glaser Scientist Awards *(Professional development/Award)* [4157]

OHTN Postdoctoral Fellowships *(Doctorate/Fellowship)* [6893]

OSU Gay, Lesbian, Bisexual and Transgender Alumni Society PFLAG Scholarships *(Undergraduate/Scholarship)* [7864]

Actuarial science

HSBC-North America Scholarship Program *(Undergraduate/Scholarship)* [4571]

International Association of Black Actuaries Scholarships *(Undergraduate/Scholarship)* [4858]

Saskatchewan Government Insurance Actuarial Science Scholarships *(Undergraduate/Scholarship)* [7996]

DW Simpson Actuarial Science Scholarship Program *(Graduate, Undergraduate/Scholarship)* [8214]

Toyota High School Scholarship Program *(Undergraduate/Scholarship)* [4581]

Women in Science and Technology Scholarships *(Doctorate, Graduate, Master's, Undergraduate/ Scholarship)* [9442]

Adult education

Adolescent Literacy Pre-doctoral Fellowships *(Doctorate/Fellowship)* [6004]

Riva Heft Hecht Scholarships *(Undergraduate/ Scholarship)* [7556]

MPAEA Memorial Scholarships *(Graduate/Scholarship)* [5941]

MPAEA Student Scholarships *(Other/Scholarship)* [5942]

NASCOE Scholarships *(Undergraduate/Scholarship)* [6070]

NCAEA Scholarships *(Graduate/Scholarship)* [6746]

Advertising (See also Public relations)

AAAA Operation Jumpstart III Scholarships *(Graduate/Scholarship)* [433]

American Advertising Federation-Cleveland College Scholarships *(Undergraduate/Scholarship)* [402]

American Advertising Federation-Cleveland High School Scholarships *(Undergraduate/Scholarship)* [403]

Bill Bernbach Diversity Scholarships *(Undergraduate/Scholarship)* [434]

HSBC-North America Scholarship Program *(Undergraduate/Scholarship)* [4571]

The Lagrant Foundation - Graduate Students Scholarships *(Graduate/Scholarship)* [5315]

The Lagrant Foundation - Undergraduate Students Scholarships *(Undergraduate/Scholarship)* [5316]

Donald Mauer Scholarships *(Undergraduate/Scholarship)* [9289]

Multicultural Advertising Intern Program *(Graduate, Undergraduate/Internship)* [435]

New York Women in Communications, Inc. Foundation Scholarships *(Graduate, Undergraduate/ Scholarship)* [6690]

Jim Springer Memorial Scholarships *(Undergraduate/Scholarship)* [2959]

Jay A. Strassberg Memorial Scholarships *(Undergraduate/Scholarship)* [2324]

Hal Tanner Jr. Scholarships *(Undergraduate/Scholarship)* [9306]

Toyota High School Scholarship Program *(Undergraduate/Scholarship)* [4581]

Worldstudio AIGA Scholarships *(Graduate, Undergraduate/Scholarship)* [9761]

Aeronautics (See also Aviation)

AIAA Foundation Scholarship Program *(Graduate, Undergraduate/Scholarship)* [836]

Civil Air Patrol Scholarships for School and Flying *(Undergraduate/Scholarship)* [2893]

Glendale Latino Association Scholarships *(High School, Undergraduate/Scholarship)* [4161]

AMA/Charles H. Grant Scholarships *(Undergraduate/Scholarship)* [29]

NORDAM Dee Howard/Etienne Fage Scholarships *(Undergraduate/Scholarship)* [6169]

PAMA Foundation Scholarship Program *(Graduate, Undergraduate/Scholarship)* [7437]

Sig Memorial Scholarships *(Undergraduate/Scholarship)* [30]

Telford Scholarships *(Undergraduate/Scholarship)* [31]

U.S. Air Force ROTC Express Scholarships *(Undergraduate/Scholarship)* [9027]

Aerospace sciences

AFROTC Scholarships *(Undergraduate/Scholarship)* [87]

Air Force Association/Grantham Scholarships *(Undergraduate/Scholarship)* [89]

Air Force Association Spouse Scholarships *(Undergraduate/Scholarship)* [90]

Jodi Callahan Memorial Scholarships *(Undergraduate/Scholarship)* [91]

Descendant Scholarships *(Undergraduate/Scholarship)* [3326]

DOE Computational Science Graduate Fellowships (DOE CSGF) *(Doctorate, Graduate/Fellowship)* [5306]

Amelia Earhart Fellowship Program *(Postdoctorate/ Fellowship)* [9811]

John and Alice Egan Multi-Year Mentioning Scholarships *(Undergraduate/Scholarship)* [3327]

Matching Scholarships Program *(Undergraduate/ Scholarship)* [3328]

Navy, Army or Air Force ROTC Scholarship Program *(Undergraduate/Scholarship)* [3329]

Edward A. O'Connor Founder's Scholarships *(Undergraduate/Scholarship)* [68]

Pitsenbarger Awards *(Undergraduate/Scholarship)* [93]

U.S. Air Force ROTC Express Scholarships *(Undergraduate/Scholarship)* [9027]

Xavier University ROTC Scholarships - Air Force ROTC *(Undergraduate/Scholarship)* [9783]

Aesthetics

KCC-JEE Graduate Fellowships *(Graduate/Fellowship)* [5279]

African studies (See also Area and ethnic studies)

African Humanities Fellowships *(Postdoctorate/Fellowship)* [673]

TIAA-CREF Ruth Simms Hamilton Research Fellowships *(Graduate/Fellowship)* [8811]

African-American studies (See also Area and ethnic studies)

African American Studies Fellowships *(Graduate, Doctorate/Fellowship)* [5668]

Muddy Waters Scholarships *(Undergraduate/Scholarship)* [2155]

Lydia Donaldson Tutt-Jones Memorial Research Grant *(Graduate, Professional development/ Grant)* [72]

Aggression and violence (See also Sociology)

Belfer-Aptman Dissertation Research Awards *(Doctorate/Grant)* [5761]

Gail Burns-Smith "Dare to Dream" Fund *(Undergraduate/Scholarship)* [4416]

Aging (See Gerontology)

Agribusiness (See also Agricultural sciences)

Alberta Agricultural Economics Association Masters Scholarships *(Graduate/Scholarship)* [203]

Alberta Agricultural Economics Association Undergraduate Scholarships *(Undergraduate/Scholarship)* [204]

Louisiana Agricultural Consultants Association Scholarships *(Graduate, Undergraduate/Scholarship)* [5517]

Douglas McRorie Memorial Scholarships *(Postgraduate/Scholarship)* [75]

National Poultry and Food Distributors Association Scholarships *(Undergraduate/Scholarship)* [6444]

NPC Scholarships *(Graduate/Scholarship)* [6442]

Progressive Dairy Producer Awards *(All/Grant)* [6233]

Agricultural sciences

Myron Asplin Foundation Scholarships *(Undergraduate/Scholarship)* [4719]

Beef Industry Scholarships *(Undergraduate/Scholarship)* [6174]

Eugene Boyko Scholarships *(Undergraduate/Scholarship)* [209]

Delmar Cengage Learning-NAAE Upper Division Scholarships *(Undergraduate/Scholarship)* [6033]

Charles Dobbins FTA Scholarships *(Undergraduate, Vocational/Occupational/Scholarship)* [4033]

Edon Farmers Cooperative Scholarships *(Undergraduate/Scholarship)* [3592]

Florida Fertilizer and Agrichemical Association Scholarships *(Graduate, Undergraduate/Scholarship)* [3834]

Carleton A. Friday Memorial Scholarships *(Undergraduate/Scholarship)* [5867]

GCSAA Student Essay Contest *(Graduate, Undergraduate/Prize)* [4188]

Jim Graham Scholarships (Undergraduate/Scholarship) [6781]

Ronald P. Guerrette Future Farmers of America Scholarship Fund (Undergraduate/Scholarship) [5579]

PPQ William F. Helms Student Scholarships (Undergraduate/Scholarship) [9402]

Don Jaques Memorial Fellowships (Graduate, Doctorate/Fellowship) [8003]

Cecil Lane Family Scholarships (Undergraduate/Scholarship) [178]

National Poultry and Food Distributors Association Scholarships (Undergraduate/Scholarship) [6444]

NGC College Scholarships (Graduate, Undergraduate/Scholarship) [6303]

Ina E. Powell Memorial Scholarships (Undergraduate/Scholarship) [179]

Progressive Dairy Producer Awards (All/Grant) [6233]

Saskatchewan Pulse Growers Undergraduate Scholarships (Undergraduate/Scholarship) [8004]

Everett Oscar Shimp Memorial Scholarships (Undergraduate/Scholarship) [7113]

Dr. Alfred E. Slinkard Scholarships (Graduate, Doctorate/Scholarship) [8005]

University of Wisconsin-Madison/CALS Continuing Student Scholarships (Undergraduate/Scholarship) [9374]

University of Wisconsin-Madison/CALS Minority Scholarships (Undergraduate/Scholarship) [9375]

The Wax Company Scholarships (Undergraduate/Scholarship) [185]

Kenneth G. Weckel Scholarships (Undergraduate/Scholarship) [5868]

Western Society of Weed Science Outstanding Student Scholarship Program (Doctorate, Graduate, Undergraduate/Scholarship) [9585]

Women's Leadership in Agriculture Scholarship Program (Undergraduate/Scholarship) [6855]

Agriculture, Economic aspects

Kyutaro & Yasuo Abiko Memorial Scholarships (Undergraduate/Scholarship) [5140]

Agriculture Future of America Community Scholarships (Undergraduate/Scholarship) [77]

Agriculture Future of America Scholarship Program (Undergraduate/Scholarship) [78]

Alberta Agricultural Economics Association Masters Scholarships (Graduate/Scholarship) [203]

Alberta Holstein Association Scholarships (Undergraduate/Scholarship) [225]

Clackamas County Farm Bureau Scholarships (Undergraduate/Scholarship) [6946]

Don Aron Scholarships (Undergraduate/Scholarship) [6208]

Keith Gilmore Foundation - Diploma Scholarships (Professional development/Scholarship) [4153]

Keith Gilmore Foundation - Postgraduate Scholarships (Postgraduate/Scholarship) [4154]

Keith Gilmore Foundation - Undergraduate Scholarships (Undergraduate/Scholarship) [4155]

HAESF Professional Internship Program (Doctorate/Internship) [4641]

Dr. M.G. "Doc" Headley Scholarships (Undergraduate/Scholarship) [8726]

Independent Professional Seed Association Student Recognition Awards (Undergraduate/Scholarship) [4720]

Gregory D. Johnson Memorial Scholarships (Doctorate, Graduate, Master's/Scholarship) [6378]

Sam S. Kuwahara Memorial Scholarships (Undergraduate/Scholarship) [5144]

The Maschhoffs Pork Production Scholarships (Undergraduate/Scholarship) [6379]

National Junior Swine Association Outstanding Member Scholarships (Graduate/Scholarship) [6380]

National Poultry and Food Distributors Association Scholarships (Undergraduate/Scholarship) [6444]

New York State Association of Agricultural Fairs Scholarships (Undergraduate/Scholarship) [6671]

NJSA Visionary Leader Scholarships (Graduate/Scholarship) [6381]

Nuffield Canada Farming Scholarships (Undergraduate/Scholarship) [6838]

Oregon Farm Bureau Memorial Scholarships (Undergraduate/Scholarship) [6947]

Claude Robinson Scholarships (Undergraduate/Scholarship) [6382]

Ellis W. Rowe Scholarships (Undergraduate/Scholarship) [4380]

John M. and Mary A. Shanley Memorial Scholarships (Undergraduate/Scholarship) [8622]

Dr. Robert and Anna Shaw Scholarships (Undergraduate/Scholarship) [267]

Pat Shimp Memorial Scholarships (Undergraduate/Scholarship) [7114]

Jason Shipley Memorial Scholarships (Undergraduate/Scholarship) [6383]

Stanley W. Strew Educational Fund Scholarships (Undergraduate/Scholarship) [2230]

Samuel Upchurch Memorial Scholarships (Undergraduate/Scholarship) [183]

Washington County Farm Bureau Scholarships (Undergraduate/Scholarship) [6948]

Willamette Valley AG Association Scholarships (Undergraduate/Scholarship) [6949]

Working for Farmers' Success Scholarships (Undergraduate/Scholarship) [9748]

Yamhill County Farm Bureau Scholarships (Undergraduate/Scholarship) [6950]

Agronomy (See Agricultural sciences)

AIDS (See Acquired immune deficiency syndrome)

Air pollution

A&WMA-GWS Scholarships (Graduate, Undergraduate/Scholarship) [111]

A&WMA Scholarships (Graduate/Scholarship) [107]

SSAWMA Scholarships (Graduate/Scholarship) [120]

Alcoholism (See Substance abuse)

Allied health (See Health sciences)

Alzheimer's disease

Sigma Kappa Foundation Alzheimer's/Gerontology Scholarships (Undergraduate/Scholarship) [8183]

American history (See History, American)

American Indian studies (See Native American studies)

American studies (See United States studies)

Ancient Greece (See Classical studies)

Anesthesiology

Baxter Corporation Canadian Research Awards in Anesthesia (Professional development/Award) [2356]

Canadian Anesthesiologists' Society Research Awards (Professional development/Award) [2357]

CAS/Vitaid-LMA Residents' Research Grant Competition (Professional development/Award) [2359]

Dale O. Heimberger CRNA Memorial Scholarship Fund (Graduate/Scholarship) [8673]

David S. Sheridan Canadian Research Awards (Professional development/Award) [2360]

Smiths Medical Canada Ltd. Research Awards (Professional development/Award) [2361]

Animal rights

ABA Scholarships (Undergraduate/Scholarship) [581]

Richard E. Andrews Memorial Scholarships (Undergraduate/Scholarship) [582]

Shaw-Worth Memorial Scholarships (Undergraduate/Scholarship) [4636]

Animal science and behavior (See also Zoology)

ABA Scholarships (Undergraduate/Scholarship) [581]

Richard E. Andrews Memorial Scholarships (Undergraduate/Scholarship) [582]

Angus Foundation Graduate Student Degree Scholarship Program (Graduate/Scholarship) [1478]

Angus/Talon Youth Educational Learning Program Endowment Fund (Graduate/Scholarship) [1479]

ASI Fellowships (Doctorate/Fellowship) [1481]

Auburn Animal Science Department Graduate Student Scholarships (Graduate/Scholarship) [176]

W.D. Farr Scholarships (Graduate/Scholarship) [6175]

Fellowships and Internships Program in Latin America (Graduate/Fellowship, Internship) [8269]

Fred Johnson Memorial Scholarships (Doctorate, Graduate, Master's/Scholarship) [6176]

Minority Visiting Students Awards (Undergraduate, Graduate/Award, Internship) [8241]

NCF Fort Dodge Animal Health Legacy Scholarships for Undergraduate Students (Undergraduate/Scholarship) [6177]

A. Stanley Rand Fellowships Program (Undergraduate, Doctorate, Postdoctorate/Fellowship) [8270]

Short-Term Fellowships (Undergraduate, Graduate, Postdoctorate/Fellowship) [8271]

Stark County Dairy Promoters Scholarships (Undergraduate/Scholarship) [8701]

Earl S. Tupper 3-year Postdoctoral Fellowships in Tropical Biology (Postdoctorate/Fellowship) [8272]

Samuel Upchurch Memorial Scholarships (Undergraduate/Scholarship) [183]

Ed Wadsworth Memorial Scholarships (Undergraduate/Scholarship) [184]

Welder Wildlife Foundation Fellowships (Doctorate, Graduate/Fellowship) [9559]

Anthropology

AAA Leadership Mentoring/Shadow Award Program (Graduate/Award) [405]

AAA Minority Dissertation Fellowship Program (Doctorate/Fellowship) [406]

AfAA Graduate Student Paper Awards (Graduate/Award) [1688]

AfAA Undergraduate Student Paper Awards (Undergraduate/Award) [1689]

Franklin Mosher Baldwin Memorial Fellowships (Master's, Doctorate/Fellowship) [5390]

Richard G. Condon Prize (Doctorate, Graduate, Undergraduate/Prize) [8469]

Fellowships and Internships Program in Latin America (Graduate/Fellowship, Internship) [8269]

Hunt Postdoctoral Fellowships (Doctorate/Fellowship) [9561]

Zora Neale Hurston Scholarships (Graduate/Scholarship) [9804]

Leakey Foundation Research Grants (Doctorate/Grant) [5391]

Larry Matfay Scholarships (Graduate, Undergraduate/Scholarship) [5287]

William P. McHugh Memorial Fund Award (Doctorate, Graduate/Fellowship) [1141]

Margaret Mead Awards (Professional development/Award) [407]

Minority Visiting Students Awards (Undergraduate, Graduate/Award, Internship) [8241]

The National Endowment for the Humanities Fellowships (Doctorate, Graduate/Fellowship) [1142]

Pi Gamma Mu Scholarships (Graduate/Scholarship) [7330]

David M. Schneider Awards (Doctorate/Award) [408]

Short-Term Fellowships (Undergraduate, Graduate, Postdoctorate/Fellowship) [8271]

Society for Linguistic Anthropology Student Essay Prize (Graduate, Undergraduate/Prize) [8365]

Earl S. Tupper 3-year Postdoctoral Fellowships in Tropical Biology (Postdoctorate/Fellowship) [8272]

The United States Department of State, Bureau of Educational & Cultural Affairs Fellowships (Doctorate, Graduate/Fellowship) [1143]

Wadsworth International Fellowships (Graduate/Fellowship) [9562]

Wenner-Gren Foundation Dissertation Fieldwork Grants (Doctorate/Grant) [9563]

Wenner-Gren Foundation Post-PhD Research Grants (Doctorate/Grant) [9564]

Applied art (See Art industries and trade)

Applied mathematics (See Mathematics and mathematical sciences)

Aquaculture

Anchor Environmental Scholarships (Graduate/Scholarship) [1471]

Aquatics Booster Club Scholarships (Undergraduate/Scholarship) [7622]

Lloyd Bridges Scholarships (Graduate, Professional development/Scholarship) [2679]

Cecilia Connelly Memorial Scholarships in Underwater Archaeology (Graduate, Undergraduate/Scholarship) [9698]

Nova Scotia Salmon Association Scholarships (All/Scholarship) [6834]

Archeology

American Philological Association Minority Student Summer Fellowships (Undergraduate/Fellowship) [986]

CCV Foundation Graduate and Undergraduate Fellowships (Doctorate, Graduate, Undergraduate/Fellowship) [2672]

Cecilia Connelly Memorial Scholarships in Underwater Archaeology (Graduate, Undergraduate/Scholarship) [9698]

Conservation Department Program Fellowships (Graduate/Fellowship) [8258]

Kenan T. Erim Fellowships for Archaeological Research at Aphrodisias (Postdoctorate/Fellowship) [1146]

Kress Pre-Doctoral Fellowships in the History of Art and Archeology in Turkey (Postdoctorate/Fellowship) [1151]

William P. McHugh Memorial Fund Award (Doctorate, Graduate/Fellowship) [1141]

Dorothy Mountain Memorial Scholarships (Graduate/Scholarship) [5532]

National Endowment for the Humanities Advanced Fellowships for Research in Turkey (Postdoctorate/Fellowship) [1153]

The National Endowment for the Humanities Fellowships (Doctorate, Graduate/Fellowship) [1142]

SAA Native American Scholarships (Graduate, Professional development, Undergraduate/Scholarship) [8293]

Smithsonian Postgraduate Fellowships in Conservation of Museum Collection Program (Postgraduate/Fellowship) [8249]

The United States Department of State, Bureau of Educational & Cultural Affairs Fellowships (Doctorate, Graduate/Fellowship) [1143]

Jane C. Waldbaum Archaeological Field School Scholarships (Undergraduate/Scholarship) [1496]

Harry Walts Memorial Graduate Scholarships (Graduate/Scholarship) [5533]

Architecture (See also Landscape architecture and design)

AAUW Legal Advocacy Fund Selected Professions Fellowships (Doctorate, Graduate/Fellowship) [18]

ACI Scholarships (Graduate/Scholarship) [631]

AIA/NEI Scholarships (Graduate, Undergraduate/Scholarship) [840]

American Association of University Women Selected Professions Fellowships (Professional development/Fellowship) [13]

Architects Association of PEI Scholarships (Undergraduate/Scholarship) [3180]

Architecture, Design and Urban Design Prize (Graduate, Undergraduate/Prize) [8231]

Association for Women in Architecture Scholarships (Undergraduate/Scholarship) [1894]

Carpenters' Company Scholarships (Undergraduate/Scholarship) [2657]

Cintas Foundation Fellowships in Architecture (Professional development/Fellowship) [2881]

Connecticut Building Congress Scholarships (Undergraduate/Scholarship) [4420]

Tom Cory Memorial Scholarships (Undergraduate/Scholarship) [1498]

D&A Florida Scholarships (Undergraduate/Scholarship) [8597]

Charles Dubose Scholarships (Undergraduate/Scholarship) [4428]

Kenan T. Erim Fellowships for Archaeological Research at Aphrodisias (Postdoctorate/Fellowship) [1146]

Generation III Scholarships (Undergraduate/Scholarship) [3586]

ACI W.R. Grace Scholarships (Graduate/Scholarship) [634]

IALD Education Trust Scholarship Program (Graduate, Undergraduate/Scholarship) [4878]

JMA Architecture Studios Scholarships (Undergraduate/Scholarship) [7498]

Kluge Fellowships (Doctorate, Graduate/Fellowship) [5274]

Samuel H. Kress Foundation Dissertation Fellowships (Doctorate/Fellowship) [8296]

Kress Pre-Doctoral Fellowships in the History of Art and Archeology in Turkey (Postdoctorate/Fellowship) [1151]

Arnold Les Larsen, FAIA, Memorial Scholarships (Graduate, Master's/Scholarship) [841]

PCH Architects/Steven J. Lehnhof Memorial Architectural Scholarships (Undergraduate/Scholarship) [7665]

Dolores Zohrab Liebmann Fund - Graduate School Fellowships (Graduate/Scholarship) [5488]

Katharine & Bryant Mather Scholarships (Graduate/Scholarship) [635]

William P. McHugh Memorial Fund Award (Doctorate, Graduate/Fellowship) [1141]

Kumar Mehta Scholarships (Graduate/Scholarship) [636]

The National Endowment for the Humanities Fellowships (Doctorate, Graduate/Fellowship) [1142]

Stuart L. Noderer Memorial Scholarships (Undergraduate/Scholarship) [7949]

Pardee Community Building Scholarships (Undergraduate/Scholarship) [7515]

Howard Brown Rickard Scholarships (Undergraduate/Scholarship) [6282]

SAH Study Tour Fellowships (Doctorate/Fellowship) [8297]

Leo and Trinidad Sanchez Scholarships (Undergraduate/Scholarship) [8208]

Galvanize the Future: Edgar K. Schutz Scholarships (Graduate, Undergraduate/Prize, Scholarship) [774]

John M. and Mary A. Shanley Memorial Scholarships (Undergraduate/Scholarship) [8622]

Study Scholarships for Artists or Musicians (Graduate/Scholarship) [4123]

Toyota High School Scholarship Program (Undergraduate/Scholarship) [4581]

Travel Fellowships in Architecture, Design and Urban Design (Graduate, Undergraduate/Fellowship) [8233]

The United States Department of State, Bureau of

Educational & Cultural Affairs Fellowships (Doctorate, Graduate/Fellowship) [1143]

Dimitri J. Ververelli Memorial Scholarships (Undergraduate/Scholarship) [4520]

Washington University Law School Olin Fellowships for Women (Graduate/Fellowship) [9533]

ACI Bertold E. Weinberg Scholarships (Graduate/Scholarship) [638]

Polaire Weissman Funds (Graduate/Fellowship) [5793]

Beverly Willis Architecture Foundation Dissertation Fellowships (Doctorate/Fellowship) [8298]

Worldstudio AIGA Scholarships (Graduate, Undergraduate/Scholarship) [9761]

Architecture, Naval

Malayalee Engineers Association Scholarships (Graduate/Fellowship) [5601]

NDSEG Fellowships (Graduate/Fellowship) [6239]

NRL Postdoctoral Fellowships (Postdoctorate/Fellowship) [6581]

Mandell and Lester Rosenblatt and Robert N. Herbert Undergraduate Scholarships (Undergraduate/Scholarship) [8417]

Society of Naval Architects and Marine Engineers Undergraduate Scholarships (Undergraduate/Scholarship) [8418]

Archival science (See Library and archival sciences)

Area and ethnic studies

AfAA Graduate Student Paper Awards (Graduate/Award) [1688]

AfAA Undergraduate Student Paper Awards (Undergraduate/Award) [1689]

Theodore E.D. Braun Research Travel Fellowships (Professional development/Fellowship) [1225]

Ruth B. Fein Prize (Graduate/Prize) [887]

Houtan Scholarships (Graduate/Scholarship) [4616]

Iranian Association of Boston's IAB Scholarships (Undergraduate/Scholarship) [6362]

Pokross/Curhan Family Fund Prize (Graduate, Undergraduate/Prize) [888]

Armenian studies (See also Area and ethnic studies)

AGBU Scholarships (Graduate/Loan) [1573]

Karekin DerAvedision Memorial Endowment Fund (Undergraduate/Scholarship) [1590]

Garikian Scholarship Fund (Undergraduate/Scholarship) [1593]

Knights of Vartan, Fresno Lodge No. 9 Scholarships (Undergraduate/Scholarship) [1601]

Dolores Zohrab Liebmann Fund - Publication Grants (Graduate/Grant) [5490]

Art (See also Performing arts; Visual arts)

Academic Promise Scholarships (Undergraduate/Scholarship) [4740]

ADAC Foundation Scholarships (Undergraduate/Scholarship) [1622]

American Watercolor Society Scholarship Program for Art Teachers (Professional development/Scholarship) [1421]

Art Institute of Colorado Scholarships (Undergraduate/Scholarship) [1624]

Art Institute's Best Teen Chef in America Culinary Scholarships (Undergraduate/Prize, Scholarship) [1625]

Joan Auld Scholarships (Undergraduate/Scholarship) [3181]

Cynthia and Alan Baran Fine Arts and Music Scholarships (Undergraduate/Scholarship) [3093]

James Beard Foundation/Art Institute of Colorado Scholarships (Undergraduate/Scholarship) [1626]

Beta Sigma Phi - Fine Arts Scholarships (Undergraduate/Scholarship) [8111]

Anne-Marie Bonner Scholarships (Undergraduate/Scholarship) [5115]

Edwin Anthony and Adelaine Bordeaux Cadogan Fellowships *(Graduate/Fellowship)* [7982]

Chautauqua Scholarships Program *(All/Scholarship)* [4969]

J. Clawson Mills Scholarships *(Doctorate/Scholarship)* [5784]

Paul Collins Scholarships *(Undergraduate/Scholarship)* [4277]

Colorado PROSTART/Art Institute of Colorado Art Scholarships for High School Seniors *(Undergraduate/Scholarship)* [1627]

Convergence Assistantship Grants *(Undergraduate/Grant)* [4386]

Dewey Lee Curtis Scholarships *(All/Scholarship)* [3356]

Chester Dale Fellowships *(Doctorate/Fellowship)* [5785]

Felicia De Bow Memorial Scholarships *(All/Scholarship)* [7037]

Walt Disney Company Foundation Scholarships *(Undergraduate/Scholarship)* [5173]

Mychajlo Dmytrenko Fine Arts Foundation Scholarships *(Undergraduate/Scholarship)* [9074]

Pauly D'Orlando Memorial Art Scholarships *(Graduate, Undergraduate/Scholarship)* [8996]

The "Drawn to Art" Fellowships *(Doctorate/Fellowship)* [417]

Evolving Perceptions Scholarships *(Undergraduate/Scholarship)* [6360]

Adrienne Zoe Fedok Art and Music Scholarships *(Undergraduate/Scholarship)* [3943]

Fine Arts Association Minority Scholarships *(Undergraduate/Scholarship)* [3749]

Fine Arts Association United Way Scholarships *(Undergraduate/Scholarship)* [3750]

Mearl K. Gable II Memorial Grants *(Professional development/Grant)* [4387]

William E. "Bill" Gallagher Scholarships *(Undergraduate/Scholarship)* [7076]

The Gallery Collection's Greeting Card Scholarships *(Undergraduate/Scholarship)* [4035]

Mathilda & Carolyn Gallmeyer Scholarships *(Undergraduate/Scholarship)* [4282]

Getty Scholar Grants *(Professional development/Grant)* [4143]

Guntley-Lorimer Science and Arts Scholarships *(Undergraduate/Scholarship)* [2119]

Ed Haas Memorial Scholarships *(Undergraduate/Scholarship)* [8724]

HAESF Professional Internship Program *(Doctorate/Internship)* [4641]

Handweavers Guild of America and Dendel Scholarships *(Graduate, Undergraduate/Scholarship)* [4388]

UAA Muriel Hannah Scholarships in Art *(Undergraduate, Vocational/Occupational/Scholarship)* [9098]

Regina Higdon Scholarships *(Undergraduate/Scholarship)* [3110]

Lucy Hilty Research Grants *(All/Grant)* [1065]

Indiana State Alumni Association Creative and Performing Arts Awards *(Undergraduate/Scholarship)* [4745]

Donald Wills Jacobs Scholarships *(Undergraduate/Scholarship)* [9154]

Gregori Jakovina Endowment Scholarships *(Undergraduate/Scholarship)* [3677]

George E. Judd Scholarships *(Undergraduate/Scholarship)* [8609]

UAA Paul G. Landis Scholarships *(Undergraduate/Scholarship)* [9104]

Jay and Deborah Last Fellowships *(Doctorate/Fellowship)* [420]

Larry McDonald Scholarships *(Undergraduate/Scholarship)* [3680]

William P. McHugh Memorial Fund Award *(Doctorate, Graduate/Fellowship)* [1141]

McNamara Family Creative Arts Project Grants *(Graduate, Undergraduate/Grant)* [4579]

Mill Creek Business Association Scholarships *(Undergraduate/Scholarship)* [5878]

Letitia Moore Art Scholarships *(Undergraduate/Scholarship)* [9789]

Jack and Gertrude Murphy Fellowships *(Graduate/Fellowship)* [7983]

National Endowment for the Humanities Advanced Fellowships for Research in Turkey *(Postdoctorate/Fellowship)* [1153]

The National Endowment for the Humanities Fellowships *(Doctorate, Graduate/Fellowship)* [1142]

Marvin R. and Pearl E. Patterson Family Scholarships Fund *(Undergraduate/Scholarship)* [4232]

Pennies for Art Scholarships *(Undergraduate/Scholarship)* [4081]

Silvio and Eugenio Petrini Grants *(Professional development/Grant)* [4389]

Phi Theta Kappa Scholarships *(Undergraduate/Scholarship)* [4752]

David G. Robinson Arts Scholarships *(Undergraduate/Scholarship)* [8619]

UAA Jack & Martha Roderick Scholarships *(Graduate, Undergraduate/Scholarship)* [9108]

Scholarships of the Arts *(Graduate, Undergraduate/Scholarship)* [3688]

Dr. Robert and Anna Shaw Scholarships *(Undergraduate/Scholarship)* [267]

Smithsonian Postgraduate Fellowships in Conservation of Museum Collection Program *(Postgraduate/Fellowship)* [8249]

John F. and Anna Lee Stacey Scholarships *(All/Scholarship)* [6229]

Marion Barr Stanfield Art Scholarships *(Graduate, Undergraduate/Scholarship)* [9002]

Robert W. and Bernice Ingalls Staton Scholarships *(Undergraduate/Scholarship)* [9314]

Cecilia Steinfeldt Fellowships for Research in the Arts and Material Culture *(Professional development/Fellowship)* [8878]

Study Scholarships for Artists or Musicians *(Graduate/Scholarship)* [4123]

UAA Emi Chance Memorial Scholarships *(Undergraduate/Scholarship)* [9119]

UAA Kimura Scholarship Fund Photography Scholarships *(Undergraduate/Scholarship)* [9123]

The United States Department of State, Bureau of Educational & Cultural Affairs Fellowships *(Doctorate, Graduate/Fellowship)* [1143]

Philip F. Vineberg Travelling Fellowships in the Humanities *(Undergraduate/Scholarship)* [5726]

Washington University Law School Olin Fellowships for Women *(Graduate/Fellowship)* [9533]

Jane and Morgan Whitney Fellowships *(Graduate/Fellowship)* [5794]

Worldstudio AIGA Scholarships *(Graduate, Undergraduate/Scholarship)* [9761]

Gwen Yarnell Theatre Scholarships *(Undergraduate/Scholarship)* [3751]

James and Joy Zana Memorial Scholarships *(Undergraduate/Scholarship)* [4266]

Art, Caricatures and cartoons

Worldstudio AIGA Scholarships *(Graduate, Undergraduate/Scholarship)* [9761]

Art, Performing (See Performing arts)

Art, Roman

Shohet Scholars Program *(Postdoctorate/Fellowship)* [4890]

Art, Visual (See Visual arts)

Art conservation

Kress Conservation Fellowships *(Graduate/Fellowship)* [5308]

Art history

Metropolitan Museum of Art Bothmer Fellowships *(Doctorate/Fellowship)* [5783]

Kenan T. Erim Fellowships for Archaeological Research at Aphrodisias *(Postdoctorate/Fellowship)* [1146]

Hench Post-Dissertation Fellowships *(Postdoctorate/Fellowship)* [419]

Louis I. Jaffe Memorial Scholarships-ODU *(Graduate/Scholarship)* [4377]

Annette Kade Fellowships *(Graduate/Fellowship)* [5787]

Kress Pre-Doctoral Fellowships in the History of Art and Archeology in Turkey *(Postdoctorate/Fellowship)* [1151]

Henry Luce Foundation Dissertation Fellowships in American Art *(Doctorate/Fellowship)* [679]

Letitia Moore Art Scholarships *(Undergraduate/Scholarship)* [9789]

Margaret B. Sevcenko Prize in Islamic Art and Culture *(Doctorate/Prize)* [4589]

Hanns Swarzenski and Brigitte Horney Swarzenski Fellowships *(Graduate/Fellowship)* [5792]

United States Capitol Historical Society Fellowships *(Graduate/Fellowship)* [9037]

Virginia Museum of Fine Arts Visual Arts Fellowships *(Graduate, Professional development, Undergraduate/Fellowship)* [9457]

Art industries and trade

Michael Beaudry Scholarships *(Undergraduate/Scholarship)* [4054]

Paul Collins Scholarships *(Undergraduate/Scholarship)* [4277]

Nortel Institute Undergraduate Scholarships *(Undergraduate/Scholarship)* [9340]

Dr. Robert and Anna Shaw Scholarships *(Undergraduate/Scholarship)* [267]

Kurt Wayne Scholarships *(Graduate/Scholarship)* [4069]

Art therapy

American Art Therapy Association Anniversary Scholarships (AATA) *(Graduate/Scholarship)* [426]

Myra Levick Scholarships *(Graduate/Scholarship)* [427]

William Philpott Scholarships *(All/Scholarship)* [2098]

Rawley Silver Awards for Excellence *(Graduate/Scholarship)* [428]

Arthritis

Arthritis Foundation Doctoral Dissertation Awards for Arthritis Health Professionals *(Professional development/Fellowship)* [1629]

Arthritis Foundation Postdoctoral Fellowships *(Doctorate/Fellowship)* [1630]

Arts

American-Scandinavian Foundation Grants to Study in Scandinavia *(Graduate/Grant)* [1170]

Art Acquisition by Application Project Grants *(Professional development/Grant)* [216]

Art Graduate Scholarships *(Graduate/Scholarship)* [239]

William E. Barto Scholarships *(Undergraduate/Scholarship)* [3525]

Hagop Bogigian Scholarship Fund *(Undergraduate/Scholarship)* [1587]

Regina Brown Undergraduate Student Fellowships *(Undergraduate/Fellowship)* [6212]

Bush Artist Fellowships *(All/Fellowship)* [2217]

Antonio Cirino Memorial Art Education Fellowships *(Undergraduate/Fellowship)* [7787]

Cultural Relations Project Grants *(Professional development/Grant)* [217]

Dance Project Grants *(Professional development/Grant)* [218]

Douglass Foundation Fellowships in American Art *(Graduate/Fellowship)* [5786]

EAA Tuition Scholarships *(College, Vocational/Occupational/Scholarship)* [3647]

EAA Workshop Scholarships *(College, Vocational/Occupational/Scholarship)* [3648]

Edgecliff McAuley Art Scholarships *(Undergraduate/Scholarship)* [9769]

Bruce T. and Jackie Mahi Erickson Grants *(Graduate, Undergraduate/Grant)* [5210]

Film and Video Arts Project Grants *(Professional development/Grant)* [219]

Helen R. Finley-Loescher and Stephen Loescher Scholarships *(Undergraduate/Scholarship)* [3149]

Florida Education Fund McKnight Doctoral Fellowships (Graduate/Fellowship) [3822]

Andrew Gronholdt Arts Scholarship Awards (Undergraduate, Vocational/Occupational, Graduate, Master's/Scholarship) [288]

John Simon Guggenheim Memorial Fellowships - U.S. and Canadian Competition (Advanced Professional/Fellowship) [4360]

Jacob K. Javits Fellowships (Doctorate, Master's/Fellowship) [6076]

Jewish Federation Academic Scholarships (Graduate, Undergraduate/Scholarship) [5161]

Literary Arts Project Grants (Professional development/Grant) [220]

Minority Visiting Students Awards (Undergraduate, Graduate/Award, Internship) [8241]

John H. Moss Scholarships (Undergraduate/Scholarship) [9339]

NCECA Graduate Student Fellowships (Graduate/Fellowship) [6213]

NHFA Scholarships (Graduate/Scholarship) [6340]

Virginia Nicklas Scholarships (Undergraduate/Scholarship) [3382]

Northwest-Shoals Community College Fine Arts Scholarships - Art (Undergraduate/Scholarship) [6823]

Prescott Fine Arts Association Scholarship Program (Undergraduate/Scholarship) [7390]

Rome Prize (Doctorate, Graduate/Prize) [400]

Leo S. Rowe Pan American Fund (Graduate, Undergraduate/Loan) [6967]

Casey Sakir Point Scholarships (Graduate, Undergraduate/Scholarship) [7366]

Scholarship Foundation of Santa Barbara Art Scholarship Program (Undergraduate/Scholarship) [8024]

Silver Nugget Gaming Ambassadors Scholarships (Undergraduate/Scholarship) [7524]

Patrick Spielman Memorial Scholarship Program (Undergraduate, Vocational/Occupational/Scholarship) [8071]

StraightForward Media's Art School Scholarships (Undergraduate/Scholarship) [8756]

The UCSD Black Alumni Scholarship for Arts and Humanities (Undergraduate/Scholarship) [7970]

The UCSD Black Alumni Scholarships for Engineering, Mathematics and Science (Undergraduate/Scholarship) [7971]

Washington University Law School Chancellor's Graduate Fellowships (Graduate/Fellowship) [9532]

Polaire Weissman Funds (Graduate/Fellowship) [5793]

Xavier University Honors Bachelor of Arts Scholarships (Undergraduate/Scholarship) [9781]

Asian studies (See Area and ethnic studies)

Astronautics

AIAA Foundation Scholarship Program (Graduate, Undergraduate/Scholarship) [836]

Astronomy and astronomical sciences

American Astronomical Society Small Research Grants (Doctorate/Grant) [568]

Annie J. Cannon Awards in Astronomy (Doctorate/Award) [569]

Chambliss Astronomy Achievement Student Awards (Undergraduate, Graduate/Award) [570]

Chretien International Research Grants (Doctorate, Professional development/Grant) [571]

DOE Computational Science Graduate Fellowships (DOE CSGF) (Doctorate, Graduate/Fellowship) [5306]

Rodger Doxsey Travel Prizes (Graduate, Postdoctorate/Prize) [572]

NPSC Fellowships (Graduate/Fellowship) [6440]

NRC-HIA Plaskett Fellowships (Doctorate/Fellowship) [6461]

Athletics

Canadian Seniors' Golf Association Scholarships (Undergraduate/Scholarship) [4181]

Earl and Countess of Wessex - World Championships in Athletics Scholarships (Undergraduate/Scholarship) [244]

Founding Fathers Leadership Scholarships (Undergraduate/Scholarship) [9676]

The Gene and John Athletic Scholarships (Undergraduate/Scholarship) [8746]

KATS Graduate Scholarships (Graduate/Scholarship) [5246]

KATS Undergraduate Scholarships (Undergraduate/Scholarship) [5247]

Mueller Undergraduate Scholarships (Undergraduate/Scholarship) [9677]

Mike Niemeyer Memorial Football Scholarships (Undergraduate/Scholarship) [7679]

Northwest-Shoals Community College Athletic Scholarships (Undergraduate/Scholarship) [6821]

Jeff Oliphant Memorial Post-Graduate Scholarships (Postgraduate/Scholarship) [9678]

Redlands High School Boy's Varsity Volleyball Scholarships (Undergraduate/Scholarship) [7691]

The Tacoma Athletic Commission Scholarships (Undergraduate, Vocational/Occupational/Scholarship) [4341]

United States Golf Association Fellowship Program (All/Fellowship) [9048]

United States Golf Association Scholarship Program (Undergraduate/Scholarship) [9049]

Atmospheric science (See also Meteorology)

A&WMA-GWS Scholarships (Graduate, Undergraduate/Scholarship) [111]

Ernest F. Hollings Undergraduate Scholarships (Undergraduate/Scholarship) [6417]

NOAA Graduate Sciences Scholarships (Graduate/Scholarship) [6418]

NOAA Undergraduate Scholarships (Undergraduate/Scholarship) [6419]

U.S. Air Force ROTC Express Scholarships (Undergraduate/Scholarship) [9027]

CASFM-Ben Urbonas Scholarships (Graduate/Scholarship) [2982]

Audiology (See Speech and language pathology/audiology)

Australian studies (See Area and ethnic studies)

Automotive technology

AIA and the Global Automotive Aftermarket Symposium Scholarships (Undergraduate/Scholarship) [1955]

ISA Aerospace Industries Division - William H. Atkinson Scholarships (Graduate, Undergraduate/Scholarship) [5052]

Auto Body Technician Certificate Scholarships (Undergraduate/Scholarship) [7991]

Automotive Technician Scholarship Program (Undergraduate/Scholarship) [5686]

Automotive Women's Alliance Foundation Scholarships (Undergraduate/Scholarship) [1970]

Larry H. Averill Memorial Scholarships (Undergraduate/Scholarship) [1937]

AVI Scholarships (Undergraduate/Scholarship) [1963]

Tom Babcox Memorial Scholarships (All/Scholarship) [1964]

Chrysler Foundation Scholarship Awards (Undergraduate/Scholarship) [4546]

Rob Copeland Memorial Scholarships (Undergraduate/Scholarship) [5421]

Richard Cossette/Gale Memorial Scholarships (All/Scholarship) [1965]

Harold Dieckmann Draper, Sr. Scholarships (Undergraduate/Scholarship) [1938]

John E. Echlin Memorial Scholarships (Undergraduate/Scholarship) [1939]

Florida Automotive Industry Scholarships (Undergraduate/Scholarship) [1966]

Carlyle Fraser/Wilton Looney Scholarships (Undergraduate/Scholarship) [1940]

Friends of Mary Automotive Scholarships (Undergraduate/Scholarship) [8115]

John Goerlich Memorial Scholarships (Undergraduate/Scholarship) [1941]

Charles V. Hagler Scholarships (Undergraduate/Scholarship) [1942]

Zenon C.R. Hansen Memorial Scholarships (Undergraduate/Scholarship) [1943]

Bob and Dawn Hardy Automotive Scholarships (Undergraduate/Scholarship) [5099]

Norman E. Huston Scholarships (Graduate, Undergraduate/Scholarship) [5053]

ISA Educational Foundation Scholarships (Graduate, Undergraduate/Scholarship) [5054]

ISA Executive Board Scholarships (Graduate, Undergraduate/Scholarship) [5055]

ISA Section and District Scholarships - Birmingham (Graduate, Undergraduate/Scholarship) [5056]

ISA Section and District Scholarships - Houston (Graduate, Undergraduate/Scholarship) [5057]

ISA Section and District Scholarships - Lehigh Valley (Graduate, Undergraduate/Scholarship) [5058]

ISA Section and District Scholarships - New Jersey (Graduate, Undergraduate/Scholarship) [5059]

ISA Section and District Scholarships - Niagara Frontier (Graduate, Undergraduate/Scholarship) [5060]

ISA Section and District Scholarships - Northern California (Graduate, Undergraduate/Scholarship) [5061]

ISA Section and District Scholarships - Richmond Hopewell (Graduate, Undergraduate/Scholarship) [5062]

ISA Section and District Scholarships - Savannah River (Graduate, Undergraduate/Scholarship) [5063]

ISA Section and District Scholarships - Southwestern Wyoming (Graduate, Undergraduate/Scholarship) [5064]

ISA Section and District Scholarships - Texas, Louisiana and Mississippi (Graduate, Undergraduate/Scholarship) [5065]

ISA Section and District Scholarships - Wilmington (Graduate, Undergraduate/Scholarship) [5066]

ISA Technical Division Scholarships - Analysis Division (Graduate, Undergraduate/Scholarship) [5067]

ISA Technical Division Scholarships - Chemical and Petroleum Industries Division (Graduate, Undergraduate/Scholarship) [5068]

ISA Technical Division Scholarships - Computer Technology Division (Graduate, Undergraduate/Scholarship) [5069]

ISA Technical Division Scholarships - Food and Pharmaceutical Industries Division (Graduate, Undergraduate/Scholarship) [5070]

ISA Technical Division Scholarships - Power Industry Division (Graduate, Undergraduate/Scholarship) [5071]

ISA Technical Division Scholarships - Process Measurement and Control Division (Graduate, Undergraduate/Scholarship) [5072]

ISA Technical Division Scholarships - Pulp and Paper Industry Division (Graduate, Undergraduate/Scholarship) [5073]

ISA Technical Division Scholarships - Test Measurement Division (Graduate, Undergraduate/Scholarship) [5074]

ISA Technical Division Scholarships - Water and Wastewater Industries Division (Graduate, Undergraduate/Scholarship) [5075]

Bob and Mary Ives Scholarships (Graduate, Undergraduate/Scholarship) [5076]

Ken and Romaine Kauffman Scholarship Fund (Undergraduate/Scholarship) [3949]

John W. Koons, Sr. Memorial Scholarships (Undergraduate/Scholarship) [1944]

Ken Krum/Bud Kouts Memorial Scholarships (Undergraduate/Scholarship) [1945]

Lewis-Clark State College Presidential Technical Out-of-State Scholarships (Undergraduate/Scholarship) [5447]

Loan Forgiveness Scholarships (Graduate, Undergraduate/Loan, Scholarship) [8634]

Leon I. Lock and Barbara R. Lock Scholarship Fund (Undergraduate/Scholarship) [3950]

Hans McCorriston Motive Power Machinist Grant Programs (Undergraduate, Vocational/Occupational/Scholarship) [1956]

Brouwer D. McIntyre Memorial Scholarships (Undergraduate/Scholarship) [1946]

The Medallion Fund Scholarships (Undergraduate, Vocational/Occupational/Scholarship) [6629]

Jim Moran Scholarships (Undergraduate/Scholarship) [1947]

Arthur Paulin Automotive Aftermarket Scholarship Awards (Postgraduate, Undergraduate/Scholarship) [1957]

Carl C. and Abbie Rebman Trust Scholarships (Undergraduate/Scholarship) [4263]

Kenneth Rogers Memorial Scholarships (Undergraduate/Scholarship) [5462]

Dorothy M. Ross Memorial Scholarships (Undergraduate/Scholarship) [1948]

SEMA Memorial Scholarships (Graduate, Undergraduate, Vocational/Occupational/Scholarship) [1959]

APSAIL's Ralph Silverman Memorial Scholarships (Undergraduate/Scholarship) [1967]

Sloan Northwood University Heavy-Duty Scholarships (Undergraduate/Scholarship) [1968]

Stuart H. Snyder Memorial Scholarships (Undergraduate/Scholarship) [1949]

Specialty Equipment Market Association Scholarships (Graduate, Undergraduate, Vocational/Occupational/Scholarship) [8635]

Walter W. Stillman Scholarships (Undergraduate/Scholarship) [1950]

Toyota High School Scholarship Program (Undergraduate/Scholarship) [4581]

TRW Foundation Scholarships (Undergraduate/Scholarship) [1951]

J. Irving Whalley Memorial Scholarships (Undergraduate/Scholarship) [1952]

M.H. Yager Memorial Scholarships (Undergraduate/Scholarship) [1953]

Aviation (See also Aeronautics)

AE Flight Training Scholarships (Professional development/Scholarship) [6721]

AE Jet Type Rating Scholarships (Professional development/Scholarship) [6722]

AE Technical Training Scholarships (Professional development/Scholarship) [6723]

Air Traffic Control Association Full-time Employee Student Scholarships (Professional development/Scholarship) [103]

Air Traffic Control Association Non-employee Student Scholarships (Undergraduate/Scholarship) [104]

Aircraft Owners and Pilots Association Scholarships (Undergraduate/Scholarship) [122]

Airports Council International-North America Scholarships (Graduate, Undergraduate/Scholarship) [149]

AMACESP Student Scholarships (Undergraduate/Scholarship) [147]

David Arver Memorial Scholarships (Undergraduate/Scholarship) [123]

Dutch and Ginger Arver Scholarships (Undergraduate/Scholarship) [124]

Association of Flight Attendants Scholarship Fund (Undergraduate/Scholarship) [1779]

Aviation Distributors and Manufacturers Association Scholarship Fund (All/Scholarship) [1972]

Donald A. Baldwin Sr. Business Aviation Management Scholarships (All/Scholarship) [6161]

Janice K. Barden Aviation Scholarships (Undergraduate/Scholarship) [6162]

Civil Air Patrol Scholarships for School and Flying (Undergraduate/Scholarship) [2893]

Alan H. Conklin Business Aviation Management Scholarships (Undergraduate/Scholarship) [6163]

Corporate Aviation Management Scholarships (Professional development/Scholarship) [6164]

John P. Culhane Memorial Scholarships (Undergraduate/Scholarship) [191]

Johnny Davis Memorial Scholarships (Undergraduate/Scholarship) [125]

Arlene Davis Scholarships (Undergraduate/Scholarship) [3408]

Distinguished Flying Cross Society Scholarships (Undergraduate/Scholarship) [3461]

F. Atlee Dodge Maintenance Scholarships (Undergraduate/Scholarship) [192]

Duncan Aviation Scholarships (Undergraduate/Scholarship) [126]

Amelia Earhart Memorial Academic Scholarships (Undergraduate/Scholarship) [6724]

Exxon Mobil Aviation and the Avitats International Operators Scholarships (All/Scholarship) [6165]

William M. Fanning Maintenance Scholarships (Undergraduate/Scholarship) [6166]

Field Aviation Co., Inc. Scholarships (Undergraduate/Scholarship) [127]

Flight Attendants/Flight Technician Scholarships (Professional development/Scholarship) [6167]

FPA Aviation Scholarships (Graduate, Undergraduate/Scholarship) [3851]

Joseph Frasca Excellence in Aviation Scholarships (Undergraduate/Scholarship) [9191]

Garmin Scholarships (Undergraduate/Scholarship) [128]

Lowell Gaylor Memorial Scholarships (Undergraduate/Scholarship) [129]

Lawrence Ginocchio Aviation Scholarships (Undergraduate/Scholarship) [6168]

Bud Glover Memorial Scholarships (Undergraduate/Scholarship) [130]

Gogos Scholarships (Undergraduate/Scholarship) [2980]

Guggenheim Fellowships (Doctorate/Fellowship) [8251]

Leon Harris/Les Nichols Memorial Scholarships to Spartan College of Aeronautics & Technology (Undergraduate/Scholarship) [131]

Don C. Hawkins Memorial Scholarships (Undergraduate/Scholarship) [132]

Helicopter Foundation International Commercial Helicopter Rating Scholarships (Professional development/Scholarship) [4508]

Helicopter Foundation International Maintenance Technician Certificate Scholarships (Professional development/Scholarship) [4509]

Honeywell Avionics Scholarships (Undergraduate, Vocational/Occupational/Scholarship) [133]

Edward L. Horne, Jr. Scholarships (All/Scholarship) [6969]

NORDAM Dee Howard/Etienne Fage Scholarships (Undergraduate/Scholarship) [6169]

The ISASI Rudolf Kapustin Memorial Scholarships (Undergraduate/Scholarship) [4988]

Eugene S. Kropf Scholarships (Undergraduate/Scholarship) [9192]

L-3 Avionics Systems Scholarships (Undergraduate, Vocational/Occupational/Scholarship) [134]

Charles A. Lindbergh Fellowships (Graduate/Fellowship) [8252]

MAF Canada Scholarship Fund (Undergraduate/Scholarship) [5908]

Maintenance Technical Reward and Career Scholarships (Undergraduate/Scholarship) [6170]

Mid-Continent Instrument Scholarships (Undergraduate/Scholarship) [135]

Joshua Esch Mitchell Aviation Scholarships (Undergraduate/Scholarship) [4293]

Monte R. Mitchell Global Scholarships (Undergraduate/Scholarship) [136]

National Black Coalition of Federal Aviation Employees Scholarships (Other, Vocational/Occupational/Scholarship) [6143]

Michelle North Scholarships for Safety (Professional development/Scholarship) [4510]

OBAP Fellowships - Airline Transport (ATP) (Professional development/Fellowship) [6970]

OBAP Fellowships - Commercial (Professional development/Fellowship) [6971]

OBAP Fellowships - Instructor Rating CFI/CFII/MEI (Professional development/Fellowship) [6972]

OBAP Fellowships - Multi-Engine (Professional development/Fellowship) [6973]

Organization of Black Aerospace Professionals General Scholarships (All/Scholarship) [6974]

PAMA Foundation Scholarship Program (Graduate, Undergraduate/Scholarship) [7437]

Chuck Peacock Memorial Scholarships (Undergraduate/Scholarship) [137]

Bob Reeve Aviation Management Scholarships (Undergraduate/Scholarship) [193]

Rockwell Collins Scholarships (Undergraduate/Scholarship) [138]

Marty Rosness Student Scholarships (Undergraduate/Scholarship) [1505]

San Diego Regional Aviation Association Scholarships (Undergraduate/Scholarship) [7961]

Bill Sanderson Aviation Maintenance Technician Scholarships (Postgraduate/Scholarship) [4511]

Scheduler and Dispatchers Scholarships (Professional development/Scholarship) [6171]

Thomas J. Slocum Memorial Scholarships to Westwood College of Aviation Technology (Undergraduate/Scholarship) [139]

Southeast Aerospace Inc. Scholarships (Undergraduate/Scholarship) [140]

Sporty's Pilot Shop/Cincinnati Avionics Scholarships (Undergraduate, Vocational/Occupational/Scholarship) [141]

Tailhook Educational Foundation Scholarship Program (Undergraduate/Scholarship) [8796]

Kei Takemoto Memorial Scholarships (Undergraduate/Scholarship) [142]

Lee Tarbox Memorial Scholarships (Undergraduate/Scholarship) [143]

Tom Taylor Memorial Scholarships to Spartan College of Aeronautics and Technology (Undergraduate/Scholarship) [144]

Texas State Technical College Scholarships (Undergraduate/Scholarship) [145]

U.S. Aircraft Insurance Group Professional Development Program (USAIG PDP) Scholarships (Undergraduate/Scholarship) [6172]

A. Verville Fellowships (All/Fellowship) [8253]

Paul A. Whelan Aviation Scholarships (Undergraduate, Graduate/Scholarship) [9193]

Dr. Harold S. Wood Awards for Excellence (Undergraduate/Award) [4072]

Banking (See also Accounting; Finance)

Bank of Canada Fellowships (Doctorate, Professional development/Fellowship) [2011]

Conference of State Bank Supervisors Graduate School Scholarships (Graduate/Award) [3213]

Tribal Business Management Program Scholarships (TBM) (Undergraduate/Scholarship) [2664]

Wells Fargo American Indian Scholarships - Graduate (Graduate/Scholarship) [828]

Wells Fargo Scholarship Program (Graduate, Undergraduate/Scholarship) [4585]

Behavioral sciences

Owen F. Aldis Scholarship Fund (Graduate/Scholarship) [4994]

Behavioral Sciences Post-Doctoral Fellowships (Postdoctorate/Fellowship) [3660]

Behavioral Sciences Student Fellowships (Graduate, Undergraduate/Fellowship) [3661]

CASBS Residential Fellowships (Doctorate, Professional development/Fellowship) [2681]

EAPSI Fellowships (Doctorate, Graduate/Fellowship) [6467]

Epilepsy Foundation Research Grants (All/Grant) [3664]

Morris County Psychological Association Scholarships (Undergraduate/Scholarship) [5933]

National Institute of Health Undergraduate Scholarship Program (Undergraduate/Scholarship) [6353]

NDSEG Fellowships (Graduate/Fellowship) [6239]

NHLBI Individual Pre-Doctoral Fellowships (Doctorate, Graduate/Fellowship) [6315]

Russell Sage Foundation Visiting Scholars (Postdoctorate/Fellowship) [7880]

SOPHE/ATSDR Student Fellowships in Environmental Health or Emergency Preparedness (Doctorate, Graduate, Master's/Fellowship) [8478]

SOPHE/CDC Student Fellowships in Child, Adolescent and School Health (Doctorate, Graduate, Master's/Fellowship) [8479]

SOPHE/CDC Student Fellowships in Injury Prevention (Graduate/Fellowship) [8480]

Louis Stokes Urban Health Policy Fellows Program (Graduate, Professional development/Fellowship) [3222]

Targeted Research Initiative for Health Outcomes (Doctorate/Grant) [3668]

Targeted Research Initiative for Mood Disorders (Doctorate/Grant) [3669]

Targeted Research Initiative for Seniors (Doctorate/Grant) [3670]

Bible studies (See also Religion; Theology)

Catholic Biblical Association of America Scholarships (Undergraduate/Scholarship) [2666]

CSF Graduate Fellowships (Graduate/Fellowship) [2787]

FTE Dissertation Fellowships (Graduate/Fellowship) [4020]

FTE Doctoral Fellowships (Doctorate, Graduate/Fellowship) [4021]

FTE North American Doctoral Fellowships (Doctorate, Graduate/Fellowship) [4023]

Biochemistry (See also Chemistry)

Epilepsy Foundation Pre-doctoral Research Training Fellowships (Graduate/Grant) [3663]

UAA Kris Knudson Memorial Scholarships (Graduate, Undergraduate/Scholarship) [9102]

Larson Aquatic Research Support Scholarships (LARS) (Doctorate, Graduate/Scholarship) [1418]

MillerCoors Engineering and Sciences Scholarships (Undergraduate/Scholarship) [47]

Bioethics (See Ethics and bioethics)

Biological and clinical sciences (See also Biology)

Barbados Cancer Association Post-Graduate Scholarships (Graduate/Scholarship) [2021]

Clinical Research Fellowship for Medical Students (Graduate/Fellowship) [3522]

Daland Fellowships in Clinical Investigation (Doctorate/Fellowship) [989]

EAPSI Fellowships (Doctorate, Graduate/Fellowship) [6467]

Endowment Fund for Education Grants (EFFE) (Undergraduate/Grant) [2093]

Endowment Fund for Education, Loans/Grants for Educational Materials (Undergraduate/Grant) [2095]

Endowment Fund for Education, Loans/Grants for Equipment (Undergraduate/Grant) [2096]

Endowment Fund for Education, Loans (Undergraduate/Loan) [2094]

Howard Hughes Medical Institute Predoctoral Fellowships (Graduate/Fellowship) [6075]

Charles A. King Trust Postdoctoral Fellowships (Postdoctorate/Fellowship) [4495]

Lewis and Clark Fund for Exploration and Field Research (Doctorate/Grant) [992]

National GEM Consortium - PhD Science Fellowships (Doctorate, Graduate/Fellowship) [6307]

OHTN Postdoctoral Fellowships (Doctorate/Fellowship) [6893]

SFP Mid-Career/Mentor Awards for Family Planning (Professional development/Grant) [8323]

SNMTS Clinical Advancement Scholarships (Professional development/Scholarship) [8422]

Louis Stokes Urban Health Policy Fellows Program (Graduate, Professional development/Fellowship) [3222]

Biology (See also Biological and clinical sciences)

AACT Undergraduate Scholarships (Undergraduate/Scholarship) [7153]

Alaska Support Industry Alliance Scholarships (Undergraduate/Scholarship) [9133]

Avista Corporation Minds in Motion Scholarships (Undergraduate/Scholarship) [5412]

Catherine H. Beattie Fellowships (Graduate/Fellowship) [2705]

Biocom Scholarships (Undergraduate/Scholarship) [7913]

BioQuip Undergraduate Scholarships (Undergraduate/Scholarship) [3653]

William L. Brown Fellowships (Graduate/Fellowship) [6978]

John and Elisabeth Buck Endowed Scholarships (Graduate, Postdoctorate/Scholarship) [5612]

C. Lalor Burdick Scholarships (Undergraduate/Scholarship) [5613]

Max M. Burger Endowed Scholarships in Embryology (Undergraduate/Scholarship) [5614]

Julian E. Carnes Scholarship Fund (Undergraduate/Scholarship) [3891]

CCV Foundation Graduate and Undergraduate Fellowships (Doctorate, Graduate, Undergraduate/Fellowship) [2672]

David and Deborah Clark Fellowships (Graduate/Fellowship) [6979]

Rexford Daubenmire Fellowships (Graduate/Fellowship) [6980]

Charles Dobbins FTA Scholarships (Undergraduate, Vocational/Occupational/Scholarship) [4033]

DOE Computational Science Graduate Fellowships (DOE CSGF) (Doctorate, Graduate/Fellowship) [5306]

Dole Food Fellowships (Graduate/Fellowship) [6981]

Dow Chemical Company Fellowships (Graduate/Fellowship) [6427]

E.I. DuPont Fellowships (Graduate/Fellowship) [6428]

Fellowships and Internships Program in Latin America (Graduate/Fellowship, Internship) [8269]

Emily P. Foster Fellowships (Graduate/Fellowship) [6982]

Thomas B. Grave and Elizabeth F. Grave Scholarships (Undergraduate/Scholarship) [5615]

Caswell Grave Scholarships (Undergraduate/Scholarship) [5616]

William Randolph Hearst Educational Endowments (Undergraduate/Scholarship) [5617]

Helm Family Scholarships (Undergraduate/Scholarship) [7932]

Benjamin Kaminer Endowed Scholarships in Physiology (Undergraduate/Scholarship) [5618]

Arthur Klorfein Scholarship and Fellowship Fund (Undergraduate/Scholarship) [5619]

Lakselaget Foundation Scholarships (Graduate, Undergraduate/Scholarship) [5320]

Lewis-Clark State College Presidential Technical Out-of-State Scholarships (Undergraduate/Scholarship) [5447]

Life Sciences Research Foundation Postdoctoral Fellowship Program (Graduate, Doctorate/Fellowship) [5494]

Frank R. Lillie Fellowships and Scholarships (Undergraduate/Scholarship) [5620]

Marine Biological Laboratory Pioneers Fund (Undergraduate/Scholarship) [5621]

S.O. Mast Founder's Scholarships (Undergraduate/Scholarship) [5622]

Dolphus E. Milligan Graduate Fellowships (Graduate/Scholarship) [6429]

Frank Morrell Endowed Memorial Scholarships (Undergraduate/Scholarship) [5623]

Barbara H. Mullin Memorial Scholarships (Graduate, Undergraduate/Scholarship) [9573]

NAAF Aboriginal Health Careers Bursary and Scholarships (Graduate, Undergraduate/Scholarship) [5992]

National Association of Biology Teachers BioClub Student Awards (Undergraduate/Award) [6035]

NDSEG Fellowships (Graduate/Fellowship) [6239]

NGC College Scholarships (Graduate, Undergraduate/Scholarship) [6303]

NOBCChE Procter and Gamble Fellowships (Graduate/Fellowship) [6430]

Pfizer Inc. Endowed Scholarships (Undergraduate/Scholarship) [5625]

Pioneer Hi-Bred International Graduate Student Fellowships (Graduate/Fellowship) [3654]

A. Stanley Rand Fellowships Program (Undergraduate, Doctorate, Postdoctorate/Fellowship) [8270]

Herbert W. Rand Fellowships and Scholarships (Undergraduate/Scholarship) [5626]

Lola Ellis Robertson Scholarships (Undergraduate/Scholarship) [5627]

Florence C. Rose and S. Meryl Rose Scholarships (Undergraduate/Scholarship) [5628]

Rowe Family Fellowships (Graduate/Fellowship) [6985]

Ruth Sager Scholarships (Undergraduate/Scholarship) [5629]

Milton L. Shifman Endowed Scholarships (Undergraduate/Scholarship) [5630]

Short-Term Fellowships (Undergraduate, Graduate, Postdoctorate/Fellowship) [8271]

SICB Fellowships of Graduate Student Travel (FGST) (Graduate/Fellowship) [8359]

SICB Grants-in-Aid of Research Program (GIAR) (Graduate/Grant) [8360]

Julia Viola Simms Science Scholarships (Postgraduate/Scholarship) [2128]

Lillian and Murray Slatkin Fellowships (Graduate/Fellowship) [6986]

Eastman Kodak Dr. Theophilus Sorrell Fellowships (Graduate/Fellowship) [6432]

Horace W. Stunkard Scholarships (Undergraduate/Scholarship) [5631]

F. Christian and Betty Thompson Fellowships (Graduate/Fellowship) [6988]

J.P. and Madeline Trinkaus Endowed Scholarships in Embryology (Undergraduate/Scholarship) [5632]

Earl S. Tupper 3-year Postdoctoral Fellowships in Tropical Biology (Postdoctorate/Fellowship) [8272]

Welder Wildlife Foundation Fellowships (Doctorate, Graduate/Fellowship) [9559]

Women in Science and Technology Scholarships (Doctorate, Graduate, Master's, Undergraduate/Scholarship) [9442]

Biology, Marine

Atlantic Salmon Federation Olin Fellowships (All/Fellowship) [1929]

Boyd N. Lyon Scholarships (Doctorate, Graduate/Scholarship) [5554]

Dr. Nancy Foster Scholarships (Doctorate, Graduate/Scholarship) [3873]

International Women's Fishing Association Scholarships (Graduate/Scholarship) [5028]

ISRS Graduate Fellowships (Doctorate, Graduate/Fellowship) [5001]

Link Foundation/Smithsonian Graduate Fellowships in Marine Science (Graduate/Fellowship) [8262]

Marine Technology Society ROV Scholarships (Graduate, Undergraduate/Scholarship) [5639]

Marine Technology Society Scholarships for Graduate and Undergraduate Students (Graduate, Undergraduate/Scholarship) [5640]

Marine Technology Society Student Scholarships for Graduating High School Seniors (Undergraduate/Scholarship) [5641]

Marine Technology Society Student Scholarships for Two-year Technical, Engineering and Community College Students (Community College, Two Year College, Undergraduate/Scholarship) [5642]

North American Rolex Scholarships (Professional development, Undergraduate/Scholarship) [7002]

Oceanic Research Group Scholarships (Graduate, Undergraduate/Scholarship) [6850]

The Paros-Digiquartz Scholarships (Graduate, Undergraduate/Scholarship) [5643]

Ellis W. Rowe Scholarships (Undergraduate/Scholarship) [4380]

Ronald L. Schmied Scholarships (Professional development, Undergraduate/Scholarship) [4362]

Biology, Molecular

Sloan Research Fellowships (Doctorate/Fellowship) [8235]

Biomedical research (See also Medical research)

Clinical Pharmacy Post-Pharm.D. Fellowships in the Biomedical Research Sciences (Postdoctorate/Fellowship) [758]

Henry Friesen Awards and Lectures (Doctorate/Award) [2601]

Gilliam Fellowships for Advanced Study (Doctorate/Fellowship) [4621]

HHMI International Student Research Fellowships (Doctorate/Fellowship) [4622]

HHMI Medical Research Fellowships (Undergraduate/Fellowship) [4623]

KFOC Biomedical Fellowships (Postdoctorate/Fellowship) [5257]

Donald A.B. Lindberg Research Fellowships (Doctorate, Graduate/Fellowship) [5744]

National Institute of Health Undergraduate Scholarship Program (Undergraduate/Scholarship) [6353]

National Space Biomedical Research Institute Postdoctoral Fellowships (Postdoctorate/Fellowship) [6521]

Pew Latin American Fellows Program in the Biomedical Sciences (Professional development/Fellowship) [7219]

SRF Post-doctoral Fellowships (Postdoctorate/Fellowship) [8061]

Helen Hay Whitney Foundation Fellowships (Doctorate, Graduate/Fellowship) [9595]

Biomedical sciences

BMES Graduate and Undergraduate Student Awards (Graduate, Undergraduate/Award) [2100]

Career Fellowship Awards for Medical Scientists (Postdoctorate, Professional development/Fellowship) [2214]

NHLBI Individual Pre-Doctoral Fellowships (Doctorate, Graduate/Fellowship) [6315]

Saul T. Wilson, Jr. Scholarships (Graduate, Undergraduate/Scholarship) [9403]

Biophysics (See also Physics)

Grass Fellowships (Doctorate, Postdoctorate/Fellowship) [4315]

Graduate Fellowship Program - Peter Verhofstadt Fellowships (GFP) (Graduate/Fellowship) [8084]

Blood banking

Canadian Blood Services Graduate Fellowships (Graduate/Fellowship) [2421]

Canadian Blood Services Postdoctoral Fellowships (Postdoctorate/Fellowship) [2422]

Botany

Garden Club of America Awards in Tropical Botany (GCA) (Doctorate/Award) [4041]

J.S. Karling Graduate Student Research Awards (Graduate/Grant) [2164]

Louisiana Agricultural Consultants Association Scholarships (Graduate, Undergraduate/Scholarship) [5517]

NGC College Scholarships (Graduate, Undergraduate/Scholarship) [6303]

Mary Perlmutter Scholarships (Postgraduate/Award) [2565]

Dennis Raveling Scholarships (Undergraduate/Scholarship) [2288]

Richard E. Schultes Research Awards (Graduate/Grant) [8316]

Welder Wildlife Foundation Fellowships (Doctorate, Graduate/Fellowship) [9559]

British studies (See also Scottish studies)

Carl H. Pforzheimer, Jr. Research Grants (Graduate, Professional development/Grant) [5225]

Broadcasting (See also Media arts)

AAJA/CNN Scholar Program (Graduate, Undergraduate/Scholarship) [1640]

AAJA/COX Foundation Scholarships (Graduate, Undergraduate/Scholarship) [1641]

The Access Intelligence Scholarships (Graduate, Undergraduate/Scholarship) [8486]

APTRA Scholarships (Undergraduate/Scholarship) [1684]

John Bayliss Broadcast Foundation Internship Programs (Undergraduate/Internship) [2030]

John Bayliss Broadcast Foundation Scholarships (Undergraduate/Scholarship) [2031]

BBM Canada Scholarships (Undergraduate/Scholarship) [2365]

Rick Brewer Scholarships (Undergraduate/Scholarship) [9261]

Mary L. Brown High School Student Scholarships (Undergraduate/Scholarship) [5037]

Colorado Broadcasters Association Continuing Education Scholarships (Professional development/Scholarship) [2984]

Joe Durso Memorial Scholarships (Undergraduate/Scholarship) [5921]

Harold E. Ennes Scholarships (Graduate, Professional development/Scholarship) [8303]

Harold E. Fellows Scholarships (All/Scholarship) [2182]

E. Lanier Finch Scholarships (Undergraduate/Scholarship) [4097]

Fisher Broadcasting Scholarships for Minorities (Undergraduate, Vocational/Occupational/Scholarship) [3802]

Stephen Gates Scholarships (Undergraduate/Scholarship) [9274]

Great Falls Broadcasters Association Scholarships (Undergraduate/Scholarship) [5922]

Robert D. Greenberg Scholarships (Graduate, Professional development/Scholarship) [8304]

Ruth Hancock Scholarships (Undergraduate/Scholarship) [2366]

Clay Huntington Sports Communications Scholarships (Undergraduate/Scholarship) [4338]

Indiana Broadcasters Association College Scholarship Program (Undergraduate/Scholarship) [4733]

Indiana Broadcasters Association High School Scholarship Program (Undergraduate/Scholarship) [4734]

ISBA General Scholarships (Undergraduate/Scholarship) [4678]

Kansas Association of Broadcasters Scholarships (Undergraduate/Scholarship) [5182]

Charles Kuralt Fellowships in International Broadcasting (Postgraduate/Scholarship) [9285]

LIN Media Minority Scholarships and Training Program (Undergraduate/Scholarship) [5501]

McNamara Family Creative Arts Project Grants (Graduate, Undergraduate/Grant) [4579]

Montana Broadcasters Association Directors' Scholarships (Undergraduate/Scholarship) [5923]

Montana Broadcasters Association Engineers' Scholarships (Undergraduate/Scholarship) [5924]

New York Women in Communications, Inc. Foundation Scholarships (Graduate, Undergraduate/Scholarship) [6690]

Ohio Association of Broadcaster's Kids Scholarships (Undergraduate/Scholarship) [6852]

Ohio Association of Broadcasters Scholarships (Undergraduate/Scholarship) [6853]

Oregon Association of Broadcasters Scholarships (Undergraduate/Scholarship) [6929]

Walter S. Patterson Scholarships (All/Scholarship) [2183]

Producers Academy Scholarships (All/Scholarship) [3264]

Linda Simmons Memorial Scholarships (Undergraduate/Scholarship) [195]

Helen J. Sioussat/Fay Wells Scholarships (All/Scholarship) [2184]

Leo Suarez Journalism Scholarships (Undergraduate/Scholarship) [3321]

Alexander M. Tanger Scholarships (All/Scholarship) [2185]

Two Year/Community Broadcast Education Association Scholarship Awards (All/Scholarship) [2186]

Abe Voron Scholarships (All/Scholarship) [2187]

Vincent T. Wasilewski Scholarships (All/Scholarship) [2188]

Wisconsin Broadcasters Association Scholarships (Undergraduate/Scholarship) [9682]

Youth Scholarships (Undergraduate/Scholarship) [8305]

Business

Evelyn Abrams Memorial Scholarships (Undergraduate/Scholarship) [7462]

Accenture American Indian Scholarship Program (Graduate, Undergraduate/Scholarship) [825]

Alaska Aerospace Development Corporation Scholarships (Undergraduate/Scholarship) [9130]

ALPFA Scholarship Programs (Postgraduate, Undergraduate/Scholarship) [1824]

American Business Women's Association Sarasota Sunrise Chapter Scholarships (Undergraduate, Vocational/Occupational/Scholarship) [3187]

American Indian Fellowship in Business Scholarships (Graduate, Master's, Undergraduate/Scholarship) [6180]

American Standard Scholarships (Undergraduate/Scholarship) [7344]

ARA Scholarship Awards (Undergraduate/Scholarship) [1961]

ASBPE Young Leaders Scholarships (All/Scholarship) [1189]

Avista Corporation Minds in Motion Scholarships (Undergraduate/Scholarship) [5412]

Bank of America Junior Achievement Scholarship Fund (Undergraduate/Scholarship) [3885]

Bank of Canada Governor's Awards (Doctorate, Professional development/Award) [2012]

Banner Bank Business Scholarships (Undergraduate/Scholarship) [5413]

Bison Transport Scholarships (Undergraduate/Scholarship) [6897]

Boeing Business Scholarships (Undergraduate/Scholarship) [4175]

Quincy Brown Memorial Scholarships (Undergraduate/Scholarship) [7634]

Business Insurance Diploma Scholarships (Undergraduate/Scholarship) [7992]

Dr. F. Ross Byrd Scholarships (Graduate, Vocational/Occupational/Scholarship) [9523]

C200 Scholar Awards (All/Scholarship) [3015]

Canadian Association for Studies in Co-operation Scholarships Lemaire Co-operative Studies Awards (CASC) (Graduate, Undergraduate/Scholarship) [2431]

Catching the Dream Scholarships (Graduate, Undergraduate/Scholarship) [817]

C.C.H.R.M.A. Scholarships (High School, Undergraduate/Scholarship) [2941]

CERT College Scholarships (Graduate, Undergraduate/Scholarship) [3272]

Melba Dawn Chiarenza Scholarship Fund (Undergraduate/Scholarship) [9554]

Citi/TELACU Scholarships (Undergraduate/Scholarship) [8820]

Clark High School Academy of Finance Scholarships (Undergraduate/Scholarship) [7476]

Clark High School Alumni Leadership Circle Scholarships (Undergraduate/Scholarship) [7477]

Congressional Scholarship Awards (Undergraduate/Scholarship) [4016]

Connecticut Mortgage Bankers Scholarships-Social Affairs Committee (Undergraduate/Scholarship) [4422]

Mable B. Crawford Memorial Scholarships (Undergraduate/Scholarship) [9146]

Critical Language Scholarships for Intensive Summer Institutes (Graduate, Undergraduate/Scholarship) [1145]

D&A Florida Scholarships (Undergraduate/Scholarship) [8597]

Canadian Association for Studies in Co-operation Scholarships - Amy and Tim Dauphinee Scholarships (CASC) (Graduate/Scholarship) [2432]

Kenneth D. and Katherine D. Davis Scholarships (Undergraduate/Scholarship) [7070]

Delta Faucet Scholarships (Undergraduate/Scholarship) [7345]

Cindy P. Dennis Scholarship Fund (Undergraduate/Scholarship) [3241]

Josephine P. White Eagle Graduate Fellowships (Graduate, Master's, Doctorate/Fellowship) [4591]

Wayne G. Failor Scholarships (High School/Scholarship) [7158]

First Security Foundation Business Scholarships (Undergraduate/Scholarship) [5427]

Florida Education Fund McKnight Doctoral Fellowships (Graduate/Fellowship) [3822]

Floto-Peel Family Scholarship Fund (Undergraduate, Vocational/Occupational/Scholarship) [4215]

UAA Michael D. Ford Memorial Scholarships (Graduate, Undergraduate/Scholarship) [9093]

UAA Jan & Glenn Fredericks Scholarships (Graduate, Undergraduate/Scholarship) [9094]

Generation III Scholarships (Undergraduate/Scholarship) [3586]

Doris Y. and John J. Gerber Scholarships (Undergraduate/Scholarship) [9524]

William R. Goldfarb Memorial Scholarships (Undergraduate/Scholarship) [1085]

Goldman Sachs/Matsuo Takabuki Commemorative Scholarships (Graduate/Scholarship) [5211]

Community Bank - Lee Guggisberg Foundation Memorial Scholarships (Undergraduate/Scholarship) [7651]

HAESF Professional Internship Program (Doctorate/Internship) [4641]

HAESF Senior Leaders and Scholars Fellowships (Professional development/Fellowship) [4642]

Gene Halker Memorial Scholarships (Graduate, Undergraduate/Scholarship) [3865]

Anna E. Hall Memorial Scholarships (Undergraduate/Scholarship) [7251]

Hilb, Rogal and Hobbs Scholarships (Undergraduate/Scholarship) [9449]

Raymond T. Hoge Scholarship Fund (Undergraduate/Scholarship) [8674]

HSBC-North America Scholarship Program (Undergraduate/Scholarship) [4571]

HSF/Nissan Community College Transfer Scholarship Program (Undergraduate/Scholarship) [4576]

HSF/Wal-Mart Stores Inc. Scholarship Program (Graduate, Undergraduate/Scholarship) [4577]

IAAP Wings Chapter Scholarships (Undergraduate, Vocational/Occupational/Scholarship) [4854]

IBEA Graduate Scholarships (Graduate/Scholarship) [4682]

IBEA Undergraduate Scholarships (Undergraduate/Scholarship) [4683]

International Dairy-Deli-Bakery Association Undergraduate Scholarships (Graduate, Undergraduate/Scholarship) [4916]

International Management Council Scholarships (IMC) (Undergraduate/Scholarship) [3155]

Dwight P. Jacobus Scholarships (Undergraduate/Scholarship) [1860]

JD/MBA Scholarships (Undergraduate/Scholarship) [7188]

Margaret G. Johnson and Marge J. Stout Scholarships (Undergraduate, Vocational/Occupational/Scholarship) [5437]

Johnson and Wales University Scholarships (Undergraduate/Scholarship) [5175]

Jane M. Klausman Women in Business Scholarships (Graduate, Undergraduate/Scholarship) [9813]

Canadian Association for Studies in Co-operation Scholarships Alexander Fraser Laidlaw Fellowships (CASC) (Graduate/Fellowship) [2433]

Paul J. Laninga Memorial Scholarship Fund (Undergraduate/Scholarship) [4226]

Las Vegas Chinatown Scholarships (Undergraduate/Scholarship) [7500]

Rick and Beverly Lattin Education Scholarship Fund (Undergraduate/Scholarship) [4227]

League of Latin American Citizens General Electric Scholarships (Undergraduate, Vocational/Occupational/Scholarship) [5386]

Doreen Legg Memorial Scholarships (Undergraduate/Scholarship) [7664]

Karen B. Lewis Career Education Scholarships (Undergraduate/Scholarship) [9441]

David C. Lizarraga Graduate Fellowships (Graduate, Master's/Fellowship) [8821]

Luso-American Education Foundation C-1 General Scholarships (Undergraduate/Scholarship) [5541]

Kaia Lynn Markwalter Endowed Scholarships (Undergraduate/Scholarship) [5453]

Mas Family Scholarships (Graduate, Undergraduate/Scholarship) [5658]

MESBEC Scholarships (Undergraduate/Scholarship) [2662]

Ruth Messmer Memorial Scholarships (Undergraduate/Scholarship) [8614]

Michaels Jewelers Foundation Scholarships for Athletes (Undergraduate/Scholarship) [4452]

Mill Creek Business Association Scholarships (Undergraduate/Scholarship) [5878]

MillerCoors National Scholarships (Undergraduate/Scholarship) [48]

George J. Mitchell Scholarships (Undergraduate/Scholarship) [9398]

Robert E. and Judy More Scholarship Fund (Undergraduate/Scholarship) [3784]

NAAF Post-Secondary Education Scholarships (Graduate, Undergraduate/Scholarship) [5993]

NABA National Scholarship Program (Graduate, Undergraduate/Scholarship) [6037]

NASE Future Entrepreneur Scholarships (Undergraduate/Scholarship) [6117]

National Honor Roll Scholarships (Undergraduate/Scholarship) [2222]

NBMBAA Graduate Scholarships Program (Graduate/Scholarship) [6152]

NBMBAA PhD Fellowship Program (Doctorate/Fellowship) [6153]

Paul and Ruth Neidhold Business Scholarships (Undergraduate/Scholarship) [3161]

Hubert A. Nelson Scholarships (Undergraduate/Scholarship) [3539]

New York Financial Writers' Associations Scholarships (Graduate, Undergraduate/Scholarship) [6667]

NHSCPA Scholarships (Graduate, Undergraduate/Scholarship) [6635]

Norfolk Southern Scholarships (Undergraduate/Scholarship) [9450]

Peggy Kommer Novosad Scholarships (Graduate, Postgraduate/Scholarship) [4295]

NSHMBA Scholarships (Graduate/Scholarship) [6508]

Office Depot Scholarships (Undergraduate/Scholarship) [4549]

Pardee Community Building Scholarships (Undergraduate/Scholarship) [7515]

Patriot Education Scholarships (Undergraduate/Scholarship) [5591]

Thomas R. Pickering Graduate Foreign Affairs Fellowships (Graduate/Fellowship) [9619]

Julia T. Pingree Student Scholarships (Undergraduate/Scholarship) [6627]

Plumbing-Heating-Cooling Contractors Association Educational Foundation Massachusetts Auxiliary Scholarships (Undergraduate/Scholarship) [7346]

Plumbing-Heating-Cooling Contractors Association Educational Foundation Need-Based Scholarships (Undergraduate/Scholarship) [7347]

Plumbing-Heating-Cooling Contractors Association Educational Foundation Scholarships (Undergraduate/Scholarship) [7348]

Progressive Dairy Producer Awards (All/Grant) [6233]

RBC Royal Bank Scholarships for Undergraduates (Undergraduate/Scholarship) [7825]

Dr. Felix H. Reyler Memorial Scholarships (Undergraduate/Scholarship) [3319]

RFDF MBA Preparation Fellowships (Graduate, Undergraduate/Fellowship) [7800]

RFDF Pre-MBA Fellowships (Graduate/Fellowship) [7801]

Dorothy Worden Ronken Scholarships (Graduate/Scholarship) [3421]

Scotiabank Scholarship for Business Studies (Graduate/Scholarship) [2127]

NASCAR/Wendell Scott Awards (Graduate, Undergraduate/Scholarship) [4550]

David and Sharon Seaver Family Scholarship Fund (Undergraduate/Scholarship) [4241]

Pat Shimp Memorial Scholarships (Undergraduate/Scholarship) [7114]

Silver Nugget Gaming Ambassadors Scholarships (Undergraduate/Scholarship) [7524]

A.O. Smith Scholarships (Undergraduate/Scholarship) [7349]

Helen D. Snow Memorial Scholarships (Undergraduate/Scholarship) [7252]

Frank H. Sobey Awards for Excellence in Business Studies (Undergraduate/Award) [8277]

Soroptimist International of Redlands Scholarships (Undergraduate/Scholarship) [7715]

Morgan Stanley Tribal Scholars Program (Undergraduate/Scholarship) [811]

Gabe Stepetin Business Scholarship Awards (Undergraduate, Vocational/Occupational, Graduate, Master's/Scholarship) [290]

StraightForward Media's Business School Scholarships (Undergraduate/Scholarship) [8757]

Edward P. Suchecki Family Scholarship Fund (Undergraduate/Scholarship) [4246]

Surety Industry Scholarship Program for Minority Students (Undergraduate/Scholarship) [8778]

Toyota High School Scholarship Program (Undergraduate/Scholarship) [4581]

Toyota/TELACU Scholarships (Undergraduate/Scholarship) [8822]

Tribal Business Management Program Scholarships (TBM) (Undergraduate/Scholarship) [2664]

Jacki Tuckfield Memorial Graduate Business Scholarship Fund (Doctorate, Graduate, Master's/Scholarship) [3323]

UAA College of Business & Public Policy Scholarships (Graduate, Undergraduate, Vocational/Occupational/Scholarship) [9118]

UAA Pignalberi Public Policy Scholarships (Graduate/Scholarship) [9124]

Urban Financial Services Coalition Scholarships (Undergraduate/Scholarship) [2129]

Martin Walmsley Fellowships for Technological Entrepreneurship (Graduate/Fellowship) [6891]

Washington University Law School Chancellor's Graduate Fellowships (Graduate/Fellowship) [9532]

Washington University Law School Olin Fellowships for Women (Graduate/Fellowship) [9533]

Seitlin Franklin E. Wheeler Scholarship Fund (Undergraduate/Scholarship) [3324]

Jerry Wheeler Scholarships (Undergraduate/Scholarship) [8559]

Bradford White Scholarships (Undergraduate/Scholarship) [7350]

Wilkinson & Company LLP Secondary School Scholarships (Undergraduate/Scholarship) [9603]

Women In Defense HORIZONS Scholarships (Graduate, Undergraduate/Scholarship) [9696]

Xavier University Williams Scholarships (Undergraduate/Scholarship) [9785]

Business administration

AAUW Legal Advocacy Fund Selected Professions Fellowships (Doctorate, Graduate/Fellowship) [18]

African American Network - Carolinas Scholarship Fund (Undergraduate/Scholarship) [3882]

American Association of University Women Selected Professions Fellowships (Professional development/Fellowship) [13]

American Society of Military Comptrollers National Scholarship Program (Undergraduate/Scholarship) [1305]

ASAC-CJAS PhD Research Grant Awards (Doctorate/Grant) [52]

Lawrence Bayer Business Administration Scholarships (Undergraduate/Scholarship) [9138]

UAA Mark A. Beltz Scholarships (Graduate, Under-

graduate, Vocational/Occupational/Scholarship)
[9087]
Bill & Nell Biggs Scholarships (Undergraduate/
Scholarship) [9140]
Wes Burton Memorial Scholarships (Undergraduate/
Scholarship) [9628]
The Rick Crane Group Real Estate Scholarship
Fund (Undergraduate/Scholarship) [5422]
CTRF Scholarships for Graduate Study in Transpor-
tation (Graduate/Scholarship) [2626]
Walt Disney Company Foundation Scholarships
(Undergraduate/Scholarship) [5173]
Richard Gregory Freeland, II Educational Scholar-
ships (High School/Scholarship) [2147]
Fuchs-Harden Educational Scholarships Fund (Un-
dergraduate/Scholarship) [4337]
HACU/Wal-Mart Achievers Scholarships (Under-
graduate/Scholarship) [4547]
Geordie Hilton Academic Scholarships (Undergradu-
ate/Scholarship) [4184]
HSF/Citi Fellows Program (Undergraduate/Scholar-
ship) [4573]
HSF/General Motors Scholarship Program (Under-
graduate/Scholarship) [4574]
Ron LaFreniere Business Scholarships (Under-
graduate/Scholarship) [8119]
Lazarian Graduate Scholarships (Graduate/Scholar-
ship) [1578]
Sue A. Malone Scholarships (Doctorate, Graduate/
Scholarship) [5188]
Minorities in Government Finance Scholarships
(Graduate, Undergraduate/Scholarship) [4199]
Native Hawaiian Chamber of Commerce Scholar-
ships (Graduate, Undergraduate/Scholarship)
[5219]
George A. Nielsen Public Investor Scholarships
(Graduate, Undergraduate/Scholarship) [4200]
OCAEOP Community Service Scholarship Program
(Undergraduate/Scholarship) [6916]
RBC Financial Group Scholarships (Graduate/
Scholarship) [2126]
Dan M. Reichard, Jr. Scholarships (Graduate, Un-
dergraduate/Scholarship) [1056]
Snodgrass Scholarships (Undergraduate/Scholar-
ship) [9175]
Wachovia Scholars Program (Undergraduate/Schol-
arship) [4551]
Urashi Zen Scholarships (Undergraduate/Scholar-
ship) [7429]

Byzantine studies (See also Area and ethnic studies)

Dumbarton Oaks Fellowships (Doctorate, Graduate/
Fellowship) [3549]
Dumbarton Oaks Junior Fellowships (Graduate/Fel-
lowship) [3550]
Post-Doctoral Teaching Fellowships (Postdoctorate/
Fellowship) [3551]

Canadian studies (See also Area and ethnic studies)

International Council for Canadian Studies Graduate
Student Scholarships (Postgraduate/Scholarship)
[4904]

Cancer (See Oncology)

Cartography/Surveying

AAGS Graduate Fellowship Awards (Undergraduate/
Fellowship) [641]
The Berntsen International Scholarships in Survey-
ing Technology (Undergraduate/Scholarship)
[642]
Canadian Hydrographic Association Student Awards
(Undergraduate/Award) [2492]
Connecticut Association of Land Surveyors Memo-
rial Scholarships (Undergraduate/Scholarship)
[3228]
Nettie Dracup Memorial Scholarships (Undergradu-
ate/Scholarship) [643]
AAGS Joseph F. Dracup Scholarship Awards (Un-
dergraduate/Scholarship) [644]

Kris M. Kunze Memorial Scholarships (Undergradu-
ate/Scholarship) [645]
The Lowell H. and Dorothy Loving Undergraduate
Scholarships (Undergraduate/Scholarship) [646]
MALSCE Scholarships (Undergraduate/Scholar-
ship) [5660]
The Cady McDonnell Memorial Scholarships (Un-
dergraduate/Scholarship) [647]
Marek Nawrot Memorial Scholarships (Undergradu-
ate/Scholarship) [7774]
Newberry Library Short-Term Fellowships in the His-
tory of Cartography (Doctorate/Fellowship) [6706]
Norman Nicholson Scholarships (Undergraduate/
Scholarship) [2424]
NSPS Board of Governors Scholarships (Under-
graduate/Scholarship) [648]
The NSPS Scholarships (Undergraduate/Scholar-
ship) [649]
Pennsylvania Land Surveyors Foundation Scholar-
ships (Undergraduate/Scholarship) [7149]
The Schonstedt Scholarships in Surveying (Under-
graduate/Scholarship) [650]

Cave studies

CCV Foundation Graduate and Undergraduate Fel-
lowships (Doctorate, Graduate, Undergraduate/
Fellowship) [2672]
NSS Sara Corrie Memorial Grants (All/Grant)
[6525]
NSS Conservation Grants (All/Grant) [6526]
NSS Education Grants (All/Grant) [6527]
Ralph W. Stone Graduate Fellowships (Graduate/
Fellowship, Grant) [6528]
Young Investigator Grants (Undergraduate/Grant)
[6529]

Central European studies (See European studies)

Chemistry (See also Biochem- istry; Electrochemistry)

AACT Undergraduate Scholarships (Undergraduate/
Scholarship) [7153]
AESF Foundation Scholarships (Graduate, Under-
graduate/Scholarship) [6127]
ASBC Foundation Graduate Scholarships (Doctor-
ate, Graduate/Scholarship) [1186]
Biocom Scholarships (Undergraduate/Scholarship)
[7913]
Burroughs Wellcome Fund Career Awards at the
Scientific Interface (Doctorate, Postdoctorate/Fel-
lowship) [2211]
Burroughs Wellcome Fund Collaborative Research
Travel Grants (Doctorate/Grant) [2212]
Julian E. Carnes Scholarship Fund (Undergraduate/
Scholarship) [3891]
Chemical Heritage Foundation Travel Grants (CHF)
(All/Grant) [2740]
D&A Florida Scholarships (Undergraduate/Scholar-
ship) [8597]
DEPS Graduate Scholarship Program (Graduate/
Scholarship) [3455]
DOE Computational Science Graduate Fellowships
(DOE CSGF) (Doctorate, Graduate/Fellowship)
[5306]
Robert E. Dougherty Scholarships (Undergraduate/
Scholarship) [3209]
Dow Chemical Company Fellowships (Graduate/
Fellowship) [6427]
E.I. DuPont Fellowships (Graduate/Fellowship)
[6428]
UAA Ardell French Memorial Scholarships (Under-
graduate/Scholarship) [9095]
Helm Family Scholarships (Undergraduate/Scholar-
ship) [7932]
Larson Aquatic Research Support Scholarships
(LARS) (Doctorate, Graduate/Scholarship) [1418]
Imelda and Ralph LeMar Scholarship Program (Un-
dergraduate/Scholarship) [3201]
Lewis-Clark State College/American Chemical Soci-
ety Scholars Program (Undergraduate/Scholar-
ship) [5440]
Lewis-Clark State College Presidential Technical

Out-of-State Scholarships (Undergraduate/Schol-
arship) [5447]
Dolphus E. Milligan Graduate Fellowships (Gradu-
ate/Fellowship) [6429]
NAAF Aboriginal Health Careers Bursary and Schol-
arships (Graduate, Undergraduate/Scholarship)
[5992]
National GEM Consortium - PhD Science Fellow-
ships (Doctorate, Graduate/Fellowship) [6307]
NDSEG Fellowships (Graduate/Fellowship) [6239]
NOBCChE Procter and Gamble Fellowships
(Graduate/Fellowship) [6430]
NPSC Fellowships (Graduate/Fellowship) [6440]
Postdoctoral Fellowships in Conservation Science
(Doctorate/Fellowship) [4145]
Lendon N. Pridgen, GlaxoSmithKline - NOBCChE
Fellowships (Graduate/Fellowship) [6431]
Rubber Division American Chemical Society Under-
graduate Scholarships (Undergraduate/Scholar-
ship) [7829]
Julia Viola Simms Science Scholarships (Postgradu-
ate/Scholarship) [2128]
Sloan Research Fellowships (Doctorate/Fellowship)
[8235]
Eastman Kodak Dr. Theophilus Sorrell Fellowships
(Graduate/Fellowship) [6432]
Graduate Fellowship Program - Peter Verhofstadt
Fellowships (GFP) (Graduate/Fellowship) [8084]
Women in Science and Technology Scholarships
(Doctorate, Graduate, Master's, Undergraduate/
Scholarship) [9442]
Xavier University Departmental Scholarships (Un-
dergraduate/Scholarship) [9780]
Xerox Technical Minority Scholarships (Graduate,
Undergraduate/Scholarship) [9787]

Child care

Alberta Child Care Association Professional Development Grants (Professional development/Grant)
[213]
Early Childhood Educators Scholarship Program
(Undergraduate/Scholarship) [5684]

Child development

Depression and ADHD Fellowships (Postdoctorate/
Fellowship) [5268]
Huenefeld/Denton Scholarships (Undergraduate/
Scholarship) [3415]
Fred Rogers Memorial Scholarships (Graduate, Un-
dergraduate/Scholarship) [35]

Chinese studies (See also Area and ethnic studies)

Comparative Perspectives on Chinese Culture and
Society Grants (Doctorate/Grant) [676]
Louise Wallace Hackney Fellowships for the Study
of Chinese Art (Doctorate, Postdoctorate/Fellow-
ship) [964]

Choreography (See Dance)

Christian education

Lewis B. Barber Memorial Scholarships (Under-
graduate/Scholarship) [8590]
Beatitudes Fellowships (Professional development/
Fellowship) [2037]
Chester H. Bruce Memorial Scholarships (Under-
graduate, Vocational/Occupational/Scholarship)
[7063]
Pamfil and Maria Bujea Family Orthodox Christian
Seminarian Scholarships (Undergraduate/Scholar-
ship) [1163]
Doris W. Frey Memorial Scholarships (Undergradu-
ate/Scholarship) [8603]
Louisville Institute Dissertation Fellowships (Doctor-
ate/Fellowship) [5527]
Louisville Institute First Book Grants for Minority
Scholars (Doctorate/Grant) [5528]
Louisville Institute Project Grants for Researchers
(Doctorate/Grant) [5529]
Louisville Institute Sabbatical Grants for Research-

ers *(Doctorate/Grant)* [5530]

Church occupations (See Religion)

Cinema

William A. Fraker Student Heritage Awards *(Graduate, Undergraduate/Award)* [1195]

Katherine Singer Kovacs Book and Essay Awards *(Professional development/Award)* [8310]

Gerald Pratley Awards *(Doctorate, Graduate/Award)* [3747]

Civil rights

Kalmen Kaplansky Scholarships in Economic and Social Rights *(Graduate/Scholarship)* [3475]

MALDEF Dream Act Student Activist Scholarships *(Undergraduate, Graduate/Scholarship)* [5805]

Minoru Yasui Memorial Scholarships *(Graduate/Scholarship)* [5147]

Classical studies (See also Area and ethnic studies)

American Philological Association Minority Student Summer Fellowships *(Undergraduate/Fellowship)* [986]

Desmond Conacher Scholarships *(Graduate/Scholarship)* [2901]

Glenn Knudsvig Memorial Scholarships *(Graduate, Undergraduate/Scholarship)* [611]

Arthur Patch McKinlay Scholarships *(Graduate, Undergraduate/Scholarship)* [612]

Ed Phinney Commemorative Scholarships *(Graduate, Undergraduate/Scholarship)* [613]

Clair Shirey Scholarships *(Undergraduate/Scholarship)* [9173]

Xavier University Departmental Scholarships *(Undergraduate/Scholarship)* [9780]

Clinical laboratory sciences

Alpha Mu Tau Undergraduate Scholarships *(Undergraduate/Scholarship)* [1197]

Luis W. Alvarez Postdoctoral Fellowships in Computational Science *(Doctorate/Fellowship)* [5380]

Ruth M. French Graduate or Undergraduate Scholarships *(Doctorate, Graduate, Undergraduate/Scholarship)* [1198]

Lawrence Livermore National Laboratory Fellowships *(Doctorate/Fellowship)* [5382]

Dorothy Morrison Undergraduate Scholarships *(Undergraduate/Scholarship)* [1199]

Clinical sciences (See Biological and clinical sciences)

Colitis (See Ileitis and colitis)

Commercial design (See Design)

Communications

Advertising Production Club of New York High School Scholarships (APC) *(Undergraduate/Scholarship)* [58]

Advertising Production Club Scholarship Awards *(Graduate, Undergraduate/Scholarship)* [59]

AFCEA Scholarship for Working Professionals *(Graduate/Scholarship)* [1554]

AGBU Scholarships *(Graduate/Loan)* [1573]

Peggy Allen Community Newspaper Internships *(Undergraduate/Internship)* [9255]

Phillip Alston Scholarships *(Undergraduate/Scholarship)* [9256]

ARRLF Mississippi Scholarships *(Undergraduate/Scholarship)* [1070]

Avista Corporation Minds in Motion Scholarships *(Undergraduate/Scholarship)* [5412]

Frances Warren Baker Memorial Scholarships *(Undergraduate/Scholarship)* [8157]

Jim Batten Community Newspaper Internships *(Undergraduate/Internship)* [9258]

Beaverbrook Media at McGill Student Paper Prize *(Graduate/Prize)* [2435]

Margaret Blanchard Dissertation Support Fund *(Postgraduate/Grant)* [9259]

Tom Bost Scholarships *(Undergraduate/Scholarship)* [9260]

William E. "Buck" Bragunier Scholarships *(Undergraduate/Scholarship)* [1556]

Lt. General Douglas D. Buchholz Memorial Scholarships *(Undergraduate/Scholarship)* [1557]

Elton Casey Scholarships *(Undergraduate/Scholarship)* [9262]

George H. Clinton Scholarship Fund *(Undergraduate/Scholarship)* [7065]

Ardis Cohoon Scholarships *(Undergraduate/Scholarship)* [9263]

Irvine W. Cook WA0CGS Scholarships *(Undergraduate/Scholarship)* [1080]

Milton E. Cooper/Young AFCEAN Graduate Scholarships *(Graduate/Scholarship)* [1558]

Charles Clarke Cordle Memorial Scholarships *(Undergraduate/Scholarship)* [1081]

Kathryn M. Cronin Scholarships *(Graduate, Undergraduate/Scholarship)* [9265]

Don and Barbara Curtis Excellence Fund for Extracurricular Student Activities *(Undergraduate/Grant)* [9266]

James Davis Scholarships *(Undergraduate/Scholarship)* [9267]

Disabled War Veterans Scholarships *(Undergraduate/Scholarship)* [1559]

Robert Winchester Dodson Scholarships *(Undergraduate/Scholarship)* [9268]

Harvey N. Dondero Communication and Journalism Excellence Scholarships *(Undergraduate/Scholarship)* [7482]

ECA Applied Urban Communication Research Grants *(Professional development/Grant)* [3575]

Vivian Edmonds Scholarships *(Undergraduate/Scholarship)* [9269]

Palmer Farley Memorial Scholarships *(Undergraduate/Scholarship)* [4372]

Reese Felts Scholarships *(Undergraduate/Scholarship)* [9270]

Charles N. Fisher Memorial Scholarships *(Undergraduate/Scholarship)* [1084]

Ameel J. Fisher Scholarships *(Undergraduate/Scholarship)* [9271]

Florida Outdoor Writers Association Scholarships *(Undergraduate/Scholarship)* [3842]

Paul B. & Aline Flynn Scholarships *(Undergraduate/Scholarship)* [8601]

Kays Gary Scholarships *(Undergraduate/Scholarship)* [9273]

Stephen Gates Scholarships *(Undergraduate/Scholarship)* [9274]

Joy Gibson Scholarships *(Undergraduate/Scholarship)* [9275]

L.C. Gifford Distinguished Journalism Scholarships *(Undergraduate/Scholarship)* [9276]

Keith Gilmore Foundation - Diploma Scholarships *(Professional development/Scholarship)* [4153]

Keith Gilmore Foundation - Postgraduate Scholarships *(Postgraduate/Scholarship)* [4154]

Keith Gilmore Foundation - Undergraduate Scholarships *(Undergraduate/Scholarship)* [4155]

Paul and Helen L. Grauer Scholarships *(Undergraduate/Scholarship)* [1087]

HAESF Professional Internship Program *(Doctorate/Internship)* [4641]

Charles Hauser Scholarships *(Undergraduate/Scholarship)* [9277]

Paul Green Houston Scholarships *(Undergraduate/Scholarship)* [9278]

HSF/Nissan Community College Transfer Scholarship Program *(Undergraduate/Scholarship)* [4576]

James F. Hurley III Bicentennial Merit Scholarships *(Undergraduate/Scholarship)* [9279]

Fred Hutchison Travel Scholarships *(Undergraduate/Scholarship)* [9280]

International Foodservice Editorial Council Scholarships *(Graduate, Undergraduate/Scholarship)* [4935]

Iowa Journalism Institute Scholarships *(Undergraduate/Scholarship)* [5043]

Harriet Irsay Scholarships *(Graduate, Undergraduate/Scholarship)* [869]

Edward Jackson International Scholarships *(Undergraduate/Scholarship)* [9281]

Gene Jackson Scholarships *(Undergraduate/Scholarship)* [9282]

Peter Lars Jacobson Scholarships *(Undergraduate/Scholarship)* [9283]

Glenn Keever Scholarships *(Undergraduate/Scholarship)* [9284]

Dr. James L. Lawson Memorial Scholarships *(Undergraduate/Scholarship)* [1092]

Norval Neil Luxon Prize for Scholarships to Juniors *(Undergraduate/Scholarship)* [9286]

Mackey-Byars Scholarships for Communication Excellence *(Undergraduate/Scholarship)* [9287]

Raleigh Mann Scholarships *(Undergraduate/Scholarship)* [9288]

Lockheed Martin Graduate Scholarships *(Graduate/Scholarship)* [1560]

Lockheed Martin IT Scholarships *(Undergraduate/Scholarship)* [1561]

Mas Family Scholarships *(Graduate, Undergraduate/Scholarship)* [5658]

Fred R. McDaniel Memorial Scholarships *(Undergraduate/Scholarship)* [1093]

McNamara Family Creative Arts Project Grants *(Graduate, Undergraduate/Grant)* [4579]

Edward Heywood Megson Scholarships *(Undergraduate/Scholarship)* [9293]

Messenger-Anderson Journalism Scholarships and Internships Program *(Undergraduate/Scholarship)* [7861]

MillerCoors National Scholarships *(Undergraduate/Scholarship)* [48]

Quincy Sharpe Mills Scholarships *(Undergraduate/Scholarship)* [9294]

Alexander Morisey Scholarships *(Undergraduate/Scholarship)* [9296]

New York Women in Communications, Inc. Foundation Scholarships *(Graduate, Undergraduate/Scholarship)* [6690]

NHFA Scholarships *(Graduate/Scholarship)* [6340]

Ohio Association of Broadcasters Scholarships *(Undergraduate/Scholarship)* [6853]

AFCEA General Emmett Paige Scholarships *(Undergraduate/Scholarship)* [1562]

Leonard M. Perryman Communications Scholarships for Ethnic Minority Students *(Undergraduate/Scholarship)* [9013]

Chuck Pezzano Scholarships *(Undergraduate, Vocational/Occupational/Scholarship)* [2166]

Pfizer Minority Medical Journalism Scholarships *(Postgraduate/Scholarship)* [9298]

PGSF-GATF Scholarships *(Graduate, Undergraduate/Scholarship)* [61]

Stephen D. Pisinski Memorial Scholarships *(Undergraduate/Scholarship)* [7539]

Robert Pittman Scholarships *(Undergraduate/Scholarship)* [9299]

Erwin Potts Scholarships *(Undergraduate/Scholarship)* [9300]

PRSSA Multicultural Affairs Scholarships *(Undergraduate/Scholarship)* [7541]

Peter DeWitt Pruden and Phyliss Harrill Pruden Scholarships *(Undergraduate/Scholarship)* [9301]

Bob Quincy Scholarships *(Undergraduate/Scholarship)* [9302]

Marjorie Usher Ragan Scholarships *(Undergraduate/Scholarship)* [9303]

Gertrude J. Robinson Book Prize *(Professional development/Prize)* [2436]

Richard J. Roth Journalism Fellowships *(Graduate/Fellowship)* [6679]

Bert Saperstein Communication Scholarships *(Undergraduate/Scholarship)* [7987]

StraightForward Media's Media and Communications Scholarships *(Undergraduate/Scholarship)* [8762]

Leo Suarez Journalism Scholarships *(Undergraduate/Scholarship)* [3321]

Hal Tanner Jr. Scholarships (Undergraduate/Scholarship) [9306]

TCA Turkish American Scholarships (Undergraduate/Scholarship) [8978]

Texas Muslims Scholarship Fund (TMSF) (Graduate, Undergraduate/Scholarship) [4006]

Jim and Pat Thacker Sports Communication Internships (Undergraduate/Internship) [9307]

Tucker Family Scholarships (Undergraduate/Scholarship) [9308]

Turf and Ornamental Communicators Association Scholarship Program (Undergraduate/Scholarship) [8974]

Veterans of Enduring Freedom (Afghanistan) and Iraqi Freedom Scholarships (Undergraduate/Scholarship) [1565]

David Julian Wichard Scholarships (Undergraduate/Scholarship) [9309]

L. Phil Wicker Scholarships (Undergraduate/Scholarship) [1113]

Tom Wicker Scholarships (Undergraduate/Scholarship) [9310]

AFCEA General John A. Wickham Scholarships (Undergraduate/Scholarship) [1566]

Glenn Wilson Broadcast Journalism Scholarships (Undergraduate/Scholarship) [7124]

Marine Corps Sgt. Jeannette L. Winters Memorial Scholarships (Undergraduate/Scholarship) [1567]

WKIX Alumni Association Scholarships (Undergraduate/Scholarship) [9311]

WTVD Endowment Scholarships (Undergraduate/Scholarship) [9312]

Communications technologies

Document Management and Graphic Communications Industry Scholarships (Undergraduate/Scholarship) [3627]

Carol A. Ratza Memorial Scholarships (Undergraduate/Scholarship) [4329]

Computer and information sciences

AAUW Legal Advocacy Fund Selected Professions Fellowships (Doctorate, Graduate/Fellowship) [18]

AeA Scholarships (Undergraduate/Scholarship) [7904]

African American Network - Carolinas Scholarship Fund (Undergraduate/Scholarship) [3882]

Air Products and Chemicals, Inc. Scholarships (Undergraduate/Scholarship) [1793]

AISES Intel Scholarships (Graduate, Undergraduate/Scholarship) [832]

Stephanie Ali Memorial Scholarships (Undergraduate/Scholarship) [9321]

American Association of University Women Selected Professions Fellowships (Professional development/Fellowship) [13]

Ann Arbor AWC Scholarships for Women in Computing (Professional development, Undergraduate/Scholarship) [1896]

Delores A. Auzenne Fellowships (Postgraduate/Fellowship) [3818]

Avista Corporation Minds in Motion Scholarships (Undergraduate/Scholarship) [5412]

Dr. Anita Borg Memorial Scholarships - USA (Graduate, Undergraduate/Scholarship) [4193]

William (Billbo) Boston Scholarships (Undergraduate/Scholarship) [7062]

Kathi Bowles Scholarships for Women in Technology (Graduate, Undergraduate/Scholarship) [1898]

Richard A. Brown Student Scholarships (Undergraduate/Scholarship) [8855]

Burroughs Wellcome Fund Career Awards at the Scientific Interface (Doctorate, Postdoctorate/Fellowship) [2211]

Burroughs Wellcome Fund Collaborative Research Travel Grants (Doctorate/Grant) [2212]

Wes Burton Memorial Scholarships (Undergraduate/Scholarship) [9628]

Julian E. Carnes Scholarship Fund (Undergraduate/Scholarship) [3891]

CDC Public Health Informatics Fellowships (Graduate, Postdoctorate/Fellowship) [2713]

CERT College Scholarships (Graduate, Undergraduate/Scholarship) [3272]

Chambersburg/Fannett-Metal School District Scholarship Fund (Undergraduate/Scholarship) [3937]

D&A Florida Scholarships (Undergraduate/Scholarship) [8597]

Document Management and Graphic Communications Industry Scholarships (Undergraduate/Scholarship) [3627]

DOE Computational Science Graduate Fellowships (DOE CSGF) (Doctorate, Graduate/Fellowship) [5306]

EAPSI Fellowships (Doctorate, Graduate/Fellowship) [6467]

ESA Foundation Computer and Video Game Scholarship Program (Undergraduate/Scholarship) [3650]

Frank Fong Scholarships (Undergraduate/Scholarship) [8290]

Richard Gregory Freeland, II Educational Scholarships (High School/Scholarship) [2147]

William R. Goldfarb Memorial Scholarships (Undergraduate/Scholarship) [1085]

Google-American Indian Science and Engineering Society Scholarships (Graduate, Undergraduate/Scholarship) [4194]

Google Hispanic College Fund Scholarships (Graduate, Undergraduate/Scholarship) [4195]

Jimmy Guild Memorial Scholarships (Undergraduate/Scholarship) [5431]

Helm Family Scholarships (Undergraduate/Scholarship) [7932]

HSBC-North America Scholarship Program (Undergraduate/Scholarship) [4571]

HSF/Wal-Mart Stores Inc. Scholarship Program (Graduate, Undergraduate/Scholarship) [4577]

IBEA Undergraduate Scholarships (Undergraduate/Scholarship) [4683]

Informatics Circle of Research Excellence Scholarships (Doctorate, Graduate/Scholarship) [248]

Internet Society Fellowships to the IETF (Doctorate/Fellowship) [5032]

Edgar Kerstan Memorial Scholarships (Undergraduate/Scholarship) [5771]

Robert E. Knight Professional Scholarships (Doctorate, Graduate/Scholarship) [8856]

Lewis-Clark State College Presidential Technical Out-of-State Scholarships (Undergraduate/Scholarship) [5447]

Malayalee Engineers Association Scholarships (Graduate/Fellowship) [5601]

John Mazurek Memorial-Morgex Insurance Scholarships (Professional development/Scholarship) [274]

Mensa Canada General Scholarships (Undergraduate/Scholarship) [5772]

MESBEC Scholarships (Undergraduate/Scholarship) [2662]

Microsoft Research Graduate Women's Scholarships (Graduate/Scholarship) [5844]

Microsoft Research PhD Fellowships (Doctorate/Fellowship) [5845]

MillerCoors Engineering and Sciences Scholarships (Undergraduate/Scholarship) [47]

NASIG Conference Student Grants (Graduate, Postdoctorate/Grant) [6743]

National GEM Consortium - PhD Science Fellowships (Doctorate, Graduate/Fellowship) [6307]

NDSEG Fellowships (Graduate/Fellowship) [6239]

Edsel Newman Scholarships (Undergraduate/Scholarship) [5476]

NPSC Fellowships (Graduate/Fellowship) [6440]

NVIDIA Graduate Fellowships (Doctorate/Fellowship) [6844]

Ray, NORP and Katie, WOKTE Pautz Scholarships (Undergraduate/Scholarship) [1098]

PHD ARA Scholarships (Doctorate, Undergraduate/Scholarship) [1100]

Faye Lynn Roberts Educational Scholarships (Undergraduate/Scholarship) [8618]

Paul and Ellen Ruckes Scholarships (Graduate, Undergraduate/Scholarship) [753]

John M. and Mary A. Shanley Memorial Scholarships (Undergraduate/Scholarship) [8622]

Everett Oscar Shimp Memorial Scholarships (Undergraduate/Scholarship) [7113]

SHPE Foundation Verizon Scholarships (Undergraduate/Scholarship) [8135]

Ralph W. Shrader Diversity Scholarships (Graduate/Scholarship) [1563]

Sloan Research Fellowships (Doctorate/Fellowship) [8235]

Snodgrass Scholarships (Undergraduate/Scholarship) [9175]

Soroptimist International of Redlands Scholarships (Undergraduate/Scholarship) [7715]

Henry D. and Ruth G. Swartz Family Scholarship Fund (Undergraduate/Scholarship) [4247]

Syncrude/Athabasca University Aboriginal Scholarships (All/Scholarship) [8791]

Texas Computer Education Association Professional Educator Grants (Professional development/Grant) [8857]

Toyota High School Scholarship Program (Undergraduate/Scholarship) [4581]

Vice Adm. Jerry O. Tuttle, USN (Ret.) and Mrs. Barbara A. Tuttle Science and Technology Scholarships (Undergraduate/Scholarship) [1564]

University of Toronto Accenture Scholarships (Undergraduate/Scholarship) [9344]

UPE/ACM Scholarship Awards (Graduate, Undergraduate/Award) [9391]

UPE Scholarship Awards (Graduate, Undergraduate/Award) [9392]

Edwin F. Wiegand Science and Technology Scholarships (Undergraduate/Scholarship) [7533]

Women In Defense HORIZONS Scholarships (Graduate, Undergraduate/Scholarship) [9696]

Women in Science and Technology Scholarships (Doctorate, Graduate, Master's, Undergraduate/Scholarship) [9442]

Frank and Betty Woodhams Memorial Scholarships (Undergraduate/Scholarship) [5773]

Xerox Technical Minority Scholarships (Graduate, Undergraduate/Scholarship) [9787]

Ralph Yetka Memorial Scholarships (Undergraduate/Scholarship) [9181]

Urashi Zen Scholarships (Undergraduate/Scholarship) [7429]

Conservation of natural resources

Gloria Barron Wilderness Society Scholarships (Graduate/Scholarship) [9601]

Conservation Guest Scholar Grants (Professional development/Grant) [4139]

Doris Duke Conservation Fellows Program (Graduate/Fellowship) [9615]

Kathryn Fuller Science for Nature Post-Doctoral Fellowships (Graduate, Postdoctorate/Fellowship) [9759]

Ann L. Holland Memorial Scholarships (Graduate, Undergraduate/Scholarship) [4077]

WDHOF Scholarships in Marine Conservation (Graduate, Undergraduate/Scholarship) [9700]

Welder Wildlife Foundation Fellowships (Doctorate, Graduate/Fellowship) [9559]

Construction

ACI BASF Construction Chemicals Student Fellowships (Graduate, Undergraduate/Fellowship) [628]

ACI President's Fellowships (Doctorate, Master's/Fellowship) [630]

Herb Adrian Memorial Scholarship Fund (Undergraduate/Scholarship) [3881]

AGC Foundation Outstanding Educator Awards (Professional development/Award) [1675]

American Society of Safety Engineers Construction Safety Scholarships (Undergraduate/Scholarship) [1331]

APS/ASU Scholarships (Undergraduate/Scholarship) [7332]

ASA Graduate Scholarships (Graduate/Scholarship) [1182]

Associated General Contractors of Connecticut Scholarships (Undergraduate/Scholarship) [3235]

ACI Elmer Baker Student Fellowships (Undergraduate/Fellowship) [633]

ACI Baker Student Fellowships *(Undergraduate/ Fellowship)* [632]

Bechtel Group Foundation Scholarships for Safety & Health *(Undergraduate/Scholarship)* [1333]

O.J. Beck, Jr. Memorial Scholarships *(Undergraduate/Scholarship)* [2936]

Carpenters' Company Scholarships *(Undergraduate/ Scholarship)* [2657]

Construction Trades Scholarships *(Undergraduate/ Scholarship)* [6131]

Cindy P. Dennis Scholarship Fund *(Undergraduate/ Scholarship)* [3241]

Lee S. Evans/National Housing Endowment Scholarships *(Graduate, Undergraduate/Scholarship)* [6344]

HSF/Wal-Mart Stores Inc. Scholarship Program *(Graduate, Undergraduate/Scholarship)* [4577]

Charles McMahon Memorial Construction Management/Engineering Scholarship Awards *(Undergraduate/Scholarship)* [1632]

National Association of Women in Construction Founders Undergraduate Scholarships *(Undergraduate/Scholarship)* [6132]

ACI Charles Pankow Foundation ACI Student Fellowships *(Graduate, Undergraduate/Fellowship)* [637]

Pardee Community Building Scholarships *(Undergraduate/Scholarship)* [7515]

Herman J. Smith Scholarships *(Undergraduate/ Scholarship)* [6345]

Toyota High School Scholarship Program *(Undergraduate/Scholarship)* [4581]

United States Society on Dams Scholarships *(Graduate/Scholarship)* [9072]

Washington Group International Safety Scholarships *(Undergraduate/Scholarship)* [1357]

Ted C. Wilson Memorial Scholarships *(Undergraduate/Scholarship)* [7441]

Consumer affairs

Geraldine Clewell Fellowships - Doctoral Student *(Graduate/Fellowship)* [7280]

Geraldine Clewell Fellowships - Masteral *(Graduate/ Fellowship)* [7281]

Geraldine Clewell Scholarships - Undergraduate *(Undergraduate/Scholarship)* [7282]

Closs/Parnitzke/Clarke Scholarships *(Undergraduate/Scholarship)* [7283]

Jean Dearth Dickerscheid Fellowships *(Graduate/ Fellowship)* [7284]

Margaret Drew Alpha Fellowships *(Graduate/Fellowship)* [7285]

Lydia Fohn-Hansen/Lola Hill Memorial Scholarships *(Undergraduate/Scholarship)* [9149]

Genevieve Forthun Scholarships *(Undergraduate/ Scholarship)* [7286]

Mary Weiking Franken Scholarships *(Undergraduate/Scholarship)* [7287]

Tommie J. Hamner Scholarships *(Undergraduate/ Scholarship)* [7288]

Jackman Scholarships *(Undergraduate/Scholarship)* [7289]

Martha Combs Jenkins Scholarships *(Undergraduate/Scholarship)* [7290]

Treva C. Kintner Scholarships *(Undergraduate/ Scholarship)* [7291]

Phi Upsilon Omicron Candle Fellowships *(Graduate/ Fellowship)* [7292]

Phi Upsilon Omicron Challenge Scholarships *(Undergraduate/Scholarship)* [7293]

Phi Upsilon Omicron Diamond Anniversary Fellowships *(Graduate/Fellowship)* [7294]

Phi Upsilon Omicron Founders Fellowships *(Graduate/Fellowship)* [7295]

Phi Upsilon Omicron Golden Anniversary Scholarships *(Undergraduate/Scholarship)* [7296]

Phi Upsilon Omicron Past Presidents Scholarships *(Undergraduate/Scholarship)* [7297]

Phi Upsilon Omicron Presidents Research Fellowships *(Graduate/Fellowship)* [7298]

Nell Bryant Robinson Scholarships *(Undergraduate/ Scholarship)* [7299]

Lucile Rust Scholarships *(Undergraduate/Scholarship)* [7300]

Margaret Jerome Sampson Scholarships *(Under-*

graduate/Scholarship) [7301]

Lillian P. Schoephoerster Scholarships *(Undergraduate/Scholarship)* [7302]

Cooley's anemia

Cooley's Anemia Foundation Research Fellowships *(Postdoctorate/Fellowship)* [3251]

Cosmetology

California Association of Private Postsecondary Schools Scholarships *(Undergraduate/Scholarship)* [2232]

Melissa Eleonor Ernest Scholarships *(Undergraduate/Scholarship)* [5096]

Joe Francis Haircare Scholarships *(Undergraduate/ Scholarship)* [3996]

Helen F. "Jerri" Rand Memorial Scholarships *(Undergraduate, Vocational/Occupational/Scholarship)* [3193]

Sally Beauty Scholarships for High School Graduates *(Undergraduate/Scholarship)* [7439]

H. Wayne Van Agtmael Cosmetology Scholarship Fund *(Undergraduate/Scholarship)* [4248]

Counseling/Guidance

ASHA Scholarships *(Graduate, Undergraduate/ Scholarship)* [1175]

ASHA Student Research Grants *(Graduate, Undergraduate/Scholarship)* [1176]

Patricia Pownder Conolly Memorial Scholarships *(Undergraduate/Scholarship)* [5777]

Lullelia W. Harrison Scholarships in Counseling *(Graduate, Undergraduate/Scholarship)* [9802]

Linda Lyons Memorial Scholarship Fund *(Undergraduate/Scholarship)* [5779]

Dottie Martin Teacher Scholarships *(Graduate, Undergraduate/Scholarship)* [6765]

NAJA Scholarships *(Graduate/Scholarship)* [6086]

Native American Leadership Education Scholarships (NALE) *(Postdoctorate, Undergraduate/Scholarship)* [2663]

OSCA Graduate Student Scholarship Program *(Graduate/Scholarship)* [6862]

Ross Trust Graduate Student Scholarships *(Graduate, Postdoctorate/Scholarship)* [685]

TCA Outstanding Graduate Student Awards *(Graduate/Award)* [8859]

Toyota High School Scholarship Program *(Undergraduate/Scholarship)* [4581]

Crafts

Joan Auld Scholarships *(Undergraduate/Scholarship)* [3181]

Craft Research Fund *(Professional development/ Grant)* [2683]

EAIA Research Grants *(Professional development/ Grant)* [3561]

Bruce T. and Jackie Mahi Erickson Grants *(Graduate, Undergraduate/Grant)* [5210]

Worldstudio AIGA Scholarships *(Graduate, Undergraduate/Scholarship)* [9761]

Creative arts (See Arts)

Creative writing

Milton Center Fellowships *(Graduate/Fellowship)* [4703]

Eleanor M. Wolfson Memorial Scholarship Fund *(Undergraduate/Scholarship)* [3797]

Criminal justice

American Criminal Justice Association Scholarships *(Graduate, Undergraduate/Scholarship)* [687]

ASC Graduate Fellowships for Ethnic Minorities *(Doctorate, Graduate/Fellowship)* [1219]

Officer Brian A. Aselton Memorial Scholarships *(Undergraduate/Scholarship)* [4410]

Peter Butler III - Rose Fortune Scholarship Program *(Undergraduate/Scholarship)* [1716]

Robert C. Carson Memorial Bursary *(Undergraduate/Scholarship)* [242]

Jorge Espejal Contreras Memorial Scholarships *(Graduate, Undergraduate/Scholarship)* [4873]

Correctional Education Association Scholarships *(Graduate, Undergraduate/Scholarship)* [3266]

Court Scholarships *(Undergraduate/Scholarship)* [3243]

Colonel Richard M. Dawson Scholarships *(Undergraduate/Scholarship)* [3105]

Libby Deschenes Prize for Applied Research *(Undergraduate/Prize)* [9581]

Thomas J. Drinan Memorial Fellowships *(All/Fellowship)* [7604]

W.E.B. Du Bois Fellowships *(Doctorate/Fellowship)* [6355]

Carli Edwards Memorial Scholarships *(Undergraduate/Scholarship)* [8114]

Brian Jimenez Memorial Scholarships *(Undergraduate/Scholarship)* [7657]

Niqui McCown Honor and Memorial Scholarship Fund *(Undergraduate/Scholarship)* [9555]

Paul R. McLaughlin Fellowships *(All/Fellowship)* [7606]

Minnesota Association County Probation Officers Scholarships *(Undergraduate/Scholarship)* [5890]

June Morrison Scholarship Fund *(Undergraduate/ Scholarship)* [9582]

National Sheriffs' Association Scholarship Program *(Graduate, Undergraduate/Scholarship)* [6474]

NIJ Visiting Fellowships *(Professional development/ Fellowship)* [6356]

Ottawa Police 150th Anniversary Scholarships *(Undergraduate/Scholarship)* [2168]

Rachael Patterson Memorial Scholarships *(Undergraduate/Scholarship)* [8987]

Pi Gamma Mu Scholarships *(Graduate/Scholarship)* [7330]

Ritchie-Jennings Memorial Scholarships *(Graduate, Undergraduate/Scholarship)* [1738]

Emmett H. Turner Scholarships *(Undergraduate/ Scholarship)* [3137]

Miki Vohryzek-Bolden Student Paper Awards *(Undergraduate/Award)* [9583]

Criminology

ASC Graduate Fellowships for Ethnic Minorities *(Doctorate, Graduate/Fellowship)* [1219]

Peter Butler III - Rose Fortune Scholarship Program *(Undergraduate/Scholarship)* [1716]

Robert C. Carson Memorial Bursary *(Undergraduate/Scholarship)* [242]

Libby Deschenes Prize for Applied Research *(Undergraduate/Prize)* [9581]

June Morrison Scholarship Fund *(Undergraduate/ Scholarship)* [9582]

Miki Vohryzek-Bolden Student Paper Awards *(Undergraduate/Award)* [9583]

Criticism (Art, Drama, Literary)

Melba Dawn Chiarenza Scholarship Fund *(Undergraduate/Scholarship)* [9554]

Northwest-Shoals Community College Fine Arts Scholarships - Drama *(Undergraduate/Scholarship)* [6824]

Wendy Y. Wolfson Memorial Scholarship Fund *(Undergraduate/Scholarship)* [3798]

Cross-cultural studies

University of Hawaii at Manoa Japan Travel Bureau Scholarships *(Graduate, Undergraduate/Scholarship)* [9209]

Culinary arts

L'Academie de Cuisine Culinary Arts Scholarships *(All, Professional development/Scholarship)* [3305]

Alliance of Black Culinarians Scholarships *(Undergraduate/Scholarship)* [7465]

American Culinary Federation Chair's Scholarship Grants *(All/Scholarship)* [689]

Balestreri/Cutino Scholarships *(Undergraduate/ Scholarship)* [690]

Canadian Hospitality Foundation College Entrance Scholarships *(Undergraduate/Scholarship)* [2488]
CANFIT Nutrition, Physical Education and Culinary Arts Scholarships *(Graduate, Undergraduate/Scholarship)* [3026]
CANFIT Scholarships *(Graduate, Undergraduate/Scholarship)* [2228]
Chaine des Rotisseurs Scholarships *(Undergraduate/Scholarship)* [691]
Julia Child Memorial Scholarships *(Undergraduate/Scholarship)* [692]
Vickie Clark-Flaherty Scholarships *(Undergraduate, Vocational/Occupational/Scholarship)* [6772]
Geri Coccodrilli Culinary Scholarship Fund *(Undergraduate/Scholarship)* [4209]
Culinary (1-Year Program) Scholarships *(Undergraduate/Scholarship)* [2490]
Culinary and Hospitality Foundation of San Benito County Scholarships *(Undergraduate/Scholarship)* [3303]
Linda Cullen Memorial Scholarships *(High School/Scholarship)* [693]
For the Love of Chocolate Foundation Scholarships *(Graduate, Professional development, Undergraduate/Scholarship)* [3857]
The French Culinary Institute Classic Pastry Arts Scholarships *(Professional development, Undergraduate/Scholarship)* [3306]
The French Culinary Institute Culinary Arts Scholarships *(All, Professional development/Scholarship)* [3307]
Golden Corral Scholarships *(Undergraduate/Scholarship)* [6773]
IFH Foodservice Distribution Scholarships *(Undergraduate/Scholarship)* [6774]
International Dairy-Deli-Bakery Association Undergraduate Scholarships *(Graduate, Undergraduate/Scholarship)* [4916]
International Foodservice Editorial Council Scholarships *(Graduate, Undergraduate/Scholarship)* [4935]
Stanley "Doc" Jensen Scholarships *(High School/Scholarship)* [694]
Johnson and Wales University Scholarships *(Undergraduate/Scholarship)* [5175]
K & W Cafeterias Scholarships *(Undergraduate/Scholarship)* [6775]
Andrew Macrina Scholarships *(High School/Scholarship)* [695]
Ray and Gertrude Marshall Scholarships *(Undergraduate/Scholarship)* [696]
Karl Mehlmann Scholarships *(Undergraduate/Scholarship)* [2988]
NC Hospitality Education Foundation Scholarships - Four Year College or University *(Undergraduate/Scholarship)* [6776]
NC Hospitality Education Foundation Scholarships - Graduate *(Graduate/Scholarship)* [6777]
NC Hospitality Education Foundation Scholarships - High School *(Undergraduate, Vocational/Occupational/Scholarship)* [6778]
NC Hospitality Education Foundation Scholarships - Two Year Community or Junior College *(Undergraduate/Scholarship)* [6779]
Oklahoma Restaurant Association Scholarships *(Graduate, Undergraduate/Scholarship)* [6871]
Hermann G. Rusch Scholarships *(Professional development/Scholarship)* [697]
Elizabeth Shafer Memorial Scholarships *(Undergraduate/Scholarship)* [7522]
South Carolina Undergraduate Scholarships *(Undergraduate/Scholarship)* [4604]
Spice Box Grants *(Professional development/Grant)* [698]
Tanana Valley Campus Culinary Arts Scholarships *(Undergraduate/Scholarship)* [8989]
Patricia Tillinghast Memorial Scholarships *(Graduate, Undergraduate/Scholarship)* [879]
Tomato Fest Scholarship Grants *(Undergraduate/Scholarship)* [699]
Charlie Trotters's Culinary Education Foundation Culinary Study Scholarships *(Professional development, Undergraduate/Scholarship)* [8962]

Culture

AAS Fellowships for Creative and Performing Artists and Writers *(All/Fellowship)* [412]
Aboriginal Traditional Arts Project Grants *(Professional development/Grant)* [215]
American Indian Program Fellowships *(Graduate/Fellowship)* [8260]
Associate Fellowships *(Doctorate/Fellowship)* [4778]
Stephen Botein Fellowships *(Doctorate/Fellowship)* [415]
Conservation Department Program Fellowships *(Graduate/Fellowship)* [8258]
Cultural Relations Project Grants *(Professional development/Grant)* [217]
Doctoral Fellowships - Dissertation *(Doctorate/Fellowship)* [4779]
Doctoral Fellowships - Graduate *(Doctorate/Fellowship)* [4780]
The "Drawn to Art" Fellowships *(Doctorate/Fellowship)* [417]
Jay and Deborah Last Fellowships *(Doctorate/Fellowship)* [420]
The Legacy Fellowships *(Doctorate/Fellowship)* [421]
Audrey Lumsden-Kouvel Fellowships *(Postdoctorate/Fellowship)* [6698]
Minority Visiting Students Awards *(Undergraduate, Graduate/Award, Internship)* [8241]
Kate B. and Hall J. Peterson Fellowships *(Doctorate/Fellowship)* [422]
Postdoctoral Fellowships *(Postdoctorate/Fellowship)* [4781]
Margaret B. Sevcenko Prize in Islamic Art and Culture *(Doctorate/Prize)* [4589]
The Joyce Tracy Fellowships *(Doctorate/Fellowship)* [424]
Uva Faculty Fellowships *(Professional development/Fellowship)* [4782]
Visiting Fellowships *(Professional development/Fellowship)* [4783]

Cystic fibrosis

CCFF Clinical Fellowships *(Doctorate, Graduate/Fellowship)* [2447]
CCFF Fellowships *(Doctorate, Graduate/Fellowship)* [2448]
CCFF Scholarships *(Doctorate, Graduate/Scholarship)* [2449]

Dairy science

Dairy Farmers of America Scholarships *(Undergraduate/Scholarship)* [3331]
Progressive Dairy Producer Awards *(All/Grant)* [6233]
South Dakota Division Scholarships *(Undergraduate/Scholarship)* [5865]
Stark County Dairy Promoters Scholarships *(Undergraduate/Scholarship)* [8701]

Dance (See also Choreography; Performing arts)

Artistic Scholarship Awards *(Undergraduate, Vocational/Occupational/Scholarship)* [2023]
Deloris Carter Hampton Scholarships *(Undergraduate/Scholarship)* [7404]
Dance Education Scholarship Program *(High School/Scholarship)* [7985]
Dance Project Grants *(Professional development/Grant)* [218]
Flamenco Student Scholarships *(Undergraduate/Scholarship)* [3808]
Graduate Student Travel Grants *(Graduate, Professional development/Grant)* [8314]
In-course Scholarships - Chinese Dance Workshop Scholarships *(Undergraduate/Scholarship)* [9333]
Indiana State Alumni Association Creative and Performing Arts Awards *(Undergraduate/Scholarship)* [4745]
Study Scholarships for Artists or Musicians *(Graduate/Scholarship)* [4123]

Upakar Indian-American Scholarships *(Undergraduate/Scholarship)* [9389]

Data processing (See also Computer and information sciences)

Bettsy Ross Educational Fund *(All, Professional development/Scholarship)* [6727]

Dental hygiene

ADHA IOH Sigma Phi Alpha Graduate Scholarships *(Graduate/Scholarship)* [707]
American Dental Hygienists' Association Institute for Oral Health Fellowships *(Master's/Fellowship)* [708]
CDA Foundation Allied Dental Student Scholarships *(All/Scholarship)* [2674]
CDA Foundation Dental Student Scholarships *(All/Scholarship)* [2675]
Dr. Princeton L. Co Emergency Fund for Dental Hygiene Scholarships *(Undergraduate/Scholarship)* [8113]
Colgate-Palmolive/HDA Foundation Scholarships *(Master's, Postgraduate/Scholarship)* [4555]
IADR David B. Ste. Scott Fellowships *(Undergraduate/Fellowship)* [4860]
Ken LaFountaine First Nations Scholarships *(Undergraduate/Scholarship)* [8118]
Latinos for Dental Careers Scholarships *(All/Scholarship)* [2676]
Wilma Motley Memorial California Merit Scholarships *(Undergraduate, Master's, Doctorate, Professional development/Scholarship)* [709]
National Dental Hygienists' Association Scholarships *(Undergraduate/Scholarship)* [6244]
Procter & Gamble Professional Oral Health/HDA Foundation Scholarships *(Undergraduate/Scholarship)* [4556]
Dr. Sidney Rafal Memorial Scholarships *(Undergraduate/Scholarship)* [4457]
Bettie Underwood Dental Assisting Scholarships *(All/Scholarship)* [2677]
Dr. Juan D. Villarreal/HDA Foundation Scholarships *(Undergraduate/Scholarship)* [4557]
Alice Hinchcliffe Williams, RDH, MS Graduate Scholarships *(Graduate/Scholarship)* [9445]
Irene Woodall Graduate Scholarships *(Master's/Scholarship)* [710]

Dental laboratory technology

CDA Foundation Allied Dental Student Scholarships *(All/Scholarship)* [2674]
CDA Foundation Dental Student Scholarships *(All/Scholarship)* [2675]
Chinese American Medical Society Summer Research Fellowships Program *(Undergraduate/Fellowship)* [2766]
Latinos for Dental Careers Scholarships *(All/Scholarship)* [2676]
Esther Lim Memorial Scholarships *(Undergraduate/Scholarship)* [2767]
Ruth Liu Memorial Scholarships *(Undergraduate/Scholarship)* [2768]
Procter & Gamble Professional Oral Health/HDA Foundation Scholarships *(Undergraduate/Scholarship)* [4556]
Bettie Underwood Dental Assisting Scholarships *(All/Scholarship)* [2677]

Dentistry

American Academy of Periodontology Educator Scholarships *(Postdoctorate/Scholarship)* [392]
American Academy of Periodontology Foundation Education Fellowships *(Postdoctorate/Fellowship)* [393]
American Academy of Periodontology Teaching Fellowships *(Postdoctorate/Fellowship)* [394]
American Dental Association Dental Assisting Scholarship Program *(Undergraduate/Scholarship)* [701]
American Dental Association Dental Hygiene Schol-

arship Program *(Undergraduate/Scholarship)* [702]

American Dental Association Dental Laboratory Technology Scholarship Program *(Undergraduate/Scholarship)* [703]

American Dental Association Dental Student Scholarships *(Undergraduate/Scholarship)* [704]

American Dental Association Minority Dental Student Scholarships *(Undergraduate/Scholarship)* [705]

AMSUS Dentist Awards *(Professional development/Award)* [1458]

ASHA Scholarships *(Graduate, Undergraduate/Scholarship)* [1175]

ASHA Student Research Grants *(Graduate, Undergraduate/Scholarship)* [1176]

CDA Foundation Allied Dental Student Scholarships *(All/Scholarship)* [2674]

CDA Foundation Dental Student Scholarships *(All/Scholarship)* [2675]

Abram and Sylvia Chasens Teaching and Research Fellowships *(Postdoctorate/Fellowship)* [395]

Colgate-Palmolive/HDA Foundation Scholarships *(Master's, Postgraduate/Scholarship)* [4555]

DAAD Study Scholarship Awards *(Graduate/Scholarship)* [4116]

Endodontic Educator Fellowship Awards *(Graduate/Fellowship)* [471]

Endodontic Research Grants *(Graduate/Grant)* [472]

Nicholas S. Hetos, DDS, Memorial Graduate Scholarships *(Graduate/Scholarship)* [4516]

Howard B. Higgins South Carolina Dental Scholarships *(Undergraduate/Scholarship)* [3906]

IADR John Ste. Clarkson Fellowships *(Postdoctorate/Fellowship)* [4861]

IADR John Ste. Gray Fellowships *(Professional development/Fellowship)* [4862]

IADR Norton Ste. Ross Fellowships *(Postgraduate/Fellowship)* [4863]

IADR Toshio Ste. Nakao Fellowships *(Professional development/Fellowship)* [4864]

Jason Lang Scholarships *(Undergraduate/Scholarship)* [252]

Latinos for Dental Careers Scholarships *(All/Scholarship)* [2676]

Richard J. Lazzara Fellowships in Advanced Implant Surgery *(Postdoctorate/Fellowship)* [396]

Dr. Mac Scholarships *(Undergraduate/Scholarship)* [3118]

NAAF Aboriginal Health Careers Bursary and Scholarships *(Graduate, Undergraduate/Scholarship)* [5992]

NAAMA Scholarships *(Undergraduate/Scholarship)* [6024]

Nicholas J. Piergrossi Scholarships *(Undergraduate/Scholarship)* [4455]

Procter & Gamble Professional Oral Health/HDA Foundation Scholarships *(Undergraduate/Scholarship)* [4556]

Dr. Sidney Rafal Memorial Scholarships *(Undergraduate/Scholarship)* [4457]

RBC Royal Bank Scholarships for First Year Medical & Dental Students *(Undergraduate/Scholarship)* [7823]

Scholarships for Emigres in the Health Sciences *(Undergraduate/Scholarship)* [5157]

Jeptha Wade Schureman Scholarship Program *(Undergraduate/Scholarship)* [3205]

John M. and Mary A. Shanley Memorial Scholarships *(Undergraduate/Scholarship)* [8622]

Dr. Kiyoshi Sonoda Memorial Scholarships *(Graduate/Scholarship)* [5146]

Bud and Linda Tarrson Fellowships *(Postdoctorate/Fellowship)* [397]

Bettie Underwood Dental Assisting Scholarships *(All/Scholarship)* [2677]

Dr. Juan D. Villarreal/HDA Foundation Scholarships *(Undergraduate/Scholarship)* [4557]

Washington Higher Education Coordinating Board Health Professional Scholarships *(Graduate/Scholarship)* [9506]

Women in Science and Technology Scholarships *(Doctorate, Graduate, Master's, Undergraduate/Scholarship)* [9442]

Design

ACI Cagley ACI Student Fellowships *(Graduate, Master's, Undergraduate/Fellowship)* [629]

ACI President's Fellowships *(Doctorate, Master's/Fellowship)* [630]

Architecture, Design and Urban Design Prize *(Graduate, Undergraduate/Prize)* [8231]

Joan Auld Scholarships *(Undergraduate/Scholarship)* [3181]

MJSA Education Foundation Scholarship Fund *(Undergraduate/Scholarship)* [5605]

Travel Fellowships in Architecture, Design and Urban Design *(Graduate, Undergraduate/Fellowship)* [8233]

Polaire Weissman Funds *(Graduate/Fellowship)* [5793]

Women's Jewelry Association Member Grants *(All/Grant)* [9726]

Diabetes

Eli Lilly Graduate Scholarships *(Graduate/Scholarship)* [2451]

The Youth Scholarship Program *(Undergraduate/Scholarship)* [2719]

Dietetics (See Nutrition)

Disabilities

AAHD Scholarships *(Graduate, Undergraduate/Scholarship)* [481]

American Speech Language Hearing Foundation Clinical Research Grants *(Doctorate/Grant)* [1381]

American Speech Language Hearing Foundation Endowed Scholarships *(Postdoctorate/Scholarship)* [1382]

American Speech Language Hearing Foundation General Scholarships *(Postgraduate/Scholarship)* [1383]

American Speech Language Hearing Foundation Scholarships for International Students *(Graduate/Scholarship)* [1384]

American Speech Language Hearing Foundation Scholarships for Students with Disability *(Graduate/Scholarship)* [1385]

ASHFA Scholarships for Minority Students *(Graduate/Scholarship)* [1386]

Katie MacDonald Memorial Scholarships *(Graduate, Undergraduate/Scholarship)* [9018]

New Century Scholars Doctoral Scholarships *(Postdoctorate/Scholarship)* [1387]

New Century Scholars Research Grants *(Doctorate/Grant)* [1388]

Siobhan Isabella Reid Memorial Scholarships *(Graduate, Undergraduate/Scholarship)* [5393]

Whitaker-Minard Memorial Scholarships *(Undergraduate/Scholarship)* [7122]

Drafting

Toyota High School Scholarship Program *(Undergraduate/Scholarship)* [4581]

Drawing (See Art; Visual arts)

Drug abuse (See Substance abuse)

Earth sciences

American Association of Stratigraphic Palynologists Student Scholarships *(Graduate/Scholarship)* [6]

J.P. Bickell Mining Scholarships *(Undergraduate/Scholarship)* [9322]

W.L. Calvert Memorial Scholarships *(Graduate/Scholarship)* [4610]

EERI/FEMA Graduate Fellowships *(Graduate/Scholarship)* [3563]

El Dorado County Mineral and Gem Society Scholarships *(Graduate, Undergraduate/Scholarship)* [3620]

Geological Association of Canada Student Prizes *(Undergraduate/Award)* [4085]

Lewis-Clark State College Presidential Technical Out-of-State Scholarships *(Undergraduate/Scholarship)* [5447]

Minority Visiting Students Awards *(Undergraduate, Graduate/Award, Internship)* [8241]

National GEM Consortium - PhD Science Fellowships *(Doctorate, Graduate/Fellowship)* [6307]

NWF Campus Ecology Fellowships *(Graduate, Undergraduate/Fellowship)* [6557]

Paleontological Society Student Research Grants *(Graduate, Undergraduate/Grant)* [7]

Dennis R. Prince Scholarships *(Undergraduate/Scholarship)* [7457]

Women's Association of the Mining Industry of Canada Foundation National Geophysics Scholarships *(Undergraduate/Scholarship)* [9713]

Women's Association of the Mining Industry of Canada Foundation National Scholarships *(Undergraduate/Scholarship)* [9714]

Women's Association of the Mining Industry of Canada Foundation Wood Bursary Awards *(Undergraduate/Award)* [9715]

East European studies (See Central European studies)

Ecology (See also Environmental science)

Fellowships and Internships Program in Latin America *(Graduate/Fellowship, Internship)* [8269]

B. Harper Bull Conservation Fellowships *(Graduate/Fellowship)* [8913]

Human Ecology Continuing Undergraduate Student Scholarships *(Undergraduate/Scholarship)* [9358]

Maude Keisling/Cumberland County Extension Homemakers Scholarships *(Undergraduate/Scholarship)* [3112]

Andrew W. Mellon Foundation Fellowships *(Graduate/Fellowship)* [6983]

Barbara H. Mullin Memorial Scholarships *(Graduate, Undergraduate/Scholarship)* [9573]

NGC College Scholarships *(Graduate, Undergraduate/Scholarship)* [6303]

A. Stanley Rand Fellowships Program *(Undergraduate, Doctorate, Postdoctorate/Fellowship)* [8270]

Dennis Raveling Scholarships *(Undergraduate/Scholarship)* [2288]

Short-Term Fellowships *(Undergraduate, Graduate, Postdoctorate/Fellowship)* [8271]

Earl S. Tupper 3-year Postdoctoral Fellowships in Tropical Biology *(Postdoctorate/Fellowship)* [8272]

Welder Wildlife Foundation Fellowships *(Doctorate, Graduate/Fellowship)* [9559]

Mary and Elliot Wood Foundation Graduate Scholarship Fund *(Graduate/Scholarship)* [3930]

Economics

Alberta Agricultural Economics Association Undergraduate Scholarships *(Undergraduate/Scholarship)* [204]

American Enterprise Institute National Research Initiative Fellowships (NRI) *(Graduate/Fellowship)* [718]

American Institute for Economic Research Student Summer Fellowships *(Doctorate, Graduate, Undergraduate/Fellowship)* [854]

American Society of Comparative Law TransCoop Programs *(All/Fellowship)* [1204]

American Society of Military Comptrollers National Scholarship Program *(Undergraduate/Scholarship)* [1305]

APS/ASU Scholarships *(Undergraduate/Scholarship)* [7332]

APS/Maricopa County Community Colleges Scholarships *(Undergraduate/Scholarship)* [7333]

Association of Government Accountants Undergraduate/Graduate Scholarships for Community Service Accomplishments *(Graduate, Undergraduate/Fellowship, Scholarship)* [1789]

Association of Government Accountants Undergraduate/Graduate Scholarships for Full-time study *(Graduate, Undergraduate/Fellowship, Scholarship)* [1790]

Association of Government Accountants Undergraduate/Graduate Scholarships for Part-time study *(Graduate, Undergraduate/Fellowship, Scholarship)* [1791]

Avista Corporation Minds in Motion Scholarships *(Undergraduate/Scholarship)* [5412]

Bank of Canada Governor's Awards *(Doctorate, Professional development/Award)* [2012]

UAA Mark A. Beltz Scholarships *(Graduate, Undergraduate, Vocational/Occupational/Scholarship)* [9087]

Chopivsky Fellowships *(Graduate/Scholarship)* [9498]

Clark High School Academy of Finance Scholarships *(Undergraduate/Scholarship)* [7476]

Clark High School Alumni Leadership Circle Scholarships *(Undergraduate/Scholarship)* [7477]

Mable B. Crawford Memorial Scholarships *(Undergraduate/Scholarship)* [9146]

CTRF Scholarships for Graduate Study in Transportation *(Graduate/Scholarship)* [2626]

Jack Ervin EDI Scholarships *(Professional development/Scholarship)* [6761]

Enid Hall Griswold Memorial Scholarships *(Undergraduate/Scholarship)* [6499]

Gene Halker Memorial Scholarships *(Graduate, Undergraduate/Scholarship)* [3865]

Anna E. Hall Memorial Scholarships *(Undergraduate/Scholarship)* [7251]

Harkness Fellowships in Health Care Policy and Practice *(Doctorate, Graduate/Fellowship)* [3020]

Hilb, Rogal and Hobbs Scholarships *(Undergraduate/Scholarship)* [9449]

Governor James E. Holshouser Professional Development Scholarships *(Professional development/Scholarship)* [6762]

HSBC-North America Scholarship Program *(Undergraduate/Scholarship)* [4571]

HSF/Citi Fellows Program *(Undergraduate/Scholarship)* [4573]

HSF/General Motors Scholarship Program *(Undergraduate/Scholarship)* [4574]

Kalmen Kaplansky Scholarships in Economic and Social Rights *(Graduate/Scholarship)* [3475]

Mas Family Scholarships *(Graduate, Undergraduate/Scholarship)* [5658]

William P. McHugh Memorial Fund Award *(Doctorate, Graduate/Fellowship)* [1141]

Douglas McRorie Memorial Scholarships *(Postgraduate/Scholarship)* [75]

MillerCoors National Scholarships *(Undergraduate/Scholarship)* [48]

Minorities in Government Finance Scholarships *(Graduate, Undergraduate/Scholarship)* [4199]

MPAC-DC Graduate Policy Fellowships *(Graduate/Fellowship)* [5960]

The National Endowment for the Humanities Fellowships *(Doctorate, Graduate/Fellowship)* [1142]

National Iranian American Council Fellowships *(Graduate, Undergraduate/Fellowship)* [6365]

NGC College Scholarships *(Graduate, Undergraduate/Scholarship)* [6303]

Nonproliferation Graduate Fellowships Program (NGFP) *(Graduate/Fellowship)* [7033]

Norfolk Southern Scholarships *(Undergraduate/Scholarship)* [9450]

UAA Diane Olsen Memorial Scholarships *(Undergraduate/Scholarship)* [9105]

Pi Gamma Mu Scholarships *(Graduate/Scholarship)* [7330]

Thomas R. Pickering Graduate Foreign Affairs Fellowships *(Graduate/Fellowship)* [9619]

Doug Purvis Prize *(Professional development/Prize)* [2368]

Betty Rendel Scholarships *(Undergraduate/Scholarship)* [6288]

Sloan Research Fellowships *(Doctorate/Fellowship)* [8235]

Helen D. Snow Memorial Scholarships *(Undergraduate/Scholarship)* [7252]

The Dan Stewart Scholarships *(Professional development/Scholarship)* [6763]

Steven M. Teutsch Prevention Effectiveness Fellowships *(Doctorate/Fellowship)* [2715]

Toyota High School Scholarship Program *(Undergraduate/Scholarship)* [4581]

Tribal Business Management Program Scholarships (TBM) *(Undergraduate/Scholarship)* [2664]

The United States Department of State, Bureau of Educational & Cultural Affairs Fellowships *(Doctorate, Graduate/Fellowship)* [1143]

Urban Financial Services Coalition Scholarships *(Undergraduate/Scholarship)* [2129]

Women In Defense HORIZONS Scholarships *(Graduate, Undergraduate/Scholarship)* [9696]

Mary and Elliot Wood Foundation Graduate Scholarship Fund *(Graduate/Scholarship)* [3930]

Editors and editing

ASBPE Young Leaders Scholarships *(All/Scholarship)* [1189]

Aubespin Scholarships *(Undergraduate/Scholarship)* [656]

Kaiser Media Fellowships in Health *(Advanced Professional/Fellowship)* [5180]

Eugene C. Pulliam Fellowships for Editorial Writing *(Professional development/Fellowship)* [8149]

Claudette Upton Scholarships *(Undergraduate/Scholarship)* [3588]

Education

AECT Foundation Mentor Endowment Scholarships *(Doctorate, Graduate/Scholarship)* [1761]

AERA-AIR Fellows Program *(Postdoctorate/Fellowship)* [714]

AERA Minority Fellowship Program in Education Research *(Postdoctorate/Fellowship)* [716]

Akao Scholarships for QFD *(Undergraduate/Scholarship)* [7552]

Alberta Teachers Association Doctoral Fellowships in Education *(Doctorate/Fellowship)* [272]

Alberta Teachers Association Educational Research Awards *(Professional development/Grant)* [273]

William Tasse Alexander Scholarship Fund *(Undergraduate/Scholarship)* [3883]

Margaret M. Alek Scholarships *(Undergraduate/Scholarship)* [3362]

American Quarter Horse Foundation Scholarships *(Undergraduate/Scholarship)* [1063]

AMS Teacher Education Scholarships *(Undergraduate/Scholarship)* [938]

Charles Lee Anderson Memorial Scholarships *(Undergraduate/Scholarship)* [3142]

APS/Maricopa County Community Colleges Scholarships *(Undergraduate/Scholarship)* [7333]

Mike Ardaw Scholarships *(Undergraduate/Scholarship)* [9137]

ARTC Glenn Moon Scholarships *(Undergraduate/Scholarship)* [4409]

ASM Undergraduate Teaching Fellowships (ASM-UTF) *(Undergraduate/Fellowship)* [1301]

Associated Women for Pepperdine Scholarships (AWP) *(Undergraduate/Scholarship)* [7167]

George C. Balch Scholarships *(Graduate, Undergraduate/Scholarship)* [9054]

Avery Bayle Barth Scholarships *(Undergraduate/Scholarship)* [3367]

Diane Basilone-Engle Memorial Scholarships *(Undergraduate/Scholarship)* [2329]

Jeannette Bautista Memorial Scholarships *(Undergraduate/Scholarship)* [7468]

Thomas M. Blake Memorial Scholarships *(Undergraduate/Scholarship)* [3230]

Susan Brager Occupational Education Scholarships *(Undergraduate/Scholarship)* [7471]

Brown Foundation College Scholarships *(Undergraduate/Scholarship)* [816]

Cecil E. Burney Scholarships *(Undergraduate/Scholarship)* [2940]

Canadian Society for the Study of Education New Scholar Fellowships (CSSE) *(Professional development/Fellowship)* [2616]

Career Colleges Scholarships *(Undergraduate/Scholarship)* [4706]

Deloris Carter Hampton Scholarships *(Undergraduate/Scholarship)* [7404]

Catching the Dream Scholarships *(Graduate, Undergraduate/Scholarship)* [817]

Delmar Cengage Learning-NAAE Upper Division Scholarships *(Undergraduate/Scholarship)* [6033]

Clark High School Teacher Education Academy Scholarships *(Undergraduate/Scholarship)* [7478]

Lula Faye Clegg Memorial Scholarship Fund *(Undergraduate/Scholarship)* [3897]

Maridell Braham Condon Scholarships *(Undergraduate/Scholarship)* [8162]

Judy Crocker Memorial Scholarship Fund *(Undergraduate/Scholarship)* [3900]

CSSE ARTS Graduate Research Awards *(Graduate/Award)* [2617]

CSSHE Masters Thesis/Project Awards *(Master's/Award)* [2619]

CSSHE Research Awards *(Professional development/Award)* [2620]

June Danby and Pat Pearse Education Scholarships *(Undergraduate/Scholarship)* [5093]

Antonia Dellas Memorial Scholarships *(Undergraduate/Scholarship)* [5094]

Rudolph Dillman Memorial Scholarships *(Graduate, Undergraduate/Scholarship)* [750]

Josephine P. White Eagle Graduate Fellowships *(Graduate, Master's, Doctorate/Fellowship)* [4591]

EAPSI Fellowships *(Doctorate, Graduate/Fellowship)* [6467]

ECT Foundation Master Scholarships *(Graduate, Master's/Scholarship)* [1763]

E.V. Erickson Field of Interest Education Scholarship Fund *(Undergraduate/Scholarship)* [4211]

Bertha M. Fase Memorial Scholarship Fund *(Undergraduate/Scholarship)* [4213]

Fraser Family Scholarships *(Undergraduate/Scholarship)* [7490]

William E. "Bill" Gallagher Scholarships *(Undergraduate/Scholarship)* [7076]

Garikian Scholarship Fund *(Undergraduate/Scholarship)* [1593]

The Gates Millennium Scholars *(Undergraduate/Scholarship)* [4569]

Laverne L. Gibson Memorial Scholarships *(Undergraduate/Scholarship)* [7077]

Guide Dogs for the Blind Dorothea and Roland Bohde Leadership Scholarships *(Postgraduate/Scholarship)* [6275]

Martha and Oliver Hansen Memorial Scholarships *(Undergraduate/Scholarship)* [5098]

Eileen Harrison Education Scholarships *(Graduate, Undergraduate/Scholarship)* [3866]

Karen Harter Recruitment Scholarship Grants *(Undergraduate/Scholarship)* [3153]

Delta Gamma Foundation Florence Margaret Harvey Memorial Scholarships *(Graduate, Undergraduate/Scholarship)* [752]

Dick and Pat Hazel Minority Scholarships *(Professional development/Scholarship)* [3061]

High School Councilors Scholarships *(Undergraduate/Scholarship)* [4707]

Raymond T. Hoge Scholarship Fund *(Undergraduate/Scholarship)* [8674]

Huenefeld/Denton Scholarships *(Undergraduate/Scholarship)* [3415]

IBEA Undergraduate Scholarships *(Undergraduate/Scholarship)* [4683]

Imagine America Scholarships *(Undergraduate/Scholarship)* [4708]

Harriet Irsay Scholarships *(Graduate, Undergraduate/Scholarship)* [869]

Dwight P. Jacobus Scholarships *(Undergraduate/Scholarship)* [1860]

Jewish Federation Academic Scholarships *(Graduate, Undergraduate/Scholarship)* [5161]

Barbara Jordan Memorial Scholarships *(Graduate, Undergraduate/Scholarship)* [1884]

Edward G. Kaelber Scholarships *(Undergraduate/Scholarship)* [5582]

Maude Keisling/Cumberland County Extension Homemakers Scholarships *(Undergraduate/Scholarship)* [3112]

Louise Nader Khourey/Kappa Delta Pi Scholarships *(Undergraduate/Scholarship)* [8681]

James Madison Foundation - Junior Fellowships *(Graduate/Fellowship)* [5564]

James Madison Foundation - Senior Fellowships *(Graduate/Fellowship)* [5565]

Edna Martin Scholarships (Undergraduate/Scholarship) [3119]

Dottie Martin Teacher Scholarships (Graduate, Undergraduate/Scholarship) [6765]

McJulien Minority Graduate Scholarships (Graduate/Scholarship) [1764]

John Alexander McLean Scholarships (Undergraduate/Scholarship) [8896]

MESBEC Scholarships (Undergraduate/Scholarship) [2662]

NAAF Post-Secondary Education Scholarships (Graduate, Undergraduate/Scholarship) [5993]

National Academy of Education Scholarships (Postdoctorate/Scholarship) [6006]

Native American Leadership Education Scholarships (NALE) (Postdoctorate, Undergraduate/Scholarship) [2663]

Nevada Parent Teacher Association Scholarships (Undergraduate/Scholarship) [7512]

North Dakota Division Scholarships (Undergraduate/Scholarship) [5862]

North Mecklenburg Teachers' Memorial Scholarships (Undergraduate/Scholarship) [3916]

Penn-Bird Family Memorial Scholarships (Undergraduate/Scholarship) [7516]

Pi Lambda Theta Scholarships (Undergraduate/Scholarship) [9366]

Poundmaker Memorial Scholarships (Undergraduate/Scholarship) [6565]

Rosa Quezada Memorial Education Scholarships (Undergraduate/Scholarship) [3231]

RCSA Cottrell Scholarships (Graduate/Scholarship) [7734]

Rechsteiner Family Scholarship Fund (Undergraduate/Scholarship) [3788]

Charles and Ruth Ronin Memorial Scholarships (Undergraduate/Scholarship) [7709]

Dorothy Worden Ronken Scholarships (Graduate/Scholarship) [3421]

School of Education Scholarships for Students from Underrepresented Groups (Undergraduate/Scholarship) [9369]

Marion A. and Ruth Sherwood Family Fund Education Scholarships (Undergraduate/Scholarship) [4243]

Everett Oscar Shimp Memorial Scholarships (Undergraduate/Scholarship) [7113]

Siemens Teacher Scholarships (Graduate, Undergraduate/Scholarship) [8142]

Lillian Smith Scholarship for Teaching Students (Graduate, Undergraduate/Scholarship) [9111]

Soroptimist International of Redlands Scholarships (Undergraduate/Scholarship) [7715]

John Soto Scholarships (Undergraduate/Scholarship) [3232]

Robert W. and Bernice Ingalls Staton Scholarships (Undergraduate/Scholarship) [9314]

Sheri Stears Education Scholarships (Undergraduate/Scholarship) [9112]

Peter T. Steinwedell Scholarships (Undergraduate/Scholarship) [4461]

Sturgulewski Family Scholarships (Graduate, Undergraduate, Vocational/Occupational/Scholarship) [9113]

John A. Sullivan Scholarships (Undergraduate/Scholarship) [3546]

Tarkanian Teacher Education Academy at Clark High School Scholarships (TEACH) (Undergraduate/Scholarship) [7530]

Nadene M. Thomas Graduate Research Scholarships (Graduate/Scholarship) [275]

Charles A. Townsend Scholarships (Undergraduate/Scholarship) [7119]

Toyota High School Scholarship Program (Undergraduate/Scholarship) [4581]

Marta Vallin Memorial Scholarships (Undergraduate/Scholarship) [3233]

Philip F. Vineberg Travelling Fellowships in the Humanities (Undergraduate/Scholarship) [5726]

Wachovia/TELACU Excellence in Teaching Scholarships (Undergraduate/Scholarship) [8823]

Richard M. Weaver Fellowships (Graduate/Fellowship) [4849]

Faye and Rendell Webb Scholarships (Undergraduate/Scholarship) [2962]

Art and Dannie Weber Scholarships (Undergraduate/Scholarship) [9660]

Louise Wachter Wichman Scholarship Fund (Undergraduate/Scholarship) [4250]

Fred Wiesner Educational Excellence Scholarships (Graduate, Undergraduate/Scholarship) [1885]

Dr. Dana Williams Scholarships (Undergraduate/Scholarship) [2964]

Winston-Salem Foundation Scholarships (Undergraduate/Scholarship) [9664]

Paul R. Wolf Memorial Scholarships (Graduate/Scholarship) [1672]

Lee Womack Scholarship Fund (Undergraduate/Scholarship) [5917]

Mary and Elliot Wood Foundation Graduate Scholarship Fund (Graduate/Scholarship) [3930]

Geoffrey H. Wood Scholarships (Undergraduate/Scholarship) [2594]

Minoru Yasui Memorial Scholarships (Graduate/Scholarship) [5147]

Education, Bilingual and cross-cultural

AECT Legacy Scholarships (Graduate, Master's, Professional development/Scholarship) [1762]

Mead Leadership Fellows Program (Professional development/Fellowship) [6796]

New Mexico Association for Bilingual Education Scholarships (Undergraduate/Scholarship) [6665]

Toyota High School Scholarship Program (Undergraduate/Scholarship) [4581]

Education, Early childhood

Patty Hamilton Early Childhood Development Scholarships (Undergraduate/Scholarship) [9152]

Carol Hoy Scholarship Fund (Undergraduate/Scholarship) [3947]

JCC Association Graduate Education Scholarships (Graduate/Scholarship) [5151]

Molly Ann Mishler Memorial Scholarships (Undergraduate/Scholarship) [9163]

National Kindergarten Alliance Graduate Scholarships (Graduate/Scholarship) [6385]

Fred Rogers Memorial Scholarships (Graduate, Undergraduate/Scholarship) [35]

Morgan Stanley Pediatrics Fellowships (Doctorate, Postdoctorate/Fellowship) [575]

Toyota High School Scholarship Program (Undergraduate/Scholarship) [4581]

Education, Elementary

AECT Legacy Scholarships (Graduate, Master's, Professional development/Scholarship) [1762]

APS/ASU Scholarships (Undergraduate/Scholarship) [7332]

Gina L. Barnhart Memorial Scholarship Fund (Undergraduate/Scholarship) [3759]

Marian Jones Donaldson Scholarship Fund (Undergraduate/Scholarship) [3769]

Albert Einstein Distinguished Educator Fellowships (Graduate, Professional development/Fellowship) [8956]

Lindsay M. Entz Memorial Scholarships (Undergraduate/Scholarship) [3770]

Jennica Ferguson Memorial Scholarships (Undergraduate/Scholarship) [6274]

Norma Gotwalt Scholarship Fund (Undergraduate/Scholarship) [3945]

Isabel M. Herson Scholarships in Education (Graduate, Undergraduate/Scholarship) [9803]

Carol Hoy Scholarship Fund (Undergraduate/Scholarship) [3947]

Carie and George Lyter Scholarship Fund (Undergraduate/Scholarship) [3951]

National Federation of the Blind Educator of Tomorrow Awards (Undergraduate/Scholarship) [6279]

Ruth Cook Pfautz Memorial Scholarship Fund (Undergraduate/Scholarship) [3956]

R.M. Princ Scholarships (Undergraduate/Scholarship) [7518]

Mary Kean White Memorial Scholarship Fund (Undergraduate/Scholarship) [8709]

Ralph Yetka Memorial Scholarships (Undergraduate/Scholarship) [9181]

Education, English as a second language

Douglas-Coldwell Foundation Scholarships in Social Affairs (Graduate/Scholarship) [3474]

Flora English Creative Writing Scholarships (Undergraduate/Scholarship) [7489]

Sarah Jane Houston Scholarships (Undergraduate/Scholarship) [3414]

Arlene Kuhner Memorial Scholarships (Undergraduate/Scholarship) [9103]

William R. Pfalzgraf Scholarships (Undergraduate/Scholarship) [7103]

Robert Roy Awards (Professional development/Award) [2406]

H.H. Stern Grant Awards (Professional development/Grant) [2407]

Education, Industrial

American Rental Association Foundation Scholarships (Graduate, Undergraduate, Vocational/Occupational/Scholarship) [1137]

Gary L. Buffington Memorial Scholarships (Undergraduate/Scholarship) [4760]

Bus and Mary Ellen Durant Timberline High School Endowed Scholarships (Undergraduate/Scholarship) [5426]

Flexible Packaging Academic Scholarships & Summer Internships Program (Undergraduate/Internship, Scholarship) [3810]

Lewis-Clark State College Presidential Technical Out-of-State Scholarships (Undergraduate/Scholarship) [5447]

Ron Marshall Scholarships (Undergraduate/Scholarship) [1138]

Material Handling Education Foundation Scholarships (Doctorate, Graduate, Undergraduate/Scholarship) [5688]

Dorothy Wellnitz Canadian Scholarships (Undergraduate/Scholarship) [1139]

Education, Medical

AAMA Houston Chapter - Medical Student Scholarships (Professional development/Scholarship) [1494]

Jonathan Alan Scholarship Fund (Undergraduate/Scholarship) [9546]

AMA Foundation Minority Scholars Awards (Undergraduate/Scholarship) [922]

AMA Foundation Physicians of Tomorrow Scholarships (Undergraduate/Scholarship) [923]

Canadian Pain Society Post-Doctoral Fellowship Awards (Doctorate/Fellowship) [2567]

Clinical Pain Management Fellowship Awards (Postgraduate/Fellowship) [2568]

CPS Excellence in Interprofessional Pain Education Awards (Professional development/Award) [2569]

CPS Interprofessional Nursing Project Awards (Professional development/Award) [2570]

CPS Knowledge Translation Research Awards (Professional development/Grant) [2571]

CPS Nursing Excellence in Pain Management Awards (Professional development/Award) [2572]

CPS Nursing Research and Education Awards (Professional development/Grant) [2573]

CPS Outstanding Pain Mentorship Awards (Professional development/Award) [2574]

CPS Toronto Poly Clinic - ROD Inter-Disciplinary Pain Education Grants (Professional development/Grant) [2575]

CPS Trainee Research Awards (Doctorate/Grant) [2576]

Davis Educational Scholarship Fund (Undergraduate, Vocational/Occupational/Scholarship) [3190]

Aleksander & Stefania Dulemba Scholarships (Undergraduate/Scholarship) [7761]

Victoria M. Gardner Scholarships (Undergraduate/Scholarship) [9272]

Victor and Ruth N. Goodman Memorial Scholarships (Graduate/Scholarship) [4373]

Zelma Gray Medical School Scholarships *(Doctorate/Fellowship)* [3876]

Alice Newell Joslyn Medical Fund *(Undergraduate/Scholarship)* [2041]

John and Lois Lamont Graduate Scholarships *(Postgraduate/Award)* [2464]

Lapeer County Medical Scholarship Fund *(Undergraduate/Scholarship)* [5351]

Lewis K. Martin II, M.D. and Cheryl Rose Martin Scholarship Fund *(Graduate/Scholarship)* [4378]

Medical Professionals of Tomorrow Scholarships *(Undergraduate, Graduate/Scholarship)* [9060]

Albert and Eloise Midyette Memorial Scholarship Fund *(Undergraduate/Scholarship)* [3913]

John J. Mingenback Memorial Scholarships *(Graduate, Undergraduate/Scholarship)* [4173]

Nebraska Hospital Association Tuition Aid and Scholarships *(Undergraduate/Scholarship)* [6606]

Herbert W. Nickens Medical Student Scholarships *(Undergraduate/Scholarship)* [1701]

Gilberto and Lennetta Pesquera Medical School Scholarships *(Graduate/Scholarship)* [4163]

Pharmavite LLC NP Doctoral Education Scholarships *(Doctorate/Scholarship)* [379]

RBC Royal Bank Scholarships for First Year Medical & Dental Students *(Undergraduate/Scholarship)* [7823]

Drs. Kirkland Ruffin & Willcox Ruffin Scholarships *(Graduate/Scholarship)* [4381]

Florence L. Smith Medical Scholarships *(Graduate/Scholarship)* [4383]

Jerome P. Webster Fellowships *(Professional development/Fellowship)* [7749]

S. William & Martha R. Goff Educational Scholarships *(Undergraduate/Scholarship)* [7123]

The Arthur N. Wilson, MD, Scholarships *(Undergraduate/Scholarship)* [924]

Education, Music

AOSA Research Grants *(All/Grant)* [959]

Bach Organ and Keyboard Music Scholarships *(Undergraduate/Scholarship)* [7786]

TCDA Jim and Glenda Casey Professional Scholarships *(Graduate, Professional development/Scholarship)* [8847]

Churchill Family Scholarships *(Undergraduate/Scholarship)* [5575]

Constant Memorial Scholarship for Aquidneck Island Resident *(Undergraduate/Scholarship)* [7788]

Dalcroze Society of America Memorial Scholarships *(Graduate/Scholarship)* [3335]

William R. Gard Memorial Scholarships *(Undergraduate/Scholarship)* [6091]

Robert C. and Judith L. Knapp Scholarships *(Graduate, Undergraduate/Scholarship)* [3867]

Donald and Idabelle Mohr Scholarships *(Undergraduate/Scholarship)* [2891]

Muddy Waters Scholarships *(Undergraduate/Scholarship)* [2155]

"Nickels for Notes" Scholarships *(Undergraduate/Scholarship)* [4080]

TCDA Abbott IPCO Professional Scholarships *(Graduate, Professional development/Scholarship)* [8849]

TCDA General Fund Scholarships *(Graduate, Undergraduate/Scholarship)* [8851]

Williams Chorale Bacardi Fallon Performing Arts Scholarships *(Undergraduate/Award, Scholarship)* [9608]

Education, Physical

American Sokol Merit Awards *(Undergraduate/Scholarship)* [1379]

Dr. Andy Anderson Young Professional Awards *(Professional development/Award)* [7317]

CANFIT Nutrition, Physical Education and Culinary Arts Scholarships *(Graduate, Undergraduate/Scholarship)* [3026]

CANFIT Scholarships *(Graduate, Undergraduate/Scholarship)* [2228]

William E. "Bill" Gallagher Scholarships *(Undergraduate/Scholarship)* [7076]

Dorothy Harris Endowed Scholarships *(Graduate/Scholarship)* [9737]

Gretchen Hauff Memorial Scholarships *(Undergraduate/Scholarship)* [7496]

Indiana State Alumni Association Creative and Performing Arts Awards *(Undergraduate/Scholarship)* [4745]

JCC Association Graduate Education Scholarships *(Graduate/Scholarship)* [5151]

R. Tait Mackenzie Awards *(Professional development/Award)* [7318]

North American Society Fellowships *(Professional development/Fellowship)* [7319]

PHE Canada Student Awards *(Undergraduate/Award)* [7321]

Physical Education Teaching Excellence (PETE) Awards *(Professional development/Award)* [7322]

Bonnie Sorenson Scudder Scholarships *(Undergraduate/Scholarship)* [3170]

Taylor Statten Memorial Fellowships *(Graduate/Scholarship)* [9342]

Education, Religious

Mary E. Bivins Foundation Religious Scholarship Program *(Graduate, Undergraduate/Scholarship)* [2104]

Emmanuel Bible College Scholarships *(Undergraduate/Scholarship)* [1592]

Father Rutilio Grande Scholarships *(Graduate, Undergraduate/Scholarship)* [7893]

International Scholarship Programs for Community Service *(All/Scholarship)* [5765]

MACC Scholarships *(Professional development/Scholarship)* [5796]

William P. McHugh Memorial Fund Award *(Doctorate, Graduate/Fellowship)* [1141]

The National Endowment for the Humanities Fellowships *(Doctorate, Graduate/Fellowship)* [1142]

The United States Department of State, Bureau of Educational & Cultural Affairs Fellowships *(Doctorate, Graduate/Fellowship)* [1143]

Philip F. Vineberg Travelling Fellowships in the Humanities *(Undergraduate/Scholarship)* [5726]

Education, Secondary

Leonore Annenberg Teaching Fellowships *(Graduate/Fellowship)* [9614]

APS/ASU Scholarships *(Undergraduate/Scholarship)* [7332]

Mary Ann Brichta Scholarships *(Undergraduate/Scholarship)* [9350]

Patricia Buchanan Memorial Scholarships *(Undergraduate/Scholarship)* [9351]

COUSE-Gram Scholarships *(Undergraduate/Scholarship)* [8596]

Marian Jones Donaldson Scholarship Fund *(Undergraduate/Scholarship)* [3769]

Albert Einstein Distinguished Educator Fellowships *(Graduate, Professional development/Fellowship)* [8956]

Jennica Ferguson Memorial Scholarships *(Undergraduate/Scholarship)* [6274]

Mollie Harter Memorial Fund *(Undergraduate/Scholarship)* [3775]

George Koeppel and Roland W. Zinns Scholarships *(Undergraduate/Scholarship)* [9361]

La Voz Latina Scholarships *(Undergraduate/Scholarship)* [3157]

John P. and Tashia F. Morgridge Scholarships *(Undergraduate/Scholarship)* [9364]

National Federation of the Blind Educator of Tomorrow Awards *(Undergraduate/Scholarship)* [6279]

Noyce Scholarships for Secondary Math and Science Education *(Undergraduate/Scholarship)* [4751]

R.M. Princ Scholarships *(Undergraduate/Scholarship)* [7518]

Carl M. Rose Memorial Scholarship Fund *(Undergraduate/Scholarship)* [7109]

University of Wisconsin-Madison Minority Teacher Loans *(Professional development, Undergraduate/Loan, Scholarship)* [9378]

Woodrow Wilson-Rockefeller Brothers Fund Fellowships for Aspiring Teachers of Color *(Graduate/Fellowship)* [9621]

Ralph Yetka Memorial Scholarships *(Undergraduate/Scholarship)* [9181]

Education, Special

AECT Legacy Scholarships *(Graduate, Master's, Professional development/Scholarship)* [1762]

APS/ASU Scholarships *(Undergraduate/Scholarship)* [7332]

Laverne L. Gibson Memorial Scholarships *(Undergraduate/Scholarship)* [7077]

Illinois Special Education Teacher Tuition Waiver Scholarships (SETTW) *(Undergraduate/Scholarship)* [4696]

Mollie Lukken Memorial Scholarships *(Graduate, Professional development/Scholarship)* [5178]

Military Order of the Purple Heart Foundation Scholarships *(Undergraduate/Scholarship)* [5455]

NAJA Scholarships *(Graduate/Scholarship)* [6086]

Siobhan Isabella Reid Memorial Scholarships *(Graduate, Undergraduate/Scholarship)* [5393]

Special Education Scholarships *(Graduate, Undergraduate/Scholarship)* [362]

Toyota High School Scholarship Program *(Undergraduate/Scholarship)* [4581]

Workshop, Inc. and Stark MRDD Fostering Diversity Through Special Needs Scholarship Fund *(Undergraduate/Scholarship)* [8710]

Education, Vocational-technical

ALOA Scholarship Foundation *(Undergraduate/Scholarship)* [1679]

APS/Maricopa County Community Colleges Scholarships *(Undergraduate/Scholarship)* [7333]

ARA Scholarship Awards *(Undergraduate/Scholarship)* [1961]

Bus and Mary Ellen Durant Timberline High School Endowed Scholarships *(Undergraduate/Scholarship)* [5426]

Laura M. Fleming Scholarships *(Undergraduate, Vocational/Occupational/Scholarship)* [3903]

Harrisville Lions Club Scholarships *(Undergraduate, Vocational/Occupational/Scholarship)* [7085]

Wilbert L. and Zora F. Holmes Scholarship Endowment Fund *(Undergraduate, Vocational/Occupational/Scholarship)* [3907]

IOIA Organic Community Initiative Scholarships *(Professional development/Scholarship)* [4716]

Virginia C. Jack and Ralph L. Jack Scholarships *(Undergraduate, Vocational/Occupational/Scholarship)* [8677]

Margaret G. Johnson and Marge J. Stout Scholarships *(Undergraduate, Vocational/Occupational/Scholarship)* [5437]

Lake Dollars for Scholars Endowment Fund *(Undergraduate, Vocational/Occupational/Scholarship)* [8683]

The Leaders of Tomorrow Scholarships *(Undergraduate, Vocational/Occupational/Scholarship)* [3572]

Lt. Colonel Robert G. Moreland Vocational/Technical Fund *(Undergraduate, Vocational/Occupational/Scholarship)* [8692]

National Dairy Herd Information Association Scholarship Program *(Undergraduate/Scholarship)* [6231]

National Slovak Society of the USA Scholarships *(Undergraduate, Vocational/Occupational/Scholarship)* [6478]

National Slovak Society of the USA Senior Scholarships *(Undergraduate, Vocational/Occupational/Scholarship)* [6479]

Northwest-Shoals Community College Applied Technology Scholarships *(Undergraduate, Vocational/Occupational/Scholarship)* [6820]

Operation Homefront Scholarships *(Undergraduate, Vocational/Occupational/Scholarship)* [6907]

William Reaser Scholarships *(Undergraduate, Vocational/Occupational/Scholarship)* [7105]

Faye Lynn Roberts Educational Scholarships *(Undergraduate/Scholarship)* [8618]

IOIA Andrew Rutherford Scholarships *(Professional development/Scholarship)* [4717]

Bill Sawyer Memorial Scholarships *(Undergraduate/Scholarship)* [5463]

Ethel Shinn Alumni-Vocational Scholarships *(Undergraduate/Scholarship)* [5465]
Mary K. Smith Rector Scholarships *(Undergraduate, Vocational/Occupational/Scholarship)* [7117]
Beatrice Drinnan Spence Scholarships *(Undergraduate, Vocational/Occupational/Scholarship)* [3573]
StraightForward Media's Vocational-Technical School Scholarships *(Undergraduate, Vocational/Occupational/Scholarship)* [8764]
Texas Mutual Scholarship Program *(Undergraduate, Vocational/Occupational/Scholarship)* [8868]
Turner Family Scholarships *(Undergraduate, Vocational/Occupational/Scholarship)* [3925]
Washington County Farm Bureau Scholarships *(Undergraduate/Scholarship)* [6948]
The Wilmore Scholarship Fund *(Undergraduate, Vocational/Occupational/Scholarship)* [3929]

Educational administration

AGBU Scholarships *(Graduate/Loan)* [1573]
Association of College and University Auditors Scholarships *(Graduate, Undergraduate/Scholarship)* [1742]
CSSHE Masters Thesis/Project Awards *(Master's/Award)* [2619]
CSSHE Research Awards *(Professional development/Award)* [2620]
Jacque Placette Chapman Master's Fellowships *(Graduate/Fellowship)* [6918]
Native American Leadership Education Scholarships (NALE) *(Postdoctorate, Undergraduate/Scholarship)* [2663]
Order of Omega Doctoral Fellowships *(Doctorate, Graduate/Fellowship)* [6919]
William J. Brennan Graduate Assistant Fellowships *(Graduate/Fellowship)* [6920]

Education--Curricula

Evelyn Abrams Memorial Scholarships *(Undergraduate/Scholarship)* [7462]
Ed Haas Memorial Scholarships *(Undergraduate/Scholarship)* [8724]
Isabel M. Herson Scholarships in Education *(Graduate, Undergraduate/Scholarship)* [9803]
Ina E. Powell Memorial Scholarships *(Undergraduate/Scholarship)* [179]
Audrey L. Wright Scholarships *(Undergraduate/Scholarship)* [4309]

Electrochemistry (See also Chemistry)

Oronzio de Nora Industrial Electrochemistry Fellowships *(Postdoctorate/Fellowship)* [3624]
Summer Fellowships of The Electrochemical Society *(Graduate/Fellowship)* [3625]

Electronics

ARRLF Mississippi Scholarships *(Undergraduate/Scholarship)* [1070]
William E. "Buck" Bragunier Scholarships *(Undergraduate/Scholarship)* [1556]
Irvine W. Cook WA0CGS Scholarships *(Undergraduate/Scholarship)* [1080]
Milton E. Cooper/Young AFCEAN Graduate Scholarships *(Graduate/Scholarship)* [1558]
Charles Clarke Cordle Memorial Scholarships *(Undergraduate/Scholarship)* [1081]
SRC NRI Hans J. Coufal Fellowships *(Graduate/Fellowship)* [8086]
Charles N. Fisher Memorial Scholarships *(Undergraduate/Scholarship)* [1084]
Paul and Helen L. Grauer Scholarships *(Undergraduate/Scholarship)* [1087]
Dr. James L. Lawson Memorial Scholarships *(Undergraduate/Scholarship)* [1092]
Johnny Lineberry Memorial Scholarships *(Undergraduate, Vocational/Occupational/Scholarship)* [9645]
Fred R. McDaniel Memorial Scholarships *(Undergraduate/Scholarship)* [1093]
Ray, NORP and Katie, WOKTE Pautz Scholarships

(Undergraduate/Scholarship) [1098]
PHD ARA Scholarships *(Doctorate, Undergraduate/Scholarship)* [1100]
Carol A. Ratza Memorial Scholarships *(Undergraduate/Scholarship)* [4329]
IRARC Memorial Joseph P. Rubino WA4MMD Scholarships *(Undergraduate/Scholarship)* [1103]
Toyota High School Scholarship Program *(Undergraduate/Scholarship)* [4581]
L. Phil Wicker Scholarships *(Undergraduate/Scholarship)* [1113]
AFCEA General John A. Wickham Scholarships *(Undergraduate/Scholarship)* [1566]

Emergency and disaster services

Gail Hartshorn Scholarships *(Undergraduate/Scholarship)* [7087]
International Association of Emergency Managers Scholarships *(Graduate, Undergraduate/Scholarship)* [4866]
William C. Leary Memorial Emergency Services Scholarships *(Undergraduate/Scholarship)* [8985]
Mary Fran Myers Scholarships *(All/Grant)* [6569]
John I. and Madeleine R. Taeni Scholarships *(Undergraduate/Scholarship)* [8627]

Endocrinology

Dr. Biljan Memorial Awards *(Graduate/Award)* [2466]
Lilly Endocrine Scholars Fellowship Awards *(Doctorate, Professional development/Fellowship)* [3638]
Summer Research Fellowships *(Graduate, Undergraduate/Fellowship)* [3639]

Energy-related areas

Alberta Innovates Graduate Student Scholarship *(Graduate/Scholarship)* [234]
American Association of Blacks in Energy Scholarships *(Undergraduate/Scholarship)* [441]
Association of Desk and Derrick Clubs Education Trust Scholarships *(Undergraduate/Scholarship)* [1749]
Association of Energy Engineers Foundation Scholarship Program *(Graduate, Undergraduate/Scholarship)* [1766]
Calgary USAEE/IAEE North American Conference Registration Fee Scholarships *(Undergraduate/Scholarship)* [9034]
DEED Student Research Grant/Internships *(Graduate, Undergraduate/Grant)* [1048]
EMLF Law Student Scholarships *(Undergraduate/Scholarship)* [3643]
Environment, Natural Resource and Energy Division Fellowships (ENRE) *(Graduate/Fellowship)* [1011]
Dennis J. O'Brien USAEE/IAEE Best Student Paper Awards *(Undergraduate/Award)* [9035]
Rocky Mountain Coal Mining Institute Technical Scholarships *(Undergraduate, Vocational/Occupational/Scholarship)* [7811]
Schatz Energy Fellowships for Graduate Studies *(Graduate/Fellowship)* [8016]

Engineering

AAAS Mass Media Science and Engineering Fellowships *(Graduate, Postgraduate, Undergraduate/Fellowship)* [430]
AAAS Science and Technology Policy Fellowships *(Postdoctorate/Fellowship)* [431]
AACE International Competitive Scholarships *(Undergraduate/Scholarship)* [4]
A&WMA Louisiana Section Scholarships *(Graduate, Undergraduate/Scholarship)* [113]
AAUW Legal Advocacy Fund Selected Professions Fellowships *(Doctorate, Graduate/Fellowship)* [18]
Accenture American Indian Scholarship Program *(Graduate, Undergraduate/Scholarship)* [825]
ACI Scholarships *(Graduate/Scholarship)* [631]
Henry Adams Scholarships *(Undergraduate/Scholarship)* [1262]
Advanced Light Source Postdoctoral Fellowship

Program *(Doctorate/Fellowship)* [5379]
AeA Scholarships *(Undergraduate/Scholarship)* [7904]
AFCEA Scholarship for Working Professionals *(Graduate/Scholarship)* [1554]
African American Network - Carolinas Scholarship Fund *(Undergraduate/Scholarship)* [3882]
AHETEMS General Scholarships *(Graduate, Undergraduate/Scholarship)* [55]
AHETEMS Professional Scholarships *(Graduate/Scholarship)* [56]
Air Force Association Excellence Scholarships *(Graduate, Master's, Undergraduate/Scholarship)* [88]
AIST Baltimore Chapter Scholarships *(Undergraduate/Scholarship)* [1799]
AIST Detroit Chapter Scholarships *(Undergraduate/Scholarship)* [1800]
AIST Northwest Chapter Scholarships *(Undergraduate/Scholarship)* [1801]
Alaska Aerospace Development Corporation Scholarships *(Undergraduate/Scholarship)* [9130]
Alberta Ingenuity Graduate Student Scholarships in Nanotechnology *(Doctorate, Graduate/Scholarship)* [231]
Alberta Ingenuity Graduate Student Scholarships *(Doctorate, Graduate/Scholarship)* [230]
Stephanie Ali Memorial Scholarships *(Undergraduate/Scholarship)* [9321]
AMEC Aboriginal Undergraduate Scholarships *(Undergraduate/Scholarship)* [2453]
AMEC Masters Scholarships *(Graduate, Master's/Scholarship)* [2454]
American Association of University Women Selected Professions Fellowships *(Professional development/Fellowship)* [13]
American Council of Engineering Companies of Illinois Scholarships *(Doctorate, Graduate, Undergraduate/Scholarship)* [660]
American Lebanese Engineering Society Scholarship Program *(Graduate, Undergraduate/Scholarship)* [892]
American Railway Engineering and Maintenance-of-Way Association Scholarships *(Undergraduate/Scholarship)* [1117]
American Society of Heating, Refrigerating, and Air-Conditioning Memorial Scholarships *(Undergraduate/Scholarship)* [1263]
American Society of Heating, Refrigerating, and Air-Conditioning Undergraduate Scholarships *(Undergraduate/Scholarship)* [1264]
ISPE/M.E. Amstutz Memorial Awards *(Undergraduate/Award)* [4690]
A.T. Anderson Memorial Scholarships *(Graduate, Undergraduate/Scholarship)* [834]
Mike Ardaw Scholarships *(Undergraduate/Scholarship)* [9137]
AREMA Committee 18 - Light Density & Short Line Railways Scholarships *(Undergraduate/Scholarship)* [1118]
AREMA Committee 24 - Education and Training Scholarships *(Undergraduate/Scholarship)* [1119]
AREMA Committee 33 - Electric Energy Utilization Scholarships *(Undergraduate/Scholarship)* [1120]
AREMA Presidential Spouse Scholarships *(Undergraduate/Scholarship)* [1121]
Armed Forces Communications and Electronics Association Fellowships *(Doctorate, Graduate/Fellowship)* [1555]
Marvin Arnold and Irene Jaquetta Heye Scholarships *(Undergraduate/Scholarship)* [7906]
ASNT Fellow Awards *(Postdoctorate/Fellowship)* [1315]
Astronaut Scholarship Foundation Scholarships *(Undergraduate/Scholarship)* [1916]
Audio Engineering Society Educational Foundation Scholarships *(Graduate/Grant)* [1931]
Delores A. Auzenne Fellowships *(Postgraduate/Fellowship)* [3818]
Avista Corporation Minds in Motion Scholarships *(Undergraduate/Scholarship)* [5412]
B&W Y-12 Scholarship Fund *(Undergraduate/Scholarship)* [3565]
Bechtel Engineering and Science Scholarships *(High School/Scholarship)* [5645]
Charles E. Behlke Engineering Memorial Scholar-

ships (Undergraduate/Scholarship) [9139]

Bill & Nell Biggs Scholarships (Undergraduate/Scholarship) [9140]

Blow Molding Division Memorial Scholarships (Graduate, Undergraduate/Scholarship) [8444]

Boeing Company Scholarships (Undergraduate/Scholarship) [8112]

William E. "Buck" Bragunier Scholarships (Undergraduate/Scholarship) [1556]

Henry Broughton, K2AE Memorial Scholarships (Undergraduate/Scholarship) [1073]

Lt. General Douglas D. Buchholz Memorial Scholarships (Undergraduate/Scholarship) [1557]

Graduate Fellowship Program - Robert M Burger Fellowships (GFP) (Doctorate, Graduate/Fellowship) [8078]

Dorothy and Dick Burgess Scholarships (Undergraduate/Scholarship) [5092]

Burroughs Wellcome Fund Career Awards at the Scientific Interface (Doctorate, Postdoctorate/Fellowship) [2211]

Burroughs Wellcome Fund Collaborative Research Travel Grants (Doctorate/Grant) [2212]

Wes Burton Memorial Scholarships (Undergraduate/Scholarship) [9628]

Cesar A. Calas/FES Miami Chapter Scholarships (Undergraduate/Scholarship) [3824]

Canadian Council of Technicians and Technologists Scholarships for Technology Students (Postgraduate/Scholarship) [2445]

Julian E. Carnes Scholarship Fund (Undergraduate/Scholarship) [3891]

Willis H. Carrier Scholarships (Undergraduate/Scholarship) [1265]

Catching the Dream Scholarships (Graduate, Undergraduate/Scholarship) [817]

CBC Spouses Cheerios Brand Health Initiative Scholarships (Undergraduate/Scholarship) [3215]

CEMF Undergraduate Engineering Scholarships (Undergraduate/Scholarship) [2455]

CEPS-Tyco Scholarships (Undergraduate/Scholarship) [9250]

CERT College Scholarships (Graduate, Undergraduate/Scholarship) [3272]

Channabasappa Memorial Scholarships (Graduate, Professional development/Scholarship) [4918]

The Churchill Scholarships (Postgraduate/Scholarship) [2789]

Frank M. Coda Scholarships (Undergraduate/Scholarship) [1266]

Committee 12 - Rail Transit Scholarships (Undergraduate/Scholarship) [1122]

Committee 27 - Maintenance-of-Way Work Equipment Scholarships (Undergraduate/Scholarship) [1123]

Connecticut Building Congress Scholarships (Undergraduate/Scholarship) [4420]

Roy Cooper Scholarships (Undergraduate/Scholarship) [5397]

Richard P. Covert, Ph.D./FHIMSS Scholarships for Management Systems (Graduate, Postgraduate, Undergraduate/Scholarship) [4504]

Robert E. Cramer Scholarships (Graduate, Undergraduate/Scholarship) [8445]

Critical Language Scholarships for Intensive Summer Institutes (Graduate, Undergraduate/Scholarship) [1145]

CSX Scholarships (Undergraduate/Scholarship) [1124]

John J. Cunningham Memorial Scholarships (Undergraduate/Scholarship) [1125]

Jason Dahnert Memorial Scholarships (Graduate, Undergraduate/Scholarship) [3863]

Robert G. Daily Scholarships (Graduate, Undergraduate/Scholarship) [8446]

D&A Florida Scholarships (Undergraduate/Scholarship) [8597]

Disabled War Veterans Scholarships (Undergraduate/Scholarship) [1559]

Document Management and Graphic Communications Industry Scholarships (Undergraduate/Scholarship) [3627]

Robert E. Dougherty Scholarships (Undergraduate/Scholarship) [3209]

EAPSI Fellowships (Doctorate, Graduate/Fellowship) [6467]

John R. Eidson Jr., Scholarships (Undergraduate/Scholarship) [2946]

Engineering Departmental Scholarships (Undergraduate/Scholarship) [9352]

Engineering Diversity Affairs Scholarships (All/Scholarship) [9353]

Engineers for Tomorrow Scholarship Program (Undergraduate/Scholarship) [5915]

Harold E. Ennes Scholarships (Graduate, Professional development/Scholarship) [8303]

Alaska Community Foundation Sven E. & Lorraine Eriksson Scholarships (Undergraduate/Scholarship) [9092]

Larry L. Etherton Scholarships (Graduate, Undergraduate/Scholarship) [1126]

AIST Benjamin F. Fairless Scholarships, American Institute of Mining, Metallurgical and Petroleum Engineers (AIME) (Undergraduate/Scholarship) [1803]

Fecon Scholarships (Undergraduate/Scholarship) [3825]

Lt. Colonel Romeo and Josephine Bass Ferretti Scholarships (Undergraduate/Scholarship) [92]

FICE Scholarships (Undergraduate/Scholarship) [3826]

Herb and Anne Fincher Memorial Scholarships (Undergraduate/Scholarship) [3057]

Reuben H. Fleet Memorial Scholarships (Undergraduate/Scholarship) [7929]

Fleming/Blaszcak Scholarships (Graduate, Undergraduate/Scholarship) [8447]

Grant H. Flint International Scholarships - Category II (Undergraduate/Scholarship) [8525]

Florida Education Fund McKnight Doctoral Fellowships (Graduate/Fellowship) [3822]

Florida Engineering Society Junior College Scholarships (Undergraduate/Scholarship) [3827]

Florida Engineering Society University Scholarships (Undergraduate/Scholarship) [3828]

Frank Fong Scholarships (Undergraduate/Scholarship) [8290]

Henry Ford Academy Scholarships (Undergraduate/Scholarship) [8384]

Michael W. and Jean D. Franke Family Foundation Scholarships (Graduate, Undergraduate/Scholarship) [1127]

Richard Gregory Freeland, II Educational Scholarships (High School/Scholarship) [2147]

Fuchs-Harden Educational Scholarships Fund (Undergraduate/Scholarship) [4337]

Future Leaders of Manufacturing Scholarships (Graduate, Undergraduate/Scholarship) [8385]

Michael and Gina Garcia Rail Engineering Scholarships (Undergraduate/Scholarship) [1129]

The Gates Millennium Scholars (Undergraduate/Scholarship) [4569]

Gauthier Family Scholarship Fund (Undergraduate/Scholarship) [4217]

Generation III Scholarships (Undergraduate/Scholarship) [3586]

Georgia Engineering Foundation Scholarships (Graduate/Scholarship) [4102]

Harold Giles Scholarships (Graduate, Undergraduate/Scholarship) [8448]

Midwest Chapter Scholarships - Jack Gill (Undergraduate/Scholarship) [1804]

Benjamin A. Gilman International Scholarships (Undergraduate/Scholarship) [9096]

Glendale Latino Association Scholarships (High School, Undergraduate/Scholarship) [4161]

Northeastern Ohio Chapter Scholarships - Alfred B. Glossbrenner and John Klusch Scholarships (Undergraduate/Scholarship) [1806]

Dr. Robert H. Goddard Memorial Scholarships (Graduate, Undergraduate/Scholarship) [6523]

William R. Goldfarb Memorial Scholarships (Undergraduate/Scholarship) [1085]

Barry M. Goldwater Scholarships (Undergraduate/Scholarship) [9357]

ACI W.R. Grace Scholarships (Graduate/Scholarship) [634]

Graduate Fellowship Program - Mahboob Khan/Advanced Micro Devices Fellowships (GFP) (Doctorate, Graduate/Fellowship) [8079]

Graduate Fellowship Program - Research Fellow-

ships (GFP) (Doctorate, Graduate/Fellowship) [8080]

GREAT MINDS Collegiate Scholarship Program (Undergraduate/Scholarship) [340]

Great Minds in STEM Scholarships (Graduate, Undergraduate/Scholarship) [4331]

Robert D. Greenberg Scholarships (Graduate, Professional development/Scholarship) [8304]

Gulf Coast Hurricane Scholarships (Graduate, Undergraduate/Scholarship) [8449]

Jerome Hake Engineering Scholarships (Graduate, Undergraduate/Scholarship) [3864]

Hamilton Industrial Environmental Association Bursaries-Mohawk College (Undergraduate/Scholarship) [4367]

Duane Hanson Scholarships (Undergraduate/Scholarship) [1267]

Claude B. Hart Memorial Scholarships (Undergraduate/Scholarship) [9641]

Helm Family Scholarships (Undergraduate/Scholarship) [7932]

Hertz Foundation's Graduate Fellowships (Doctorate/Fellowship) [6074]

The Homeland Security Undergraduate Scholarships (Undergraduate/Scholarship) [9039]

Jane Hood Memorial Fund (Undergraduate/Scholarship) [3776]

HSF/Nissan Community College Transfer Scholarship Program (Undergraduate/Scholarship) [4576]

IDA Fellowship Awards (Professional development/Fellowship) [4919]

Informatics Circle of Research Excellence Scholarships (Doctorate, Graduate/Scholarship) [248]

Injection Molding Division Scholarships (Graduate, Undergraduate/Scholarship) [8450]

ISPE Advantage Award/Foundation Scholarships (Undergraduate/Scholarship) [4691]

ITEEA FTE Scholarships (Undergraduate/Scholarship) [5010]

ITEEA Greer/FTE Grants (Professional development/Grant) [5011]

ITEEA Litherland/FTE Scholarships (Undergraduate/Scholarship) [5012]

Nancy Lorraine Jensen Memorial Scholarships (Undergraduate/Scholarship) [8531]

Joseph C. Johnson Memorial Grants (Undergraduate/Scholarship) [1191]

Robert C. and Judith L. Knapp Scholarships (Graduate, Undergraduate/Scholarship) [3867]

AIST Willy Korf Memorial Fund (Undergraduate/Scholarship) [1807]

Lamar University College of Engineering Scholarships (Undergraduate/Scholarship) [6257]

Laser Technology, Engineering and Applications Scholarships (Graduate, Undergraduate/Scholarship) [8639]

Harold Leeming Memorial Scholarships (Undergraduate/Scholarship) [7663]

Gerald J. Levandoski Memorial Scholarship Fund (Undergraduate/Scholarship) [3779]

Erwin Lew Memorial Scholarships (Graduate, Undergraduate/Scholarship) [8451]

Lewis-Clark State College Presidential Technical Out-of-State Scholarships (Undergraduate/Scholarship) [5447]

Dolores Zohrab Liebmann Fund - Graduate School Fellowships (Graduate/Fellowship) [5488]

AIST Ronald E. Lincoln Memorial Scholarships (Undergraduate/Scholarship) [1808]

David C. Lizarraga Graduate Fellowships (Graduate, Master's/Fellowship) [8821]

David F. Ludovici Scholarships (Undergraduate/Scholarship) [3829]

Robert Mack Scholarships (Graduate, Undergraduate/Scholarship) [5556]

CEMF Claudette MacKay-Lassonde Graduate Scholarships (Doctorate, Postdoctorate/Scholarship) [2456]

Thermoset Division/James I. Mackenzie and James H. Cunningham Scholarships (Graduate, Undergraduate/Scholarship) [8452]

MAES Founders Scholarships (Graduate, Undergraduate/Scholarship) [5798]

MAES General Scholarships (Graduate, Undergraduate/Scholarship) [5799]

MAES Graduate Scholarships *(Graduate/Scholarship)* [5800]

MAES Padrino/Madrina Scholarships *(Graduate, Undergraduate/Scholarship)* [5801]

MAES Pipeline Scholarships *(Graduate, Undergraduate/Scholarship)* [5802]

MAES Presidential Scholarships *(Graduate, Undergraduate/Scholarship)* [5803]

Malayalee Engineers Association Scholarships *(Graduate/Fellowship)* [5601]

Maley/FTE Scholarships *(Graduate/Scholarship)* [5013]

Marine Corps Engineer Association Assistance Fund *(Graduate, High School, Undergraduate/Scholarship)* [5635]

Lockheed Martin Graduate Scholarships *(Graduate/Scholarship)* [1560]

Lockheed Martin IT Scholarships *(Undergraduate/Scholarship)* [1561]

Mas Family Scholarships *(Graduate, Undergraduate/Scholarship)* [5658]

Master's Scholarships Program (MSP) *(Graduate, Master's/Scholarship)* [8081]

Katharine & Bryant Mather Scholarships *(Graduate/Scholarship)* [635]

Midwest Chapter Scholarships - Betty McKern *(Undergraduate/Scholarship)* [1809]

Charles McMahon Memorial Construction Management/Engineering Scholarship Awards *(Undergraduate/Scholarship)* [1632]

Kumar Mehta Scholarships *(Graduate/Scholarship)* [636]

MESBEC Scholarships *(Undergraduate/Scholarship)* [2662]

Bernard Michel Scholarships *(Undergraduate/Scholarship)* [2348]

Michigan Society of Professional Engineers Scholarships *(Undergraduate/Scholarship)* [5829]

Michigan Tech Alumni Scholarships *(Graduate, Undergraduate/Scholarship)* [1130]

John G. and Betty J. Mick Scholarship Fund *(Undergraduate/Scholarship)* [8691]

Midwest Chapter Scholarships - Engineering *(Undergraduate/Scholarship)* [1810]

Midwest Chapter Scholarships - Western States Awards *(Undergraduate/Scholarship)* [1812]

Raymond W. Miller, PE and Alice E. Miller Scholarships *(Undergraduate, Graduate/Scholarship)* [3830]

Raymond W. Miller, PE Scholarships *(Undergraduate/Scholarship)* [3831]

Ralph Modjeski Scholarships *(Graduate, Undergraduate/Scholarship)* [7369]

Montana Broadcasters Association Engineers' Scholarships *(Undergraduate/Scholarship)* [5924]

Robert E. and Judy More Scholarship Fund *(Undergraduate/Scholarship)* [3784]

NAAF Post-Secondary Education Scholarships *(Graduate, Undergraduate/Scholarship)* [5993]

National Association of Multicultural Engineering Program Advocates Beginning Freshmen Awards (NAMEPA) *(Undergraduate/Scholarship)* [6088]

National Association of Multicultural Engineering Program Advocates Transfer Engineering Student Awards (NAMEPA) *(Undergraduate/Scholarship)* [6089]

The National Board Technical Scholarships *(Undergraduate/Scholarship)* [6159]

National Co-op Scholarship Program *(Undergraduate/Scholarship)* [9750]

National GEM Consortium - MS Engineering Fellowships *(Graduate/Fellowship)* [6305]

National GEM Consortium - PhD Engineering Fellowships *(Doctorate, Graduate/Fellowship)* [6306]

National Security Technology Engineering and Science Scholarships *(Undergraduate/Scholarship)* [7510]

Midwest Chapter Scholarships - Don Nelson *(Undergraduate/Scholarship)* [1813]

Ted and Ruth Neward Scholarships *(Graduate, Undergraduate/Scholarship)* [8453]

Edsel Newman Scholarships *(Undergraduate/Scholarship)* [5476]

Alwin B. Newton Scholarships *(Undergraduate/Scholarship)* [1268]

Donald E. Nichols Scholarships *(Undergraduate/Scholarship)* [1269]

Midwest Chapter Scholarships - Mel Nickel *(Undergraduate/Scholarship)* [1814]

Nixon Family Scholarship Fund *(Undergraduate/Scholarship)* [9556]

Stuart L. Noderer Memorial Scholarships *(Undergraduate/Scholarship)* [7949]

Norfolk Southern Foundation Scholarships *(Undergraduate/Scholarship)* [1131]

Nortel Institute Undergraduate Scholarships *(Undergraduate/Scholarship)* [9340]

Robert Noyce Scholarship Program *(Undergraduate/Scholarship)* [7160]

Nuts, Bolts and Thingamajigs Scholarships *(Undergraduate, Vocational/Occupational/Scholarship)* [6842]

Ocean Industries Student Research Awards *(Undergraduate, Graduate/Award)* [7736]

Ohio Space Grant Consortium Graduate Fellowships *(Doctorate, Graduate/Fellowship)* [6864]

Ohio Space Grant Consortium Special Minority Fellowships *(Doctorate, Graduate/Fellowship)* [6865]

Ohio Valley Chapter Scholarships *(Undergraduate/Scholarship)* [1815]

Patricia & Armen Oumedian Scholarships *(Undergraduate/Scholarship)* [4296]

AFCEA General Emmett Paige Scholarships *(Undergraduate/Scholarship)* [1562]

Joseph M. Parish Memorial Grants *(Undergraduate/Scholarship)* [1192]

PB Rail Engineering Scholarships *(Undergraduate/Scholarship)* [1132]

Pennsylvania Society of Professional Engineers Scholarships *(Undergraduate/Scholarship)* [7156]

William Pigott Memorial Scholarships *(Undergraduate/Scholarship)* [3164]

Pitsco/Hearlihy/FTE Grants *(Professional development/Grant)* [5014]

Plastics Pioneers Association Scholarships *(Graduate, Undergraduate/Scholarship)* [8454]

Polymer Modifiers and Additives Division Scholarships *(Graduate, Undergraduate/Scholarship)* [8455]

Eric Primavera Memorial Scholarships *(Undergraduate/Scholarship)* [3832]

Josef Princ Memorial Scholarships *(Undergraduate/Scholarship)* [7517]

Graduate Fellowship Program - GRC/John L. Prince Fellowships (GFP) *(Graduate/Fellowship)* [8082]

Purdue Krannert School of Management SHPE Scholarships *(Undergraduate, Master's/Scholarship)* [8130]

REMSA Scholarships *(Undergraduate/Scholarship)* [1133]

Howard Brown Rickard Scholarships *(Undergraduate/Scholarship)* [6282]

RA Consulting Service/Maria Riley Scholarships *(Graduate, Undergraduate/Scholarship)* [6297]

Rocky Mountain Coal Mining Institute Engineering/Geology Scholarships *(Undergraduate/Scholarship)* [7810]

Barnes W. Rose, Jr. and Eva Rose Nichol Scholarship Fund *(Undergraduate/Scholarship)* [282]

Paul and Ellen Ruckes Scholarships *(Graduate, Undergraduate/Scholarship)* [753]

AIST David H. Samson Scholarships *(Undergraduate/Scholarship)* [1816]

Saskatchewan Government Insurance Graduate Student Traffic Safety Research Scholarhips *(Graduate/Scholarship)* [7999]

Saskatchewan Pulse Growers Undergraduate Scholarships *(Undergraduate/Scholarship)* [8004]

Kurt H. and Donna M. Schuler Cash Grants *(Undergraduate/Scholarship)* [1193]

AIST William E. Schwabe Memorial Scholarships *(Undergraduate/Scholarship)* [1817]

NASCAR/Wendell Scott Awards *(Graduate, Undergraduate/Scholarship)* [4550]

SDF Community College Transfer Scholarships for Math and Science *(Undergraduate/Scholarship)* [7964]

John M. and Mary A. Shanley Memorial Scholarships *(Undergraduate/Scholarship)* [8622]

Dr. Robert and Anna Shaw Scholarships *(Undergraduate/Scholarship)* [267]

Shell Incentive Scholarship Fund *(Undergraduate/Scholarship)* [8103]

Shell Process Technology Scholarships *(Undergraduate/Scholarship)* [8104]

Shell Technical Scholarships *(Undergraduate/Scholarship)* [8105]

Marion A. and Ruth K. Sherwood Family Fund Engineering Scholarships *(Undergraduate/Scholarship)* [4244]

SHPE Foundation Dissertation Scholarships *(Doctorate/Scholarship)* [8131]

SHPE Foundation General Scholarships *(High School, Undergraduate, Graduate/Scholarship)* [8132]

SHPE Foundation Northrop Grumman Scholarships *(Undergraduate/Scholarship)* [8133]

SHPE Foundation Professional Scholarships *(Master's, Doctorate/Scholarship)* [8134]

SMART Scholarships *(Graduate, Undergraduate/Scholarship)* [8056]

Society of Manufacturing Engineers Ford PAS Scholarships (SME) *(Undergraduate/Scholarship)* [8401]

Society of Plastics Engineers General Scholarships *(Graduate, Undergraduate/Scholarship)* [8456]

Society of Plastics Engineers Pittsburgh Section Scholarships *(Graduate, Undergraduate/Scholarship)* [8457]

Society of Women Engineers Scholarships *(Undergraduate/Scholarship)* [8516]

Sons of Norway Foundation Scholarships to Oslo International School *(Undergraduate/Scholarship)* [8532]

Soroptimist International of Redlands Scholarships *(Undergraduate/Scholarship)* [7715]

Southeast Member Chapter Scholarships *(Undergraduate/Scholarship)* [1818]

SPEATBC Scholarships *(Undergraduate/Scholarship)* [8482]

SREB-State Doctoral Scholarships *(Doctorate, Graduate/Scholarship)* [8585]

Robert P. Stearns/SCS Engineers Scholarships *(Graduate/Scholarship)* [8526]

StraightForward Media's Engineering Scholarships *(Undergraduate/Scholarship)* [8758]

Sturgulewski Family Scholarships *(Graduate, Undergraduate, Vocational/Occupational/Scholarship)* [9113]

Graduate Fellowship Program - GRC/Al Tasch Fellowships (GFP) *(Graduate/Fellowship)* [8083]

Texas Society of Professional Engineers Scholarships *(Undergraduate/Scholarship)* [8872]

Anil and Neema Thakrar Family Fund *(Undergraduate/Scholarship)* [3963]

Thermoforming Division Memorial Scholarships *(Graduate, Undergraduate/Scholarship)* [8458]

Thermoplastic Materials and Foams Division Scholarships *(Graduate, Undergraduate/Scholarship)* [8459]

Thermoplastics Elastomers Special Interest Group Scholarships *(Graduate, Undergraduate/Scholarship)* [8460]

Thompson Scholarships for Women in Safety *(Graduate/Scholarship)* [1355]

Toronto Rehabilitation Institute Graduate Student Scholarships - Ontario Student Opportunities Trust Fund (OSOTF) *(Graduate/Scholarship)* [8919]

Toyota/TELACU Scholarships *(Undergraduate/Scholarship)* [8822]

Reuben Trane Scholarships *(Undergraduate/Scholarship)* [1270]

Vice Adm. Jerry O. Tuttle, USN (Ret.) and Mrs. Barbara A. Tuttle Science and Technology Scholarships *(Undergraduate/Scholarship)* [1564]

UAA Quanterra Scholarships *(Undergraduate/Scholarship)* [9125]

United Engineering Foundation Grants *(All/Grant)* [9009]

U.S. Air Force ROTC Express Scholarships *(Undergraduate/Scholarship)* [9027]

University of Toronto Accenture Scholarships *(Undergraduate/Scholarship)* [9344]

Vale Inco Limited Masters Scholarships *(Graduate/Scholarship)* [2457]

VEF Fellowship Program *(Doctorate, Master's/Fellowship)* [9424]

VEF Visiting Scholars Program *(Doctorate/Scholarship)* [9425]

Veolia ES Waste-to-Energy/Terrence L. Guest Memorial Awards (Graduate/Scholarship) [8527]
Dimitri J. Ververelli Memorial Scholarships (Undergraduate/Scholarship) [4520]
Veterans of Enduring Freedom (Afghanistan) and Iraqi Freedom Scholarships (Undergraduate/Scholarship) [1565]
Vinyl Plastics Division Scholarships (Graduate, Undergraduate/Scholarship) [8461]
Gary Wagner, K3OMI Scholarships (Undergraduate/Scholarship) [1111]
Washington University Law School Chancellor's Graduate Fellowships (Graduate/Fellowship) [9532]
Washington University Law School Olin Fellowships for Women (Graduate/Fellowship) [9533]
Allen and Loureena Weber Scholarships (Undergraduate/Scholarship) [8404]
ACI Bertold E. Weinberg Scholarships (Graduate/Scholarship) [638]
William E. Weisel Scholarships (Undergraduate/Scholarship) [8405]
AFCEA General John A. Wickham Scholarships (Undergraduate/Scholarship) [1566]
Ted C. Wilson Memorial Scholarships (Undergraduate/Scholarship) [7441]
Marine Corps Sgt. Jeannette L. Winters Memorial Scholarships (Undergraduate/Scholarship) [1567]
Women In Defense HORIZONS Scholarships (Graduate, Undergraduate/Scholarship) [9696]
Women in Science and Technology Scholarships (Doctorate, Graduate, Master's, Undergraduate/Scholarship) [9442]
Yasme Foundation Scholarships (Undergraduate/Scholarship) [1115]
Ralph Yetka Memorial Scholarships (Undergraduate/Scholarship) [9181]

Engineering, Aerospace/Aeronautical/Astronautical

DEPS Graduate Scholarship Program (Graduate/Scholarship) [3455]
Amelia Earhart Fellowship Program (Postdoctorate/Fellowship) [9811]
NDSEG Fellowships (Graduate/Fellowship) [6239]
Science Foundation Arizona Graduate Research Fellowships (GRF) (Graduate/Fellowship) [8054]

Engineering, Agricultural

NPC Scholarships (Graduate/Scholarship) [6442]

Engineering, Architectural

AISC/Great Lakes Fabricators and Erectors Association Fellowships (Graduate/Fellowship) [871]
AISC/Rocky Mountain Steel Construction Association Fellowships (Graduate/Fellowship) [872]
AISC/Southern Association of Steel Fabricators Fellowships (Graduate/Fellowship) [873]
AISC/Southern Association of Steel Fabricators Scholarships (Undergraduate/Scholarship) [874]
AISC/Structural Steel Education Council Fellowships (Graduate/Fellowship) [875]
AISC/US Steel Fellowships (Graduate/Fellowship) [876]
Michael Baker Inc. Scholarships for Diversity in Engineering (Undergraduate/Scholarship) [1794]
Carpenters' Company Scholarships (Undergraduate/Scholarship) [2657]
Edilia and Francois Auguste de Montequin Fellowships (Doctorate/Fellowship) [8295]
Janusz & Roma Drzymala Scholarships (Undergraduate/Scholarship) [7760]
AISC/Fred R. Havens Fellowships (Graduate, Undergraduate/Fellowship) [877]
HDR Engineering, Inc. Scholarships for Diversity in Engineering (Undergraduate/Scholarship) [1796]
PCH Architects/Steven J. Lehnhof Memorial Architectural Scholarships (Undergraduate/Scholarship) [7665]
J.W. "Bill" Neese Scholarships (Undergraduate/Scholarship) [4900]
Snodgrass Scholarships (Undergraduate/Scholarship) [9175]

Structural Engineering Travel Fellowships (Doctorate, Graduate, Undergraduate/Fellowship) [8232]
William J. Tangye Scholarships (Undergraduate/Scholarship) [4902]

Engineering, Automotive

Larry H. Averill Memorial Scholarships (Undergraduate/Scholarship) [1937]
Harold Dieckmann Draper, Sr. Scholarships (Undergraduate/Scholarship) [1938]
John E. Echlin Memorial Scholarships (Undergraduate/Scholarship) [1939]
Carlyle Fraser/Wilton Looney Scholarships (Undergraduate/Scholarship) [1940]
John Goerlich Memorial Scholarships (Undergraduate/Scholarship) [1941]
Charles V. Hagler Scholarships (Undergraduate/Scholarship) [1942]
Zenon C.R. Hansen Memorial Scholarships (Undergraduate/Scholarship) [1943]
John W. Koons, Sr. Memorial Scholarships (Undergraduate/Scholarship) [1944]
Ken Krum/Bud Kouts Memorial Scholarships (Undergraduate/Scholarship) [1945]
Brouwer D. McIntyre Memorial Scholarships (Undergraduate/Scholarship) [1946]
Jim Moran Scholarships (Undergraduate/Scholarship) [1947]
Dorothy M. Ross Memorial Scholarships (Undergraduate/Scholarship) [1948]
Stuart H. Snyder Memorial Scholarships (Undergraduate/Scholarship) [1949]
Walter W. Stillman Scholarships (Undergraduate/Scholarship) [1950]
TRW Foundation Scholarships (Undergraduate/Scholarship) [1951]
J. Irving Whalley Memorial Scholarships (Undergraduate/Scholarship) [1952]
M.H. Yager Memorial Scholarships (Undergraduate/Scholarship) [1953]

Engineering, Biomedical

Biocom Scholarships (Undergraduate/Scholarship) [7913]
DOE Computational Science Graduate Fellowships (DOE CSGF) (Doctorate, Graduate/Fellowship) [5306]
Toyota High School Scholarship Program (Undergraduate/Scholarship) [4581]
Women in Science and Technology Scholarships (Doctorate, Graduate, Master's, Undergraduate/Scholarship) [9442]

Engineering, Chemical

SEE Education Foundation Scholarships (Doctorate, Graduate, Undergraduate/Scholarship) [4992]
ACI BASF Construction Chemicals Student Fellowships (Graduate, Undergraduate/Fellowship) [628]
AESF Foundation Scholarships (Graduate, Undergraduate/Scholarship) [6127]
Air Products and Chemicals, Inc. Scholarships (Undergraduate/Scholarship) [1793]
APS/ASU Scholarships (Undergraduate/Scholarship) [7332]
APS/Maricopa County Community Colleges Scholarships (Undergraduate/Scholarship) [7333]
Canadian Technical Asphalt Association Scholarships (Undergraduate/Scholarship) [2624]
DEPS Graduate Scholarship Program (Graduate/Scholarship) [3455]
Dow Chemical Company Fellowships (Graduate/Fellowship) [6427]
E.I. DuPont Fellowships (Graduate/Fellowship) [6428]
Marathon Oil Corporation College Scholarship Program (Graduate, Undergraduate/Scholarship) [4578]
John J. McKetta Undergraduate Scholarships (Undergraduate/Scholarship) [846]
Dolphus E. Milligan Graduate Fellowships (Graduate/Fellowship) [6429]
Minority Scholarship Awards for College Students (Undergraduate/Scholarship) [847]

Minority Scholarship Awards for Incoming College Freshmen (Undergraduate/Scholarship) [848]
NDSEG Fellowships (Graduate/Fellowship) [6239]
NOBCChE Procter and Gamble Fellowships (Graduate/Fellowship) [6430]
Nonproliferation Graduate Fellowships Program (NGFP) (Graduate/Fellowship) [7033]
NPSC Fellowships (Graduate/Fellowship) [6440]
AIChE/Donald F. and Mildred Topp Othmer National Scholarship Awards (Undergraduate/Scholarship) [849]
Rubber Division American Chemical Society Undergraduate Scholarships (Undergraduate/Scholarship) [7829]
Ralph W. Shrader Diversity Scholarships (Graduate/Scholarship) [1563]
Eastman Kodak Dr. Theophilus Sorrell Fellowships (Graduate/Fellowship) [6432]
Evald Torokvei Foundation Scholarships (Graduate/Scholarship) [9343]
Toyota High School Scholarship Program (Undergraduate/Scholarship) [4581]
Xerox Technical Minority Scholarships (Graduate, Undergraduate/Scholarship) [9787]

Engineering, Civil

AGC New York State Chapter Scholarship Program (Undergraduate/Scholarship) [1677]
AHETEMS/ExxonMobil Scholarships (Undergraduate/Scholarship) [54]
AISC/Rocky Mountain Steel Construction Association Fellowships (Graduate/Fellowship) [872]
AISC/Southern Association of Steel Fabricators Fellowships (Graduate/Fellowship) [873]
AISC/Southern Association of Steel Fabricators Scholarships (Undergraduate/Scholarship) [874]
AISC/Structural Steel Education Council Fellowships (Graduate/Fellowship) [875]
AISC/US Steel Fellowships (Graduate/Fellowship) [876]
Amos Joe Alter ASCE Section Alaska Section Scholarships (Undergraduate/Scholarship) [9136]
Arsham Amirikian Engineering Scholarships (Undergraduate/Scholarship) [1429]
APS/ASU Scholarships (Undergraduate/Scholarship) [7332]
APS/Maricopa County Community Colleges Scholarships (Undergraduate/Scholarship) [7333]
APWA Engineering Scholarships (Undergraduate/Scholarship) [1059]
Associated General Contractors of Connecticut Scholarships (Undergraduate/Scholarship) [3235]
Association of State Dam Safety Officials Undergraduate Scholarships (Undergraduate/Scholarship) [1877]
Michael Baker Inc. Scholarships for Diversity in Engineering (Undergraduate/Scholarship) [1794]
ACI Baker Student Fellowships (Undergraduate/Fellowship) [632]
Canadian Technical Asphalt Association Scholarships (Undergraduate/Scholarship) [2624]
Warren E. "Whitey" Cole American Society of Highway Engineers Scholarships (Undergraduate/Scholarship) [3764]
AISC/Fred R. Havens Fellowships (Graduate, Undergraduate/Fellowship) [877]
HDR Engineering, Inc. Scholarships for Diversity in Engineering (Undergraduate/Scholarship) [1796]
HSF/Wal-Mart Stores Inc. Scholarship Program (Graduate, Undergraduate/Scholarship) [4577]
International Association of Foundation Drilling Scholarships for Civil Engineering Students (Postgraduate/Scholarship) [1756]
International Association of Foundation Drilling Scholarships for Part-time Civil Engineering Graduate School Students (Postgraduate/Scholarship) [1757]
MALSCE Scholarships (Undergraduate/Scholarship) [5660]
Marathon Oil Corporation College Scholarship Program (Graduate, Undergraduate/Scholarship) [4578]
NDSEG Fellowships (Graduate/Fellowship) [6239]
Pardee Community Building Scholarships (Undergraduate/Scholarship) [7515]

Galvanize the Future: Edgar K. Schutz Scholarships *(Graduate, Undergraduate/Prize, Scholarship)* [774]

SHPE Foundation Verizon Scholarships *(Undergraduate/Scholarship)* [8135]

Charles Smith Memorial Scholarship Awards *(Undergraduate/Scholarship)* [1633]

Structural Engineering Travel Fellowships *(Doctorate, Graduate, Undergraduate/Fellowship)* [8232]

TAC Foundation-Armtec Scholarships *(Undergraduate/Scholarship)* [8933]

Toyota High School Scholarship Program *(Undergraduate/Scholarship)* [4581]

Larry Wilson Scholarships for Undergraduate Civil Engineering Students *(Undergraduate/Scholarship)* [1539]

WRI Education Foundation Scholarships - Graduate *(Graduate/Scholarship)* [9670]

WRI Education Foundation Scholarships - High School Seniors *(Undergraduate/Scholarship)* [9671]

WRI Education Foundation Scholarships - Undergraduate *(Undergraduate/Scholarship)* [9672]

Engineering, Computer

AISES Intel Scholarships *(Graduate, Undergraduate/Scholarship)* [832]

Zachary Barriger Memorial Scholarships *(Undergraduate/Scholarship)* [2935]

Dr. Anita Borg Memorial Scholarships - USA *(Graduate, Undergraduate/Scholarship)* [4193]

Chambersburg/Fannett-Metal School District Scholarship Fund *(Undergraduate/Scholarship)* [3937]

Google-American Indian Science and Engineering Society Scholarships *(Graduate, Undergraduate/Scholarship)* [4194]

Google Hispanic College Fund Scholarships *(Graduate, Undergraduate/Scholarship)* [4195]

HSBC-North America Scholarship Program *(Undergraduate/Scholarship)* [4571]

NVIDIA Graduate Fellowships *(Doctorate/Fellowship)* [6844]

SHPE Foundation Verizon Scholarships *(Undergraduate/Scholarship)* [8135]

Toyota High School Scholarship Program *(Undergraduate/Scholarship)* [4581]

Xerox Technical Minority Scholarships *(Graduate, Undergraduate/Scholarship)* [9787]

Engineering, Electrical

AHETEMS/ExxonMobil Scholarships *(Undergraduate/Scholarship)* [54]

AISES Intel Scholarships *(Graduate, Undergraduate/Scholarship)* [832]

APS/ASU Scholarships *(Undergraduate/Scholarship)* [7332]

APS/Maricopa County Community Colleges Scholarships *(Undergraduate/Scholarship)* [7333]

Zachary Barriger Memorial Scholarships *(Undergraduate/Scholarship)* [2935]

Chrysler Foundation Scholarship Awards *(Undergraduate/Scholarship)* [4546]

DEPS Graduate Scholarship Program *(Graduate/Scholarship)* [3455]

DOE Computational Science Graduate Fellowships (DOE CSGF) *(Doctorate, Graduate/Fellowship)* [5306]

Belknap Freeman Carnegie Mellon Scholarships *(Undergraduate/Scholarship)* [1128]

Perry F. Hadlock Memorial Scholarships *(Undergraduate/Scholarship)* [1089]

HSF/General Motors Scholarship Program *(Undergraduate/Scholarship)* [4574]

HSF/Wal-Mart Stores Inc. Scholarship Program *(Graduate, Undergraduate/Scholarship)* [4577]

Julia Kiene Fellowships in Electrical Energy *(Graduate/Fellowship)* [9723]

Louis T. Klauder Scholarships *(Graduate, Undergraduate/Scholarship)* [1054]

League of Latin American Citizens General Electric Scholarships *(Undergraduate, Vocational/Occupational/Scholarship)* [5386]

Imelda and Ralph LeMar Scholarship Program *(Undergraduate/Scholarship)* [3201]

Lyle Mamer Fellowships *(Graduate/Fellowship)* [9724]

Marathon Oil Corporation College Scholarship Program *(Graduate, Undergraduate/Scholarship)* [4578]

Edmond A. Metzger Scholarships *(Undergraduate/Scholarship)* [1094]

Microsoft Research Graduate Women's Scholarships *(Graduate/Scholarship)* [5844]

Microsoft Research PhD Fellowships *(Doctorate/Fellowship)* [5845]

MillerCoors Engineering and Sciences Scholarships *(Undergraduate/Scholarship)* [47]

NASA Aeronautics Scholarships - Undergraduate Program *(Undergraduate/Scholarship)* [1241]

NDSEG Fellowships *(Graduate/Fellowship)* [6239]

NPSC Fellowships *(Graduate/Fellowship)* [6440]

NVIDIA Graduate Fellowships *(Doctorate/Fellowship)* [6844]

Ralph W. Shrader Diversity Scholarships *(Graduate/Scholarship)* [1563]

Xerox Technical Minority Scholarships *(Graduate, Undergraduate/Scholarship)* [9787]

Engineering, Geological

CCV Foundation Graduate and Undergraduate Fellowships *(Doctorate, Graduate, Undergraduate/Fellowship)* [2672]

HDR Engineering, Inc. Scholarships for Diversity in Engineering *(Undergraduate/Scholarship)* [1796]

Marliave Scholarship Fund *(Undergraduate/Scholarship)* [1768]

Rocky Mountain Coal Mining Institute Engineering/Geology Scholarships *(Undergraduate/Scholarship)* [7810]

Martin L. Stout Scholarships *(Undergraduate/Scholarship)* [1769]

Engineering, Hydraulic

Channabasappa Memorial Scholarships *(Graduate, Professional development/Scholarship)* [4918]

IDA Fellowship Awards *(Professional development/Fellowship)* [4919]

Engineering, Industrial

Chapter 17 - St. Louis Scholarships *(Undergraduate/Scholarship)* [8372]

Chapter 31 - Peoria Endowed Scholarships *(Undergraduate/Scholarship)* [8375]

Chapter 52 - Wichita Scholarships *(Graduate, Undergraduate/Scholarship)* [8377]

Chapter 56 - Fort Wayne Scholarships *(Graduate, Undergraduate/Scholarship)* [8378]

Chapter 67 - Phoenix Scholarships *(Undergraduate/Scholarship)* [8380]

Chapter 198 - Downriver Detroit Scholarships *(Graduate, Undergraduate/Scholarship)* [8373]

Chapter 311 - Tri City Scholarships *(Undergraduate/Scholarship)* [8376]

John S.W. Fargher Scholarships *(Graduate/Scholarship)* [4800]

Future Leaders of Manufacturing Scholarships *(Graduate, Undergraduate/Scholarship)* [8385]

Dwight D. Gardner Scholarships *(Undergraduate/Scholarship)* [4801]

Gilbreth Memorial Fellowships *(Graduate/Scholarship)* [4802]

HSF/General Motors Scholarship Program *(Undergraduate/Scholarship)* [4574]

HSF/Wal-Mart Stores Inc. Scholarship Program *(Graduate, Undergraduate/Scholarship)* [4577]

IIE Council of Fellows Undergraduate Scholarships *(Undergraduate/Scholarship)* [4803]

John L. Imhoff Scholarships *(Graduate, Undergraduate/Scholarship)* [4804]

Harold and Inge Marcus Scholarships *(Undergraduate/Scholarship)* [4805]

Marvin Mundel Memorial Scholarships *(Undergraduate/Scholarship)* [4806]

Clarence and Josephine Myers Scholarships *(Graduate, Undergraduate/Scholarship)* [8394]

North Central, Region 9 Scholarships *(Undergraduate/Scholarship)* [8395]

Presidents Scholarships *(Undergraduate/Scholarship)* [4807]

A.O. Putnam Memorial Scholarships *(Undergraduate/Scholarship)* [4808]

Tom D. Ralls Memorial Scholarships *(Professional development/Scholarship)* [3849]

Steven M. Teutsch Prevention Effectiveness Fellowships *(Doctorate/Fellowship)* [2715]

United Parcel Service Scholarships for Female Students *(Undergraduate/Scholarship)* [4810]

United Parcel Service Scholarships for Minority Students *(Undergraduate/Scholarship)* [4811]

Chapter 4 - Lawrence A. Wacker Memorial Awards *(Undergraduate/Scholarship)* [8402]

Allen and Loureena Weber Scholarships *(Undergraduate/Scholarship)* [8404]

Lisa Zaken Awards For Excellence *(Graduate, Undergraduate/Award)* [4812]

Engineering, Marine

Marine Technology Society Student Scholarships for Two-year Technical, Engineering and Community College Students *(Community College, Two Year College, Undergraduate/Scholarship)* [5642]

Mandell and Lester Rosenblatt and Robert N. Herbert Undergraduate Scholarships *(Undergraduate/Scholarship)* [8417]

Society of Naval Architects and Marine Engineers Undergraduate Scholarships *(Undergraduate/Scholarship)* [8418]

SUT Houston Graduate Scholarships *(Graduate/Scholarship)* [8508]

SUT Houston Undergraduate Scholarships *(Undergraduate/Scholarship)* [8509]

Engineering, Materials

Electronics Division Lewis C. Hoffman Scholarships *(Undergraduate/Scholarship)* [606]

NDSEG Fellowships *(Graduate/Fellowship)* [6239]

Galvanize the Future: Edgar K. Schutz Scholarships *(Graduate, Undergraduate/Prize, Scholarship)* [774]

ACI Richard N. White Student Fellowships *(Master's/Fellowship)* [639]

Engineering, Mechanical

AESF Foundation Scholarships *(Graduate, Undergraduate/Scholarship)* [6127]

AHETEMS/ExxonMobil Scholarships *(Undergraduate/Scholarship)* [54]

Air Products and Chemicals, Inc. Scholarships *(Undergraduate/Scholarship)* [1793]

APS/ASU Scholarships *(Undergraduate/Scholarship)* [7332]

APS/Maricopa County Community Colleges Scholarships *(Undergraduate/Scholarship)* [7333]

Association of Desk and Derrick Clubs Education Trust Scholarships *(Undergraduate/Scholarship)* [1749]

Auxiliary Undergraduate Scholarships *(Graduate, High School, Undergraduate/Scholarship)* [1659]

Chapter 198 - Downriver Detroit Scholarships *(Graduate, Undergraduate/Scholarship)* [8373]

Chrysler Foundation Scholarship Awards *(Undergraduate/Scholarship)* [4546]

Lucy and Charles W.E. Clarke Scholarships *(Undergraduate/Scholarship)* [1660]

DOE Computational Science Graduate Fellowships (DOE CSGF) *(Doctorate, Graduate/Fellowship)* [5306]

HSF/General Motors Scholarship Program *(Undergraduate/Scholarship)* [4574]

Louis T. Klauder Scholarships *(Graduate, Undergraduate/Scholarship)* [1054]

Imelda and Ralph LeMar Scholarship Program *(Undergraduate/Scholarship)* [3201]

Marathon Oil Corporation College Scholarship Program *(Graduate, Undergraduate/Scholarship)* [4578]

MillerCoors Engineering and Sciences Scholarships *(Undergraduate/Scholarship)* [47]

Clarence and Josephine Myers Scholarships *(Graduate, Undergraduate/Scholarship)* [8394]

NASA Aeronautics Scholarships - Undergraduate

Program *(Undergraduate/Scholarship)* [1241]

North Central, Region 9 Scholarships *(Undergraduate/Scholarship)* [8395]

NPSC Fellowships *(Graduate/Fellowship)* [6440]

Elizabeth M. and Winchell M. Parson Scholarships *(Doctorate/Scholarship)* [1661]

Rice-Cullimore Scholarships *(Graduate/Scholarship)* [1662]

Marjorie Roy Rothermel Scholarships *(Graduate/Scholarship)* [1663]

Rubber Division American Chemical Society Undergraduate Scholarships *(Undergraduate/Scholarship)* [7829]

Chapter 4 - Lawrence A. Wacker Memorial Awards *(Undergraduate/Scholarship)* [8402]

Allen and Loureena Weber Scholarships *(Undergraduate/Scholarship)* [8404]

Albert E. Wischmeyer Memorial Scholarships *(Undergraduate/Scholarship)* [8406]

Xerox Technical Minority Scholarships *(Graduate, Undergraduate/Scholarship)* [9787]

Engineering, Metallurgical

AESF Foundation Scholarships *(Graduate, Undergraduate/Scholarship)* [6127]

Engineering, Mining and Mineral

Samuel C. Kraus, Jr. Memorial Scholarships *(Undergraduate/Scholarship)* [6534]

SME Coal and Energy Division Scholarships *(Undergraduate/Scholarship)* [8414]

SME Environmental Division Scholarships *(Undergraduate/Scholarship)* [8415]

Engineering, Naval

American Society of Naval Engineers Scholarships (ASNE) *(Graduate, Undergraduate/Scholarship)* [1309]

Engineering, Nuclear

SEE Education Foundation Scholarships *(Doctorate, Graduate, Undergraduate/Scholarship)* [4992]

American Nuclear Society Incoming Freshman Scholarships *(Undergraduate/Scholarship)* [948]

American Nuclear Society Nevada Section Scholarships *(Undergraduate/Scholarship)* [7466]

American Nuclear Society Undergraduates Scholarships *(Undergraduate/Scholarship)* [949]

Association of Desk and Derrick Clubs Education Trust Scholarships *(Undergraduate/Scholarship)* [1749]

DOE Computational Science Graduate Fellowships (DOE CSGF) *(Doctorate, Graduate/Fellowship)* [5306]

Engineering, Ocean

NDSEG Fellowships *(Graduate/Fellowship)* [6239]

Mandell and Lester Rosenblatt and Robert N. Herbert Undergraduate Scholarships *(Undergraduate/Scholarship)* [8417]

Society of Naval Architects and Marine Engineers Undergraduate Scholarships *(Undergraduate/Scholarship)* [8418]

Engineering, Optical

BACUS Scholarships *(Graduate, Undergraduate/Scholarship)* [8637]

IS&T Raymond Davis Scholarships *(Graduate, Undergraduate/Scholarship)* [8352]

DEPS Graduate Scholarship Program *(Graduate/Scholarship)* [3455]

Robert S. Hilbert Memorial Student Travel Grants *(Graduate, Undergraduate/Grant)* [6911]

Michael Kidger Memorial Scholarships in Optical Design *(Graduate/Scholarship)* [8638]

D.J. Lovell Scholarships *(Graduate, Undergraduate/Scholarship)* [8640]

Optical Design and Engineering Scholarships *(Graduate, Undergraduate/Scholarship)* [8641]

Student Travel Grants *(Graduate, Undergraduate/Grant)* [8642]

Xerox Technical Minority Scholarships *(Graduate, Undergraduate/Scholarship)* [9787]

Engineering, Petroleum

AHETEMS/ExxonMobil Scholarships *(Undergraduate/Scholarship)* [54]

Alaska Support Industry Alliance Scholarships *(Undergraduate/Scholarship)* [9133]

Association of Desk and Derrick Clubs Education Trust Scholarships *(Undergraduate/Scholarship)* [1749]

CADE Bursary *(Undergraduate/Scholarship)* [2374]

CADE Scholarships *(Undergraduate/Scholarship)* [2375]

Marathon Oil Corporation College Scholarship Program *(Graduate, Undergraduate/Scholarship)* [4578]

Petroleum Engineering Scholarships *(Graduate, Undergraduate/Scholarship)* [8436]

English language and literature (See also Linguistics; Literature)

Dick Depaolis Memorial Scholarships *(Undergraduate/Scholarship)* [3196]

Indiana State Alumni Association Creative and Performing Arts Awards *(Undergraduate/Scholarship)* [4745]

NCTE Research Foundation Grants *(Professional development/Grant)* [6218]

NEMLA Book Prize *(Professional development/Prize)* [6798]

Susan P. Schroeder Memorial Scholarships *(Undergraduate/Scholarship)* [5464]

Swensrud Teacher Fellowships at MHS (Massachusetts Historical Society) *(Professional development/Fellowship)* [5679]

Edwyna Wheadon Postgraduate Training Scholarship Fund *(Professional development/Scholarship)* [6219]

Enology

American Wine Society Educational Foundation Scholarships *(Graduate/Scholarship)* [1450]

Nancy Johnston Memorial Scholarships *(Graduate, Undergraduate/Scholarship)* [8837]

Entomology

American Association of Professional Apiculturists Research Scholarships *(Graduate, Undergraduate/Scholarship)* [541]

Stan Beck Fellowships *(Graduate, Undergraduate/Fellowship)* [3652]

Nancy Johnston Memorial Scholarships *(Graduate, Undergraduate/Scholarship)* [8837]

Louisiana Agricultural Consultants Association Scholarships *(Graduate, Undergraduate/Scholarship)* [5517]

North Carolina Commercial Flower Growers Association Floriculture Scholarships *(Graduate, Undergraduate/Scholarship)* [6757]

Environmental conservation

Bat Conservation International Student Research Scholarships *(Graduate, Undergraduate/Scholarship)* [2028]

VPPPA Stephen Brown Scholarships *(Graduate, Undergraduate/Scholarship)* [9474]

Antenore C. "Butch" Davanzo Scholarships *(Graduate, Undergraduate/Scholarship)* [5840]

Delta/VPPPA Safety, Health and Environmental Scholarships *(Undergraduate, Vocational/Occupational, Graduate/Scholarship)* [9475]

Grand Canyon Historical Society Scholarships *(Graduate/Scholarship)* [4205]

John P. Hennessey Scholarships *(Graduate, Undergraduate/Scholarship)* [5841]

NGC College Scholarships *(Graduate, Undergraduate/Scholarship)* [6303]

VPPPA William Sullivan Scholarships *(Graduate, Undergraduate/Scholarship)* [9476]

Switzer Environmental Fellowships *(Graduate/Fellowship)* [8787]

VPPPA June Brothers Scholarships *(Graduate, Undergraduate/Scholarship)* [9477]

Jack H. Wagner Scholarships *(Graduate, Undergraduate/Scholarship)* [5842]

Frederick K. Weyerhaeuser Forest History Fellowships *(Graduate/Fellowship)* [3860]

Environmental design

Worldstudio AIGA Scholarships *(Graduate, Undergraduate/Scholarship)* [9761]

Environmental law

A&WMA Scholarships *(Graduate/Scholarship)* [107]

The Lela Breitbart Memorial Scholarship Fund *(All/Scholarship)* [8892]

EMLF Law Student Scholarships *(Undergraduate/Scholarship)* [3643]

Property and Environment Research Center Graduate Fellowships *(Graduate/Fellowship)* [7452]

SSAWMA Scholarships *(Graduate/Scholarship)* [120]

Switzer Environmental Fellowships *(Graduate/Fellowship)* [8787]

Environmental science (See also Ecology)

A&WMA-GWS Scholarships *(Graduate, Undergraduate/Scholarship)* [111]

A&WMA NCNJ Chapter Scholarships *(Graduate, Undergraduate/Scholarship)* [118]

Anchor Environmental Scholarships *(Graduate/Scholarship)* [1471]

Avista Corporation Minds in Motion Scholarships *(Undergraduate/Scholarship)* [5412]

J.P. Bickell Mining Scholarships *(Undergraduate/Scholarship)* [9322]

Carol Bond Community College Scholarships *(Undergraduate/Scholarship)* [6748]

Carol Bond Environmental Educator Scholarships *(Professional development/Scholarship)* [6749]

Carol Bond University Scholarships *(Undergraduate/Scholarship)* [6750]

Bridgestone Americas Fellowships *(Graduate/Fellowship)* [9414]

Rachel Carson Prize *(Professional development/Prize)* [1246]

CFERP Masters Fellowships *(Graduate/Fellowship)* [3030]

Chopivsky Fellowships *(Graduate/Scholarship)* [9498]

Community-based Natural Resource Management Assistantships *(All/Internship)* [3031]

CTFS Research Grants Program *(Graduate, Postdoctorate, Professional development/Grant)* [8268]

Cushing Academy Fellowships on Environmental History *(Graduate, Doctorate/Fellowship)* [5669]

Frank L. Dautriel Memorial Scholarships for Graduates *(Graduate/Scholarship)* [5519]

Frank L. Dautriel Memorial Scholarships for Undergraduates *(Undergraduate/Scholarship)* [5520]

DOE Computational Science Graduate Fellowships (DOE CSGF) *(Doctorate, Graduate/Fellowship)* [5306]

EMLF Law Student Scholarships *(Undergraduate/Scholarship)* [3643]

Environmental History of Quebec Scholarships *(Postdoctorate, Postgraduate/Scholarship)* [6617]

Grant H. Flint International Scholarships - Category II *(Undergraduate/Scholarship)* [8525]

GFLC-A&WMA Scholarships *(Graduate, Undergraduate/Scholarship)* [109]

Greater Research Opportunities Undergraduate Fellowships (GRO) *(Undergraduate/Fellowship)* [9041]

Samuel P. Hays Research Fellowships *(Professional development/Fellowship)* [1248]

Marjorie M. Hendricks Environmental Education

Scholarship Fund (Undergraduate/Scholarship) [4221]

Gus and Henrietta Hill Scholarships (Undergraduate/Scholarship) [3532]

Dannie Jasmine Scholarships (Undergraduate/Scholarship) [5944]

N.G. Kaul Memorial Scholarships (Doctorate, Graduate/Scholarship) [6687]

Legacy Inc. College Undergraduate and Graduate Scholarships (Graduate, Undergraduate/Scholarship) [5400]

George Perkins Marsh Prize (Professional development/Prize) [1249]

Randall Matthis for Environmental Studies Scholarships (Graduate, Undergraduate/Scholarship) [1537]

Ben Meadows Natural Resource Scholarships - Academic Achievement Scholarships (Undergraduate/Scholarship) [2054]

Ben Meadows Natural Resource Scholarships - Leadership Scholarships (Undergraduate/Scholarship) [2055]

National Environmental Health Association Scholarship Fund (Graduate, Undergraduate/Scholarship) [6269]

New York Water Environment Association Scholarships (Undergraduate/Scholarship) [6688]

Eric Niemitalo Scholarships in Earth and Environmental Science (Undergraduate/Scholarship) [8121]

A. Stanley Rand Fellowships Program (Undergraduate, Doctorate, Postdoctorate/Fellowship) [8270]

Republic Services Environmental Studies Scholarships (Undergraduate/Scholarship) [7521]

Hal Rothman Dissertation Fellowships (Doctorate/Fellowship) [1252]

Royal Palm Audubon Society Environmental Fellowships (Postgraduate/Fellowship) [3820]

Science to Achieve Results Fellowships (STAR) (Graduate/Fellowship) [9042]

Miller G. Sherwood Family Scholarship Fund (Undergraduate/Scholarship) [4245]

Robert P. Stearns/SCS Engineers Scholarships (Graduate/Scholarship) [8526]

Switzer Environmental Fellowships (Graduate/Fellowship) [8787]

Judith A. Towle Environmental Studies Fund (Undergraduate/Fellowship) [5082]

Udall Scholarships (Undergraduate/Scholarship) [9197]

Veolia ES Waste-to-Energy/Terrence L. Guest Memorial Awards (Graduate/Scholarship) [8527]

WALPA Lake Scholarships (Graduate, Undergraduate/Scholarship) [9526]

Larry Wilson for Environmental Studies Scholarships (Graduate, Undergraduate/Scholarship) [1538]

Mary and Elliot Wood Foundation Graduate Scholarship Fund (Graduate/Scholarship) [3930]

Environmental technology

A&WMA NCNJ Chapter Scholarships (Graduate, Undergraduate/Scholarship) [118]

AESF Foundation Scholarships (Graduate, Undergraduate/Scholarship) [6127]

Alberta Innovates Graduate Student Scholarship (Graduate/Scholarship) [234]

Arkansas Society of Professional Sanitarians Scholarships (Undergraduate/Scholarship) [1547]

Jim Bourque Scholarships (Postgraduate, Undergraduate/Scholarship) [1501]

Frank L. Dautriel Memorial Scholarships for Graduates (Graduate/Scholarship) [5519]

Frank L. Dautriel Memorial Scholarships for Undergraduates (Undergraduate/Scholarship) [5520]

Charles and Margaret Foster Scholarships (Undergraduate/Scholarship) [8602]

Hamilton Industrial Environmental Association Bursaries-Mohawk College (Undergraduate/Scholarship) [4367]

Hampton Roads Sanitation District Environmental Scholarships (Graduate/Scholarship) [4375]

Switzer Environmental Fellowships (Graduate/Fellowship) [8787]

Thompson Scholarships for Women in Safety

(Graduate/Scholarship) [1355]

Morris K. Udall Scholarships (Undergraduate/Scholarship) [8991]

Epidemiology (See also Infectious diseases)

Alex's Lemonade Stand Foundation Epidemiology Grants (Doctorate, Professional development/Grant) [292]

OHTN Postdoctoral Fellowships (Doctorate/Fellowship) [6893]

Epilepsy

Behavioral Sciences Post-Doctoral Fellowships (Postdoctorate/Fellowship) [3660]

Behavioral Sciences Student Fellowships (Graduate, Undergraduate/Fellowship) [3661]

Epilepsy Foundation Post-doctoral Research Fellowships (Postdoctorate, Professional development/Fellowship) [3662]

Epilepsy Foundation Pre-doctoral Research Training Fellowships (Graduate/Grant) [3663]

Epilepsy Foundation Research Grants (All/Grant) [3664]

Epilepsy Foundation Research and Training Fellowships for Clinicians (Doctorate, Professional development/Grant) [3665]

Health Sciences Student Fellowships (Doctorate, Graduate/Fellowship) [3666]

Robert S. Morison Fellowships (Doctorate, Graduate/Fellowship) [720]

Partnership for Pediatric Epilepsy Research (Doctorate/Grant) [3667]

Savoy Foundation Postdoctoral and Clinical Research Fellowships (Postdoctorate/Fellowship) [8012]

Targeted Research Initiative for Health Outcomes (Doctorate/Grant) [3668]

Targeted Research Initiative for Mood Disorders (Doctorate/Grant) [3669]

Targeted Research Initiative for Seniors (Doctorate/Grant) [3670]

Equine studies

Alabama Horse Council Scholarships (Undergraduate/Scholarship) [175]

Ethics and bioethics

ARRS/Leonard Berlin Scholarships in Medical Professionalism (Professional development/Scholarship) [1160]

Ethnography

Conservation Department Program Fellowships (Graduate/Fellowship) [8258]

European studies (See also Central European studies; East European studies)

CES Conference Travel Grants (Graduate, Professional development/Grant) [3274]

CES Dissertation Completion Fellowships (Graduate/Fellowship) [3275]

CES Pre-Dissertation Research Fellowships (Graduate/Fellowship) [3276]

Dissertation Fellowships in East European Studies (Doctorate/Fellowship) [677]

Early Career Postdoctoral Fellowships in East European Studies (Postdoctorate/Fellowship) [678]

Educational and Cultural Affairs Alumni Small Grants Program (ECA) (Professional development/Grant) [4980]

First Article Prize (Professional development/Prize) [3277]

Dr. Guido Goldman Fellowships (Doctorate, Postdoctorate/Fellowship) [666]

Individual Advanced Research Opportunities Program For Master's Students (IARO) (Graduate/Grant) [4981]

Individual Advanced Research Opportunities Program For Pre-doctoral Students (IARO) (Postgraduate/Grant) [4982]

Individual Advanced Research Opportunities Program For Professionals (IARO) (Professional development/Grant) [4983]

Individual Advanced Research Opportunities Program for Postdoctoral Scholars (IARO) (Postdoctorate/Grant) [4984]

Kade-Heideking Fellowships (Doctorate/Fellowship) [4128]

Kress Curatorial Fellowships (Doctorate/Fellowship) [5309]

Kress Fellowships in Art History at Foreign Institutions (Doctorate/Fellowship) [5310]

Kress Travel Fellowships in the History of Art (Doctorate/Fellowship) [5311]

McGill University Scholarships for Research Trips to Europe (Graduate/Scholarship) [5725]

NEH Fellowships for Senior Scholars (Doctorate/Fellowship) [2695]

Prins Foundation Fellowship for Senior Scholars (Doctorate/Fellowship) [2696]

Prins Foundation Post-Doctoral and Early Career Fellowship for Emigrating Scholars (Professional development, Postdoctorate/Fellowship) [2697]

Thyssen-Heideking Fellowships (Postdoctorate/Fellowship) [4129]

Family planning

Geraldine Clewell Fellowships - Doctoral Student (Graduate/Fellowship) [7280]

Geraldine Clewell Fellowships - Masteral (Graduate/Fellowship) [7281]

Geraldine Clewell Scholarships - Undergraduate (Undergraduate/Scholarship) [7282]

Closs/Parnitzke/Clarke Scholarships (Undergraduate/Scholarship) [7283]

Jean Dearth Dickerscheid Fellowships (Graduate/Fellowship) [7284]

Margaret Drew Alpha Fellowships (Graduate/Fellowship) [7285]

Lydia Fohn-Hansen/Lola Hill Memorial Scholarships (Undergraduate/Scholarship) [9149]

Genevieve Forthun Scholarships (Undergraduate/Scholarship) [7286]

Mary Weiking Franken Scholarships (Undergraduate/Scholarship) [7287]

Tommie J. Hamner Scholarships (Undergraduate/Scholarship) [7288]

Phyllis P. Harris Scholarships (Postgraduate/Award) [2463]

Jackman Scholarships (Undergraduate/Scholarship) [7289]

Martha Combs Jenkins Scholarships (Undergraduate/Scholarship) [7290]

Treva C. Kintner Scholarships (Undergraduate/Scholarship) [7291]

Phi Upsilon Omicron Candle Fellowships (Graduate/Fellowship) [7292]

Phi Upsilon Omicron Challenge Scholarships (Undergraduate/Scholarship) [7293]

Phi Upsilon Omicron Diamond Anniversary Fellowships (Graduate/Fellowship) [7294]

Phi Upsilon Omicron Founders Fellowships (Graduate/Fellowship) [7295]

Phi Upsilon Omicron Golden Anniversary Scholarships (Undergraduate/Scholarship) [7296]

Phi Upsilon Omicron Past Presidents Scholarships (Undergraduate/Scholarship) [7297]

Phi Upsilon Omicron Presidents Research Fellowships (Graduate/Fellowship) [7298]

Nell Bryant Robinson Scholarships (Undergraduate/Scholarship) [7299]

Lucile Rust Scholarships (Undergraduate/Scholarship) [7300]

Margaret Jerome Sampson Scholarships (Undergraduate/Scholarship) [7301]

Lillian P. Schoephoerster Scholarships (Undergraduate/Scholarship) [7302]

SFP Junior Investigator's Career Development Awards (Professional development/Grant) [8322]

SFP Mid-Career/Mentor Awards for Family Planning (Professional development/Grant) [8323]

SFP Student and Resident Research Grants (Graduate/Grant) [8324]

Family/Marital therapy

AAMFT Minority Fellowships (Doctorate, Graduate/ Fellowship) [511]

Fashion design

Paul Arnold Memorial Scholarships (Undergraduate/ Scholarship) [7396]

Bridging the GAP for Hispanic Success Awards (Undergraduate/Scholarship) [4545]

California Association of Family and Consumer Sciences -San Diego Chapter Scholarships (CAFCS) (Graduate, Undergraduate, Vocational/Occupational/Scholarship) [7917]

S. Penny Chappell Scholarships (Undergraduate/ Scholarship) [7279]

Edith Head Scholarships (Undergraduate/Scholarship) [3411]

HSF/Wal-Mart Stores Inc. Scholarship Program (Graduate, Undergraduate/Scholarship) [4577]

Casey Sakir Point Scholarships (Graduate, Undergraduate/Scholarship) [7366]

Sutherland/Purdy Scholarships (Undergraduate/ Scholarship) [7303]

Women's Jewelry Association Member Grants (All/ Grant) [9726]

Worldstudio AIGA Scholarships (Graduate, Undergraduate/Scholarship) [9761]

Filmmaking (See also Media arts)

AAS Fellowships for Creative and Performing Artists and Writers (All/Fellowship) [412]

Anne Friedberg Innovative Scholarship Awards (Professional development/Scholarship) [8309]

Film and Video Arts Project Grants (Professional development/Grant) [219]

Steve Kaplan TV and Film Studies Scholarships (Professional development/Scholarship) [1212]

MANAA Media Scholarships (Graduate, Undergraduate/Scholarship) [5737]

McNamara Family Creative Arts Project Grants (Graduate, Undergraduate/Grant) [4579]

Scott Pearlman Field Awards for Science and Exploration (Professional development/Award) [3698]

Fred Rogers Memorial Scholarships (Graduate, Undergraduate/Scholarship) [35]

David Rose Scholarships (Undergraduate/Scholarship) [1215]

SCMS Dissertation Awards (Postdoctorate/Award) [8311]

SCMS Student Writing Awards (Graduate/Award) [8312]

SFFS Education Colleges & Universities Scholarship Program (Undergraduate, Graduate/Scholarship) [7980]

Worldstudio AIGA Scholarships (Graduate, Undergraduate/Scholarship) [9761]

Finance (See also Accounting; Banking)

Herb Adrian Memorial Scholarship Fund (Undergraduate/Scholarship) [3881]

African American Network - Carolinas Scholarship Fund (Undergraduate/Scholarship) [3882]

ALPFA Scholarship Programs (Postgraduate, Undergraduate/Scholarship) [1824]

American Society of Military Comptrollers National Scholarship Program (Undergraduate/Scholarship) [1305]

APS/ASU Scholarships (Undergraduate/Scholarship) [7332]

APS/Maricopa County Community Colleges Scholarships (Undergraduate/Scholarship) [7333]

ASCEND/ING Scholarships (Undergraduate/Scholarship) [1635]

Association of College and University Auditors Scholarships (Graduate, Undergraduate/Scholarship) [1742]

ASWA 2-Year College Scholarships (Undergraduate/ Scholarship) [1374]

ASWA Undergraduate Scholarships (Undergraduate/ Scholarship) [1375]

Bank of Canada Governor's Awards (Doctorate, Professional development/Award) [2012]

Sharon D. Banks Undergraduate Memorial Scholarships (Undergraduate/Scholarship) [9739]

Stuart Cameron and Margaret McLeod Memorial Scholarships (SCMS) (Graduate, Undergraduate/ Scholarship loan) [4814]

Chrysler Foundation Scholarship Awards (Undergraduate/Scholarship) [4546]

Clark High School Academy of Finance Scholarships (Undergraduate/Scholarship) [7476]

Clark High School Alumni Leadership Circle Scholarships (Undergraduate/Scholarship) [7477]

Ernst and Young/Ascend Leadership Scholarship Program (Undergraduate/Scholarship) [1636]

Daniel B. Goldberg Scholarships (Graduate/Scholarship) [4197]

Frank L. Greathouse Government Accounting Scholarships (Graduate, Undergraduate/Scholarship) [4198]

Hilb, Rogal and Hobbs Scholarships (Undergraduate/Scholarship) [9449]

HSBC-North America Scholarship Program (Undergraduate/Scholarship) [4571]

HSF/Citi Fellows Program (Undergraduate/Scholarship) [4573]

HSF/General Motors Scholarship Program (Undergraduate/Scholarship) [4574]

HSF/Wal-Mart Stores Inc. Scholarship Program (Graduate, Undergraduate/Scholarship) [4577]

IMA Memorial Education Fund Scholarships (MEF) (Graduate, Undergraduate/Scholarship loan) [4815]

Robert A. Kleckner Scholarships (Undergraduate/ Scholarship) [8612]

Ann Koby Legacy Scholarships (Undergraduate/ Scholarship) [9740]

Douglas McRorie Memorial Scholarships (Postgraduate/Scholarship) [75]

Minorities in Government Finance Scholarships (Graduate, Undergraduate/Scholarship) [4199]

Robert E. and Judy More Scholarship Fund (Undergraduate/Scholarship) [3784]

NABA National Scholarship Program (Graduate, Undergraduate/Scholarship) [6037]

Networks Scholarships College of Business (Undergraduate/Scholarship) [4750]

New York Financial Writers' Associations Scholarships (Graduate, Undergraduate/Scholarship) [6667]

George A. Nielsen Public Investor Scholarships (Graduate, Undergraduate/Scholarship) [4200]

Norfolk Southern Scholarships (Undergraduate/ Scholarship) [9450]

Helene M. Overly Memorial Scholarships (Undergraduate/Scholarship) [9741]

Public Employee Retirement Research and Administration Scholarships (Graduate/Scholarship) [4201]

Dr. Felix H. Reyler Memorial Scholarships (Undergraduate/Scholarship) [3319]

South Carolina Association for Financial Professionals Certified Treasury Professional Scholarships (Professional development/Scholarship) [8544]

South Carolina Association for Financial Professionals College Education Scholarships (Undergraduate/Scholarship) [8545]

Surety Industry Scholarship Program for Minority Students (Undergraduate/Scholarship) [8778]

Robert Toigo Foundation Fellowships (Master's/Fellowship) [8911]

Tribal Business Management Program Scholarships (TBM) (Undergraduate/Scholarship) [2664]

Urban Financial Services Coalition Scholarships (Undergraduate/Scholarship) [2129]

Wachovia Scholars Program (Undergraduate/Scholarship) [4551]

Wells Fargo American Indian Scholarships - Graduate (Graduate/Scholarship) [828]

Wells Fargo Scholarship Program (Graduate, Undergraduate/Scholarship) [4585]

Fine arts (See Art)

Finnish studies (See Area and ethnic studies)

Fires and fire prevention

Randall Brown and Associates Awards (Postgraduate/Award) [2468]

Fire Safety Awards (Postgraduate/Award) [2469]

International Association of Wildland Fire Graduate-Level Scholarships (Doctorate, Graduate/Scholarship) [4880]

Junior Firefighter Scholarships (Undergraduate/ Scholarship) [6555]

Leber Rubes Inc. Awards (Postgraduate/Award) [2470]

Joseph C. Menezes Scholarships (Undergraduate/ Scholarship) [5571]

Nadine International Inc. Awards (Postgraduate/ Award) [2471]

Rachael Patterson Memorial Scholarships (Undergraduate/Scholarship) [8987]

Snodgrass Scholarships (Undergraduate/Scholarship) [9175]

Thompson Scholarships for Women in Safety (Graduate/Scholarship) [1355]

Underwriters' Laboratories of Canada Awards (Postgraduate/Award) [2472]

John Charles Wilson Scholarships (Undergraduate/ Scholarship) [4856]

Fisheries sciences/management

Anchor Environmental Scholarships (Graduate/ Scholarship) [1471]

Norman S. Baldwin Fishery Science Scholarships (Doctorate, Graduate/Scholarship) [4868]

Ted Bjornn University of Idaho Graduate Student Scholarships (Graduate/Scholarship) [4661]

Ted Bjornn University of Idaho Undergraduate Student Scholarships (Undergraduate/Scholarship) [4662]

Jack B. Fisher Scholarship Fund (Undergraduate/ Scholarship) [8665]

B. Harper Bull Conservation Fellowships (Graduate/ Fellowship) [8913]

ICAFS Idaho Graduate Student Scholarships (Graduate/Scholarship) [4663]

ICAFS Idaho High School Student Scholarships (Undergraduate/Scholarship) [4664]

ICAFS Idaho Undergraduate Student Scholarships (Undergraduate/Scholarship) [4665]

Susan B. Martin Memorial Scholarships (Graduate/ Scholarship) [4666]

Ben Meadows Natural Resource Scholarships - Academic Achievement Scholarships (Undergraduate/Scholarship) [2054]

Ben Meadows Natural Resource Scholarships - Leadership Scholarships (Undergraduate/Scholarship) [2055]

Barbara H. Mullin Memorial Scholarships (Graduate, Undergraduate/Scholarship) [9573]

Ronald L. Schmied Scholarships (Professional development, Undergraduate/Scholarship) [4362]

West Coast Sea Grant Fellowships (Graduate/Fellowship) [2279]

Floriculture

NGC College Scholarships (Graduate, Undergraduate/Scholarship) [6303]

Joseph Shinoda Memorial Scholarships (Undergraduate/Scholarship) [8109]

Folklore

Muddy Waters Scholarships (Undergraduate/Scholarship) [2155]

Food science and technology

AACT Undergraduate Scholarships (Undergraduate/ Scholarship) [7153]

American Association of Cereal Chemists Graduate Fellowships *(Graduate/Fellowship)* [455]

Margaret J. Andrew Memorial Scholarships *(Undergraduate/Scholarship)* [8156]

California Association of Family and Consumer Sciences -San Diego Chapter Scholarships (CAFCS) *(Graduate, Undergraduate, Vocational/Occupational/Scholarship)* [7917]

Career Development Scholarships *(Postdoctorate, Postgraduate/Scholarship)* [3855]

Carleton A. Friday Memorial Scholarships *(Undergraduate/Scholarship)* [5867]

Institute of Food Technologists Graduate Scholarships *(Graduate/Scholarship)* [4791]

Institute of Food Technologists Junior/Senior Scholarships *(Undergraduate/Scholarship)* [4792]

Institute of Food Technologists Sophomore Scholarships *(Undergraduate/Scholarship)* [4793]

International Foodservice Editorial Council Scholarships *(Graduate, Undergraduate/Scholarship)* [4935]

Les Dames D'Escoffier New York Scholarships *(Undergraduate/Scholarship)* [5405]

Maine Nutrition Council Scholarships *(Undergraduate/Scholarship)* [5599]

E.H. Marth Food and Environmental Scholarships *(Undergraduate/Scholarship)* [9674]

National Poultry and Food Distributors Association Scholarships *(Undergraduate/Scholarship)* [6444]

PMCA Graduate Fellowships for Confectionery Research at Pennsylvania State University *(Graduate/Fellowship)* [7154]

Stark County Dairy Promoters Scholarships *(Undergraduate/Scholarship)* [8701]

John D. Utterback Scholarship Program *(Undergraduate/Scholarship)* [324]

Kenneth G. Weckel Scholarships *(Undergraduate/Scholarship)* [5868]

Food service careers

Harvey and Laura Alpert Scholarship Awards *(Undergraduate/Scholarship)* [4929]

California Association of Family and Consumer Sciences -San Diego Chapter Scholarships (CAFCS) *(Graduate, Undergraduate, Vocational/Occupational/Scholarship)* [7917]

Career Development Scholarships *(Postdoctorate, Postgraduate/Scholarship)* [3855]

Letitia B. Carter Scholarships *(All/Scholarship)* [7745]

Nancy Curry Scholarships *(Postgraduate, Vocational/Occupational/Scholarship)* [8028]

GED Jump Start Scholarships *(Undergraduate/Scholarship)* [8029]

Marcia S. Harris Legacy Fund Scholarships *(Undergraduate/Scholarship)* [7746]

Hospitality Food Service Scholarships *(Undergraduate/Scholarship)* [6621]

IFSEA Worthy Goal Scholarships *(Four Year College, Two Year College, Undergraduate, Vocational/Occupational/Scholarship)* [4933]

International Dairy-Deli-Bakery Association Undergraduate Scholarships *(Graduate, Undergraduate/Scholarship)* [4916]

International Foodservice Editorial Council Scholarships *(Graduate, Undergraduate/Scholarship)* [4935]

Oklahoma Restaurant Association Scholarships *(Graduate, Undergraduate/Scholarship)* [6871]

RAMEF Co-Branded Scholarships for High School Seniors *(Undergraduate/Scholarship)* [7747]

Al Schuman Ecolab Undergraduate Entrepreneurial Scholarships *(Undergraduate/Scholarship)* [6463]

Schwan's Food Service Scholarships *(Undergraduate, Vocational/Occupational/Scholarship)* [8030]

Jeff Siegel Scholarships *(Undergraduate/Scholarship)* [6669]

SNF Professional Growth Scholarships *(Graduate, Undergraduate/Scholarship)* [8031]

UAA Wells Fargo Career Scholarships *(Graduate/Scholarship)* [9127]

Winston Scholarships *(Graduate, Undergraduate, Vocational/Occupational/Scholarship)* [8032]

Foreign languages

Pete and Ellen Bensley Memorial Scholarship Fund *(Undergraduate/Scholarship)* [3886]

National Security Education Program - David L. Boren Fellowships *(Undergraduate/Fellowship)* [9204]

Palo Verde High School - Barbara Edwards Memorial Scholarships *(Undergraduate/Scholarship)* [7485]

Fellowships for Intensive Advanced Turkish Language Study in Turkey *(Graduate, Undergraduate/Fellowship)* [1148]

German Society Scholarships *(Undergraduate/Scholarship)* [4137]

Michael J. Hogan Fellowships *(Graduate/Fellowship)* [8340]

ISCALC International Scholarship Fund *(Undergraduate/Scholarship)* [3777]

Italian Language Scholarships *(Undergraduate/Scholarship)* [6922]

Louise Nader Khourey/Kappa Delta Pi Scholarships *(Undergraduate/Scholarship)* [8681]

Kor Memorial Scholarships *(Graduate, Undergraduate/Scholarship)* [5270]

Language Teacher Bursary Program Awards *(Professional development/Award)* [253]

Languages In Teacher Education Scholarships *(Undergraduate/Scholarship)* [254]

MACC Scholarships *(Professional development/Scholarship)* [5796]

Mead Leadership Fellows Program *(Professional development/Fellowship)* [6796]

Thomas R. Pickering Graduate Foreign Affairs Fellowships *(Graduate/Fellowship)* [9619]

Richard J. Schmeelk Fellowships *(Graduate/Fellowship)* [8020]

Starr Foundation Graduate Fellowships in Asian Studies *(Graduate/Grant)* [9205]

Audrey L. Wright Scholarships *(Undergraduate/Scholarship)* [4309]

Forestry

CFERP Masters Fellowships *(Graduate/Fellowship)* [3030]

Chopivsky Fellowships *(Graduate/Scholarship)* [9498]

Tommy Crabb Scholarship Fund *(Undergraduate/Scholarship)* [4480]

Robert E. Dougherty Scholarships *(Undergraduate/Scholarship)* [3209]

James L. and Genevieve H. Goodwin Scholarships *(Undergraduate/Scholarship)* [4433]

B. Harper Bull Conservation Fellowships *(Graduate/Fellowship)* [8913]

Ben Meadows Natural Resource Scholarships - Academic Achievement Scholarships *(Undergraduate/Scholarship)* [2054]

Ben Meadows Natural Resource Scholarships - Leadership Scholarships *(Undergraduate/Scholarship)* [2055]

NGC College Scholarships *(Graduate, Undergraduate/Scholarship)* [6303]

NTHA College Forest Resources Scholarships *(Undergraduate/Scholarship)* [6807]

Dr. Harry V. Pfautz Memorial Scholarship Fund *(Undergraduate/Scholarship)* [3955]

Ina E. Powell Memorial Scholarships *(Undergraduate/Scholarship)* [179]

Frederick K. Weyerhaeuser Forest History Fellowships *(Graduate/Fellowship)* [3860]

WFI International Fellowships *(Undergraduate/Fellowship)* [9754]

French studies (See also Area and ethnic studies)

Alliance Francaise of Hartford Harpin/Rohinsky Scholarships *(Undergraduate/Scholarship)* [4406]

Fellowships for Full-time Studies in French *(Undergraduate/Fellowship)* [245]

Walter J. Jensen Fellowships *(Professional development/Fellowship)* [7248]

Mary Isabel Sibley Fellowships *(Doctorate/Fellowship)* [7249]

Funeral services (See also Mortuary science)

ABFSE National Scholarship Program *(Undergraduate/Scholarship)* [584]

NFDA Professional Women's Conference Scholarships *(Undergraduate/Scholarship)* [4031]

Gaming industry

Wells Fargo American Indian Scholarships - Graduate *(Graduate/Scholarship)* [828]

Gemology

Michael Beaudry Scholarships *(Undergraduate/Scholarship)* [4054]

ColorMasters Scholarships *(Undergraduate/Scholarship)* [4055]

GIA Endowment Scholarships - Distance Education *(Graduate/Scholarship)* [4056]

GIA Endowment Scholarships - On Campus *(Graduate/Scholarship)* [4057]

William Goldberg Diamond Corp. Scholarships *(Undergraduate/Scholarship)* [4058]

Marion H. Halfacre Scholarships *(Graduate/Scholarship)* [4059]

Morris Hanauer Scholarships *(Undergraduate/Scholarship)* [4060]

George W. Juno Memorial Scholarships *(Graduate/Scholarship)* [4062]

Richard T. Liddicoat Scholarships *(Graduate/Scholarship)* [4063]

Mikimoto Scholarships *(Graduate/Scholarship)* [4065]

Daniel Swarovski and Company Scholarships *(Graduate/Scholarship)* [4068]

Kurt Wayne Scholarships *(Graduate/Scholarship)* [4069]

Genealogy

ASG Scholar Awards *(Professional development/Scholarship)* [1257]

General studies/Field of study not specified

4th Infantry Division Association Scholarships *(All/Scholarship)* [5990]

The "21" Endowed Scholarships *(Undergraduate/Scholarship)* [5409]

92109 Community Fund-Mark and Karla Stuart Family Scholarships *(Undergraduate, Vocational/Occupational/Scholarship)* [7903]

AAAA Scholarship Program *(Undergraduate/Scholarship)* [1611]

AAIB Scholarships *(Undergraduate/Scholarship)* [485]

AAJUW Scholarships *(Graduate, Undergraduate/Scholarship)* [487]

AAS-American Society for Eighteenth Century Studies Fellowships *(Postdoctorate/Fellowship)* [411]

AAS CIAC Small Grants *(Graduate/Grant)* [1709]

AAS Korean Studies Scholarship Program *(Doctorate, Graduate/Scholarship)* [1710]

AAUW Legal Advocacy Fund American Fellowships *(Doctorate/Fellowship)* [15]

AAUW Legal Advocacy Fund Career Development Grants *(Professional development/Grant)* [16]

AAUW Legal Advocacy Fund International Fellowships *(Doctorate, Graduate/Fellowship)* [17]

Anthony Abbene Scholarships *(Undergraduate/Scholarship)* [4650]

Clifford V. Abbott Memorial Scholarships *(Undergraduate/Scholarship)* [8714]

Alejandro "Alex" Abecia Reaching High Scholarships *(Undergraduate, Vocational/Occupational/Scholarship)* [2932]

Abercrombie and Fitch Global Diversity Scholar Awards *(High School/Scholarship)* [6501]

The Frederick B. Abramson Memorial Foundation Scholarships *(Undergraduate/Scholarship)* [22]

ACHE/American Legion Auxiliary Scholarships *(Undergraduate/Scholarship)* [155]

GENERAL STUDIES/FIELD OF STUDY NOT SPECIFIED

Field of Study Index

ACHE/American Legion Scholarships (Undergraduate/Scholarship) [156]

ACHE Junior and Community College Athletic Scholarships (Undergraduate/Scholarship) [157]

ACHE Police Officers and Firefighters Survivors' Educational Assistance Programs (Undergraduate/Scholarship) [159]

ACHE Senior Adult Scholarships (Undergraduate/Scholarship) [160]

ACHE Two-Year College Academic Scholarships (Undergraduate/Scholarship) [161]

Ken and Pat Ackerman Family Scholarship Fund (Undergraduate/Scholarship) [3755]

Wayne D. Ackerman Family Scholarship Fund (Undergraduate/Scholarship) [8655]

ACMS Faculty Research Fellowships (Professional development/Fellowship) [600]

ACMS Intensive Mongolian Language Fellowship Program (Undergraduate/Fellowship) [601]

ACMS Research Fellowships (Doctorate, Postdoctorate/Fellowship) [603]

ACMS U.S.-Mongolia Field Research Fellowship Program (Graduate, Undergraduate/Fellowship) [604]

ACSO Scholarships (Undergraduate/Scholarship) [1520]

ACSUS Distinguished Dissertation Awards (Doctorate/Award) [1731]

Nancy Ashley Adams/Ashley Adams Koetje Scholarships (Undergraduate/Scholarship) [3360]

Adams Family Scholarships (Undergraduate/Scholarship) [3361]

Ruth D. Adams Fund (Undergraduate/Scholarship) [3756]

Mamie Adams Memorial Awards (Undergraduate/Scholarship) [5410]

The Clarke B. Adams Memorial Foundation Lapeer County Community Foundation Fund (Undergraduate/Scholarship) [5347]

Lt. Holly Adams Memorial Scholarships (Undergraduate/Scholarship) [3091]

Ruth Adams Memorial Scholarships (Undergraduate/Scholarship) [7615]

Beaver Medical Clinic-Glen Adams Scholarship Awards (Undergraduate/Scholarship) [7616]

Henry S. and Carolyn Adams Scholarship Fund (Undergraduate/Scholarship) [3880]

Frederick G. Adams Scholarships (Undergraduate/Scholarship) [4405]

Adelante Fund Hope Scholarships, CPS Energy Dependents (Undergraduate/Scholarship) [43]

Adelante Fund Hope Scholarships, San Antonio, TX Students (Undergraduate/Scholarship) [44]

Adelante Fund UPS Scholarships (Undergraduate/Scholarship) [45]

Carl Joseph Adelhardt Memorial Scholarships (Undergraduate/Scholarship) [4050]

Adelson Family Scholarships (Undergraduate/Scholarship) [7463]

Bob Adkins Memorial Scholarships (Undergraduate/Scholarship) [7057]

Chris Nance Adler Scholarship Fund (High School/Scholarship) [2933]

Adult Students in Scholastic Transition Scholarships (ASIST) (All/Scholarship) [3693]

AEBC Toronto Chapter Scholarships (Graduate, Undergraduate, Vocational/Occupational/Scholarship) [335]

AFSA Chapter 155 Division 1 Scholarships - Category 1 (Undergraduate/Scholarship) [97]

AFSA Chapter 155 Division 1 Scholarships - Category 2 (Undergraduate/Scholarship) [98]

AFSA Chapter 155 Division 1 Scholarships - Category 3 (Undergraduate/Scholarship) [99]

After-the-Fires Scholarships (Undergraduate, Vocational/Occupational/Scholarship) [7905]

Patty Ahearn Victoria Elementary Scholarships (Undergraduate/Scholarship) [7617]

Ahepa Buckeye Scholarship Awards (Undergraduate/Scholarship) [85]

Ahepa District No. 1 Scholarship Program (Graduate, Undergraduate/Scholarship) [790]

AIBS Junior Fellowships (Doctorate/Fellowship) [843]

AIBS Senior Fellowships (Doctorate, Postdoctorate/Fellowship) [844]

AIDS Awareness Scholarships (Undergraduate/Scholarship) [7843]

AIGC Fellowships - Graduate (Graduate/Fellowship) [826]

AIMS Long-term Research Grants (Doctorate, Postdoctorate/Grant) [860]

AIMS Short-term Research Grants (Doctorate, Postdoctorate/Grant) [861]

Air Force ROTC Enhanced HBCU Scholarships (Undergraduate/Scholarship) [9023]

Air Force Sergeants Association Scholarship Program (Undergraduate/Scholarship) [95]

AISES Summer Internships (Graduate, Undergraduate/Internship) [833]

AIST San Francisco Chapter Scholarships (Undergraduate/Scholarship) [1802]

AJL Convention Travel Grants (All/Grant) [1820]

Ak-Sar-Ben Scholarships (Undergraduate/Scholarship) [296]

Crown Prince Akihito Scholarship Foundation (Graduate/Scholarship) [5132]

Alabama Gi Dependents Educational Benefit Program (Undergraduate/Scholarship) [162]

Alabama National Guard Educational Assistance Program (Undergraduate/Scholarship) [163]

Alabama Power Scholarships (Undergraduate/Scholarship) [6809]

Alabama Scholarships for Dependents of Blind Parents (Undergraduate/Scholarship) [164]

Alabama Student Assistance Programs (Undergraduate/Scholarship) [165]

Alabama Student Grant Programs (Undergraduate, Vocational/Occupational/Grant) [166]

Alaska Kidney Foundation-ASN Research Grants (Doctorate/Grant) [1311]

Alaska Native Medical Center Auxiliary Scholarships (Undergraduate/Scholarship) [9131]

Alaska Yukon Pioneer Memorial Scholarships (Undergraduate/Scholarship) [9135]

Alberta Blue Cross Scholarships for Aboriginal Students (Undergraduate/Scholarship) [211]

Alberta Centennial Premier's Scholarships - Alberta (Undergraduate/Scholarship) [237]

Alberta Press Council Scholarships (Undergraduate/Scholarship) [270]

Alberta Ukrainian Centennial Commemorative Scholarships (Graduate/Scholarship) [9496]

Victor Albright Scholarships-Dane County (Undergraduate/Scholarship) [9347]

Victor Albright Scholarships (Undergraduate/Scholarship) [9348]

ALCOA Foundation Scholarships (Undergraduate, Graduate/Scholarship) [4317]

ALD Graduate Fellowships (Graduate/Fellowship) [6019]

Anne L. Alexander and Blaise Robert Alexander Memorial Scholarships (Undergraduate/Scholarship) [3757]

Hon. Lincoln Alexander Scholarships (Undergraduate/Scholarship) [2109]

Horatio Alger Ak-Sar-Ben Scholarships (Undergraduate/Scholarship) [297]

Horatio Alger Delaware Scholarships (Undergraduate/Scholarship) [298]

Horatio Alger District of Columbia, Maryland and Virginia Scholarships (Undergraduate/Scholarship) [299]

Horatio Alger Florida Scholarships (Undergraduate/Scholarship) [300]

Horatio Alger Franklin Scholarships (Undergraduate/Scholarship) [301]

Horatio Alger Georgia Scholarships (Undergraduate/Scholarship) [302]

Horatio Alger Idaho University Scholarships (Undergraduate/Scholarship) [303]

Horatio Alger Illinois Scholarships (Undergraduate/Scholarship) [304]

Horatio Alger Indiana Scholarships (Undergraduate/Scholarship) [305]

Horatio Alger Kentucky Scholarships (Undergraduate/Scholarship) [306]

Horatio Alger Lola and Duane Hagadone Idaho Scholarships (Undergraduate/Scholarship) [307]

Horatio Alger Louisiana Scholarships (Undergraduate/Scholarship) [308]

Horatio Alger Minnesota Scholarships (Undergraduate/Scholarship) [309]

Horatio Alger Missouri Scholarships (Undergraduate/Scholarship) [310]

Horatio Alger Montana Scholarships (Undergraduate/Scholarship) [311]

Horatio Alger National Scholarships (Undergraduate/Scholarship) [312]

Horatio Alger North Dakota Scholarships (Undergraduate/Scholarship) [313]

Horatio Alger Pennsylvania Scholarships (Undergraduate/Scholarship) [314]

Horatio Alger South Dakota Scholarships (Undergraduate/Scholarship) [315]

Horatio Alger Texas - Fort Worth Scholarships (Undergraduate/Scholarship) [316]

Horatio Alger Texas Scholarships (Undergraduate/Scholarship) [317]

Horatio Alger Utah Scholarships (Undergraduate/Scholarship) [318]

Horatio Alger Washington Scholarships (Undergraduate/Scholarship) [319]

Horatio Alger Wyoming Scholarships (Undergraduate/Scholarship) [320]

All-Ink Scholarships (Graduate, Undergraduate/Scholarship) [322]

Paul Shearman Allen and Associate Scholarships (Undergraduate/Scholarship) [9062]

Robinson G. Allen Athletic Memorial Scholarships (Undergraduate/Scholarship) [7618]

Frances C. Allen Fellowships (Graduate/Fellowship) [6692]

William A. Allen Memorial Metal Shop/Auto Body Scholarships (Undergraduate/Scholarship) [7619]

Dan Allen Memorial Scholarships (Undergraduate/Scholarship) [7844]

Alpha Chi Sigma Scholarship Awards (Graduate, Undergraduate/Scholarship) [348]

Alpha Delta Gamma Educational Foundation Scholarships (ADGEF) (All/Scholarship) [350]

Alpha Eta Scholarships (Undergraduate/Scholarship) [3363]

Alpha Kappa Alpha - Educational Advancement Foundation Financial Need-Based Scholarships (Graduate, Undergraduate/Scholarship) [352]

Alpha Kappa Alpha - Educational Advancement Foundation Merit Scholarships (Graduate, Undergraduate/Scholarship) [353]

Alpha Rho Leadership Scholarships (Undergraduate/Scholarship) [3364]

Alpha Tau Omega Graduate Scholarships (Graduate/Scholarship) [365]

Alpha Tau Omega Undergraduate Scholarships (Undergraduate/Scholarship) [366]

Justin Scot Alston Memorial Scholarships (Undergraduate/Scholarship) [4651]

Altrusa International of Grand Rapids Scholarships (Undergraduate/Scholarship) [4270]

Lou Amen Legacy Scholarships (Undergraduate/Scholarship) [2240]

American Association of University Women American Fellowships (Doctorate, Postdoctorate/Fellowship) [9]

American Association of University Women Career Development Grants (Postgraduate/Grant) [10]

American Association of University Women International Fellowships (Graduate, Postgraduate/Fellowship) [11]

American Association for Women in Community Colleges Regional Scholarships (Undergraduate/Scholarship) [565]

American Association for Women in Community Colleges Scholarship Leaders Institute (Professional development/Scholarship) [566]

American Composites Manufacturers Association Scholarships (Undergraduate/Scholarship) [625]

American Composites Manufacturers Association Western Chapter Scholarships (Undergraduate/Scholarship) [626]

American Council of the Blind Scholarships (Graduate, Undergraduate/Scholarship) [658]

American Council of Learned Societies Fellowships (Postdoctorate/Fellowship) [674]

American Division Veterans Association Scholarships (Undergraduate, Vocational/Occupational/Scholarship) [712]

1329

American Dream Scholarship Program (Undergraduate/Scholarship) [7890]

American Fire Sprinkler Association Scholarships (Undergraduate/Scholarship) [4407]

American Foreign Service Association Scholarship Fund (Undergraduate/Scholarship) [744]

American GI Forum of San Jose Scholarships (Undergraduate/Scholarship) [780]

American Indian Endowed Scholarships (Graduate, Undergraduate/Scholarship) [9503]

American Legion Boys/Girls State Scholarships (Undergraduate/Scholarship) [5411]

American Legion Eagle Scout of the Year Scholarships (High School/Scholarship) [6246]

The American Legion Legacy Scholarships (Undergraduate/Scholarship) [894]

The American Legion National High School Oratorical Scholarships Contest (Undergraduate/Scholarship) [895]

American Paint Horse Foundation Scholarships (Undergraduate/Scholarship) [976]

American-Scandinavian Foundation Fellowships and Grants to Study in America (Graduate/Fellowship, Grant) [1168]

American-Scandinavian Foundation Fellowships to Study in Scandinavia (Graduate/Fellowship) [1169]

American-Scandinavian Foundation Translation Prize (Professional development/Prize) [1171]

American Society for Environmental History Minority Travel Grants (Graduate, Professional development/Grant) [1245]

American Water Ski Educational Foundation Scholarships (Undergraduate/Scholarship) [1414]

Americans for Informed Democracy Global Scholar Tuition (Undergraduate/Scholarship) [1454]

AmeriGlide Achiever Scholarships (All/Scholarship) [1456]

AMLN Scholarships (Graduate, Undergraduate/Scholarship) [934]

Bernard Amtmann Fellowships (Postgraduate, Professional development/Fellowship) [2087]

AMVETS National Scholarships - Entering College Freshmen (Undergraduate/Scholarship) [1464]

AMVETS National Scholarships - For Veterans (Undergraduate/Scholarship) [1465]

AMVETS National Scholarships - JROTC (Undergraduate/Scholarship) [1466]

Anaheim Police Survivors and Scholarship Fund (Undergraduate/Scholarship) [1469]

Anchor Scholarship Foundation (Undergraduate/Scholarship) [8780]

Andersen Nontraditional Scholarships for Women's Education and Retraining (Undergraduate/Scholarship) [3884]

Judge Isaac Anderson, Jr. Scholarships (Undergraduate/Scholarship) [8589]

Jane E. Anderson Scholarships (Undergraduate/Scholarship) [3365]

Kathy D. and Stephen J. Anderson Scholarships (Graduate/Scholarship) [3092]

Redlands Rotary Club - Donald C. Anderson Scholarships (Undergraduate/Scholarship) [7620]

Warren M. Anderson Scholarships (Undergraduate/Scholarship) [4741]

Cindy Andrews Educational Scholarships (Undergraduate/Scholarship) [7621]

William H. Andrews/HAWS Scholarships (Undergraduate/Scholarship) [9623]

Androscoggin County Chamber of Commerce Adult Scholarships (Undergraduate/Scholarship) [1475]

Angus Foundation General Undergraduate Student Scholarships (High School, Undergraduate/Scholarship) [1477]

Angus Foundation Scholarships (Undergraduate/Scholarship) [6374]

Jack Anson Fellowships (Graduate/Fellowship) [6738]

APA Minority Fellowships Program (Postdoctorate/Fellowship) [1646]

APC Tuition-Assist Scholarship Awards (Graduate, Undergraduate/Scholarship) [60]

APIASF Scholarships (Undergraduate/Scholarship) [1655]

APT US&C Scholarships (All/Scholarship) [1847]

ARAFCS Doctoral Scholarships (Doctorate/Scholarship) [1534]

ARAFCS Masters Scholarships (Graduate/Scholarship) [1535]

Frank G. Araujo Memorial Scholarships (Undergraduate/Scholarship) [7623]

A.R.F.O.R.A. Undergraduate Scholarships for Women (Undergraduate/Scholarship) [1162]

Arizona Christian School Tuition Organization Scholarships (Undergraduate/Scholarship) [1515]

Rick Arkans Eagle Scout Scholarships (High School/Scholarship) [6247]

Arkansas State University Mountain Home Scholarships (Undergraduate/Scholarship) [1551]

Connie "Chelo" Armendariz Memorial Scholarships (Undergraduate, Vocational/Occupational/Scholarship) [7624]

Armenian American Citizen's League Scholarships (Undergraduate/Scholarship) [1580]

Armenian General Athletic Union Scholarships (Undergraduate/Scholarship) [1583]

Armenian Professional Society Scholarship Fund (Graduate/Scholarship) [1575]

Armenian Relief Society Scholarships (Graduate, Undergraduate/Scholarship) [1584]

Aaron Edward Arnoldsen Memorial Scholarships (Undergraduate/Scholarship) [1620]

Judge Sidney M. Aronovitz Memorial Scholarships (High School, Undergraduate/Scholarship) [3314]

Merle Aronson Point Scholarships (Graduate, Undergraduate/Scholarship) [7354]

ARREOLA/CBSPM Scholarships (Undergraduate, Vocational/Occupational/Scholarship) [7907]

ARS Undergraduate Scholarships (Undergraduate/Scholarship) [1577]

Chester Arzell and Helen Miller Montgomery Scholarships (Undergraduate/Scholarship) [9624]

ASBA College Scholarship Program (Undergraduate/Scholarship) [1180]

ASBC Foundation Undergraduate Scholarships (Undergraduate/Scholarship) [1187]

ASECS Graduate Student Research Paper Awards (Graduate/Award) [1221]

ASECS Innovative Course Design Competition (Undergraduate/Award) [1222]

Asian American Scholarships (Undergraduate/Scholarship) [9063]

Asian and Pacific Islander Queers Sisters Scholarships (Undergraduate/Scholarship) [7397]

ASIS Foundation Chapter Matching Scholarships (Undergraduate/Scholarship) [1657]

Michael M. Assarian Scholarships (Undergraduate/Scholarship) [1585]

Darrell and Palchie Asselin Scholarships (Undergraduate/Scholarship) [3524]

Association for the Advancement of Baltic Studies Dissertation Grants for Graduate Students (Doctorate/Grant) [1686]

Association on American Indian Affairs Emergency Aid Scholarships (Undergraduate/Scholarship) [815]

Association for Compensatory Educators of Texas Paraprofessionals Scholarships (Professional development/Scholarship) [1746]

Association for Compensatory Educators of Texas Scholarships (Undergraduate/Scholarship) [1747]

Association of Donor Recruitment Professionals Hughes Scholarships (Professional development/Scholarship) [1751]

Association of Donor Recruitment Professionals Presidential Scholarships (Professional development/Scholarship) [1752]

Association of the United States Navy Scholarships (Undergraduate/Scholarship) [1887]

Association of Universities and Colleges of Canada Public Scholarships (Undergraduate/Scholarship) [1889]

Athletic Equipment Managers Association College Scholarships (Undergraduate/Scholarship) [1918]

Atlanta Alumnae Achievement Scholarships (Undergraduate/Scholarship) [3366]

Atlantic Provinces Library Association Memorial Awards (Professional development/Scholarship) [1926]

Atlas Shrugged Essay Contest (Graduate, Undergraduate/Prize) [7591]

Herzog August Bibliothek Wolfenbuttel Fellowships (Doctorate/Fellowship) [6693]

AWMA Niagara Frontier Section College Scholarships (Graduate, Undergraduate/Scholarship) [115]

AXA Achievement Scholarships (Undergraduate/Scholarship) [1989]

Susan Ayers Memorial Scholarships (Undergraduate/Scholarship) [7467]

John M. Azarian Memorial Armenian Youth Scholarship Fund (Undergraduate/Scholarship) [1586]

B-Brave McMahon/Stratton Scholarship Fund (Undergraduate/Scholarship) [3758]

Paula Backscheider Archival Fellowships (Professional development/Fellowship) [1224]

BAEO Children's Scholarship Fund (High School/Scholarship) [2106]

BAFTX Early Starters Awards (Undergraduate/Scholarship) [2175]

BAFTX Graduate Awards (Undergraduate/Scholarship) [2176]

BAFTX Junior Achievers Awards (Undergraduate/Scholarship) [2177]

BAFTX Undergraduate Awards (Undergraduate/Scholarship) [2178]

Baha'i Faith Scholarships for Racial Harmony (Undergraduate/Scholarship) [7625]

The Bailey Family Foundation College Scholarship Program (Undergraduate/Scholarship) [1994]

The Bailey Family Foundation High School Scholarships Program (Undergraduate/Scholarship) [1995]

Lincoln C. Bailey Memorial Scholarship Fund (Undergraduate/Scholarship) [4986]

Bambi Bailey Scholarships (Undergraduate/Scholarship) [3078]

Barbara Bailey Scholarships (Undergraduate/Scholarship) [7399]

Sandra Sebrell Bailey Scholarships (Undergraduate/Scholarship) [3406]

Marian Wood Baird Scholarships (Undergraduate/Scholarship) [9407]

Richard L. Baker Memorial Scholarships (Undergraduate/Scholarship) [8717]

Robby Baker Memorial Scholarships (Undergraduate/Scholarship) [277]

Lloyd G. Balfour Fellowships (Graduate/Fellowship) [6739]

Ballard Family Foundation Scholarships (Undergraduate, Vocational/Occupational/Scholarship) [7909]

G. Thomas Balsbaugh Memorial Scholarship Fund (Undergraduate/Scholarship) [3935]

Brenda S. Bank Educational Workshop Scholarships (Undergraduate/Scholarship) [8326]

CSF Michael Bany Memorial Scholarships (Undergraduate/Scholarship) [2793]

Barakat Trust and Barakat Foundation Scholarships (Graduate/Scholarship) [1491]

Joe Barbarow Memorial Scholarships (Undergraduate/Scholarship) [7060]

Edgar Barge Memorial Scholarships (Undergraduate/Scholarship) [4256]

Robbie Baron Memorial Scholarships (Undergraduate/Scholarship) [3936]

Laura Beckley Barsotti Memorial Scholarships (Undergraduate/Scholarship) [4652]

CSF Walter and Marilyn Bartlett Scholarships (Undergraduate/Scholarship) [2794]

Elsa Barton Educational Scholarship Fund (Undergraduate, Vocational/Occupational/Scholarship) [1023]

Guthikonda BasavapunnaRao & Umadevi Scholarships (Graduate/Scholarship) [8829]

Bascom Hill Society Scholarships (Undergraduate/Scholarship) [9349]

Charles A. Bassett Endowed Memorial Scholarship Fund (Undergraduate/Scholarship) [4207]

Lewis and Gurry Batten/Sand Plains Educational Trust Scholarships (Undergraduate/Scholarship) [7061]

Hazel Reed Baumeister Scholarship Program (Undergraduate/Scholarship) [8197]

Timothy Baylink Good Fellowship Awards (Undergraduate/Fellowship) [7626]

BCCC Foundation Scholarships (Undergraduate/ Scholarship) [2002]

BCCC Foundation Workforce Scholarships (Undergraduate/Scholarship) [2003]

BCPA Bursaries (Undergraduate/Scholarship) [2180]

BDC Visiting Fellowships (Doctorate/Fellowship) [2196]

Beacon of Hope Scholarships (Undergraduate/ Scholarship) [2035]

Jane Beattie Memorial Scholarships (All/Scholarship) [8362]

Beau Gunn Redlands Baseball For Youth Scholarships (Undergraduate/Scholarship) [7627]

Suzanne Beauregard Scholarships (Undergraduate/ Scholarship) [4180]

Beaver Medical Clinic-H.E.A.R.T. Scholarship Awards (Undergraduate/Scholarship) [7628]

Beaver Medical Clinic-Premed Scholarship Awards (Undergraduate/Scholarship) [7629]

Don C. Beaver Memorial Scholarships (Undergraduate/Scholarship) [2241]

BECA Foundation-CUSM Scholarships (Undergraduate/Scholarship) [2039]

BECA Foundation General Scholarships Fund (Undergraduate/Scholarship) [2040]

Dennis J. Beck Memorial Scholarships (Undergraduate, Vocational/Occupational/Scholarship) [5091]

Garvin L. Beck Scholarships (Undergraduate/Scholarship) [7630]

Raymond and Donald Beeler Memorial Scholarships (Undergraduate/Scholarship) [7631]

Notah Begay III Scholarship Program (Undergraduate/Scholarship) [278]

John Bell and Lawrence Thornton Scholarship Fund (Undergraduate/Scholarship) [4412]

Ray and Mary Bell Memorial Scholarships (Undergraduate/Scholarship) [7911]

Alfred D. Bell Travel Grants (All/Grant) [3859]

Bellevue PFLAG Scholarships (Undergraduate/ Scholarship) [7401]

CSF Johnny Bench Scholarships (Undergraduate/ Scholarship) [2795]

H. Y. Benedict Fellowships (Graduate/Fellowship) [342]

Louise Bennett-Coverley Scholarships (Undergraduate/Scholarship) [2110]

Reverend E.F. Bennett Scholarships (Undergraduate/Scholarship) [2937]

Bergman Scholarships (Undergraduate/Scholarship) [6783]

The Joseph Berkman, and Michael and Sarah Chipkin Holocaust/Genocide Studies Awards (Graduate/Scholarship) [8738]

Richard L. Bernardi Memorial Scholarships (Undergraduate/Scholarship) [3143]

Donald H. Bernstein/John B. Talbert, Jr. Scholarships (Undergraduate/Scholarship) [3887]

James R. and Geraldine F. Bertelsen Scholarships (Undergraduate/Scholarship) [7912]

Beta Gamma Memorial Scholarships (Undergraduate/Scholarship) [3368]

Beta Omega Scholarships (Undergraduate/Scholarship) [8158]

Beta Sigma Scholarships (Undergraduate/Scholarship) [8159]

Bethune-Cookman University Excelsior Scholarships (Undergraduate/Scholarship) [2079]

Bethune-Cookman University Presidential Scholarships (Undergraduate/Scholarship) [2080]

BIA Higher Education Grants (Graduate, Postgraduate, Undergraduate/Grant) [1509]

BIE-Loan for Service for Graduates (Graduate/ Loan) [827]

BIGALA Scholarships (Bisexual Gay and Lesbian Alliance) (Undergraduate/Scholarship) [7845]

James L. Biggane Fellowships in Finance (Graduate/Fellowship) [6677]

James Bilder Scholarships (Undergraduate, Vocational/Occupational/Scholarship) [8591]

BioRx/Hemophilia of North Carolina Educational Scholarships (Undergraduate/Scholarship) [6317]

Birmingham-Southern College Eagle Scout Scholarships (Undergraduate/Scholarship) [6248]

Birmingham Student Scholarship Fund Association

(Undergraduate/Scholarship) [2102]

BISA's Scholarship Assistance Program (High School/Scholarship) [2146]

Lebbeus F. Bissell Scholarships (Undergraduate/ Scholarship) [4413]

Dr. Richard E. Bjork Memorial Graduate Study Awards (Graduate/Scholarship) [8739]

Norman Blachford Point Scholarships (Graduate, Undergraduate/Scholarship) [7355]

Black Canadian Scholarships (Undergraduate/ Scholarship) [6994]

Black Student Fund (High School/Scholarship) [2107]

William T. Blackwell Scholarship Fund (Undergraduate/Scholarship) [6358]

Alex Blaski Memorial Scholarships (Undergraduate/ Scholarship) [7757]

Bloch-Selinger Education Fund (Undergraduate/ Scholarship) [3760]

Lawrence Bloomberg Entrance Awards (Postgraduate/Award) [8034]

F.A. and Charlotte Blount Scholarships (Undergraduate/Scholarship) [9625]

Blues Ambassador Scholarships (Undergraduate/ Scholarship) [7469]

Jordan ABDO/Michael Bluett Memorial Scholarships (Undergraduate/Scholarship) [8592]

Harry and Edith Blunt Scholarships (Undergraduate/ Scholarship) [608]

BMO Financial Group Scholarships (Undergraduate/ Scholarship) [2111]

Sandra Bobbitt Continuing Education Scholarships (Undergraduate/Scholarship) [1836]

Edith and Arnold N. Bodtker Grants (All/Grant) [3339]

Bolick Foreign Student Scholarships (Undergraduate/Scholarship) [9141]

Dorothy M. Bolyard Memorial Scholarships (Undergraduate/Scholarship) [7914]

BOMA/NY Scholarships (Undergraduate/Scholarship) [2207]

Steve Bonk Scholarships (Postgraduate/Scholarship) [2634]

Lorne and Ruby Bonnell Scholarships (Undergraduate/Scholarship) [3182]

Barbara Bonnema Memorial Scholarships (Undergraduate/Scholarship) [7633]

Scott Bonners Memorial Scholarships (Undergraduate/Scholarship) [2330]

Admiral Mike Boorda Scholarship Program (Undergraduate, Vocational/Occupational/Scholarship) [6592]

Diane Booth Memorial Scholarships (Undergraduate/Scholarship) [3761]

Tom Boots Memorial Scholarships (Undergraduate/ Scholarship) [6601]

Maria and Czeslaw Borek Scholarships (Undergraduate/Scholarship) [7758]

David L. Boren Undergraduate Scholarships (Graduate, Undergraduate/Scholarship) [1784]

Geraldine Geistert Boss Scholarships (Undergraduate/Scholarship) [4272]

Boston City Federation "Return to School" Scholarships (Graduate, Undergraduate/Scholarship) [4074]

Dr. George T. Bottomley Scholarships (Undergraduate/Scholarship) [5707]

Miranda Bouldin General Scholarships (Undergraduate/Scholarship) [5513]

William R. Bowen Scholarships (Undergraduate/ Scholarship) [3052]

Billy Bowling Memorial Scholarships (Undergraduate/Scholarship) [6810]

Dr. Betty J. Boyd-Beu & Edwin G. Beu, Jr. Scholarships (Undergraduate/Scholarship) [9142]

W. Scott Boyd Group Grants (All/Grant) [4884]

Dody Boyd Scholarships (Undergraduate/Scholarship) [3096]

Verna Curry Boyer Scholarships (Undergraduate/ Scholarship) [8718]

Charles Bradley Memorial Scholarships (Undergraduate/Scholarship) [4397]

W. Philip Braender and Nancy Coleman Braender Scholarships (Undergraduate/Scholarship) [4415]

The Helen and Edward Brancati Teacher Develop-

ment Scholarships (Professional development/ Scholarship) [2644]

Gladys Kamakakuokalani 'Ainoa Brandt Scholarships (Graduate, Undergraduate/Scholarship) [5209]

Kenneth H. Breeden Scholarships (Undergraduate/ Scholarship) [5343]

Marion Luna Brem/Pat McNeil Health and Education Scholarships (Undergraduate/Scholarship) [2938]

Breslauer Family Scholarships (Undergraduate/ Scholarship) [7915]

Hilda E. Bretzlaff Foundation Scholarships (Undergraduate/Grant) [2173]

Louise A. Broderick San Diego County Scholarships (Undergraduate, Vocational/Occupational/Scholarship) [7916]

Louis J. Brody Q.C. Entrance Scholarships (Postgraduate/Scholarship) [8035]

Ross P. Broesamle Educational Scholarship Fund (Undergraduate/Scholarship) [5348]

John G. Brokaw Scholarships (Undergraduate/ Scholarship) [6585]

Peter F. Bronfman Entrance Awards (Postgraduate/ Award) [8036]

Peter F. Bronfman Scholarships of Merit (Postgraduate/Scholarship) [8037]

Seth R. and Corrine H. Brooks Memorial Scholarships (All/Scholarship) [2075]

Carl E. Brooks Scholarships (Undergraduate/Scholarship) [8593]

Dorothy B. Brothers Executive Scholarship Program (High School/Scholarship) [9717]

Brown Dental Scholarships (Undergraduate/Scholarship) [5116]

Diana Brown Endowed Scholarships (Undergraduate/Scholarship) [5414]

Marjorie M. Brown Fellowship Program (Postdoctorate/Fellowship) [5201]

The John Carter Brown Library Long-Term Fellowships (All/Fellowship) [2198]

The John Carter Brown Library Short-Term Fellowships (Doctorate, Postdoctorate/Fellowship) [2199]

Jesse Brown Memorial Youth Scholarship Program (All/Scholarship) [3459]

JoAhn Brown-Nash Memorial Scholarships (Undergraduate/Scholarship) [3097]

Ron Brown Scholars Program (Undergraduate/ Scholarship) [2201]

James W. Jr. and Jane T. Brown Scholarship Fund (Undergraduate/Scholarship) [4208]

CSF M. and E. Brown Scholarships (Undergraduate/Scholarship) [2796]

D.C. and Virginia Brown Scholarships (High School, Undergraduate/Scholarship) [2939]

Harry and Lucille Brown Scholarships (Undergraduate/Scholarship) [4273]

Jack H. Brown Scholarships (Undergraduate/Scholarship) [2242]

Bernard B. and Mary L. Brusin Scholarships (Undergraduate/Scholarship) [3526]

William and Clara Bryan Scholarships (Undergraduate/Scholarship) [3098]

BSA Educational Scholarships (Undergraduate/ Scholarship) [2224]

BSF Science and Medicine Research Grants (Professional development/Grant) [2026]

Walter and Louise Buell Graduate Scholarships (Graduate/Scholarship) [3862]

Susan Thompson Buffett Foundation Scholarships (Undergraduate/Scholarship) [2205]

Tien Bui Memorial Scholarships (Undergraduate/ Scholarship) [9627]

Builders Association of Northeast Indiana Scholarships (Undergraduate/Scholarship) [8719]

Armen H. Bululian Scholarships (Undergraduate/ Scholarship) [1588]

Charles E. Bunnell Scholarships (Undergraduate/ Scholarship) [9143]

William T. Burbage Family Memorial Scholarships (Undergraduate/Scholarship) [3053]

George M. Burditt Scholarships (Undergraduate/ Scholarship) [1781]

Freda Burge Scholarships (Undergraduate/Scholarship) [7064]

Burger King Employee Scholars Program (Under-

graduate/Scholarship) [4474]

Burger King Scholars Program (Undergraduate/Scholarship) [4475]

Loyal D. Burkett Memorial Scholarships (Undergraduate/Scholarship) [9144]

Kathy Bush Memorial Scholarships (Undergraduate/Scholarship) [7635]

Business, Education and Technology Scholarships (Graduate, Undergraduate, Vocational/Occupational/Scholarship) [336]

Lindsay Buster Memorial Scholarships (Undergraduate/Scholarship) [3144]

Leon C. Bynoe Memorial Scholarships (Undergraduate/Scholarship) [9323]

Joe Bynum/Raymond James Investment Services Technical Excellence Scholarship Fund (Undergraduate/Scholarship) [3033]

Robert C. Byrd Honors Scholarships (Undergraduate/Scholarship) [4694]

George J. Bysiewicz Scholarship Fund (Undergraduate/Scholarship) [3079]

CAA National Capital Region Writing Contest (All/Prize) [2417]

Cabrillo Clubs of California Scholarships (Undergraduate/Scholarship) [7377]

Dr. Aurelio M. Caccomo Family Foundation Memorial Scholarships (Undergraduate/Scholarship) [1467]

CAG Health and Health Care Study Group Awards (Graduate/Award) [2378]

Cal State San Macros Alumna Scholarships (Undergraduate/Scholarship) [2286]

Tese Caldarelli Memorial Scholarships (Graduate, Undergraduate/Scholarship) [6045]

Calhoun County Auduburn University Scholarships (Undergraduate/Scholarship) [3034]

Hermione Grant Calhoun Scholarships (Undergraduate/Scholarship) [6273]

Calhoun Scholarships (Undergraduate/Scholarship) [2226]

California Groundwater Association Scholarships (Undergraduate/Scholarship) [2258]

California Scottish Rite Foundation Scholarships (Undergraduate/Scholarship) [2275]

California Shopping Cart Retrieval Corporation Inc. Scholarships (Undergraduate/Scholarship) [2243]

Calista Scholarships (Graduate, Undergraduate, Vocational/Occupational/Scholarship) [2290]

Harry D. Callahan Educational Trust (Undergraduate/Scholarship) [8659]

Calvin Alumni Association Arizona Central Chapter Scholarships (Undergraduate/Scholarship) [2292]

Calvin Alumni Association-Black Alumni Chapter Scholarships (Undergraduate/Scholarship) [2293]

Calvin Alumni Association British Columbia Scholarships (Undergraduate/Scholarship) [2294]

Calvin Alumni Association California- Bay Area Scholarships (Undergraduate/Scholarship) [2295]

Calvin Alumni Association Colorado Chapter Scholarships (Undergraduate/Scholarship) [2296]

Calvin Alumni Association Florida-Gulf Coast Scholarships (Undergraduate/Scholarship) [2297]

Calvin Alumni Association-Illinois Scholarships (Undergraduate/Scholarship) [2298]

Calvin Alumni Association-Iowa/Pella Scholarships (Undergraduate/Scholarship) [2299]

Calvin Alumni Association-Maryland/Baltimore Scholarships (Undergraduate/Scholarship) [2300]

Calvin Alumni Association-Michigan Lakeshore Scholarships (Undergraduate/Scholarship) [2301]

Calvin Alumni Association-Michigan, Lansing Scholarships (Undergraduate/Scholarship) [2302]

Calvin Alumni Association-New Jersey Scholarships (Undergraduate/Scholarship) [2303]

Calvin Alumni Association-New York, Rochester Scholarships (Undergraduate/Scholarship) [2304]

Calvin Alumni Association-South Florida Scholarships (Undergraduate/Scholarship) [2305]

Calvin Alumni Association-South Florida Sophomore Scholarships (Undergraduate/Scholarship) [2306]

Calvin Alumni Association-Southeast Michigan Scholarships (Undergraduate/Scholarship) [2307]

Calvin Alumni Association-Southeastern Wisconsin Scholarships (Undergraduate/Scholarship) [2308]

Calvin Alumni Association Southern California Chapter Scholarships (Undergraduate/Scholarship) [2309]

Calvin Alumni Association-Southwest Michigan, Kalamazoo Scholarships (Undergraduate/Scholarship) [2310]

Calvin Alumni Association-Washington, D.C. Scholarships (Undergraduate/Scholarship) [2311]

Calvin Alumni Association-Washington, Lynden Scholarships (Undergraduate/Scholarship) [2312]

Calvin Alumni Association-Washington-Seattle/Tacoma Scholarships (Undergraduate/Scholarship) [2313]

Camden County College Employee Memorial Scholarships (Undergraduate/Scholarship) [2331]

Camden County College Foundation Scholarships (Undergraduate/Scholarship) [2332]

Camden County Retired Educators Association Scholarships (Undergraduate/Scholarship) [2333]

Cameco Northern Scholarships - Technical Institute (Undergraduate/Scholarship) [2346]

Cameco Northern Scholarships - University (Undergraduate/Scholarship) [2347]

Wesley C. Cameron Scholarships (Undergraduate/Scholarship) [6586]

Lois Campbell Scholarship Awards (Undergraduate/Scholarship) [4930]

Lucille Campbell Scholarship Fund (Undergraduate/Scholarship) [9550]

Robert G. Campbell Scholarships (Undergraduate/Scholarship) [7636]

Theodore R. Campbell Scholarships (Undergraduate/Scholarship) [240]

Campus Discovery Scholarships (Graduate, Undergraduate/Scholarship) [2352]

Canada-Ukraine Parliamentary Program Internship Scholarships (CUPP) (Undergraduate/Scholarship) [9497]

Canadian Evaluation Society Educational Fund Scholarships (Graduate/Scholarship) [2459]

Canadian Federation of Independent Grocers National Scholarships (Undergraduate/Scholarship) [2461]

Canadian Federation of University Women Etobicoke Bursary (Undergraduate/Scholarship) [9324]

Canadian Hard of Hearing Association Scholarships (Undergraduate/Scholarship) [2481]

Canadian Iranian Foundation Scholarships (Undergraduate/Scholarship) [2509]

Canadian Parking Association Scholarships (Undergraduate/Scholarship) [2581]

Canadian Polar Commission Scholarships (Doctorate, Graduate/Scholarship) [1734]

Canadian Sanitation Supply Association Scholarships (Undergraduate/Scholarship) [2592]

Canadian Seniors' Golf Association Scholarships (Undergraduate/Scholarship) [4181]

Canadian Society for the Study of Education Mentorship Awards (Professional development/Award) [2615]

Cancer for College Scholarships (Graduate, Undergraduate/Scholarship) [2636]

Cancer Survivors' Fund Scholarships (Undergraduate/Scholarship) [2640]

Agustin C. Cano Memorial Scholarships (Undergraduate/Scholarship) [7472]

Commander Ronald J. Cantin Scholarships (Undergraduate/Scholarship) [2921]

CAODC Occupational Health and Safety Scholarships (Professional development/Scholarship) [2399]

CAODC Scholarship Program (Undergraduate/Scholarship) [2400]

John Caoile Memorial Scholarships (Undergraduate/Scholarship) [7473]

Cape Fear Community College Merit Scholarships (Undergraduate, Vocational/Occupational/Scholarship) [2647]

Kasie Ford Capling Memorial Scholarship Endowment Fund (Undergraduate/Scholarship) [3890]

Lester J. Cappon Fellowships in Documentary Editing (Postdoctorate/Fellowship) [6694]

Daniel Cardillo Charitable Fund (All/Scholarship) [5573]

Career Advancement Scholarships (Undergraduate/Scholarship) [2220]

CareerFitter Scholarships (Graduate, Undergraduate/Scholarship) [2651]

Beth Carew Memorial Scholarships (Undergraduate/Scholarship) [6318]

William F. Carl Scholarships (Undergraduate, Vocational/Occupational/Scholarship) [6771]

AABA Read Carlock Memorial Scholarship Fund (Professional development/Scholarship) [1507]

Glen and Babs Carlson Endowed Scholarships (Undergraduate/Scholarship) [5415]

Carmangay Home and School Association Scholarships (Undergraduate/Scholarship) [241]

Walta Wilkinson Carmichael Scholarships (Undergraduate/Scholarship) [8160]

Carnegie Observatories Graduate Research Fellowships (Doctorate, Graduate/Fellowship) [2655]

Herb Carnegie Scholarships (Undergraduate/Scholarship) [2113]

Carolina Panthers Scholarship Fund (Graduate/Scholarship) [3892]

Carolina's Gay & Lesbian Scholarships (Undergraduate/Scholarship) [7846]

Carolinas-Virginias Retail Hardware Scholarships (Undergraduate/Scholarship) [3893]

Walter & Elsie Carr Endowed Scholarships (Undergraduate/Scholarship) [5416]

Commander James Carr Forensic Science Scholarships (Undergraduate/Scholarship) [356]

CSF Eugene Carroll Scholarships (Undergraduate/Scholarship) [2797]

Karen D. Carsel Memorial Scholarships (Graduate/Scholarship) [749]

Orin Carver Scholarships (Undergraduate/Scholarship) [3183]

CASAA Leaders of Distinction Scholarships (Professional development/Scholarship) [2409]

CASAA Scholarships (Undergraduate/Scholarship) [2410]

Local 827 Peter J. Casey Scholarships (Undergraduate/Scholarship) [4888]

Fraser Milner Casgrain LLP Scholarships (Undergraduate/Scholarship) [2114]

George H. and Anna Casper Fund (Undergraduate/Scholarship) [8660]

Orrie & Dorothy Cassada Scholarships (Undergraduate/Scholarship) [4274]

Catholic Aid Association's Post-High School Tuition Scholarships (Undergraduate/Scholarship) [2670]

Marshall Cavendish Scholarships (Graduate/Scholarship) [899]

CAWEE International Student Fellowships (Postgraduate/Fellowship) [8038]

Christine Kerr Cawthorne Scholarships (Undergraduate/Scholarship) [8161]

CBC Spouses Education Scholarship Fund (Doctorate, Graduate, Undergraduate/Scholarship) [3216]

CBC Spouses Flexible Education Scholarships (Graduate, Master's, Undergraduate/Scholarship) [3217]

CBCF Congressional Fellows Program (Professional development/Fellowship) [3220]

CC Times Scholarships (Undergraduate/Scholarship) [2770]

CCSD School Counselors' Scholarships (Undergraduate/Scholarship) [7474]

CCU Alumni Endowed Scholarships (Undergraduate/Scholarship) [2986]

Betty J. Cecere Memorial Scholarship Endowment Fund (Undergraduate/Scholarship) [9551]

Cedarcrest Farms Scholarships (Graduate, Undergraduate/Scholarship) [884]

Center for the Education of Women Scholarships (Graduate, Undergraduate/Scholarship) [2687]

Centerville-Abington Dollars for Scholars (Undergraduate/Scholarship) [9552]

Central Maine Power Scholarship Fund (Undergraduate/Scholarship) [5574]

Certified Municipal Clerk Scholarships (CMC) (Professional development/Scholarship) [4957]

Cerutti Group Scholarships (Undergraduate, Graduate/Scholarship) [4318]

CFT/ACPSOP Scholarships (Undergraduate/Scholarship) [2798]

CGPF Endowments Conference Scholarships (Professional development/Scholarship) [2478]

Logan S. Chambers Individual Scholarships *(Professional development/Scholarship)* [4885]

Mary Anne Chambers Scholarships *(Undergraduate/Scholarship)* [5117]

Jason Chaney Memorial Scholarship Fund *(Undergraduate/Scholarship)* [9553]

Harry H. and Floy B. Chapin Scholarships *(Undergraduate/Scholarship)* [3145]

Nancy J. Chapman Scholarships *(Professional development/Scholarship)* [1753]

Charles "Chuck" McAdams Memorial Scholarships *(Graduate, Undergraduate/Scholarship)* [8809]

Charlotte Housing Authority Scholarship Fund (CHASF) *(Undergraduate, Vocational/Occupational/Scholarship)* [3894]

Charlotte-Mecklenburg Schools Scholarship Incentive Program *(Undergraduate/Scholarship)* [3895]

Chateau Ste. Michelle Scholarship Fund *(Undergraduate/Scholarship)* [2975]

Cesar E. Chavez Scholarships *(Undergraduate/Scholarship)* [7637]

CHEA Undergraduate Scholarship Program for Students with Disabilities *(High School, Undergraduate/Scholarship)* [2260]

CHEA Vocational Grants *(High School/Grant)* [2261]

Cheatham County Scholarships *(Undergraduate/Scholarship)* [3100]

Cheerful Giver Scholarships *(Undergraduate/Scholarship)* [7918]

Chernos Essay Competition *(High School/Prize)* [2429]

Cherokee Nation Graduate Scholarships *(Graduate/Scholarship)* [2742]

Cherokee Nation Pell Scholarships *(Undergraduate/Scholarship)* [2743]

Cherokee Nation Scholarships *(Undergraduate/Scholarship)* [2744]

Sgt. Michael F. Cherven Memorial Scholarships *(Undergraduate/Scholarship)* [5666]

Buena M. Chesshir Memorial Women's Educational Scholarships *(Graduate, Master's, Undergraduate/Scholarship)* [9440]

Cheyenne High School Faculty Memorial Scholarships *(Undergraduate/Scholarship)* [7475]

Chi Chapter Undergraduate Scholarships *(Undergraduate/Scholarship)* [3369]

Chicago Division Scholarships *(Undergraduate/Scholarship)* [5858]

Chicana Latina Scholarship Fund *(Graduate, Undergraduate/Scholarship)* [2750]

Child of Alumni Book Voucher Awards *(Undergraduate/Scholarship)* [4742]

Kevin Child Scholarships *(Undergraduate/Scholarship)* [6319]

John and Ruth Childe Scholarships *(Undergraduate/Scholarship)* [8594]

Children of Evangeline Section Scholarships *(Graduate, Undergraduate/Scholarship)* [8435]

Children of Unitarian Universalist Ministers College Scholarships *(Undergraduate/Scholarship)* [8995]

Children's Scholarship Fund of Charlotte *(Undergraduate/Scholarship)* [3896]

Chinese Professionals Association of Canada BMO Diversity Scholarships *(Undergraduate/Scholarship)* [2771]

Chinese Professionals Association of Canada Education Foundation Awards *(High School/Award)* [2772]

Chinese Professionals Association of Canada Journalism Scholarships *(Undergraduate/Scholarship)* [2773]

Chinese Professionals Association of Canada Professional Achievement Awards *(Professional development/Award)* [2774]

Choose Your Future Scholarships *(Undergraduate/Scholarship)* [3101]

Commander Daniel J. Christovich Scholarship Fund *(Undergraduate/Scholarship)* [2922]

Chrysler Technical Scholarship Fund *(Undergraduate/Scholarship)* [3358]

CHS - Bursary Program Scholarships *(Undergraduate/Scholarship)* [2483]

CHS - Mature Student Bursary Program Scholarships *(Professional development/Scholarship)* [2484]

CHS Scholarships *(Undergraduate, Vocational/Occupational/Scholarship)* [2485]

Church Family Scholarships *(Undergraduate/Scholarship)* [5418]

CIA Undergraduate Scholarships *(Undergraduate/Scholarship)* [1785]

CIBC Scholarships *(Undergraduate/Scholarship)* [2115]

Cincinnati High School Scholarships *(High School/Scholarship)* [2799]

CIP Fellow's Travel Scholarships *(Postgraduate/Scholarship)* [2502]

Carlos Enrique Cisneros Point Scholarships *(Graduate, Undergraduate/Scholarship)* [7356]

Citi Foundation Scholarship Program *(Undergraduate/Scholarship)* [805]

Citizens' Scholarship Foundation of Wakefield Scholarships *(All/Scholarship)* [2885]

City of Sanibel Employee Dependent Scholarships *(Undergraduate/Scholarship)* [8595]

Civitan Shropshire Scholarships *(Undergraduate, Vocational/Occupational/Scholarship)* [2895]

Claes Nobel Academic Scholarships for Members *(High School/Scholarship)* [6502]

Cecil Earl Clapp, Sr. Memorial Scholarships *(Undergraduate/Scholarship)* [6811]

Fisher Clark Memorial Endowed Scholarships *(Undergraduate/Scholarship)* [5419]

Andrew Blake Clark Memorial Scholarships *(Undergraduate/Scholarship)* [9629]

Thomas Arkle Clark Scholar-Leader of the Year Endowed Scholarships *(Graduate, Undergraduate/Scholarship)* [7254]

Classic Wines of California Scholarships *(Undergraduate/Scholarship)* [2244]

James L. Clifford Prize *(Professional development/Prize)* [1227]

David H. Clift Scholarships *(Graduate/Scholarship)* [900]

Bryan Cline Memorial Soccer Scholarship Program *(Undergraduate/Scholarship)* [279]

The Club at Morningside Scholarships *(Undergraduate, Vocational/Occupational/Scholarship)* [7919]

CMSF Scholarships *(Graduate, Undergraduate/Scholarship)* [2781]

CNST Scholarships *(Doctorate, Graduate/Scholarship)* [1735]

Coast Guard Foundation Enlisted Education Grants *(All/Grant)* [2923]

Coast Guard Foundation Scholarships *(Undergraduate/Scholarship)* [2924]

The Helena B. Cobb Annual Scholarships *(Undergraduate, Vocational/Occupational/Scholarship)* [9728]

The Helena B. Cobb Four-Year Higher Education Grants *(Undergraduate, Vocational/Occupational/Scholarship)* [9729]

Coca-Cola First Generation Scholarships *(Undergraduate/Scholarship)* [806]

Coca-Cola Scholars Foundation Four-Year Awards for Seniors *(Undergraduate/Scholarship)* [2966]

CODY Foundation Fund *(Undergraduate/Scholarship)* [3938]

Coeur d'Alene Alumni Scholarships *(Undergraduate/Scholarship)* [5420]

Steven L. Coffey Memorial Scholarships *(Undergraduate/Scholarship)* [3568]

Thomas D. Coffield Scholarships *(Undergraduate/Scholarship)* [4276]

Donald O. Coffman Scholarships *(Undergraduate/Scholarship)* [7405]

COHEAO Scholarships *(Undergraduate/Scholarship)* [2919]

Marshall A. Cohen Entrance Awards *(Postgraduate/Award)* [8039]

Cole Foundation Undergraduate Scholarship Program *(Undergraduate/Scholarship)* [3898]

The College Club of Hartford Scholarships *(Undergraduate/Scholarship)* [4418]

College of Marin Gay and Lesbian Student Scholarships *(Undergraduate/Scholarship)* [7847]

Irene Culver Collins and Louis Franklin Collins Scholarships *(Undergraduate/Scholarship)* [3054]

Captain Winifred Quick Collins Scholarships *(Undergraduate/Scholarship)* [6587]

Elmer and Rosa Lee Collins Scholarships *(Undergraduate/Scholarship)* [9630]

Erma Collins Scholarships *(Undergraduate/Scholarship)* [2116]

Lloyd E. and Rachel S. Collins Scholarships *(Undergraduate/Scholarship)* [9631]

Columbus Citizens Foundation College Scholarships *(Undergraduate/Scholarship)* [3012]

Columbus Citizens Foundation High School Scholarships *(High School/Scholarship)* [3013]

Commonwealth Fund/Harvard University Fellowships in Minority Health Policy *(Professional development/Fellowship)* [3019]

Commonwealth "Good Citizen" Scholarships *(Undergraduate/Scholarship)* [1795]

Communal Studies Association Research Fellowships *(Graduate/Grant)* [3022]

Communications Workers of America Scholarships *(Undergraduate/Scholarship)* [3024]

Community-based Natural Resource Management Assistantships *(All/Internship)* [3031]

The Community Foundation DBI Scholarships *(Undergraduate, Vocational/Occupational/Scholarship)* [3103]

Community Foundation of the Fox River Valley Scholarships *(Undergraduate/Scholarship)* [3073]

Community Foundation of Sarasota County Adult Learner Scholarships *(Undergraduate, Vocational/Occupational/Scholarship)* [3189]

Community Foundation Scholarships *(Undergraduate/Scholarship)* [3146]

The Community Foundation Student Education Loans *(Undergraduate/Loan)* [3104]

Community Foundation of Western Massachusetts Community Scholarship Program *(Undergraduate/Scholarship)* [3207]

Compassionate Care Scholarships *(Undergraduate/Scholarship)* [7408]

Alan Compton and Bob Stanley Professional Scholarships *(Undergraduate/Scholarship)* [2016]

Congressional Hispanic Caucus Institute Scholarships *(Community College, Graduate, Undergraduate/Scholarship)* [3226]

CSF T.L. Conlan Memorial Scholarships *(Undergraduate/Scholarship)* [2800]

Connecticut Association of Latinos in Higher Education Scholarships *(Undergraduate/Scholarship)* [4419]

Connecticut Capitol Scholarship Program *(Undergraduate/Scholarship)* [4421]

Connecticut Nurserymen's Foundation Scholarships *(Undergraduate/Scholarship)* [4423]

Dwight O. Conner and Ellen Conner Lepp/Danhart Scholarships *(Undergraduate/Scholarship)* [7066]

Karen Connick Memorial Scholarships *(Undergraduate/Scholarship)* [4257]

Connor/Spafford Scholarships *(Undergraduate/Scholarship)* [4182]

Constantinople Armenian Relief Society Scholarships (CARS) *(Undergraduate/Scholarship)* [1589]

The Continental Group Scholarship Fund *(High School, Undergraduate/Scholarship)* [3316]

James & Maryetta Cook Scholarships *(Undergraduate/Scholarship)* [2334]

John Kent Cooke Foundation Graduate Scholarships *(Graduate/Scholarship)* [3245]

John Kent Cooke Foundation Undergraduate Transfer Scholarships *(Undergraduate/Scholarship)* [3246]

John Kent Cooke Foundation Young Scholars *(High School/Scholarship)* [3247]

George Joseph Cooper Awards *(Undergraduate/Scholarship)* [6995]

Madison and Edith Cooper Scholarships *(Undergraduate, Vocational/Occupational/Scholarship)* [7920]

COPA Scholarship Fund *(Undergraduate/Scholarship)* [2563]

Cope Middle School PTSA Scholarships *(Undergraduate/Scholarship)* [7639]

Copnick/Hilliard Scholarships *(Professional development/Scholarship)* [2578]

Copper and Brass Servicenter Association Inc. Scholarship Program *(Undergraduate/Scholarship)* [3253]

Corbett-Porter Building Bridges Scholarships *(Un-

dergraduate/Scholarship) [7479]

Beta Nu/Caryl Cordis D'hondt Scholarships (Undergraduate/Scholarship) [8163]

Theta/Caryl Cordis D'hondt Scholarships (Undergraduate/Scholarship) [8164]

Cornaro Scholarships for Graduate Studies (Graduate/Scholarship) [5191]

D.C. Cornelius Memorial Scholarships (Undergraduate/Scholarship) [9632]

The Corp - Students of Georgetown Inc. Coke Scholarships (Undergraduate/Scholarship) [3257]

The Corp - Students of Georgetown Inc. Textbook Scholarships (Undergraduate/Scholarship) [3258]

The Corp - Students of Georgetown Inc.-Word Scholarships (Undergraduate/Scholarship) [3259]

Cotner Family Scholarships (Undergraduate/Scholarship) [3765]

Courage to Grow Scholarships (Undergraduate/Scholarship) [3286]

Soozie Courter Sharing a Brighter Tomorrow Hemophilia Scholarship Program (Graduate, Undergraduate, Vocational/Occupational/Scholarship) [6320]

The Joe E. Covington Awards for Research on Bar Admissions Testing (Doctorate, Graduate/Award) [6204]

Steve Cowan Memorial Scholarships (Undergraduate/Scholarship) [3290]

Reuben R. Cowles Youth Awards (Undergraduate/Award) [885]

Justin Forrest Cox "Beat the Odds" Memorial Scholarships (Undergraduate/Scholarship) [2942]

Crafton Elementary School PTA Scholarships (Undergraduate/Scholarship) [7640]

Crafton Hills College Foundation Scholarships (Undergraduate/Scholarship) [7641]

Margaret T. Craig Community Service Scholarships (Undergraduate/Scholarship) [3147]

J. Craig and Page T. Smith Scholarships (Undergraduate/Scholarship) [8239]

Crain Educational Grant Program (Undergraduate/Scholarship) [8198]

Crawford Scholarships (Undergraduate/Scholarship) [7921]

Creative Glass Center of America Fellowships (All/Fellowship) [3288]

CRMA Scholarships (Graduate, Undergraduate/Scholarship) [2748]

Redlands Rotary Club - Ernest L. Cronemeyer Memorial Scholarships (Undergraduate/Scholarship) [7642]

CrossLites Scholarships (Graduate, High School, Undergraduate/Scholarship) [3297]

R.G. and Ruth Crossno Memorial Scholarships (Undergraduate/Scholarship) [3569]

Crowder Scholarships (Undergraduate/Scholarship) [3901]

CRS Scholarships (Undergraduate/Scholarship) [2785]

Lydia Cruz and Sandra Maria Ramos Scholarships (Undergraduate/Scholarship) [3404]

The Crystal Green Blood Assurance Memorial Scholarships (Undergraduate/Scholarship) [2153]

CSA Fraternal Life Scholarships (Undergraduate/Scholarship) [3299]

CSF Ach Family Scholarships (Undergraduate/Scholarship) [2801]

CSF Barr Foundation Scholarships (Undergraduate/Scholarship) [2802]

CSF Barrett Family Scholarships (Undergraduate/Scholarship) [2803]

CSF Bigg's/Curtis Breeden Scholarships (Undergraduate/Scholarship) [2804]

CSF Borden Inc. Scholarships (Undergraduate/Scholarship) [2805]

CSF Castellini Foundation Scholarships (Undergraduate/Scholarship) [2806]

CSF Cincinnati Bell Scholarships (Undergraduate/Scholarship) [2807]

CSF Cincinnati Financial Corporation Scholarships (Undergraduate/Scholarship) [2808]

CSF Cincinnati Milacron Scholarships (Undergraduate/Scholarship) [2809]

CSF Crosset Family Scholarships (Undergraduate/Scholarship) [2810]

CSF Dater Foundation Scholarships (Undergraduate/Scholarship) [2811]

CSF Duke Energy Scholarships (Undergraduate/Scholarship) [2812]

CSF Farmer Family Foundation Scholarships (Undergraduate/Scholarship) [2813]

CSF Fifth Third Bank Combined Scholarships (Undergraduate/Scholarship) [2814]

CSF Fletemeyer Family Scholarships (Undergraduate/Scholarship) [2815]

CSF Gardner Foundation Scholarships (Undergraduate/Scholarship) [2816]

CSF G.E. Aircraft Engines Scholarships (Undergraduate/Scholarship) [2817]

CSF Goldman, Sachs and Company Scholarships (Undergraduate/Scholarship) [2818]

CSF Greater Cincinnati Scholarships Association (Undergraduate/Scholarship) [2819]

CSF Heidelberg Distributing Co. Scholarships (Undergraduate/Scholarship) [2820]

CSF Heinz Pet Products Scholarships (Undergraduate/Scholarship) [2821]

CSF Juilfs Foundation Scholarships (Undergraduate/Scholarship) [2822]

CSF Kroger Cincinnati/Dayton Scholarships (Undergraduate/Scholarship) [2823]

CSF Lazarus/Federated Scholarships (Undergraduate/Scholarship) [2824]

CSF McCall Educational Scholarships (Undergraduate/Scholarship) [2825]

CSF Midland Company Scholarships (Undergraduate/Scholarship) [2826]

CSF Nethercott Family Scholarships (Undergraduate/Scholarship) [2827]

CSF Ohio National Foundation Scholarships (Undergraduate/Scholarship) [2828]

CSF Pepper Family Scholarships (Undergraduate/Scholarship) [2829]

CSF Pichler Family Scholarships (Undergraduate/Scholarship) [2830]

CSF PNC Bank Scholarships (Undergraduate/Scholarship) [2831]

CSF Procter and Gamble Scholarships (Undergraduate/Scholarship) [2832]

CSF SC Johnson, A Family Company Scholarships (Undergraduate/Scholarship) [2833]

CSF Scripps Headliners Scholarships (Undergraduate/Scholarship) [2834]

CSF Semple Foundation Scholarships (Undergraduate/Scholarship) [2835]

CSF Union Central 135th Anniversary Scholarships (Undergraduate/Scholarship) [2836]

CSF U.S. Bank N.A. Scholarships (Undergraduate/Scholarship) [2837]

CSF Western-Southern Foundation Scholarships (Undergraduate/Scholarship) [2838]

CSF Woodward Trustees Scholarships (Undergraduate/Scholarship) [2839]

CSF Wynne Family Memorial Scholarships (Undergraduate/Scholarship) [2840]

CSOHNS Fellowships (Graduate/Fellowship) [2611]

Murtha Cullina Scholarships (Undergraduate/Scholarship) [3080]

Brian Cummins Memorial Scholarships (Undergraduate/Scholarship) [4424]

John S. and Marjoria R. Cunningham Camp Scholarships (All/Scholarship) [5576]

Laura Moore Cunningham Foundation General Scholarships (Undergraduate/Scholarship) [5423]

Tsutako Curo Scholarships (Undergraduate/Scholarship) [7480]

Curry Awards for Girls and Young Women (Undergraduate/Scholarship) [8199]

Cindy Curry Memorial Scholarships (Undergraduate/Scholarship) [7069]

Michael D. Curtin Renaissance Student Memorial Scholarships (Undergraduate/Scholarship) [3570]

C.V. Starr Scholarships (Undergraduate, Graduate/Scholarship) [2690]

CWEDA Scholarship Program (Undergraduate/Scholarship) [2354]

Cystic Fibrosis Scholarship Foundation (Undergraduate, Vocational/Occupational/Scholarship) [3312]

DAAD Undergraduate Scholarship Program (Undergraduate/Scholarship) [4117]

Daddy Longlegs Scholarships (Undergraduate, Vocational/Occupational/Scholarship) [7922]

Daggy Youth/Student Scholarships (Professional development/Scholarship) [5016]

Dalai Lama Trust Graduate Scholarships (Graduate/Scholarship) [3333]

Serena D. Dalton Scholarships (Undergraduate/Scholarship) [9633]

Marvin E. Daly Memorial Scholarships (Undergraduate/Scholarship) [6812]

D&R Sobey Scholarships (Undergraduate/Scholarship) [8276]

Robin M. Daniels Memorial Scholarships (Undergraduate/Scholarship) [7481]

Arthur H. Daniels Scholarships (Undergraduate/Scholarship) [7643]

Dante Prizes (Undergraduate/Prize) [3341]

Danville Education Association Scholarship Fund (Undergraduate/Scholarship) [3766]

Danville High School Class of 1963 Scholarship Fund (Undergraduate/Scholarship) [3767]

Danville Rotary Scholarships (Undergraduate/Scholarship) [3768]

Mary Mouzon Darby Undergraduate Scholarships (Undergraduate/Scholarship) [4627]

Daughters of the American Revolution American Indian Scholarships (Undergraduate/Scholarship) [818]

David Library Fellowships (Doctorate, Postdoctorate/Fellowship) [3344]

Kenneth and Kathleen Davis Endowed Scholarships (Undergraduate/Scholarship) [5424]

Davis Family Scholarships (Undergraduate/Scholarship) [7923]

The William H. Davis, Jr. Scholarship Fund (Undergraduate/Scholarship) [3086]

Davis Memorial Foundation Scholarship Awards Program (Graduate, Undergraduate/Scholarship) [3346]

CSF Estelle Davis Memorial Scholarships (Undergraduate/Scholarship) [2841]

Dwight F. Davis Memorial Scholarships (Undergraduate/Scholarship) [9408]

Larry Dean Davis Scholarship Program (Undergraduate, Vocational/Occupational/Scholarship) [2171]

Lawrence E. Davis Scholarships (Undergraduate/Scholarship) [7071]

Brian M. Day Scholarships (Undergraduate/Scholarship) [7409]

Elsie De Wolfe Point Scholarships (Graduate, Undergraduate/Scholarship) [7357]

Dean Prim Scholarships (Undergraduate/Scholarship) [9634]

B.J. Dean Scholarships (Undergraduate/Scholarship) [3106]

Derek Lee Dean Soccer Scholarships (High School/Scholarship) [2943]

Don Debolt Franchising Scholarship Program (Undergraduate/Scholarship) [4939]

Walter M. Decker Point Scholarships (Graduate, Undergraduate/Scholarship) [7358]

Laurence Decore Awards for Student Leadership (Undergraduate/Scholarship) [243]

Anthony R. Dees Educational Workshop Scholarships (Undergraduate/Scholarship) [8327]

Jan DiMartino Delany Memorial Scholarships (Undergraduate/Scholarship) [3939]

Vine Deloria Jr. Memorial Scholarships (Graduate/Scholarship) [807]

Eric Delson Memorial Scholarships (High School, Undergraduate, Vocational/Occupational/Scholarship) [6321]

Delta Chi Alumnae Memorial Scholarships (Undergraduate/Scholarship) [8165]

Delta Epsilon Sigma Graduate Fellowships (Graduate/Fellowship) [3395]

Delta Epsilon Sigma Undergraduate Scholarships (Undergraduate/Scholarship) [3396]

Delta Iota Alumni Scholarships (Undergraduate/Scholarship) [8218]

Delta Phi Epsilon Educational Foundation Scholarships (Undergraduate/Scholarship) [3402]

Delta Zeta Undergraduate Scholarships (Undergraduate/Scholarship) [3409]

C. Rodney Demarest Memorial Scholarships (Un-

dergraduate/Scholarship) [4425]

Law Offices of Michael A. DeMayo Scholarships (Undergraduate/Scholarship) [5364]

Christopher Demetris Scholarships (Undergraduate/Scholarship) [4513]

Ruth DeMoss Scholarships (Undergraduate/Scholarship) [7924]

Michael Denton Scholarships (Undergraduate/Scholarship) [6813]

Denver Scholarship Foundation Scholarships (Undergraduate/Scholarship) [3428]

Tommy Depaola Scholarship Awards (Undergraduate/Scholarship) [4931]

Herman H. Derksen Scholarships (Undergraduate, Vocational/Occupational/Scholarship) [7925]

Pat Dermargosian Memorial Scholarships (Undergraduate/Scholarship) [7644]

Achille & Irene Despres, William & Andre Scholarships (Undergraduate/Scholarship) [4278]

Detroit Economic Club Scholarships (Undergraduate/Scholarship) [3197]

Helen L. Dewar Scholarships (Undergraduate/Scholarship) [8894]

Albert and Jane Dewey Scholarships (Undergraduate/Scholarship) [4426]

Diabetes Hope Foundation Scholarships (Undergraduate/Scholarship) [3434]

Julio C. Diaz Memorial Scholarship Fund (High School/Scholarship) [8662]

Bill Dickey Scholarship Association Scholarships (Undergraduate/Scholarship) [3440]

Rob Digiacomo Scholarship Fund (Undergraduate/Scholarship) [8663]

The E.R. and Lilian B. Dimmette Scholarship Fund (Undergraduate/Scholarship) [3902]

Distinguished Young Women Scholarships (Undergraduate/Scholarship) [3463]

Dr. Allan A. Dixon Memorial Scholarships (Postgraduate/Scholarship) [2596]

Julian Dobranowski Memorial Scholarships (Undergraduate/Scholarship) [7759]

Doddridge County Promise Scholarships (Undergraduate/Scholarship) [7072]

Hans H. and Margaret B. Doe Scholarships (Graduate, Undergraduate, Vocational/Occupational/Scholarship) [7926]

Emmett J. Doerr Memorial Distinguished Scout Scholarships (High School/Scholarship) [6249]

Dofflemyer Scholarships (Undergraduate/Scholarship) [6250]

Dokmo Family Scholarships (Undergraduate/Scholarship) [7927]

Dollar-A-Day Academic Scholarships (Graduate, Undergraduate/Scholarship) [3467]

Dolphin Scholarships (Undergraduate/Scholarship) [3469]

Doniphan Community Foundation Scholarships (Undergraduate/Scholarship) [4258]

Harry A. Donn Scholarships (Undergraduate/Scholarship) [4427]

Mickey Donnelly Memorial Scholarships (Undergraduate/Scholarship) [7483]

Jim Doogan Memorial Scholarships (Undergraduate/Scholarship) [9185]

Doraine Pursuit of Educational Excellence Scholarships (Undergraduate/Scholarship) [2944]

Dr. Michael Dorizas Memorial Scholarships (Undergraduate/Scholarship) [4514]

Eric Dostie Memorial College Scholarships (Undergraduate/Scholarship) [6322]

Father Connie Dougherty Scholarships (Undergraduate, Vocational/Occupational/Scholarship) [3191]

Tommy Douglas Scholarships (Undergraduate/Scholarship) [6548]

Downeast Energy Scholarships (Undergraduate/Scholarship) [3477]

Jay Downes Memorial Scholarships (Undergraduate/Scholarship) [2945]

Wilma Sackett Dressel Scholarships (Undergraduate/Scholarship) [8166]

Charles Drew Scholarships (Professional development/Scholarship) [1754]

Drinkwater Family Scholarships (Undergraduate/Scholarship) [7928]

Mary Ellen Driscoll Scholarships (Undergraduate/Scholarship) [4183]

Lillian Cooper Droke Memorial Scholarships (Undergraduate/Scholarship) [5778]

Drum Major Institute Scholars (Undergraduate/Scholarship) [8144]

Sergeant Major Douglas R. Drum Memorial Scholarship Fund (Undergraduate/Scholarship) [936]

Lee Dubin Scholarship Fund (Undergraduate/Scholarship) [7848]

Deborah Gandee Dudding Memorial Scholarships (Undergraduate/Scholarship) [7073]

Edward Leon Duhamel Freemasons Scholarships (Undergraduate/Scholarship) [7789]

Doris Duke Conservation Fellows Program (Graduate/Fellowship) [9615]

Duluth Building and Construction Trades Council Scholarships (Undergraduate, Vocational/Occupational/Scholarship) [3527]

Duluth Central High School Alumni Scholarships (Undergraduate/Scholarship) [3528]

Dunbar Heritage Scholarships (Undergraduate/Scholarship) [8599]

Wade and Marcelene Duncan Scholarships (Undergraduate/Scholarship) [9635]

Lord Dundonald Chapter Imperial Order Daughters of the Empire Scholarships (IODE) (Undergraduate/Scholarship) [6996]

Travis Dunning Memorial Scholarships (Undergraduate/Scholarship) [7484]

Durning Sisters Scholarships (Graduate/Scholarship) [3370]

Joshua Dyke Family Scholarships (Undergraduate/Scholarship) [8895]

Howard G. and Gladys A. Eakes Memorial Scholarships (Undergraduate/Scholarship) [4259]

Fernandez Earle Undergraduate Entrance Scholarships (Undergraduate/Scholarship) [3559]

Eastern Orthodox Scouting Scholarships (High School/Scholarship) [6251]

Eastern Shore Building Industry Association Scholarships (Undergraduate/Scholarship) [3055]

Ellen Eberhardt Memorial Scholarships (Undergraduate/Scholarship) [8720]

ECA Centennial Scholarships (Master's, Doctorate/Scholarship) [3576]

Edgecliff Alumni Awards (Undergraduate/Scholarship) [9768]

Melanie and Todd Edmonson Memorial Scholarships (Undergraduate/Scholarship) [3035]

Edmonton Epilepsy Continuing Education Scholarships (Undergraduate/Scholarship) [3590]

Education Factor Scholarships (Graduate, Undergraduate/Scholarship) [5735]

Education is Power Scholarships (Undergraduate, Vocational/Occupational/Scholarship) [6323]

Education Resource Center Scholarships (ERC) (Undergraduate, Vocational/Occupational/Scholarship) [8211]

Educational Administration Scholarship Awards (Postgraduate/Scholarship) [545]

Educational Enrichment Awards (Undergraduate/Scholarship) [1510]

Educational Leadership Foundation Grants (Undergraduate/Grant) [2973]

Educational Portal of the Americas Graduate Scholarships (Postgraduate/Scholarship) [3604]

Educational Portal of the Americas Undergraduate Scholarships (Undergraduate/Scholarship) [3605]

Educational and Professional Achievement Scholarships (Undergraduate, Vocational/Occupational/Scholarship) [1933]

Jimmy Edwards Scholarships (Undergraduate/Scholarship) [3107]

Christine H. Eide Memorial Scholarships (Graduate, Undergraduate/Scholarship) [5496]

Hillel Einhorn New Investigator Awards (Doctorate/Award) [8363]

El Pomar Fellowships (Graduate/Fellowship) [3622]

George & Isabelle Elanjian Scholarships (Undergraduate/Scholarship) [1591]

W. Eldridge and Emily Lowe Scholarships (Undergraduate/Scholarship) [8219]

Elks National Foundation Scholarships (Undergraduate/Scholarship) [3629]

Mark Jonathan Elliot Scholarship Fund (Graduate,

Undergraduate/Scholarship) [4722]

Dr. Robert Elliott Memorial Scholarships (Undergraduate/Scholarship) [5708]

Clay Elliott Scholarship Foundation Scholarships (Undergraduate/Scholarship) [3631]

Pauline Elliott Scholarships (Undergraduate/Scholarship) [5709]

CSF Thomas J. Emery Memorial Scholarships (Undergraduate/Scholarship) [2842]

Thomas O. Enders Graduate Fellowships (Graduate/Fellowship) [1732]

Priscilla Maxwell Endicott Scholarships (Undergraduate/Scholarship) [4429]

Vice Admiral Donald D. Engen Scholarships (Undergraduate/Scholarship) [6577]

Epsilon Epsilon Scholarships (Undergraduate/Scholarship) [8167]

Epsilon Tau Pi's Soaring Eagle Scholarships (Undergraduate/Scholarship) [6252]

Epsilon Tau Scholarships (Undergraduate/Scholarship) [8168]

Alan R. Epstein "Reach for the Stars" Scholarships (Undergraduate/Scholarship) [3317]

eQuality Scholarships (Undergraduate/Scholarship) [7849]

Erb Group Companies Service to Community Scholarships (Undergraduate/Scholarship) [6898]

Robert C. Erb Sr. Scholarships (Undergraduate/Scholarship) [5710]

ERCA Community Contribution Scholarships (Undergraduate/Scholarship) [3607]

Harriet Erich Graduate Fellowships (Graduate/Fellowship) [3371]

Ernest Hemingway Research Grants (Professional development/Grant) [4524]

The Eleonor A. Ernest Scholarships (Undergraduate/Scholarship) [5095]

Robert P. Ernest Scholarships (Undergraduate/Scholarship) [5097]

Boomer Esiason Foundation Scholarship Program (All/Scholarship) [3685]

European College of Liberal Arts Scholarships (ECLA) (Undergraduate/Scholarship) [9075]

Eustace-Kwan Family Foundation Scholarships (Undergraduate, Vocational/Occupational/Scholarship) [8200]

Chick Evans Caddie Scholarships (Undergraduate/Scholarship) [9575]

CSF Lyle and Arlene Everingham Scholarships (Undergraduate/Scholarship) [2844]

CSF Lyle Everingham Scholarships (Undergraduate/Scholarship) [2843]

Evjue Foundation, Inc./Capital Times Scholarships (Undergraduate/Scholarship) [9354]

Excel Staffing Companies Scholarships for Excellence in Continuing Education (Undergraduate/Scholarship) [280]

Executive Women International Scholarship Program (EWISP) (High School/Scholarship) [3694]

Exercise For Life Athletic Scholarships Program (Undergraduate/Scholarship) [3686]

FACT Graduating Senior Scholarship Program (Undergraduate/Scholarship) [3736]

Faculty Research Visit Grants (Doctorate/Grant) [4118]

Fairbanks Chapter Legacy Scholarships (Undergraduate/Scholarship) [9186]

The Fallen Heroes Scholarships (Undergraduate/Scholarship) [2925]

James Mackenzie Fallows Scholarships Honoring Gertrude Baccus (Undergraduate/Scholarship) [7645]

Families of Freedom Scholarship Fund - America Scholarships (Undergraduate, Vocational/Occupational/Scholarship) [3704]

Farmers State Bank Scholarships (Undergraduate, Vocational/Occupational/Scholarship) [8721]

Farmington UNICO Scholarships (Undergraduate/Scholarship) [4430]

David Edward Farson Scholarships (Undergraduate/Scholarship) [7074]

Anne M. Fassett Scholarships (Undergraduate/Scholarship) [8600]

Federal Communication Bar Association Foundation Scholarships (Undergraduate/Scholarship) [3720]

Federal Employee Education and Assistance Fund

Scholarships *(Undergraduate/Scholarship)* [3724]

Federalsburg Rotary Club Scholarships *(Undergraduate/Scholarship)* [3056]

FEEA-NTEU Scholarships *(Graduate, Postgraduate, Undergraduate/Scholarship)* [3725]

Nolan W. Feeser Scholarship Fund *(Undergraduate/Scholarship)* [3771]

FEF Scholarships *(Graduate/Scholarship)* [3700]

Virginia Valk Fehsenfeld Scholarships *(Undergraduate/Scholarship)* [4279]

Symee Ruth Feinburg Memorial Scholarships *(Undergraduate/Scholarship)* [4431]

Edward R. and Hazel N. Felber Scholarships *(Undergraduate/Scholarship)* [9355]

Fellowships for Intensive Advanced Turkish Language Study in Turkey *(Graduate, Undergraduate/Fellowship)* [1148]

Fellowships in the PMAC-AGPC *(Professional development/Fellowship)* [7450]

Dr. Joan W. Fernandez Point Scholarships *(Graduate, Undergraduate/Scholarship)* [7359]

Field Museum Graduate Student Fellowships *(Graduate/Fellowship)* [3742]

Beth K. Fields Scholarships *(Undergraduate/Scholarship)* [9211]

Sakura Finetek Student Scholarships *(Undergraduate/Scholarship)* [6511]

Gordy Fink Memorial Scholarships *(Undergraduate/Scholarship)* [7488]

First Church of Christ in Wethersfield - Metcalf Scholarships *(Undergraduate/Scholarship)* [4432]

First Friday Breakfast Club Scholarships *(Undergraduate/Scholarship)* [7850]

Martin Fischer Awards *(All/Award)* [2479]

St. Stephen A.M.E. Allison E. Fisher Book Awards *(Undergraduate/Scholarship)* [3804]

Joseph L. Fisher Doctoral Dissertation Fellowships *(Graduate/Fellowship)* [7743]

Arthur and Juna Fisher Memorial Track Scholarships *(Undergraduate/Scholarship)* [7646]

Sergeant Paul Fisher Scholarships *(Undergraduate/Scholarship)* [6235]

Carol C. Fitzgerald Scholarship Program *(Professional development/Scholarship)* [3722]

Gloria Flaherty Scholarships *(Graduate/Scholarship)* [4171]

FLEOA Foundation Scholarship Program *(Undergraduate/Scholarship)* [3727]

Grant H. Flint International Scholarships - Category I *(Undergraduate/Scholarship)* [8524]

Walter & Anna Flis Memorial Scholarships *(Undergraduate/Scholarship)* [7762]

Florida Atlantic Planning Society Graduate Fellowships for Academic Excellence *(Postgraduate/Fellowship)* [3819]

Barney Flynn Memorial Scholarships *(High School/Scholarship)* [2947]

John Flynn Memorial Scholarships *(Undergraduate/Scholarship)* [3150]

FMA-FEEA Scholarship Program *(Undergraduate/Scholarship)* [3729]

Alice J. Foit Scholarships *(Undergraduate/Scholarship)* [8666]

Ford Foundation Dissertation Fellowships *(Doctorate/Fellowship)* [5999]

Ford Foundation Diversity Fellowships *(Doctorate/Fellowship)* [6000]

Ford Foundation Predoctoral Fellowships *(Postgraduate/Fellowship)* [6002]

Ford Motor Company Scholarship Program *(Undergraduate/Scholarship)* [4568]

Anne Ford Scholarships *(Undergraduate/Scholarship)* [6186]

Foresters Scholarships *(Undergraduate/Scholarship)* [4714]

Forsyth County United Way Scholarships *(Undergraduate/Scholarship)* [5344]

Andrew Foster Scholarships *(Undergraduate/Scholarship)* [6146]

Fostering Hope Scholarships Fund *(Undergraduate/Scholarship)* [7075]

Foundation for the Advancement of Aboriginal Youth Bursary Program *(Undergraduate/Scholarship)* [2440]

Foundation for the Advancement of Aboriginal Youth Scholarships *(Undergraduate/Scholarship)* [2441]

Foundation for the Carolinas Rotary Scholarship Fund *(Undergraduate/Scholarship)* [3904]

Foundation of the Federal Bar Association Public Service Scholarships *(Undergraduate/Scholarship)* [3966]

Foundation Scholarships *(Undergraduate/Scholarship)* [5231]

Terry Fox Memorial Scholarships *(Undergraduate/Scholarship)* [6549]

Captain Ernest Fox Perpetual Scholarships *(Undergraduate/Scholarship)* [2926]

Parker B. Francis Respiratory Research Grants *(Professional development/Grant)* [1155]

Joey and Florence Franco Legacy Scholarships *(Undergraduate/Scholarship)* [2245]

Joe Francomano Scholarships *(Undergraduate/Scholarship)* [5174]

Johnny and Sarah Frank Scholarships *(Undergraduate/Scholarship)* [9150]

John Hope Franklin Dissertation Fellowships *(Doctorate/Fellowship)* [990]

James Franklin and Dorothy J. Warnell Scholarship Fund *(Undergraduate, Vocational/Occupational/Scholarship)* [3192]

Franklin Elementary School PTA Scholarships *(Undergraduate/Scholarship)* [7647]

Franklin Research Grants *(Postgraduate/Grant)* [991]

John and Victory E. Frantz Scholarship Fund *(Undergraduate/Scholarship)* [4216]

Fraser Stryker Diversity Scholarships *(Undergraduate/Scholarship)* [3998]

FRAXA Postdoctoral Fellowships *(Postdoctorate/Fellowship)* [4000]

Freedom Alliance Scholarships *(Undergraduate/Scholarship)* [4004]

Freepali Scholarships *(Graduate, Undergraduate/Scholarship)* [4008]

Dale E. Fridell Memorial Scholarships *(Undergraduate, Vocational/Occupational/Scholarship)* [8750]

Marc Friedlaender Fellowships *(Graduate, Doctorate/Fellowship)* [5671]

CSF William A. Friedlander Scholarships *(Undergraduate/Scholarship)* [2845]

A.E. Robert Friedman Scholarships *(Undergraduate/Scholarship)* [7035]

Phil Friel Scholarships *(Undergraduate/Scholarship)* [5711]

Joel R. Friend Scholarships *(Undergraduate/Scholarship)* [2060]

Kennedy T. Friend Scholarships *(Graduate, Undergraduate/Scholarship)* [327]

Friends of Coal Scholarships *(Undergraduate/Scholarship)* [9566]

Friends of Megan Bolton Memorial Fund *(Undergraduate/Scholarship)* [3944]

Dean A. Froehlich Endowed Scholarships *(Undergraduate/Scholarship)* [5428]

Melbourne & Alice E. Frontjes Scholarships *(Undergraduate/Scholarship)* [4280]

Marian Johnson Frutiger Scholarships *(Undergraduate/Scholarship)* [8169]

Gerard Swartz Fudge Memorial Scholarships *(Undergraduate/Scholarship)* [4653]

Keiko Fukuda Scholarships *(Undergraduate/Scholarship)* [9056]

Daniel G. and Helen I. Fultz Scholarship Fund *(Undergraduate/Scholarship)* [3772]

Gaddy Student Scholarships *(Undergraduate/Scholarship)* [9638]

Gaebe Eagle Scout Awards *(Undergraduate/Scholarship)* [6253]

Harry Gairey Scholarships *(Undergraduate/Scholarship)* [2117]

Farley Moody Galbraith Scholarship Fund *(Undergraduate/Scholarship)* [3037]

Louise Bales Gallagher Scholarships *(Undergraduate/Scholarship)* [3372]

Whitney Laine Gallahar Memorial Scholarship Fund *(Undergraduate/Scholarship)* [3038]

Carolyn Gallmeyer Scholarships *(Undergraduate/Scholarship)* [4281]

Gallo Blue Chip Scholarships *(Undergraduate/Scholarship)* [4398]

CSF Priscilla Gamble Scholarships *(Undergraduate/Scholarship)* [2846]

Gamma Iota Scholarships - Gamma Tau *(Undergraduate/Scholarship)* [8170]

Gamma Iota Scholarships - Kappa Eta *(Undergraduate/Scholarship)* [8171]

Gamma Iota Scholarships - Zeta Kappa *(Undergraduate/Scholarship)* [8172]

Gamma Iota Scholarships - Zeta Nu *(Undergraduate/Scholarship)* [8173]

Gamma Sigma Alpha Graduate Scholarships *(Graduate/Scholarship)* [4039]

Veronica Gantt Memorial Scholarships *(Undergraduate/Scholarship)* [7491]

Garden State Rotary Club of Cherry Hill Scholarships *(Undergraduate/Scholarship)* [2335]

Peter M. Gargano Scholarship Fund *(Undergraduate/Scholarship)* [3529]

Gail Garner R.I.S.E. Memorial Scholarships *(Undergraduate/Scholarship)* [7648]

Marcus Mosiah Garvey Scholarships *(Undergraduate/Scholarship)* [5118]

Edwin W. Gaston Scholarships *(Undergraduate/Scholarship)* [343]

Gates Cambridge Scholarships *(Doctorate, Postgraduate/Scholarship)* [6072]

Raffin Gathercole Scholarships *(Undergraduate/Scholarship)* [4051]

David A. and Pamela A. Gault Charitable Fund *(Undergraduate/Scholarship)* [8668]

A.R.F.O.R.A. Martha Gavrila Scholarships for Women *(Postgraduate/Scholarship)* [1164]

GAWP Graduate Scholarships *(Graduate/Fellowship)* [4099]

Gay, Lesbian, Bisexual, Transgender Alumni Council Scholarships *(Undergraduate/Scholarship)* [9356]

GCABS Youth Scholarship Awards *(High School, Undergraduate/Scholarship)* [4147]

Gehring Memorial Foundation Scholarships *(Graduate, Undergraduate/Scholarship)* [4723]

Victoria S. and Bradley L. Geist Scholarships *(Undergraduate/Scholarship)* [4477]

Irma Gelhausen Scholarship Fund *(Undergraduate/Scholarship)* [5349]

General Falcon Scholarships *(Undergraduate/Scholarship)* [7372]

General Mills Foundation Scholarships *(Undergraduate/Scholarship)* [808]

Georgetown Working League Scholarships *(Undergraduate/Scholarship)* [4090]

Gerber Foundation Merit Scholarships *(Undergraduate/Scholarship)* [4112]

Daniel Gerber, Sr. Medallion Scholarships *(Undergraduate/Scholarship)* [4113]

German Historical Institute Fellowships at the Horner Library *(Doctorate/Fellowship)* [4127]

Getty GRI-NEH Postdoctoral Fellowships *(Postdoctorate/Fellowship)* [4140]

Getty Postdoctoral Fellowships *(Postdoctorate/Fellowship)* [4141]

Getty Predoctoral Fellowships *(Doctorate/Fellowship)* [4142]

Getty Research Exchange Fellowship Program for Cultural Heritage Preservation *(Doctorate/Fellowship)* [1149]

GFWC Women's Club of South County Scholarships *(Undergraduate/Scholarship)* [7790]

Tom Gifford Scholarships *(Undergraduate/Scholarship)* [4218]

Shane Gilbert Memorial Scholarships *(Undergraduate/Scholarship)* [7078]

William Harrison Gill Education Fund *(Undergraduate/Scholarship)* [2061]

Benjamin A. Gilman International Scholarships *(Undergraduate/Scholarship)* [9096]

Ethel Z. Gilman Scholarships *(Professional development/Scholarship)* [8804]

Leo Gilmartin Scholarships *(High School/Scholarship)* [7352]

Susan Kay Munson Gilmore Memorial Scholarships *(Undergraduate, Vocational/Occupational/Scholarship)* [3151]

Nick Giorgione Hope for Hearts Scholarships *(Undergraduate/Scholarship)* [7493]

Alex Gissler Memorial Scholarships *(Undergraduate/Scholarship)* [5712]

Ann and Brad Glassco Scholarships *(Undergraduate/Scholarship)* [7649]

GLATA Living Memorial Doctorate Scholarships (Doctorate, Graduate/Fellowship) [4325]

GLATA Living Memorial Undergraduate/Graduate Scholarships (Graduate, Undergraduate/Fellowship, Scholarship) [4326]

Glazing Industry Scholarships (Undergraduate/Scholarship) [7494]

Gleaner Life Insurance Scholarship Foundation (Undergraduate/Scholarship) [4159]

Franciszek Glogowski Memorial Scholarships (Undergraduate/Scholarship) [7764]

Irene Carlson Gnaedinger Memorial Scholarships (Undergraduate/Scholarship) [5429]

Glenn Godfrey Memorial Scholarships (Graduate, Undergraduate, Vocational/Occupational/Scholarship) [5283]

Godparents for Tanzania Scholarships (Undergraduate/Scholarship) [4169]

Gold Award/Eagle Scout Scholarships (Undergraduate/Scholarship) [6254]

Gold Key Scholarships (Undergraduate/Scholarship) [5232]

Golden Key Graduate Scholar Awards (Postgraduate, Professional development/Fellowship) [6073]

Golden Key International Honour Society Study Abroad Scholarships (Undergraduate/Scholarship) [4176]

Rhode Island Commission on Women/Freda H. Goldman Education Awards (Undergraduate/Award) [7791]

Alois and Marie Goldmann Scholarship Fund (Undergraduate/Scholarship) [4669]

Joshua Gomes Memorial Scholarship Fund (Graduate, Undergraduate/Scholarship) [6324]

Millie Gonzalez Memorial Scholarships (Undergraduate, Vocational/Occupational/Scholarship) [6325]

J.O. Goodman Scholarship Awards (Undergraduate/Scholarship) [6899]

David B. Goodstein Point Scholarships (Graduate, Undergraduate/Scholarship) [7360]

Richard Goolsby Scholarship Fund (Graduate, Undergraduate/Scholarship) [3905]

Lucille May Gopie Scholarships (Undergraduate/Scholarship) [2118]

L. Gordon, Jr. and June D. Pfefferkorn Scholarships (Undergraduate/Scholarship) [9640]

Barnett D. Gordon Scholarships (Graduate, Undergraduate/Scholarship) [4724]

Pauline LaFon Gore Scholarships (Undergraduate/Scholarship) [3108]

Richard C. Gorecki Scholarships (Undergraduate/Scholarship) [7373]

Nettie and Jesse Gorov Scholarships (Undergraduate/Scholarship) [3152]

American Association of University Women-Mary Sue Gottcent Memorial Scholarships (Undergraduate/Scholarship) [8604]

Louis Gottschalk Prize (Professional development/Prize) [1228]

Carl W. Gottschalk Research Scholar Grants (Doctorate/Grant) [1312]

Charles F. Gould Endowment Scholarships (Undergraduate/Scholarship) [9151]

Graduate Student Scholarships (Graduate/Scholarship) [246]

Rachel Graham Memorial Scholarships (Undergraduate/Scholarship) [7650]

Grand Rapids Scholarship Association (Undergraduate/Scholarship) [4283]

Grande Prairie 4-H District Scholarships (Undergraduate/Scholarship) [199]

Charles Hall Grandgent Awards (Graduate/Award) [3342]

Granger Business Association College Scholarships (Undergraduate/Scholarship) [4313]

Russ Grant Memorial Scholarship for Tennis (Undergraduate/Scholarship) [7079]

Lucile Cheever Graubart/Lambda Scholarships (Undergraduate/Scholarship) [8174]

Grays Harbor Community Foundation Scholarships (Graduate, Undergraduate/Scholarship) [4323]

Greater Seattle Business Association Scholarships (Undergraduate/Scholarship) [4333]

Bishop Charles P. Greco Graduate Fellowships (Graduate/Fellowship) [5277]

Greek Orthodox Archdiocese of America Paleologos Graduate Scholarships (Graduate/Scholarship) [4345]

Green Hill Yacht and Country Club Scholarships (Undergraduate, Vocational/Occupational/Scholarship) [3058]

Green Knight Economic Development Corporation Scholarships (GKEDC) (Undergraduate/Scholarship) [4347]

James H. and Shirley L. Green Scholarship Fund (Undergraduate/Scholarship) [8670]

Curt Greene Memorial Scholarships (Undergraduate/Scholarship) [4399]

Greenwich Scholarship Association Scholarships (GSA) (Undergraduate/Scholarship) [4351]

Frances Harris Gresham Scholarships (Undergraduate/Scholarship) [8606]

Griffin Foundation Scholarships (Undergraduate/Scholarship) [4353]

Homajean Grisham Memorial Scholarships (Undergraduate/Scholarship) [6814]

Reginald K. Groome Memorial Scholarships (Undergraduate/Scholarship) [8065]

Katherin F. Gruber Scholarship Program (All/Scholarship) [2151]

Jack & Mary Lou Gruber Scholarships (Undergraduate/Scholarship) [5430]

Gruwell Scholarships (Undergraduate/Scholarship) [3059]

Guelph Caribbean Canadian Association Scholarships (Undergraduate/Scholarship) [4355]

Melissa Guerra Scholarships (Undergraduate/Scholarship) [2948]

Bobette Bibo Gugliotta Memorial Scholarships for Creative Writing (Undergraduate/Scholarship) [8202]

GuildScholar Awards (Undergraduate/Scholarship) [5159]

Hai Guin Scholarships Association (Undergraduate/Scholarship) [1594]

Guin-Stanford Scholarships (Professional development/Scholarship) [3039]

Calouste Gulbenkian Foundation Scholarships (Graduate, Undergraduate/Scholarship) [1595]

Larry Gulley Scholarships (Undergraduate/Scholarship) [8328]

Patricia S. Gustafson '56 Memorial Scholarships (Undergraduate/Scholarship) [3530]

Guzkowski Family Scholarships (Undergraduate/Scholarship) [7652]

Sara Gwisdalla Memorial Scholarships (Undergraduate/Scholarship) [7080]

Wesley R. Habley NACADA Summer Institute Scholarships (Professional development/Scholarship) [5996]

Jaye Haddad Memorial Fund (Undergraduate/Scholarship) [7851]

HAESF Graduate Scholarships (Graduate/Scholarship) [4640]

Nathaniel Hafer Memorial Scholarships (Undergraduate/Scholarship) [7081]

Sophia Hagopian Memorial Fund (Undergraduate/Scholarship) [1596]

Leslie Jane Hahn Memorial Scholarships (Undergraduate/Scholarship) [7931]

Hall of Achievement Scholarships (Undergraduate/Scholarship) [2246]

Joyce C. Hall College Scholarships (Undergraduate/Scholarship) [7165]

Chappie Hall Scholarship Program (Graduate, Postgraduate, Undergraduate/Scholarship) [2]

Guy D. & Mary Edith Halladay Graduate Scholarships (Undergraduate/Scholarship) [4284]

Alice Hamilton Prize (Professional development/Prize) [1247]

Al Hamilton Scholarships (Undergraduate/Scholarship) [2120]

Stan Hamilton Scholarships (Undergraduate/Scholarship) [7993]

George and Mary Josephine Hamman Foundation Scholarships (Undergraduate/Scholarship) [4369]

Jay Hammond Memorial Scholarships (Undergraduate/Scholarship) [9187]

Adam Hampton Memorial Scholarship Fund (Undergraduate/Scholarship) [3773]

Hancock Family Snow Hill High School Scholar-

ships (Undergraduate/Scholarship) [3060]

H. Pauline Hand Memorial Scholarships (Undergraduate/Scholarship) [8725]

Ilse and George Hanfmann Fellowships (Doctorate/Fellowship) [1150]

Byron Hanke Fellowships (Doctorate, Graduate, Undergraduate/Fellowship) [3933]

Clayburn and Garnet R. Hanna Scholarships (Undergraduate/Scholarship) [7082]

Zenon C.R. Hansen Leadership Scholarships (Undergraduate/Scholarship) [6255]

Clem T. Hanson Scholarship Fund (Undergraduate/Scholarship) [5916]

Haraldson Foundation Scholarships (Graduate, Undergraduate/Scholarship) [4391]

Isaac and Mary Harbottle Scholarships (Graduate, Undergraduate/Scholarship) [5212]

H.G. Hardbarger Science and Mathematics Awards (Undergraduate/Award) [7083]

Matt Harmon Memorial Scholarships (Undergraduate/Scholarship) [8607]

North Las Vegas Firefighters - William J. Harnedy Memorial Scholarships (Undergraduate/Scholarship) [7495]

Harness Tracks of America Scholarship Fund (Undergraduate/Scholarship) [4401]

Walter and Lucille Harper Scholarships (Undergraduate/Scholarship) [5233]

Harris Corporation Merit Scholarships (Undergraduate/Scholarship) [4403]

Ruth Harris Memorial Scholarships (Undergraduate/Scholarship) [7084]

Frank and Charlene Harris Scholarships (Undergraduate/Scholarship) [3109]

Peg Hart Harrison Memorial Scholarships (Undergraduate/Scholarship) [3373]

Evelyn W. Harrison Point Scholarships (Graduate, Undergraduate/Scholarship) [7361]

Morton Harrison Scholarship Fund (Undergraduate/Scholarship) [3774]

Carroll Hart Scholarships (Graduate/Scholarship) [8329]

Hartford Foundation College Scholarship Program (Undergraduate/Scholarship) [4437]

Hartford Grammar School Scholarships (Undergraduate/Scholarship) [4438]

Hartford Whalers Booster Club Scholarships (Undergraduate/Scholarship) [4440]

Harry C. Hartleben III. Scholarships (Undergraduate/Scholarship) [7086]

William T. Hartzell Memorial Scholarships (Undergraduate/Scholarship) [7653]

Gregory Lynn Haught Citizenship Awards (Undergraduate/Award) [7088]

Dorcas Edmonson Haught Scholarships (Undergraduate/Scholarship) [7089]

Hawaii Community Foundation Scholarships (Undergraduate, Graduate/Scholarship) [4478]

R. Garn Haycock Memorial Scholarships (Undergraduate/Scholarship) [7654]

Erin Kumelos Heard Memorial Scholarships (Undergraduate/Scholarship) [3374]

Elizabeth Heath Technical, Trades Training and Development Awards (Undergraduate/Scholarship) [6997]

Dr. James H. Heckaman Memorial Scholarship Fund (Undergraduate/Scholarship) [8672]

Professor Ulla Hedner Scholarships (Undergraduate, Vocational/Occupational/Scholarship) [6326]

CSF Richard Heekin Scholarships (Undergraduate/Scholarship) [2847]

Howell Heflin Memorial Scholarships (Undergraduate/Scholarship) [6815]

Lavonne Heghinian Scholarships (Undergraduate/Scholarship) [3412]

Barbara and Nicole Heicox Foreign Travel and Study Scholarship Fund (Undergraduate/Scholarship) [4220]

Hemlow Prize in Burney Studies (Graduate/Prize) [1229]

Jeanne H. Hemmingway Scholarships (Undergraduate/Scholarship) [3531]

Hemophilia Health Services Memorial Scholarship Program (Graduate, Undergraduate/Scholarship) [6327]

Henderson Memorial Endowed Scholarships (Un-

dergraduate/Scholarship) [5432]

Melvin Henderson-Rubio Scholarships (Undergraduate/Scholarship) [9605]

John B. Henderson Scholarships (Undergraduate/Scholarship) [9153]

Dr. E. Bruce Hendrick Scholarships (All/Scholarship) [8647]

Gene Henson Scholarships (High School, Undergraduate/Scholarship) [1922]

Herb Kohl Educational Foundation Excellence Scholarships (Undergraduate/Scholarship) [4530]

Herb Kohl Educational Foundation Fellowships (Professional development/Fellowship) [4531]

Herb Kohl Educational Foundation Initiative Scholarships (High School/Scholarship) [4532]

Michael Herman Memorial Scholarship Fund (Undergraduate, Vocational/Occupational/Scholarship) [4222]

Manuel Hernandez, Jr. Foundation Scholarships (Undergraduate, Vocational/Occupational/Scholarship) [2949]

Ella Beren Hersch Scholarships (Undergraduate/Scholarship) [7090]

Peter Hess Scholarships (Undergraduate/Scholarship) [4061]

HHS Memorial Scholarships (Graduate, Undergraduate/Scholarship) [37]

HIAA Graduate Student Travel Grants (Graduate/Grant) [4588]

CSF Dwight Hibbard Scholarships (Undergraduate/Scholarship) [2848]

Jim Hierlihy Memorial Scholarships (Undergraduate/Scholarship) [3672]

D. Glenn Hilts Scholarships (Graduate, Undergraduate/Scholarship) [1872]

Jim & Nancy Hinkle Travel Grants (Postdoctorate/Grant) [4525]

Hispanic Association of Colleges and Universities Scholarships (Undergraduate/Scholarship) [4548]

Hispanic Association on Corporate Responsibility Scholarship Program (Undergraduate/Scholarship) [4553]

Hispanic Metropolitan Chamber Scholarships (Graduate, Undergraduate/Scholarship) [4564]

Hispanic Scholarship Fund College Scholarship Program (HSF) (Graduate, Undergraduate/Scholarship) [4570]

Hispanic Serving Institution Scholarships (HSIS) (Undergraduate/Scholarship) [9024]

Historically Black College or University Scholarships (HBCUS) (Undergraduate/Scholarship) [9025]

Lucy Hsu Ho Scholarships (Undergraduate/Scholarship) [2062]

C.V. Hoar Scholarship Awards (Undergraduate/Scholarship) [6900]

C.H.(Chuck) Hodgson Scholarships (Undergraduate/Scholarship) [9591]

James E. Hoff, S.J. Scholars (Undergraduate/Scholarship) [9771]

CSF Florette B. Hoffheimer Scholarships (Undergraduate/Scholarship) [2849]

Hoffman Family Scholarship Fund (Undergraduate/Scholarship) [4224]

Henry Hoffman Memorial Scholarship Fund (Undergraduate/Scholarship) [6064]

Irving J. Hoffman Memorial Scholarships (Undergraduate/Scholarship) [9331]

The Thelma S. Hoge Memorial Scholarship Fund (Undergraduate/Scholarship) [3087]

Michael J. Hoggard Memorial Scholarships (Undergraduate/Scholarship) [7497]

Cleve Holloway Memorial Scholarship Fund (Undergraduate/Scholarship) [3040]

Robert Holmes Scholarships (Undergraduate/Scholarship) [3198]

Herbert Hoover Uncommon Student Awards (Undergraduate/Scholarship) [4597]

Hope for the Warriors Spouses Scholarships (Graduate, Master's, Undergraduate, Vocational/Occupational/Scholarship) [4599]

Hopi Education Awards (Doctorate, Undergraduate/Award) [1511]

Frank and Gladys Hopkins Endowed Scholarships (Undergraduate/Scholarship) [5434]

Minnie Hopkins Memorial Scholarship Fund of Lath-

rop/Compton School (Undergraduate/Scholarship) [8675]

Sam J. Hord Memorial Scholarships (Undergraduate/Scholarship) [8563]

Hormel Foods Charitable Trust Scholarships (Undergraduate/Scholarship) [4601]

Detroit Tigers Willie Horton Scholarships (Undergraduate/Scholarship) [3199]

Hosinec Family Scholarships (Graduate, Undergraduate/Scholarship) [9332]

Max and Julia Houghton Duluth Central Scholarships (Undergraduate/Scholarship) [3533]

Houston Alumnae Chapter Graduate Fellowships (Graduate/Fellowship) [3375]

Kaspar Hovannisian Memorial Scholarships (Graduate/Scholarship) [1597]

Hirair and Anna Hovnanian Foundation Presidential Scholarships (Undergraduate/Scholarship) [1598]

Hirair and Anna Hovnanian Foundation Scholarships (Undergraduate/Scholarship) [1599]

C.D. Howard Scholarships (Undergraduate/Scholarship) [4898]

CSF Roger and Joyce Howe Family Scholarships (Undergraduate/Scholarship) [2850]

Christopher Hoy/ERT Scholarships (Graduate, Master's/Scholarship) [901]

HSF/Atrisco Heritage Foundation Scholarship Program (Graduate, Undergraduate/Scholarship) [4572]

HSF/IDT Hope High School Scholarship Program (Undergraduate/Scholarship) [4575]

Albert W. and Mildred Hubbard Scholarships (Undergraduate/Scholarship) [7934]

William Peyton Hubbard Scholarships (Undergraduate/Scholarship) [2121]

Amber Huber Memorial Scholarships (Undergraduate/Scholarship) [3154]

Hudson River Graduate Fellowships (Doctorate, Master's/Fellowship) [4618]

Puedo Scholarships - Joseph Huerta (Undergraduate/Scholarship) [2950]

Dale Hughes, Jr. Memorial Scholarships (Undergraduate/Scholarship) [8727]

Roger K. Hughes Legacy Scholarships (Undergraduate/Scholarship) [2247]

Hughes Memorial Foundation Scholarships (Graduate/Scholarship) [4625]

James Hughes Memorial Scholarship Fund (Undergraduate/Scholarship) [7159]

Paul A. Hughes Memorial Scholarships (Undergraduate/Scholarship) [2248]

Humane Studies Fellowships (Graduate/Fellowship) [4798]

Humber College Institute of Technology and Advanced Learning Scholarships (Undergraduate/Scholarship) [5119]

Kevin Hummer Point Scholarships (Graduate, Undergraduate/Scholarship) [7363]

Donald & Florence Hunting Scholarships (Undergraduate/Scholarship) [4286]

Doc Hurley Scholarships (Undergraduate/Scholarship) [4442]

Mike Hylton and Ron Niederman Memorial Scholarships (Undergraduate/Scholarship) [6328]

I Have a Dream Scholarships (Undergraduate/Scholarship) [5120]

IAESTE United States Scholarships (Undergraduate/Scholarship) [3309]

IAHCSMM - Purdue University Scholarship Awards (Professional development/Scholarship) [4870]

ICDA Graduate Scholarships (Graduate/Scholarship) [5034]

ICDA Research Grants (Graduate/Grant) [5035]

Ice Skating Institute of America Education Foundation Scholarships (Undergraduate/Scholarship) [4657]

Idaho Attorney General Scholarships (Undergraduate/Scholarship) [5435]

Idaho Promise Category B Scholarships (Undergraduate/Scholarship) [5436]

Ella R. Ifill Fund (Undergraduate/Scholarship) [5580]

Illinois Association of Chamber of Commerce Executives Scholarships (Postdoctorate/Scholarship) [4680]

Illinois Student Assistance Commission Merit Rec-

ognition Scholarships (MRS) (Undergraduate/Scholarship) [4698]

Illuminator Educational Foundation Scholarships (Undergraduate/Scholarship) [2249]

IMCEA Memorial Scholarships (Graduate, Undergraduate/Scholarship) [4960]

Independent Lubricant Manufacturers Association Scholarships (Undergraduate/Scholarship) [4712]

Independent University Alumni Association Scholarships (Graduate, Undergraduate/Scholarship) [4725]

Indiana Alumni Scholarships (Undergraduate/Scholarship) [9772]

Indiana State Alumni Association Academic Excellence Scholarships (Undergraduate/Scholarship) [4744]

Indiana State Alumni Association Incentive Scholarships (Undergraduate/Scholarship) [4746]

Indiana State Alumni Association President's Scholarships (Undergraduate/Scholarship) [4747]

Indiana State Alumni Association Transfer Student Scholarships (Undergraduate/Scholarship) [4749]

Informatics Post Doctoral Fellowships (Doctorate/Fellowship) [7227]

Informatics Pre Doctoral Fellowships (Doctorate/Fellowship) [7228]

Informatics Research Starter Grants (Doctorate/Grant) [7229]

Informatics Sabbatical Fellowships (Doctorate, Postdoctorate/Fellowship) [7230]

Information Age Publishing Graduate Student Book Scholarships (Doctorate, Graduate/Scholarship) [4762]

Barbara Ingram, Janet W. McCarthy and W.J.P. Jack Robertson Memorial Scholarships (Undergraduate/Scholarship) [6998]

Jennifer Ingrum Scholarships (Undergraduate/Scholarship) [3111]

INIA Scholarships Program (Undergraduate/Scholarship) [4965]

Inland Northwest Business Alliance Scholarships (INBA) (Undergraduate/Scholarship) [7411]

Institute for Anarchist Studies Grants for Radical Writers and Translators (Professional development/Grant) [4785]

Institute for the International Education of Students Faculty Fellowships (Professional development/Fellowship) [6695]

Institute of Turkish Studies Undergraduate Study Grants (Undergraduate/Grant) [4831]

International Code Council Foundation General Scholarship Fund (Undergraduate/Scholarship) [4899]

International Door Association Scholarship Foundation Program (Undergraduate, Vocational/Occupational/Scholarship) [4921]

International Education Awards - Ukraine (Undergraduate/Scholarship) [249]

International Executive Housekeepers Association Education Foundation Scholarship Awards (Undergraduate/Scholarship) [4923]

International Executive Housekeepers Association Spartan Scholarship Awards (Undergraduate/Scholarship) [4924]

International Grenfell Association Bursary (Undergraduate/Scholarship) [4946]

International Grenfell Association Secondary/High School Scholarships (Undergraduate/Scholarship) [4947]

International Grenfell Association University/College Scholarships (Undergraduate/Scholarship) [4948]

International Harvester Collectors Scholarships (Undergraduate/Scholarship) [4950]

International Order of the King's Daughters and Sons North American Indian Scholarship Program (Undergraduate/Scholarship) [820]

International Peace Scholarships (Undergraduate/Scholarship) [7305]

International Radio and Television Society Foundation Summer Fellowships Program (Graduate, Undergraduate/Fellowship) [4973]

International Study Abroad Scholarships (Graduate, Undergraduate/Scholarship) [4078]

Interracial Scholarship Fund of Greater Hartford (Undergraduate/Scholarship) [4443]

Iowa Division Scholarships *(Undergraduate/Scholarship)* [5859]

The Iranian-American Scholarship Fund *(Graduate, Undergraduate/Scholarship)* [6361]

Iranian Federated Women's Club Scholarships *(Undergraduate/Scholarship)* [6363]

Irish-American Research Travel Fellowships *(Professional development/Fellowship)* [1230]

Greg Irons Student Scholarships *(Undergraduate/Scholarship)* [3534]

Hazel D. Isbell Fellowships *(Graduate/Fellowship)* [3376]

Gunnar Isberg Student Scholarships *(Undergraduate/Scholarship)* [5896]

ISDS Graduate Student Scholarships *(Doctorate, Graduate/Scholarship)* [4990]

ISF Excellence in Community Service Scholarships *(Undergraduate/Scholarship)* [5048]

ISF Undergraduate Scholarships *(Undergraduate/Scholarship)* [5049]

Island Institute Scholarship Fund *(Undergraduate/Scholarship)* [5581]

Broughton Isom Memorial Scholarships *(Undergraduate/Scholarship)* [6816]

Italian Language Scholarships *(Undergraduate/Scholarship)* [6922]

Jack Family Scholarships *(Undergraduate/Scholarship)* [4287]

The Jackson Club Scholarships *(Undergraduate/Scholarship)* [3535]

Jackson High School Alumni Scholarship Fund *(Undergraduate/Scholarship)* [8678]

Sylvia E. Jackson Scholarships *(Undergraduate/Scholarship)* [8728]

Holly Jackson-Wuller Memorial Scholarships *(Undergraduate/Scholarship)* [7091]

Freddy L. Jacobs Scholarships *(Undergraduate/Scholarship)* [4886]

Eric L. Jacobson Memorial Scholarships *(Undergraduate/Scholarship)* [7655]

Louis I. Jaffe Memorial Scholarships-NSU Alumni *(Graduate/Scholarship)* [4376]

Cory Jam Awards *(Undergraduate/Scholarship)* [3536]

Jamaica Day Basil Duncan Memorial Scholarships *(Undergraduate/Scholarship)* [5121]

Jamaica National Building Society Scholarships *(Undergraduate/Scholarship)* [5122]

Jamaican Canadian Association Alberta Scholarship Program *(Undergraduate/Scholarship)* [5130]

Jamail/Long Challenge Grant Scholarships *(Graduate, Undergraduate/Scholarship)* [4559]

Dr. Ali Jarrahi Merit Scholarships *(Undergraduate/Scholarship)* [5050]

Carl and Lucille Jarrett Scholarship Fund *(Graduate, Undergraduate/Scholarship)* [3778]

Right Hon. Michaelle Jean Legacy Scholarships *(Undergraduate/Scholarship)* [2122]

Jefferson Graduate Fellowships *(Doctorate, Graduate/Fellowship)* [5153]

Erin L. Jenkins Memorial Scholarship Fund *(Undergraduate/Scholarship)* [3948]

Elise Reed Jenkins Memorial Scholarships - Gamma Lambda *(Undergraduate/Scholarship)* [8175]

Elise Reed Jenkins Memorial Scholarships - Gamma Psi *(Undergraduate/Scholarship)* [8176]

Ruth E. Jenkins Scholarships *(Undergraduate/Scholarship)* [7936]

Mike Jensen R.I.S.E. Memorial Scholarships *(Undergraduate/Scholarship)* [7656]

Kenneth Jernigan Scholarships *(Undergraduate/Scholarship)* [6276]

Harry Jerome Scholarships *(Undergraduate/Scholarship)* [2123]

James Jesinski Scholarships *(Undergraduate/Scholarship)* [9359]

James V. Johnson Scholarship Fund *(Undergraduate/Scholarship)* [3908]

Camilla C. Johnson Scholarships *(Undergraduate/Scholarship)* [4288]

Chip Johnson Scholarships *(Undergraduate/Scholarship)* [8608]

CSF Ella Wilson Johnson Scholarships *(Undergraduate/Scholarship)* [2851]

Stella B. Johnson Scholarships *(Undergraduate/Scholarship)* [9643]

OOIDA Mary Johnston Scholarships *(Undergraduate/Scholarship)* [7025]

George E. Jonas Scholarships *(Graduate, Undergraduate/Scholarship)* [5167]

Napoleon A. Jones, III Memorial Scholarships *(Undergraduate/Scholarship)* [7937]

Annabel Lambeth Jones Scholarships *(Undergraduate/Scholarship)* [3909]

CSF David J. Joseph Company Scholarships *(Undergraduate/Scholarship)* [2852]

JQSOW Scholarships *(Undergraduate/Scholarship)* [5149]

Kazimiera Juchniewicz Memorial Scholarships *(Undergraduate/Scholarship)* [7765]

Junior Achievement of East Central Ohio, Inc. Scholarship Fund *(Undergraduate/Scholarship)* [8679]

Junior Women of the Contemporary Club Scholarships *(Undergraduate/Scholarship)* [7658]

Just Out Scholarship Fund *(Undergraduate/Scholarship)* [3678]

Juvenile Arthritis Scholarships *(Undergraduate/Scholarship)* [4444]

K-12 Edu-Grants *(Other/Grant)* [6329]

Stefan & Weronika Kacperski Memorial Scholarships *(Undergraduate/Scholarship)* [7766]

Daniel Kahikina and Millie Akaka Scholarships *(Graduate, Undergraduate/Scholarship)* [5213]

David A. Kaiser Memorial Scholarship Fund *(Undergraduate/Scholarship)* [8680]

Kamehameha Schools Class of 1968 "Ka Poli O Kaiona" Scholarships *(Graduate, Undergraduate/Scholarship)* [5214]

Kamehameha Schools Class of 1972 Scholarships *(Graduate, Undergraduate/Scholarship)* [5215]

Martin S. Kane Memorial Community Service Award Scholarships *(Undergraduate/Scholarship)* [3062]

Kansas City Division Scholarships *(All/Scholarship)* [5860]

CSF M. Kantor and Brothers Scholarships *(Undergraduate/Scholarship)* [2853]

Walter Kapala Scholarships *(Undergraduate/Scholarship)* [4445]

Joseph Kaplan Fund *(Graduate, Undergraduate/Scholarship)* [4726]

Don Kaplan Legacy Scholarships *(Undergraduate/Scholarship)* [2250]

Kaplan Test Prep and Admission Scholarships for NSHSS Members *(High School/Scholarship)* [6503]

Kappa Chapter Centennial Scholarships *(Undergraduate/Scholarship)* [3377]

Kappa Kappa Gamma Graduate Scholarships *(Graduate/Scholarship)* [5193]

Kappa Kappa Gamma Undergraduate Scholarships *(Undergraduate/Scholarship)* [5194]

Kappa Zeta Scholarships *(Undergraduate/Scholarship)* [8177]

Josephine de Karman Fellowships *(Graduate, Undergraduate/Fellowship)* [5205]

Philip R. Karr, III Scholarship Fund *(Graduate/Fellowship)* [4100]

K.A.S.A Memorial Scholarships *(Undergraduate/Scholarship)* [7092]

KASF Chair Scholarships *(Graduate, Undergraduate/Scholarship)* [5292]

KASF Designated Scholarships *(Graduate, Undergraduate/Scholarship)* [5293]

KASF General Scholarships *(Graduate, Undergraduate/Scholarship)* [5294]

Ka'u Chamber of Commerce College Scholarships *(Undergraduate/Scholarship)* [5207]

William and Beatrice Kavanaugh Scholarships *(Undergraduate/Scholarship)* [5100]

Kawano Family Scholarships *(Undergraduate/Scholarship)* [7938]

Doc Keen Memorial Scholarships *(Undergraduate, Vocational/Occupational/Scholarship)* [8610]

Keepers Preservation Education Fund *(Undergraduate/Award)* [5583]

KEF Academic Scholarships *(Graduate, Undergraduate, Vocational/Occupational/Scholarship)* [5284]

KEF College/University Basic Scholarships *(Gradu-*

ate, Undergraduate, Vocational/Occupational/Scholarship)* [5285]

KEF Vocational Education Scholarship *(Vocational/Occupational/Scholarship)* [5286]

Keiser College Coast Guard Scholarships *(Undergraduate/Scholarship)* [2927]

Annette and Ernest Keith Scholarships *(Undergraduate/Scholarship)* [7659]

Kellogg Company Career Scholarships *(Undergraduate/Scholarship)* [5234]

Dr. Charles Kelly Memorial Scholarships *(Undergraduate/Scholarship)* [7093]

Oscar Kenshur Book Prize *(Professional development/Prize)* [1231]

Raymond A. Kent-Navy V-12/ROTC Scholarships *(Undergraduate/Scholarship)* [9212]

Kentucky Alumni Club Scholarships - Capital Region Alumni Club *(Undergraduate/Scholarship)* [9213]

Kentucky Alumni Club Scholarships - Central Kentucky Alumni Club *(Undergraduate/Scholarship)* [9214]

Kentucky Alumni Club Scholarships - Lake Cumberland Alumni Club *(Undergraduate/Scholarship)* [9215]

Kentucky Alumni Club Scholarships - Northern Kentucky Alumni Club *(Undergraduate/Scholarship)* [9216]

Kentucky Educational Excellence Scholarships *(Graduate, Undergraduate/Scholarship)* [2090]

Judge Oliver Kessel Memorial Scholarships - Ripley Rotary *(Undergraduate/Scholarship)* [7094]

Ashley E. Ketcher Memorial Scholarships *(Undergraduate/Scholarship)* [3156]

Luella Akins Key Scholarships *(Undergraduate/Scholarship)* [3378]

KFC Colonel's Scholars Program *(Undergraduate/Scholarship)* [5249]

Khaki University and Y.M.C.A. Memorial Scholarships *(Undergraduate/Scholarship)* [9334]

Bill Kidder Fund Awards *(Undergraduate/Scholarship)* [7853]

Mary and Millard Kiker Scholarships *(Undergraduate/Scholarship)* [3910]

Kilbuck Family Native American Scholarships *(Undergraduate/Scholarship)* [2063]

Kildonan Education Awards *(Undergraduate/Scholarship)* [6999]

Helen and George Kilik Scholarships *(Undergraduate/Scholarship)* [250]

Killam Fellowships Program *(Undergraduate/Fellowship)* [9100]

Killingworth Foundation Scholarships *(Undergraduate/Scholarship)* [5260]

Kimberly Elementary School PTA Scholarships *(Undergraduate/Scholarship)* [7660]

Dr. Martin Luther King & Coretta Scott King Student Leadership Scholarships *(Undergraduate/Scholarship)* [2336]

Arthur M. and Berdena King Eagle Scout Scholarships *(High School/Scholarship)* [6256]

Mackenzie King Open Scholarships *(Graduate/Scholarship)* [5723]

Kingsbury Elementary School PTA Scholarships *(Undergraduate/Scholarship)* [7661]

Isabel Mayer Kirkpatrick Scholarships *(Undergraduate/Scholarship)* [8611]

Dr. Elemer and Eva Kiss Scholarship Fund *(Undergraduate/Scholarship)* [4638]

Tamo Kitaura Scholarships *(Professional development/Scholarship)* [9057]

Kiwanis Club of Escondido Scholarships II *(Undergraduate, Vocational/Occupational/Scholarship)* [7940]

Kiwanis Club of Escondido Scholarships I *(Undergraduate/Scholarship)* [7939]

Gerda and Kurt Klein Scholarships *(High School/Scholarship)* [4606]

Stefan & Janina Klimt Scholarships *(Undergraduate/Scholarship)* [7767]

CSF Raymond and Augusta Klink Scholarships *(Undergraduate/Scholarship)* [2854]

Bryan L. Knapp Point Scholarships *(Graduate, Undergraduate/Scholarship)* [7364]

J. Merrill Knapp Research Fellowships *(Undergraduate/Fellowship)* [782]

Kemper K. Knapp Scholarships *(Undergraduate/Scholarship)* [9360]

Iver & Cora Knapstad Scholarships *(Undergraduate/Scholarship)* [9155]

Knights of Pythias Scholarships *(Undergraduate/Scholarship)* [7499]

Jane Shaw Knox Graduate Scholarships *(Graduate/Scholarship)* [3868]

Knox-Hume Scholarships *(Undergraduate/Scholarship)* [3113]

Ina Knutsen Scholarships *(Undergraduate/Scholarship)* [8117]

Seth Koehler Central High School Scholarship Fund *(Undergraduate, Vocational/Occupational/Scholarship)* [4225]

CSF Bob and Linda Kohlhepp Scholarships *(Undergraduate/Scholarship)* [2855]

George Kokocinski Memorial Scholarships *(Undergraduate/Scholarship)* [7768]

Gwin J. and Ruth Kolb Travel Fellowships *(Doctorate, Professional development/Fellowship)* [1232]

Anna and John Kolesay Memorial Scholarships *(Undergraduate/Scholarship)* [251]

Bernie Kom Memorial Awards *(Postgraduate/Award)* [8040]

Susan G. Komen for the Cure College Scholarship Awards *(Undergraduate/Award, Scholarship)* [5281]

Herman P. Kopplemann Scholarships *(Undergraduate/Scholarship)* [4446]

Robert Wade Korn Endowed Scholarships *(Undergraduate/Scholarship)* [9156]

Eugene & Elinor Kotur Scholarship Trust Fund *(Undergraduate, Graduate/Scholarship)* [9499]

Marjorie Kovler Research Fellowships *(All/Fellowship)* [5239]

Eve Kraft Education and College Scholarships *(Undergraduate/Scholarship)* [9409]

Norman Kramer Scholarship Awards *(Undergraduate/Scholarship)* [5837]

Krawczyk-Krane Family Scholarships *(Undergraduate/Scholarship)* [7769]

Sharon Kreikemeier Memorial Scholarships *(Undergraduate/Scholarship)* [6602]

Robert Krembil Scholarships of Merit *(Postgraduate/Scholarship)* [8041]

Melvin Kruger Endowed Scholarship Program *(Undergraduate, Vocational/Occupational/Scholarship)* [6465]

Melvin Kruger Endowed Scholarships *(Graduate, Undergraduate, Vocational/Occupational/Scholarship)* [7817]

Judith Keller Marx Krumholz Scholarships *(Undergraduate/Scholarship)* [7941]

Kuchler-Killian Memorial Scholarships *(Undergraduate/Scholarship)* [6277]

Heloise Werthan Kuhn Scholarships *(Undergraduate/Scholarship)* [3116]

Kumin Scholars Program *(Undergraduate/Scholarship)* [8204]

Jan Kuropas Memorial Scholarships *(Undergraduate/Scholarship)* [7770]

Chris Kurzweil Scholarships *(Undergraduate/Scholarship)* [3200]

Gretchen Laatsch Scholarships *(Graduate/Scholarship)* [1740]

Lavina Laible Scholarships *(Undergraduate/Scholarship)* [4289]

Casey Laine Armed Forces Scholarships *(Undergraduate/Scholarship)* [2951]

Lake George Dollars for Scholars Awards *(Undergraduate/Scholarship)* [5318]

Lalor Foundation Post-Doctoral Fellowships *(Postdoctorate/Fellowship)* [5322]

Lam Research Corporation Core Values Scholarships *(Undergraduate/Scholarship)* [5324]

Lamaku Post-Secondary Scholarships *(Undergraduate/Scholarship)* [83]

Lambda Alumni, UCLA Lesbian & Gay Alumni Association Scholarships Program *(Undergraduate/Scholarship)* [7854]

Allen T. Lambert Scholarships *(Postgraduate/Scholarship)* [8042]

Frank S. Land Scholarships *(Undergraduate/Scholarship)* [3425]

Gloria Landis Bursary *(Undergraduate, Vocational/Occupational/Scholarship)* [5398]

The Lanford Family Highway Worker Memorial Scholarship Program *(Undergraduate/Scholarship)* [1157]

Langfitt-Ambrose Trust Funds *(Undergraduate/Scholarship)* [7097]

Stephen Lankester Scholarships *(Undergraduate/Scholarship)* [4290]

The Otis and Florence Lapham Memorial Scholarships *(Undergraduate/Scholarship)* [5101]

Peter and Jody Larkin Legacy Scholarships *(Undergraduate/Scholarship)* [2251]

Joseph C. Larson Entrepreneurial Scholarships *(Undergraduate/Scholarship)* [7942]

Las Limas Community Scholarships *(Undergraduate/Scholarship)* [8730]

Las Vegas Elks Scholarships for the Physically Challenged *(Undergraduate, Vocational/Occupational/Scholarship)* [7502]

Las Vegas Elks Scholarships *(Undergraduate, Vocational/Occupational/Scholarship)* [7501]

Stanislaw & Aniela Lasek Scholarships *(Undergraduate/Scholarship)* [7771]

Austin E. Lathrop Scholarships *(Undergraduate/Scholarship)* [9157]

Kenneth Laundy Entrance Scholarships *(Postgraduate/Scholarship)* [8043]

Robert G. Lawrence Prize *(Doctorate, Graduate, Professional development/Prize)* [2412]

Willie D. Lawson, Jr. Memorial Scholarships *(Doctorate, Graduate, Professional development/Scholarship)* [6150]

Lawton Minority Retention Grants *(Undergraduate/Scholarship)* [9362]

Sue Kay Lay Memorial Scholarships *(Undergraduate/Scholarship)* [2952]

Danny T. Le Memorial Scholarships *(High School, Undergraduate/Scholarship)* [9431]

Franklin M. Leach Scholarships *(Undergraduate/Scholarship)* [9158]

LeaderShape Institute Scholarships *(Undergraduate/Grant)* [5202]

Leadership 1000 Scholarships *(Undergraduate/Scholarship)* [2976]

LEAGUE Foundation Scholarships *(Undergraduate/Scholarship)* [7855]

Jack W. Leatherman Family Scholarship Fund *(Graduate/Scholarship)* [4228]

Patrick Ledden Honorary Scholarships *(Undergraduate/Scholarship)* [7943]

Ken Lee Memorial Scholarships *(Undergraduate/Scholarship)* [7944]

Bruce Lee Scholarships *(Undergraduate/Scholarship)* [9064]

Legacy Scholarship Program *(Undergraduate/Scholarship)* [8870]

Jay C. and B. Nadine Leggett Charitable Scholarship Fund *(Undergraduate/Scholarship)* [8684]

Herbert Lehman Education Scholarships *(Undergraduate/Scholarship)* [5971]

Lehman Family Scholarships *(Undergraduate/Scholarship)* [7945]

Lemelson Center Fellowships *(Doctorate, Postdoctorate, Professional development/Fellowship)* [8255]

Lemelson Center Travel to Collections Awards *(Graduate, Professional development/Award)* [8256]

The Lemon Grove Education Foundation Scholarships *(Undergraduate, Vocational/Occupational/Scholarship)* [7946]

Stan Lencki Scholarships *(Undergraduate/Scholarship)* [5713]

Franklin A. Lentesty Scholarships *(Undergraduate/Scholarship)* [6817]

V.A. Leonard Scholarships *(Graduate, Undergraduate/Scholarship)* [357]

Leopold Education Project Scholarships *(Undergraduate/Scholarship)* [3158]

Sherman L. & Mabel C. Lepard Scholarships *(Undergraduate/Scholarship)* [4291]

Irwin S. Lerner Student Scholarships *(Undergraduate/Scholarship)* [6513]

Carol Anne Letheren Entrance Awards *(Postgraduate/Award)* [8044]

The Irving Leuchter Memorial Scholarships *(All/Scholarship)* [6714]

Jack A. and Louise S. Levine Memorial Scholarships *(Undergraduate/Scholarship)* [7666]

Lewis-Clark Coin Club Endowed Scholarships *(Undergraduate/Scholarship)* [5439]

Lewis-Clark State College Foundation Scholars Scholarships *(Undergraduate/Scholarship)* [5441]

Lewis-Clark State College Freshman Scholarships *(Undergraduate/Scholarship)* [5442]

Lewis-Clark State College Non-Traditional Student Scholarships *(Undergraduate/Scholarship)* [5445]

Lewis-Clark State College Presidential Out-of-State Scholarships *(Undergraduate/Scholarship)* [5446]

Lewis-Clark State College Provost Scholarships *(Undergraduate/Scholarship)* [5448]

Lewis-Clark State College Transfer Scholarships *(Undergraduate/Scholarship)* [5449]

Lewis-Clark State College Valley Scholarships *(Undergraduate/Scholarship)* [5450]

George T. Lewis, Jr. Academic Scholarship Fund *(Undergraduate/Scholarship)* [3912]

Jonathan D. Lewis Point Scholarships *(Graduate, Undergraduate/Scholarship)* [7365]

Marvin Lewis Scholarships *(Undergraduate/Scholarship)* [5471]

Lewiston Clarkston Kiwanis Club Scholarships *(Undergraduate/Scholarship)* [5451]

Lewiston Service League Memorial Scholarships *(Undergraduate/Scholarship)* [5452]

Lexington Alumni Scholarships *(Undergraduate/Scholarship)* [5473]

Lexington Community Foundation Annual Scholarships *(Undergraduate/Scholarship)* [5474]

Lexington Community Foundation/CCC Scholarships *(Undergraduate/Scholarship)* [5475]

Library Research Grants *(All/Grant)* [4144]

Dolores Zohrab Liebmann Fund - Independent Research/Study Grants *(Graduate/Grant)* [5489]

LIFE Lessons Scholarship Program *(Undergraduate/Scholarship)* [5492]

Lighthouse International Scholarships - College-bound Awards *(High School, Undergraduate/Scholarship)* [5497]

Lighthouse International Scholarships - Graduate Awards *(Graduate/Scholarship)* [5498]

Lighthouse International Scholarships - Undergraduate Awards *(Undergraduate/Scholarship)* [5499]

Lilly Reintegration Scholarships *(All, Vocational/Occupational/Scholarship)* [2707]

Linda's Scholarships *(All/Scholarship)* [5882]

Lindenwood University Scouting Scholarships *(Undergraduate/Scholarship)* [6258]

CSF Carl H. Lindner Family Scholarships *(Undergraduate/Scholarship)* [2856]

Lawrence Lipking Fellowships at the Newberry Library *(Graduate/Fellowship)* [6697]

Ruth Lister Scholarships *(Undergraduate, Vocational/Occupational/Scholarship)* [8986]

LIT Scholarships *(Graduate, Undergraduate/Scholarship)* [5328]

Ian Lithgow Memorial Awards *(Postgraduate/Award)* [8045]

Live Out Loud Annual Scholarships *(Undergraduate/Scholarship)* [7856]

LLN Scholarships *(Community College/Scholarship)* [5358]

E.C. Lloyd and J.C.U. Johnson Scholarship Fund *(Undergraduate/Scholarship)* [3042]

Lo Family Scholarships *(Undergraduate/Scholarship)* [9335]

Virgil K. Lobring Scholarships *(Undergraduate/Scholarship)* [3202]

Audrey Loftus Memorial Scholarships *(Undergraduate/Scholarship)* [9188]

Stephen Logan Memorial Scholarships *(Undergraduate/Scholarship)* [4052]

London Goodenough Association of Canada Scholarships *(Graduate/Scholarship)* [5515]

Lone Star GIA Associate and Alumni Scholarships *(Undergraduate/Scholarship)* [4064]

Lawrence A. Long Memorial Law Scholarships *(Undergraduate/Scholarship)* [368]

L.D. and Elsie Long Memorial Scholarships *(Graduate/Scholarship)* [9646]

Long-Term Research Fellowship Programs *(Profes-*

sional development/Fellowship) [5672]

Megan Nicole Longwell Scholarships *(Undergraduate/Scholarship)* [7098]

Audre Lord Scholarships *(Graduate, Undergraduate/Scholarship)* [7857]

Sir James Lougheed Awards of Distinction *(Doctorate, Graduate/Award)* [255]

Love of Bonita Empowerment Scholarships *(Undergraduate/Scholarship)* [8613]

First Lieutenant Scott McClean Love Memorial Scholarship - Children of Soldiers *(Undergraduate, Vocational/Occupational/Scholarship)* [1615]

First Lieutenant Scott McClean Love Memorial Scholarship - Spouses of Soldiers *(Undergraduate, Vocational/Occupational/Scholarship)* [1616]

Diane G. Lowe and John Gomez, IV Scholarships *(Undergraduate/Scholarship)* [3117]

H.B. Paul Lowenberg Lions Scholarships *(Undergraduate/Scholarship)* [4447]

Elsa Ludeke Graduate Scholarships *(Graduate/Scholarship)* [3417]

Lugonia Alumni/Harrison Lightfoot Scholarships *(Undergraduate/Scholarship)* [7667]

Luso-American Fraternal Federation B-2 Scholarships *(Postgraduate/Scholarship)* [5545]

Luso-American Fraternal Federation B-3 Scholarships *(All, Vocational/Occupational/Scholarship)* [5546]

Luso-American Fraternal Federation B-4 Scholarships *(All/Scholarship)* [5547]

Melissa A. Lyles Memorial Scholarships *(Undergraduate/Scholarship)* [7503]

John Mabry Forestry Scholarships *(Undergraduate/Scholarship)* [7587]

MAC Emeritus Scholarships for First-Time Meeting Attendees *(All/Scholarship)* [5855]

Bill MacAloney Legacy Scholarships *(Undergraduate/Scholarship)* [2252]

John Macara, Barrister of Goderich, Scholarships *(Undergraduate/Scholarship)* [9336]

Nate Mack/Cindi Turner Scholarships *(Undergraduate/Scholarship)* [7504]

James Mackenzie Fallows Scholarships Honoring William Cunningham *(Undergraduate/Scholarship)* [7668]

Carol E. Macpherson Memorial Scholarship and Alumnae Society Scholarships *(Graduate, Undergraduate/Scholarship)* [9244]

Lawrence Madeiros Scholarships *(Undergraduate/Scholarship)* [6330]

The Brandon Magalassi Memorial Scholarship Foundation Scholarships *(Undergraduate/Scholarship)* [5567]

John T. & Frances Maghielse Scholarships *(Undergraduate/Scholarship)* [4292]

Sonia S. Maguire Outstanding Scholastic Achievement Awards *(Graduate, Undergraduate/Scholarship)* [8782]

Dan and Rachel Mahi Educational Scholarships *(Graduate, Undergraduate/Scholarship)* [5216]

Rick Mahoney Scholarships *(Undergraduate/Scholarship)* [5714]

Mary Main Memorial Scholarships *(Undergraduate/Scholarship)* [4449]

Maine Community Foundation - Rice Scholarships *(Undergraduate/Scholarship)* [5585]

Maine Vietnam Veterans Scholarships *(All/Scholarship)* [5586]

Joseph J. Malone Fellowships in Arab and Islamic Studies *(Professional development/Fellowship)* [6227]

Dr. Julianne Malveaux Scholarships *(Undergraduate/Scholarship)* [6093]

Manchester Scholarship Foundation Scholarships *(Undergraduate/Scholarship)* [4450]

Mangasar M. Mangasarian Scholarship Fund *(Graduate/Scholarship)* [1602]

Horace Mann Insurance Scholarships *(High School/Scholarship)* [6878]

Mansfield Soccer Association Scholarships *(Undergraduate/Scholarship)* [5603]

Stephen T. Marchello Scholarships *(Undergraduate/Scholarship)* [5609]

The Eric Marder Scholarships *(Undergraduate/Scholarship)* [4710]

Aurella Varallo Mariani Scholarship Program *(Under-*

graduate/Scholarship) [5985]

Marine Corps League National Scholarships *(Undergraduate/Scholarship)* [5637]

Mariposa Elementary School PTA Scholarships *(Undergraduate, Vocational/Occupational/Scholarship)* [7669]

Markley Family Scholarship Fund *(Undergraduate/Scholarship)* [8687]

Markley Scholarships *(Graduate, Undergraduate/Scholarship)* [6046]

Markowski-Leach Scholarship Fund *(Graduate, Undergraduate/Scholarship)* [7858]

Carl J. Marrara Memorial Scholarship Fund *(Undergraduate/Scholarship)* [3780]

Barry H. Marshal Scholarships *(Undergraduate/Scholarship)* [7859]

Marshall Memorial Fellowships *(Professional development/Fellowship)* [4132]

Sarah Shinn Marshall Scholarships *(Undergraduate/Scholarship)* [3379]

Marshall Undergraduate Scholars Program *(Undergraduate/Award)* [5650]

Bryce-Lietzke Martin Scholarships *(Undergraduate/Scholarship)* [7099]

Martin Sisters Scholarships *(Undergraduate/Scholarship)* [3380]

John S. Martinez and Family Scholarship Fund *(Undergraduate/Scholarship)* [3081]

Eric Martinez Memorial Scholarships *(Graduate, Undergraduate/Scholarship)* [9019]

Michael L. Marx and Donald K. Marshall Scholarships *(Undergraduate/Scholarship)* [7860]

Beverly Mascoll Scholarships *(Undergraduate/Scholarship)* [2124]

Master Municipal Clerks Academy Scholarships *(Professional development/Scholarship)* [4958]

Matanuska-Susitna College Regent's Scholarships *(Undergraduate/Scholarship)* [9160]

Rene Matos Memorial Scholarships *(Undergraduate, Vocational/Occupational/Scholarship)* [6338]

The Renardo A. Matteucci Scholarship Fund *(Undergraduate/Scholarship)* [3088]

Antonio Mattos Memorial Scholarships *(Undergraduate/Scholarship)* [5548]

Mature Student Scholarships *(Undergraduate/Scholarship)* [3673]

Aaron Matusek Memorial Scholarships *(Undergraduate/Scholarship)* [7506]

Edmund F. Maxwell Scholarships *(Undergraduate/Scholarship)* [5698]

Juliann and Joseph Maxwell Scholarships *(Undergraduate/Scholarship)* [3120]

Juliann King Maxwell Scholarships for Riverview High School Students *(Undergraduate, Vocational/Occupational/Scholarship)* [3121]

May-Cassioppi Scholarships *(Undergraduate/Scholarship)* [3159]

John E. Mayfield ABLE Scholarships *(Undergraduate/Scholarship)* [3122]

John E. Mayfield Scholarships for Cheatham County Central High School *(Undergraduate/Scholarship)* [3123]

John E. Mayfield Scholarships for Harpeth High School *(Undergraduate/Scholarship)* [3124]

John E. Mayfield Scholarships Pleasant View Christian School *(Undergraduate/Scholarship)* [3125]

John E. Mayfield Scholarships for Sycamore High School *(Undergraduate/Scholarship)* [3126]

Bill Maynes Fellowships *(Professional development/Fellowship)* [3691]

Joseph W. Mayo ALS Scholarships *(Undergraduate/Scholarship)* [5587]

Tadeusz Maziarz Scholarships *(Undergraduate/Scholarship)* [7772]

Bill McAdam Scholarships *(Undergraduate/Scholarship)* [6331]

McBurney Disability Scholarships *(Undergraduate/Scholarship)* [9363]

Bill McCarthy Scout Scholarship Fund *(Undergraduate/Scholarship)* [8688]

Walter A. and Nan C. McCloskey Memorial Scholarships *(Undergraduate/Scholarship)* [3781]

Dave McCloud Aviation Memorial Scholarships *(Undergraduate/Scholarship)* [9161]

McDaniel College Eagle Scout Scholarships *(Undergraduate/Scholarship)* [6259]

Ronald McDonald House Charities African American Future Achievers Scholarships *(Undergraduate/Scholarship)* [5700]

Ronald McDonald House Charities of Hispanic Heritage *(Undergraduate/Scholarship)* [5701]

Ronald McDonald House Charities of Las Vegas Scholarships *(Undergraduate/Scholarship)* [7507]

Ronald McDonald House Charities Scholarships in Asia *(Undergraduate/Scholarship)* [5702]

Ronald McDonald House Charities Scholarships *(Undergraduate/Scholarship)* [5703]

McDonald's USA National Employee Scholarship Program *(Undergraduate/Scholarship)* [5705]

McFarffels Scholarships *(Undergraduate/Scholarship)* [7412]

Nancy B. Woolridge McGee Graduate Fellowships *(Graduate/Fellowship)* [9806]

Lucile E. McGee Scholarships *(Undergraduate/Scholarship)* [5102]

McKelvey Foundation Entrepreneurial Scholarships *(Undergraduate/Scholarship)* [5728]

McKelvey Scholarships *(Undergraduate/Scholarship)* [5729]

McKinley Elementary School PTA Scholarships *(Undergraduate, Vocational/Occupational/Scholarship)* [7670]

John L. and Eleanore I. Mckinley Scholarships *(Undergraduate/Scholarship)* [3418]

Louise McKinney Post-secondary Scholarships *(Undergraduate/Scholarship)* [256]

McKinney Sisters Undergraduate Scholarships *(Undergraduate/Scholarship)* [3381]

Elizabeth McKissick Memorial Scholarships *(Undergraduate/Scholarship)* [5454]

James H. McLaughlin Scholarships *(Undergraduate/Scholarship)* [6740]

Joan Reagin McNeill Scholarships - Alpha Theta *(Undergraduate/Scholarship)* [8178]

Joan Reagin McNeill Scholarships - Theta Phi *(Undergraduate/Scholarship)* [8179]

David Meador Student Scholarships *(Undergraduate/Scholarship)* [6622]

Jack Meadows Memorial Awards *(Undergraduate/Scholarship)* [7000]

The Medalist Club Post Graduate Scholarships *(Postgraduate/Scholarship)* [5733]

Medicus Student Exchange Scholarships *(Graduate, Undergraduate/Scholarship)* [8783]

Augustine and Sandra Medina Memorial Scholarships *(Undergraduate/Scholarship)* [7671]

Dr. Ernest and Minnie Mehl Scholarships *(Undergraduate/Scholarship)* [257]

Mellon Advanced Fellowships in Turkey for East European Scholars *(Doctorate/Fellowship)* [1152]

Richard Mellon Endowment Scholarships *(Undergraduate/Scholarship)* [9162]

Andrew W. Mellon Fellowships *(Graduate, Doctorate/Fellowship)* [5675]

E.V. and Nancy Melosi Travel Grants *(Graduate, Professional development/Grant)* [1250]

Menominee Tribal Scholarships *(Graduate, Undergraduate/Scholarship)* [5769]

Mensa Education and Research Foundation U.S. Scholarships *(Graduate, Undergraduate, Vocational/Occupational/Scholarship)* [5775]

Benchwarmers of Redlands-Jess Mercado Football Scholarships *(Undergraduate/Scholarship)* [7672]

Al Mercury Scholarships *(Undergraduate/Scholarship)* [9338]

MESA Graduate Student Paper Prize *(Graduate/Prize)* [5851]

MESA Student Travel Fund *(Undergraduate/Grant)* [5852]

Mesothelioma Memorial Scholarships *(Undergraduate, Vocational/Occupational/Scholarship)* [8751]

Mesquite Club Evening Chapter Scholarships *(Undergraduate/Scholarship)* [7508]

MetroPCS Community Scholars Program *(Undergraduate/Scholarship)* [5781]

Mexican American Alumni Association Scholarships *(Graduate, Undergraduate/Scholarship)* [9400]

MHS Health Career Scholarships *(Undergraduate/Scholarship)* [5750]

Michigan Council of Women in Technology High School Program *(Undergraduate/Scholarship)* [5816]

Michigan Council of Women in Technology Undergraduate Scholarship Program *(Graduate, Undergraduate/Scholarship)* [5817]

Michigan Education Association Scholarships *(Undergraduate/Scholarship)* [5819]

Bronislaw Michno Memorial Scholarships *(Undergraduate/Scholarship)* [7773]

Beth Middleton Memorial Scholarships *(Undergraduate/Scholarship)* [3709]

Midwest Chapter Scholarships - Non-Engineering *(Undergraduate/Scholarship)* [1811]

Midwest Chapter Scholarships - Western States Awards *(Undergraduate/Scholarship)* [1812]

Midwest Modern Language Association Fellowships *(Doctorate/Fellowship)* [6699]

Keith Miffioli Scholarships *(Undergraduate/Scholarship)* [3160]

Mihaly Russin Scholarship Awards *(Graduate/Scholarship)* [7837]

Milan Getting Scholarships *(Undergraduate/Scholarship)* [8522]

Eunice Miles Scholarships *(Undergraduate/Scholarship)* [4066]

Military Intelligence Corps Association Scholarships *(Undergraduate, Vocational/Occupational/Scholarship)* [5872]

Robbie Miller Memorial Scholarships *(Undergraduate/Scholarship)* [5456]

Brian and Colleen Miller Scholarships *(Undergraduate/Scholarship)* [2953]

Miller Thomson Foundation Scholarships *(Undergraduate/Scholarship)* [5884]

MillerCoors Chicago Scholarships *(Community College, Undergraduate/Scholarship)* [46]

Carolina Panthers Players Sam Mills Memorial Scholarship Fund *(Undergraduate/Scholarship)* [3914]

Minerva Scholarships *(Undergraduate/Scholarship)* [2125]

Minneapolis Camp Scholarships *(Undergraduate/Scholarship)* [5888]

Minnesota Division Scholarships *(Undergraduate/Scholarship)* [5861]

Minnesota GLBT Educational Fund *(Undergraduate/Scholarship)* [7862]

Minnesota Power Community Involvement Scholarships *(Undergraduate/Scholarship)* [3537]

Minnesota State Archery Association Scholarships Program *(Undergraduate/Scholarship)* [5902]

MiraCosta College Two-Year Colleges Scholarships *(Undergraduate/Scholarship)* [5906]

Missigman Scholarship Fund *(Undergraduate/Scholarship)* [3783]

N.W. Mitchell-Piedmont Federal Savings and Loans Endowed Scholarships *(Undergraduate/Scholarship)* [9647]

George J. Mitchell Postgraduate Scholarships *(Postgraduate/Scholarship)* [6077]

Dorothy Mitchell Scholarships *(Undergraduate/Scholarship)* [7673]

Robert L. & Hilda Treasure Mitchell Scholarships *(Undergraduate/Scholarship)* [4294]

Sam Mizrahi Memorial Scholarships *(Undergraduate/Scholarship)* [3952]

MKC Scholarships *(Undergraduate/Scholarship)* [7948]

MMUF Dissertation Grants *(Doctorate/Grant)* [9616]

MMUF Travel and Research Grants *(Doctorate/Grant)* [9617]

MOAA American Patriot Scholarships *(Undergraduate/Scholarship)* [5874]

MOAA Base/Post Scholarships *(Undergraduate/Scholarship)* [5875]

Modern Woodmen of America Scholarships *(Undergraduate/Scholarship)* [3538]

Molecular Evolution Fellowships *(Doctorate/Fellowship)* [8242]

Momeni Foundation Scholarships *(Undergraduate/Scholarship)* [6364]

Murray Montague Memorial Scholarships *(Undergraduate/Scholarship)* [4268]

Hugh and Elizabeth Montgomery Scholarships *(Undergraduate/Scholarship)* [5590]

Cary Moore Memorial Scholarship Fund *(Undergraduate/Scholarship)* [3203]

Moore Middle School PTA Scholarships *(Undergraduate/Scholarship)* [7674]

Farmers Union Marketing and Processing Foundation Stanley Moore Scholarships *(Undergraduate, Vocational/Occupational/Scholarship)* [6784]

Stanley Moore Scholarships *(Undergraduate, Vocational/Occupational/Scholarship)* [6785]

Dr. Blanca Moore-Velez Woman of Substance Scholarships *(Undergraduate/Scholarship)* [6094]

More Uncommon Grounds Scholarships (MUG) *(Undergraduate/Scholarship)* [3260]

Kyle Moreland Memorial Endowment Scholarship Fund *(Undergraduate/Scholarship)* [4230]

Leo F. Moro Baseball Memorial Scholarships *(Undergraduate/Scholarship)* [3953]

James B. Morris Scholarships *(Undergraduate/Scholarship)* [5935]

Mortar Board National Foundation Fellowships *(Postdoctorate/Fellowship)* [5937]

Dwight Mosley Scholarships *(Undergraduate/Scholarship)* [9410]

John R. Mott Scholarships *(Undergraduate/Scholarship)* [5939]

MPI CRV Scholarships *(Professional development/Scholarship)* [5757]

Ruth Mu-Lan and James S.C. Chao Scholarships *(Undergraduate/Scholarship)* [9065]

Brittany Mueller Memorial Scholarships *(High School/Scholarship)* [6603]

Dudley Mullins/Cabot Corporation Scholarships *(Undergraduate/Scholarship)* [7100]

Muncy Rotary Club Scholarship Fund *(Undergraduate/Scholarship)* [3785]

Muncy Scholars Award Fund *(Undergraduate/Award)* [3786]

Harry Munoz Memorial Scholarships *(Undergraduate/Scholarship)* [7675]

Rick Munoz Memorial Scholarships *(Undergraduate/Scholarship)* [7676]

Anthony Munoz Scholarships *(Undergraduate/Scholarship)* [5948]

Daniel Murphy Scholarships *(High School/Scholarship)* [5950]

Carolyn Murray Memorial Scholarships *(Undergraduate/Scholarship)* [2337]

Muscle Shoals Kiwanis/Wal-Mart Scholarships *(Undergraduate/Scholarship)* [6818]

Muslim Sister Scholarships *(Undergraduate/Scholarship)* [8224]

MyApartmentMap Housing Scholarships *(Undergraduate/Scholarship)* [5962]

NACA East Coast Graduate Student Scholarships *(Graduate, Postdoctorate/Scholarship)* [6047]

NACA East Coast Higher Education Research Scholarships *(Postgraduate/Scholarship)* [6048]

NACA East Coast Undergraduate Scholarships for Student Leaders *(Undergraduate/Scholarship)* [6049]

NACA Foundation Graduate Scholarships *(Graduate, Master's, Postdoctorate/Scholarship)* [6050]

NACA Regional Council Student Leadership Scholarships *(Undergraduate/Scholarship)* [6051]

NACA Southeast Student Leadership Scholarships *(Undergraduate/Scholarship)* [6052]

NACADA Scholarships *(Doctorate, Graduate/Scholarship)* [5997]

Irwin Allen Nadal Entrance Awards *(Postgraduate/Award)* [8046]

Miles Spencer Nadal Entrance Awards *(Postgraduate/Award)* [8047]

NAED/Spencer Dissertation Fellowship Program *(Doctorate/Fellowship)* [6005]

NAFEO Internship Program *(Undergraduate/Internship)* [6068]

Jack Nagasaka Memorial Scholarships *(Undergraduate/Scholarship)* [7677]

NANBPWC National Scholarships *(Undergraduate/Scholarship)* [6095]

Robyn Nance Memorial Scholarships *(Undergraduate/Scholarship)* [7678]

Chereddi NarayanaRao & Radhamanohari Scholarships *(Graduate/Scholarship)* [8830]

NARFE-FEEA Scholarship Awards Program *(Undergraduate/Scholarship)* [6011]

NARRP Student Conference Scholarships *(Graduate, Undergraduate/Scholarship)* [6111]

Kermit B. Nash Academic Scholarships *(Undergraduate/Scholarship)* [8137]

Elizabeth Nash Foundation Scholarships *(Graduate, Undergraduate/Scholarship)* [5983]

Archie Hartwell Nash Memorial Scholarships *(Graduate, Undergraduate/Scholarship)* [3127]

Mike Nash Memorial Scholarships *(Undergraduate/Scholarship)* [9427]

National AAHAM Scholarships *(Undergraduate/Scholarship)* [483]

National Air Filtration Association Scholarship Fund *(Undergraduate/Scholarship)* [6015]

National Association for Armenian Studies and Research Scholarships *(Graduate, Postgraduate/Scholarship)* [1603]

National Association of Campus Activities Multicultural Scholarship Programs *(Undergraduate/Scholarship)* [6053]

National Association of Campus Activities Scholarships for Student Leaders *(Undergraduate/Scholarship)* [6054]

National Association for the Self-Employed Scholarships *(Undergraduate/Scholarship)* [6118]

National Beta Club Scholarships *(Undergraduate/Scholarship)* [6139]

National Black Deaf Advocate Scholarships *(Graduate, Undergraduate/Scholarship)* [6147]

National Center for Health Statistics Postdoctoral Research Awards *(Postdoctorate/Fellowship)* [2714]

National Coal Transportation Association At Large Scholarships *(Undergraduate/Scholarship)* [6190]

National College Scholarship Awards *(Undergraduate/Scholarship)* [5088]

National Collegiate Athletic Association Postgraduate Scholarships *(Postgraduate/Scholarship)* [6194]

National Collegiate Cancer Foundation Scholarships *(Undergraduate/Scholarship)* [6196]

National Costumers Association Scholarships *(Undergraduate/Scholarship)* [6210]

National Huguenot Society Scholarships *(Undergraduate/Scholarship)* [6347]

National Merit Scholarship Program *(Undergraduate/Scholarship)* [6405]

National Organization of Italian-American Women Scholarships *(All/Scholarship)* [6425]

National Pathfinder Scholarships *(Graduate, Master's, Undergraduate/Scholarship)* [6287]

National Preservation Institute Scholarships *(All/Scholarship)* [6446]

National Technical Honor Society Scholarships *(Undergraduate/Scholarship)* [3710]

National Women's Studies Association Lesbian Caucus Scholarships *(Doctorate, Graduate/Scholarship)* [6560]

Native American Community Scholars Awards *(Graduate/Award)* [8243]

Native American Education Grants *(Graduate, Undergraduate/Grant)* [821]

Native American Visiting Student Awards *(Graduate/Award)* [8244]

Naval Helicopter Association Scholarships *(Graduate, Undergraduate/Scholarship)* [6575]

The Nazareth Scholarships *(Undergraduate/Scholarship)* [6597]

NCBWL Scholarships *(High School/Scholarship)* [5986]

H.N. Neal Memorial Scholarships *(Undergraduate/Scholarship)* [2338]

Nebraska Farm Bureau Young Farmers and Ranchers Greater Horizon Scholarships *(Undergraduate/Scholarship)* [6599]

Bill Nelson Scholarship Endowment *(Graduate, Undergraduate/Scholarship)* [7004]

Judge William J. Nelson Scholarships *(Undergraduate/Scholarship)* [8615]

NEMLA Summer Fellowships *(Graduate, Professional development/Fellowship)* [6799]

NEMRA Educational Scholarship Foundation *(Undergraduate, Vocational/Occupational/Scholarship)* [6267]

Andrew Nerland Endowment Scholarships *(Undergraduate/Scholarship)* [9164]

NERRS Graduate Research Fellowships (GRF) *(Graduate, Master's/Fellowship)* [6271]

Dr. Ezra Nesbeth Scholarships *(Undergraduate/Scholarship)* [5123]

Amelia and Emanuel Nessell Scholarships *(Undergraduate/Scholarship)* [3540]

Netherlands-Florida Scholarship Foundation Scholarships *(Doctorate, Graduate/Scholarship)* [6615]

Reverend John S. Nettled Scholarships *(Undergraduate/Scholarship)* [3045]

Nevada Black Police Association Scholarships *(Undergraduate/Scholarship)* [7511]

Alan H. Neville Memorial Scholarships *(Graduate, Undergraduate, Vocational/Occupational/Scholarship)* [337]

New Hampshire Snowmobile Association Scholarships *(Undergraduate, Vocational/Occupational/Scholarship)* [6633]

New Mexico Manufactured Housing Association Scholarship Program *(Undergraduate/Scholarship)* [281]

New York State Senate - Legislative Fellowships *(Graduate, Postgraduate/Fellowship)* [6678]

The New York Times College Scholarships *(Undergraduate/Scholarship)* [6685]

Newberry Consortium on American Indian Studies Graduate Student Fellowships *(Doctorate/Fellowship)* [6702]

Newberry Library ACM/GLCA Faculty Fellowships *(Professional development/Fellowship)* [6703]

Newberry Library/British Academy Fellowships for Study in Great Britain *(Doctorate/Fellowship)* [6704]

Newberry Library/Ecole Nationale des Chartes Exchange Fellowships *(Graduate/Fellowship)* [6705]

Newberry Library Short-Term Resident Fellowships for Individual Research *(Postdoctorate/Fellowship)* [6707]

Newcomer Supply Student Scholarships *(Undergraduate/Scholarship)* [6514]

Frank Newman Leadership Awards *(Undergraduate/Scholarship)* [2350]

Newman University Scouting Scholarships *(Undergraduate/Scholarship)* [6260]

Jerry Newson Scholarships *(Undergraduate/Scholarship)* [3128]

NFPA Youth Scholarships *(Undergraduate, Vocational/Occupational/Scholarship)* [6299]

NGAT Educational Scholarships *(Graduate, Undergraduate/Scholarship)* [6313]

Le Hoang Nguyen College Scholarships (LHN) *(High School/Scholarship)* [9432]

The Thuy Nguyen Scholarships *(High School/Scholarship)* [9433]

NHAEOP Member Scholarships *(Undergraduate/Scholarship)* [6626]

NHPGA Apprentice Scholarships *(Undergraduate/Scholarship)* [5715]

NHS National Scholarships *(Undergraduate/Scholarship)* [6342]

NIAF Scholarships - General Category I *(Undergraduate/Scholarship)* [6369]

NIBA Presidential Scholarships *(Undergraduate/Scholarship)* [6351]

Mike Niemeyer Memorial Football Scholarships *(Undergraduate/Scholarship)* [7679]

Evelyn S. Nish Scholarships *(Undergraduate/Scholarship)* [8180]

Anderson Niskanen Scholarships *(Undergraduate/Scholarship)* [3541]

Nissan North America, Inc. Scholarships *(Undergraduate/Scholarship)* [809]

CSF Corwin Nixon Scholarships *(Undergraduate/Scholarship)* [2857]

NLBRA/Wrangler Academic Scholarships *(Undergraduate/Scholarship)* [6398]

NMCRS Gold Star Scholarship Program *(Undergraduate, Vocational/Occupational/Scholarship)* [6593]

NMSC College and University Sponsorship of Merit Scholarship Awards *(Undergraduate/Scholarship)* [6406]

NMSC Corporate-Sponsored Achievement Scholarship Awards *(Undergraduate/Scholarship)* [6407]

NMSC National Achievement Scholarship Program *(Undergraduate/Scholarship)* [6408]

NMSC Special Scholarships *(Undergraduate/Scholarship)* [6409]

Charles S. Noble Scholarships for Study at Harvard *(Undergraduate/Scholarship)* [258]

Edna A. Noblin Dawsonville Lions Club Scholarships *(Undergraduate/Scholarship)* [5345]

Alfred H. Nolle Scholarships *(Undergraduate/Scholarship)* [344]

Non Commissioned Officers Association Scholarships *(Undergraduate/Scholarship)* [6726]

Nor' Easters Scholarships - Four-year Program *(Undergraduate/Scholarship)* [6732]

Nor' Easters Scholarships - Two-year Program *(Undergraduate/Scholarship)* [6733]

Norall Scholarship Trust *(Undergraduate/Scholarship)* [5477]

Nordic Ski Association of Anchorage Scholarships *(Undergraduate/Scholarship)* [197]

North Carolina Heroes Fund Scholarships *(All/Scholarship)* [6767]

North Dakota Farmers Union Co-op House Scholarships *(Undergraduate/Scholarship)* [6786]

North Dakota Farmers Union Scholarships *(Undergraduate/Scholarship)* [6787]

North Texas GIA Alumni Association Scholarships *(Undergraduate/Scholarship)* [4067]

Northern Alberta Development Council Bursary Awards *(Undergraduate/Award)* [259]

Northern Alberta Development Council Bursary Partnership Program *(Undergraduate/Award)* [260]

Northern Arizona Native-American Foundation Scholarships *(Undergraduate, Vocational/Occupational/Scholarship)* [6801]

Northern Resident Scholarships *(Doctorate, Graduate/Scholarship)* [1736]

Northern Virginia Alumnae Chapter Scholarships *(Undergraduate/Scholarship)* [3383]

Eugene Northrup Scholarships *(Undergraduate/Scholarship)* [5457]

Northwest Community Center Scholarships *(Undergraduate/Scholarship)* [3162]

Northwest-Shoals Community College Academic Scholarships *(Undergraduate/Scholarship)* [6819]

Northwest-Shoals Community College Athletic Scholarships *(Undergraduate/Scholarship)* [6821]

Northwest-Shoals Community College Bank Independent Scholarships *(Undergraduate/Scholarship)* [6822]

Northwest-Shoals Community College High School Academic Scholarships *(Undergraduate/Scholarship)* [6826]

Northwest-Shoals Community College Independent Computer Scholarships *(Undergraduate/Scholarship)* [6827]

Northwest-Shoals Community College Student Activities Scholarships *(Undergraduate/Scholarship)* [6828]

Notre Dame Club of Canton Scholarships *(Undergraduate/Scholarship)* [8693]

NSHSS Academic Paper Awards *(High School/Scholarship)* [6504]

NSHSS National Scholar Awards *(High School/Scholarship)* [6505]

NSSA/NSCA Collegiate Scholarships *(Undergraduate/Scholarship)* [6531]

NWAG Georgia, USA Scholarships *(High School/Scholarship)* [6718]

NWAG Nigeria Scholarships *(Undergraduate/Scholarship)* [6719]

NWF's Women for Sustainable Development Scholarships (WSD) *(Undergraduate/Scholarship)* [8145]

NWSA Distinguished Fellowships *(All/Fellowship)* [6561]

NWSA Graduate Scholarships *(Graduate/Scholarship)* [6562]

AEBC Rick Oakes Scholarships for the Arts *(Graduate, Undergraduate, Vocational/Occupational/Scholarship)* [338]

Obrzut Ling Scholarships *(Undergraduate, Vocational/Occupational/Scholarship)* [7414]

Katharine H. Obye Scholarship Awards *(Undergraduate/Scholarship)* [3163]

Odd Fellows Lodge No. 8 Endowed Scholarships *(Undergraduate/Scholarship)* [5458]

Captain Jennifer Shafer Odom Memorial Scholarships - Children of Soldiers *(Undergraduate, Vocational/Occupational/Scholarship)* [1617]

Captain Jennifer Shafer Odom Memorial Scholarships - Spouses of Soldiers *(Undergraduate, Vocational/Occupational/Scholarship)* [1618]

Don & Jan O'Dowd/SWAA Scholarships *(Undergraduate/Scholarship)* [9166]

Ohio War Orphan Scholarships *(Undergraduate/Scholarship)* [9773]

O'Jays Scholarship Fund *(Undergraduate, Vocational/Occupational/Scholarship)* [8694]

Roy C. and Dorothy Jean Olson Memorial Scholarships *(Undergraduate/Scholarship)* [4961]

Olympia Tumwater Foundation Traditional Scholarships *(Undergraduate/Scholarship)* [6875]

Olympia Tumwater Foundation Transitional (non-traditional) Scholarships *(Undergraduate/Scholarship)* [6876]

Charlie O'Meilia Scholarships *(Undergraduate/Scholarship)* [4901]

Omicron Delta Kappa Foundation Scholarships *(Graduate/Scholarship)* [6880]

Ontario Hockey Association War Memorial Scholarships *(Undergraduate/Scholarship)* [9341]

Open Society Fellowships *(Professional development/Fellowship)* [6903]

Sheldon Oppenheim Memorial Scholarships *(Undergraduate/Scholarship)* [7863]

Optimist Club Of Redlands - Ralph Maloof Scholarships *(Undergraduate/Scholarship)* [7680]

Optimist Club of Redlands - Virginia Elliott Scholarships *(Undergraduate/Scholarship)* [7681]

Order Sons of Italy Foundation General Scholarships *(Graduate, Undergraduate/Scholarship)* [6923]

Oregon Logging Conference Scholarships *(Undergraduate/Scholarship)* [5459]

Doris Orenstein Memorial Convention Travel Grants *(All/Grant)* [1822]

Organization of American States Academic Scholarships *(Undergraduate/Scholarship)* [6963]

Organization of American States AOS-Placed Scholarships *(Graduate, Undergraduate/Scholarship)* [6964]

Organization of American States Graduate Scholarships *(Doctorate, Graduate/Scholarship)* [6965]

Organization of American States Self-Placed Scholarships *(Doctorate, Graduate/Scholarship)* [6966]

Organization of Chinese Americans Scholarships *(Undergraduate/Scholarship)* [6976]

OSU Gay, Lesbian, Bisexual and Transgender Alumni Society PFLAG Scholarships *(Undergraduate/Scholarship)* [7864]

OTA Education Foundation Scholarships *(Undergraduate/Scholarship)* [6901]

Alvin G. Ott Fish and Wildlife Scholarships *(Undergraduate/Scholarship)* [9167]

Ted H. Ousley Scholarship Fund *(Undergraduate/Scholarship)* [3917]

Outlaw Student's Minority Scholarships *(Undergraduate/Scholarship)* [8753]

Outstanding Undergraduate Scholarships, Student Organization for Alumni Relations (SOAR) *(Undergraduate/Scholarship)* [9217]

Victoria Ovis Memorial Scholarships *(Undergraduate/Scholarship)* [6387]

Charles and Melva T. Owen Memorial Scholarships *(Undergraduate/Scholarship)* [6280]

Ozarks Division Scholarships *(Undergraduate/Scholarship)* [5863]

The Pac-10 Postgraduate Scholarships *(Graduate/Scholarship)* [7027]

Dr. Nicholas Padis Memorial Graduate Scholarships *(Graduate/Scholarship)* [4517]

Casilda Pagan Educational/Vocational Scholarships *(Graduate, Undergraduate/Scholarship)* [4608]

Ben Palacio Scholarships *(Undergraduate/Scholarship)* [9058]

Robert R. Palmer Research Travel Fellowships *(Professional development/Fellowship)* [1234]

Pan-Macedonian National Scholarships *(Undergraduate/Scholarship)* [7039]

The PanHellenic Scholarships *(Undergraduate/Scholarship)* [7041]

Panther Cafe Scholarships *(Undergraduate/Scholarship)* [7514]

Paper Stock Industries Chapter of ISRI Scholarship Program *(Undergraduate/Scholarship)* [7047]

Paper Stock Industries/RRF Scholarships *(Undergraduate/Scholarship)* [7045]

Cissy McDaniel Parker Scholarships *(Undergraduate/Scholarship)* [3384]

E.U. Parker Scholarships *(Undergraduate/Scholarship)* [6281]

Parking Industry Institute Scholarship Program *(Undergraduate/Scholarship)* [6436]

Carl Parsell Scholarship Fund *(Undergraduate/Scholarship)* [5810]

Pasteur Foundation Postdoctoral Fellowships *(Graduate/Fellowship)* [7130]

PATCH Early Childhood Education Scholarships *(Professional development/Scholarship)* [7132]

James H. Patrenos Memorial Scholarships *(Undergraduate/Scholarship)* [8220]

Gail Patrick Charitable Trust Scholarships *(Undergraduate/Scholarship)* [3420]

Q.O.(Quint) Patrick Scholarships *(Undergraduate/Scholarship)* [9592]

Alice Conger Patterson Scholarships *(Undergraduate/Scholarship)* [9649]

Joanne Holbrook Patton Military Spouse Scholarships *(Graduate, Undergraduate/Scholarship)* [6411]

Joanne Holbrook Patton Military Spouse Scholarships for Spouses of the Fallen *(Graduate, Undergraduate/Scholarship)* [6412]

Joanne Holbrook Patton Military Spouse Scholarships for Spouses of the Wounded *(Graduate, Undergraduate/Scholarship)* [6413]

Paul and Inger Friend 4-H Scholarships *(Undergraduate/Scholarship)* [8731]

PEA Bursaries *(Undergraduate/Scholarship)* [7443]

PEA Scholarships *(Undergraduate/Scholarship)* [7444]

Charles S. Pearce Scholarships *(Undergraduate/Prize, Scholarship)* [9365]

Pearman Family Scholarships *(Undergraduate/Scholarship)* [7950]

Mario Pedrozzi Scholarships *(Graduate, Undergraduate, Vocational/Occupational/Scholarship)* [7145]

Peierls Rising Star Scholarship Program *(Undergraduate/Scholarship)* [4580]

Pellegrini Scholarships *(Graduate, Undergraduate, Vocational/Occupational/Scholarship)* [8784]

Dorothy E. Hofmann Pembroke Scholarships *(Undergraduate/Scholarship)* [4454]

Robert B. and Dorothy Pence Scholarships *(Undergraduate/Scholarship)* [8616]

Penndelphia Scholarship Foundation *(Undergraduate, Vocational/Occupational/Scholarship)* [7147]

Pennsboro Alumni Scholarship Fund *(Undergraduate/Scholarship)* [7101]

P.E.O. Chapter Scholarship Fund *(Undergraduate, Vocational/Occupational/Scholarship)* [4233]

PEO Educational Loan Funds *(Graduate, Undergraduate, Vocational/Occupational/Loan)* [7306]

Pepsi Wood County Technical/Caperton Center Scholarship Fund *(Undergraduate/Scholarship)* [7102]

Pepsico Scholarships *(Undergraduate/Scholarship)* [9066]

Joaquin Pereira Memorial Scholarships *(Undergraduate/Scholarship)* [5549]

Zoe Gore Perrin Scholarships *(Undergraduate/Scholarship)* [3385]

Eleanor Perry Memorial Endowed Scholarships *(Undergraduate/Scholarship)* [5461]

Perry Township School Memorial Scholarship Fund *(Undergraduate/Scholarship)* [8695]

Dr. Connell Persico Scholarships *(Undergraduate/Scholarship)* [7865]

Persons Case Scholarships *(Undergraduate, Graduate/Scholarship)* [261]

Peter Buck Fellowships Program - Graduate *(Graduate/Fellowship)* [8263]

Peter Buck Fellowships Program - Postdoctoral *(Postdoctorate/Fellowship)* [8264]

Peter R. Weitz Prize *(Professional development/Prize)* [4133]

Jerome Peters Family Scholarships *(Undergraduate/Scholarship)* [5592]

William H. and Lena M. Petree Scholarships *(Undergraduate/Scholarship)* [9650]

Pfafftown Jaycees/Lynn Canada Memorial Scholarships *(Undergraduate/Scholarship)* [9651]

Pfizer Epilepsy Scholarships *(Graduate, Undergraduate/Scholarship)* [7221]

Marshall Phelps Athletic Memorial Scholarships *(Undergraduate/Scholarship)* [7682]

Phi Eta Sigma Distinguished Member Scholarships (Graduate or Professional) *(Graduate, Professional development/Scholarship)* [7255]

Phi Eta Sigma Distinguished Member Scholarships (Undergraduate) *(Undergraduate/Scholarship)* [7256]

Phi Eta Sigma Undergraduate Scholarship Awards *(Undergraduate/Scholarship)* [7257]

Phi Kappa Phi Fellowships *(Graduate, Undergraduate/Fellowship)* [7259]

Phi Kappa Sigma Need-Based Scholarships *(Undergraduate/Scholarship)* [7261]

Phi Kappa Sigma Participation-Based Scholarships *(Undergraduate/Scholarship)* [7262]

Philip Morris USA Scholarships *(Undergraduate/Scholarship)* [9067]

Walter T. Philippy Scholarships *(Undergraduate/Scholarship)* [5716]

CSF Charles and Claire Phillips Scholarships *(Undergraduate/Scholarship)* [2858]

Phillips Scholarships *(Undergraduate/Scholarship)* [3184]

Howard and Mildred Phoenix Scholarships *(Undergraduate/Scholarship)* [7683]

Eleonora Pidperyhora Scholarship *(Undergraduate/Scholarship)* [7775]

Herschel Pifer Memorial Scholarships *(Undergraduate/Scholarship)* [7104]

Christopher Pitkin Memorial Scholarships *(Undergraduate, Vocational/Occupational/Scholarship)* [6332]

Day Pitney LLP Scholarships *(Undergraduate/Scholarship)* [4456]

Peter George Pitsakis Memorial Scholarships *(Undergraduate/Scholarship)* [4518]

Al Plamann Legacy Scholarships *(Undergraduate/Scholarship)* [2253]

TFC Edward A. Plank, Jr. Memorial Scholarships *(Undergraduate/Scholarship)* [3063]

Katherine Barton Platt Excavation Fellowships *(Professional development, Undergraduate/Fellowship)* [1178]

Platt Family Scholarship Prize Essay Contest *(Graduate, Undergraduate/Prize, Scholarship)* [5503]

Pleasantview Public Schools Fund *(Undergraduate/Scholarship)* [4261]

PLSCA Scholarships *(Undergraduate/Scholarship)* [5505]

Henry DeWitt Plyler Scholarship Fund *(Undergraduate/Scholarship)* [3918]

Point Foundation Scholarships *(Graduate, Postgraduate, Undergraduate/Scholarship)* [7866]

Point Lay Memorial Scholarships *(Undergraduate/Scholarship)* [9168]

Tibor T. Polgar Fellowships *(Graduate, Undergraduate/Fellowship)* [4619]

Pollard-Bailey Scholarships *(Undergraduate/Scholarship)* [7952]

CSF George and Amy Polley Scholarships *(Undergraduate/Scholarship)* [2859]

David J. Pollini Scholarships *(Undergraduate/Scholarship)* [5717]

Henry Belin du Pont Dissertation Fellowships *(Doctorate, Graduate/Fellowship)* [4364]

Buster Pool Memorial Scholarships *(Undergraduate/Scholarship)* [3130]

Pope Scholarship Awards *(Undergraduate/Scholarship)* [5718]

Port with No Borders Scholarships *(Undergraduate/Scholarship)* [7953]

Gail Porterfield Memorial Scholarships *(Undergraduate/Scholarship)* [7684]

Portland Area Business Association Scholarships *(Undergraduate/Scholarship)* [3681]

Portuguese-American Scholarship Foundation *(Undergraduate/Scholarship)* [7378]

Poteet Strawberry Festival Association Scholarships *(Graduate, Undergraduate/Scholarship)* [7382]

Gerald Powell Scholarships *(Undergraduate/Scholarship)* [3046]

The Power to Continue Learning Scholarships *(Undergraduate, Vocational/Occupational/Scholarship)* [7685]

Susan Kelly Power and Helen Hornbeck Tanner Fellowships *(Doctorate, Postdoctorate/Fellowship)* [6708]

J.R. (Joe) Power National Scholarships *(Postgraduate/Scholarship)* [7546]

Powers-Knapp Scholarships *(Undergraduate/Scholarship)* [9367]

Master Sergeant Neal E. Powers Memorial Scholarships *(Undergraduate/Scholarship)* [100]

Prairie Baseball Academy Scholarships *(Undergraduate/Scholarship)* [262]

Jim and Dee Price Scholarships *(Undergraduate/Scholarship)* [4262]

Pride Foundation Regional Scholarships *(Undergraduate/Scholarship)* [7416]

Pride Foundation Scholarships *(Undergraduate/Scholarship)* [7867]

Pride of the Rose Scholarship Fund *(Undergraduate/Scholarship)* [3682]

Prince Henry Society Scholarships *(Undergraduate/Scholarship)* [7433]

Private High School Awards *(Undergraduate/Award)* [1512]

Miguel Pro Scholarships *(Undergraduate/Scholarship)* [9774]

Procida Tile Importers Scholarships *(Undergraduate/Scholarship)* [7519]

Professional Association Leadership Alumni Scholarships (PAL) *(Graduate/Scholarship)* [8805]

Professional Institute of the Public Service of Canada Expanded Scholarships *(Undergraduate/Scholarship)* [7446]

Progress Lane Scholarships *(Undergraduate/Scholarship)* [3064]

Project Red Flag Academic Scholarships for Women with Bleeding Disorders *(Undergraduate/Scholarship)* [6333]

Provincial and Regional 4-H Scholarships *(Undergraduate/Scholarship)* [200]

ProWorld Study Abroad Scholarships *(Undergraduate/Scholarship)* [4178]

Pryor Graduate Fellowships *(Graduate/Fellowship)* [345]

Cheryl White Pryor Memorial Scholarships *(Undergraduate/Scholarship)* [3386]

PSAC - Coughlin National Scholarships *(Postgraduate/Scholarship)* [7547]

PSAC - Groulx National Scholarships *(Postgraduate/Scholarship)* [7548]

PSAC National Scholarships *(Postgraduate/Scholarship)* [7549]

PSAC Regional Scholarships *(Postgraduate/Scholarship)* [7550]

PSHF Good Idea Grants *(Professional development/Grant)* [7544]

Public Agency Training Council Criminal Justice Scholarships *(Undergraduate/Scholarship)* [358]

Public Education Foundation Opportunity Scholarships *(Undergraduate/Scholarship)* [7520]

Duane V. Puerde Memorial Scholarships *(Undergraduate, Vocational/Occupational/Scholarship)* [3065]

Puget Sound LGBT Leadership Scholarships Fund *(Undergraduate/Scholarship)* [7868]

Harry B. Pulver Scholarships *(Undergraduate/Scholarship)* [4164]

Elizabeth Pusey Scholarships *(Undergraduate/Scholarship)* [3066]

Davis Putter Scholarships Fund *(Undergraduate/Scholarship)* [7869]

Qualcomm San Diego Science, Technology, Engineering and Mathematics Scholarships *(Undergraduate/Scholarship)* [7954]

Queen Elizabeth II Graduate Scholarship Program *(Doctorate, Graduate/Scholarship)* [263]

Queer Foundation Effective Writing and Scholarships *(Undergraduate/Prize, Scholarship)* [7560]

Michael J. Quill Scholarships *(Undergraduate/Scholarship)* [8929]

Salvatore E. Quinci Foundation Scholarships *(Un-*

dergraduate, Vocational/Occupational/Scholarship) [6334]

Dr. J. Glenn Radcliffe Memorial Scholarships (Undergraduate/Scholarship) [8732]

J.J. Rains Memorial Scholarships (High School/Scholarship) [2954]

Rainwater Family Scholarships (Undergraduate/Scholarship) [6399]

The NASSCO Jeffrey D. Ralston Memorial Scholarships (Undergraduate/Scholarship) [5988]

Guthikonda Ramabrahmam & Balamani (Graduate/Scholarship) [8831]

Rambus Scholarship Fund (Undergraduate/Scholarship) [8205]

Raul Ramirez Memorial Scholarships (Undergraduate/Scholarship) [7686]

CSF Marvin Rammelsberg Memorial Scholarships (Undergraduate/Scholarship) [2860]

Rancho Bernardo/Smith Scholarships (Undergraduate/Scholarship) [7955]

Ayn Rand Institute Anthem Essay Contest (High School, Undergraduate/Prize) [7592]

Ayn Rand Institute Former Participants' Essay Contest (High School, Undergraduate/Prize) [7593]

Ayn Rand Institute Fountainhead Essay Contest (High School, Undergraduate/Prize) [7594]

Ayn Rand Institute We the Living Essay Contest (High School, Undergraduate/Prize) [7595]

James Randi Educational Foundation Scholarships (Graduate, Undergraduate/Scholarship) [7597]

The Jennings Randolph Peace Scholar Dissertation Program (Doctorate/Scholarship) [9081]

United States Institute of Peace Jennings Randolph Senior Fellowship Program (All/Fellowship) [9082]

Jeannette Rankin Scholarships (Undergraduate, Vocational/Occupational/Scholarship) [7601]

General John Paul Ratay Educational Grants (Undergraduate/Grant) [5876]

Dr. Mark Rathke Family Scholarships (Undergraduate/Scholarship) [3542]

Mary C. Rawlins Scholarships (Undergraduate/Scholarship) [4458]

W.B. Ray HS Class of '56 Averill Johnson Scholarships (Undergraduate/Scholarship) [2955]

Raytheon Scholarship Program (Undergraduate/Scholarship) [7611]

RBC Royal Bank Scholarships for New Canadians (Undergraduate/Scholarship) [7824]

RBPA Scholarships (All/Scholarship) [7589]

Ronald Reagan College Leaders Scholarship Program (Undergraduate/Scholarship) [7313]

CSF Robert H. Reakirt Foundation Scholarships (Undergraduate/Scholarship) [2861]

Realize the Dream Scholarships (Undergraduate/Scholarship) [2977]

Redlands Area Interfaith Council Scholarships (Undergraduate/Scholarship) [7687]

Redlands Community Scholarship Foundation Scholarships (Undergraduate/Scholarship) [7688]

Redlands Council PTA - Dorathy Jolley Memorial Scholarships (Undergraduate/Scholarship) [7689]

Redlands High School Academic Decathalon Scholarships (Undergraduate/Scholarship) [7690]

Redlands High School Boy's Varsity Volleyball Scholarships (Undergraduate/Scholarship) [7691]

Redlands High School Girls' Volleyball Boosters Scholarship Awards (Undergraduate/Scholarship) [7693]

Redlands High School Mock Trial Scholarships (Undergraduate/Scholarship) [7694]

Redlands High School-PTSA Scholarships (Undergraduate, Vocational/Occupational/Scholarship) [7695]

Redlands High School Soccer Boosters Scholarship Awards (Undergraduate/Scholarship) [7696]

Redlands High School Softball Booster Scholarship Awards (Undergraduate/Scholarship) [7697]

Redlands High School Speech Boosters Scholarship Awards (Undergraduate/Scholarship) [7698]

Redlands High School Spiritleaders Scholarships (Undergraduate/Scholarship) [7699]

Redlands High School Terrier Band Boosters Club Scholarships (Undergraduate/Scholarship) [7700]

Redlands High School Vocal Music Boosters Scholarship Awards (Undergraduate/Scholarship) [7701]

Redlands Morning Kiwanis Club Foundation Scholarships (Undergraduate, Vocational/Occupational/Scholarship) [7702]

Redlands Noon Kiwanis Club Foundation Scholarships (Undergraduate/Scholarship) [7703]

Redlands Noon Kiwanis Club - Martin and Dorothy Munz Scholarships (Undergraduate/Scholarship) [7704]

Redlands Rotary Club Foundation Discretionary Scholarships (Undergraduate/Scholarship) [7705]

Redlands Teachers Association Scholarships (Undergraduate/Scholarship) [7706]

Registered Apprenticeship Program Scholarships (RAP) (Undergraduate/Scholarship) [264]

J.H. Stewart Reid Memorial Fellowship Trust (Doctorate/Fellowship) [2415]

J.H. Stewart Reid Memorial Fellowships (Doctorate, Graduate/Fellowship) [7730]

Henry J. Reilly Memorial Scholarships - For Freshmen in College (Undergraduate/Scholarship) [7738]

Henry J. Reilly Memorial Scholarships - For Graduating High School Seniors (Undergraduate/Scholarship) [7739]

Henry J. Reilly Memorial Scholarships - For Sophomores and Juniors in College (Undergraduate/Scholarship) [7740]

Henry J. Reilly Memorial Scholarships - Graduate Program (Graduate, Professional development/Scholarship) [7741]

Jacob L. Reinecke Memorial Scholarship Fund (Undergraduate/Scholarship) [4235]

Daniel L. Reiss Memorial Scholarship Fund (Undergraduate/Scholarship) [4236]

Paul Resnick and Bruce Donnelly Scholarships (Undergraduate/Scholarship) [2928]

Retail Packaging Association Scholarships (RPA) (Undergraduate/Scholarship) [7751]

Retired League Postmasters Scholarship Program (Undergraduate/Scholarship) [7755]

W. Reymonta Scholarships (Undergraduate/Scholarship) [7777]

Lori Rhett Memorial Scholarships (Graduate, Undergraduate/Scholarship) [6055]

Rhode Island Association of Former Legislators Scholarships (Undergraduate/Scholarship) [7793]

Barbara Hagan Richards Scholarships (Undergraduate/Scholarship) [3131]

James Edward "Bill" Richards Scholarships (Undergraduate/Scholarship) [3132]

Ellen Swallow Richards Travel Grants (Graduate, Professional development/Grant) [1251]

Phillip Guy Richardson Memorial Scholarships (Undergraduate/Scholarship) [5103]

John S. and Jacqueline P. Rider Scholarships (Undergraduate/Scholarship) [9652]

Jasper Ridge Restoration Fellowships Jasper Ridge Biological Preserve (Graduate, Postdoctorate/Fellowship) [3580]

CSF William J. Rielly/MCURC Scholarships (Undergraduate/Scholarship) [2862]

Jerrothia Allenfonzo Riggs & Anna & Dorothy Mae Barnes Scholarships (Undergraduate/Scholarship) [2339]

Riggs Cove Foundation Scholarships (Undergraduate/Scholarship) [4091]

Benjamin Riggs Scholarships (Undergraduate/Scholarship) [4092]

Susan E. Riley Scholarships (Undergraduate/Scholarship) [3387]

Lana K. Rinehart Scholarships (Undergraduate/Scholarship) [3067]

Harold and Eleonor Ringelberg Scholarship Fund (Undergraduate/Scholarship) [4237]

Josephine Ringold Scholarships (Undergraduate/Scholarship) [4297]

Riverside Sheriffs Association Member Scholarship Program (Graduate, Undergraduate/Scholarship) [7803]

Jean Wiggin Roach Scholarships (Undergraduate/Scholarship) [3388]

Lawrence and Louise Robbins Scholarships (Undergraduate/Scholarship) [5593]

James H. Roberts Athletic Scholarships (Undergraduate/Scholarship) [7106]

Marion Roberts Memorial Scholarships (Undergraduate/Scholarship) [1958]

Smiley Elementary School PTA - Beverly Roberts Memorial Scholarships (Undergraduate/Scholarship) [7708]

CSF Mary Roberts Scholarships (Undergraduate/Scholarship) [2863]

Thomas Warren Roberts Scholarships (Undergraduate/Scholarship) [7107]

A.D. 'Al' Robertson Memorial Scholarships (Undergraduate/Scholarship) [9169]

Ben Robinette Scholarship Endowment Fund (Undergraduate/Scholarship) [3919]

Robinhood Marine Center Scholarships (Undergraduate/Scholarship) [4093]

Jackie Robinson Foundation Minority Scholarships (Undergraduate/Scholarship) [822]

James Robinson Memorial Scholarships (Undergraduate/Scholarship) [7108]

Jackie Robinson Scholarships (Undergraduate/Scholarship) [7808]

August M. Rocco Scholarship Fund (Undergraduate/Scholarship) [8696]

James and Marilyn Rockfeller Scholarships (Undergraduate/Scholarship) [5594]

Rockford Area Habitat for Humanity College Scholarships (Undergraduate/Scholarship) [3166]

Rockford Chapter Daughters of the American Revolution Memorial Scholarships (Undergraduate/Scholarship) [3167]

Rockin' Christmas Fund Scholarships (Undergraduate/Scholarship) [8620]

Rocky Mountain Research Fellowships (Graduate/Fellowship) [7815]

R.O.E.A. Dumitru Golea Goldy-Gemu Scholarships (Undergraduate/Scholarship) [1165]

Kimberly Marie Rogers Memorial Scholarship Fund (Undergraduate, Vocational/Occupational/Scholarship) [3789]

Pat and Cliff Rogers Nursing Scholarships (Undergraduate/Scholarship) [9170]

Geraldine Ruth Rogers Scholarships (Undergraduate/Scholarship) [8897]

Mary Stuart Rogers Scholarships (Undergraduate/Scholarship) [9606]

Richard C. Rolfs Scholarships (Undergraduate/Scholarship) [7418]

Mary Louise Roller Pan-Hellenic Scholarships (Undergraduate/Scholarship) [6741]

Roothbert Fund Scholarships (Undergraduate/Scholarship) [7819]

ROP - Rob Bruce Memorial Scholarships (Undergraduate/Scholarship) [7710]

Dr. Wayne F. Rose Scholarship Fund (Undergraduate/Scholarship) [3790]

Ollie Rosenberg Educational Trust (Undergraduate/Scholarship) [3958]

Rosenberg-Ibarra Scholarships (Undergraduate/Scholarship) [7419]

Jean and Tom Rosenthal Scholarship Program (Undergraduate/Scholarship) [3204]

Ross-Fahey Scholarships (Graduate, Postgraduate/Scholarship) [6056]

The Bea and Harry Ross Scholarship Endowment (Graduate/Scholarship) [8743]

The Rotary Club of Cape Coral Goldcoast Scholarship Fund (Undergraduate/Scholarship) [2645]

Rotary Club of Corpus Christi Scholarships (Undergraduate/Scholarship) [2956]

The Rotary Club of Rancho Bernardo Sunrise Abraxas Student Scholarships (Undergraduate, Vocational/Occupational/Scholarship) [7956]

The Rotary Foundation Ambassadorial Scholarships (Undergraduate/Scholarship) [7821]

Bernard Rotberg Memorial Scholarships (Undergraduate/Scholarship) [5163]

Mike Ruben Scholarships (Undergraduate/Scholarship) [7111]

Lawrence E. & Mabel Jackson Rudberg Scholarships (Undergraduate/Scholarship) [3543]

Anna M. Rundquist Memorial Scholarships (Undergraduate/Scholarship) [4340]

Ruppert Educational Grant Program (Undergraduate/Grant) [8207]

Rural Telephone Company Scholarships (Under-

graduate/Scholarship) [7835]

Norman K. Russell Scholarships (Doctorate, Graduate/Scholarship) [6434]

Michael A. Russo Memorial Scholarships (Undergraduate/Scholarship) [7711]

Alexander Rutherford Scholarships for High School Achievement (Undergraduate/Scholarship) [266]

Rutherford Scholars (Undergraduate/Scholarship) [265]

Ralph and Clara Rutledge Memorial Scholarships (Graduate/Scholarship) [3869]

Charles and Eleonor Rycenga Education Scholarship Fund (Undergraduate/Scholarship) [4238]

Deborah Jean Rydberg Memorial Scholarships (Undergraduate/Scholarship) [3168]

Ryerson Scholarships (Undergraduate/Scholarship) [5124]

Jeanne Graves Ryland Scholarships (Undergraduate/Scholarship) [3389]

SACHS Foundation Graduate Scholarships (Graduate/Scholarship) [7840]

SACHS Foundation Undergraduate Scholarships for Colorado Black Students (High School/Scholarship) [7841]

Sacks For CF Scholarships (All/Scholarship) [3687]

Julie Anne Sadlier Memorial Scholarships (Undergraduate/Scholarship) [3390]

Virginia Hartford Saharov Memorial Scholarships (Undergraduate/Scholarship) [3391]

Saint Andrews Scholarships (Undergraduate/Scholarship) [7882]

St. Francis Xavier Scholarships (Undergraduate/Scholarship) [9775]

St. James Armenian Church Memorial Scholarships (All/Scholarship) [1604]

St. Louis Division Scholarships (Undergraduate/Scholarship) [5864]

Saint Paul University Excellence Scholarships (Undergraduate/Scholarship) [7887]

Saint Paul University Financial Aid Bursaries (Undergraduate/Scholarship) [7888]

Saint Vincent College Eagle Scout Scholarships (Undergraduate/Scholarship) [6261]

Saints Cyril and Methodius Scholarships (Undergraduate/Scholarship) [7838]

Joseph and Amelia Saks Scholarship Fund (Undergraduate/Scholarship) [3047]

The Sallie Mae 911 Education Fund (Undergraduate/Scholarship) [7891]

Henry Salvatori Scholarships (Undergraduate/Scholarship) [6924]

Samalot - Sebastian Scholarship Fund (High School/Scholarship) [3320]

The Walter Samek III Memorial Scholarship Fund (Undergraduate/Scholarship) [3089]

SAMFund Scholarships (Graduate, Undergraduate/Scholarship) [7897]

Ray and Pearl Sams Scholarships (Undergraduate/Scholarship) [9653]

Samsung American Legion Scholarships (Undergraduate/Scholarship) [897]

San Angelo Area Foundation Scholarships (All/Scholarship) [7901]

San Diego City College Study Abroad Scholarships (Undergraduate/Scholarship) [7957]

The San Diego Foundation Community Scholarships II (Undergraduate/Scholarship) [7959]

The San Diego Foundation Community Scholarships I (Undergraduate, Vocational/Occupational/Scholarship) [7958]

San Diego National Bank Scholarships (Undergraduate, Vocational/Occupational/Scholarship) [7960]

San Pasqual Academy Scholarships (Undergraduate, Vocational/Occupational/Scholarship) [7962]

Sand Hill Scholars Program (Undergraduate/Scholarship) [8209]

Saskatchewan Government Insurance Anniversary Scholarships (Undergraduate/Scholarship) [7997]

Saskatchewan Government Insurance Corporate Scholarships (Undergraduate/Scholarship) [7998]

Saskatchewan School Boards Association Education Scholarships (Undergraduate/Scholarship) [8007]

Saskatchewan School Boards Association Graduate

Student Awards (Graduate, Doctorate/Award) [8008]

Saskatchewan Trucking Association Scholarships (Undergraduate/Scholarship) [8010]

Roger C. Sathre Memorial Scholarship Fund (Undergraduate/Scholarship) [4673]

Malini E. Sathyadev Memorial Scholarships (Undergraduate/Scholarship) [7963]

Dave Sauer Memorial College Scholarships (Undergraduate/Scholarship) [116]

Dr. William A. and Marcelein J. Sautter Hanover-Horton High School Youth of Promise Scholarships (Undergraduate/Scholarship) [5104]

Save Mart Legacy Scholarships (Undergraduate/Scholarship) [2254]

John A. Savoy Scholarship Fund (Undergraduate/Scholarship) [3792]

SBA Four-Year Scholarships Program (Undergraduate/Scholarship) [8644]

SBA One-Year Scholarship Program (Undergraduate, Vocational/Occupational/Scholarship) [8645]

Leslie and Mary Ella Scales Memorial Scholarships (Undergraduate/Scholarship) [3048]

Edith Scandlyn/Sammie Lynn Scandlyn Puett Memorial Scholarships (Undergraduate/Scholarship) [3392]

Mary Turnbull Schacht Memorial Scholarships (Undergraduate/Scholarship) [8181]

David W. Schacht Native American Student Scholarships (Undergraduate/Scholarship) [2064]

Millicent M. Schaffner Endowed Memorial Scholarships (Undergraduate/Scholarship) [4239]

Leopold Schepp Foundation Scholarships (Doctorate, Graduate, Undergraduate/Scholarship) [8018]

Robert C. and Margaret A. Schikora Scholarships (Undergraduate/Scholarship) [8621]

Henry L.P. Schmelzer College Transitions Scholarships (Undergraduate/Scholarship) [5595]

CSF Charlotte R. Schmidlapp Scholarships (Undergraduate/Scholarship) [2864]

Richard J. Schnell Memorial Scholarships (Postdoctorate/Scholarship) [3169]

Scholarship Awards of The Aliant Pioneer Volunteers (Postgraduate/Scholarship) [2531]

The Scholarship Foundation of St. Louis Scholarships (Graduate, Undergraduate/Scholarship) [8022]

Scholarship for Junior PHS Commissioned Officers (Undergraduate, Vocational/Occupational/Scholarship) [7315]

Scholarships for Aboriginal Canadians (Undergraduate/Scholarship) [6550]

Scholarships for Visible Minorities (Undergraduate/Scholarship) [6551]

Schoolsfirst Federal Credit Union Scholarships (Undergraduate/Scholarship) [7712]

CSF H.C. Schott Foundation Scholarships (Undergraduate/Scholarship) [2865]

Tanna H. Schulich MBA Entrance Scholarships (Postgraduate/Scholarship) [8048]

Alice Southworth Schulman Simmons Scholarships for UU Women (Undergraduate/Scholarship) [9000]

David and Ginny Schultz Family Scholarship Fund (Undergraduate/Scholarship) [4240]

CSF Nelson Schwab Jr. Family Scholarships (Undergraduate/Scholarship) [2866]

CSF Judge Benjamin Schwartz Scholarships (Undergraduate/Scholarship) [2867]

Evalee C. Schwarz Educational Loans (Graduate, Undergraduate/Loan) [8052]

SCLEOA Scholarships (Undergraduate/Scholarship) [8547]

CSF E.W. Scripps Scholarships (Undergraduate/Scholarship) [2868]

Seaman Family Scholarships (Undergraduate/Scholarship) [2957]

Seaspace Scholarships (Graduate, Undergraduate/Scholarship) [8073]

Margery J. Seeger Scholarships (Undergraduate/Scholarship) [4298]

Elisabeth Seegmiller Recruitment Scholarship Grants (Undergraduate/Scholarship) [3171]

Aaron Seesan Memorial Scholarship Fund (Undergraduate/Scholarship) [8697]

Detective Cheryl Seiden Memorial Scholarships (Undergraduate/Scholarship) [359]

Seldovia Native Association Achievement Scholarships (Undergraduate, Graduate/Scholarship) [8075]

Seldovia Native Association General Scholarships (Undergraduate, Graduate/Scholarship) [8076]

D. Mitchell Self Memorial Scholarships (Undergraduate/Scholarship) [6829]

Senior Memorial Scholarships (Undergraduate/Scholarship) [3172]

Sentinels of Freedom "Life Scholarships" (All/Scholarship) [7890]

William "Buddy" Sentner Scholarship Awards (Undergraduate/Scholarship) [539]

Felix R. Sepulveda Memorial Scholarships - Northside Booster Club (Undergraduate/Scholarship) [7713]

Servus Credit Union 4-H Scholarships (Undergraduate/Scholarship) [201]

Captain Anthony D. Sesow Scholarships (Undergraduate/Scholarship) [6578]

Hubert K. Seymour Scholarships (Undergraduate/Scholarship) [6788]

Al Shackleford and Dan Martin Professional Scholarships (Undergraduate/Scholarship) [2017]

Charles Shafae' Scholarships (Undergraduate/Prize, Scholarship) [7043]

Josephine Hooker Shain Scholarships (Undergraduate/Scholarship) [4094]

Judge Terry Sharnsie Scholarships (High School/Scholarship) [2958]

William H. Shannon Fellowships (Graduate, Undergraduate/Fellowship) [5017]

Commander Dan F. Shanower Scholarships (Undergraduate/Scholarship) [6579]

Ken and Sandy Sharkey Family Scholarship Fund (Undergraduate/Scholarship) [4242]

Lal Bahadur Shastri Student Prize (Graduate, Undergraduate/Prize) [8099]

W.L. Shattuck Scholarships (Undergraduate/Scholarship) [4674]

Regina B. Shearn Scholarships (Graduate, Undergraduate/Scholarship) [360]

Jim Sheerin Scholarships (Undergraduate/Scholarship) [5719]

Nettie and Edward Shelah Scholarships (Undergraduate/Scholarship) [8733]

Bruce Shelton Scholarships (Undergraduate/Scholarship) [9654]

Matthew Shepard Scholarships (Undergraduate/Scholarship) [7870]

Robert P. Sheppard Leadership Awards (High School/Scholarship) [6506]

Morgan and Jeanie Sherwood Travel Grants (Graduate, Professional development/Grant) [1253]

Drs. Poh Shien and Judy Young Scholarships (Undergraduate/Scholarship) [9068]

CSF S. David Shor Scholarships (Undergraduate/Scholarship) [2869]

Shoreline Community College Academic Excellence Scholarships for Graduating High School Seniors (Undergraduate/Scholarship) [8123]

Shoreline Community College Academic Improvement Scholarships for Graduating High School Seniors (Undergraduate/Scholarship) [8124]

Shoreline Community College Continuing Students Scholarships (Undergraduate/Scholarship) [8125]

Shoreline Community College Part-Time Students Scholarships (Undergraduate/Scholarship) [8126]

Tom Shown Scholarships (Undergraduate/Scholarship) [9655]

Phil Shykes Memorial Scholarships (Undergraduate, Vocational/Occupational/Scholarship) [3544]

Don and Madalyn Sickafoose Educational Trust (Undergraduate/Scholarship) [8698]

Norman Siegel Research Scholar Grants (Doctorate/Grant) [1313]

Sigma Diagnostics Student Scholarships (Undergraduate/Scholarship) [6517]

Sigma Kappa Foundation Alumnae Continuing Education Scholarships (Undergraduate/Scholarship) [8182]

Sigma Kappa Foundation Founders' Scholarships (Undergraduate/Scholarship) [8184]

Sigma Kappa Foundation Michigan Scholarships *(Undergraduate/Scholarship)* [8186]

Silver Nugget Family Scholarships *(Undergraduate/Scholarship)* [7523]

Meyer and Dorothy Silverman Scholarships *(Undergraduate/Scholarship)* [3133]

Harvey L. Simmons Memorial Scholarships *(Undergraduate/Scholarship)* [7965]

Simon Youth Foundation Community Scholarships *(Undergraduate, Vocational/Occupational/Scholarship)* [8212]

Simonton Windows Scholarships *(Undergraduate, Vocational/Occupational/Scholarship)* [7115]

CSF Lowe Simpson Scholarships *(Undergraduate/Scholarship)* [2870]

Single Parent Scholarships *(Graduate, Undergraduate/Scholarship)* [1549]

Aaron B. Singleton Memorial Scholarships *(Undergraduate/Scholarship)* [6830]

Gadde Sitaramamma & Tirupataiah Scholarships *(Graduate/Scholarship)* [8832]

Wiggsy Sivertsen Scholarships *(Undergraduate/Scholarship)* [7871]

Bill Six Memorial Scholarship Fund *(Undergraduate/Scholarship)* [7116]

Leif and Inger Sjoberg Awards *(Professional development/Award)* [1173]

R. Skeeles Memorial Scholarship Fund *(Undergraduate/Scholarship)* [8699]

CSF Frank Foster Skillman Scholarships *(Undergraduate/Scholarship)* [2871]

Francelene Skinner Memorial Scholarships *(Undergraduate/Scholarship)* [5478]

SLEAMC Scholarships *(Graduate, Undergraduate/Scholarship)* [8107]

Robert W. Sledge Fellowships *(Graduate/Fellowship)* [346]

J. Ward Sleichter and Frances F. Sleichter Memorial Scholarship Fund *(Undergraduate/Scholarship)* [3960]

Eva Smith Bursary *(Undergraduate/Scholarship)* [5125]

Ryan and Jamie Smith Essay Contest *(Graduate, Postgraduate/Scholarship)* [8237]

David W. Smith Fellowships *(Postdoctorate/Fellowship)* [2605]

Gladys Ann Smith Greater Los Angeles Women's Council Scholarships *(Undergraduate/Scholarship)* [6588]

Boy Scouts of America Troop 3 Scholarships - Art Till/Nathan E. Smith Memorial Scholarships *(Undergraduate, Vocational/Occupational/Scholarship)* [7714]

Drew Smith Memorial Scholarships *(Undergraduate/Scholarship)* [3068]

Tacy Ana Smith Memorial Scholarships *(Undergraduate/Scholarship)* [3921]

Smith-Reynolds Founder Fellowships *(Graduate/Fellowship)* [4526]

Ralph and Josephine Smith Scholarship Fund *(Undergraduate/Scholarship)* [3793]

Brian Smith Scholarships *(Undergraduate/Scholarship)* [2169]

Esther M. Smith Scholarships *(Undergraduate/Scholarship)* [3069]

Helen J. and Harold Gilman Smith Scholarships *(Graduate, Undergraduate/Scholarship)* [2065]

Joseph Sumner Smith Scholarships *(All/Scholarship)* [9001]

Smith's Personal Best Scholarships *(Undergraduate/Scholarship)* [7525]

Gladys Snauble Scholarships *(Undergraduate/Scholarship)* [4299]

SNMTS Bachelor's Degree Completion Scholarships *(Undergraduate/Scholarship)* [8421]

Boleslaw & Irena Sobczak Scholarships *(Undergraduate/Scholarship)* [7779]

Arnold Sobel Scholarships *(Undergraduate/Scholarship)* [2929]

Sobeys & Empire Work Experience & Scholarship Program - Future Leaders Awards *(Professional development/Award)* [8278]

Social Equity Venture Fund Teaching Fellowships *(Professional development/Fellowship)* [8280]

Society of Allied Weight Engineers Scholarships *(Undergraduate/Scholarship)* [8291]

Society of Marine Port Engineers Scholarship Loans *(Undergraduate/Scholarship loan, Loan)* [8408]

Dale and Betty George Sola Scholarships *(Undergraduate/Scholarship)* [3545]

SON Scholarships *(Undergraduate/Scholarship)* [7899]

Sons of Union Veterans of the Civil War Scholarships *(Undergraduate/Scholarship)* [8534]

Christine Soper Scholarships *(Undergraduate/Scholarship)* [4300]

Soroptimist International of Chambersburg Scholarship Fund *(Undergraduate/Scholarship)* [3961]

Paul and Daisy Soros Fellowships *(Graduate/Fellowship)* [8536]

Lily and Catello Sorrentino Memorial Scholarships *(Undergraduate/Scholarship)* [7794]

Sourdough Reunion Memorial Scholarships *(Undergraduate/Scholarship)* [9176]

South Central Modern Language Association Fellowships *(Doctorate/Fellowship)* [6709]

South Central Power Scholarships *(Undergraduate, Vocational/Occupational/Scholarship)* [8556]

South Coast Area High School Senior Honors Scholarship Program *(Undergraduate/Scholarship)* [8025]

South Jersey Golf Association Scholarships *(Undergraduate/Scholarship)* [8561]

South Kentucky RECC High School Senior Scholarships *(Undergraduate/Scholarship)* [8564]

Southern Maine Women's Golf Association Scholarships *(All/Scholarship)* [8583]

Southern Nevada Sports Hall of Fame Athletic Scholarships *(Undergraduate/Scholarship)* [7526]

Southern Scholarship Foundation Scholarships *(Undergraduate/Scholarship)* [8587]

Southwest Florida Community Foundation College Assistance Scholarships *(Undergraduate/Scholarship)* [8623]

Southwest Movers Association Scholarships *(Undergraduate/Scholarship)* [8629]

Sovereign Nations Scholarships *(Undergraduate/Scholarship)* [810]

Master Sergeant William Sowers Memorial Scholarships *(Undergraduate/Scholarship)* [101]

Kathy Spadoni Memorial Scholarships *(Undergraduate/Scholarship)* [7421]

Nathan Sparks Memorial Scholarships *(Undergraduate/Scholarship)* [3049]

Spartan Staff Scholarships *(Undergraduate/Scholarship)* [7527]

Faith Speckhard Scholarships *(Undergraduate, Vocational/Occupational/Scholarship)* [5106]

Spencer Foundation Research Grants *(All/Grant)* [6007]

Lawrence Alan Spiegel Remembrance Scholarships *(Undergraduate/Scholarship)* [4595]

Spirit of Allison Graduation Awards *(Undergraduate/Award)* [3806]

The Spirit Square Center for Arts and Education Scholarship Fund *(Undergraduate/Scholarship)* [3922]

Spouse Tuition Aids Program (STAP) *(Graduate, Undergraduate/Loan)* [6594]

SSC-Building Environmental Campus Community Fellowships (BECC) *(Undergraduate/Scholarship)* [8146]

SSOC Scholarships *(Undergraduate/Scholarship)* [8014]

Ernest and Charlene Stachowiak Memorial Scholarships *(Undergraduate/Scholarship)* [3173]

Matt Stager Memorial Scholarship Fund *(Undergraduate/Scholarship)* [9538]

A.R.O.Y. Stanitz Scholarships *(Undergraduate/Scholarship)* [1166]

Starker Fellowships for White Matter Disease Clinical Research *(Doctorate, Professional development/Fellowship)* [5113]

Starr Foundation Graduate Fellowships in Asian Studies *(Graduate/Grant)* [9205]

State of Idaho Scholarships Category A *(Undergraduate, Vocational/Occupational/Scholarship)* [5466]

Minnie Patton Stayman Scholarships *(Undergraduate/Scholarship)* [7161]

Harry Steele Entrance Awards *(Postgraduate/Award)* [8049]

CSF Helen Steiner Rice Scholarships *(Undergraduate/Scholarship)* [2872]

Elin J. Stene/Xi Scholarships *(Undergraduate/Scholarship)* [8187]

Step Up Scholarships *(Undergraduate/Scholarship)* [7966]

Elizabeth Coulter Stephenson Scholarships *(Undergraduate/Scholarship)* [3422]

CSF Joseph S. Stern, Jr. Scholarships *(Undergraduate/Scholarship)* [2873]

Richie Stevenson Scholarships *(Undergraduate, Vocational/Occupational/Scholarship)* [3135]

Stewart Title Firefighters Scholarships *(High School, Undergraduate/Scholarship)* [2960]

Mary Stewart and William T. Covington, Jr. Scholarship Fund *(Undergraduate/Scholarship)* [3923]

Dr. Gunnar B. Stickler Scholarships *(Undergraduate, Vocational/Occupational/Scholarship)* [8735]

The Richard Stockton College of New Jersey Foundation Alumni Association Graduate Awards *(Graduate/Scholarship)* [8744]

David Stockwood Memorial Prize *(Professional development/Prize)* [66]

James E. Stoner Memorial Scholarships *(Undergraduate/Scholarship)* [1777]

Stop Hunger Scholarships *(Undergraduate/Scholarship)* [546]

Bonnie Strangio Education Scholarships *(Graduate, Undergraduate/Scholarship)* [3689]

Marlene Streit Golf Scholarships *(Undergraduate/Scholarship)* [4185]

George and Pearl Strickland Scholarships *(Graduate, Undergraduate/Scholarship)* [3076]

Striving for Success Scholarships *(Undergraduate/Scholarship)* [7528]

Stultz Scholarships *(Undergraduate/Scholarship)* [9656]

Subic Bay-Cubi Point 1 Scholarships *(Undergraduate/Scholarship)* [6589]

Vallabhaneni Sukundamma & Lakshmaiah Scholarships *(Graduate/Scholarship)* [8833]

Phil Sullivan Scholarships *(Undergraduate/Scholarship)* [7422]

William A. Sullivan Scholarships *(Undergraduate/Scholarship)* [6590]

Summerside-Natick Hockey Scholarships *(Undergraduate/Scholarship)* [3185]

Sun Life Financial Peer Support Scholarships *(Professional development/Scholarship)* [2579]

Bruce and Marjorie Sundlun Scholarships *(Undergraduate/Scholarship)* [7795]

Super Kutz Scholarships *(Undergraduate/Scholarship)* [8776]

Sussman-Miller Educational Assistance Award Program *(Undergraduate/Scholarship)* [283]

Lorraine E. Swain Scholarships *(Undergraduate/Scholarship)* [8188]

Hugh B. Sweeny Scholarships *(Undergraduate/Scholarship)* [5176]

Jeffery Tyler Sweitzer Wrestling Memorial Scholarship Fund *(Undergraduate/Scholarship)* [8702]

Timothy S. Sweterlitsch Memorial Scholarship Fund *(Undergraduate/Scholarship)* [8703]

SWFL Deputy Sheriffs Association Fund Scholarships *(Undergraduate/Scholarship)* [8625]

SWFL Professional Golfers Association Scholarships *(Undergraduate/Scholarship)* [8626]

Hazaros Tabakoglu Scholarship Fund *(Undergraduate/Scholarship)* [1605]

Tagged for Greatness Scholarships *(Undergraduate/Scholarship)* [180]

Taiwanese American Community Scholarships *(Undergraduate/Scholarship)* [8798]

Tall Awareness Scholarships *(Undergraduate/Scholarship)* [7529]

Tall Clubs International Student Scholarships *(Undergraduate/Scholarship)* [8802]

TANA Foundation Graduate Scholarships *(Graduate/Scholarship)* [8834]

CSF Martha W. Tanner Memorial Scholarships *(Undergraduate/Scholarship)* [2874]

Jack Tate/ThinkCOLLEGE Scholarship Fund *(Undergraduate/Scholarship)* [3924]

Ryan "Munchie" Taylor Memorial Scholarships *(Undergraduate/Scholarship)* [5550]

USHJA General Scholarships (Undergraduate/Scholarship) [9051]

USHJA Postgraduate Scholarships (Postgraduate/Scholarship) [9052]

USS Coral Sea Remembrance Scholarships (Undergraduate/Scholarship) [9405]

USS Tennessee Scholarship Fund (Undergraduate, Vocational/Occupational/Scholarship) [6595]

USTA Serves College Education Scholarships (Undergraduate/Scholarship) [9411]

USTA Tennis and Education Foundation College Textbook Scholarships (Undergraduate/Scholarship) [9412]

Utility Workers Union of America Scholarship Program (Undergraduate/Scholarship) [70]

Valley Alliance of Mentors for Opportunities and Scholarship Program (VAMOS) (Undergraduate/Scholarship) [4584]

Hurad Van Der Bedrosian Memorial Scholarships (Graduate/Scholarship) [1608]

The Vander Putten Family Scholarships (All/Scholarship) [2930]

Keith C. Vanderhyde Scholarships (Undergraduate/Scholarship) [4305]

Jacob R. & Mary M. VanLoo & Lenore K. VanLoo Scholarships (Undergraduate/Scholarship) [4306]

Kodali Veeraiah & Sarojini Scholarships (Graduate/Scholarship) [8835]

Helen Veress-Mitchell Scholarship Fund (Graduate, Undergraduate/Scholarship) [2649]

Chester M. Vernon Memorial Eagle Scout Scholarships (High School/Scholarship) [6263]

Veterans of Foreign Wars Scout of the Year (High School/Scholarship) [6264]

Vilas Equity Scholarships (Undergraduate/Scholarship) [9383]

William F. Vilas Scholarships (Undergraduate/Scholarship) [9384]

Visiting Scholars Fellowships (Postdoctorate/Fellowship) [2043]

Irma E. Voigt Memorial Scholarships (Undergraduate/Scholarship) [8191]

CSF Dee Wacksman Memorial Scholarships (Undergraduate/Scholarship) [2876]

Bruce Wade Memorial Scholarships for Lesbian, Gay and Bisexual (Undergraduate/Scholarship) [7875]

Mercedes Laurie Wade Scholarships (Undergraduate/Scholarship) [2341]

Robert & Barbara Wade Scholarships (Undergraduate/Scholarship) [5480]

WAEPA Scholarship Program (Undergraduate, Vocational/Occupational/Scholarship) [9763]

Nell and Spencer Waggoner Scholarships (Undergraduate/Scholarship) [9659]

Laramie Walden Memorial Fund (Undergraduate/Scholarship) [3927]

Margaret E. Waldron Scholarship Fund (Undergraduate/Scholarship) [3794]

Walmart Associate Scholarships (Undergraduate/Scholarship) [9479]

Robert E. Walter Memorial Scholarships (Undergraduate/Scholarship) [5558]

Sam Walton Community Scholarships (Undergraduate/Scholarship) [9480]

Walton Family Foundation Scholarships (Undergraduate/Scholarship) [9481]

War Memorial Doctoral Scholarships (Postgraduate/Scholarship) [6188]

Rachel Warner Memorial Scholarships (Graduate, Undergraduate/Scholarship) [6336]

Washington College Bound Scholarships (Undergraduate/Scholarship) [9504]

Washington Higher Education Coordinating Board Educational Opportunity Grants (Undergraduate/Grant) [9505]

Washington Higher Education Coordinating Board - State Need Grants (SNG) (Undergraduate/Grant) [9507]

Washington Reciprocity Out-of-State Scholarships (Undergraduate/Scholarship) [5469]

Washington State Governors' Scholarship for Foster Youth (Undergraduate/Scholarship) [2978]

Stand Watie Scholarships (Undergraduate/Scholarship) [8529]

Watson-Brown Scholarships (Undergraduate/Scholarship) [9540]

Thomas J. Watson Fellowships (Graduate/Fellowship) [9544]

Glenn Watson Scholarships (Undergraduate/Scholarship) [8576]

Watsontown Volunteer Fire Company Scholarships (Undergraduate/Scholarship) [2342]

Wayne County Bank Scholarships (Undergraduate/Scholarship) [6832]

Wayne-Meador-Elliott Scholarships (Undergraduate/Scholarship) [7120]

WBSN Foundation Scholarships (Graduate, Professional development/Scholarship) [9719]

Lester and Eleanor Webster Charitable Trust Fund (Undergraduate/Scholarship) [8707]

Frank L. Weil Memorial Eagle Scout Scholarships (Undergraduate/Scholarship) [6265]

Arthur Weinberg Fellowships for Independent Scholars (Professional development/Fellowship) [6710]

The Bee Winkler Weinstein Scholarship Fund (All, Vocational/Occupational/Scholarship) [8748]

Weissbuch Family Scholarships (Undergraduate/Scholarship) [7973]

Edward Kent Welch Memorial Scholarships (Undergraduate/Scholarship) [9661]

Wells Fargo Scholarships (Undergraduate/Scholarship) [7425]

Donald M. Wells Scholarships (Undergraduate/Scholarship) [4307]

Francis X. Weninger Scholarships (Undergraduate/Scholarship) [9777]

John R. and Joan F. Werren Scholarships Fund (Undergraduate/Scholarship) [8708]

West Virginia PTA Scholarships (Undergraduate/Scholarship) [9568]

Redlands Evening Lions Club - Barbara Westen Scholarships (Undergraduate/Scholarship) [7716]

Western Governors University Scholarship Program (Undergraduate/Scholarship) [4586]

Western Society of Weed Science Outstanding Student Scholarship Program (Doctorate, Graduate, Undergraduate/Scholarship) [9585]

Robert B. Westover Scholarships (Undergraduate/Scholarship) [4070]

Wheelchair Success Foundation Scholarships (Undergraduate/Scholarship) [2963]

Whidbey Island Giving Circle Scholarships (Undergraduate/Scholarship) [7426]

Wayne F. White and Bob Evans Legacy Scholarships (Undergraduate/Scholarship) [3878]

White House Fellows (Professional development/Fellowship) [7392]

White Rose Scholarships (Undergraduate/Scholarship) [7876]

Portia White Scholarships (Undergraduate/Scholarship) [2130]

Robert B. and Sophia Whiteside Scholarships (Undergraduate/Scholarship) [3547]

Ann Cook Whitman Scholarships for Perry High School (Undergraduate/Scholarship) [3615]

Ann Cook Whitman Washington, DC Scholarships (Undergraduate/Scholarship) [3616]

Donna Axum Whitworth Scholarships (Undergraduate/Scholarship) [3393]

Why Get Your Blue On? Video Scholarships (Graduate, Undergraduate/Award, Scholarship) [9587]

Dwight Whylie Scholarships (Undergraduate/Scholarship) [2131]

Alice Hersey Wick Scholarships (Undergraduate/Scholarship) [8192]

Wicomico High School Class of '55 Scholarships (Undergraduate/Scholarship) [3070]

WIEA Scholarships (Doctorate, Graduate, Undergraduate, Vocational/Occupational/Scholarship) [9687]

Barbara Wiedner and Dorothy Vandercook Memorial Peace Scholarships (Undergraduate/Scholarship) [4311]

Elmo Wierenga Alumni Scholarships (Undergraduate/Scholarship) [4308]

Elie Wiesel Prize in Ethics (Undergraduate/Prize) [9597]

WIGA Scholarships (Postgraduate, Professional development, Undergraduate/Scholarship) [9512]

Fred C. Wikoff, Jr. Scholarships (Undergraduate, Vocational/Occupational/Scholarship) [3928]

Teddy Wilburn Scholarships (Undergraduate/Scholarship) [3138]

Wiley Publishing Inc. Scholarships (Undergraduate/Scholarship) [3711]

Andrea Will Memorial Scholarships (Undergraduate/Scholarship) [8193]

M. William and Frances J. Tilghman Scholarships (Undergraduate/Scholarship) [3071]

Williams Foundation Scholarships (Undergraduate/Scholarship) [7534]

Rodney Williams Legacy Scholarships (Undergraduate/Grant) [9218]

John G. Williams Scholarship Fund (Undergraduate/Scholarship) [9610]

CSM Virgil R. Williams Scholarships (Undergraduate/Scholarship) [3645]

Elizabeth T. Williams Scholarships (Undergraduate/Scholarship) [9662]

Randy Williams Scholarships (Undergraduate, Vocational/Occupational/Scholarship) [7975]

Redlands Footlighters, Inc. - Merle and Peggy Williams Scholarships (Undergraduate/Scholarship) [7717]

RS Williamson and Eliford Mott Memorial Scholarships (Undergraduate/Scholarship) [9593]

Edwin H. and Louise N. Williamson Endowed Scholarships (Undergraduate/Scholarship) [9663]

Mary Katherine "Kathy" Williamson Scholarship Fund (Undergraduate/Scholarship) [3050]

Williamsport-Lycoming Community Foundation - Benjamin Franklin Scholarships (Undergraduate, Vocational/Occupational/Scholarship) [3796]

Woodrow Wilson International Center for Scholars Fellowships (Doctorate/Fellowship) [9612]

Bob Wilson Legacy Scholarships (Undergraduate/Scholarship) [2256]

John D. Wirth Travel Grants for International Scholars (Graduate, Professional development/Grant) [1254]

Wisconsin High School Scholarships (Undergraduate/Scholarship) [9385]

Wisconsin Region Student Leadership Scholarships (Graduate, Undergraduate/Scholarship) [6057]

CSF HCRTA/Glen O. and Wyllabeth Wise Scholarships (Undergraduate/Scholarship) [2877]

Woksape Oyate: "Wisdom of the People" Distinguished Scholars Awards (Undergraduate/Scholarship) [813]

Deborah Partridge Wolfe International Fellowships (Graduate, Undergraduate/Fellowship) [9807]

Tim Wolfred Scholarships (Undergraduate/Scholarship) [7877]

Woman In Rural Electrification Scholarships (WIRE) (Undergraduate/Scholarship) [8565]

Woman's Club of Grand Haven Scholarships Fund (Undergraduate/Scholarship) [4251]

The Woman's Club of Nashville Scholarships (Undergraduate/Scholarship) [3139]

Women in Coaching National Coaching Institute Scholarships (Undergraduate/Scholarship) [2917]

Women's Army Corps Veterans Association Scholarships (Undergraduate/Scholarship) [9711]

Women's Independence Scholarship Programs (Undergraduate/Scholarship) [8774]

Women's Italian Club of Boston Scholarships (Undergraduate/Scholarship) [4083]

Women's Overseas and Service League Scholarships for Women (Undergraduate/Scholarship) [9733]

Carolyn Wones Recruitment Scholarship Grants (Undergraduate/Scholarship) [3176]

Mary and Elliot Wood Foundation Undergraduate Scholarship Fund (Undergraduate/Scholarship) [3931]

Rolla F. Wood Graduate Scholarships (Graduate/Scholarship) [7277]

Hugh and Helen Wood Nepales Scholarships (Undergraduate/Scholarship) [2066]

Woodex Bearing Company Scholarships (Undergraduate/Scholarship) [4095]

Betsy B. Woodward Scholarships (Undergraduate/Scholarship) [1782]

Woodyard Family Scholarships (Undergraduate/Scholarship) [4265]

CSF L and T Woolfolk Memorial Scholarships (Un-

dergraduate/Scholarship) [2878]

Donald Worster Travel Grants *(Graduate, Professional development/Grant)* [1255]

James and Colin Lee Wozumi Scholarships *(Undergraduate/Scholarship)* [7427]

WREI Congressional Fellows on Women and Public Policy *(Doctorate, Graduate, Master's/Fellowship)* [9735]

WSAJ American Justice Essay Scholarships *(Undergraduate/Scholarship)* [9519]

WSAJ Presidents' Scholarships *(Undergraduate/Scholarship)* [9521]

WSSA Students Paper Competition *(Undergraduate/Award)* [9579]

WYCUP Scholarships *(Professional development/Scholarship)* [9752]

Margaret Wyeth Scholarships *(Undergraduate/Scholarship)* [3177]

Xavier Community-Engaged Fellowships *(Undergraduate/Fellowship)* [9778]

Xavier University Chancellor Scholarships *(Undergraduate/Scholarship)* [9779]

Xavier University Legacy Scholarships *(Undergraduate/Scholarship)* [9782]

Pang Xiaoyan Scholarships *(Undergraduate/Scholarship)* [2775]

Yale Graduate and Professional Students Research Fellowships *(Graduate, Professional development/Fellowship)* [2044]

William J. Yankee Memorial Scholarships *(Undergraduate/Scholarship)* [1021]

Vera Yip Memorial Scholarships *(Undergraduate, Vocational/Occupational/Scholarship)* [2760]

York Graduate Scholarships *(Graduate/Scholarship)* [8050]

York Regional Police Scholarships *(Undergraduate/Scholarship)* [5127]

York Rite Grand Chapter Royal Arch Masons Scholarships *(Undergraduate/Scholarship)* [3426]

Jack and Edna May Yost Scholarships *(Undergraduate/Scholarship)* [3964]

You Go Girl! Scholarships *(Undergraduate/Scholarship)* [7428]

Alma H. Young Emerging Scholar Awards *(Doctorate/Scholarship)* [9394]

Young People For Fellowships (YP4) *(Undergraduate/Fellowship)* [8147]

Donnell B. Young Scholarships *(Undergraduate/Scholarship)* [286]

Elmer Cooke Young - Taylor Young Scholarships *(Undergraduate/Scholarship)* [4463]

Youth Affairs Committee Rising Star Scholarships *(Undergraduate/Scholarship)* [5128]

Youth Empowerment Summit Scholarships *(Undergraduate/Scholarship)* [6148]

Youth Leadership Scholarships *(Undergraduate/Scholarship)* [2265]

Youth Partners Accessing Capital (PAC) *(Graduate, Undergraduate/Scholarship)* [354]

Nettie Tucker Yowell Scholarships *(Undergraduate/Scholarship)* [9443]

YWA Foundation Scholarships *(Graduate, Undergraduate/Scholarship)* [9793]

Zagunis Student Leader Scholarships *(Graduate, Undergraduate/Scholarship)* [6058]

CSF L.B. Zapoleon Scholarships *(Undergraduate/Scholarship)* [2879]

Zenko Family Scholarship Fund *(Undergraduate/Scholarship)* [4252]

Zeta Chapter Memorial Scholarship Awards *(Undergraduate/Scholarship)* [3178]

Zeta Phi Beta Sorority General Graduate Scholarships *(Graduate, Postdoctorate/Scholarship)* [9808]

Zeta Phi Beta Sorority General Undergraduate Scholarships *(Undergraduate/Scholarship)* [9809]

Zimmermann Scholarships *(Graduate/Scholarship)* [8785]

A.R. Zipf Fellowships *(Graduate/Fellowship)* [3280]

Jacob Ziskind Memorial Fund for Upperclassmen *(Graduate, Undergraduate/Scholarship)* [4728]

Morris L. and Rebecca Ziskind Memorial Scholarships *(Undergraduate/Scholarship)* [4655]

Ruth and Sherman Zudekoff Scholarships *(Undergraduate/Scholarship)* [3084]

Genetics

Epilepsy Foundation Pre-doctoral Research Training Fellowships *(Graduate/Grant)* [3663]

Fred Johnson Memorial Scholarships *(Doctorate, Graduate, Master's/Scholarship)* [6176]

Welder Wildlife Foundation Fellowships *(Doctorate, Graduate/Fellowship)* [9559]

Geography (See also Cartography/Surveying)

Robin P. Armstrong Memorial Prize for Excellence in Native Studies Awards *(Doctorate, Graduate/Award)* [2377]

Association of American Geographers IGIF Graduate Research Awards *(Graduate, Undergraduate/Scholarship)* [1691]

Association of American Geographers IGIF Student Travel Grants *(Graduate, Undergraduate/Grant)* [1692]

Canadian Association of Geographers Historical Geography Study Group Awards *(Doctorate, Graduate, Undergraduate/Award)* [2379]

CCV Foundation Graduate and Undergraduate Fellowships *(Doctorate, Graduate, Undergraduate/Fellowship)* [2672]

CTRF Scholarships for Graduate Study in Transportation *(Graduate/Scholarship)* [2626]

Excellence in Geographic Information Systems Scholarships *(Undergraduate/Scholarship)* [9148]

Darrel Hess Community College Geography Scholarships *(Undergraduate/Scholarship)* [1693]

Michael Marucci Memorial Scholarships *(Undergraduate/Scholarship)* [6278]

Eric Niemitalo Scholarships in Earth and Environmental Science *(Undergraduate/Scholarship)* [8121]

Pi Gamma Mu Scholarships *(Graduate/Scholarship)* [7330]

Geology

American Association of Stratigraphic Palynologists Student Scholarships *(Graduate/Scholarship)* [6]

Association of Desk and Derrick Clubs Education Trust Scholarships *(Undergraduate/Scholarship)* [1749]

J.P. Bickell Mining Scholarships *(Undergraduate/Scholarship)* [9322]

Charles F. Brandenburg Memorial Scholarships *(Undergraduate/Scholarship)* [2622]

Cameco Corporation Scholarships in the Geological Sciences - Continuing Students *(Undergraduate/Scholarship)* [2344]

Cameco Corporation Scholarships in the Geological Sciences - Entering Students *(Undergraduate/Scholarship)* [2345]

CCV Foundation Graduate and Undergraduate Fellowships *(Doctorate, Graduate, Undergraduate/Fellowship)* [2672]

Chugach Gem & Mineral Society Scholarships *(Undergraduate/Scholarship)* [9089]

Farouk El-Baz Student Research Grants *(Doctorate, Graduate, Undergraduate/Grant)* [4087]

Geological Society of America Graduate Student Research Grants *(Doctorate, Graduate/Grant)* [4088]

HSF/Wal-Mart Stores Inc. Scholarship Program *(Graduate, Undergraduate/Scholarship)* [4577]

Samuel C. Kraus, Jr. Memorial Scholarships *(Undergraduate/Scholarship)* [6534]

Marathon Oil Corporation College Scholarship Program *(Graduate, Undergraduate/Scholarship)* [4578]

McColl Family Fellowships *(Professional development/Fellowship)* [776]

Eric Niemitalo Scholarships in Earth and Environmental Science *(Undergraduate/Scholarship)* [8121]

NPSC Fellowships *(Graduate/Fellowship)* [6440]

Paleontological Society Student Research Grants *(Graduate, Undergraduate/Grant)* [7]

Geophysics (See also Physics)

Association of Desk and Derrick Clubs Education Trust Scholarships *(Undergraduate/Scholarship)* [1749]

J.P. Bickell Mining Scholarships *(Undergraduate/Scholarship)* [9322]

CfA Postdoctoral Fellowships *(Postdoctorate/Fellowship)* [4471]

Clay Postdoctoral Fellowships *(Postdoctorate/Fellowship)* [4472]

CSEG Scholarship Trust Fund *(Graduate, Undergraduate/Scholarship)* [2607]

Marathon Oil Corporation College Scholarship Program *(Graduate, Undergraduate/Scholarship)* [4578]

Geosciences

AGI Minority Participation Program Geoscience Student Scholarships (AGI-MPP) *(Graduate, Undergraduate/Scholarship)* [778]

AWG Minority Scholarships *(Undergraduate/Scholarship)* [1900]

Chrysalis Scholarships *(Graduate/Grant)* [1901]

AWG Maria Luisa Crawford Field Camp Scholarships *(Undergraduate/Scholarship)* [1902]

EAPSI Fellowships *(Doctorate, Graduate/Fellowship)* [6467]

Global Volcanism Program for Visiting Scientist/ Postdoctoral Fellowships *(Postdoctorate/Fellowship)* [8261]

Penelope Hanshaw Scholarships *(Graduate, Undergraduate/Scholarship)* [1903]

HGS Foundation Scholarships *(Undergraduate/Scholarship)* [4611]

NDSEG Fellowships *(Graduate/Fellowship)* [6239]

Glen Ruby Memorial Scholarships *(Undergraduate/Scholarship)* [2613]

William Rucker Greenwood Scholarships *(Graduate, Undergraduate/Scholarship)* [1904]

Shell Incentive Scholarship Fund *(Undergraduate/Scholarship)* [8103]

Shell Process Technology Scholarships *(Undergraduate/Scholarship)* [8104]

Shell Technical Scholarships *(Undergraduate/Scholarship)* [8105]

Society of Exploration Geophysicists Foundation Scholarships *(Graduate, Undergraduate/Scholarship)* [8320]

Janet Cullen Tanaka Scholarships *(Undergraduate/Scholarship)* [1905]

United States Geospatial Intelligence Foundation Graduate Scholarships *(Postgraduate/Scholarship)* [9044]

United States Geospatial Intelligence Foundation High School Scholarships *(Undergraduate/Scholarship)* [9045]

United States Geospatial Intelligence Foundation Undergraduate Scholarships *(Undergraduate/Scholarship)* [9046]

Mary-Claire Ward Geoscience Awards *(Graduate/Award)* [7458]

German studies (See also Area and ethnic studies)

Leo Baeck Institute - DAAD Fellowships *(Doctorate/Fellowship)* [4115]

German Historical Institute Doctoral and Postdoctoral Fellowships *(Doctorate, Postgraduate/Fellowship)* [4126]

German Society Scholarships *(Undergraduate/Scholarship)* [4137]

German Studies Research Grants *(Undergraduate/Grant)* [4119]

Dr. Guido Goldman Fellowships *(Doctorate, Postdoctorate/Fellowship)* [666]

Dr. Richard M. Hunt Fellowships *(Doctorate, Postdoctorate/Fellowship)* [667]

Intensive Language Course Grants *(Doctorate/Grant)* [4120]

Kade-Heideking Fellowships *(Doctorate/Fellowship)* [4128]

Learn German in Germany Grants *(Doctorate/Grant)* [4122]

NEH Fellowships for Senior Scholars (Doctorate/Fellowship) [2695]

Prins Foundation Fellowship for Senior Scholars (Doctorate/Fellowship) [2696]

Prins Foundation Post-Doctoral and Early Career Fellowship for Emigrating Scholars (Professional development, Postdoctorate/Fellowship) [2697]

Thyssen-Heideking Fellowships (Postdoctorate/Fellowship) [4129]

University Summer Course Grants (Undergraduate/Grant) [4124]

Gerontology

AFAR Scholarships (Graduate, Undergraduate/Scholarship) [746]

Alberta Association of Gerontology Student Awards - Edmonton Chapter (Graduate, Undergraduate/Award) [207]

Alberta Association of Gerontology Student Awards (Graduate/Award) [206]

Anne Beckingham Scholarships (Graduate, Professional development/Scholarship) [2474]

Behavioral Gerontology SIG Student Research Awards (Undergraduate/Award) [1712]

CAG Margery Boyce Bursary Awards (Postgraduate/Award) [2381]

Brookdale Leadership in Aging Fellowships (Professional development/Fellowship) [2194]

Canadian Evaluation Society Memorial Scholarships (Graduate, Professional development/Scholarship) [2475]

Extendicare Scholarships in Gerontology (Graduate/Scholarship) [2540]

Aracelis Francis Minority Scholarships in Gerontology (Master's/Scholarship) [1787]

HPGS/ALOH Graduate Scholarships (Graduate/Scholarship) [4485]

HPGS Undergraduate Scholarships (Undergraduate/Scholarship) [4486]

Annie Kirshenblatt Memorial Scholarships (Graduate, Undergraduate/Scholarship) [8915]

CAG Donald Menzies Bursary Awards (Postgraduate/Award) [2382]

Dr. Helen K. Mussallem Fellowships (Graduate/Scholarship) [2549]

Shoshana Philipp (Kirshenblatt) R.N. Memorial Scholarships (Graduate, Undergraduate/Scholarship) [8917]

SCA Nursing Scholarships (Graduate, Professional development/Scholarship) [2476]

Sigma Kappa Foundation Alzheimer's/Gerontology Scholarships (Undergraduate/Scholarship) [8183]

Sigma Kappa Foundation Gerontology Scholarships (Undergraduate/Scholarship) [8185]

Government (See also Political science)

George Oliver Benton Memorial Scholarships (Undergraduate/Scholarship) [3095]

Center for Women in Government and Civil Society Fellowships (Graduate/Fellowship) [2709]

Enid Hall Griswold Memorial Scholarships (Undergraduate/Scholarship) [6499]

Bryce Harlow Fellowship Program (Graduate/Fellowship) [4395]

Gary Merrill Memorial Scholarships (Undergraduate/Scholarship) [5588]

Minnesota Association of Township Scholarships (Undergraduate, Vocational/Occupational/Scholarship) [5894]

Police Explorer Scholarships Program (Undergraduate/Scholarship) [3844]

Political Studies Scholarships (Undergraduate, Graduate/Scholarship) [9447]

Betty Rendel Scholarships (Undergraduate/Scholarship) [6288]

Women In Defense HORIZONS Scholarships (Graduate, Undergraduate/Scholarship) [9696]

Mary and Elliot Wood Foundation Graduate Scholarship Fund (Graduate/Scholarship) [3930]

Graphic art and design (See also Art)

Advertising Production Club of New York High School Scholarships (APC) (Undergraduate/Scholarship) [58]

Advertising Production Club Scholarship Awards (Graduate, Undergraduate/Scholarship) [59]

Paul Arnold Memorial Scholarships (Undergraduate/Scholarship) [7396]

Don Bailey Scholarships (Undergraduate/Scholarship) [6309]

Cadmus Communications Corporation Graphics Scholarship Endowment Fund (Undergraduate/Scholarship) [3889]

ESA Foundation Computer and Video Game Scholarship Program (Undergraduate/Scholarship) [3650]

The Gallery Collection's Greeting Card Scholarships (Undergraduate/Scholarship) [4035]

GEF Scholarship Program (Undergraduate, Graduate/Scholarship) [4319]

Elizabeth Greenhalgh Memorial Scholarships in Journalism, Graphic Arts, or Photography (Graduate, Undergraduate/Scholarship) [9699]

International Foodservice Editorial Council Scholarships (Graduate, Undergraduate/Scholarship) [4935]

Lewis-Clark State College Presidential Technical Out-of-State Scholarships (Undergraduate/Scholarship) [5447]

Maine Graphic Arts Association Scholarships (Undergraduate/Scholarship) [5597]

Andrew Oliver Research Fellowships (Graduate, Doctorate/Fellowship) [5677]

PGSF-GATF Scholarships (Graduate, Undergraduate/Scholarship) [61]

Print Graphics Scholarship Foundation (PGSF) (Graduate, Undergraduate/Fellowship, Scholarship) [7435]

Harry V. Quadracci Memorial Scholarships (Undergraduate, Graduate/Scholarship) [4321]

Society of Graphic Designers of Canada Adobe Scholarships (Undergraduate/Scholarship) [8331]

Society of Graphic Designers of Canada Applied Arts Scholarships (Undergraduate/Scholarship) [8332]

Society of Graphic Designers of Canada Veer Scholarships (Undergraduate/Scholarship) [8333]

Tag and Label Manufacturers Institute Scholarships - Four-Year Colleges (Undergraduate/Scholarship) [8793]

Worldstudio AIGA Scholarships (Graduate, Undergraduate/Scholarship) [9761]

Greek studies (See also Area and ethnic studies)

Hellenic University Club of Philadelphia Founders Scholarships (Undergraduate/Scholarship) [4515]

Mary Isabel Sibley Fellowships (Doctorate/Fellowship) [7249]

Health care services

ACMPE Scholarship Fund Program (Graduate, Undergraduate/Scholarship) [5739]

Adelson Scholarships (Undergraduate/Scholarship) [7464]

American Cancer Society - Postdoctoral Fellowships (Doctorate/Fellowship) [594]

AMSUS Physician Awards (Professional development/Award) [1460]

APS/Maricopa County Community Colleges Scholarships (Undergraduate/Scholarship) [7333]

Association of Health Care Journalists Media Fellowships on Health Performance (Professional development/Fellowship) [3017]

Australian-American Health Policy Fellowships (Doctorate, Graduate/Fellowship) [3018]

Leslie Baranowski Scholarships for Professional Excellence (All/Scholarship) [4764]

Ellis J. Bonner Scholarships (Doctorate, Graduate, Undergraduate/Scholarship) [6080]

Maria Gonzales Borrero Scholarships (Undergraduate/Scholarship) [4414]

Corris Boyd Scholarships (Master's/Scholarship) [1891]

Dvora Brodie Scholarships (Graduate, Postgraduate, Undergraduate/Scholarship) [4503]

Joe Q. Bryant American Council on Exercise Educational Scholarships (Undergraduate/Scholarship) [662]

Cancer Treatment Centers of America Post-Graduate Management Fellowships (Postgraduate/Fellowship) [2642]

Rhea Sourifman Caplin Memorial Scholarships (Undergraduate/Scholarship) [4417]

Leigh Carter Scholarships (Undergraduate/Scholarship) [3099]

Casey Family Scholars Scholarships (Undergraduate, Vocational/Occupational/Scholarship) [3871]

CBC Spouses Cheerios Brand Health Initiative Scholarships (Undergraduate/Scholarship) [3215]

CentraState Associated Auxiliaries Scholarships (Undergraduate/Scholarship) [2723]

CentraState Healthcare Foundation Health Professional Scholarships (Undergraduate/Scholarship) [2725]

Children's Memorial Hospital Postgraduate Administrative Fellowships (Postgraduate/Fellowship) [5539]

DHCC Board Scholarships (Graduate, Professional development, Undergraduate/Scholarship) [3442]

Eagles Fly for Leukemia Scholarships (Undergraduate/Scholarship) [2755]

Foundation for Seacoast Health Scholarships (Graduate, Undergraduate/Scholarship) [3992]

Gardner Foundation Infusion Nurses Society Education Scholarships (All/Scholarship) [4765]

Florence S. Gaynor Scholarships (Doctorate, Graduate, Undergraduate/Scholarship) [6081]

John Glaser Scholarships (Undergraduate/Scholarship) [2971]

Harkness Fellowships in Health Care Policy and Practice (Doctorate, Graduate/Fellowship) [3020]

Health and Aging Policy Fellows (Professional development/Fellowship) [1018]

Healthcare Information Management Systems Scholarships (Graduate, Postgraduate, Undergraduate/Scholarship) [4505]

HFMA Connecticut Chapter Scholarships (Graduate, Undergraduate/Scholarship) [4501]

HRET Health Career Scholarships (Graduate, Undergraduate/Scholarship) [6644]

Michael A. Hunter Memorial Scholarships (Undergraduate/Scholarship) [2757]

IHRDP Post-doctoral Fellowships (Doctorate, Graduate, Master's, Postdoctorate/Fellowship, Scholarship) [4756]

Gaynold Jensen Education Stipends (Postdoctorate, Professional development/Scholarship) [3443]

Oliver Joel and Ellen Pell Denny Healthcare Scholarship Fund (Undergraduate/Scholarship) [9642]

The Robert Wood Johnson Health Policy Fellowship Program (All/Fellowship) [1019]

Kaiser Permanente Northwest Pride Scholarships (Undergraduate/Scholarship) [3679]

Rhonda Knopp Memorial Scholarships (Undergraduate/Scholarship) [7095]

David A. Kronick Travelling Fellowships (Doctorate/Fellowship) [5743]

LGBT HEART Scholarships (Graduate/Scholarship) [5407]

Donald A.B. Lindberg Research Fellowships (Doctorate, Graduate/Fellowship) [5744]

Robert Mack Scholarships (Graduate, Undergraduate/Scholarship) [5556]

Mat-Su Health Foundation Scholarships (Undergraduate/Scholarship) [9159]

William J. Merriman American Council on Exercise Educational Scholarships (Undergraduate/Scholarship) [663]

MSPT Sports Medicine Scholarships (Undergraduate/Scholarship) [7509]

NOHIMSS Student Scholarship Program (Undergraduate, Master's, Doctorate/Scholarship) [6805]

North Carolina Association of Health Care Recruiters Scholarships (Undergraduate/Scholarship) [6755]

Northern California Chapter of HIMSS Scholarships

(Graduate, Postgraduate, Undergraduate/Scholarship) [4506]
NTHS/HOSA Scholarships *(Undergraduate/Scholarship)* [6544]
Outlaw Student's Medical Professions Scholarships *(Undergraduate/Scholarship)* [8752]
George Phillips Scholarships *(Undergraduate/Scholarship)* [5509]
Portuguese American Police Association Scholarships *(Undergraduate/Scholarship)* [7380]
Reid Hospital Graduate Student Scholarships *(Graduate/Scholarship)* [9557]
Haynes Rice Scholarships *(Doctorate, Graduate, Undergraduate/Scholarship)* [6082]
Violet D. Ruelokke Primary Health Care Awards *(Graduate, Professional development/Scholarship)* [1852]
SALEF Health Career Scholarships *(Graduate, Undergraduate/Scholarship)* [7894]
Major General Jerry Sanders Scholarship Program *(High School, Undergraduate/Scholarship)* [1461]
Schaible Health Care Services Scholarships *(Undergraduate/Scholarship)* [8988]
Victor E. Schimmel Memorial Nursing Scholarships *(Doctorate, Graduate, Master's/Scholarship)* [1725]
Lewis L. Seaman Junior Enlisted Awards for Outstanding Operational Support *(Professional development/Award)* [1462]
June M. Seneca Scholarships *(Graduate/Scholarship)* [8088]
Service League Volunteer Scholarships *(Undergraduate/Scholarship)* [9510]
William Shannon American Council on Exercise Certification Scholarships *(Professional development, Undergraduate/Scholarship)* [664]
Pat Shimp Memorial Scholarships *(Undergraduate/Scholarship)* [7114]
The Eileen J. Smith, R.N. Memorial Scholarships *(Undergraduate/Scholarship)* [5105]
Society for the Arts in Healthcare Environmental Research Grants *(Professional development/Grant)* [8300]
Society for the Arts in Healthcare Student Scholarships *(Doctorate, Graduate, Undergraduate/Scholarship)* [8301]
Soroptimist International of Redlands Scholarships *(Undergraduate/Scholarship)* [7715]
Ken Stanley Memorial Scholarships *(Undergraduate/Scholarship)* [5511]
Matt Stauffer Memorial Scholarships *(Undergraduate, Vocational/Occupational/Scholarship)* [2758]
Louis Stokes Health Scholars Program *(Undergraduate, Vocational/Occupational/Scholarship)* [3221]
Paul Tejada Memorial Scholarships *(Undergraduate/Scholarship)* [5107]
Vincent Trotter Health Care Scholarships *(Undergraduate, Vocational/Occupational/Scholarship)* [7969]
Udall Scholarships *(Undergraduate/Scholarship)* [9197]
Villers Fellowships for Health Care Justice *(Graduate/Fellowship)* [3706]
Leon Williams Scholarships *(Undergraduate/Scholarship)* [7974]
David A. Winston Health Policy Scholarships *(Graduate/Scholarship)* [1892]
Marilyn Yetso Memorial Scholarships *(Undergraduate, Vocational/Occupational/Scholarship)* [2759]

Health education

AAHD Scholarships *(Graduate, Undergraduate/Scholarship)* [481]
ACS/ASA Health Policy and Management Scholarships *(Professional development/Scholarship)* [1398]
Dr. Andy Anderson Young Professional Awards *(Professional development/Award)* [7317]
Jane B. Aron Doctoral Fellowships *(Doctorate/Fellowship)* [6120]
ASHA Scholarships *(Graduate, Undergraduate/Scholarship)* [1175]
ASHA Student Research Grants *(Graduate, Undergraduate/Scholarship)* [1176]

Association of American Indian Physicians Scholarships *(Graduate, Undergraduate/Scholarship)* [1699]
Cathy L. Brock Memorial Scholarships *(Graduate/Scholarship)* [4787]
Diversified Investment Advisors Leaders in Healthcare Scholarships *(Graduate/Scholarship)* [4788]
Vivian Drenckhahn Student Scholarships *(Graduate, Undergraduate/Scholarship)* [8477]
Emergency Medicine Physician Scholarships for Health Information Management Program *(Undergraduate/Scholarship)* [8664]
NSPF Ray B. Essick Scholarship Awards *(Professional development/Scholarship)* [6538]
Foundation for Seacoast Health Scholarships *(Graduate, Undergraduate/Scholarship)* [3992]
Steven Huesing Scholarships *(Graduate, Undergraduate/Scholarship)* [2915]
JCC Association Graduate Education Scholarships *(Graduate/Scholarship)* [5151]
Kaiser Media Fellowships in Health *(Advanced Professional/Fellowship)* [5180]
KHIMA Graduate Scholarships *(Graduate/Scholarship)* [5187]
David B. Larson Fellowships in Health and Spirituality *(Doctorate/Fellowship)* [5275]
Les Dames D'Escoffier New York Scholarships *(Undergraduate/Scholarship)* [5405]
LGBT HEART Scholarships *(Graduate/Scholarship)* [5407]
R. Tait Mackenzie Awards *(Professional development/Award)* [7318]
Sue A. Malone Scholarships *(Doctorate, Graduate/Scholarship)* [5188]
Randall Matthis for Environmental Studies Scholarships *(Graduate, Undergraduate/Scholarship)* [1537]
Migrant Health Scholarships *(Professional development/Scholarship)* [6182]
Minnesota Health Information Management Association Scholarships *(Undergraduate/Scholarship)* [5898]
National Swimming Pool Foundation Board of Directors' Scholarship Awards *(Professional development/Scholarship)* [6539]
National Swimming Pool Foundation Scholarship Awards *(Professional development/Scholarship)* [6540]
North American Society Fellowships *(Professional development/Fellowship)* [7319]
PHE Canada Health Educator Awards *(Professional development/Award)* [7320]
PHE Canada Student Awards *(Undergraduate/Award)* [7321]
Terry Linda Potter Scholarship Fund *(Undergraduate/Scholarship)* [4234]
Elliott C. Roberts Scholarships *(Graduate/Scholarship)* [4789]
SALEF Health Career Scholarships *(Graduate, Undergraduate/Scholarship)* [7894]
Karen Schuvie Scholarships *(Undergraduate/Scholarship)* [5189]
SOPHE/ATSDR Student Fellowships in Environmental Health or Emergency Preparedness *(Doctorate, Graduate, Master's/Fellowship)* [8478]
SOPHE/CDC Student Fellowships in Child, Adolescent and School Health *(Doctorate, Graduate, Master's/Fellowship)* [8479]
SOPHE/CDC Student Fellowships in Injury Prevention *(Graduate/Fellowship)* [8480]
Louis Stokes Health Scholars Program *(Undergraduate, Vocational/Occupational/Scholarship)* [3221]

Health sciences

Dr. Anderson Abbott Awards *(Undergraduate/Scholarship)* [9320]
Alberta Innovates Graduate Student Scholarship *(Graduate/Scholarship)* [234]
Allied Health Care Professional Scholarships *(Undergraduate/Scholarship)* [4693]
American Lung Association/AAAAI Allergic Respiratory Diseases Awards *(Doctorate/Grant)* [908]
American Lung Association Biomedical Research Grants *(Doctorate/Grant)* [909]

American Lung Association Clinical Patient Care Research Grants *(Doctorate/Grant)* [910]
American Lung Association Dalsemer Research Grants *(Doctorate/Grant)* [911]
American Lung Association DeSousa Awards *(Doctorate/Grant)* [912]
American Lung Association Lung Cancer Discovery Awards *(Doctorate/Grant)* [913]
American Lung Association Senior Research Training Fellowships *(Doctorate/Fellowship)* [914]
American Lung Association Social-Behavioral Research Grants *(Doctorate/Grant)* [915]
American Society of Electroneurodiagnostic Technologists Student Education Grants (ASET) *(Undergraduate/Grant)* [1238]
Bill Bendiner and Doug Morgenson Scholarships *(Undergraduate/Scholarship)* [7402]
Robert Browning Scholarships *(Undergraduate/Scholarship)* [7403]
Richard J. Burk, Jr. Fellowships *(Graduate/Fellowship)* [4488]
Joseph R. Calder, Jr., MD Scholarship Fund *(Undergraduate/Scholarship)* [3763]
California Association of Private Postsecondary Schools Scholarships *(Undergraduate/Scholarship)* [2232]
CentraState Band Aid Open Committee Scholarships *(Undergraduate/Scholarship)* [2724]
Gordon W. and Agnes P. Cobb Scholarships *(Undergraduate/Scholarship)* [3567]
Davis Foundation Postdoctoral Fellowships *(Postdoctorate/Fellowship)* [4494]
DCH Freehold Toyota Scholarships *(Undergraduate/Scholarship)* [2726]
Josephine P. White Eagle Graduate Fellowships *(Graduate, Master's, Doctorate/Fellowship)* [4591]
Fanconi Anemia Research Grants *(Postdoctorate/Grant)* [3713]
Florida Education Fund McKnight Doctoral Fellowships *(Graduate/Fellowship)* [3822]
Robert Gardner Memorial Fellowships *(Graduate/Fellowship)* [4489]
Health Outcomes Post Doctoral Fellowships *(Postdoctorate/Fellowship)* [7223]
Health Outcomes Pre Doctoral Fellowships *(Doctorate/Fellowship)* [7224]
Health Outcomes Research Starter Grants *(Doctorate/Grant)* [7225]
Health Outcomes Sabbatical Fellowships *(Postdoctorate/Fellowship)* [7226]
Health Sciences Student Fellowships *(Doctorate, Graduate/Fellowship)* [3666]
Health, Sport, and Fitness SIG Student Research Awards *(Undergraduate/Award)* [1714]
HLS/MLA Professional Development Grants *(Professional development/Grant)* [5742]
Houston/Nancy Holliman Scholarships *(Undergraduate/Scholarship)* [3413]
HRET Health Career Scholarships *(Graduate, Undergraduate/Scholarship)* [6644]
Indian Health Service Scholarship Program *(Undergraduate/Scholarship)* [819]
The Robert Wood Johnson Health Policy Fellowship Program *(All/Fellowship)* [1019]
KFOC Allied Health Fellowships *(Doctorate/Fellowship)* [5255]
KFOC Allied Health Scholarships *(Graduate/Scholarship)* [5256]
Charles A. King Trust Postdoctoral Fellowships *(Postdoctorate/Fellowship)* [4495]
Robert S. Landauer, Sr. Memorial Fellowships *(Graduate/Fellowship)* [4490]
S. Evelyn Lewis Memorial Scholarships in Medical Health Sciences *(Graduate, Undergraduate/Scholarship)* [9805]
LGBT HEART Scholarships *(Graduate/Scholarship)* [5407]
Lung Health Dissertation Grants *(Graduate/Grant)* [916]
Richard Marks Educational Fund *(Graduate/Scholarship)* [5217]
Medical Library Association Scholarships for Minority Students *(Graduate/Scholarship)* [5745]
Medical Staff Scholarships *(Undergraduate/Scholarship)* [9509]

George Hi'ilani Mills Perpetual Fellowships *(Graduate/Fellowship)* [5218]

MLA/NLM Spectrum Scholarship Program *(Undergraduate/Scholarship)* [5746]

MLA Research, Development, and Demonstration Project Grants *(Graduate/Grant)* [5747]

Burton J. Moyer Memorial Fellowships *(Graduate/Fellowship)* [4491]

National Biosafety and Biocontainment Training Program Fellowships *(Graduate/Fellowship)* [6141]

NLM Associate Fellowships *(Graduate, Postgraduate/Fellowship)* [6396]

Helen Woodruff Nolop Scholarships in Audiology and Allied Fields *(Graduate/Scholarship)* [3419]

Norkus Charitable Foundation Scholarships *(Undergraduate/Scholarship)* [2727]

Patterson Trust Postdoctoral Fellowships in Brain Circuitry *(Postdoctorate/Fellowship)* [4496]

Scholarships for Disadvantaged Students *(Undergraduate/Scholarship)* [4499]

Dr. Robert Norman Shaw Scholarships *(Undergraduate/Scholarship)* [268]

J. Newell Stannard Fellowships *(Graduate/Fellowship)* [4492]

Louis Stokes Health Scholars Program *(Undergraduate, Vocational/Occupational/Scholarship)* [3221]

Louis Stokes Urban Health Policy Fellows Program *(Graduate, Professional development/Fellowship)* [3222]

Steven M. Teutsch Prevention Effectiveness Fellowships *(Doctorate/Fellowship)* [2715]

Thomson Reuters/MLA Doctoral Fellowships *(Doctorate/Fellowship)* [5748]

TMA Research Fellowships *(Graduate, Postdoctorate/Grant)* [5967]

Star and Barry Tobias Scholarships *(Undergraduate/Scholarship)* [2728]

Vanier Canada Graduate Scholarships *(Graduate/Scholarship)* [6573]

Health services administration

Ellis J. Bonner Scholarships *(Doctorate, Graduate, Undergraduate/Scholarship)* [6080]

Cathy L. Brock Memorial Scholarships *(Graduate/Scholarship)* [4787]

City of Toronto Scholarships for Aboriginal Students *(Graduate, Undergraduate/Scholarship)* [9328]

Diversified Investment Advisors Leaders in Healthcare Scholarships *(Graduate/Scholarship)* [4788]

Florence S. Gaynor Scholarships *(Doctorate, Graduate, Undergraduate/Scholarship)* [6081]

GE Healthcare Management Scholarship Program *(Graduate/Scholarship)* [1323]

Haynes Rice Scholarships *(Doctorate, Graduate, Undergraduate/Scholarship)* [6082]

Elliott C. Roberts Scholarships *(Graduate/Scholarship)* [4789]

Louis Stokes Health Scholars Program *(Undergraduate, Vocational/Occupational/Scholarship)* [3221]

Steven M. Teutsch Prevention Effectiveness Fellowships *(Doctorate/Fellowship)* [2715]

Toronto Rehabilitation Institute Graduate Student Scholarships - Ontario Student Opportunities Trust Fund (OSOTF) *(Graduate/Scholarship)* [8919]

Hearing and deafness

AG BELL College Scholarship Awards *(Undergraduate/Scholarship)* [2048]

Elizabeth Benson Scholarship Awards *(Undergraduate/Scholarship)* [7727]

Houston/Nancy Holliman Scholarships *(Undergraduate/Scholarship)* [3413]

NAJA Scholarships *(Graduate/Scholarship)* [6086]

George H. Nofer Scholarships for Law and Public Policy *(Doctorate, Graduate/Scholarship)* [2049]

Daniel H. Pokorny Memorial Scholarship Awards *(Undergraduate/Scholarship)* [7728]

School Age Financial Aid Program *(Undergraduate/Scholarship)* [2050]

Sertoma Communicative Disorders Scholarships *(Graduate/Scholarship)* [8094]

Sertoma Hard of Hearing and Deaf Scholarships

(Undergraduate/Scholarship) [8095]

Heating, air conditioning, and refrigeration

Lewis-Clark State College Presidential Technical Out-of-State Scholarships *(Undergraduate/Scholarship)* [5447]

Dave Nelsen Scholarships *(Undergraduate/Scholarship)* [6097]

Snodgrass Scholarships *(Undergraduate/Scholarship)* [9175]

Hematology

Aplastic Anemia and Myelosdysplasia Scholarships *(Graduate/Scholarship)* [2533]

Hemophilia

Hemophilia Federation of America Educational Scholarships *(Undergraduate/Scholarship)* [4528]

Gail Posluns Fellowships in Hematology *(Postdoctorate/Fellowship)* [5537]

Herpetology

Peace Frogs Fellowships *(Graduate/Fellowship)* [6984]

Hispanic American studies

Latin American Educational Foundation Scholarships *(Undergraduate, Vocational/Occupational/Scholarship)* [5356]

LULAC GM Scholarships *(Graduate, High School, Undergraduate, Vocational/Occupational/Award)* [5387]

LULAC National Scholarship Fund *(Graduate, High School, Undergraduate, Vocational/Occupational/Scholarship)* [5388]

Histology

Robert A. Clark Memorial Educational Scholarships *(Postgraduate/Scholarship)* [6510]

Fisher Healthcare Educational Scholarships *(Postgraduate/Scholarship)* [6512]

Leonard Noble Educational Scholarships *(Postgraduate/Scholarship)* [6515]

Dezna C. Sheehan Memorial Educational Scholarships *(Postgraduate/Scholarship)* [6516]

Thermo Scientific Educational Scholarships *(Postgraduate/Scholarship)* [6518]

Ventana Medical Systems In Situ Hybridization Awards *(Professional development/Award)* [6519]

Historic preservation

Association for Preservation Technology International Student Scholarships *(Graduate, Undergraduate/Scholarship)* [1843]

J.E. Caldwell Centennial Scholarships *(Undergraduate/Scholarship)* [6498]

Death Valley '49ers Scholarships *(Undergraduate/Scholarship)* [3352]

Grand Canyon Historical Society Scholarships *(Graduate/Scholarship)* [4205]

Mildred Colodny Diversity Scholarships for Graduate Study in Historic Preservation *(Graduate/Scholarship)* [6546]

National Alliance of Preservation Commission Student Scholarships *(Undergraduate/Scholarship)* [6017]

The Aaron and Rita Slom Scholarships *(Undergraduate/Scholarship)* [8923]

History

American Indian Program Fellowships *(Graduate/Fellowship)* [8260]

Cecil E. Burney Scholarships *(Undergraduate/Scholarship)* [2940]

Rachel Carson Prize *(Professional development/Prize)* [1246]

Dick Depaolis Memorial Scholarships *(Undergraduate/Scholarship)* [3196]

Dr. Feroz Ahmed Memorial Educational Post-Graduate Scholarships *(Doctorate, Postgraduate/Scholarship)* [8216]

Douglas-Coldwell Foundation Scholarships in Social Affairs *(Graduate/Scholarship)* [3474]

UAA Governor William A. Egan Scholarships *(Undergraduate/Scholarship)* [9091]

Environmental History of Quebec Scholarships *(Postdoctorate, Postgraduate/Scholarship)* [6617]

Faculty Advisor Research Grants *(Professional development/Grant)* [7240]

Fellowships in Aerospace History *(Doctorate/Fellowship)* [792]

Franciszek Gadzala Memorial Scholarships *(Undergraduate/Scholarship)* [7763]

William E. "Bill" Gallagher Scholarships *(Undergraduate/Scholarship)* [7076]

Margaret S. Gilbert Scholarship Fund *(Undergraduate/Scholarship)* [8669]

Gilder Lehrman Short-Term Fellowships *(Graduate, Postdoctorate/Fellowship)* [4151]

Grand Canyon Historical Society Scholarships *(Graduate/Scholarship)* [4205]

Randy Green Memorial Scholarship Fund *(High School/Scholarship)* [3318]

Velma Shotwell Griffin Memorial Scholarship Fund *(Undergraduate/Scholarship)* [8671]

Enid Hall Griswold Memorial Scholarships *(Undergraduate/Scholarship)* [6499]

Samuel P. Hays Research Fellowships *(Professional development/Fellowship)* [1248]

Hench Post-Dissertation Fellowships *(Postdoctorate/Fellowship)* [419]

Catarino and Evangelina Hernandez Research Fellowships in Latino History *(Professional development/Fellowship)* [8874]

Brooke Hindle Postdoctoral Fellowships *(Postdoctorate/Fellowship)* [8344]

Mary M. Hughes Research Fellowships in Texas History *(Professional development/Fellowship)* [8875]

Huguenot Society of South Carolina Graduate Scholarships *(Graduate/Scholarship)* [4628]

Harriet Irsay Scholarships *(Graduate, Undergraduate/Scholarship)* [869]

The J. Franklin Jameson Fellowships in American History *(Doctorate/Fellowship)* [793]

John H. Jenkins Research Fellowships in Texas History *(Professional development/Fellowship)* [8876]

Mary Jon and J. P. Bryan Leadership in Education Awards *(Professional development/Award)* [8877]

Melvin Kranzberg Dissertation Fellowships *(Doctorate/Fellowship)* [8345]

Lazarian Graduate Scholarships *(Graduate/Scholarship)* [1578]

Lerner-Scott Dissertation Prizes *(Doctorate/Prize)* [6959]

Suzanne and Caleb Loring Research Fellowships *(Graduate, Doctorate/Fellowship)* [5673]

George Perkins Marsh Prize *(Professional development/Prize)* [1249]

Michael Marucci Memorial Scholarships *(Undergraduate/Scholarship)* [6278]

Larry Matfay Scholarships *(Graduate, Undergraduate/Scholarship)* [5287]

William P. McHugh Memorial Fund Award *(Doctorate, Graduate/Fellowship)* [1141]

Thomas S. Morgan Memorial Scholarships *(Graduate, Master's/Scholarship)* [7241]

National Council on Public History Graduate Student Travel Awards *(Doctorate, Graduate/Grant)* [6215]

National Council on Public History Student Project Awards *(Undergraduate/Award)* [6216]

National Endowment for the Humanities Advanced Fellowships for Research in Turkey *(Postdoctorate/Fellowship)* [1153]

The National Endowment for the Humanities Fellowships *(Doctorate, Graduate/Fellowship)* [1142]

North American Conference on British Studies Dissertation Year Fellowships *(Doctorate, Postdoctorate/Fellowship)* [6735]

North American Conference on British Studies-

Huntington Library Fellowships (Doctorate, Post-doctorate/Fellowship) [6736]

OAH-IEHS Huggins-Quarles Dissertation Awards (Doctorate/Grant) [6960]

William E. Parrish Scholarships (Graduate, Master's/Scholarship) [7242]

Louis Pelzer Memorial Awards (Graduate/Award) [6961]

Petroleum History Society Graduate Scholarships (Graduate/Scholarship) [7215]

Phi Alpha Theta Doctoral Scholarships (Doctorate/Scholarship) [7243]

Pi Gamma Mu Scholarships (Graduate/Scholarship) [7330]

John Pine Memorial Scholarships (Doctorate/Scholarship) [7244]

D.F. Plett Graduate Fellowships (Graduate/Fellowship) [7342]

A. Stanley Rand Fellowships Program (Undergraduate, Doctorate, Postdoctorate/Fellowship) [8270]

Charles and Ruth Ronin Memorial Scholarships (Undergraduate/Scholarship) [7709]

Hal Rothman Dissertation Fellowships (Doctorate/Fellowship) [1252]

Everett Oscar Shimp Memorial Scholarships (Undergraduate/Scholarship) [7113]

Benjamin F. Stevens Fellowships (Graduate, Doctorate/Fellowship) [5678]

Graydon A. Tunstall Undergraduate Student Scholarships (Undergraduate/Scholarship) [7245]

The United States Department of State, Bureau of Educational & Cultural Affairs Fellowships (Doctorate, Graduate/Fellowship) [1143]

W.B.H. Dowse Fellowships (Graduate, Doctorate/Fellowship) [5680]

Frederick K. Weyerhaeuser Forest History Fellowships (Graduate/Fellowship) [3860]

Xavier University Departmental Scholarships (Undergraduate/Scholarship) [9780]

A.F. Zimmerman Scholarships (Graduate, Master's/Scholarship) [7246]

Blanche Raper Zimmerman Scholarships (Professional development/Scholarship) [9665]

History, American

AAS Fellowships for Creative and Performing Artists and Writers (All/Fellowship) [412]

AAS-Northeast Modern Language Association Fellowships (All/Fellowship) [414]

American History Scholarships (Undergraduate/Scholarship) [6496]

Stephen Botein Fellowships (Doctorate/Fellowship) [415]

Cromwell Fellowships (Undergraduate/Fellowship) [1291]

German Historical Institute Doctoral and Postdoctoral Fellowships (Doctorate, Postgraduate/Fellowship) [4126]

Woody Guthrie Fellowships (All/Fellowship) [2158]

Kade-Heideking Fellowships (Doctorate/Fellowship) [4128]

The Legacy Fellowships (Doctorate/Fellowship) [421]

Lloyd Lewis Fellowships in American History (Postdoctorate/Fellowship) [6696]

James Madison Foundation - Junior Fellowships (Graduate/Fellowship) [5564]

James Madison Foundation - Senior Fellowships (Graduate/Fellowship) [5565]

Massachusetts Society of the Cincinnati Fellowships (Graduate, Doctorate/Fellowship) [5674]

Kate B. and Hall J. Peterson Fellowships (Doctorate/Fellowship) [422]

Arthur M. Schlesinger, Jr. Fellowships (All/Fellowship) [5240]

Tadeusz Sendzimir Scholarships (Undergraduate/Scholarship) [4460]

Swensrud Teacher Fellowships at MHS (Massachusetts Historical Society) (Professional development/Fellowship) [5679]

Thyssen-Heideking Fellowships (Postdoctorate/Fellowship) [4129]

The Joyce Tracy Fellowships (Doctorate/Fellowship) [424]

United States Capitol Historical Society Fellowships (Graduate/Fellowship) [9037]

Virginia Historical Society Research Fellowships (Doctorate/Fellowship) [9453]

History, Ancient

Fellowships in the Humanities and Social Sciences in Turkey (Postdoctorate/Fellowship) [1147]

History, Art (See Art history)

History, Economic

Armed Forces Communications and Electronics Association Fellowships (Doctorate, Graduate/Fellowship) [1555]

Arthur H. Cole Grants in Aid (Doctorate/Grant) [3582]

EHA Exploratory Travel and Data Grants (Doctorate/Grant) [3583]

EHA Graduate Dissertation Fellowships (Doctorate/Fellowship) [3584]

History, Medical

Hannah Junior General Scholarships (Graduate/Scholarship) [1681]

Hannah Senior General Scholarships (Graduate/Scholarship) [1682]

History, Military

ABC-Clio Research Grants (Graduate/Grant) [8412]

Marshall-Baruch Fellowships (Doctorate/Fellowship) [5649]

Women In Defense HORIZONS Scholarships (Graduate, Undergraduate/Scholarship) [9696]

History, United States (See History, American)

History of printing (See Printing--History)

History of science (See Science--History)

Home Economics

Hettie M. Anthony Fellowships (Postdoctorate/Fellowship) [5200]

California Association of Family and Consumer Sciences -San Diego Chapter Scholarships (CAFCS) (Graduate, Undergraduate, Vocational/Occupational/Scholarship) [7917]

FACS Graduate Fellowships (Graduate/Fellowship) [6129]

Kappa Omicron Nu National Alumni Fellowships (Graduate/Fellowship) [5196]

Eileen C. Maddex Fellowships (Graduate/Fellowship) [5198]

Omicron Nu Research Fellowships (Postdoctorate/Fellowship) [5203]

Homosexuality

Carolina's Gay & Lesbian Scholarships (Undergraduate/Scholarship) [7846]

Center for Lesbian and Gay Studies Fellowships (Graduate/Fellowship) [2701]

Martin Duberman Fellowships (Professional development/Fellowship) [2702]

GAPA Scholarships (Undergraduate/Scholarship) [4048]

Joan Heller-Diane Bernard Fellowships (Graduate, Undergraduate/Fellowship) [2703]

Bruce Wade Memorial Scholarships for Lesbian, Gay and Bisexual (Undergraduate/Scholarship) [7875]

Horticulture

American Conifer Society Scholarships (Undergraduate/Scholarship) [652]

American Society for Horticultural Science Student Travel Grants (Graduate, Undergraduate/Grant) [1272]

Arizona Nursery Association Scholarships (Undergraduate/Scholarship) [1524]

ASHS Industry Division Student Travel Grants (Graduate, Undergraduate/Grant) [1273]

ASHS Scholars Awards (Undergraduate/Scholarship) [1274]

Ball Horticultural Company Scholarships (Undergraduate/Scholarship) [724]

Vic and Margaret Ball Student Intern Scholarships (Undergraduate/Internship) [725]

Catherine H. Beattie Fellowships (Graduate/Fellowship) [2705]

Harold Bettinger Scholarships (Undergraduate/Scholarship) [726]

Leonard Bettinger Vocational Scholarships (Undergraduate, Vocational/Occupational/Scholarship) [727]

James Bridenbaugh Memorial Scholarships (Undergraduate/Scholarship) [728]

John Carew Memorial Scholarships (Undergraduate/Scholarship) [729]

Christmas Tree Chapter Scholarship Awards (Undergraduate/Scholarship) [6933]

Clackamas Chapter Scholarship Awards (Undergraduate/Scholarship) [6934]

Howard A. Clark Horticulture Scholarships (Undergraduate/Scholarship) [3102]

James H. Davis Scholarships (Undergraduate/Scholarship) [3838]

Earl Deadman Memorial Scholarships (Undergraduate/Scholarship) [730]

Dosatron International Inc. Scholarships (Undergraduate/Scholarship) [731]

Bill Egan Scholarship Program (Undergraduate/Scholarship) [6935]

Emerald Empire Chapter Scholarship Awards (Undergraduate/Scholarship) [6936]

Miklos Faust International Travel Awards (Doctorate/Fellowship) [1275]

Paris Fracasso Production Floriculture Scholarships (Undergraduate/Scholarship) [732]

Fruits and Vegetable Industries Scholarships (Undergraduate/Scholarship) [5831]

Garden Club Council of Winston-Salem and Forsyth County Council (Undergraduate/Scholarship) [9639]

Katherine M. Grosscup Scholarships (Graduate, Undergraduate/Scholarship) [4042]

Hill Country Master Gardeners Horticulture Scholarships (Graduate, Undergraduate/Scholarship) [4543]

Idaho Nursery and Landscape Association Scholarships (Undergraduate/Scholarship) [4676]

Illinois Landscape Contractors Association Scholarships (Undergraduate/Scholarship) [4688]

Joseph H. Klupenger Scholarship Awards (Undergraduate/Scholarship) [6937]

Louisiana Agricultural Consultants Association Scholarships (Graduate, Undergraduate/Scholarship) [5517]

Ed Markham International Scholarships (Undergraduate/Scholarship) [733]

The Master Gardeners of Pierce County Scholarships (Undergraduate/Scholarship) [4339]

Mt. Hood Chapter Scholarship Awards (Undergraduate/Scholarship) [6938]

Nashville Unit Scholarships (Undergraduate/Scholarship) [4534]

National Greenhouse Manufacturers Association Scholarships (Undergraduate/Scholarship) [734]

National Junior Horticultural Association Alumni Scholarships (Undergraduate/Scholarship) [6376]

NGC College Scholarships (Graduate, Undergraduate/Scholarship) [6303]

North Carolina Commercial Flower Growers Association Floriculture Scholarships (Graduate, Undergraduate/Scholarship) [6757]

North Carolina Nursery and Landscape Association Horticulture Scholarships (Undergraduate/Scholarship) [6769]

Mike and Flo Novovesky Scholarships (Undergraduate/Scholarship) [735]
Nurseries Foundation Scholarship Awards (Undergraduate/Scholarship) [6939]
Nurseries Memorial Scholarship Awards (Graduate/Scholarship) [6940]
Lawrence "Bud" Ohlman Memorial Scholarships (Undergraduate/Scholarship) [736]
Oregon Association of Nurseries Scholarship Program (Undergraduate/Scholarship) [6941]
Pennsylvania Heartland Unit Scholarships (Undergraduate/Scholarship) [4535]
Jim Perry Vocational Scholarships (Undergraduate, Vocational/Occupational/Scholarship) [737]
Rain Bird Intelligent Use of Water Scholarships (Undergraduate/Scholarship) [5336]
James K. Rathmell Jr. Scholarships (Undergraduate/Scholarship) [738]
Bertha and Byron L. Reppert Scholarship Fund (Undergraduate/Scholarship) [3957]
Retail Chapter Scholarship Awards (Undergraduate/Scholarship) [6942]
Seed Companies Scholarships (Undergraduate/Scholarship) [739]
Stanley Smith Horticultural Fellowships (Graduate, Undergraduate/Fellowship) [6987]
South Texas Unit Scholarships (Undergraduate/Scholarship) [4536]
Marco Polo Stufano Garden Conservancy Fellowships (Professional development/Fellowship) [4044]
Jordan B. Tatter Scholarships (Undergraduate/Scholarship) [5832]
John Tomasovic, Sr. Scholarships (Undergraduate/Scholarship) [740]
Edward Tuinier Memorial Scholarships (Undergraduate/Scholarship) [741]
Jacob VanNamen-Vans Marketing Scholarships (Undergraduate/Scholarship) [742]
West Michigan Nursery and Landscape Association Scholarship Fund (Undergraduate/Scholarship) [4249]
Western Reserve Herb Society Scholarships (Undergraduate/Scholarship) [4537]
Willamette Chapter Scholarship Awards (Undergraduate/Scholarship) [6943]
Ed Wood Memorial Scholarship Awards (Undergraduate/Scholarship) [6944]
Francis Sylvia Zverina Scholarships (Undergraduate/Scholarship) [4538]

Hospitals--Administration

Jessica King Scholarships (Professional development/Scholarship) [3310]

Hotel, institutional, and restaurant management

The American Automobile Association Five Diamond Hospitality Scholarships (AAA) (Undergraduate/Scholarship) [795]
American Express Professional Development Scholarships (Professional development/Scholarship) [796]
The American Express Scholarship Competition (Undergraduate/Scholarship) [797]
Applied Hospitality Degree Scholarships (Undergraduate/Scholarship) [2487]
Canadian Hospitality Foundation College Entrance Scholarships (Undergraduate/Scholarship) [2488]
Canadian Hospitality Foundation University Entrance Scholarships (Undergraduate/Scholarship) [2489]
Caribbean Hotel and Tourism Association Academic Scholarships (Graduate, Undergraduate/Scholarship) [2653]
Vickie Clark-Flaherty Scholarships (Undergraduate, Vocational/Occupational/Scholarship) [6772]
Epicurean Charitable Foundation Scholarships (Undergraduate/Scholarship) [7487]
FHSMAI Scholarship Program (Graduate/Scholarship) [3970]
Golden Corral Scholarships (Undergraduate/Scholarship) [6773]
R.W. "Bob" Holden Memorial Scholarships (Under-

graduate/Scholarship) [4482]
The Hyatt Hotels Fund For Minority Lodging Management Students (Undergraduate/Scholarship) [798]
The Steve Hymans Extended Stay Scholarship Program (Undergraduate/Scholarship) [799]
IFH Foodservice Distribution Scholarships (Undergraduate/Scholarship) [6774]
International Foodservice Editorial Council Scholarships (Graduate, Undergraduate/Scholarship) [4935]
Clem Judd Jr. Memorial Scholarships (Undergraduate/Scholarship) [4483]
K & W Cafeterias Scholarships (Undergraduate/Scholarship) [6775]
Lodging Management Program Scholarships (LMP) (Undergraduate/Scholarship) [800]
Jay Magazine Memorial Fund College Scholarships (JMMF) (Graduate, Undergraduate/Scholarship) [5759]
NC Hospitality Education Foundation Scholarships - Four Year College or University (Undergraduate/Scholarship) [6776]
NC Hospitality Education Foundation Scholarships - Graduate (Graduate/Scholarship) [6777]
NC Hospitality Education Foundation Scholarships - High School (Undergraduate, Vocational/Occupational/Scholarship) [6778]
NC Hospitality Education Foundation Scholarships - Two Year Community or Junior College (Undergraduate/Scholarship) [6779]
Oklahoma Restaurant Association Scholarships (Graduate, Undergraduate/Scholarship) [6871]
Ontario Women's Institute Scholarships (Undergraduate/Scholarship) [3734]
The Arthur J. Packard Memorial Scholarship Competition (Undergraduate/Scholarship) [801]
Pepsi Scholarships (Undergraduate/Scholarship) [802]
Rama Scholarships for the American Dream (Graduate, Undergraduate/Scholarship) [803]
Tribal Business Management Program Scholarships (TBM) (Undergraduate/Scholarship) [2664]

Housing

California Association of Family and Consumer Sciences -San Diego Chapter Scholarships (CAFCS) (Graduate, Undergraduate, Vocational/Occupational/Scholarship) [7917]
NACCED Annual John C. Murphy Scholarships (Graduate, Undergraduate/Scholarship) [6066]

Human relations

Bill Bendiner and Doug Morgenson Scholarships (Undergraduate/Scholarship) [7402]
Derivative Duo Scholarships (Undergraduate/Scholarship) [7410]
Phyllis P. Harris Scholarships (Postgraduate/Award) [2463]
David C. Maloney Scholarships (Undergraduate/Scholarship) [6423]
UAA April Relyea Scholarships (Graduate, Undergraduate, Vocational/Occupational/Scholarship) [9107]

Human rights

Alberta Award for the Study of Canadian Human Rights and Multiculturalism (Doctorate, Graduate/Award) [236]
Beverlee Bell Scholarships in Human Rights and Democracy (Graduate/Scholarship) [3473]
Canadian Japanese-Mennonite Scholarships (Graduate/Scholarship) [5767]
Henigson Human Rights Fellowships (Graduate/Fellowship) [4467]
HRP Global Human Rights Fellowships (Graduate/Fellowship) [4468]
Satter Human Rights Fellowships (Graduate/Fellowship) [4469]
Upper Midwest Human Rights Fellowship Program (Professional development/Fellowship) [9246]
Minoru Yasui Memorial Scholarships (Graduate/Scholarship) [5147]

Humanities

AAS National Endowment for the Humanities Long-Term Fellowships (Postdoctorate/Fellowship) [413]
ACLS Collaborative Research Fellowships (Doctorate/Fellowship) [671]
ACLS Digital Innovation Fellowships (Doctorate/Fellowship) [672]
African Humanities Fellowships (Postdoctorate/Fellowship) [673]
American Research in the Humanities in China Fellowships (Doctorate/Fellowship) [675]
American Society of Comparative Law TransCoop Programs (All/Fellowship) [1204]
ACLS Frederick Burkhardt Residential Fellowships (Professional development/Fellowship) [416]
Canada Graduate Scholarship Program (Graduate/Scholarship) [8285]
Critical Language Scholarships for Intensive Summer Institutes (Graduate, Undergraduate/Scholarship) [1145]
Dissertation Fellowships in East European Studies (Doctorate/Fellowship) [677]
Dissertation Proposal Development Fellowships (Doctorate/Fellowship) [8282]
Dr. Feroz Ahmed Memorial Educational Post-Graduate Scholarships (Doctorate, Postgraduate/Scholarship) [8216]
Early Career Postdoctoral Fellowships in East European Studies (Postdoctorate/Fellowship) [678]
Fellowships in the Humanities and Social Sciences in Turkey (Postdoctorate/Fellowship) [1147]
First Article Prize (Professional development/Prize) [3277]
Getty Scholar Grants (Professional development/Grant) [4143]
Harry Frank Guggenheim Fellowships (Doctorate/Fellowship) [4357]
Harry Frank Guggenheim Foundation Research Grants (All/Grant) [4358]
John Simon Guggenheim Memorial Fellowships - U.S. and Canadian Competition (Advanced Professional/Fellowship) [4360]
Woody Guthrie Fellowships (All/Fellowship) [2158]
Ed Haas Memorial Scholarships (Undergraduate/Scholarship) [8724]
Lois Hole Humanities and Social Sciences Scholarships (Undergraduate/Scholarship) [247]
International Society for Humor Studies Graduate Student Awards (GSA) (Graduate/Award) [4996]
International Society for Humor Studies Scholarly Contribution Awards (SCA) (Professional development/Award) [4997]
Islamic Scholarship Fund Scholarships (ISF) (Postgraduate, Undergraduate/Scholarship) [5078]
Louis I. Jaffe Memorial Scholarships-ODU (Graduate/Scholarship) [4377]
Jacob K. Javits Fellowships (Doctorate, Master's/Fellowship) [6076]
Kluge Fellowships (Doctorate, Graduate/Fellowship) [5274]
Korean Studies Dissertation Workshop Funds (Graduate/Fellowship, Grant) [8283]
Library Resident Research Fellowships (Doctorate/Fellowship) [993]
Dolores Zohrab Liebmann Fund - Graduate School Fellowships (Graduate/Fellowship) [5488]
Major Collaborative Research Initiatives Grants (Graduate/Grant) [8286]
David C. Maloney Scholarships (Undergraduate/Scholarship) [6423]
Larry McDonald Scholarships (Undergraduate/Scholarship) [3680]
McNeil Dissertation Fellowships (All/Fellowship) [9667]
Andrew W. Mellon Dissertation Completion Fellowships (Doctorate/Fellowship) [680]
Mellon Fellowships (Doctorate, Graduate/Fellowship) [3279]
Multi-Country Research Fellowships (Doctorate/Fellowship) [3270]
NAFA International Dissertation Research Fellowships (Graduate/Fellowship) [6078]
National Endowment for the Humanities Advanced Fellowships for Research in Turkey (Postdoctorate/Fellowship) [1153]

National Endowment for the Humanities Fellowships *(Doctorate/Fellowship)* [6700]

National Humanities Center Fellowships *(Doctorate, Postdoctorate/Fellowship)* [6349]

NEH Fellowships for Senior Scholars *(Doctorate/Fellowship)* [2695]

Charlotte W. Newcombe Doctoral Dissertation Fellowships *(Doctorate/Fellowship)* [9618]

Persian Language Study in Tehran Scholarships *(Doctorate, Graduate/Fellowship)* [856]

Post-doctoral Residential Research and Teaching Fellowships *(Postdoctorate/Fellowship)* [9743]

Post-Doctoral Summer Travel-Research Grants *(Doctorate/Grant)* [4832]

Pre-doctoral Residential Research Fellowships *(Doctorate/Fellowship)* [9744]

Prins Foundation Fellowship for Senior Scholars *(Doctorate/Fellowship)* [2696]

Prins Foundation Post-Doctoral and Early Career Fellowship for Emigrating Scholars *(Professional development, Postdoctorate/Fellowship)* [2697]

Rome Prize *(Doctorate, Graduate/Prize)* [400]

Ellis W. Rowe Scholarships *(Undergraduate/Scholarship)* [4380]

Charles A. Ryskamp Research Fellowships *(Doctorate/Fellowship)* [681]

SHAFR Dissertation Completion Fellowships *(Doctorate/Fellowship)* [8342]

Short-term Senior Fellowships in Iranian Studies *(Doctorate, Graduate/Fellowship)* [858]

Social Sciences and Humanities Research Council of Canada Standard Research Grants *(Doctorate, Graduate/Grant)* [8287]

SSHRC Doctoral Fellowship Program *(Doctorate/Fellowship, Scholarship)* [8288]

Robert W. and Bernice Ingalls Staton Scholarships *(Undergraduate/Scholarship)* [9314]

Summer Language Study Grants in Turkey *(Graduate/Grant)* [4833]

Trudeau Foundation Doctoral Scholarships *(Doctorate/Scholarship)* [8968]

The UCSD Black Alumni Scholarship for Arts and Humanities *(Undergraduate/Scholarship)* [7970]

The UCSD Black Alumni Scholarships for Engineering, Mathematics and Science *(Undergraduate/Scholarship)* [7971]

Vanier Canada Graduate Scholarships *(Graduate/Scholarship)* [6573]

Winterthur Research Fellowships *(All/Fellowship)* [9668]

Mary and Elliot Wood Foundation Graduate Scholarship Fund *(Graduate/Scholarship)* [3930]

Huntington's disease

HDSA Research Grants *(Professional development/Grant)* [4644]

Hereditary Disease Foundation Research Grants *(Postdoctorate/Grant)* [4540]

Huntington's Disease Society of America Research Fellowships *(Postdoctorate/Fellowship)* [4645]

Don King Student Fellowships *(Undergraduate/Fellowship)* [4646]

John J. Wasmuth Postdoctoral Fellowships *(Postdoctorate/Fellowship)* [4541]

Hydrology

Arizona Hydrological Society Scholarships *(Graduate, Undergraduate/Scholarship)* [1522]

B. Harper Bull Conservation Fellowships *(Graduate/Fellowship)* [8913]

Hydro Research Foundation Fellowships *(Master's/Fellowship)* [4648]

CASFM-Ben Urbonas Scholarships *(Graduate/Scholarship)* [2982]

Ileitis and colitis

ROFY Scholarships *(Undergraduate/Scholarship)* [7613]

Illustrators and illustrations

Inez Demonet Scholarships *(Graduate/Scholarship)* [9421]

UAA Kimura Scholarship Fund Illustration Scholar-

ships *(Undergraduate/Scholarship)* [9122]

Vesalius Trust Student Scholarships *(Graduate, Undergraduate/Scholarship)* [9422]

Worldstudio AIGA Scholarships *(Graduate, Undergraduate/Scholarship)* [9761]

Immigration

Abba P. Schwartz Research Fellowships *(All/Fellowship)* [5241]

Immunology

Irvington Institute Fellowships of the Cancer Research Institute *(Postdoctorate/Fellowship)* [2638]

UAA Kris Knudson Memorial Scholarships *(Graduate, Undergraduate/Scholarship)* [9102]

Indian studies (Asia)

SHOT-NASA Fellowships *(Doctorate, Postdoctorate/Fellowship)* [8346]

Industrial and labor relations

Mackenzie King Travelling Scholarships *(Graduate/Scholarship)* [5724]

NPELRA Foundation Scholarships *(Graduate/Scholarship)* [6836]

The Anthony C. Russo Scholarships *(Graduate/Scholarship)* [6457]

Industrial design

Flexible Packaging Academic Scholarships & Summer Internships Program *(Undergraduate/Internship, Scholarship)* [3810]

IDSA Gianninoto Graduate Scholarships *(Graduate/Scholarship)* [4758]

Tag and Label Manufacturers Institute Scholarships - Two-Year Colleges *(Undergraduate/Scholarship)* [8794]

Worldstudio AIGA Scholarships *(Graduate, Undergraduate/Scholarship)* [9761]

Industrial hygiene

Thompson Scholarships for Women in Safety *(Graduate/Scholarship)* [1355]

Industry and trade

Bruce Clement Post-Secondary Education Scholarships *(Undergraduate/Scholarship)* [6631]

EAIA Research Grants *(Professional development/Grant)* [3561]

Karen B. Lewis Career Education Scholarships *(Undergraduate/Scholarship)* [9441]

Oil and Gas Trades and Technology Bursary and Scholarships (OGTT) *(All/Scholarship)* [5994]

Syncrude/Athabasca University Aboriginal Scholarships *(All/Scholarship)* [8791]

Infectious diseases (See also Epidemiology)

Investigators in the Pathogenesis of Infectious Disease Awards *(Doctorate, Postdoctorate/Grant)* [2215]

Information science and technology

AFFIRM University Scholarships *(Undergraduate/Scholarship)* [1775]

Alberta Innovates Graduate Student Scholarship *(Graduate/Scholarship)* [234]

APALA Scholarships *(Doctorate, Graduate/Scholarship)* [1648]

APS/ASU Scholarships *(Undergraduate/Scholarship)* [7332]

APS/Maricopa County Community Colleges Scholarships *(Undergraduate/Scholarship)* [7333]

Boeing Company Scholarships *(Undergraduate/Scholarship)* [8112]

Kathi Bowles Scholarships for Women in Technol-

ogy *(Graduate, Undergraduate/Scholarship)* [1898]

Chrysler Foundation Scholarship Awards *(Undergraduate/Scholarship)* [4546]

HSF/Wal-Mart Stores Inc. Scholarship Program *(Graduate, Undergraduate/Scholarship)* [4577]

iCORE ICT Graduate Student Scholarships *(Doctorate, Graduate, Master's/Scholarship)* [232]

Iowa Library Association Foundation Scholarships *(Graduate/Scholarship)* [5039]

Christian Larew Memorial Scholarships *(Graduate/Scholarship)* [5484]

Lewis-Clark State College Presidential Technical Out-of-State Scholarships *(Undergraduate/Scholarship)* [5447]

Eli Lilly and Company/Black Data Processing Associates Scholarships *(High School/Scholarship)* [2033]

Robert V. McKenna Scholarships *(Undergraduate/Scholarship)* [8818]

NAAF Post-Secondary Education Scholarships *(Graduate, Undergraduate/Scholarship)* [5993]

Arthur L. Norberg Travel Grants *(All/Grant)* [1991]

Office Depot Scholarships *(Undergraduate/Scholarship)* [4549]

Fritz Schwartz Serials Education Scholarships *(Graduate, Professional development/Scholarship)* [6744]

Symantec Research Labs Graduate Fellowships *(Doctorate, Graduate/Fellowship)* [8789]

Syncrude/Athabasca University Aboriginal Scholarships *(All/Scholarship)* [8791]

Thomson Reuters/MLA Doctoral Fellowships *(Doctorate/Fellowship)* [5748]

Jack E. Tillson Scholarships *(Graduate/Scholarship)* [5040]

The Adelle and Erwin Tomash Fellowships *(Doctorate/Fellowship)* [1992]

Urban Financial Services Coalition Scholarships *(Undergraduate/Scholarship)* [2129]

Wells Fargo American Indian Scholarships - Graduate *(Graduate/Scholarship)* [828]

Insurance and insurance-related fields

CPCU Loman Education Foundation Scholarships *(Professional development/Scholarship)* [4838]

Founders Circle Professional Scholarships *(Professional development/Scholarship)* [4839]

Gongaware Scholarships *(Undergraduate/Scholarship)* [4743]

Insurance and Risk Management Scholarships - Grant MacEwan *(Undergraduate/Scholarship)* [7994]

Insurance Scholarship Foundation of America College Scholarships *(Undergraduate/Scholarship)* [4840]

Insurance Scholarship Foundation of America Professional Scholarships *(Professional development/Scholarship)* [4841]

Intermediaries and Reinsurance Underwriters Association Internships *(Undergraduate/Internship)* [4852]

Marsh College Scholarships *(Undergraduate/Scholarship)* [4842]

William H. McGannon Foundation Scholarships *(Graduate, Undergraduate/Scholarship)* [5721]

Patriot Education Scholarships *(Undergraduate/Scholarship)* [5591]

Risk Management and Insurance Scholarships - University of Calgary *(Undergraduate/Scholarship)* [7995]

State Farm Insurance Doctoral Dissertation Awards *(Doctorate/Award)* [8712]

Surety Industry Scholarship Program for Minority Students *(Undergraduate/Scholarship)* [8778]

Seitlin Franklin E. Wheeler Scholarship Fund *(Undergraduate/Scholarship)* [3324]

Intelligence service

Jorge Espejal Contreras Memorial Scholarships *(Graduate, Undergraduate/Scholarship)* [4873]

The Henley Putnam University Scholarships *(Professional development/Scholarship)* [4874]

Interdisciplinary studies

BSF General Scholarship Awards (Undergraduate, Vocational/Occupational/Scholarship) [2024]

Interior design

Paul Arnold Memorial Scholarships (Undergraduate/ Scholarship) [7396]

ASF/Annika Teig/Skidmore, Owings and Merril Fellowships (Undergraduate/Fellowship) [1172]

Irene Winifred Eno Grants (All/Grant) [1277]

International Furnishings and Design Association Educational Foundation Student Scholarships (Undergraduate/Scholarship) [4942]

International Furnishings and Design Association Part-time Student Scholarships (Undergraduate/ Scholarship) [4943]

Legacy Scholarships for Graduate Students (Graduate/Scholarship) [1278]

Charles D. Mayo Student Scholarships (Undergraduate/Scholarship) [4944]

Eloise Pitts O'More Scholarships (Undergraduate/ Scholarship) [3129]

Worldstudio AIGA Scholarships (Graduate, Undergraduate/Scholarship) [9761]

International affairs and relations

AGBU Scholarships (Graduate/Loan) [1573]

Samuel Flagg Bemis Dissertation Research Grants (Doctorate, Graduate/Grant) [8335]

Stuart L. Bernath Dissertation Grants (Doctorate, Graduate/Grant) [8336]

Myrna F. Bernath Fellowships (Doctorate, Graduate/ Fellowship) [8337]

D&A Florida Scholarships (Undergraduate/Scholarship) [8597]

Robert A. and Barbara Divine Graduate Student Travel Grants (Graduate/Grant) [8338]

Mayme and Herb Frank Scholarship Program (Graduate, Undergraduate/Scholarship) [1638]

Lawrence Gelfand - Armin Rappaport Fellowships (Doctorate, Graduate/Fellowship, Grant) [8339]

W. Stull Holt Dissertation Fellowships (Doctorate, Graduate/Fellowship, Grant) [8341]

Harriet Irsay Scholarships (Graduate, Undergraduate/Scholarship) [869]

ISCALC International Scholarship Fund (Undergraduate/Scholarship) [3777]

Mackenzie King Travelling Scholarships (Graduate/ Scholarship) [5724]

Lazarian Graduate Scholarships (Graduate/Scholarship) [1578]

Mas Family Scholarships (Graduate, Undergraduate/Scholarship) [5658]

MPAC-DC Graduate Policy Fellowships (Graduate/ Fellowship) [5960]

National Iranian American Council Fellowships (Graduate, Undergraduate/Fellowship) [6365]

Nonproliferation Graduate Fellowships Program (NGFP) (Graduate/Fellowship) [7033]

Pi Gamma Mu Scholarships (Graduate/Scholarship) [7330]

Thomas R. Pickering Graduate Foreign Affairs Fellowships (Graduate/Fellowship) [9619]

Rangel Graduate Fellowships (Graduate/Fellowship) [7599]

SHAFR Dissertation Completion Fellowships (Doctorate/Fellowship) [8342]

TCA Turkish American Scholarships (Undergraduate/Scholarship) [8978]

Texas Muslims Scholarship Fund (TMSF) (Graduate, Undergraduate/Scholarship) [4006]

University of Hawaii at Manoa Japan Travel Bureau Scholarships (Graduate, Undergraduate/Scholarship) [9209]

Women In Defense HORIZONS Scholarships (Graduate, Undergraduate/Scholarship) [9696]

International trade

Malcolm Baldrige Scholarships (Undergraduate/ Scholarship) [4411]

HSBC-North America Scholarship Program (Undergraduate/Scholarship) [4571]

Interracial studies

Research Fellowships in Iranian Studies, Resident Director-Tehran (Doctorate, Graduate/Fellowship) [857]

Short-term Senior Fellowships in Iranian Studies (Doctorate, Graduate/Fellowship) [858]

Italian studies (See also Area and ethnic studies)

Italian Language Scholarships (Undergraduate/ Scholarship) [6922]

NIAF Scholarships - General Category II (Undergraduate/Scholarship) [6370]

Japanese studies (See also Area and ethnic studies)

Mary Jane Hendrie Memorial Scholarships (Graduate, Undergraduate/Scholarship) [9330]

Japan Foundation, New York Doctoral Fellowship Program (Doctorate/Fellowship) [5134]

Japan Foundation, New York Research Fellowship Program (Undergraduate/Fellowship) [5135]

Japan Foundation, New York Short-Term Fellowship Program (Doctorate/Fellowship) [5136]

KCC-JEE Graduate Fellowships (Graduate/Fellowship) [5279]

The Shincho Graduate Fellowships for Study in Japan (Graduate/Fellowship) [5227]

Jewish studies (See also Area and ethnic studies)

Berkowitz Fellowships (Professional development/ Fellowship) [8902]

Maurice and Marilyn Cohen Fund for Doctoral Dissertation Fellowships in Jewish Studies (Doctorate/Fellowship) [3974]

Furman-Tikvah Scholarships (Graduate/Scholarship) [8903]

Graduate Research Fellowships (Doctorate/Fellowship) [2694]

International Doctoral Scholarships for Studies Specializing in Jewish Fields (Doctorate/Scholarship) [5763]

International Fellowships in Jewish Studies (Professional development/Fellowship) [5764]

International Scholarship Programs for Community Service (All/Scholarship) [5765]

Israeli Fellowships (Doctorate, Postdoctorate/Fellowship) [2685]

J.D. Graduate Tikvah Scholarships (Graduate/Scholarship) [8904]

J.D. or LL.M. Tikvah Scholarships (Graduate/Scholarship) [8905]

Jewish Caucus Scholarships (Undergraduate/Scholarship) [6559]

NEH Fellowships for Senior Scholars (Doctorate/ Fellowship) [2695]

Post-Doctoral Tikvah Scholarships (Postdoctorate/ Scholarship) [8906]

Prins Foundation Fellowship for Senior Scholars (Doctorate/Fellowship) [2696]

Prins Foundation Post-Doctoral and Early Career Fellowship for Emigrating Scholars (Professional development, Postdoctorate/Fellowship) [2697]

Joseph S. Steinberg Emerging Jewish Filmmaker Fellowships (Undergraduate, Graduate/Fellowship) [2698]

Tikvah Fellowships (Graduate, Professional development/Fellowship) [8909]

Visiting Doctoral Tikvah Scholarships (Doctorate/ Scholarship) [8907]

Visiting Scholars Program (Doctorate/Fellowship) [2699]

Wexner Graduate Fellowships/Davidson Scholars (Graduate/Fellowship) [9589]

Journalism

AAJA/CNN Scholar Program (Graduate, Undergraduate/Scholarship) [1640]

AAJA/COX Foundation Scholarships (Graduate, Undergraduate/Scholarship) [1641]

Leroy F. Aaron Scholarships (Graduate, Undergraduate/Scholarship) [6391]

AAS Fellowships for Creative and Performing Artists and Writers (All/Fellowship) [412]

Kyutaro & Yasuo Abiko Memorial Scholarships (Undergraduate/Scholarship) [5140]

Al Muammar Scholarships for Journalism (Undergraduate/Scholarship) [1490]

Alaska Press Club Scholarships (Undergraduate/ Scholarship) [9132]

Floyd S. Alford Jr. Scholarships (Undergraduate/ Scholarship) [9254]

Peggy Allen Community Newspaper Internships (Undergraduate/Internship) [9255]

Phillip Alston Scholarships (Undergraduate/Scholarship) [9256]

American Political Science Association Journalists Fellowships (Professional development/Fellowship) [1015]

American Political Science Association/MCI Scholarships (Postdoctorate/Scholarship) [1016]

American Quarter Horse Foundation Scholarships (Undergraduate/Scholarship) [1063]

Fred Archibald Communications Internships (Undergraduate/Internship) [8465]

Association of Electronic Journalists Presidents Scholarships (Undergraduate/Scholarship) [7572]

AT&T Business Internship Awards (Postgraduate/ Internship) [9257]

Atkinson Fellowships in Public Policy (Professional development/Fellowship) [1920]

UAA Elaine Atwood Scholarships (Undergraduate/ Scholarship) [9084]

Frances Warren Baker Memorial Scholarships (Undergraduate/Scholarship) [8157]

Jim Batten Community Newspaper Internships (Undergraduate/Internship) [9258]

Bob Baxter Scholarships (Graduate, Undergraduate/ Scholarship) [6448]

N.S. Beinstock Fellowships (Professional development/Fellowship) [7573]

Pete and Ellen Bensley Memorial Scholarship Fund (Undergraduate/Scholarship) [3886]

Lester G. Benz Memorial Scholarships for College Journalism Study (Professional development/ Scholarship) [7562]

Reid Blackburn Scholarships (Undergraduate/Scholarship) [6449]

Tom Bost Scholarships (Undergraduate/Scholarship) [9260]

Ed Bradley Scholarships (Undergraduate/Scholarship) [7574]

Rick Brewer Scholarships (Undergraduate/Scholarship) [9261]

Broadcast News Management Fellowships (Professional development/Scholarship) [7575]

Carlos M. Castaneda Journalism Scholarships (Graduate/Scholarship) [4027]

CJF Canadian Journalism Fellowships (Graduate, Professional development, Undergraduate/Fellowship) [2513]

Michelle Clark Fellowships (Undergraduate/Fellowship) [7576]

Greg Clerk Awards (Professional development/ Award) [2514]

Ardis Cohoon Scholarships (Undergraduate/Scholarship) [9263]

Kathryn M. Cronin Scholarships (Graduate, Undergraduate/Scholarship) [9265]

D&A Florida Scholarships (Undergraduate/Scholarship) [8597]

James Davis Scholarships (Undergraduate/Scholarship) [9267]

Harvey N. Dondero Communication and Journalism Excellence Scholarships (Undergraduate/Scholarship) [7482]

Harold K. Douthit Regional Scholarships (Undergraduate/Scholarship) [6857]

Richard Drukker Memorial Scholarships (Undergraduate/Scholarship) [6651]

Bob East Scholarships *(Graduate, Undergraduate/Scholarship)* [6450]

Vivian Edmonds Scholarships *(Undergraduate/Scholarship)* [9269]

Don English Memorial Scholarships *(Undergraduate/Scholarship)* [7486]

Reese Felts Scholarships *(Undergraduate/Scholarship)* [9270]

Allison E. Fisher Scholarships *(Graduate, Undergraduate/Scholarship)* [3805]

Ameel J. Fisher Scholarships *(Undergraduate/Scholarship)* [9271]

Florida Outdoor Writers Association Scholarships *(Undergraduate/Scholarship)* [3842]

Paul B. & Aline Flynn Scholarships *(Undergraduate/Scholarship)* [8601]

George Foreman Tribute to Lyndon B. Johnson Scholarships *(Undergraduate/Scholarship)* [7577]

Denise Franklin Journalism Scholarships *(Undergraduate/Scholarship)* [9637]

Emanuel R. Freedman Scholarships *(Graduate, Undergraduate/Scholarship)* [7012]

Guy P. Gannett Scholarships *(Undergraduate/Scholarship)* [5578]

Joel Garcia Memorial Scholarships *(Undergraduate/Scholarship)* [2237]

Garikian Scholarship Fund *(Undergraduate/Scholarship)* [1593]

Kays Gary Scholarships *(Undergraduate/Scholarship)* [9273]

Joy Gibson Scholarships *(Undergraduate/Scholarship)* [9275]

L.C. Gifford Distinguished Journalism Scholarships *(Undergraduate/Scholarship)* [9276]

Keith Gilmore Foundation - Diploma Scholarships *(Professional development/Scholarship)* [4153]

Keith Gilmore Foundation - Postgraduate Scholarships *(Postgraduate/Scholarship)* [4154]

Keith Gilmore Foundation - Undergraduate Scholarships *(Undergraduate/Scholarship)* [4155]

Elizabeth Greenhalgh Memorial Scholarships in Journalism, Graphic Arts, or Photography *(Graduate, Undergraduate/Scholarship)* [9699]

Charles Hauser Scholarships *(Undergraduate/Scholarship)* [9277]

Paul Green Houston Scholarships *(Undergraduate/Scholarship)* [9278]

James F. Hurley III Bicentennial Merit Scholarships *(Undergraduate/Scholarship)* [9279]

Fred Hutchison Travel Scholarships *(Undergraduate/Scholarship)* [9280]

INF Scholarships *(Undergraduate/Scholarship)* [5042]

Inter American Press Association Scholarships *(Undergraduate/Scholarship)* [4846]

International Foodservice Editorial Council Scholarships *(Graduate, Undergraduate/Scholarship)* [4935]

InternXchange Internships *(Undergraduate/Internship)* [4121]

Iowa Journalism Institute Scholarships *(Undergraduate/Scholarship)* [5043]

Harriet Irsay Scholarships *(Graduate, Undergraduate/Scholarship)* [869]

Edward Jackson International Scholarships *(Undergraduate/Scholarship)* [9281]

Gene Jackson Scholarships *(Undergraduate/Scholarship)* [9282]

Peter Lars Jacobson Scholarships *(Undergraduate/Scholarship)* [9283]

Sister Rita Jeanne Scholarships *(Undergraduate/Scholarship)* [5169]

Kaiser Media Fellowships in Health *(Advanced Professional/Fellowship)* [5180]

Ken Kashiwara Scholarships *(Undergraduate/Scholarship)* [7578]

Glenn Keever Scholarships *(Undergraduate/Scholarship)* [9284]

Alexander Kendrick Memorial Scholarships *(Graduate, Undergraduate/Scholarship)* [7013]

Bernard Kilgore Memorial Scholarships *(Undergraduate/Scholarship)* [6652]

Kit C. King Graduate Scholarships *(Graduate/Scholarship)* [6451]

John S. Knight Fellowships *(Professional development/Fellowship)* [8653]

Harold Knopp Scholarships *(Undergraduate/Scholarship)* [7096]

William D. Krahling Excellence in Journalism Scholarships *(Undergraduate/Scholarship)* [367]

Irene Corbally Kuhn Scholarships *(Graduate, Undergraduate/Scholarship)* [7014]

Lazarian Graduate Scholarships *(Graduate/Scholarship)* [1578]

Flora Lewis Memorial Scholarships *(Graduate, Undergraduate/Scholarship)* [7015]

Lily Scholarships in Religion for Journalists *(Professional development/Scholarship)* [7732]

LIN Media Minority Scholarships and Training Program *(Undergraduate/Scholarship)* [5501]

Kay Longscope Scholarships *(Graduate, Undergraduate/Scholarship)* [6392]

Raleigh Mann Scholarships *(Undergraduate/Scholarship)* [9288]

Mas Family Scholarships *(Graduate, Undergraduate/Scholarship)* [5658]

Maxwell Graduate Scholarships in Medical Journalism *(Postgraduate/Scholarship)* [9290]

Durwood McAlister Scholarships *(Undergraduate/Scholarship)* [4107]

McClatchy Scholarships *(Undergraduate/Scholarship)* [8552]

Anne O'Hare McCormick Scholarship Fund *(Graduate/Scholarship)* [6716]

C.A. "Pete" McKnight Scholarships *(Undergraduate/Scholarship)* [9292]

Edward Heywood Megson Scholarships *(Undergraduate/Scholarship)* [9293]

Messenger-Anderson Journalism Scholarships and Internships Program *(Undergraduate/Scholarship)* [7861]

Quincy Sharpe Mills Scholarships *(Undergraduate/Scholarship)* [9294]

Jacque I. Minnotte Health Reporting Fellowships *(Professional development/Fellowship)* [7579]

Alexander Morisey Scholarships *(Undergraduate/Scholarship)* [9296]

Morris Newspaper Corp. Scholarships *(Undergraduate/Scholarship)* [4108]

Muddy Waters Scholarships *(Undergraduate/Scholarship)* [2155]

National Iranian American Council Fellowships *(Graduate, Undergraduate/Fellowship)* [6365]

N.C. Psychoanalytic Foundation Journalism Scholarships *(Graduate, Postgraduate/Scholarship)* [9297]

Edward J. Nell Memorial Scholarships in Journalism *(Undergraduate/Scholarship)* [7563]

Elizabeth Neuffer Fellowships *(Professional development/Fellowship)* [5030]

New York Financial Writers' Associations Scholarships *(Graduate, Undergraduate/Scholarship)* [6667]

New York Women in Communications, Inc. Foundation Scholarships *(Graduate, Undergraduate/Scholarship)* [6690]

AAJA/S.I. Newhouse Foundation Scholarships *(Graduate, Undergraduate/Scholarship)* [1642]

NPPF Still and Multimedia Scholarships *(Undergraduate/Scholarship)* [6452]

Ohio Newspaper Association Minority Scholarships *(Undergraduate/Scholarship)* [6858]

Ohio Newspaper Association University Journalism Scholarships *(Undergraduate/Scholarship)* [6859]

Ohio Newspaper Association Women's Scholarships *(Undergraduate/Scholarship)* [6860]

Frank del Olmo Memorial Scholarships *(Undergraduate/Scholarship)* [2238]

Overseas Press Club Foundation Harper's Magazine Scholarships *(Graduate, Undergraduate/Scholarship)* [7016]

Overseas Press Club Foundation Reuters Scholarships *(Graduate, Undergraduate/Scholarship)* [7017]

Scott Pearlman Field Awards for Science and Exploration *(Professional development/Award)* [3698]

Leonard M. Perryman Communications Scholarships for Ethnic Minority Students *(Undergraduate/Scholarship)* [9013]

Steve Petix Journalism Scholarships *(Undergraduate/Scholarship)* [7951]

Pfizer Minority Medical Journalism Scholarships

(Postgraduate/Scholarship) [9298]

PHD ARA Scholarships *(Doctorate, Undergraduate/Scholarship)* [1100]

Stephen D. Pisinski Memorial Scholarships *(Undergraduate/Scholarship)* [7539]

Robert Pittman Scholarships *(Undergraduate/Scholarship)* [9299]

Carter Pitts Scholarships *(Undergraduate/Scholarship)* [5044]

Erwin Potts Scholarships *(Undergraduate/Scholarship)* [9300]

Lou and Carole Prato Sports Reporting Scholarships *(Undergraduate/Scholarship)* [7580]

Peter DeWitt Pruden and Phyliss Harrill Pruden Scholarships *(Undergraduate/Scholarship)* [9301]

Pulliam/Kilgore Freedom of Information Internships *(Undergraduate/Internship)* [8466]

Bob Quincy Scholarships *(Undergraduate/Scholarship)* [9302]

Chips Quinn Scholarships *(Graduate, Undergraduate/Scholarship)* [7565]

Marjorie Usher Ragan Scholarships *(Undergraduate/Scholarship)* [9303]

Mike Reynolds Journalism Scholarships *(Undergraduate/Scholarship)* [7581]

Eugene L. Roberts Jr. Prize *(Undergraduate/Prize)* [9304]

William C. Rogers Scholarships *(Undergraduate/Scholarship)* [4109]

Richard J. Roth Journalism Fellowships *(Graduate/Fellowship)* [6679]

Isaac Roth Newspaper Carrier Scholarship Program *(Undergraduate/Scholarship)* [6653]

Roy Rowan Scholarships *(Graduate, Undergraduate/Scholarship)* [7018]

SAJA Journalism Scholarships *(Graduate, Undergraduate/Scholarship)* [8540]

Abe Schecter Graduate Scholarships *(Postgraduate/Scholarship)* [7582]

David R. Schweisberg Memorial Scholarships *(Graduate, Undergraduate/Scholarship)* [7019]

Carole Simpson Scholarships *(Undergraduate/Scholarship)* [7583]

Ward Sims Memorial Scholarships *(Undergraduate/Scholarship)* [9174]

Drue Smith/Society of Professional Journalists Scholarships *(Undergraduate/Scholarship)* [3134]

A.C. Snow Scholarships *(Undergraduate/Scholarship)* [9305]

South Carolina Scholastic Press Association Scholarships *(Undergraduate/Scholarship)* [8553]

South Carolina Scholastic Press Association Yearbook Scholarships *(Undergraduate/Scholarship)* [8554]

Standard and Poor's Award for Economic and Business Reporting - S&P Scholarships *(Graduate, Undergraduate/Scholarship)* [7020]

H.L. Stevenson Scholarships *(Graduate, Undergraduate/Scholarship)* [7021]

Jay A. Strassberg Memorial Scholarships *(Undergraduate/Scholarship)* [2324]

Sturgulewski Family Scholarships *(Graduate, Undergraduate, Vocational/Occupational/Scholarship)* [9113]

Leo Suarez Journalism Scholarships *(Undergraduate/Scholarship)* [3321]

Kirk Sutlive Scholarships *(Undergraduate/Scholarship)* [4110]

Stan Swinton Scholarships *(Graduate, Undergraduate/Scholarship)* [7022]

Taylor/Blakeslee University Fellowships *(Professional development, Undergraduate/Fellowship)* [3268]

Television News Scholarships *(Undergraduate/Scholarship)* [6453]

Templeton-Cambridge Journalism Fellowships *(All/Fellowship)* [8839]

Texas Muslims Scholarship Fund (TMSF) *(Graduate, Undergraduate/Scholarship)* [4006]

Tucker Family Scholarships *(Undergraduate/Scholarship)* [9308]

UAA Anchorage Daily News Journalism Scholarships *(Undergraduate/Scholarship)* [9117]

UAA GCI, Inc. Scholarships *(Undergraduate/Scholarship)* [9121]

UAA Kimura Scholarship Fund Photography Scholarships (*Undergraduate/Scholarship*) [9123]

David Julian Wichard Scholarships (*Undergraduate/Scholarship*) [9309]

Tom Wicker Scholarships (*Undergraduate/Scholarship*) [9310]

Glenn Wilson Broadcast Journalism Scholarships (*Undergraduate/Scholarship*) [7124]

Pete Wilson Graduate Scholarships (*Graduate, Undergraduate/Scholarship*) [7584]

Pete Wilson Journalism Scholarships (*Graduate, Undergraduate/Scholarship*) [7585]

Theo Wilson Scholarships (*Graduate, Undergraduate/Scholarship*) [7023]

Wisconsin-Madison Journalism Scholarships (*Undergraduate/Scholarship*) [9386]

The Working Press Internships (*Undergraduate/Internship*) [8467]

WTVD Endowment Scholarships (*Undergraduate/Scholarship*) [9312]

Korean studies

Fall Fellowships in Korean Studies (*Professional development/Fellowship*) [5289]

Korean Language Study Awards (*Graduate/Scholarship*) [5290]

Labor relations (See Industrial and labor relations)

Laboratory technology (See Medical laboratory technology)

Land economics (See Land management)

Land management

Anchor Environmental Scholarships (*Graduate/Scholarship*) [1471]

Appraisal Institute Education Trust Scholarships (*Graduate, Undergraduate/Scholarship*) [1488]

Ivanhoe Foundation Fellowships (*Master's/Fellowship*) [5086]

Marathon Oil Corporation College Scholarship Program (*Graduate, Undergraduate/Scholarship*) [4578]

Mined Land Reclamation Educational Grant Program (*Undergraduate/Grant*) [6125]

NGC College Scholarships (*Graduate, Undergraduate/Scholarship*) [6303]

Landscape architecture and design

AIA Alaska Scholarships (*Graduate, Undergraduate/Scholarship*) [838]

Alabama Architectural Foundation Scholarships (*Postgraduate, Undergraduate/Scholarship*) [153]

American Society of Landscape Architects Council of Fellow Scholarships (*Undergraduate/Scholarship*) [1282]

Anchor Environmental Scholarships (*Graduate/Scholarship*) [1471]

ASF/Annika Teig/Skidmore, Owings and Merril Fellowships (*Undergraduate/Fellowship*) [1172]

ASLA Council of Fellows Scholarships (*Undergraduate/Scholarship*) [5330]

CLASS Fund Irrigation Scholarship Program (*Graduate, Undergraduate/Scholarship*) [5331]

CLCA Landscape Educational Advancement Foundation Scholarships (*Undergraduate/Scholarship*) [2263]

Paul Courtland Scholarships (*Undergraduate/Scholarship*) [5332]

Garden Club Council of Winston-Salem and Forsyth County Council (*Undergraduate/Scholarship*) [9639]

Edith H. Henderson Scholarships (*Undergraduate/Scholarship*) [1283]

Steven G. King Play Environments Scholarships (*Undergraduate/Scholarship*) [5333]

LAF/Class Fund AILA/YAMAGAMI/Hope Fellowships

(*Postgraduate/Fellowship*) [1284]

Landscape Forms Design for People Scholarships (*Undergraduate/Scholarship*) [5334]

William J. Locklin Scholarships (*Undergraduate/Scholarship*) [1285]

Michigan Nursery and Landscape Association Scholarships (*Undergraduate/Scholarship*) [5823]

NGC College Scholarships (*Graduate, Undergraduate/Scholarship*) [6303]

Raymond E. Page Scholarships (*Undergraduate/Scholarship*) [1286]

Peridian International, Inc./Rae L. Price, FASLA Scholarships (*Undergraduate/Scholarship*) [5335]

Rae L. Price Scholarships (*Undergraduate/Scholarship*) [1287]

Rain Bird Intelligent Use of Water Scholarships (*Undergraduate/Scholarship*) [5336]

Enid W. and Bernard B. Spigel Architectural Scholarships (*Graduate, Undergraduate/Scholarship*) [4384]

Harriet Barnhart Wimmer Scholarships (*Undergraduate/Scholarship*) [1288]

David T. Woolsey Scholarships (*Undergraduate/Scholarship*) [1289]

Hawaii Chapter/David T. Woolsey Scholarships (*Graduate, Undergraduate/Scholarship*) [5337]

Worldstudio AIGA Scholarships (*Graduate, Undergraduate/Scholarship*) [9761]

Languages (See Foreign languages)

Latin American studies (See also Area and ethnic studies)

FAIC Latin American and Caribbean Scholars Program (*Professional development/Scholarship*) [851]

Foundation of American Institute for Conservation Lecture Grants (*Professional development/Grant*) [852]

Leo S. Rowe Pan American Fund (*Graduate, Undergraduate/Loan*) [6967]

Arthur M. Schlesinger, Jr. Fellowships (*All/Fellowship*) [5240]

Thesaurus Linguae Latinae Fellowships (TTL) (*Doctorate/Fellowship*) [987]

UC MEXUS Grants for Dissertation Research (*Graduate/Grant*) [9199]

UC MEXUS Short-Term Projects (*Master's, Doctorate, Postdoctorate/Grant*) [9200]

Law

AAJ Trial Advocacy Scholarships (*Undergraduate/Scholarship*) [489]

AALL Leadership Academy Grants (*Professional development/Grant*) [507]

AALL Research Funds (*Professional development/Grant*) [495]

AAUW Legal Advocacy Fund Selected Professions Fellowships (*Doctorate, Graduate/Fellowship*) [18]

ABA Legal Opportunity Scholarship Funds (*Undergraduate/Scholarship*) [4566]

ABF Doctoral Fellowships (*Doctorate, Graduate/Fellowship*) [577]

The Frederick B. Abramson Public Interest Fellowships Awards (*All/Fellowship*) [23]

Accenture American Indian Scholarship Program (*Graduate, Undergraduate/Scholarship*) [825]

ACS Law Fellowships (*Graduate/Fellowship*) [654]

Adler Pollock & Sheehan Diversity Scholarships (*Undergraduate/Scholarship*) [50]

Affirmative Action Mini Grants and Student Scholarships (*All/Grant*) [25]

AGBU Scholarships (*Graduate/Loan*) [1573]

Akron Bar Association Foundation Scholarships (*Undergraduate/Scholarship*) [151]

Neil Alexander Scholarships (*Undergraduate/Scholarship*) [6013]

Alliance Defense Fund - Blackstone Legal Fellowships (*Undergraduate/Fellowship*) [333]

ALL-SIS CONELL Grants (*Professional development/Grant*) [508]

Tillie B. Alperin Scholarships (*Undergraduate/Scholarship*) [9220]

American Association of Law Libraries Library School Scholarships (*Graduate, Postgraduate/Scholarship*) [498]

American Association of University Women Selected Professions Fellowships (*Professional development/Fellowship*) [13]

American Counsel Association Scholarships (*Undergraduate/Scholarship*) [683]

American Enterprise Institute National Research Initiative Fellowships (NRI) (*Graduate/Fellowship*) [718]

American Judges Association Law Student Essay Competition (*Undergraduate/Prize*) [890]

American Psychology-Law Society Dissertation Awards (*Graduate/Award*) [1043]

American Psychology-Law Society Early Career Professional Grants-In-Aid (*Professional development/Grant*) [1044]

American Psychology-Law Society Student Grants-In-Aid (*Graduate/Grant*) [1045]

American Society of Comparative Law TransCoop Programs (*All/Scholarship*) [1204]

Anheuser-Busch NAPABA Law Foundation Presidential Scholarships (*Undergraduate/Scholarship*) [6026]

APBASV Scholarships (*All/Scholarship*) [1652]

Arent Fox Diversity Scholarships (*Undergraduate/Scholarship*) [1503]

Armenian Bar Association Graduate Scholarships in Law (*Graduate/Scholarship*) [1569]

Arthur Lockwood Beneventi Law Scholarships (*Undergraduate/Scholarship*) [6497]

Benjamin Asbell Memorial Scholarships (*Undergraduate/Scholarship*) [2315]

Asian American Lawyers Associations of Massachusetts Scholarships (*Undergraduate/Scholarship*) [1644]

Asian/Pacific Bar Association of Sacramento Law Foundation Scholarships (*Graduate, Postgraduate/Scholarship*) [1650]

Associated Women for Pepperdine Scholarships (AWP) (*Undergraduate/Scholarship*) [7167]

Attorney-CPA Foundation Scholarships (*Undergraduate/Scholarship*) [439]

H. Thomas Austern Memorial Writing Competition (*Undergraduate/Prize*) [3853]

William Stone Ayres Scholarships (*Undergraduate/Scholarship*) [3479]

Jaimes F. Bailey, Jr. Scholarships (*Undergraduate/Scholarship*) [5111]

Baker Donelson Diversity Scholarships (*Undergraduate/Scholarship*) [1997]

Baker and Hostetler Diversity Fellowships (*Undergraduate/Fellowship*) [1999]

Donald W. Banner Corporate Intern Scholarships (*Undergraduate/Scholarship*) [4844]

Donald W. Banner Diversity Scholarships for Law Students (*Undergraduate/Scholarship*) [2014]

Mark T. Banner Scholarships for Law Students (*Graduate, Undergraduate/Scholarship*) [7798]

Barbri Scholarships for Bar Preparation (*Undergraduate/Scholarship*) [4561]

Helen Bassett Commemorative Scholarships (*Undergraduate/Scholarship*) [6567]

Bay Area Minority Law Student Scholarships (*Graduate, Undergraduate/Scholarship*) [2019]

Beck-Pfann Memorial Scholarships (*Undergraduate/Scholarship*) [7168]

Harvey Bell Memorial Prize (*Graduate/Prize*) [6564]

The Viscount Bennett Fellowships (*Graduate/Fellowship*) [2419]

Berkowitz Fellowships (*Professional development/Fellowship*) [8902]

Hon. Peggy Bernheim Memorial Scholarships (*Undergraduate/Scholarship*) [2190]

Beverly Estate Scholarships (*Undergraduate/Scholarship*) [3480]

Thomas F. Black, Jr. Memorial Scholarships (*Undergraduate/Scholarship*) [7784]

William Verbon Black Scholarships (*Undergraduate/Scholarship*) [187]

Lucie and Thornton Blackburn Scholarships (*Undergraduate/Scholarship*) [2363]

David and Camille Boatwright Endowed Scholar-

ships *(Undergraduate/Scholarship)* [7169]
Bohemian Lawyers Association of Chicago Scholarships *(Graduate/Scholarship)* [2162]
George and Mary Brammer Scholarships *(Undergraduate/Scholarship)* [3481]
Ann Marie Bredefeld Scholarships *(Undergraduate/Scholarship)* [7170]
Margaret Martin Brock Scholarships in Law *(Undergraduate/Scholarship)* [7171]
Kae and Kay Brockermeyer Endowed Scholarships *(Undergraduate/Scholarship)* [7172]
Shirley J. Brooke Endowed Scholarships *(Undergraduate/Scholarship)* [7173]
Peggy Browning Fund - Chicago School-Year Fellowships *(Graduate, Undergraduate/Fellowship)* [2203]
Gregory Brunk Scholarships *(Undergraduate/Scholarship)* [3482]
Buder Scholarships for American Indian Law Students *(Undergraduate/Scholarship)* [9530]
Sam Bull Memorial Scholarships *(Undergraduate/Scholarship)* [227]
Business and Transactional Law Center Scholarships *(Undergraduate/Scholarship)* [9485]
BWEL Law Student Scholarships *(Undergraduate/Scholarship)* [2142]
Donald C. and Doris K. Byers Scholarships *(Undergraduate/Scholarship)* [3483]
Johnston Cabaniss Scholarships *(Undergraduate/Scholarship)* [188]
CALL/ACBD Education Reserve Fund Grants *(Graduate/Grant)* [2388]
Canadian Association of Law Libraries CALL Research Grants *(Graduate/Grant)* [2389]
Canadian Association of Law Teachers Award for Academic Excellence *(Professional development/Award)* [2393]
Canadian Association for the Practical Study of Law in Education Fellowships *(Graduate/Fellowship)* [2402]
Canadian IT Law Association Student Writing Contest *(Doctorate/Prize)* [2511]
Robert C. Carson Memorial Bursary *(Undergraduate/Scholarship)* [242]
Catzman Awards for Professionalism and Civility *(Professional development/Award)* [65]
CCLA Summer Legal Internships *(Undergraduate, Graduate/Internship)* [2428]
Child and Family Advocacy Fellowships *(Undergraduate/Scholarship)* [9486]
Almeric Christian Memorial Scholarships *(Graduate/Scholarship)* [9438]
CIHR Health Law and Policy Fellowships *(Graduate/Fellowship)* [2791]
CISDL Associate Fellows *(Graduate/Fellowship)* [2730]
CISDL Legal Research Fellows *(Graduate/Fellowship)* [2731]
CISDL Senior Research Fellows *(Professional development/Fellowship)* [2732]
CLA Student Summer Internship Program *(Undergraduate/Internship)* [2517]
Athalie Clarke Endowed Scholarships *(Undergraduate/Scholarship)* [7174]
Brian Dane Cleary Memorial Scholarships *(Undergraduate/Scholarship)* [7175]
Justice Robert L. Clifford Fellowships *(All/Fellowship)* [5930]
Frank M. Coffin Family Law Fellowships *(Graduate/Fellowship)* [5569]
Claude T. Coffman Memorial Scholarships *(Undergraduate/Scholarship)* [9221]
Columbian Lawyers Association of Westchester County Scholarships *(Undergraduate/Scholarship)* [3009]
Consumer Law Public Service Fellowships *(All/Fellowship)* [7603]
Hon. Joseph W. Cowgill Memorial Scholarships *(Undergraduate/Scholarship)* [2316]
Mable B. Crawford Memorial Scholarships *(Undergraduate/Scholarship)* [9146]
CTRF Scholarships for Graduate Study in Transportation *(Graduate/Scholarship)* [2626]
Cuban American Bar Association Scholarships *(All/Scholarship)* [3301]
Angela D. Dales Merit Scholarship Program *(Under-

graduate/Scholarship)* [1486]
Dallas Hispanic Bar Association Scholarships *(Undergraduate/Scholarship)* [3337]
D&A Florida Scholarships *(Undergraduate/Scholarship)* [8597]
Hugh and Hazel Darling Dean Scholarships *(Undergraduate/Scholarship)* [7176]
Darling Foundation Endowed School of Law Scholarships *(Undergraduate/Scholarship)* [7177]
DBA Law School Scholarship Program *(Undergraduate/Scholarship)* [3471]
Alexander A. Delle Cese Memorial Scholarships *(Undergraduate/Scholarship)* [2191]
Martha Delman and Milton Arthur Krug Endowed Scholarships *(Undergraduate/Scholarship)* [7178]
Edward D. Di Loreto-Odell S. McConnell Scholarships *(Undergraduate/Scholarship)* [7179]
Carol DiMaiti Scholarship Awards *(Undergraduate/Scholarship)* [5662]
Raymond DiPaglia Endowment Scholarships *(Undergraduate/Scholarship)* [3484]
Diversity Fellowship Program (DFP) *(Undergraduate/Fellowship)* [5928]
Diversity Scholars Awards *(Graduate/Award)* [3239]
Daniel B. Dixon Scholarships *(Undergraduate/Scholarship)* [326]
Grace O. Doane Scholarships *(Undergraduate/Scholarship)* [3485]
Hon. Ralph W.E. Donges Memorial Scholarships *(Undergraduate/Award)* [2317]
Joseph M. Dorgan Scholarships *(Undergraduate/Scholarship)* [3486]
Drake University Law School Law Opportunity Scholarships - Disadvantage *(Undergraduate/Scholarship)* [3487]
Drake University Law School Law Opportunity Scholarships - Diversity *(Undergraduate/Scholarship)* [3488]
Drake University Law School Public Service Scholarships *(Undergraduate/Scholarship)* [3489]
Cleveland Drennon, Jr. Memorial Scholarships *(Undergraduate/Scholarship)* [9222]
DRI Law Student Diversity Scholarships *(Undergraduate/Scholarship)* [2144]
Thomas J. Drinan Memorial Fellowships *(All/Fellowship)* [7604]
DuBois Brothers Scholarships *(Undergraduate/Scholarship)* [2318]
Josephine P. White Eagle Graduate Fellowships *(Graduate, Master's, Doctorate/Fellowship)* [4591]
Robert E. Early Memorial Scholarships *(Undergraduate/Scholarship)* [3490]
East Tennessee Foundation Scholarships *(Undergraduate/Scholarship)* [9223]
Mike Eidson Scholarships *(Graduate, Undergraduate/Scholarship)* [490]
Electric Cooperative Pioneer Trust Fund Scholarships *(Undergraduate/Scholarship)* [3491]
Herman E. Elgar Memorial Scholarships *(Undergraduate/Scholarship)* [3492]
Equal Access to Justice Scholarships *(Undergraduate/Scholarship)* [6134]
Equal Justice Works Fellowship Program *(Graduate, Undergraduate/Fellowship)* [3675]
Judge Samuel J. Ervin, III Fellowships *(Graduate/Fellowship)* [5402]
R. Wayne Estes Endowed Scholarships *(Undergraduate/Scholarship)* [7180]
Evans and Petree Law Firm Scholarships *(Undergraduate/Scholarship)* [9224]
Clifton W. Everett, Sr. Community Lawyer Fellowships *(Graduate/Fellowship)* [5403]
Faegre & Benson Diversity Scholarships *(Undergraduate/Scholarship)* [3702]
D.J. Fairgrave Education Trust *(Undergraduate/Scholarship)* [3493]
Farella Braun Martel LLP Diversity Scholarships *(Undergraduate/Scholarship)* [3715]
Judge McIntyre Faries Scholarships *(Undergraduate/Scholarship)* [7181]
Federal Court Bench and Bar Scholarships *(Undergraduate/Scholarship)* [9225]
Fellowships to Promote Research on the Legal Framework for Civil Society in Latin America, Africa and Asia *(All/Fellowship)* [4892]
John E. Fenton, Jr. Public Service Fellowships

(Postgraduate/Fellowship) [7605]
Filipino Bar Association of Northern California Scholarships (FBANC) *(All/Scholarship)* [1653]
Finnegan, Henderson, Farabow, Garrett & Dunner, LLP Diversity Scholarships *(Undergraduate/Scholarship)* [3753]
Fish & Richardson 1L Diversity Fellowships *(Undergraduate/Scholarship)* [3800]
Scott A. Flahive Memorial Scholarship Fund *(Undergraduate/Scholarship)* [4214]
Foreign, Comparative & International Law - Schaffer Grants for Foreign Law Librarians *(Professional development/Grant)* [499]
Leland Stanford Forrest Scholarships *(Undergraduate/Scholarship)* [3494]
Howard Fox Memorial Law Scholarships *(Undergraduate/Scholarship)* [2068]
Franchise Law Diversity Scholarship Awards *(Undergraduate/Scholarship)* [4940]
John Hope Franklin Prize *(Professional development/Prize)* [5366]
Fredrikson and Byron Foundation Minority Scholarships *(Undergraduate/Scholarship)* [4002]
Fried, Frank, Harris, Shriver and Jacobson Fellowships *(Graduate/Fellowship)* [4010]
Froberg-Suess JD/MBA Scholarships *(Undergraduate/Scholarship)* [7182]
Furman-Tikvah Scholarships *(Graduate/Scholarship)* [8903]
Gerald Garner Memorial Scholarships *(Undergraduate/Scholarship)* [7183]
William H. Gates Public Service Law Scholarships *(Undergraduate/Scholarship)* [4046]
Joseph H. Gellert/Dutchess County Bar Association Scholarships *(Undergraduate/Scholarship)* [3555]
John J. Gibbons Fellowships in Public Interest and Constitutional Law *(All/Fellowship)* [4149]
Terry M. Giles Honor Scholarships *(Undergraduate/Scholarship)* [7184]
Senator James Gladstone Memorial Scholarships *(Graduate, Undergraduate/Scholarship)* [228]
Jane S. Glenn Memorial Endowed Scholarships *(Undergraduate/Scholarship)* [7805]
Government Documents Special Interest Section - Veronica Maclay Student Grants *(Master's/Grant)* [509]
Wilford Hayes Gowen Scholarships *(Undergraduate/Scholarship)* [9226]
William L. Graddy Law School Scholarships *(Undergraduate/Scholarship)* [8605]
Graham & Dunn 1L Diversity Fellowships *(Graduate/Fellowship)* [4203]
Alexander G. Gray, Jr. Scholarships *(Graduate/Scholarship)* [5682]
Philip F. Greco Memorial Scholarships *(Undergraduate/Scholarship)* [5560]
Michael Greenberg Student Writing Competition *(Graduate/Prize, Scholarship)* [6394]
Guy P. Greenwald Jr. Endowed Scholarships *(Undergraduate/Scholarship)* [7185]
F.C. Grote Fund Scholarships *(Graduate, Undergraduate/Scholarship)* [328]
Warren and Rosalie Gummow Endowed Scholarships *(Undergraduate/Scholarship)* [7186]
The Richard D. Hailey AAJ Law Student Scholarships *(Undergraduate/Scholarship)* [491]
Vincent S. Haneman-Joseph B. Perskie Memorial Foundation Scholarships *(Graduate, Undergraduate/Scholarship)* [1924]
Lex and Scott Hawkins Endowed Scholarships *(Undergraduate/Scholarship)* [3495]
Thomas T. Hayashi Memorial Scholarships *(Graduate, Undergraduate/Scholarship)* [5142]
Edward and Cora Hayes Scholarships *(Undergraduate/Scholarship)* [3496]
Annamae Heaps Law Scholarships *(Undergraduate/Scholarship)* [3497]
Joseph T. Helling Scholarship Fund *(Undergraduate/Scholarship)* [4730]
John M. Helmick Law Scholarships *(Undergraduate/Scholarship)* [3498]
ASIL Arthur C. Helton Fellowship Program *(All/Fellowship)* [1280]
Herbert Herff Presidential Law Scholarships *(Undergraduate/Scholarship)* [9227]

Alia Herrera Memorial Scholarships (Undergraduate/Scholarship) [492]

Mark and Michelle Hiepler Endowed Scholarships (Undergraduate/Scholarship) [7187]

Hierholzer-Fojtik Scholarship Fund (Undergraduate/Scholarship) [4223]

Judge Delmas C. Hill Scholarships (Undergraduate/Scholarship) [9487]

HIPLA Judicial Fellowships (Undergraduate/Fellowship) [4613]

HIPLA Scholarships for University of Houston Law Center Students (Graduate, Undergraduate/Scholarship) [4614]

Robert and Elaine Hoffman Memorial Scholarships (Undergraduate/Scholarship) [9228]

Alan Holoch Memorial Grants (Professional development/Grant) [500]

Kathryn Hookanson Law Fellowships (Undergraduate/Scholarship) [9229]

John C. "Jack" Hough Memorial Law Scholarships (Undergraduate/Scholarship) [9230]

Lloyd Houlden Research Fellowships (Professional development/Fellowship) [2386]

HSF/Wal-Mart Stores Inc. Scholarship Program (Graduate, Undergraduate/Scholarship) [4577]

John Peter Humphrey Student Fellowships (Graduate/Fellowship) [2443]

Cecil C. Humphreys Law Fellowships (Undergraduate/Fellowship) [9231]

IBA Law Student Scholarship Foundation Scholarships (Undergraduate/Scholarship) [4754]

Indiana Continuing Legal Education Forum Scholarship Fund (Undergraduate/Scholarship) [4731]

International Association of Law Libraries Scholarship Program (Professional development/Scholarship) [4876]

International Municipal Lawyers Association Canadian Scholarships (Professional development/Scholarship) [4963]

International Trademark Association-Ladas Memorial Awards (Professional development, Undergraduate/Award) [5019]

Internships in International Civil Society Law (Undergraduate/Internship) [4893]

Iranian American Bar Association Scholarships (Undergraduate/Scholarship) [5046]

James P. Irish Scholarships (Undergraduate/Scholarship) [3499]

Islamic Scholarship Fund Scholarships (ISF) (Postgraduate, Undergraduate/Scholarship) [5078]

Italian American Lawyers Association Annual Scholarships (Undergraduate/Scholarship) [5084]

Jan Jancin Competition Awards (Undergraduate/Award) [881]

Japanese American Bar Association Scholarships (Graduate, Undergraduate/Scholarship) [5138]

J.D. Graduate Tikvah Scholarships (Graduate/Scholarship) [8904]

J.D. or LL.M. Tikvah Scholarships (Graduate/Scholarship) [8905]

JD/MBA Scholarships (Undergraduate/Scholarship) [7188]

Jewish Federation Academic Scholarships (Graduate, Undergraduate/Scholarship) [5161]

JLTLA Scholarships (Undergraduate/Scholarship) [8981]

MCCA Lloyd M. Johnson, Jr. Scholarships (Undergraduate/Scholarship) [5904]

Bernadine Johnson-Marshall and Martha Bell Williams Scholarships (Undergraduate/Award) [1718]

Edward H. Jones Scholarships (Undergraduate/Scholarship) [3500]

JSR Foundation Endowed School of Law Scholarships (Undergraduate/Scholarship) [7189]

Woodrow Judkins Endowed Scholarships (Undergraduate/Scholarship) [7190]

Kaplan Scholarships (Undergraduate/Scholarship) [4562]

Kegler Brown Minority Merit Scholarships (Undergraduate/Scholarship) [5229]

Kerr Foundation Scholarships (Undergraduate/Scholarship) [6867]

Kerrigan Scholarships (Undergraduate/Scholarship) [7191]

James N. Kincanon Scholarships (Undergraduate/Scholarship) [7806]

Martin Luther King Law Scholarships (Undergraduate/Scholarship) [3501]

Forest A. King Scholarships (Undergraduate/Scholarship) [3502]

Kluge Fellowships (Doctorate, Graduate/Fellowship) [5274]

AALL/Wolters Kluwer Law & Business Grants (Professional development/Grant) [501]

Koch Scholarships (Undergraduate/Scholarship) [9488]

Senator Carl O. Koella, Jr. Memorial Scholarships (Undergraduate/Scholarship) [3114]

Marcia J. Koslov Scholarships (Professional development/Scholarship) [502]

Krist-Reavley Minority Scholarships (Undergraduate/Scholarship) [7192]

Cooley Godward Kronish Diversity Fellowships (Graduate, Undergraduate/Fellowship) [3249]

George F. Kugler, Jr. Scholarships (Undergraduate/Scholarship) [2319]

Julia Kwan Endowed Scholarships (Graduate/Scholarship) [7193]

The Labor Law Scholarships (Undergraduate/Scholarship) [6660]

James D. Lang Memorial Scholarships (Undergraduate/Scholarship) [2390]

Frank H. Lang Merit Scholarships (Undergraduate/Scholarship) [5341]

Jason Lang Scholarships (Undergraduate/Scholarship) [252]

Latham Diversity Scholars (Undergraduate/Scholarship) [5354]

Law Foundation of British Columbia Graduate Fellowships (Graduate/Fellowship) [5360]

Law Foundation of Ontario Community Leadership in Justice Fellowships (Professional development/Fellowship) [5362]

Law and Social Science Dissertation Fellowship and Mentoring Program (Doctorate, Graduate/Fellowship) [578]

Law and Society Association Article Prize (Professional development/Prize) [5367]

Law and Society Association Dissertation Prize (Professional development/Prize) [5368]

Law and Society Association International Prize (Professional development/Prize) [5369]

Law and Society Association Student Paper Prize (Graduate, Undergraduate/Prize) [5370]

Law Society of British Columbia Scholarships (Graduate, Undergraduate/Scholarship) [5373]

Law Student Diversity Scholarships (Undergraduate/Scholarship) [5814]

Verne Lawyer Scholarships (Undergraduate/Scholarship) [3503]

Lazarian Graduate Scholarships (Graduate/Scholarship) [1578]

League of Attorneys' Wives Scholarships (Undergraduate/Scholarship) [3504]

Albert J. and Mae Lee Memorial Scholarships (Undergraduate/Scholarship) [7194]

The Leesfield/AAJ Law Student Scholarships (Undergraduate/Scholarship) [493]

Judge William B. Leffler Scholarships (Undergraduate/Scholarship) [9232]

Legal Research Service Scholarships (Undergraduate/Scholarship) [3505]

Craig Lensch Memorial Scholarships (Undergraduate/Scholarship) [2192]

Frederick D. Lewis Jr. Scholarships (Undergraduate/Scholarship) [3506]

Liberty Bell Award Law Scholarships (Graduate/Scholarship) [2736]

Dolores Zohrab Liebmann Fund - Graduate School Fellowships (Graduate/Fellowship) [5488]

Lim, Ruger and Kim Scholarships (Undergraduate/Scholarship) [6027]

George N. Lindsay Civil Rights Legal Fellowships (Graduate/Fellowship) [5384]

Abram D. and Maxine H. Londa Scholarships (Undergraduate/Scholarship) [6661]

The C. Lyons Fellowship Program (All/Fellowship) [6389]

Gordon and Delores Madson Scholarships (Undergraduate/Scholarship) [3507]

MALDEF Dream Act Student Activist Scholarships (Undergraduate, Graduate/Scholarship) [5805]

Sue A. Malone Scholarships (Doctorate, Graduate/Scholarship) [5188]

Honorable Carol Los Mansmann Memorial Scholarships (Graduate, Undergraduate/Scholarship) [329]

Howard T. Markey Memorial Scholarships (Undergraduate/Scholarship) [3717]

Abraham Lincoln Marovitz Public Interest Law Scholarships (Undergraduate/Scholarship) [2746]

Right Honourable Paul Martin Sr. Scholarships (Graduate/Scholarship) [2500]

Massachusetts Bar Foundation Legal Intern Fellowship Program (LIFP) (All/Fellowship) [5664]

Greg Matthews Memorial Scholarships (Undergraduate/Scholarship) [7195]

Monna Mawson Scholarships (Undergraduate/Scholarship) [4659]

McCleary Law Fellows Program (Graduate, Undergraduate/Fellowship) [4634]

Niqui McCown Honor and Memorial Scholarship Fund (Undergraduate/Scholarship) [9555]

J. McDonald and Judy Williams School of Law Scholarships (Undergraduate/Scholarship) [7196]

H.H. McKnight Memorial Scholarships (Undergraduate/Scholarship) [9233]

Paul R. McLaughlin Fellowships (All/Fellowship) [7606]

R. Roy McMurty Fellowships in Legal History (Doctorate, Graduate/Fellowship) [6992]

Memphis Access and Diversity Law Scholarships (Undergraduate/Scholarship) [9234]

John Merrick Law Scholarships (Undergraduate/Scholarship) [7197]

Sanders J. Mestel Legal Scholarship Fund (Undergraduate/Scholarship) [8689]

Mexican American Legal Defense and Educational Fund Law School Scholarships (Undergraduate/Scholarship) [5806]

Milbank Diversity Scholarships (Undergraduate/Scholarship) [5870]

Minority Leadership Development Awards (Graduate/Award) [503]

Minority Presence Grant Program for Doctoral Study (Doctorate, Graduate/Grant) [9295]

Jake S. More Scholarships (Undergraduate/Scholarship) [3508]

Thomas More Scholarships (Undergraduate/Scholarship) [4191]

Sonia Morgan Scholarships (Undergraduate/Scholarship) [6662]

Linda J. Murphy Scholarships (Undergraduate/Scholarship) [9704]

My Life As A Lawyer Scholarships (Graduate, Undergraduate/Scholarship) [3262]

Sam A. Myar Jr. Law Scholarships (Undergraduate/Scholarship) [9235]

NAAF Post-Secondary Education Scholarships (Graduate, Undergraduate/Scholarship) [5993]

NALS of Detroit Scholarships (Undergraduate/Scholarship) [5977]

NAPABA Law Foundation Scholarships (Undergraduate/Scholarship) [6028]

National Italian American Bar Association Scholarships (Postgraduate/Scholarship) [6367]

National Judges Association Scholarships (Professional development/Scholarship) [6372]

National Sheriffs' Association Scholarship Program (Graduate, Undergraduate/Scholarship) [6474]

NCLEJ Law School Graduate Fellows and Volunteers (Graduate/Fellowship) [6184]

Nebraska Paralegal Association Student Scholarships (Undergraduate/Scholarship) [6610]

Charles I. Nelson Endowed Scholarships (Undergraduate/Scholarship) [7198]

New Brunswick Law Foundation Graduate Scholarships in Law (Graduate/Scholarship) [5375]

Gunnar Nicholson Endowed Scholarships (Undergraduate/Scholarship) [7199]

Helen W. Nies Memorial Scholarships (Undergraduate/Scholarship) [3718]

Peggy Kommer Novosad Scholarships (Graduate, Postgraduate/Scholarship) [4295]

NSCLC Post-Graduate Fellowships (Postgraduate/Fellowship) [6472]

Oklahoma City University Merit Scholarships (Undergraduate/Scholarship) [6868]

Olin/Searle Fellows in Law *(Professional development/Fellowship)* [3731]

Faith E. O'Neal Scholarships *(Undergraduate/Scholarship)* [7558]

Dwight D. Opperman Scholarships *(Undergraduate/Scholarship)* [3509]

PABA Foundation Community Service Scholarships *(Graduate, Undergraduate/Scholarship)* [7308]

PABA Foundation Fellowships *(Postdoctorate/Fellowship)* [7309]

PABA Foundation Incentive Scholarships *(Graduate, Undergraduate/Scholarship)* [7310]

PABA Foundation Merit Scholarships *(Graduate, Undergraduate/Scholarship)* [7311]

PACE/Columbian Lawyers Association of Westchester County Endowed Scholarships *(Undergraduate/Scholarship)* [3010]

Pacific Legal Foundation Faculty Grants *(All/Grant)* [7031]

Pathways to Success Scholarships *(Undergraduate/Scholarship)* [3954]

Pepperdine University Armenian Student Scholarships *(Undergraduate/Scholarship)* [7200]

Pepperdine University Dean's Scholarships *(Doctorate, Graduate/Scholarship)* [7201]

Pepperdine University Diversity Scholarships *(Doctorate, Graduate/Scholarship)* [7202]

Pepperdine University Faculty Scholarships *(Doctorate, Graduate/Scholarship)* [7203]

Jerome S. Petz, S.J., Scholarships *(Undergraduate/Scholarship)* [3510]

William R. Pfalzgraf Scholarships *(Undergraduate/Scholarship)* [7103]

Jamie Phillips Endowed Scholarships *(Undergraduate/Scholarship)* [7204]

Pi Gamma Mu Scholarships *(Graduate/Scholarship)* [7330]

Pittsburg State University Distinguished Graduate Scholarships *(Undergraduate/Scholarship)* [9489]

Harold and Harriet Plum Memorial Scholarships *(Undergraduate/Scholarship)* [2320]

Donald and Susie Polden Dean's Scholarships *(Undergraduate/Scholarship)* [9236]

Political Leadership Scholarships *(Undergraduate/Scholarship)* [7415]

Political Studies Scholarships *(Undergraduate, Graduate/Scholarship)* [9447]

Justice Stewart G. Pollock Fellowships *(All/Fellowship)* [5931]

Polsinelli Diversity Scholarships *(Undergraduate/Scholarship)* [9490]

Louis C. Portella Memorial Scholarships *(Graduate/Scholarship)* [2321]

Post-Doctoral Tikvah Scholarships *(Postdoctorate/Scholarship)* [8906]

George V. Powell Diversity Scholarships *(Undergraduate/Scholarship)* [5339]

Practising Law Institute Law Student Scholarships *(Undergraduate/Scholarship)* [7384]

Diana M. Priestly Memorial Scholarships *(Undergraduate/Scholarship)* [2391]

Prince Edward Island Law Student Scholarships *(Undergraduate/Scholarship)* [5377]

Public Interest Environmental Law Fellowships *(Postgraduate/Fellowship)* [3656]

Public Interest Scholarships *(Undergraduate/Scholarship)* [2234]

Public Service International Law Fellowships *(All/Fellowship)* [7607]

John Purfield Endowed Scholarships *(Undergraduate/Scholarship)* [7205]

Frederick Rakestraw Law Scholarships *(Graduate/Scholarship)* [6803]

Rappaport Fellows Program in Law and Public Policy *(All/Fellowship)* [7608]

Ratner and Sugarmon Scholarships *(Undergraduate/Scholarship)* [9237]

Janet Reynoldson Memorial Scholarships *(Undergraduate/Scholarship)* [3511]

William S. Richardson Commemorative Scholarships *(Graduate/Scholarship)* [5221]

Howard Brown Rickard Scholarships *(Undergraduate/Scholarship)* [6282]

Honorable Joseph H. Ridge Memorial Scholarships *(Undergraduate/Scholarship)* [330]

Isador M. Robinson Endowment Scholarships *(Undergraduate/Scholarship)* [3512]

Rosenthal Bar Exam Scholarships *(Undergraduate/Scholarship)* [2235]

Hon. Rudolph J. Rossetti Memorial Scholarships *(Undergraduate/Award)* [2322]

Joe Rudd Scholarships *(Undergraduate/Scholarship)* [7813]

SABA Foundation Fellowships *(Undergraduate/Fellowship)* [8538]

Santa Clara La Raza Lawyers Scholarships *(Graduate/Scholarship)* [5313]

Saratoga County Bar Association Law Student Scholarships *(All/Scholarship)* [7989]

SCCLA Fellowships *(All/Fellowship)* [8578]

SCCLA Scholarships *(All/Scholarship)* [8579]

Jeptha Wade Schureman Scholarship Program *(Undergraduate/Scholarship)* [3205]

Marla Schwartz Grants *(Professional development, Graduate/Grant)* [504]

Walter and Rita Selvy Scholarships *(Undergraduate/Scholarship)* [3513]

Serbian Bar Association of America Scholarships *(Undergraduate/Scholarship)* [8092]

Seton Hall Law School's Merit Scholarship Program *(Undergraduate/Scholarship)* [8097]

Barbara A. Shacochis Scholarships *(Undergraduate/Scholarship)* [7206]

Saleem Shah Early Career Development Awards *(Doctorate/Award)* [1046]

Shamberg Scholarships *(Undergraduate/Scholarship)* [9491]

The Ivan Shandor Memorial Ukrainian American Bar Association Scholarships *(Master's/Scholarship)* [9500]

John M. and Mary A. Shanley Memorial Scholarships *(Undergraduate/Scholarship)* [8622]

Benjamin G. Shatz Scholarships *(Undergraduate/Scholarship)* [7207]

Bill and Ann Sheperd Legal Scholarship Fund *(Undergraduate/Scholarship)* [3683]

Joseph Henry Shepherd Scholarships *(Undergraduate/Scholarship)* [9238]

Justice Janie L. Shores Scholarships *(Undergraduate/Scholarship)* [189]

Sidley Prelaw Scholars Initiative *(Undergraduate/Scholarship)* [8140]

Stuart Silverman Scholarships *(Undergraduate/Scholarship)* [7208]

Skadden Fellowships *(Graduate/Fellowship)* [8229]

James I. Smith, III Notre Dame Law School Scholarship Fund *(Graduate, Undergraduate/Scholarship)* [331]

Louis B. Sohn Fellowships in Human Rights and Environment *(Graduate/Fellowship)* [2692]

Soroptimist International of Redlands Scholarship *(Undergraduate/Scholarship)* [7715]

Amy E. Spain Memorial Scholarships *(Undergraduate/Scholarship)* [9239]

Special Law School Scholarships *(Undergraduate/Scholarship)* [7209]

Spring Internships in International Civil Society Law *(Undergraduate/Internship)* [4894]

James F. and Donna Springfield Scholarships *(Undergraduate/Scholarship)* [9240]

Otto M. Stanfield Law Scholarships *(Graduate/Scholarship)* [9003]

Stark County Bar Association Fund *(Undergraduate/Scholarship)* [8700]

Tom Steel Post-Graduate Fellowships *(Postgraduate, Professional development/Fellowship)* [7431]

StraightForward Media's Law School Scholarships *(Undergraduate/Scholarship)* [8760]

Jay A. Strassberg Memorial Scholarships *(Undergraduate/Scholarship)* [2324]

Suffolk Public Interest Law Group Summer Fellowships (SPILG) *(All/Fellowship)* [7609]

Summer Research Diversity Fellowships in Law and Social Science *(Undergraduate/Fellowship)* [579]

Hatton W. Sumners Scholarships *(Undergraduate/Scholarship)* [6869]

Michael Bendix Sutton Foundation *(Undergraduate/Scholarship)* [6335]

Robert M. Takasugi Public Interest Fellowships *(Postgraduate/Fellowship)* [8800]

Charles "Buck" and Dora Taylor Endowed Law Scholarships *(Undergraduate/Scholarship)* [3514]

Technical Services Special Interest Section Grants *(Professional development/Grant)* [506]

Tennessee Bar Foundation IOLTA Law School Scholarships *(Undergraduate/Scholarship)* [9241]

Texas Muslims Scholarship Fund (TMSF) *(Graduate, Undergraduate/Scholarship)* [4006]

The Rodney Thaxton Justice Fund *(Undergraduate/Scholarship)* [3322]

Dean James Thomas Memorial Scholarships *(Undergraduate/Scholarship)* [9680]

Honorable Raymond Thompson Endowed Scholarships *(Undergraduate/Scholarship)* [7210]

Daniel B. Toll Memorial Scholarships *(Undergraduate/Scholarship)* [2325]

William Tomar Memorial Scholarships *(Undergraduate/Scholarship)* [2326]

Davis Wright Tremaine 1L Diversity Scholarships *(Undergraduate/Scholarship)* [3348]

Thomas and Glenna Trimble Endowed Scholarships *(Undergraduate/Scholarship)* [7211]

Trustees College Scholarships *(Undergraduate/Scholarship)* [5561]

Trustees Law School Scholarships *(Undergraduate/Scholarship)* [5562]

VABANC Scholarships *(Graduate, Undergraduate/Scholarship)* [9429]

Wallace Vail Scholarships *(Undergraduate/Scholarship)* [6663]

Philip F. Vineberg Travelling Fellowships in the Humanities *(Undergraduate/Scholarship)* [5726]

Visiting Doctoral Tikvah Scholarships *(Doctorate/Scholarship)* [8907]

John D. Voelker Foundation Native American Scholarships *(Undergraduate/Scholarship)* [9470]

Gary Walker Memorial Scholarships *(Professional development/Scholarship)* [3972]

Bruce A. Wallace Memorial Scholarships *(Undergraduate/Scholarship)* [2327]

Warner Norcross & Judd LLP Minorty Scholarships *(Undergraduate/Scholarship)* [9483]

Earl Warren Civil Rights Training Scholarships *(Graduate/Scholarship)* [5972]

Earl Warren Shearman and Sterling Scholarships *(Graduate/Scholarship)* [5973]

Washington University Law School Chancellor's Graduate Fellowships *(Graduate/Fellowship)* [9532]

J.L. Weigand, Jr. Legal Education Trust Scholarships *(Undergraduate/Scholarship)* [9492]

Haemer Wheatcraft Scholarships *(Undergraduate/Scholarship)* [3515]

Stan Wheeler Mentorship Awards *(Professional development/Award)* [5371]

Brian J. White Endowed Law Scholarships *(Undergraduate/Scholarship)* [7212]

Howard A. White Endowed Scholarships *(Undergraduate/Scholarship)* [7213]

Richard S. White Fellowships *(Undergraduate/Fellowship)* [4522]

Paul D. White Scholarships *(Undergraduate/Award)* [2000]

Sidney B. Williams, Jr. Scholarships *(Undergraduate/Scholarship)* [882]

Women In Defense HORIZONS Scholarships *(Graduate, Undergraduate/Scholarship)* [9696]

Women of WSAJ Bar Preparation Scholarships *(Undergraduate/Scholarship)* [9518]

Wood County Bar Association Memorial Scholarships *(Undergraduate/Scholarship)* [7125]

Marilyn Graboys Wool Scholarships *(Undergraduate/Scholarship)* [7796]

WSAJ Diversity Bar Preparation Scholarships *(Undergraduate/Scholarship)* [9520]

Wyatt, Tarrant and Combs, LLP Scholarships *(Undergraduate/Scholarship)* [9242]

Minoru Yasui Memorial Scholarships *(Graduate/Scholarship)* [5147]

Searle Young Legal Scholars Research Fellowships *(Professional development/Fellowship)* [3732]

Diane Yu Loan Repayment Assistance Program *(Undergraduate/Loan)* [6029]

Yukon Law Foundation Scholarships *(Undergraduate/Scholarship)* [9799]

Michael A. Zamperini/W. Clay Burchell Scholarships *(Undergraduate/Scholarship)* [7878]

Zarley, McKee, Thomte, Voorhees, Sease Law

Scholarships *(Undergraduate/Scholarship)* [3516]

Law enforcement

Jack Ackroyd Scholarships *(Professional development/Scholarship)* [2372]

American Association of State Troopers Scholarship Foundation First Scholarships *(Undergraduate/Scholarship)* [550]

American Association of State Troopers Scholarship Foundation Second Scholarships *(Undergraduate/Scholarship)* [551]

American Federation of Police and Concerned Citizen Scholarships *(Undergraduate, Vocational/Occupational/Scholarship)* [722]

Benjamin Asbell Memorial Scholarships *(Undergraduate/Scholarship)* [2315]

Sheriff W. Bruce Umpleby Law Enforcement Scholarship Fund *(Undergraduate/Scholarship)* [8658]

Peter Butler III - Rose Fortune Scholarship Program *(Undergraduate/Scholarship)* [1716]

Canadian Identification Society Essay Scholarship Awards *(Professional development/Prize)* [2494]

Alphonso Deal Scholarship Awards *(Undergraduate/Scholarship)* [6157]

William Donald Dixon Research Grants *(Graduate/Grant)* [2495]

Edward Foster Awards *(All/Award)* [2496]

Charles D. Gonthier Research Fellowships *(Graduate, Professional development/Fellowship)* [2498]

Wayne Hildebrant Police Scholarship Fund *(Undergraduate/Scholarship)* [5350]

IAWP International Recognition and Scholarship Awards *(Professional development/Scholarship)* [4882]

Frederick George James Memorial Scholarships *(Undergraduate/Scholarship)* [7935]

V.J. Johnson Memorial Scholarships *(Undergraduate/Scholarship)* [552]

John W. Kelley Memorial Scholarships *(Undergraduate/Scholarship)* [8729]

Christopher J. Kohlmeier Scholarships *(Undergraduate/Scholarship)* [7662]

Law Enforcement Memorial Scholarship Fund *(Undergraduate/Scholarship)* [3911]

National Association of School Safety and Law Enforcement Officers Scholarships (NASSLEO) *(Undergraduate/Scholarship)* [6115]

National Organization of Black Law Enforcement Executives Fellowship Programs *(All/Fellowship)* [6421]

Pan Pacific Law Enforcement Scholarships *(Undergraduate/Scholarship)* [7978]

Portuguese American Police Association Scholarships *(Undergraduate/Scholarship)* [7380]

Newell S. Rand Jr. Memorial Scholarships *(Undergraduate/Scholarship)* [7055]

StraightForward Media's Law Enforcement Scholarships *(Professional development, Undergraduate/Scholarship)* [8759]

The WIFLE Scholarship Fund *(Graduate, Postdoctorate, Undergraduate/Scholarship)* [9702]

Leadership, Institutional and community

Alliance Pipeline Scholarships *(Professional development/Scholarship)* [2005]

Bush Leadership Fellows Program *(Professional development/Fellowship)* [2218]

Diversity Executive Leadership Program Scholarships *(Professional development/Scholarship)* [1184]

Fraser Milner Casgrain Scholarships *(Professional development/Scholarship)* [2006]

Greenlining Institute Fellowships *(Graduate/Fellowship)* [4349]

Investors Group Scholarships for Not-For-Profit Leaders *(Professional development/Scholarship)* [2007]

Kappa Omicron Nu Undergraduate Scholarships *(Undergraduate/Scholarship)* [5197]

Lafarge Community Leaders Scholarships *(Professional development/Scholarship)* [2008]

Marmot Leadership Scholarships *(Postgraduate,*

Professional development, Undergraduate/Scholarship) [7008]

Outward Bound Leadership Scholarships for Educators *(Professional development/Scholarship)* [7009]

Outward Bound Wilderness Leadership Awards for Youth *(High School, Professional development/Award)* [7010]

Scholarships for Leadership Training and Coaching *(Professional development/Scholarship)* [3457]

Youth or the Environment Scholarships *(Professional development/Scholarship)* [2009]

Leukemia

E.D. Thomas Post Doctoral Fellowships *(Postdoctorate/Fellowship)* [4014]

Liberal arts

Cecil E. Burney Scholarships *(Undergraduate/Scholarship)* [2940]

Elizabeth M. Gruber Scholarships *(Graduate/Scholarship)* [3410]

Doris Hendren Memorial Scholarships *(Undergraduate/Scholarship)* [7933]

Harriet Irsay Scholarships *(Graduate, Undergraduate/Scholarship)* [869]

Islamic Scholarship Fund Scholarships (ISF) *(Postgraduate, Undergraduate/Scholarship)* [5078]

Bernard Michel Scholarships *(Undergraduate/Scholarship)* [2348]

StraightForward Media's Liberal Arts Scholarships *(Undergraduate/Scholarship)* [8761]

Jeannette K. Watson Fellowships *(Undergraduate/Fellowship)* [9542]

Dennis Wong and Associates Scholarships *(Graduate, Undergraduate/Scholarship)* [5223]

Library and archival sciences

AALL Leadership Academy Grants *(Professional development/Grant)* [507]

AALL Scholarships for Continuing Education Classes *(Postgraduate/Scholarship)* [496]

AALL Scholarships for Library School Graduates Seeking a Non-Law Degree *(Postgraduate/Scholarship)* [497]

Above and Beyond Scholarships *(Graduate/Scholarship)* [2269]

ACMS Library Fellowships *(Graduate, Professional development/Fellowship)* [602]

AECT Legacy Scholarships *(Graduate, Master's, Professional development/Scholarship)* [1762]

AILA Scholarships *(Graduate/Scholarship)* [830]

AJL Scholarship Program *(Graduate/Scholarship)* [1821]

ALL-SIS CONELL Grants *(Professional development/Grant)* [508]

American Association of Law Libraries Library School Scholarships *(Graduate, Postgraduate/Scholarship)* [498]

APALA Scholarships *(Doctorate, Graduate/Scholarship)* [1648]

ArLA Scholarships *(Graduate, Master's/Scholarship)* [1541]

Atlantic Provinces Library Association Memorial Awards *(Professional development/Scholarship)* [1926]

Beard Scholarships *(Master's/Scholarship)* [4104]

Bound to Stay Bound Books Scholarships (BTSB) *(Graduate/Scholarship)* [1826]

Rev. Andrew L. Bouwhuis Memorial Scholarship Program *(Graduate/Scholarship)* [2668]

MAC Louisa Bowen Memorial Scholarships for Graduate Students in Archival Administration *(Graduate/Scholarship)* [5854]

Carol June Bradley Awards *(All/Grant)* [5955]

Rick Chace Foundation Scholarships *(Graduate/Scholarship)* [1829]

Continuing Education Awards *(Graduate/Grant)* [5741]

CLA/ACB Dafoe Scholarships *(Graduate/Scholarship)* [2519]

DEMCO New Leaders Travel Grants *(All/Grant)* [7536]

Dena Epstein Awards for Archival and Library Re-

search in American Music *(All/Grant)* [5956]

Foreign, Comparative & International Law - Schaffer Grants for Foreign Law Librarians *(Professional development/Grant)* [499]

Kevin Freeman Travel Grants *(Graduate, Professional development/Grant)* [5957]

Jewels Gardiner Scholarships *(Undergraduate/Scholarship)* [2270]

Eugene Garfield Doctoral Dissertation Fellowships *(Doctorate, Graduate/Fellowship)* [2070]

The Gates Millennium Scholars *(Undergraduate/Scholarship)* [4569]

Walter Gerboth Awards *(Professional development/Grant)* [5958]

Government Documents Special Interest Section - Veronica Maclay Student Grants *(Master's/Grant)* [509]

Grow Your Own Your Library Institutional Scholarships *(Graduate, Professional development/Scholarship)* [7537]

Caroline M. Hewins Scholarships *(Graduate/Scholarship)* [4465]

D. Glenn Hilts Scholarships *(Graduate, Undergraduate/Scholarship)* [1872]

HLS/MLA Professional Development Grants *(Professional development/Grant)* [5742]

Alan Holoch Memorial Grants *(Professional development/Grant)* [500]

Hubbard Scholarships *(Master's/Scholarship)* [4105]

Huenefeld/Denton Scholarships *(Undergraduate/Scholarship)* [3415]

Indiana Library Federation AIME Scholarships *(Undergraduate/Scholarship)* [4736]

Iowa Library Association Foundation Scholarships *(Graduate/Scholarship)* [5039]

E.J. Josey Scholarships *(Graduate/Scholarship)* [2133]

Kodak Fellowships in Film Preservation *(Graduate/Fellowship)* [1830]

Marcia J. Koslov Scholarships *(Professional development/Scholarship)* [502]

Christian Larew Memorial Scholarships *(Graduate/Scholarship)* [5484]

Library Media Teacher Scholarships *(Graduate/Scholarship)* [2271]

LITA and LSSI Minority Scholarships *(Graduate/Scholarship)* [5485]

LITA/OCLC Minority Scholarships *(Graduate/Scholarship)* [5486]

Louisiana Library Association Scholarships *(Graduate, Master's/Scholarship)* [5522]

Lillian Grace Mahan Scholarship Fund *(Graduate/Scholarship)* [8685]

Medical Library Association Scholarships for Minority Students *(Graduate/Scholarship)* [5745]

Frederic G. Melcher Scholarships *(Graduate/Scholarship)* [1827]

Minority Leadership Development Awards *(Graduate/Award)* [503]

Mary Moore Mitchell Scholarships *(Graduate, Master's/Scholarship)* [5523]

MLA Research, Development, and Demonstration Project Grants *(Graduate/Grant)* [5747]

Mook & Blanchard Honorary Scholarships *(Graduate/Scholarship)* [2272]

Archie Motley Memorial Scholarships for Minority Students *(Graduate/Scholarship)* [5856]

NELA Scholarships *(Graduate, Master's/Scholarship)* [6624]

Louise A. Nixon Scholarships *(Graduate/Scholarship)* [6608]

NJLA Scholarships *(Graduate, Postgraduate/Scholarship)* [6646]

Katharine Pantzer Fellowships in the British Book Trades *(Professional development/Fellowship)* [2085]

Pennsylvania Library Association Scholarships for MLS Students *(Graduate/Scholarship)* [7151]

Mary Pickford Scholarships *(Graduate/Scholarship)* [1831]

Henry Belin du Pont Fellowships *(Graduate/Fellowship)* [4365]

Sarah Rebecca Reed Scholarships *(Graduate/Scholarship)* [2071]

REFORMA Scholarship Program *(Doctorate, Gradu-*

ate, Professional development/Scholarship)
[7721]

Esther Schlundt Memorial Scholarships *(Graduate/ Scholarship)* [4737]

School Library Paraprofessional Scholarships *(Graduate/Scholarship)* [2273]

Marla Schwartz Grants *(Professional development, Graduate/Grant)* [504]

Fritz Schwartz Serials Education Scholarships *(Graduate, Professional development/Scholarship)* [6744]

Frank B. Sessa Scholarships for Continuing Professional Education *(Professional development/ Scholarship)* [2072]

CFI Sid Solow Scholarships *(Graduate/Scholarship)* [1832]

Carin Alma E. Somers Scholarship Trust *(Undergraduate/Scholarship)* [1927]

Sony Pictures Scholarships *(Graduate/Scholarship)* [1833]

AALL & Thomson West - George A. Strait Minority Scholarship Endowments *(Postgraduate/Scholarship)* [505]

Roger K. Summit Scholarships for North America *(Graduate/Scholarship)* [3436]

Technical Services Special Interest Section Grants *(Professional development/Grant)* [506]

Thomson Reuters/MLA Doctoral Fellowships *(Doctorate/Fellowship)* [5748]

Jack E. Tillson Scholarships *(Graduate/Scholarship)* [5040]

Universal Studios Preservation Scholarships *(Graduate/Scholarship)* [1834]

Philip F. Vineberg Travelling Fellowships in the Humanities *(Undergraduate/Scholarship)* [5726]

Vorgin-Bell Scholarships *(Graduate, Master's, Undergraduate/Scholarship)* [6848]

Sue Marsh Weller Memorial Scholarships *(Graduate, Postgraduate, Undergraduate/Scholarship)* [4738]

H.W. Wilson Scholarships *(Graduate/Scholarship)* [2520]

Blance E. Woolls Scholarships *(Graduate/Scholarship)* [2073]

World Book Graduate Scholarships in Library and Information Science *(Graduate/Scholarship)* [2521]

Life sciences

Dow Chemical Company Fellowships *(Graduate/ Fellowship)* [6427]

E.I. DuPont Fellowships *(Graduate/Fellowship)* [6428]

Foundation for the Preservation of Honey Bees Graduate Scholarships *(Graduate/Scholarship)* [3990]

Life Sciences Research Foundation Postdoctoral Fellowship Program *(Graduate, Doctorate/Fellowship)* [5494]

Michigan Society of Fellows Three-Year Fellowships *(Postdoctorate/Fellowship)* [5827]

Dolphus E. Milligan Graduate Fellowships *(Graduate/Fellowship)* [6429]

NOBCChE Procter and Gamble Fellowships *(Graduate/Fellowship)* [6430]

Paul and Ellen Ruckes Scholarships *(Graduate, Undergraduate/Scholarship)* [753]

Sino-American Pharmaceutical Professionals Association Scholarships *(Undergraduate/Scholarship)* [8222]

Eastman Kodak Dr. Theophilus Sorrell Fellowships *(Graduate/Fellowship)* [6432]

UNESCO-L'Oreal for Women in Science International Fellowships *(Doctorate, Postdoctorate/Fellowship)* [6927]

University of Wisconsin-Madison/CALS Continuing Student Scholarships *(Undergraduate/Scholarship)* [9374]

University of Wisconsin-Madison/CALS Minority Scholarships *(Undergraduate/Scholarship)* [9375]

Lighting science

IALD Education Trust Scholarship Program *(Graduate, Undergraduate/Scholarship)* [4878]

Linguistics

ETS Postdoctoral Fellowships *(Postdoctorate/Fellowship)* [3609]

Harold Gulliksen Psychometric Research Fellowships *(Doctorate, Graduate/Fellowship)* [3610]

Sylvia Taylor Johnson Minority Fellowships in Educational Measurement *(Doctorate/Fellowship)* [3611]

National Endowment for the Humanities Advanced Fellowships for Research in Turkey *(Postdoctorate/Fellowship)* [1153]

Literature

D&A Florida Scholarships *(Undergraduate/Scholarship)* [8597]

R.L. Gillette Scholarships *(Undergraduate/Scholarship)* [751]

Gene Halker Memorial Scholarships *(Graduate, Undergraduate/Scholarship)* [3865]

Hench Post-Dissertation Fellowships *(Postdoctorate/Fellowship)* [419]

Literary Arts Project Grants *(Professional development/Grant)* [220]

William P. McHugh Memorial Fund Award *(Doctorate, Graduate/Fellowship)* [1141]

National Endowment for the Humanities Advanced Fellowships for Research in Turkey *(Postdoctorate/Fellowship)* [1153]

The National Endowment for the Humanities Fellowships *(Doctorate, Graduate/Fellowship)* [1142]

Virginia Nicklas Scholarships *(Undergraduate/Scholarship)* [3382]

Ameen Rihani Scholarship Program *(Undergraduate/Scholarship)* [1492]

Luci Shaw Fellowships *(Undergraduate/Fellowship)* [4704]

The United States Department of State, Bureau of Educational & Cultural Affairs Fellowships *(Doctorate, Graduate/Fellowship)* [1143]

Aubrey L. Williams Research Travel Fellowships *(Professional development/Fellowship)* [1236]

Literature, Children's

Hannah Beiter Graduate Student Research Grants *(Doctorate, Graduate/Grant)* [2762]

Local government

Congressional Scholarship Awards *(Undergraduate/ Scholarship)* [4016]

Logistics

Academic Scholarship Program A *(Undergraduate/ Scholarship)* [6241]

Academic Scholarship Program B *(Undergraduate/ Scholarship)* [6242]

Sharon D. Banks Undergraduate Memorial Scholarships *(Undergraduate/Scholarship)* [9739]

Bison Transport Scholarships *(Undergraduate/ Scholarship)* [6897]

James Costello Memorial Scholarships *(Undergraduate/Scholarship)* [5023]

Ginger and Fred Deines Canada Scholarships *(Undergraduate, Vocational/Occupational/Scholarship)* [8949]

Ginger and Fred Deines Mexico Scholarships *(Undergraduate, Vocational/Occupational/Scholarship)* [8950]

Delta Nu Alpha Foundation Scholarships *(Undergraduate/Scholarship)* [3400]

Hooper Memorial Scholarships *(Undergraduate, Vocational/Occupational/Scholarship)* [8951]

Ann Koby Legacy Scholarships *(Undergraduate/ Scholarship)* [9740]

Denny Lydic Scholarships *(Undergraduate, Vocational/Occupational/Scholarship)* [8952]

Marathon Oil Corporation College Scholarship Program *(Graduate, Undergraduate/Scholarship)* [4578]

Helene M. Overly Memorial Scholarships *(Undergraduate/Scholarship)* [9741]

Texas Transportation Scholarships *(Undergraduate, Vocational/Occupational/Scholarship)* [8953]

Alice Glaisyer Warfield Scholarships *(Undergraduate, Vocational/Occupational/Scholarship)* [8954]

Management

Herb Adrian Memorial Scholarship Fund *(Undergraduate/Scholarship)* [3881]

APS/Maricopa County Community Colleges Scholarships *(Undergraduate/Scholarship)* [7333]

Bridging the GAP for Hispanic Success Awards *(Undergraduate/Scholarship)* [4545]

George M. Brooker Collegiate Scholarships for Minorities *(Graduate, Postgraduate, Undergraduate/ Scholarship)* [4818]

California Association of Family and Consumer Sciences -San Diego Chapter Scholarships (CAFCS) *(Graduate, Undergraduate, Vocational/Occupational/Scholarship)* [7917]

Stuart Cameron and Margaret McLeod Memorial Scholarships (SCMS) *(Graduate, Undergraduate/ Scholarship loan)* [4814]

CDC Presidential Management Fellows Program *(Graduate/Fellowship)* [2711]

Club Managers Association of America Research Grants (CMAA) *(All/Grant)* [2910]

CMAA Student Conference Travel Grants *(All/ Grant)* [2911]

CTP Scholarship Program *(Professional development/Scholarship)* [6455]

Diversity Executive Leadership Program Scholarships *(Professional development/Scholarship)* [1184]

Harold E. Eisenberg Foundation Scholarships *(Professional development/Scholarship)* [4906]

Donald M. Furbush Professional Development Grants *(Professional development/Grant)* [4819]

HACU/Wal-Mart Achievers Scholarships *(Undergraduate/Scholarship)* [4547]

Robert Hancock Memorial Scholarship Awards *(Undergraduate/Scholarship)* [5836]

HRH Prince Alwaleed Bin Talal ISNA Fellowships *(Graduate/Fellowship)* [5080]

HSBC-North America Scholarship Program *(Undergraduate/Scholarship)* [4571]

HSF/Wal-Mart Stores Inc. Scholarship Program *(Graduate, Undergraduate/Scholarship)* [4577]

IFMA Foundation Certificate Program Scholarships *(Graduate/Scholarship)* [4926]

IFMA Foundation Graduate/Undergraduate Scholarships *(Graduate, Undergraduate/Scholarship)* [4927]

IMA Memorial Education Fund Scholarships (MEF) *(Graduate, Undergraduate/Scholarship loan)* [4815]

Willmoore H. Kendall Scholarships *(Postgraduate/ Scholarship)* [2912]

David A. Kronick Travelling Fellowships *(Doctorate/ Fellowship)* [5743]

Val Mason Scholarships *(Postgraduate/Scholarship)* [2603]

NBMBAA PhD Fellowship Program *(Doctorate/Fellowship)* [6153]

Ontario Women's Institute Scholarships *(Undergraduate/Scholarship)* [3734]

PARMA Scholarships *(Undergraduate/Scholarship)* [7460]

Kenyon T. Payne Outstanding Student Awards *(Undergraduate/Award)* [5838]

Joe Perdue Scholarships *(Undergraduate/Scholarship)* [2913]

John T. Riordan Professional Education Scholarships *(Professional development/Scholarship)* [4909]

Paul H. Rittle Sr. Professional Development Grants *(Professional development/Grant)* [4820]

Stanley M. Schoenfeld Memorial Scholarships *(Postgraduate/Fellowship)* [6673]

NASCAR/Wendell Scott Awards *(Graduate, Undergraduate/Scholarship)* [4550]

Surety Industry Scholarship Program for Minority Students *(Undergraduate/Scholarship)* [8778]

Syncrude/Athabasca University Aboriginal Scholarships *(All/Scholarship)* [8791]

Tag and Label Manufacturers Institute Scholarships - Four-Year Colleges *(Undergraduate/Scholarship)* [8793]

Tribal Business Management Program Scholarships (TBM) *(Undergraduate/Scholarship)* [2664]

Wells Fargo American Indian Scholarships - Graduate *(Graduate/Scholarship)* [828]

Manufacturing

Malcolm Baldridge Scholarships *(Undergraduate/Scholarship)* [4411]

Walt Bartram Memorial Education Award, Region 12 and Chapter 119 *(Undergraduate/Scholarship)* [8369]

Boeing Company Scholarships *(Undergraduate/Scholarship)* [8112]

Caterpillar Scholars Award *(Undergraduate/Scholarship)* [8370]

Arthur and Gladys Cervenka Scholarships *(Undergraduate/Scholarship)* [8371]

Chapter 6 Fairfield County Scholarships *(Undergraduate/Scholarship)* [8379]

Chapter 17 - St. Louis Scholarships *(Undergraduate/Scholarship)* [8372]

Chapter 23 - Quad Cities Iowa/Illinois Scholarships *(Undergraduate/Scholarship)* [8374]

Chapter 31 - Peoria Endowed Scholarships *(Undergraduate/Scholarship)* [8375]

Chapter 52 - Wichita Scholarships *(Graduate, Undergraduate/Scholarship)* [8377]

Chapter 56 - Fort Wayne Scholarships *(Graduate, Undergraduate/Scholarship)* [8378]

Chapter 67 - Phoenix Scholarships *(Undergraduate/Scholarship)* [8380]

Chapter 93 - Albuquerque Scholarships *(Undergraduate/Scholarship)* [8381]

Chapter 198 - Downriver Detroit Scholarships *(Graduate, Undergraduate/Scholarship)* [8373]

Chapter 311 - Tri City Scholarships *(Undergraduate/Scholarship)* [8376]

Chapter One - Detroit Founding Chapter Scholarships *(Graduate, Undergraduate/Scholarship)* [8382]

Dake Community Manufacturing Scholarships *(Undergraduate/Scholarship)* [4210]

Chapter 116 - Kalamazoo - Roscoe Douglas Scholarships *(Undergraduate/Scholarship)* [8383]

Future Leaders of Manufacturing Scholarships *(Graduate, Undergraduate/Scholarship)* [8385]

Connie and Robert T. Gunter Scholarships *(Undergraduate/Scholarship)* [8386]

Clinton J. Helton Manufacturing Scholarships *(Undergraduate/Scholarship)* [8387]

HSF/General Motors Scholarship Program *(Undergraduate/Scholarship)* [4574]

Lucile B. Kaufman Women's Scholarships *(Undergraduate/Scholarship)* [8388]

E. Wayne Kay Co-op Scholarships *(Undergraduate/Scholarship)* [8389]

E. Wayne Kay Community College Scholarships *(Undergraduate/Scholarship)* [8390]

E. Wayne Kay High School Scholarships *(Undergraduate/Scholarship)* [8391]

Giuliano Mazzetti Scholarships *(Undergraduate/Scholarship)* [8392]

Chapter 63 - Portland James E. Morrow Scholarships *(Graduate, Undergraduate/Scholarship)* [8393]

Clarence and Josephine Myers Scholarships *(Graduate, Undergraduate/Scholarship)* [8394]

North Central, Region 9 Scholarships *(Undergraduate/Scholarship)* [8395]

Nuts, Bolts and Thingamajigs Scholarships *(Undergraduate, Vocational/Occupational/Scholarship)* [6842]

Edward S. Roth Manufacturing Engineering Scholarships *(Graduate, Undergraduate/Scholarship)* [8396]

Prof. George Schneider, Jr. Manufacturing Technology Education Scholarships *(Undergraduate/Scholarship)* [8397]

SME Directors Scholarships *(Undergraduate/Scholarship)* [8398]

SME Education Foundation Family Scholarships *(Undergraduate/Scholarship)* [8399]

Chapter 63 - Portland Uncle Bud Smith Scholarships *(Graduate, Undergraduate/Scholarship)* [8400]

Chapter 4 - Lawrence A. Wacker Memorial Awards *(Undergraduate/Scholarship)* [8402]

Myrtle and Earl Walker Scholarships *(Undergraduate/Scholarship)* [8403]

Allen and Loureena Weber Scholarships *(Undergraduate/Scholarship)* [8404]

Albert E. Wischmeyer Memorial Scholarships *(Undergraduate/Scholarship)* [8406]

Women of Today's Manufacturing Scholarships *(Undergraduate/Scholarship)* [3175]

Marine biology (See Biology, Marine)

Marine engineering (See Engineering, Marine)

Maritime studies

LaRue A. Ditmore Music Scholarships *(Undergraduate/Scholarship)* [9706]

Dr. Nancy Foster Scholarships *(Doctorate, Graduate/Scholarship)* [3873]

Lily H. Gridley Memorial Scholarships *(Undergraduate/Scholarship)* [9707]

Norm Manly - YMTA Maritime Educational Scholarships *(Undergraduate/Scholarship)* [9795]

Corporal Joseph Martinez U.S. Army Memorial Scholarships *(Undergraduate/Scholarship)* [7505]

Ethyl and Armin Wiebke Memorial Scholarships *(Undergraduate/Scholarship)* [9708]

WMA Memorial Scholarships *(Undergraduate/Scholarship)* [9709]

Marketing and distribution

All-American Vector Marketing Scholarship Program *(Undergraduate/Scholarship)* [9416]

American Marketing Association-Connecticut Chapter, Anna C. Klune Memorial Scholarships *(Graduate/Scholarship)* [4408]

Anchor Plastics Scholarships *(Graduate, Undergraduate/Scholarship)* [7264]

APS/Maricopa County Community Colleges Scholarships *(Undergraduate/Scholarship)* [7333]

Mike Buoncristiano Memorial Scholarship Fund *(Undergraduate/Scholarship)* [3445]

Chrysler Foundation Scholarship Awards *(Undergraduate/Scholarship)* [4546]

Mark Duda Scholarship Fund *(Graduate, Undergraduate/Scholarship)* [3446]

Harold E. Eisenberg Foundation Scholarships *(Professional development/Scholarship)* [4906]

Enterprise Rent-A-Car Scholarships *(Graduate, Undergraduate/Scholarship)* [7265]

Lee Epstein Scholarship Fund *(Graduate, Undergraduate/Scholarship)* [3447]

Federated Insurance Scholarships *(Graduate, Undergraduate/Scholarship)* [7266]

Dave Florence Scholarship Fund *(Undergraduate/Scholarship)* [3448]

Richard A. Hammill Scholarship Fund *(Undergraduate/Scholarship)* [918]

William H. Harris Memorial Scholarships *(Graduate, Undergraduate/Scholarship)* [7267]

Hilb, Rogal and Hobbs Scholarships *(Undergraduate/Scholarship)* [9449]

HSBC-North America Scholarship Program *(Undergraduate/Scholarship)* [4571]

HSF/Wal-Mart Stores Inc. Scholarship Program *(Graduate, Undergraduate/Scholarship)* [4577]

IBEA Undergraduate Scholarships *(Undergraduate/Scholarship)* [4683]

Debbie Khalil Memorial Scholarships *(Graduate, Undergraduate/Scholarship)* [7268]

Don Kuhn Memorial Scholarship Fund *(Graduate/Scholarship)* [3449]

The Lagrant Foundation - Graduate Students Scholarships *(Graduate/Scholarship)* [5315]

The Lagrant Foundation - Undergraduate Students Scholarships *(Undergraduate/Scholarship)* [5316]

Robert J. Lavidge Nonprofit Marketing Research Scholarships *(Professional development/Scholarship)* [919]

Reba Malone Scholarships *(Graduate, Undergraduate/Scholarship)* [1055]

Marathon Oil Corporation College Scholarship Program *(Graduate, Undergraduate/Scholarship)* [4578]

MillerCoors National Scholarships *(Undergraduate/Scholarship)* [48]

MPower Scholarships *(Graduate, Undergraduate/Scholarship)* [7269]

New York Women in Communications, Inc. Foundation Scholarships *(Graduate, Undergraduate/Scholarship)* [6690]

Northwestern Mutual Financial Network Scholarships *(Graduate, Undergraduate/Scholarship)* [7270]

Office Depot Scholarships *(Undergraduate/Scholarship)* [4549]

Sanky Perlowin Memorial Scholarships *(Undergraduate/Scholarship)* [3453]

Phi Sigma Epsilon Past National President Scholarships *(Graduate, Undergraduate/Scholarship)* [7271]

John T. Riordan Professional Education Scholarships *(Professional development/Scholarship)* [4909]

Jim Springer Memorial Scholarships *(Undergraduate/Scholarship)* [2959]

Tag and Label Manufacturers Institute Scholarships - Four-Year Colleges *(Undergraduate/Scholarship)* [8793]

Valpak Scholarships *(Graduate, Undergraduate/Scholarship)* [7272]

Valuing Diversity PhD Scholarships *(Doctorate/Scholarship)* [920]

Vector Marketing Canadian Scholarship Awards *(Undergraduate/Scholarship)* [9417]

Vector Marketing Scholarships *(Graduate, Undergraduate/Scholarship)* [7273]

Whan Memorial Scholarships *(Graduate, Undergraduate/Scholarship)* [7274]

Glenn Wilson Broadcast Journalism Scholarships *(Undergraduate/Scholarship)* [7124]

Willa Yeck Memorial Scholarship Fund *(Undergraduate/Scholarship)* [3450]

Lorraine Zitone Memorial Scholarship Fund *(Undergraduate/Scholarship)* [3451]

Materials handling

IFMA Foundation Certificate Program Scholarships *(Graduate/Scholarship)* [4926]

IFMA Foundation Graduate/Undergraduate Scholarships *(Graduate, Undergraduate/Scholarship)* [4927]

Materials research/science

ACI Scholarships *(Graduate/Scholarship)* [631]

AESF Foundation Scholarships *(Graduate, Undergraduate/Scholarship)* [6127]

ASNT Fellowship Awards *(Graduate/Fellowship)* [1316]

DEPS Graduate Scholarship Program *(Graduate/Scholarship)* [3455]

DOE Computational Science Graduate Fellowships (DOE CSGF) *(Doctorate, Graduate/Fellowship)* [5306]

ACI W.R. Grace Scholarships *(Graduate/Scholarship)* [634]

Electronics Division Lewis C. Hoffman Scholarships *(Undergraduate/Scholarship)* [606]

Katharine & Bryant Mather Scholarships *(Graduate/Scholarship)* [635]

Kumar Mehta Scholarships *(Graduate/Scholarship)* [636]

NPSC Fellowships *(Graduate/Fellowship)* [6440]

Robert B. Oliver ASNT Scholarships *(Undergraduate/Scholarship)* [1317]

ACI Bertold E. Weinberg Scholarships *(Graduate/Scholarship)* [638]

Xerox Technical Minority Scholarships *(Graduate, Undergraduate/Scholarship)* [9787]

Mathematics and mathematical sciences

AAPM Summer Undergraduate Fellowships *(Undergraduate/Fellowship)* [530]

AeA Scholarships *(Undergraduate/Scholarship)* [7904]

AFCEA Math and Science Teachers Scholarships *(Graduate, Undergraduate/Scholarship)* [1553]

AFCEA Scholarship for Working Professionals *(Graduate/Scholarship)* [1554]

African American Network - Carolinas Scholarship Fund *(Undergraduate/Scholarship)* [3882]

AHETEMS General Scholarships *(Graduate, Undergraduate/Scholarship)* [55]

AHETEMS Professional Scholarships *(Graduate/Scholarship)* [56]

Air Force Association Excellence Scholarships *(Graduate, Master's, Undergraduate/Scholarship)* [88]

Alaska Aerospace Development Corporation Scholarships *(Undergraduate/Scholarship)* [9130]

AMS Centennial Fellowships *(Postdoctorate/Fellowship)* [2738]

A.T. Anderson Memorial Scholarships *(Graduate, Undergraduate/Scholarship)* [834]

Armed Forces Communications and Electronics Association Fellowships *(Doctorate, Graduate/Fellowship)* [1555]

Astronaut Scholarship Foundation Scholarships *(Undergraduate/Scholarship)* [1916]

Delores A. Auzenne Fellowships *(Postgraduate/Fellowship)* [3818]

Avista Corporation Minds in Motion Scholarships *(Undergraduate/Scholarship)* [5412]

B&W Y-12 Scholarship Fund *(Undergraduate/Scholarship)* [3565]

Bill & Nell Biggs Scholarships *(Undergraduate/Scholarship)* [9140]

Sam L. Booke, Sr. Scholarships *(Undergraduate/Scholarship)* [9626]

William E. "Buck" Bragunier Scholarships *(Undergraduate/Scholarship)* [1556]

Lt. General Douglas D. Buchholz Memorial Scholarships *(Undergraduate/Scholarship)* [1557]

Burroughs Wellcome Fund Career Awards at the Scientific Interface *(Doctorate, Postdoctorate/Fellowship)* [2211]

Burroughs Wellcome Fund Collaborative Research Travel Grants *(Doctorate/Grant)* [2212]

Wes Burton Memorial Scholarships *(Undergraduate/Scholarship)* [9628]

Career Awards for Science and Mathematics Teachers *(Professional development/Award)* [2213]

CERT College Scholarships *(Graduate, Undergraduate/Scholarship)* [3272]

The Churchill Scholarships *(Postgraduate/Scholarship)* [2789]

City of Toronto Graduate Scholarships for Women in Mathematics *(Graduate/Scholarship)* [9325]

Mike Crapo Math and Science Scholarship Fund *(Undergraduate/Scholarship)* [4668]

CRM-ISM Postdoctoral Fellowships *(Postdoctorate/Fellowship)* [2734]

Disabled War Veterans Scholarships *(Undergraduate/Scholarship)* [1559]

DOE Computational Science Graduate Fellowships (DOE CSGF) *(Doctorate, Graduate/Fellowship)* [5306]

EAPSI Fellowships *(Doctorate, Graduate/Fellowship)* [6467]

Emerging Teacher-Leaders in Elementary School Mathematics Grants for Grades K-5 Teachers *(Professional development/Grant)* [6221]

Kevin Ernst Memorial Scholarship Fund *(Undergraduate/Scholarship)* [4212]

Fields Research Immersion Fellowships *(Postdoctorate/Fellowship)* [3744]

Herb and Anne Fincher Memorial Scholarships *(Undergraduate/Scholarship)* [3057]

Reuben H. Fleet Memorial Scholarships *(Undergraduate/Scholarship)* [7929]

Frank Fong Scholarships *(Undergraduate/Scholarship)* [8290]

The Gates Millennium Scholars *(Undergraduate/Scholarship)* [4569]

Dr. Virginia Gilbert Memorial Scholarships *(Undergraduate/Scholarship)* [7492]

Margaret S. Gilbert Scholarship Fund *(Undergraduate/Scholarship)* [8669]

Glendale Latino Association Scholarships *(High School, Undergraduate/Scholarship)* [4161]

Golden Key Math Scholarships *(Undergraduate/Scholarship)* [4177]

Barry M. Goldwater Scholarships *(Undergraduate/Scholarship)* [9357]

GREAT MINDS Collegiate Scholarship Program *(Undergraduate/Scholarship)* [340]

Great Minds in STEM Scholarships *(Graduate, Undergraduate/Scholarship)* [4331]

Jimmy Guild Memorial Scholarships *(Undergraduate/Scholarship)* [5431]

Claude B. Hart Memorial Scholarships *(Undergraduate/Scholarship)* [9641]

Hilb, Rogal and Hobbs Scholarships *(Undergraduate/Scholarship)* [9449]

The Homeland Security Undergraduate Scholarships *(Undergraduate/Scholarship)* [9039]

Jane Hood Memorial Fund *(Undergraduate/Scholarship)* [3776]

ISM Doctoral Fellowships *(Doctorate/Fellowship)* [4775]

ISM Scholarships for Graduate Studies *(Graduate/Scholarship)* [4776]

Dr. Bill Johnson Scholarships *(Undergraduate/Scholarship)* [8116]

Edgar Kerstan Memorial Scholarships *(Undergraduate/Scholarship)* [5771]

Robert C. and Judith L. Knapp Scholarships *(Graduate, Undergraduate/Scholarship)* [3867]

Lakselaget Foundation Scholarships *(Graduate, Undergraduate/Scholarship)* [5320]

Lewis-Clark State College Presidential Technical Out-of-State Scholarships *(Undergraduate/Scholarship)* [5447]

Carie and George Lyter Scholarship Fund *(Undergraduate/Scholarship)* [3951]

MAES Founders Scholarships *(Graduate, Undergraduate/Scholarship)* [5798]

MAES General Scholarships *(Graduate, Undergraduate/Scholarship)* [5799]

MAES Graduate Scholarships *(Graduate/Scholarship)* [5800]

MAES Padrino/Madrina Scholarships *(Graduate, Undergraduate/Scholarship)* [5801]

MAES Pipeline Scholarships *(Graduate, Undergraduate/Scholarship)* [5802]

MAES Presidential Scholarships *(Graduate, Undergraduate/Scholarship)* [5803]

Lockheed Martin Graduate Scholarships *(Graduate/Scholarship)* [1560]

Lockheed Martin IT Scholarships *(Undergraduate/Scholarship)* [1561]

Mensa Canada General Scholarships *(Undergraduate/Scholarship)* [5772]

Mentoring Travel Grants for Women *(Postdoctorate/Scholarship)* [1907]

MESBEC Scholarships *(Undergraduate/Scholarship)* [2662]

Microsoft Research Graduate Women's Scholarships *(Graduate/Scholarship)* [5844]

Microsoft Research PhD Fellowships *(Doctorate/Fellowship)* [5845]

National Co-op Scholarship Program *(Undergraduate/Scholarship)* [9750]

National GEM Consortium - PhD Science Fellowships *(Doctorate, Graduate/Fellowship)* [6307]

Robert Noyce Scholarship Program *(Undergraduate/Scholarship)* [7160]

Noyce Scholarships for Secondary Math and Science Education *(Undergraduate/Scholarship)* [4751]

Ohio Space Grant Consortium Graduate Fellowships *(Doctorate, Graduate/Fellowship)* [6864]

Ohio Space Grant Consortium Special Minority Fellowships *(Doctorate, Graduate/Fellowship)* [6865]

AFCEA General Emmett Paige Scholarships *(Undergraduate/Scholarship)* [1562]

PIMS Postdoctoral Fellowships *(Doctorate/Fellowship)* [7029]

Postdoctoral Fellowships at the Fields Institute *(Postdoctorate/Fellowship)* [3745]

Josef Princ Memorial Scholarships *(Undergraduate/Scholarship)* [7517]

Prospective Secondary Teacher Course Work Scholarships *(Postgraduate/Scholarship)* [6222]

Purdue Krannert School of Management SHPE Scholarships *(Undergraduate, Master's/Scholarship)* [8130]

Joseph Wood Rogers Memorial Scholarships *(Undergraduate/Scholarship)* [8122]

School In-Service Training Grants for Grades 6-8 Teachers *(High School/Grant)* [6223]

School In-Service Training Grants for Grades 9-12 Teachers *(High School/Grant)* [6224]

School In-Service Training Grants for Grades K-5 Teachers *(High School/Grant)* [6225]

SDF Community College Transfer Scholarships for Math and Science *(Undergraduate/Scholarship)* [7964]

Everett Oscar Shimp Memorial Scholarships *(Undergraduate/Scholarship)* [7113]

SHPE Foundation Dissertation Scholarships *(Doctorate/Scholarship)* [8131]

SHPE Foundation General Scholarships *(High School, Undergraduate, Graduate/Scholarship)* [8132]

SHPE Foundation Northrop Grumman Scholarships *(Undergraduate/Scholarship)* [8133]

SHPE Foundation Professional Scholarships *(Master's, Doctorate/Scholarship)* [8134]

Ralph W. Shrader Diversity Scholarships *(Graduate/Scholarship)* [1563]

Julia Viola Simms Science Scholarships *(Postgraduate/Scholarship)* [2128]

Sloan Research Fellowships *(Doctorate/Fellowship)* [8235]

SMART Scholarships *(Graduate, Undergraduate/Scholarship)* [8056]

SREB-State Doctoral Scholarships *(Doctorate, Graduate/Scholarship)* [8585]

Margaret Svec Scholarships *(Undergraduate/Scholarship)* [8127]

Anil and Neema Thakrar Family Fund *(Undergraduate/Scholarship)* [3963]

Travel Grants for Women Researchers *(Postdoctorate/Scholarship)* [1908]

VEF Fellowship Program *(Doctorate, Master's/Fellowship)* [9424]

VEF Visiting Scholars Program *(Doctorate/Scholarship)* [9425]

Graduate Fellowship Program - Peter Verhofstadt Fellowships (GFP) *(Graduate/Fellowship)* [8084]

Veterans of Enduring Freedom (Afghanistan) and Iraqi Freedom Scholarships *(Undergraduate/Scholarship)* [1565]

AFCEA General John A. Wickham Scholarships *(Undergraduate/Scholarship)* [1566]

Marine Corps Sgt. Jeannette L. Winters Memorial Scholarships *(Undergraduate/Scholarship)* [1567]

Women In Defense HORIZONS Scholarships *(Graduate, Undergraduate/Scholarship)* [9696]

Women in Science and Technology Scholarships *(Doctorate, Graduate, Master's, Undergraduate/Scholarship)* [9442]

Woodcock Family Education Scholarship Program *(Undergraduate/Scholarship)* [284]

Frank and Betty Woodhams Memorial Scholarships *(Undergraduate/Scholarship)* [5773]

Xavier University Departmental Scholarships *(Undergraduate/Scholarship)* [9780]

Leo Zupin Memorial Scholarship Fund *(Undergraduate, Vocational/Occupational/Scholarship)* [4253]

Mechanics and repairs

Caterpillar Scholarships in Diesel Mechanics *(Undergraduate/Scholarship)* [5417]

ISOPE Offshore Mechanics Scholarships for Outstanding Students *(Graduate/Scholarship)* [4999]

Media arts

AAAS Mass Media Science and Engineering Fellowships *(Graduate, Postgraduate, Undergraduate/Fellowship)* [430]

Aboriginal Traditional Arts Project Grants *(Professional development/Grant)* [215]

Academy of Motion Picture Arts and Sciences Student Academy Awards (Undergraduate/Award) [33]

Anne Friedberg Innovative Scholarship Awards (Professional development/Scholarship) [8309]

Association for Women in Sports Media Internship Program (Graduate, Undergraduate/Internship) [1910]

Dalton Camp Awards (All/Prize) [4012]

Canadian Picture Pioneers Scholarships (Undergraduate/Scholarship) [2583]

UFVA Carole Fielding Student Grants (Graduate, Undergraduate/Grant) [9202]

HAESF Professional Internship Program (Doctorate/Internship) [4641]

HBO Point Scholarships (Graduate, Undergraduate/Scholarship) [7362]

HSF/Nissan Community College Transfer Scholarship Program (Undergraduate/Scholarship) [4576]

Clay Huntington Sports Communications Scholarships (Undergraduate/Scholarship) [4338]

Harriet Irsay Scholarships (Graduate, Undergraduate/Scholarship) [869]

McNamara Family Creative Arts Project Grants (Graduate, Undergraduate/Grant) [4579]

New York Women in Communications, Inc. Foundation Scholarships (Graduate, Undergraduate/Scholarship) [6690]

NHFA Scholarships (Graduate/Scholarship) [6340]

Fred Rogers Memorial Scholarships (Graduate, Undergraduate/Scholarship) [35]

Barbara Sanchez Scholarships (Undergraduate/Scholarship) [8348]

SCMS Dissertation Awards (Postdoctorate/Award) [8311]

SCMS Student Writing Awards (Graduate/Award) [8312]

StraightForward Media's Media and Communications Scholarships (Undergraduate/Scholarship) [8762]

Tribeca Film Institute Film and Video Fellowships (Professional development/Fellowship) [8958]

Tribeca Film Institute Media Arts Fellowships in Mexico (Professional development/Fellowship) [8959]

Tribeca Film Institute New Media Fellowships (Professional development/Fellowship) [8960]

Sandy Ulm Scholarships (Undergraduate/Scholarship) [3816]

Visual Arts and New Media Project Grants (Professional development/Grant) [223]

Medical assisting

Northampton County Medical Society Alliance Scholarships (Undergraduate/Scholarship) [6794]

TMA Research Fellowships (Graduate, Postdoctorate/Grant) [5967]

Maxine Williams Scholarships (Postdoctorate/Scholarship) [513]

Medical laboratory technology

CSMLS Student Scholarship Awards (Postgraduate/Scholarship) [2609]

NAAF Aboriginal Health Careers Bursary and Scholarships (Graduate, Undergraduate/Scholarship) [5992]

Medical library science (See Library and archival sciences)

Medical research (See also Biomedical research)

AHNS-ACS Career Development Awards (Professional development/Grant) [784]

AHNS Pilot Research Grants (Professional development/Grant) [785]

AHNS Young Investigator Awards (Professional development/Grant) [786]

American Cancer Society - Research Scholar Grants (Doctorate, Professional development/Grant) [595]

American Liver Foundation Liver Scholar Awards (Doctorate/Award) [903]

American Liver Foundation Special Research Initiatives (Doctorate/Award) [904]

Ballantyne Resident Research Grants (Professional development/Grant) [787]

CAHR Master's Level Scholarships (Master's/Scholarship) [2384]

CAS/GE Healthcare Canada Inc. Research Awards (Professional development/Award) [2358]

CSCI Distinguished Scientist Lectures and Awards (Doctorate/Award) [2600]

Cystic Fibrosis Cholestatic Liver Disease Liver Scholarships (Doctorate/Award) [905]

Deafness Research Foundation Research Grants (Doctorate/Grant) [3350]

FXRFC Medical Research Postdoctoral Fellowships (Postdoctorate/Fellowship) [3994]

ITNS Research Grants (Professional development/Grant) [5021]

Robert Wood Johnson Clinical Scholarships (Graduate/Scholarship) [5165]

Mentored Research Scholar Grant in Applied and Clinical Research (Doctorate, Professional development/Grant) [598]

NFID Advanced Vaccinology Course Travel Grants (Postdoctorate/Grant) [6301]

Postdoctoral Research Fellowships (Postdoctorate/Award) [906]

Damon Runyon Cancer Research Foundation Fellowships (Doctorate, Graduate, Postdoctorate/Fellowship) [7831]

Damon Runyon Clinical Investigator Awards (Doctorate, Graduate, Postdoctorate/Fellowship) [7832]

Damon Runyon-Rachleff Innovation Awards (Postdoctorate/Fellowship) [7833]

SSF Research Grants (Professional development/Grant) [8226]

SSF Student Fellowships (Graduate, Undergraduate/Fellowship) [8227]

Surgeon Scientist Career Development Awards (Professional development/Grant) [788]

Tarrson Regeneration Scholarships (Postdoctorate/Scholarship) [398]

E.D. Thomas Post Doctoral Fellowships (Postdoctorate/Fellowship) [4014]

Toronto Rehab Scholarships in Rehabilitation-Related Research (Graduate/Scholarship) [8918]

Medical technology

Chinese American Medical Society Summer Research Fellowships Program (Undergraduate/Fellowship) [2766]

Margaret Dowell-Gravatt, M.D. Scholarships (Undergraduate/Scholarship) [2059]

Illinois Student Assistance Commission Medical Student Scholarships (Undergraduate/Scholarship) [4697]

Esther Lim Memorial Scholarships (Undergraduate/Scholarship) [2767]

Ruth Liu Memorial Scholarships (Undergraduate/Scholarship) [2768]

SPSmedical CS Scholarships (Professional development/Scholarship) [4871]

Medicine (See also specific diseases)

AAMA Houston Chapter - Medical Student Scholarships (Professional development/Scholarship) [1494]

AAUW Legal Advocacy Fund Selected Professions Fellowships (Doctorate, Graduate/Fellowship) [18]

Dr. Anderson Abbott Awards (Undergraduate/Scholarship) [9320]

Accenture American Indian Scholarship Program (Graduate, Undergraduate/Scholarship) [825]

Advanced Cardiovascular Surgery Fellowships (Graduate, Postdoctorate/Fellowship) [561]

AFPPA Student Scholarships (Undergraduate/Scholarship) [1773]

AGBU Scholarships (Graduate/Loan) [1573]

Henry and Maria Ahrens Scholarships (Graduate/Scholarship) [4255]

Allegheny County Medical Society Medical Student Scholarships (ACMS) (Undergraduate/Scholarship) [3983]

Alliance Medical Education Scholarship Fund (AMES) (Undergraduate/Scholarship) [3984]

American Association of University Women Selected Professions Fellowships (Professional development/Fellowship) [13]

American Parkinson Disease Association Medical Students Summer Fellowships (Doctorate/Fellowship) [978]

A.T. Anderson Memorial Scholarships (Graduate, Undergraduate/Scholarship) [834]

Armenian American Medical Association Scholarships (Undergraduate/Scholarship) [1581]

ASHA Scholarships (Graduate, Undergraduate/Scholarship) [1175]

ASHA Student Research Grants (Graduate, Undergraduate/Scholarship) [1176]

Dr. Noyes L. Avery, Jr. & Ann E. Avery Scholarships (Undergraduate/Scholarship) [4271]

Benign Essential Blepharospasm Research Foundation Research Grants (Doctorate, Postdoctorate/Grant) [2057]

Linn Benton Scholarships (Undergraduate/Scholarship) [6952]

Eleanor McWilliams Burke Fund (Undergraduate/Scholarship) [3762]

Joseph R. Calder, Jr., MD Scholarship Fund (Undergraduate/Scholarship) [3763]

Dr. John Big Canoe Memorial Scholarships (Undergraduate/Scholarship) [2523]

Career Mobility Scholarship Awards (Doctorate, Undergraduate/Scholarship) [27]

CBC Spouses Cheerios Brand Health Initiative Scholarships (Undergraduate/Scholarship) [3215]

CCFA Career Development Awards (Doctorate, Graduate/Grant) [3292]

CCFA Research Fellowship Awards (Doctorate, Graduate/Fellowship) [3293]

CCFA Student Research Fellowship Awards (Graduate, Undergraduate/Grant) [3294]

CDC Preventive Medicine Residency and Fellowships (Professional development/Fellowship) [2712]

Edward D. Churchill Research Scholarships (Professional development/Scholarship) [562]

Clinical Laboratory Management Association High School Senior Scholarships (High School/Scholarship) [2907]

Clinical Laboratory Management Association Undergraduate Scholarships (Undergraduate/Scholarship) [2908]

Crohn's and Colitis Foundation of America Senior Research Awards (Doctorate, Graduate/Grant) [3295]

DAAD Study Scholarship Awards (Graduate/Scholarship) [4116]

D&A Florida Scholarships (Undergraduate/Scholarship) [8597]

Steve Dearduff Scholarships (Graduate, Undergraduate/Scholarship) [3075]

Margaret Dowell-Gravatt, M.D. Scholarships (Undergraduate/Scholarship) [2059]

Family and Children's Services of Lebanon County Fund (Undergraduate/Scholarship) [3942]

Dr. Joseph J. Fitzsimmons Scholarships (Doctorate/Scholarship) [9055]

Doris W. Frey Memorial Scholarships (Undergraduate/Scholarship) [8603]

William and Francis Fry Honorary Fellowships for Contributions to Therapeutic Ultrasound (Professional development/Fellowship) [5003]

William R. Goldfarb Memorial Scholarships (Undergraduate/Scholarship) [1085]

Scott A. Gunder, MD, DCMS Presidential Scholarships (Undergraduate/Scholarship) [3985]

HAESF Professional Internship Program (Doctorate/Internship) [4641]

Hall County Medical Society Scholarships (Graduate/Scholarship) [4260]

Lillie Hope-McGarvey Health Scholarship Awards (Undergraduate, Vocational/Occupational, Graduate, Master's/Scholarship) [289]

Dr. James L. Hutchinson and Evelyn Ribbs Hutchinson Medical School Scholarship Fund (Undergraduate/Scholarship) [8203]

ISTU Student Prize (All/Prize) [5004]

Jewish Federation Academic Scholarships (Graduate, Undergraduate/Scholarship) [5161]

Magoichi & Shizuko Kato Memorial Scholarships (Graduate/Scholarship) [5143]

Jason Lang Scholarships (Undergraduate/Scholarship) [252]

Lazarian Graduate Scholarships (Graduate/Scholarship) [1578]

Rebecca Lee, M.D. Scholarships (Undergraduate/Scholarship) [1720]

S. Evelyn Lewis Memorial Scholarships in Medical Health Sciences (Graduate, Undergraduate/Scholarship) [9805]

Dolores Zohrab Liebmann Fund - Graduate School Fellowships (Graduate/Fellowship) [5488]

Lycoming County Medical Society Scholarships (LCMS) (Undergraduate/Scholarship) [3986]

Irene and Daisy MacGregor Memorial Scholarships (Graduate/Scholarship) [4448]

Dr. Edward May Magruder Medical Scholarships (Undergraduate/Scholarship) [609]

Dr. Frank and Florence Marino Scholarships (Undergraduate/Scholarship) [4451]

Mission Bay Hospital Auxiliary Scholarships (Undergraduate/Scholarship) [7947]

Montgomery County Medical Society Scholarships (MCMS) (Undergraduate/Scholarship) [3987]

NAAF Aboriginal Health Careers Bursary and Scholarships (Graduate, Undergraduate/Scholarship) [5992]

National Ataxia Foundation Research Fellowships (Professional development/Fellowship) [6136]

National Ataxia Foundation Research Grants (Professional development/Fellowship) [6137]

National Biosafety and Biocontainment Training Program Fellowships (Graduate/Fellowship) [6141]

National Medical Fellowships Need-Based Scholarships (Undergraduate/Scholarship) [6403]

OPSF Scholarships (Graduate/Scholarship) [6846]

Sylvia Parkinson Scholarships (Undergraduate/Scholarship) [4453]

PKD Foundation Fellowships (Doctorate, Graduate/Fellowship) [7335]

Providence Alaska Medical Center Auxiliary Scholarships (Undergraduate/Scholarship) [9106]

Howard Brown Rickard Scholarships (Undergraduate/Scholarship) [6282]

Paul S. Robinson Scholarships (Undergraduate/Scholarship) [8318]

Alice W. Rooke Scholarships (Undergraduate/Scholarship) [4459]

RSDSA Research Grants (Postdoctorate, Professional development/Grant) [7719]

Scholarships for Emigres in the Health Sciences (Undergraduate/Scholarship) [5157]

Jeptha Wade Schureman Scholarship Program (Undergraduate/Scholarship) [3205]

SCLMA Scholarships (Graduate, Undergraduate/Scholarship) [8581]

John M. and Mary A. Shanley Memorial Scholarships (Undergraduate/Scholarship) [8622]

Myrtle Siegfried, MD and Michael Vigilante, MD Scholarships (Undergraduate/Scholarship) [3988]

Julia Viola Simms Science Scholarships (Postgraduate/Scholarship) [2128]

Nadine Barrie Smith Student Awards (All/Award) [5005]

Dr. William E. & Norma Sprague Scholarships (Undergraduate/Scholarship) [4301]

Summer Intern Scholarships in Cardiothoracic Surgery (Undergraduate/Scholarship) [563]

Marvin H. and Kathleen G. Teget Leadership Scholarships (Undergraduate/Scholarship) [8768]

Dr. Peter A. Theodos Memorial Graduate Scholarships (Graduate/Scholarship) [4519]

Thompson Scholarships for Women in Safety (Graduate/Scholarship) [1355]

Sam Tughan Scholarships (Undergraduate/Scholarship) [2593]

VEF Fellowship Program (Doctorate, Master's/Fellowship) [9424]

VEF Visiting Scholars Program (Doctorate/Scholarship) [9425]

The Sibyl Jennings Vorheis Memorial Undergraduate Scholarships (Undergraduate/Scholarship) [3926]

Washington University Law School Olin Fellowships for Women (Graduate/Fellowship) [9533]

Women in Science and Technology Scholarships (Doctorate, Graduate, Master's, Undergraduate/Scholarship) [9442]

Worcester District Medical Society Scholarship Fund (Undergraduate/Scholarship) [9746]

Medicine, Cardiology

APACVS Scholarships (Postgraduate, Professional development/Scholarship) [1841]

Canadian Association of Cardiac Rehabilitation Graduate Scholarship Awards (Graduate/Scholarship) [2370]

DeBakey International Society Fellowship Awards (Professional development/Award) [3354]

Medicine, Chiropractic

Beatrice K. Blair Scholarships (Undergraduate/Scholarship) [2149]

F. Maynard Lipe Scholarship Awards (Postdoctorate, Postgraduate/Scholarship) [615]

Medicine, Geriatric

APDA Postdoctoral Fellowships (Professional development/Fellowship) [979]

BAGNC Predoctoral Scholarships (Doctorate, Graduate/Scholarship) [382]

Claire M. Fagin Fellowships (Doctorate/Fellowship) [383]

Hartford Geriatrics Health Outcomes Research Scholars Award Program (Professional development/Grant) [80]

HPGS/ALOH Graduate Scholarships (Graduate/Scholarship) [4485]

HPGS Undergraduate Scholarships (Undergraduate/Scholarship) [4486]

Pharmacy Faculty Fellowships in Geriatric Pharmacy/Geriatric Pharmaceutical Science (Postdoctorate/Fellowship) [763]

T. Franklin Williams Research Scholars Award Program (Professional development/Grant) [81]

Medicine, Gynecological and obstetrical

SMFM/AAOGF Scholarship Awards (Graduate/Scholarship) [8410]

Medicine, Internal

Epilepsy Foundation Research and Training Fellowships for Clinicians (Doctorate, Professional development/Grant) [3665]

Medicine, Nuclear

Paul Cole Scholarships (Undergraduate/Scholarship) [8420]

Medicine, Orthopedic

AOA Research Grants (Graduate/Grant) [63]

AOFAS Research Grants Program (Graduate/Grant) [966]

Orthopaedic Trauma Association Research Grants (Professional development/Grant) [6990]

Orthopedic Foot and Ankle Fellowships (Graduate/Fellowship) [967]

Medicine, Osteopathic

AACOM Scholar in Residence Program (Graduate, Undergraduate/Scholarship) [461]

Amgen Scholars Fellowships (Doctorate, Professional development/Fellowship) [3637]

William G. Anderson, DO, Minority Scholarships (Undergraduate/Scholarship) [969]

Humanism in Medicine Scholarships (Undergraduate/Scholarship) [8766]

Illinois Student Assistance Commission Medical Student Scholarships (Undergraduate/Scholarship) [4697]

Kansas Osteopathic Medical Service Scholarships (Graduate, Professional development/Scholarship) [5185]

McCaughan Heritage Scholarships (Undergraduate/Scholarship) [970]

NAAMA Scholarships (Undergraduate/Scholarship) [6024]

New Jersey Association of Osteopathic Physicians and Surgeons Scholarships (Undergraduate/Scholarship) [6637]

Procter and Gamble Complex PE Scholars Grant (Undergraduate/Award) [971]

Scleroderma Foundation Established Investigator Grants (Doctorate/Grant) [8058]

Scleroderma Foundation New Investigator Grants (Doctorate/Grant) [8059]

Morgan Stanley Pediatrics Fellowships (Doctorate, Postdoctorate/Fellowship) [575]

Student Osteopathic Medical Student Fellowships and Research (Undergraduate/Fellowship) [8767]

Marvin H. and Kathleen G. Teget Leadership Scholarships (Undergraduate/Scholarship) [8768]

Welch Scholars Grants (Undergraduate/Grant) [972]

Medicine, Pediatric

American Pediatric Surgical Nurses Association Educational Grants (Professional development/Grant) [984]

ASHA Scholarships (Graduate, Undergraduate/Scholarship) [1175]

ASHA Student Research Grants (Graduate, Undergraduate/Scholarship) [1176]

Daland Fellowships in Clinical Investigation (Doctorate/Fellowship) [989]

John W. Duckett Jr., AFUD Pediatric Research Scholarships (Undergraduate/Scholarship) [8432]

Gerber Fellowships in Pediatric Nutrition (Undergraduate/Fellowship) [6401]

National Association of Pediatric Nurse Practitioners McNeil Rural and Underserved Scholarships (Graduate/Scholarship) [6107]

Lizette Peterson Homer Injury Prevention Grant Awards (Professional development, Undergraduate/Grant) [8426]

Marion and Donald Routh Student Research Grants (Undergraduate/Grant) [8427]

Society for Pediatric Urology Research Grant Program (Undergraduate/Grant) [8433]

Morgan Stanley Pediatrics Fellowships (Doctorate, Postdoctorate/Fellowship) [575]

Medicine, Sports

MSPT Sports Medicine Scholarships (Undergraduate/Scholarship) [7509]

Swede Swanson Memorial Scholarships (Undergraduate/Scholarship) [6604]

Medicine, Veterinary (See Veterinary science and medicine)

Medieval studies

Birgit Baldwin Fellowships (Graduate/Fellowship) [5752]

Fellowships in the Humanities and Social Sciences in Turkey (Postdoctorate/Fellowship) [1147]

Medieval Academy Dissertation Grants (Graduate/Grant) [5753]

Schallek Awards (Graduate/Award) [5754]

Schallek Fellowships (Graduate/Fellowship) [5755]

Meniere's disease

AOS Research Training Fellowships (Graduate/Fellowship) [974]

Mental health

ADAA Career Development Travel Awards *(Professional development/Award)* [1483]
ADAA Junior Faculty Research Grants *(Professional development/Grant)* [1484]
ASA Minority Fellowship Program *(Doctorate, Master's/Fellowship)* [1377]
Council on Social Work Education Minority Fellowship Programs *(Postdoctorate/Fellowship)* [3282]
CVS/All Kids Can Scholars Program *(Undergraduate, Vocational/Occupational/Scholarship)* [1935]
Derivative Duo Scholarships *(Undergraduate/Scholarship)* [7410]
Family and Children's Services of Lebanon County Fund *(Undergraduate/Scholarship)* [3942]
Maine Community Foundation - CWG Scholarship Fund *(Graduate/Scholarship)* [5584]
NAJA Scholarships *(Graduate/Scholarship)* [6086]
OMHF Postdoctoral Fellowships *(Postdoctorate/Fellowship)* [6895]
Don Renschler Scholarships *(Graduate/Scholarship)* [7417]
Scholarships for Lutheran College Students *(Undergraduate/Scholarship)* [2077]

Metallurgy

AIST Baltimore Chapter Scholarships *(Undergraduate/Scholarship)* [1799]
AIST Detroit Chapter Scholarships *(Undergraduate/Scholarship)* [1800]
Edward J. Dulis Scholarships *(Undergraduate/Scholarship)* [5690]
AIST Benjamin F. Fairless Scholarships, American Institute of Mining, Metallurgical and Petrolium Engineers (AIME) *(Undergraduate/Scholarship)* [1803]
Dayton E. Finnigan Scholarships *(Undergraduate/Scholarship)* [4336]
Globe-Trotters Chapter Scholarships *(Undergraduate/Scholarship)* [1805]
Northeastern Ohio Chapter Scholarships - Alfred B. Glossbrenner and John Klusch Scholarships *(Undergraduate/Scholarship)* [1806]
Nicholas J. Grant Scholarships *(Undergraduate/Scholarship)* [5691]
John M. Haniak Scholarships *(Undergraduate/Scholarship)* [5692]
H.H. Harris Foundation Scholarships *(Undergraduate/Scholarship)* [772]
AIST Willy Korf Memorial Fund *(Undergraduate/Scholarship)* [1807]
AIST Ronald E. Lincoln Memorial Scholarships *(Undergraduate/Scholarship)* [1808]
Materials Information Society National Merit Scholarships *(Undergraduate/Scholarship)* [5693]
MJSA Educational Foundation Jewelry Scholarships *(Undergraduate/Scholarship)* [7792]
Ohio Valley Chapter Scholarships *(Undergraduate/Scholarship)* [1815]
William Park Woodside Founder's Scholarships *(Undergraduate/Scholarship)* [5694]
George A. Roberts Scholarships *(Undergraduate/Scholarship)* [5695]
AIST William E. Schwabe Memorial Scholarships *(Undergraduate/Scholarship)* [1817]
Sheet Metal And Air Conditioning Contractors' National Association College of Fellows Scholarships *(Undergraduate/Scholarship)* [8101]
SME Coal and Energy Division Scholarships *(Undergraduate/Scholarship)* [8414]
SME Environmental Division Scholarships *(Undergraduate/Scholarship)* [8415]
Lucille and Charles A. Wert Scholarships *(Undergraduate/Scholarship)* [5696]

Meteorology (See also Atmospheric science)

AMS Freshman Undergraduate Scholarships *(Undergraduate/Scholarship)* [928]
AMS Industry/Government Graduate Fellowships *(Graduate/Fellowship)* [930]
AMS/Industry Minority Scholarships *(Undergraduate/Scholarship)* [931]

AMS Undergraduate Named Scholarships *(Undergraduate/Scholarship)* [932]
Roger Daley Postdoctoral Publication Awards *(Postdoctorate/Award)* [2525]
Tertia M.C. Hughes Memorial Graduate Student Prizes *(Graduate/Prize)* [2526]
Naval Weather Service Association Scholarships *(High School, Undergraduate/Scholarship)* [6583]
President's Prize *(Professional development/Prize)* [2527]
Francois J. Saucier Prize in Applied Oceanography *(Professional development/Prize)* [2528]
Dr. Andrew Thomson Prize in Applied Meteorology *(Professional development/Prize)* [2529]
CASFM-Ben Urbonas Scholarships *(Graduate/Scholarship)* [2982]

Microbiology (See also Biology)

American Society for Microbiology International Fellowships for Africa *(Postdoctorate/Fellowship)* [1295]
American Society for Microbiology International Fellowships for Asia *(Postdoctorate/Fellowship)* [1296]
American Society for Microbiology International Fellowships for Latin America and the Caribbean *(Postdoctorate/Fellowship)* [1297]
American Society for Microbiology Undergraduate Research Fellowships (URF) *(Undergraduate/Fellowship)* [1298]
ASM/CCID Program in Infectious Disease and Public Health Microbiology *(Postdoctorate/Fellowship)* [1299]
ASM Undergraduate Research Capstone Program *(Undergraduate/Fellowship)* [1300]
Margaret Dowell-Gravatt, M.D. Scholarships *(Undergraduate/Scholarship)* [2059]
UAA Kris Knudson Memorial Scholarships *(Graduate, Undergraduate/Scholarship)* [9102]
National Biosafety and Biocontainment Training Program Fellowships *(Graduate/Fellowship)* [6141]
Selman A. Waksman Endowed Scholarships in Microbial Diversity *(Undergraduate/Scholarship)* [5633]
Robert D. Watkins Graduate Research Fellowships *(Postdoctorate/Fellowship)* [1303]

Middle Eastern studies (See Near Eastern studies)

Midwifery

ACNM Foundation, Inc. Fellowships for Graduate Education *(Doctorate, Postdoctorate/Fellowship)* [617]
Basic Midwifery Student Scholarship Program *(Undergraduate/Scholarship)* [618]
Hazel Corbin/Childbirth Connection Grants for Evidence-based Midwifery Care *(Professional development/Grant)* [619]
Washington Higher Education Coordinating Board Health Professional Scholarships *(Graduate/Scholarship)* [9506]

Military science and education

Sergeant Douglas and Charlotte DeHorse Scholarships *(Graduate, Undergraduate/Scholarship)* [2661]
NMIA Scholarship Program *(Undergraduate/Scholarship)* [6415]
Reserve Officers Training Corps Scholarships (ROTC) *(Undergraduate/Scholarship)* [9368]
Colonel Nate Smith Memorial Scholarships *(Graduate, Undergraduate/Scholarship)* [5731]
Xavier University ROTC Scholarships - Army ROTC *(Undergraduate/Scholarship)* [9784]

Mineralogy

EMLF Law Student Scholarships *(Undergraduate/Scholarship)* [3643]

Ludo Frevel Crystallography Scholarships *(Graduate/Scholarship)* [4896]
Mineralogical Association of Canada Scholarships *(Doctorate, Postgraduate/Scholarship)* [5886]
SME Coal and Energy Division Scholarships *(Undergraduate/Scholarship)* [8414]
SME Environmental Division Scholarships *(Undergraduate/Scholarship)* [8415]

Mining

American Society of Mining and Reclamation Memorial Scholarships *(Undergraduate/Scholarship)* [1307]
J.P. Bickell Mining Scholarships *(Undergraduate/Scholarship)* [9322]
Joseph A. Holmes Safety Association Scholarships *(Graduate, Undergraduate/Scholarship)* [4593]
National Association of Abandoned Mine Land Programs Scholarships *(Undergraduate/Scholarship)* [6031]
SME Coal and Energy Division Scholarships *(Undergraduate/Scholarship)* [8414]
SME Environmental Division Scholarships *(Undergraduate/Scholarship)* [8415]
Women's Association of the Mining Industry of Canada Foundation National Geophysics Scholarships *(Undergraduate/Scholarship)* [9713]
Women's Association of the Mining Industry of Canada Foundation National Scholarships *(Undergraduate/Scholarship)* [9714]
Women's Association of the Mining Industry of Canada Foundation Wood Bursary Awards *(Undergraduate/Award)* [9715]

Ministry (See Religion)

Modern languages

Fellowships in the Humanities and Social Sciences in Turkey *(Postdoctorate/Fellowship)* [1147]
NEMLA Book Prize *(Professional development/Prize)* [6798]
Xavier University Departmental Scholarships *(Undergraduate/Scholarship)* [9780]

Mortuary science (See also Funeral services)

ABFSE National Scholarship Program *(Undergraduate/Scholarship)* [584]
Brenda Renee Horn Memorial Scholarship *(Undergraduate/Scholarship)* [4029]
Joseph E. Hagan Memorial Scholarships *(Undergraduate/Scholarship)* [4030]
NFDA Professional Women's Conference Scholarships *(Undergraduate/Scholarship)* [4031]

Motherhood

Childbirth Educator Program Scholarships *(All/Scholarship)* [5326]

Muscular dystrophy

Dystonia Medical Research Foundation Fellowships *(Postdoctorate/Fellowship)* [3557]
MDA Development Grants *(Doctorate/Grant)* [5952]
MDA Research Grants *(Doctorate/Grant)* [5953]
MDF Post-Doctoral Fellowships *(Postdoctorate/Fellowship)* [5969]

Museum science

Rick Chace Foundation Scholarships *(Graduate/Scholarship)* [1829]
Kodak Fellowships in Film Preservation *(Graduate/Fellowship)* [1830]
Betsy B. and Garold A. Leach Scholarships for Museum Studies *(Undergraduate/Scholarship)* [3416]
Lee Kimche McGrath Worldwide Fellowships *(Professional development/Fellowship)* [1870]
Metropolitan Museum of Art Conservation and Sci-

entific Research Fellowships (Graduate/Fellowship) [5788]

Metropolitan Museum of Art Research Scholarships in Photograph Conservation (Graduate/Scholarship) [5789]

Mary Pickford Scholarships (Graduate/Scholarship) [1831]

Smithsonian Fellowships in Museum Practice (Professional development/Fellowship) [8266]

CFI Sid Solow Scholarships (Graduate/Scholarship) [1832]

Sony Pictures Scholarships (Graduate/Scholarship) [1833]

United States Capitol Historical Society Fellowships (Graduate/Fellowship) [9037]

Universal Studios Preservation Scholarships (Graduate/Scholarship) [1834]

Music

Ed Adams Memorial Scholarships (Professional development/Scholarship) [7753]

Margaret M. Alkek Scholarships (Undergraduate/Scholarship) [3362]

Allen - Marty Allen Scholarships (High School, Undergraduate, Vocational/Occupational/Scholarship) [2934]

Martin K. Alsup Scholarships (Undergraduate/Scholarship) [7058]

American Guild of Organists, Canton Chapter Charitable Fund (Undergraduate/Scholarship) [8656]

The Anderson Group Summer Institute Scholarships (Professional development/Scholarship) [1473]

Anonymous Scholarship Fund (Graduate/Scholarship) [9547]

AOSA Research Grants (All/Grant) [959]

AOSA Research Partnership Grants (All/Grant) [960]

Louis Armstrong Scholarships (High School/Scholarship) [1206]

Artistic Scholarship Awards (Undergraduate, Vocational/Occupational/Scholarship) [2023]

Bernt Balchen, Jr. Hardingfele Scholarships (All, Professional development/Scholarship) [4393]

Cynthia and Alan Baran Fine Arts and Music Scholarships (Undergraduate/Scholarship) [3093]

Barta-Lehman Musical Scholarships (Undergraduate/Scholarship) [7910]

Willa Beach-Porter Music Scholarships (Undergraduate/Scholarship) [2721]

Norbert J. Beihoff Scholarships (Undergraduate/Scholarship) [2888]

Belmont University Commercial Music Scholarships (Undergraduate/Scholarship) [3094]

Charlotte V. Bergen Scholarships (Undergraduate/Scholarship) [1207]

Carol June Bradley Awards (All/Grant) [5955]

Erika A. and George E. Brattain Sr. Scholarship Fund (Undergraduate/Scholarship) [9548]

Ralph Burkhardt Scholarship Fund (Undergraduate/Scholarship) [9549]

Cecil E. Burney Scholarships (Undergraduate/Scholarship) [2940]

Jeffrey Carollo Music Scholarships (Undergraduate/Scholarship) [6648]

Llewellyn L. Cayvan String Instrument Scholarships (Undergraduate/Scholarship) [4275]

Cherry Lane Foundation/Music Alive! Scholarships (Undergraduate/Scholarship) [1208]

UAA Edward Rollin Clinton Memorial for Music (Undergraduate/Scholarship) [9090]

Ruth M. Cogan Scholarship Fund (Undergraduate/Scholarship) [8661]

Dennis Coleman Choral Conducting Scholarships (Undergraduate/Scholarship) [7407]

Contemporary Club Scholarships (Undergraduate/Scholarship) [7638]

Bill Cormack Scholarships (Undergraduate/Scholarship) [8865]

Fran Morgenstern Davis Scholarships (Undergraduate/Scholarship) [1209]

John Denver Music Scholarships (Undergraduate/Scholarship) [1210]

Louis Dreyfus Warner-Chappell City College Scholarships (Undergraduate/Scholarship) [1211]

ECMS Scholarships (Undergraduate/Scholarship) [3578]

Edgecliff McAuley Music Scholarships (Undergraduate/Scholarship) [9770]

Dena Epstein Awards for Archival and Library Research in American Music (All/Grant) [5956]

Alaska Community Foundation Sven E. & Lorraine Eriksson Scholarships (Undergraduate/Scholarship) [9092]

Adrienne Zoe Fedok Art and Music Scholarships (Undergraduate/Scholarship) [3943]

Charles and Margaret Foster Scholarships (Undergraduate/Scholarship) [8602]

Brandon Fradd Fellowships in Music Competition (Professional development/Fellowship) [2883]

Kevin Freeman Travel Grants (Graduate, Professional development/Grant) [5957]

William R. Gard Memorial Scholarships (Undergraduate/Scholarship) [6091]

Garikian Scholarship Fund (Undergraduate/Scholarship) [1593]

Walter Gerboth Awards (Professional development/Grant) [5958]

R.L. Gillette Scholarships (Undergraduate/Scholarship) [751]

Velma Shotwell Griffin Memorial Scholarship Fund (Undergraduate/Scholarship) [8671]

Guy D. & Mary Edith Halladay Music Scholarships (Graduate, Undergraduate/Scholarship) [4285]

Hench Post-Dissertation Fellowships (Postdoctorate/Fellowship) [419]

Indiana State Alumni Association Creative and Performing Arts Awards (Undergraduate/Scholarship) [4745]

Ruth K. Jacobs Memorial Scholarships (Graduate, Undergraduate/Scholarship) [2779]

Alvin H. Johnson AMS Dissertation Fellowships (Graduate/Fellowship) [940]

Steve Kaplan TV and Film Studies Scholarships (Professional development/Scholarship) [1212]

Gunild Keetman Scholarships (Professional development, Undergraduate/Scholarship) [6957]

Douglas Gray Kimel Scholarships (Undergraduate/Scholarship) [9644]

Leiber and Stoller Music Scholarships (Undergraduate/Scholarship) [1213]

Harold A. Levin Scholarships (Undergraduate/Scholarship) [2890]

Paul Mansur Scholarships (Undergraduate/Scholarship) [4952]

American Turkish Society Arif Mardin Music Fellowships (Professional development/Fellowship) [8976]

Howard Mayer Brown Fellowships (Graduate/Fellowship) [941]

Christopher Mesi Memorial Music Scholarships (Undergraduate/Scholarship) [2659]

Glenn Miller Scholarships (Undergraduate/Scholarship) [5880]

Muddy Waters Scholarships (Undergraduate/Scholarship) [2155]

Music Project Grants (Professional development/Grant) [221]

Albert and Alice Nacinovich Music Scholarships (Undergraduate/Scholarship) [3787]

National Association of Pastoral Musicians Academic Scholarships (Graduate, Undergraduate/Scholarship) [6102]

Northwest-Shoals Community College Fine Arts Scholarships - Music (Undergraduate/Scholarship) [6825]

NPM Program Scholarships (Undergraduate/Scholarship) [6103]

Rudy Perez Songwriting Scholarships (Undergraduate/Scholarship) [1214]

William R. Pfalzgraf Scholarships (Undergraduate/Scholarship) [7103]

Barbara Potter Scholarships (All/Scholarship) [961]

Presbyterian Association of Musicians Scholarships (All/Scholarship) [7386]

Redlands High School Terrier Band Boosters Club Scholarships (Undergraduate/Scholarship) [7700]

Redlands High School Vocal Music Boosters Scholarship Awards (Undergraduate/Scholarship) [7701]

Mark A. Reid Memorial Scholarship Grants (Under-

graduate/Scholarship) [3165]

Fred Rogers Memorial Scholarships (Graduate, Undergraduate/Scholarship) [35]

David Rose Scholarships (Undergraduate/Scholarship) [1215]

S. Byrl Ross Memorial Scholarship Fund (Undergraduate/Scholarship) [7110]

Curtis M. Saulsbury Scholarship Fund (Undergraduate/Scholarship) [3082]

UAA Brown Schoenheit Memorial Scholarships (Undergraduate/Scholarship) [9109]

Shields-Gillespie Scholarships (All, Professional development/Scholarship) [962]

Robert W. and Bernice Ingalls Staton Scholarships (Undergraduate/Scholarship) [9314]

Joseph L. and Vivian E. Steele Music Scholarship Fund (Undergraduate/Scholarship) [3962]

Study Scholarships for Artists or Musicians (Graduate/Scholarship) [4123]

Texas Music Educators Association Past-Presidents Memorial Scholarships (Undergraduate/Scholarship) [8866]

Johnny Trombly Scholarships (Undergraduate/Scholarship) [5919]

Barry Tuckwell Scholarships (All/Scholarship) [4953]

University of Wisconsin-Madison Music Scholarships (Undergraduate/Scholarship) [9379]

Upakar Indian-American Scholarships (Undergraduate/Scholarship) [9389]

Philip F. Vineberg Travelling Fellowships in the Humanities (Undergraduate/Scholarship) [5726]

Violin Society of America Scholarships (Undergraduate/Scholarship) [9436]

Gary S. Wilmer RAMI Music Scholarships (Undergraduate/Scholarship) [3174]

Wisconsin-Madison Music Clinic Scholarships (Undergraduate/Scholarship) [9387]

Wendy Y. Wolfson Memorial Scholarship Fund (Undergraduate/Scholarship) [3798]

John W. Work III Memorial Foundation Scholarships (Undergraduate/Scholarship) [3140]

Marusia Yaworska Entrance Scholarships (Graduate/Scholarship) [9501]

YMF Scholarships (All/Scholarship) [9791]

Music, Classical

Gladys C. Anderson Memorial Scholarships (Graduate, Undergraduate/Scholarship) [748]

Lou Drane Music Scholarships (Undergraduate/Scholarship) [3940]

Music, Jazz

Central Florida Jazz Society Scholarships (Undergraduate/Award, Scholarship) [2717]

Hartford Jazz Society Scholarships (Undergraduate/Scholarship) [4439]

Music, Opera (See Opera)

Music, Piano

Chopin Foundation of the United States Scholarships (Undergraduate/Scholarship) [2777]

"Nickels for Notes" Scholarships (Undergraduate/Scholarship) [4080]

Music, Vocal

John D. Anello Sr. and Albert A. Silverman Memorial Scholarships (Undergraduate/Scholarship) [2887]

Elizabeth W. Boyce Scholarships (Undergraduate/Scholarship) [2889]

Dorchester Woman's Club Scholarships (Undergraduate/Scholarship) [4076]

Institutional Grants: Educational and Research Projects (All/Grant) [9472]

"Nickels for Notes" Scholarships (Undergraduate/Scholarship) [4080]

Music composition

Pete Carpenter Fellowships *(All/Fellowship)* [2157]
John Lennon Scholarships *(All/Prize, Scholarship)* [2159]
Peermusic Latin Scholarships *(All/Prize, Scholarship)* [2160]

Music therapy

"Nickels for Notes" Scholarships *(Undergraduate/Scholarship)* [4080]

Musicology

Woody Guthrie Fellowships *(All/Fellowship)* [2158]

Myasthenia Gravis

Myasthenia Gravis Foundation of America Nursing Fellowships *(Undergraduate/Fellowship)* [5964]
Myasthenia Gravis Foundation of America Student Fellowships *(Graduate, Undergraduate/Fellowship)* [5965]

National security

Rieser Fellowships *(Undergraduate/Fellowship)* [2209]
Women In Defense HORIZONS Scholarships *(Graduate, Undergraduate/Scholarship)* [9696]

Native American studies

Larry Matfay Scholarships *(Graduate, Undergraduate/Scholarship)* [5287]
Newberry Consortium on American Indian Studies Faculty Fellowships *(Professional development/Fellowship)* [6701]
Adolph Van Pelt Special Fund for Indians Scholarships *(Undergraduate/Scholarship)* [1696]
Phillips Fund Grants for Native American Research *(Graduate/Grant)* [994]
Allogan Slagle Memorial Scholarships *(All/Scholarship)* [1697]
Morris K. Udall Scholarships *(Undergraduate/Scholarship)* [8991]

Natural resources

A.T. Anderson Memorial Scholarships *(Graduate, Undergraduate/Scholarship)* [834]
Avista Corporation Minds in Motion Scholarships *(Undergraduate/Scholarship)* [5412]
EMLF Law Student Scholarships *(Undergraduate/Scholarship)* [3643]
Environment, Natural Resource and Energy Division Fellowships (ENRE) *(Graduate/Fellowship)* [1011]
Grand Haven Offshore Challenge Scholarship Fund *(Undergraduate/Scholarship)* [4219]
Great Lakes Commission Sea Grant Fellowships *(Graduate/Scholarship)* [4328]
Randall Matthis for Environmental Studies Scholarships *(Graduate, Undergraduate/Scholarship)* [1537]
Ben Meadows Natural Resource Scholarships - Academic Achievement Scholarships *(Undergraduate/Scholarship)* [2054]
Ben Meadows Natural Resource Scholarships - Leadership Scholarships *(Undergraduate/Scholarship)* [2055]
Property and Environment Research Center Graduate Fellowships *(Graduate/Fellowship)* [7452]
Property and Environment Research Center Lone Mountain Fellowships *(Professional development/Fellowship)* [7453]
Property and Environment Research Center Media Fellowships *(Professional development/Fellowship)* [7454]
Julian Simon Fellowships *(Professional development/Fellowship)* [7455]
Smithsonian Institution Graduate Student Fellowships *(Graduate/Fellowship)* [8245]
Smithsonian Institution Postdoctoral Fellowships *(Doctorate/Fellowship)* [8246]
Smithsonian Institution Predoctoral Fellowships *(Doctorate/Fellowship)* [8247]
Smithsonian Institution Senior Fellowships *(Doctorate/Fellowship)* [8248]
Guy A. Woodings Scholarships *(Undergraduate/Scholarship)* [9180]

Natural sciences

A&WMA Louisiana Section Scholarships *(Graduate, Undergraduate/Scholarship)* [113]
Alexander Graham Bell Canada Graduate Scholarship Program *(Doctorate, Master's/Scholarship)* [6571]
Lorraine Allison Scholarships *(Graduate/Scholarship)* [1500]
Ora E. Anderson Scholarships *(Undergraduate/Scholarship)* [3875]
CTFS Research Grants Program *(Graduate, Postdoctorate, Professional development/Grant)* [8268]
Margaret S. Gilbert Scholarship Fund *(Undergraduate/Scholarship)* [8669]
John Simon Guggenheim Memorial Fellowships - U.S. and Canadian Competition *(Advanced Professional/Fellowship)* [4360]
Dolores Zohrab Liebmann Fund - Graduate School Fellowships *(Graduate/Fellowship)* [5488]
Multi-Country Research Fellowships *(Doctorate/Fellowship)* [3270]
Natural Sciences and Engineering Research Council Postgraduate Scholarships *(Doctorate/Scholarship)* [6572]
Newkirk Center for Science and Society Graduate Student Fellowships *(Doctorate, Graduate/Fellowship)* [6712]
Laura Ann Peck Memorial Endowed Scholarships *(Undergraduate/Scholarship)* [5460]
Howard Brown Rickard Scholarships *(Undergraduate/Scholarship)* [6282]
Saskatchewan Pulse Growers Undergraduate Scholarships *(Undergraduate/Scholarship)* [8004]
Susan P. Schroeder Memorial Scholarships *(Undergraduate/Scholarship)* [5464]
Vanier Canada Graduate Scholarships *(Graduate/Scholarship)* [6573]

Naval art and science

NRL Postdoctoral Fellowships *(Postdoctorate/Fellowship)* [6581]

Near Eastern studies

Garikian Scholarship Fund *(Undergraduate/Scholarship)* [1593]

Nephrology

American Nephrology Nurses' Association Evidence-Based Research Grants *(Professional development/Grant)* [943]
American Nephrology Nurses' Association Research Grants *(Doctorate, Graduate/Grant)* [944]
KFOC Allied Health Fellowships *(Doctorate/Fellowship)* [5255]
KFOC Allied Health Scholarships *(Graduate/Scholarship)* [5256]
KFOC Biomedical Scholarships *(Doctorate/Scholarship)* [5258]
Nephrology Nurse Researcher Awards *(Doctorate, Graduate/Award)* [945]
Barbara F. Prowant Nursing Research Grants *(Graduate/Grant)* [946]

Neurology

AANS Medical Student Summer Research Fellowships (MSSRF) *(Undergraduate/Fellowship)* [515]
American Australian Association Neurological Fellowships *(Graduate/Fellowship)* [574]
Clinical Research Training Fellowships *(Professional development/Fellowship)* [373]
George C. Cotzias, MD Memorial Fellowships *(Professional development/Fellowship)* [981]
Daland Fellowships in Clinical Investigation *(Doctorate/Fellowship)* [989]
Roger C. Duvoisin, MD Research Grants *(Professional development/Grant)* [982]

Epilepsy Foundation Research and Training Fellowships for Clinicians *(Doctorate, Professional development/Grant)* [3665]
Grass Fellowships *(Doctorate, Postdoctorate/Fellowship)* [4315]
Medical Student Summer Research Scholarships *(Undergraduate/Scholarship)* [374]
NJCBIR Individual Research Grants *(Professional development/Grant)* [6639]
NJCBIR Pilot Research Grants *(Professional development/Grant)* [6640]
NJCBIR Postdoctoral and Graduate Student Fellowships *(Graduate, Postdoctorate/Fellowship)* [6641]
NJCBIR Programmatic Multi-Investigator Project Grants *(Professional development/Grant)* [6642]
William P. Van Wagenen Fellowships *(Undergraduate/Fellowship)* [516]

Neurophysiology

Grass Fellowships *(Doctorate, Postdoctorate/Fellowship)* [4315]

Neuroscience

ASET Educational Seminars, Courses and Program Scholarships *(All, Professional development/Scholarship)* [1239]
Lynn Ann Baldwin Scholarships *(Master's/Scholarship)* [2395]
Certified Neuroscience Registered Nurse Recertification Grant Program (CNRN) *(Professional development/Grant)* [518]
Epilepsy Foundation Post-doctoral Research Fellowships *(Postdoctorate, Professional development/Fellowship)* [3662]
Epilepsy Foundation Pre-doctoral Research Training Fellowships *(Graduate/Grant)* [3663]
Fellowships and Internships Program in Latin America *(Graduate/Fellowship, Internship)* [8269]
Grass Fellowships *(Doctorate, Postdoctorate/Fellowship)* [4315]
Integra Foundation NNF Research Grant Awards *(Professional development/Grant)* [519]
Klingenstein Fellowships in the Neurosciences *(Doctorate, Professional development/Fellowship)* [5266]
NNF Scholarship Program *(Graduate, Undergraduate/Scholarship)* [520]
Nueroscience Certification Bursary Awards *(Professional development/Award)* [2396]
Short-Term Fellowships *(Undergraduate, Graduate, Postdoctorate/Fellowship)* [8271]
Sloan Research Fellowships *(Doctorate/Fellowship)* [8235]
Earl S. Tupper 3-year Postdoctoral Fellowships in Tropical Biology *(Postdoctorate/Fellowship)* [8272]
Jessie Young Bursary Awards *(Professional development/Award)* [2397]

Nonprofit sector

ARNOVA Emerging Scholar Awards *(Graduate, Undergraduate/Award)* [1858]

Nuclear science

American Nuclear Society Nevada Section Scholarships *(Undergraduate/Scholarship)* [7466]
American Nuclear Society Undergraduates Scholarships *(Undergraduate/Scholarship)* [949]
Nonproliferation Graduate Fellowships Program (NGFP) *(Graduate/Fellowship)* [7033]

Nursing

AAACN Scholarships *(Undergraduate/Scholarship)* [437]
AACN Continuing Professional Development Scholarships *(Graduate, Professional development/Scholarship)* [469]
AACN Minority Nurse Faculty Scholarships *(Graduate/Scholarship)* [457]
Mandel & Lauretta Abrahamer Scholarships *(Undergraduate/Scholarship)* [8715]

ACNL Research Scholarships *(Graduate/Scholarship)* [1722]

ACNP Nurse Practitioner Student Scholarship Awards *(Undergraduate/Scholarship)* [621]

AfterCollege/AACN Nursing Scholarships *(Graduate, Undergraduate/Scholarship)* [458]

American Pediatric Surgical Nurses Association Educational Grants *(Professional development/Grant)* [984]

American Quarter Horse Foundation Scholarships *(Undergraduate/Scholarship)* [1063]

AMSUS Nursing Awards *(Professional development/Award)* [1459]

ANCA Scholarships *(Graduate, Undergraduate/Scholarship)* [1613]

Roy Anderson Memorial Scholarships *(Graduate, Undergraduate/Scholarship)* [2990]

AORN Foundation Scholarship Program *(Undergraduate/Scholarship)* [1839]

APS/ASU Scholarships *(Undergraduate/Scholarship)* [7332]

Arizona Nurses Foundation Scholarships *(Doctorate, Graduate, Undergraduate/Scholarship)* [1526]

ASHA Scholarships *(Graduate, Undergraduate/Scholarship)* [1175]

ASHA Student Research Grants *(Graduate, Undergraduate/Scholarship)* [1176]

Association of Rehabilitation Nurses Scholarship Program *(Undergraduate/Scholarship)* [1855]

AstraZeneca RURAL Scholarships *(Doctorate/Scholarship)* [2534]

Bachelor of Science in Nursing Academic Scholarships *(Graduate/Scholarship)* [6099]

Dr. Johnella Banks Memorial Scholarships *(Undergraduate/Scholarship)* [2137]

Banner Health System - McKee Medical Center, Loveland: Nightingale Scholarships *(Graduate, Undergraduate/Scholarship)* [2991]

Banner Health System - North Colorado Medical Center, Greeley: Nightingale Scholarships *(Graduate, Undergraduate/Scholarship)* [2992]

Leslie Baranowski Scholarships for Professional Excellence *(All/Scholarship)* [4764]

Basic Midwifery Student Scholarship Program *(Undergraduate/Scholarship)* [618]

BCEN Undergraduate Scholarships *(Undergraduate/Scholarship)* [3633]

Anne Beckingham Scholarships *(Graduate, Professional development/Scholarship)* [2474]

Dr. Ann C. Beckingham Scholarships *(Doctorate/Scholarship)* [2535]

Reckitt Benckiser Student Scholarships *(Graduate/Scholarship)* [6105]

Linn Benton Scholarships *(Undergraduate/Scholarship)* [6952]

Dr. Noorali & Sabiya Bharwani Endowment *(Undergraduate/Scholarship)* [2082]

Hussein Jina Bharwani Memorial Endowment *(Undergraduate/Scholarship)* [2083]

Birks Family Foundation Scholarships *(Undergraduate/Scholarship)* [2536]

Joan Blend Scholarship Fund *(Undergraduate/Scholarship)* [8657]

Barbara Brantley Nursing Education Scholarships *(Graduate/Scholarship)* [1723]

Breakthrough to Nursing Scholarships *(Undergraduate/Scholarship)* [3976]

Ruby A. Brown Memorial Scholarships *(Undergraduate/Scholarship)* [3566]

Eleanor McWilliams Burke Fund *(Undergraduate/Scholarship)* [3762]

byourself Scholarship Fund *(Undergraduate, Vocational/Occupational/Scholarship)* [3188]

Joseph R. Calder, Jr., MD Scholarship Fund *(Undergraduate/Scholarship)* [3763]

California Association of Private Postsecondary Schools Scholarships *(Undergraduate/Scholarship)* [2232]

The California Endowment and AACN Minority Nurse Faculty Scholarships *(Graduate/Scholarship)* [459]

Canadian Evaluation Society Memorial Scholarships *(Graduate, Professional development/Scholarship)* [2475]

Canadian Nurses Foundation - Baxter Corporation Scholarships *(Graduate/Scholarship)* [2537]

Canadian Nurses Foundation Northern Scholarships *(Undergraduate/Scholarship)* [2538]

Canadian Nurses Foundation Scholarships *(Undergraduate/Scholarship)* [2539]

Rhea Sourifman Caplin Memorial Scholarships *(Undergraduate/Scholarship)* [4417]

Career Mobility Scholarship Awards *(Doctorate, Undergraduate/Scholarship)* [27]

Career Mobility Scholarships *(Graduate, Undergraduate, Vocational/Occupational/Scholarship)* [3977]

Certified Neuroscience Registered Nurse Recertification Grant Program (CNRN) *(Professional development/Grant)* [518]

CFIDS Association of America NP Student Scholarships *(Graduate/Scholarship)* [376]

Melba Dawn Chiarenza Scholarship Fund *(Undergraduate/Scholarship)* [9554]

Patricia Smith Christensen Scholarships *(Postdoctorate/Scholarship)* [8195]

Frances N. Christian Memorial Endowment Nursing Scholarships *(Graduate, Undergraduate/Scholarship)* [8740]

City of Toronto Queen Elizabeth II Sesquicentennial Scholarships in Community Health Nursing for Graduates *(Graduate/Scholarship)* [9326]

City of Toronto Queen Elizabeth II Sesquicentennial Scholarships in Community Health Nursing for Undergraduates *(Undergraduate/Scholarship)* [9327]

CLN Scholarships *(Graduate, Undergraduate/Scholarship)* [3237]

Jennet Colliflower Nursing Scholarships *(Undergraduate/Scholarship)* [3315]

Colorado Nurses Association: Nightingale Scholarships *(Graduate, Undergraduate/Scholarship)* [2993]

Colorado Nurses Foundation Nightingale Scholarships *(Graduate, Undergraduate/Scholarship)* [2994]

Colorado Organization of Nursing Leaders Scholarships *(Graduate, Undergraduate/Scholarship)* [2995]

Hazel Corbin/Childbirth Connection Grants for Evidence-based Midwifery Care *(Professional development/Grant)* [619]

Claire V. Cunningham Masonic Fund for Supporting Leadership in Nursing Scholarships *(Professional development/Scholarship)* [1724]

Jane Delano Student Nurse Scholarships *(Undergraduate/Scholarship)* [1135]

Gretchen Dimico Memorial Scholarships *(Undergraduate/Scholarship)* [5425]

Dr. Feroz Ahmed Memorial Educational Post-Graduate Scholarships *(Doctorate, Postgraduate/Scholarship)* [8216]

Doctoral Degree Scholarships in Cancer Nursing *(Doctorate/Scholarship)* [596]

Doctors IRA & UDAYA Nursing Scholarships *(Undergraduate/Scholarship)* [8598]

Margaret Dowell-Gravatt, M.D. Scholarships *(Undergraduate/Scholarship)* [2059]

Bus and Mary Ellen Durant Timberline High School Endowed Scholarships *(Undergraduate/Scholarship)* [5426]

Emergency Nurses Association Undergraduate Scholarships *(Undergraduate/Scholarship)* [3634]

Ruth Murphy Evans Scholarships *(Undergraduate/Scholarship)* [4335]

ExeptionalNurse.com College Scholarships *(Graduate, Undergraduate/Scholarship)* [3696]

Faculty Doctoral Scholarships *(Doctorate/Scholarship)* [3635]

Family and Children's Services of Lebanon County Fund *(Undergraduate/Scholarship)* [3942]

Red and Lola Fehr: Nightingale Scholarships *(Graduate, Undergraduate/Scholarship)* [2996]

Florida Education Fund McKnight Doctoral Fellowships *(Graduate/Fellowship)* [3822]

Florida Nurses Foundation Scholarships *(All/Scholarship)* [3840]

Floto-Peel Family Scholarship Fund *(Undergraduate, Vocational/Occupational/Scholarship)* [4215]

Forsyth County Nursing Scholarships *(Undergraduate/Scholarship)* [9636]

Barbara Palo Foster Memorial Scholarships *(Graduate, Undergraduate/Scholarship)* [2756]

The Foundation of the National Student Nurses' Association Scholarships *(Graduate, Undergraduate/Scholarship)* [6536]

Doris W. Frey Memorial Scholarships *(Undergraduate/Scholarship)* [8603]

Don and Eileen Fulton Nursing Scholarships *(Undergraduate/Scholarship)* [8722]

Arkansas Nursing Foundation - Dorothea Fund Scholarships *(Professional development/Scholarship)* [1543]

Gadsden State/McClellan Campus Nursing Scholarship Awards *(Undergraduate/Scholarship)* [3036]

Gardner Foundation Infusion Nurses Society Education Scholarships *(All/Scholarship)* [4765]

Elaine Gelman Scholarship Awards *(Undergraduate/Scholarship)* [6106]

Mary Ghezzi Nursing Scholarships *(Undergraduate/Scholarship)* [8983]

Dr. Helen Preston Glass Fellowships *(Doctorate/Fellowship)* [2541]

William R. Goldfarb Memorial Scholarships *(Undergraduate/Scholarship)* [1085]

Goodfellow Nursing Scholarships *(Master's, Undergraduate/Scholarship)* [5507]

Goodfellow Professional Development Fund *(Professional development/Scholarship)* [5508]

Baxter Corporation - Jean Goodwill Scholarships *(Postgraduate/Scholarship)* [20]

Graduate Scholarships in Cancer Nursing Practice *(Master's, Doctorate/Scholarship)* [597]

Arkansas Nursing Foundation - Mary Gray Scholarships *(Professional development/Scholarship)* [1544]

William G. and Mayme J. Green Scholarships *(Undergraduate/Scholarship)* [4434]

Helen R. Greenamyer Memorial Scholarships *(Undergraduate/Scholarship)* [8723]

Judy Hill Scholarships *(Undergraduate/Scholarship)* [2542]

Ann L. Holland Memorial Scholarships *(Graduate, Undergraduate/Scholarship)* [4077]

Caroline Holt Nursing Scholarships *(Undergraduate/Scholarship)* [4441]

Roberta L. Houpt Scholarship Fund *(Undergraduate/Scholarship)* [3946]

HRET Health Career Scholarships *(Graduate, Undergraduate/Scholarship)* [6644]

Idaho Nursing Scholarships *(Undergraduate/Scholarship)* [4670]

Illinois Student Assistance Commission Nurse Educator Scholarships (NESP) *(Undergraduate/Scholarship)* [4699]

Illinois Student Assistance Commission Nursing Education Scholarships *(Undergraduate/Scholarship)* [4700]

Integra Foundation NNF Research Grant Awards *(Professional development/Grant)* [519]

Susan K. Ipacs Nursing Legacy Scholarships *(Undergraduate/Scholarship)* [3877]

Virginia C. Jack and Ralph L. Jack Scholarships *(Undergraduate, Vocational/Occupational/Scholarship)* [8677]

Johnson and Johnson: Nightingale Scholarships *(Graduate, Undergraduate/Scholarship)* [2997]

Johnson & Johnson Scholarships *(Undergraduate/Scholarship)* [2543]

Kaiser Permanente: Nightingale Scholarships *(Graduate, Undergraduate/Scholarship)* [2998]

Dr. Dorothy J. Kergin Scholarships *(Doctorate/Scholarship)* [2544]

Edyie G. Kirby Nursing Scholarship Awards *(Undergraduate/Scholarship)* [3041]

Lake Dollars for Scholars Endowment Fund *(Undergraduate, Vocational/Occupational/Scholarship)* [8683]

Tecla Lin & Nelia Laroza Memorial Scholarships *(Undergraduate/Scholarship)* [2545]

Gertie S. Lowe Nursing Scholarship Awards *(Undergraduate/Scholarship)* [3043]

Pat Lyon Nursing Fellowships *(Graduate/Fellowship)* [8916]

Mallet Nursing Scholarships *(Undergraduate/Scholarship)* [8120]

March of Dimes Graduate Nursing Scholarships

(Graduate/Scholarship) [5607]

Eleanor Jean Martin Scholarships (Graduate/Scholarship) [2546]

Master's Degree with a Major in Nursing Academic Scholarships (Graduate/Scholarship) [6100]

John Mazurek Memorial-Morgex Insurance Scholarships (Professional development/Scholarship) [274]

Senator Patricia K. McGee Nursing Faculty Scholarships (Doctorate, Graduate/Scholarship) [6675]

McKesson Scholarships (Undergraduate/Scholarship) [3978]

McLean Scholarships (Undergraduate/Scholarship) [1797]

National Association of Pediatric Nurse Practitioners McNeil Rural and Underserved Scholarships (Graduate/Scholarship) [6107]

Jerry Medforth Nursing Scholarship Awards (Undergraduate/Scholarship) [3044]

Michigan League for Nursing Scholarships (Undergraduate/Scholarship) [5821]

Michigan Nurses Foundation Scholarships (Doctorate, Undergraduate/Scholarship) [5825]

Albert and Eloise Midyette Memorial Scholarship Fund (Undergraduate/Scholarship) [3913]

Mary Ann Mikulic Scholarships (Professional development/Scholarship) [1856]

Ruth Milan-Altrusa Scholarships (Undergraduate/Scholarship) [5589]

Military Nurses Association Scholarships (Graduate, Master's/Scholarship) [2547]

Joseph and Catherine Missigman Memorial Nursing Scholarships (Undergraduate/Scholarship) [3782]

MODNA Nursing Education Scholarships (Doctorate, Graduate/Fellowship) [5849]

Dan Mordecai Educational Scholarships (Graduate, Undergraduate/Scholarship) [6619]

H.M. Muffly Memorial Scholarships (Graduate, Undergraduate/Scholarship) [2999]

Margaret Munro Scholarships (Undergraduate/Scholarship) [2548]

NAAF Aboriginal Health Careers Bursary and Scholarships (Graduate, Undergraduate/Scholarship) [5992]

National American Arab Nurses Association Scholarships (Master's, Undergraduate/Scholarship) [6022]

National Black Nurses Association Scholarships (Undergraduate/Scholarship) [6155]

National Heartburn Alliance NP Student Scholarships (Graduate/Scholarship) [377]

National Slovak Society of the USA Scholarships (Undergraduate, Vocational/Occupational/Scholarship) [6478]

New Brunswick Nurses Association Scholarships (Graduate/Scholarship) [2550]

Sharon Nield Memorial Scholarships (Undergraduate/Scholarship) [2551]

NNF Scholarship Program (Graduate, Undergraduate/Scholarship) [520]

North Carolina League for Nursing Academic Scholarships (Graduate/Scholarship) [3915]

North Ottawa Hospital Auxiliary Scholarship Fund (Undergraduate/Scholarship) [4231]

Northampton County Medical Society Alliance Scholarships (Undergraduate/Scholarship) [6794]

NOVA Foundation Scholarships (Doctorate, Graduate, Undergraduate/Scholarship) [6840]

Nursing Scholarship Program (Undergraduate/Scholarship) [4498]

Orthopaedic Specialists Nursing Scholarships (Undergraduate/Scholarship) [9648]

Outlaw Student's Nursing School Scholarships (Undergraduate/Scholarship) [8754]

Senator Norman Paterson Fellowships (Doctorate/Fellowship) [2552]

Colorado Nurses Association: Virginia Paulson Memorial Scholarships (Graduate, Undergraduate/Scholarship) [3000]

Margaret Pemberton Scholarships (Undergraduate/Scholarship) [2138]

Florrie Penney, RN Rehabilitation Nursing Bursaries (Graduate, Professional development/Scholarship) [1850]

Pfizer Inc. NP Student Scholarships (Graduate/Scholarship) [378]

Pharmavite LLC NP Doctoral Education Scholarships (Doctorate/Scholarship) [379]

Shoshana Philipp (Kirshenblatt) R.N. Memorial Scholarships (Graduate, Undergraduate/Scholarship) [8917]

Donald E. Pizzini Memorial Nurse Scholarships (Professional development/Scholarship) [5926]

Post Basic Course Bursaries (Graduate, Professional development/Scholarship) [1851]

Poudre Valley Health System, Fort Collins: Nightingale Scholarships (Graduate, Undergraduate/Scholarship) [3001]

Carl C. and Abbie Rebman Trust Scholarships (Undergraduate/Scholarship) [4263]

Pat Redden Memorial Scholarships (Undergraduate/Scholarship) [5510]

Faye Lynn Roberts Educational Scholarships (Undergraduate/Scholarship) [8618]

Liz Roberts Memorial Scholarships (Undergraduate/Scholarship) [7707]

Ellis W. Rowe Scholarships (Undergraduate/Scholarship) [4380]

Lucille and Edward R. Roybal Foundation Public Health Scholarships (Graduate, Undergraduate/Scholarship) [7827]

St. Anthony's Hospitals, Denver: Nightingale Scholarships (Graduate, Undergraduate/Scholarship) [3002]

St. Clare's Mercy Hospital School of Nursing Alumni Association Scholarships (Graduate/Scholarship) [1853]

St. Joseph's Hospital School of Nursing Alumnae Scholarships (Undergraduate/Scholarship) [7112]

Sanofi Pasteur Scholarships (Graduate/Scholarship) [2553]

SCA Nursing Scholarships (Graduate, Professional development/Scholarship) [2476]

Victor E. Schimmel Memorial Nursing Scholarships (Doctorate, Graduate, Master's/Scholarship) [1725]

Scholarships for Emigres in the Health Sciences (Undergraduate/Scholarship) [5157]

Jeptha Wade Schureman Scholarship Program (Undergraduate/Scholarship) [3205]

Pat Shimp Memorial Scholarships (Undergraduate/Scholarship) [7114]

Sigma Theta Tau International Scholarships (Doctorate/Scholarship) [2554]

Hazel Simms Nursing Scholarships (Professional development/Scholarship) [5352]

Society of Pediatric Nurses Educational Scholarships (Graduate, Professional development/Scholarship) [8424]

Specialty Nursing Scholarships (Undergraduate/Scholarship) [3979]

Spotlight on Nursing Graduate Nursing Scholarships (Graduate/Scholarship) [8651]

Anne Sturrock Nursing Scholarships (Undergraduate/Scholarship) [8624]

Syncrude/Athabasca University Aboriginal Scholarships (All/Scholarship) [8791]

John I. and Madeleine R. Taeni Scholarships (Undergraduate/Scholarship) [8627]

Virginia Elizabeth and Alma Vane Taylor Student Nurse Scholarships (Undergraduate/Scholarship) [9657]

TD Meloche-Monnex Scholarships (Doctorate/Scholarship) [2555]

UAA Alaska Kidney Foundation Scholarships (Graduate, Undergraduate/Scholarship) [9115]

UAA RRANN Program Scholarships (Undergraduate/Scholarship) [9126]

UCB, Inc. NP Student Scholarships (Graduate/Scholarship) [380]

United Health Foundation National Association of Hispanic Nurses Scholarships (Graduate, Undergraduate/Scholarship) [6084]

John Vanderlee Scholarships (Undergraduate/Scholarship) [2556]

The Sibyl Jennings Vorheis Memorial Undergraduate Scholarships (Undergraduate/Scholarship) [3926]

Sue Walicki Nursing Scholarships (Undergraduate/Scholarship) [5109]

Patty Walter Memorial Scholarships (Graduate, Undergraduate/Scholarship) [3003]

Imogene Ward Nursing Scholarships (Undergraduate/Scholarship) [3814]

Washington County Farm Bureau Scholarships (Undergraduate/Scholarship) [6948]

Washington Higher Education Coordinating Board Health Professional Scholarships (Graduate/Scholarship) [9506]

Washington State Nurses Association Foundation Scholarships (WSNF) (Graduate, Undergraduate/Scholarship) [9528]

West Virginia Nurses Association District No. 3 Scholarships (Undergraduate/Scholarship) [7121]

Lois Widley Student Scholarships (Graduate, Undergraduate/Scholarship) [4967]

WOCN Accredited Nursing Education Scholarships (Graduate, Undergraduate/Scholarship) [9765]

WOCN Advanced Education Scholarships (Doctorate, Graduate, Undergraduate/Scholarship) [9766]

Jean Wright-Elson Scholarships (Doctorate, Graduate, Undergraduate/Scholarship) [7976]

Joan C. Yoder Memorial Nursing Scholarships (Undergraduate/Scholarship) [9182]

Yukon Delta Fisheries Development Association Scholarships (Undergraduate/Scholarship) [9183]

Nursing, Cardiovascular and cerebrovascular

Epilepsy Foundation Pre-doctoral Research Training Fellowships (Graduate/Grant) [3663]

Nursing, Neonatal

Foundation for Neonatal Research and Education Scholarships (Doctorate, Graduate, Postgraduate, Undergraduate/Scholarship) [3981]

Nursing, Oncological

Oncology Nursing Society Foundation - Doctoral Scholarships (Doctorate/Scholarship) [6885]

Oncology Nursing Society Foundation - Master's and Post-Master's NP Certificate Scholarships (Master's/Scholarship) [6886]

Oncology Nursing Society Foundation - Non-RN Bachelors Scholarships (Graduate/Scholarship) [6887]

Oncology Nursing Society Foundation - Non-RNHS Bachelors Scholarships (Undergraduate/Scholarship) [6888]

Oncology Nursing Society Foundation - RN Bachelors Scholarships (Graduate/Scholarship) [6889]

Nursing, Pediatric

Eight and Forty Lung and Respiratory Disease Nursing Scholarships (Professional development/Scholarship) [896]

Nancy Llewellyn, RN Pediatric Nursing Bursaries (Graduate, Professional development/Scholarship) [1849]

Pediatric Endocrinology Nursing Society Academic Education Scholarships (Undergraduate/Scholarship) [7136]

Pediatric Endocrinology Nursing Society Convention Reimbursement Awards (Undergraduate/Award) [7137]

Nursing, Psychiatric

Associates in Behavioral Health Scholarships (Graduate/Scholarship) [7398]

Irene and Daisy MacGregor Memorial Scholarships (Graduate/Scholarship) [4448]

RPNAS Baccalaureate Level Program Scholarships (Graduate/Scholarship) [7723]

RPNAS Doctorate Level Program Scholarships (Doctorate/Scholarship) [7724]

RPNAS Master's Level Program Scholarships (Graduate, Master's/Scholarship) [7725]

Nursing administration

Barbara Brantley Nursing Education Scholarships (Graduate/Scholarship) [1723]

Nutrition

ASHA Scholarships (Graduate, Undergraduate/Scholarship) [1175]

ASHA Student Research Grants (Graduate, Undergraduate/Scholarship) [1176]

Birmingham District Alabama Dietetic Association Scholarships (Graduate, Undergraduate/Scholarship) [168]

Eleanor McWilliams Burke Fund (Undergraduate/Scholarship) [3762]

California Association of Family and Consumer Sciences -San Diego Chapter Scholarships (CAFCS) (Graduate, Undergraduate, Vocational/Occupational/Scholarship) [7917]

CANFIT Nutrition, Physical Education and Culinary Arts Scholarships (Graduate, Undergraduate/Scholarship) [3026]

CANFIT Scholarships (Graduate, Undergraduate/Scholarship) [2228]

CBC Spouses Cheerios Brand Health Initiative Scholarships (Undergraduate/Scholarship) [3215]

Margaret Drew Alpha Fellowships (Graduate/Fellowship) [7285]

International Foodservice Editorial Council Scholarships (Graduate, Undergraduate/Scholarship) [4935]

Maine Nutrition Council Scholarships (Undergraduate/Scholarship) [5599]

North Alabama Dietetic Association Scholarships (Graduate, Undergraduate/Scholarship) [169]

North Dakota Division Scholarships (Undergraduate/Scholarship) [5862]

Northeast Alabama District Dietetic Association Scholarships (Graduate, Undergraduate/Scholarship) [170]

Nell Bryant Robinson Scholarships (Undergraduate/Scholarship) [7299]

Margaret Jerome Sampson Scholarships (Undergraduate/Scholarship) [7301]

Saskatchewan Pulse Growers Undergraduate Scholarships (Undergraduate/Scholarship) [8004]

William E. Smith Scholarships (Graduate/Scholarship) [171]

Southeast Alabama Dietetic Association Scholarships (Graduate, Undergraduate/Scholarship) [172]

Stark County Dairy Promoters Scholarships (Undergraduate/Scholarship) [8701]

WDA Full-Time Graduate Scholarships (Graduate/Scholarship) [9684]

WDA Part-Time Graduate Scholarships (Graduate/Scholarship) [9685]

Mary and Elliot Wood Foundation Graduate Scholarship Fund (Graduate/Scholarship) [3930]

Wood Fruitticher Grocery Company, Inc. Scholarships (Graduate, Undergraduate/Scholarship) [173]

Occupational safety and health

AAOHN Professional Development Scholarships - Academic Study (Graduate, Undergraduate/Scholarship) [522]

AAOHN Professional Development Scholarships - Continuing Education (Professional development/Scholarship) [523]

America Responds Memorial Scholarships (Undergraduate/Scholarship) [1330]

American Society of Safety Engineers Construction Safety Scholarships (Undergraduate/Scholarship) [1331]

ASSE Diversity Committee Scholarships (Graduate, Undergraduate/Scholarship) [1332]

Bechtel Group Foundation Scholarships for Safety & Health (Undergraduate/Scholarship) [1333]

VPPPA Stephen Brown Scholarships (Graduate, Undergraduate/Scholarship) [9474]

Warren K. Brown Scholarships (Undergraduate/Scholarship) [1334]

CNA Foundation Scholarships (Graduate, Undergraduate/Scholarship) [1335]

Delta/VPPPA Safety, Health and Environmental Scholarships (Undergraduate, Vocational/Occupational, Graduate/Scholarship) [9475]

Scott Dominguez - Craters of the Moon Chapter Scholarships (Graduate, Undergraduate/Scholarship) [1336]

Gold Country Section & Region II Scholarships (Graduate, Undergraduate/Scholarship) [1337]

Gulf Coast Past President's Scholarships (Undergraduate/Scholarship) [1338]

George Gustafson HSE Memorial Scholarships (Graduate, Undergraduate/Scholarship) [1339]

David Iden Memorial Safety Scholarships (Undergraduate/Scholarship) [1340]

IRSST Doctoral Scholarships Abroad (Doctorate/Fellowship) [4768]

IRSST Doctoral Scholarships Supplement (Doctorate/Fellowship) [4769]

IRSST Doctoral Scholarships (Doctorate/Fellowship) [4767]

IRSST Masters Scholarships Supplement (Graduate/Fellowship) [4771]

IRSST Masters Scholarships (Graduate/Fellowship) [4770]

IRSST Postdoctoral Scholarships Abroad (Doctorate/Fellowship) [4773]

IRSST Postdoctoral Scholarships (Doctorate/Fellowship) [4772]

Karl A. Jacobson Scholarships (Undergraduate/Scholarship) [1341]

Greater Baton Rouge Chapter - Don Jones Excellence in Safety Scholarships (Undergraduate/Scholarship) [1342]

Southwest Chapter Roy Kinslow Scholarships (Undergraduate/Scholarship) [1343]

James P. Kohn Memorial Scholarships (Graduate/Scholarship) [1344]

Central Indiana ASSE Jim Kriner Memorial Scholarships (Graduate, Undergraduate/Scholarship) [1345]

Leadership Development Scholarships (Professional development/Scholarship) [524]

Liberty Mutual Scholarships (Undergraduate/Scholarship) [1346]

Marsh Risk Consulting Scholarships (Undergraduate/Scholarship) [1347]

Dick Martin Scholarships (Postgraduate/Scholarship) [2426]

Rixio Medina and Associates Hispanics in Safety Scholarships (Graduate, Undergraduate/Scholarship) [1348]

North Florida Chapter Safety Education Scholarships (Graduate, Undergraduate/Scholarship) [1349]

Northeastern Illinois Chapter Scholarships (Graduate, Undergraduate/Scholarship) [1350]

PDC Scholarships (Undergraduate/Scholarship) [1351]

Harold F. Polston Scholarships (Graduate, Undergraduate/Scholarship) [1352]

William C. Ray, CIH, CSP Arizona Scholarships (Graduate, Undergraduate/Scholarship) [1353]

Julie Schmid Research Scholarships (All/Scholarship) [1837]

Louis Stokes Health Scholars Program (Undergraduate, Vocational/Occupational/Scholarship) [3221]

VPPPA William Sullivan Scholarships (Graduate, Undergraduate/Scholarship) [9476]

Harry Taback 9/11 Memorial Scholarships (Undergraduate/Scholarship) [1354]

Thompson Scholarships for Women in Safety (Graduate/Scholarship) [1355]

UPS Diversity Scholarships (Undergraduate/Scholarship) [1356]

VPPPA June Brothers Scholarships (Graduate, Undergraduate/Scholarship) [9477]

Washington Group International Safety Scholarships (Undergraduate/Scholarship) [1357]

Occupational therapy

AMBUCS Scholarships for Therapists Program (Graduate, Undergraduate/Scholarship) [371]

Ethel Beard Burstein Scholarship Program (Postgraduate/Scholarship) [951]

Canadian Occupational Therapy Foundation Graduate Scholarships (Graduate/Scholarship) [2558]

Canadian Occupational Therapy Foundation Invac-

are Master's Scholarships (Graduate/Scholarship) [2559]

Thelma Cardwell Scholarships (Graduate/Scholarship) [2560]

Dave Couch Memorial Scholarships (Undergraduate/Scholarship) [7067]

Margaret Dowell-Gravatt, M.D. Scholarships (Undergraduate/Scholarship) [2059]

Goldwin Howland Scholarships (Graduate/Scholarship) [2561]

Kappa Delta Phi Scholarship Program (Postgraduate/Scholarship) [952]

Mary Minglen Scholarship Program (Postgraduate/Scholarship) [953]

NorthCoast Medical Scholarship Program (Postgraduate/Scholarship) [954]

Frank Oppenheimer Scholarship Program (Postgraduate/Scholarship) [955]

Willard and Spackman Scholarship Program (Postgraduate/Scholarship) [956]

Edith Weingarten Scholarship Program (Postgraduate/Scholarship) [957]

Ocean engineering (See Engineering, Ocean)

Oceanography

Boyd N. Lyon Scholarships (Doctorate, Graduate/Scholarship) [5554]

Roger Daley Postdoctoral Publication Awards (Postdoctorate/Award) [2525]

DOE Computational Science Graduate Fellowships (DOE CSGF) (Doctorate, Graduate/Fellowship) [5306]

Dr. Nancy Foster Scholarships (Doctorate, Graduate/Scholarship) [3873]

Ernest F. Hollings Undergraduate Scholarships (Undergraduate/Scholarship) [6417]

Tertia M.C. Hughes Memorial Graduate Student Prizes (Graduate/Prize) [2526]

Naval Weather Service Association Scholarships (High School, Undergraduate/Scholarship) [6583]

NDSEG Fellowships (Graduate/Fellowship) [6239]

NOAA Graduate Sciences Scholarships (Graduate/Scholarship) [6418]

NOAA Undergraduate Scholarships (Undergraduate/Scholarship) [6419]

President's Prize (Professional development/Prize) [2527]

Francois J. Saucier Prize in Applied Oceanography (Professional development/Prize) [2528]

Dr. Andrew Thomson Prize in Applied Meteorology (Professional development/Prize) [2529]

Oncology

Alex's Lemonade Stand Foundation Epidemiology Grants (Doctorate, Professional development/Grant) [292]

Alex's Lemonade Stand Foundation Innovation Grants (Professional development/Grant) [293]

Alex's Lemonade Stand Foundation Young Investigator Grants (Doctorate, Professional development/Grant) [294]

American Association for Cancer Research - GlaxoSmithKline Clinical Cancer Research Scholar Awards (Graduate, Postdoctorate/Award) [449]

American Association for Cancer Research Minority Scholar Awards (Graduate/Award) [450]

American College of Radiation Oncology Resident Scholarships (Graduate/Scholarship) [623]

Aplastic Anemia and Myelosdysplasia Scholarships (Graduate/Scholarship) [2533]

Barbados Cancer Association Post-Graduate Scholarships (Graduate/Scholarship) [2021]

Basic Research Fellowships (Postdoctorate/Fellowship) [586]

CARO-ELEKTA Research Fellowship Program (Professional development/Fellowship) [2404]

Childhood Cancer Foundation Scholarships (Undergraduate/Scholarship) [2752]

Childhood Cancer Survivor Scholarships (All/Scholarship) [2753]

Jane Coffin Childs Memorial Fund - Medical Research Fellowships (Doctorate/Fellowship) [2764]

Norm Hollend Fellowships in Oncology (Postdoctorate/Fellowship) [5535]

Institute Community Support Publication Prizes (Doctorate, Graduate, Undergraduate/Prize) [2507]

Kimmel Scholarships (Doctorate, Graduate/Fellowship) [5264]

LRF Post-Doctoral Fellowships (Doctorate, Graduate/Fellowship) [5552]

David McColm Fellowships in Lung Cancer Research (Postdoctorate/Fellowship) [5536]

Minority-Serving Institution Faculty Scholar Awards (Doctorate/Award) [452]

Ryan Mullaly Second Chance Fund Scholarships (Undergraduate, Vocational/Occupational/Scholarship) [5946]

Prevent Cancer Foundation Fellowships (Doctorate, Graduate/Fellowship) [7394]

Barbara Rosenblum Cancer Dissertation Scholarships (Doctorate, Graduate/Fellowship) [8520]

Morgan Stanley Pediatrics Fellowships (Doctorate, Postdoctorate/Fellowship) [575]

E.D. Thomas Post Doctoral Fellowships (Postdoctorate/Fellowship) [4014]

Women in Cancer Research Scholar Awards (Graduate, Postdoctorate/Award) [453]

Opera

Bel Canto Vocal Scholarship Foundation Vocal Competition (All/Award, Scholarship) [2046]

Opera Foundation Scholarships (Professional development/Scholarship) [6905]

Operations research

Steven M. Teutsch Prevention Effectiveness Fellowships (Doctorate/Fellowship) [2715]

Optics

BACUS Scholarships (Graduate, Undergraduate/Scholarship) [8637]

Jean Bennett Memorial Student Travel Grants (Graduate, Undergraduate/Grant) [6909]

Corning Outstanding Student Paper Competition (Graduate, Undergraduate/Award) [6910]

Michael Kidger Memorial Scholarships in Optical Design (Graduate/Scholarship) [8638]

D.J. Lovell Scholarships (Graduate, Undergraduate/Scholarship) [8640]

Maiman Student Paper Competition (Graduate, Undergraduate/Award) [6912]

Optical Design and Engineering Scholarships (Graduate, Undergraduate/Scholarship) [8641]

Harvey M. Pollicove Memorial Scholarships (Undergraduate/Scholarship) [6913]

Student Travel Grants (Graduate, Undergraduate/Grant) [8642]

Emil Wolf Outstanding Student Paper Competition (Graduate, Undergraduate/Award) [6914]

Xerox Technical Minority Scholarships (Graduate, Undergraduate/Scholarship) [9787]

Optometry

The William C. Ezell Fellowships (Postgraduate/Fellowship) [385]

FFB-C Postdoctoral Fellowships (Postdoctorate/Fellowship) [3968]

Terrance Ingraham Pediatric Optometry Residency Awards (Graduate/Award) [386]

Kansas Optometry Service Scholarships (Graduate, Undergraduate/Scholarship) [5184]

VISTAKON George Mertz and Sheldon Wechsler Residency Awards (All/Award) [387]

Antoinette M. Molinari Memorial Scholarships (Doctorate/Scholarship) [388]

Lucille and Edward R. Roybal Foundation Public Health Scholarships (Graduate, Undergraduate/Scholarship) [7827]

VISTAKON Research Grants (All/Grant) [389]

VSP Research Grants (All/Grant) [390]

Ornithology

Welder Wildlife Foundation Fellowships (Doctorate, Graduate/Fellowship) [9559]

Orthotics prosthetics technology

The Eneslow Pedorthic Institute Scholarships (Undergraduate/Scholarship) [7139]

The Dawn Janisse Scholarships (Undergraduate/Scholarship) [7140]

The Aristotle Mirones Scholarships (Undergraduate/Scholarship) [7141]

The Sidney M. Pols Scholarships (Undergraduate/Scholarship) [7142]

The Dr. William M. Scholl College of Podiatric Medicine Scholarships (Undergraduate/Scholarship) [7143]

Otology

AOS Research Training Fellowships (Graduate/Fellowship) [974]

Otosclerosis

AOS Research Training Fellowships (Graduate/Fellowship) [974]

Packaging

Petroleum Packaging Council Scholarships (Undergraduate/Scholarship) [7217]

Painting (See also Art)

American Watercolor Society Scholarship Program for Art Teachers (Professional development/Scholarship) [1421]

Theodore Rousseau Fellowships (Graduate/Fellowship) [5790]

Slifka Foundation Interdisciplinary Fellowships (Doctorate/Fellowship) [5791]

Pakistani studies

AIPS Post-Doctoral Fellowships (Doctorate/Fellowship) [863]

AIPS Pre-Doctoral Fellowships (Doctorate, Graduate/Fellowship) [864]

Paleontology

Fellowships and Internships Program in Latin America (Graduate/Fellowship, Internship) [8269]

Short-Term Fellowships (Undergraduate, Graduate, Postdoctorate/Fellowship) [8271]

Earl S. Tupper 3-year Postdoctoral Fellowships in Tropical Biology (Postdoctorate/Fellowship) [8272]

Paralegal studies

AAFPE LEX Scholarships (Undergraduate/Scholarship) [526]

AALL Research Funds (Professional development/Grant) [495]

Therese A. Cannon Educational Scholarships (Professional development/Scholarship) [4971]

Gail Goodell Folsom Memorial Scholarships (Undergraduate/Award) [5975]

Judge and Mrs. Robert D. Horowitz Legal Scholarship Fund (Graduate/Scholarship) [8676]

Robert V.A. Jones Canadians Corporate Counsel Awards (Professional development/Award) [2438]

Kentucky Paralegal Association Student Scholarships (Undergraduate/Scholarship) [5251]

AALL/Wolters Kluwer Law & Business Grants (Professional development/Grant) [501]

Samuel Krugliak Legal Scholarship Fund (Undergraduate/Scholarship) [8682]

Monna Mawson Scholarships (Undergraduate/Scholarship) [4659]

NALS of Detroit Scholarships (Undergraduate/Scholarship) [5977]

NALS of Michigan Scholarships (Undergraduate/Award) [5979]

NFPA/PACE Scholarships (Professional development/Scholarship) [6284]

NFPA and Thomson West Scholarships (Undergraduate/Scholarship) [6285]

Pathways to Success Scholarships (Undergraduate/Scholarship) [3954]

St. Louis Paralegal Association Student Scholarships (Undergraduate/Scholarship) [7884]

Ann S. Salsberg Scholarship Awards (Undergraduate/Award, Scholarship) [2323]

SPA Certified Legal Assistant Scholarships (Professional development/Scholarship) [7885]

Hartman E. Stime Scholarships (Undergraduate/Scholarship) [3553]

Vermont Paralegal Organization Scholarships (Undergraduate/Scholarship) [9419]

John D. Voelker Foundation Native American Scholarships (Undergraduate/Scholarship) [9470]

Warner Norcross & Judd LLP Minorty Scholarships (Undergraduate/Scholarship) [9483]

Paramedics

Gail Hartshorn Scholarships (Undergraduate/Scholarship) [7087]

John I. and Madeleine R. Taeni Scholarships (Undergraduate/Scholarship) [8627]

Parapsychology

Eileen J. Garrett Scholarships (Undergraduate/Scholarship) [7052]

Parapsychological Association Research Endowments (All/Grant) [7049]

Alex Tanous Scholarship Awards (Undergraduate/Scholarship) [8807]

Parkinson's disease

APDA Postdoctoral Fellowships (Professional development/Fellowship) [979]

APDA Research Grants (Professional development/Grant) [980]

Clinician Scientist Development Awards (Postgraduate/Fellowship) [7127]

Parkinson's Disease Foundation International Research Grants Program (Postdoctorate/Grant) [7128]

Parks and recreation

National Recreation and Park Association Diversity Scholarships (Undergraduate/Scholarship) [6459]

Thomas and Ruth River International Scholarships (Undergraduate, Graduate/Scholarship) [9756]

George Torkildsen Literary Awards (Professional development/Award) [9757]

Pathology

The Eneslow Pedorthic Institute Scholarships (Undergraduate/Scholarship) [7139]

The Dawn Janisse Scholarships (Undergraduate/Scholarship) [7140]

The Aristotle Mirones Scholarships (Undergraduate/Scholarship) [7141]

The Sidney M. Pols Scholarships (Undergraduate/Scholarship) [7142]

The Dr. William M. Scholl College of Podiatric Medicine Scholarships (Undergraduate/Scholarship) [7143]

Peace studies

Post-Doctoral or Sabbatical Fellowships (Doctorate/Fellowship) [9248]

Rieser Fellowships (Undergraduate/Fellowship) [2209]

Herbert Scoville Jr. Peace Fellowships (Graduate/Fellowship) [8067]

Mary and Elliot Wood Foundation Graduate Scholarship Fund (Graduate/Scholarship) [3930]

Performing arts

AAS Fellowships for Creative and Performing Artists and Writers *(All/Fellowship)* [412]

ACHE Junior and Community College Performing Arts Scholarships *(Undergraduate/Scholarship)* [158]

ASTR Research Fellowships *(Professional development/Fellowship)* [1359]

CBC Spouses Heineken USA Performing Arts Scholarships *(Undergraduate/Scholarship)* [3218]

The John L. Dales Scholarship Fund *(Undergraduate, Vocational/Occupational/Scholarship)* [8069]

Florida Education Fund McKnight Doctoral Fellowships *(Graduate/Fellowship)* [3822]

UAA Ken Gray Endowment Scholarships *(Undergraduate/Scholarship)* [9097]

George E. Judd Scholarships *(Undergraduate/Scholarship)* [8609]

Liberace Scholarship Fund *(Undergraduate/Scholarship)* [5482]

McNamara Family Creative Arts Project Grants *(Graduate, Undergraduate/Grant)* [4579]

Muddy Waters Scholarships *(Undergraduate/Scholarship)* [2155]

Redlands High School Drama Boosters Awards *(Undergraduate/Scholarship)* [7692]

Star-Ledger Scholarships for the Performing Arts *(Undergraduate/Scholarship)* [6649]

Theatre and Performance Art Project Grants *(Professional development/Grant)* [222]

UAA Friends of the Performing Arts Scholarships *(Undergraduate/Scholarship)* [9120]

Wolf Trap Foundation Scholarship Program for Performing Arts Teachers *(Professional development/Scholarship)* [9693]

The Wolf Trap Internship Program *(Graduate, Professional development, Undergraduate/Internship)* [9694]

Personnel administration/human resources

Bison Transport Scholarships *(Undergraduate/Scholarship)* [6897]

C.C.H.R.M.A. Scholarships *(High School, Undergraduate/Scholarship)* [2941]

HSF/General Motors Scholarship Program *(Undergraduate/Scholarship)* [4574]

NPELRA Foundation Scholarships *(Graduate/Scholarship)* [6836]

Barbara Sanchez Scholarships *(Undergraduate/Scholarship)* [8348]

SHRM Certification Scholarships - Individual *(Graduate/Scholarship)* [8349]

SHRM Foundation Regional Academic Scholarships *(Graduate, Undergraduate/Scholarship)* [8350]

Pesticide science

Professional Women in Pest Management Scholarships (PWIPM) *(Graduate, Professional development/Scholarship)* [6438]

Pharmaceutical sciences

American Foundation for Pharmaceutical Education Gateway Research Scholarships *(Professional development/Scholarship)* [756]

American Foundation for Pharmaceutical Education Pre-Doctoral Fellowships in the Pharmaceutical Sciences *(Doctorate/Fellowship)* [757]

Dr. Feroz Ahmed Memorial Educational Post-Graduate Scholarships *(Doctorate, Postgraduate/Scholarship)* [8216]

Minority Pharmacy Faculty New Investigator Grants *(Professional development/Grant)* [759]

Minority Student Pre-Doctoral Fellowship Program *(Doctorate, Graduate/Fellowship)* [761]

Pharmacy Faculty Fellowships in Community Pharmacy Practice *(Postdoctorate/Fellowship)* [762]

Pharmacy Faculty Fellowships in Geriatric Pharmacy/Geriatric Pharmaceutical Science *(Postdoctorate/Fellowship)* [763]

Pharmacology

Epilepsy Foundation Pre-doctoral Research Training Fellowships *(Graduate/Grant)* [3663]

Pharmacology/Toxicology Post Doctoral Fellowships *(Postdoctorate/Fellowship)* [7235]

Pharmacology/Toxicology Pre Doctoral Fellowships *(Doctorate/Fellowship)* [7236]

Pharmacology/Toxicology Research Starter Grants *(Doctorate/Grant)* [7237]

Pharmacology/Toxicology Sabbatical Fellowships *(Postdoctorate/Fellowship)* [7238]

School of Pharmacy Continuing Student Scholarships *(Undergraduate/Scholarship)* [9370]

University of Wisconsin-Madison Pharmacy New Student Scholarships *(Undergraduate/Scholarship)* [9381]

Pharmacy

Armenian American Pharmacists' Association Scholarships *(Doctorate, Graduate/Scholarship)* [1582]

ASHP Student Research Awards *(Doctorate/Award)* [1259]

Eleanor McWilliams Burke Fund *(Undergraduate/Scholarship)* [3762]

Joseph R. Calder, Jr., MD Scholarship Fund *(Undergraduate/Scholarship)* [3763]

Christian Pharmacist Fellowship International *(All/Fellowship)* [2783]

J.C. and Rheba Cobb Memorial Scholarships *(Undergraduate/Scholarship)* [6198]

DAAD Study Scholarship Awards *(Graduate/Scholarship)* [4116]

Epilepsy Foundation Pre-doctoral Research Training Fellowships *(Graduate/Grant)* [3663]

Thomas W. Gallagher Scholarships Fund *(Undergraduate/Scholarship)* [8667]

John W. Webb Lecture Awards *(Professional development/Award)* [1260]

Jason Lang Scholarships *(Undergraduate/Scholarship)* [252]

Maryland Poison Center Clinical Toxicology Fellowships *(Doctorate, Graduate/Fellowship)* [5654]

Merck Frosst Canada Ltd. Postgraduate Pharmacy Fellowships *(Doctorate, Postgraduate/Fellowship)* [1771]

Minority Pharmacy Faculty New Investigator Grants *(Professional development/Grant)* [759]

Minority Student Gateway to Research Scholarships *(Professional development/Scholarship)* [760]

NAAF Aboriginal Health Careers Bursary and Scholarships *(Graduate, Undergraduate/Scholarship)* [5992]

National Community Pharmacists Association Presidential Scholarships *(Undergraduate/Scholarship)* [6199]

National Community Pharmacists Association Summer Internship Programs *(Undergraduate/Internship)* [6200]

Pharmaceutics Post Doctoral Fellowships *(Postdoctorate/Fellowship)* [7231]

Pharmaceutics Pre Doctoral Fellowships *(Doctorate/Fellowship)* [7232]

Pharmaceutics Research Starter Grants *(Doctorate/Grant)* [7233]

Pharmaceutics Sabbatical Fellowships *(Postdoctorate/Fellowship)* [7234]

Pharmacy Faculty Fellowships in Community Pharmacy Practice *(Postdoctorate/Fellowship)* [762]

Pharmacy Faculty New Investigator Grants Program *(Doctorate/Grant)* [764]

Pharmacy Student Scholarship Program *(Postdoctorate/Scholarship)* [6060]

Neil Pruitt, Sr. Memorial Scholarships *(Undergraduate/Scholarship)* [6201]

Rho Chi, AFPE First Year Graduate Fellowships *(Doctorate, Graduate/Fellowship)* [7781]

Rho Chi Society Clinical Research Scholarships *(Postdoctorate/Scholarship)* [7782]

Lucille and Edward R. Roybal Foundation Public Health Scholarships *(Graduate, Undergraduate/Scholarship)* [7827]

Scholarships for Emigres in the Health Sciences *(Undergraduate/Scholarship)* [5157]

School of Pharmacy Continuing Student Scholarships *(Undergraduate/Scholarship)* [9370]

Willard B. Simmons Sr. Memorial Scholarships *(Undergraduate/Scholarship)* [6202]

TSHP R&E Foundation Scholarship Program *(Undergraduate, Graduate/Scholarship)* [8972]

University of Wisconsin-Madison Pharmacy New Student Scholarships *(Undergraduate/Scholarship)* [9381]

Washington Higher Education Coordinating Board Health Professional Scholarships *(Graduate/Scholarship)* [9506]

Western Michigan Society of Health-System Pharmacists Scholarships *(Undergraduate/Scholarship)* [9577]

Philanthropy

William Diaz Fellowships *(Professional development/Fellowship)* [6729]

Edward G. Kaelber Scholarships *(Undergraduate/Scholarship)* [5582]

David Stevenson Fellowships *(Doctorate, Graduate, Professional development/Fellowship)* [6730]

Philology

Thesaurus Linguae Latinae Fellowships (TTL) *(Doctorate/Fellowship)* [987]

Philosophy

Father Rutilio Grande Scholarships *(Graduate, Undergraduate/Scholarship)* [7893]

Ameen Rihani Scholarship Program *(Undergraduate/Scholarship)* [1492]

Photogrammetry

Robert E. Altenhofen Memorial Scholarships *(Graduate, Undergraduate/Scholarship)* [1665]

ERDAS Internships *(Graduate/Internship)* [1667]

Francis H. Moffitt Memorial Scholarships *(Graduate, Undergraduate/Scholarship)* [1670]

The Kenneth J. Osborn Memorial Scholarships *(Undergraduate/Scholarship)* [1671]

Paul R. Wolf Memorial Scholarships *(Graduate/Scholarship)* [1672]

Z/I Imaging Scholarships *(Graduate/Scholarship)* [1673]

Photography

Bob Baxter Scholarships *(Graduate, Undergraduate/Scholarship)* [6448]

Reid Blackburn Scholarships *(Undergraduate/Scholarship)* [6449]

Donald Franklin Bradley Memorial Scholarships *(Undergraduate/Scholarship)* [7470]

IS&T Raymond Davis Scholarships *(Graduate, Undergraduate/Scholarship)* [8352]

Bob East Scholarships *(Graduate, Undergraduate/Scholarship)* [6450]

Don English Memorial Scholarships *(Undergraduate/Scholarship)* [7486]

Bruce T. and Jackie Mahi Erickson Grants *(Graduate, Undergraduate/Grant)* [5210]

Allison E. Fisher Scholarships *(Graduate, Undergraduate/Scholarship)* [3805]

The Gallery Collection's Greeting Card Scholarships *(Undergraduate/Scholarship)* [4035]

Glendale Latino Association Scholarships *(High School, Undergraduate/Scholarship)* [4161]

Elizabeth Greenhalgh Memorial Scholarships in Journalism, Graphic Arts, or Photography *(Graduate, Undergraduate/Scholarship)* [9699]

International Foodservice Editorial Council Scholarships *(Graduate, Undergraduate/Scholarship)* [4935]

Kit C. King Graduate Scholarships *(Graduate/Scholarship)* [6451]

Manzer-Keener-Wefler Scholarships *(Undergraduate/Scholarship)* [8686]

NPPF Still and Multimedia Scholarships *(Undergraduate/Scholarship)* [6452]

Scott Pearlman Field Awards for Science and Exploration *(Professional development/Award)* [3698]

Television News Scholarships *(Undergraduate/Scholarship)* [6453]

UAA Kimura Scholarship Fund Photography Scholarships *(Undergraduate/Scholarship)* [9123]
Worldstudio AIGA Scholarships *(Graduate, Undergraduate/Scholarship)* [9761]

Photography, Journalistic

AAJA/COX Foundation Scholarships *(Graduate, Undergraduate/Scholarship)* [1641]
Tom Hanson Photojournalism Awards *(Professional development/Internship)* [2515]

Physical sciences

A&WMA Louisiana Section Scholarships *(Graduate, Undergraduate/Scholarship)* [113]
American Council of Independent Laboratories Scholarships *(Undergraduate/Scholarship)* [669]
American Sokol Merit Awards *(Undergraduate/Scholarship)* [1379]
Casey Bennett Scholarships *(Undergraduate/Scholarship)* [3740]
CEPS-Tyco Scholarships *(Undergraduate/Scholarship)* [9250]
Roy Cooper Scholarships *(Undergraduate/Scholarship)* [5397]
Harold Leeming Memorial Scholarships *(Undergraduate/Scholarship)* [7663]
Michigan Society of Fellows Three-Year Fellowships *(Postdoctorate/Fellowship)* [5827]
Ohio Valley Chapter Scholarships *(Undergraduate/Scholarship)* [1815]
Postdoctoral Fellowships in Conservation Science *(Doctorate/Fellowship)* [4145]
Paul and Ellen Ruckes Scholarships *(Graduate, Undergraduate/Scholarship)* [753]
Graduate Fellowship Program - Peter Verhofstadt Fellowships (GFP) *(Graduate/Fellowship)* [8084]

Physical therapy

The Achieve Physical Therapy & Fitness Scholarships *(Doctorate/Scholarship)* [8737]
AMBUCS Scholarships for Therapists Program *(Graduate, Undergraduate/Scholarship)* [371]
APTA Minority Scholarships - Faculty Development Scholarships *(Postdoctorate/Scholarship)* [999]
APTA Minority Scholarships - Physical Therapist Assistant Students *(All/Scholarship)* [1000]
APTA Minority Scholarships - Physical Therapist Students *(All/Scholarship)* [1001]
Eleanor McWilliams Burke Fund *(Undergraduate/Scholarship)* [3762]
Dave Couch Memorial Scholarships *(Undergraduate/Scholarship)* [7067]
Margaret Dowell-Gravatt, M.D. Scholarships *(Undergraduate/Scholarship)* [2059]
MPTA Doctoral Scholarships *(Doctorate/Scholarship)* [5913]
The Shanon Newberry Physical Therapy Scholarship Endowment *(Doctorate/Scholarship)* [8741]
The Physical Therapy Faculty Scholarship Endowment *(Graduate/Scholarship)* [8742]
Scholarships for Emigres in the Health Sciences *(Undergraduate/Scholarship)* [5157]
Everett Oscar Shimp Memorial Scholarships *(Undergraduate/Scholarship)* [7113]
The Sibyl Jennings Vorheis Memorial Undergraduate Scholarships *(Undergraduate/Scholarship)* [3926]
Monica M. Weaver Memorial Fund *(Undergraduate/Scholarship)* [3795]

Physics

AAPM Fellowships for Graduate Study in Medical Physics *(Graduate/Fellowship)* [528]
AAPM Minority Undergraduate Summer Experience Fellowships (MUSE) *(Undergraduate/Fellowship)* [529]
AAPM Summer Undergraduate Fellowships *(Undergraduate/Fellowship)* [530]
AFCEA Scholarship for Working Professionals *(Graduate/Scholarship)* [1554]
Alaska Aerospace Development Corporation Scholarships *(Undergraduate/Scholarship)* [9130]
American Institute of Physics Congressional Sci-

ence Fellowships *(Doctorate/Fellowship)* [866]
American Institute of Physics State Department Science Fellowships *(Doctorate/Fellowship)* [867]
American Physical Society Minority Undergraduate Scholarships *(Undergraduate/Scholarship)* [996]
Michael P. Anderson Scholarships in Space Science *(Undergraduate/Scholarship)* [6484]
APS Scholarships for Minority Undergraduate Physics Majors *(Undergraduate/Scholarship)* [6485]
Armed Forces Communications and Electronics Association Fellowships *(Doctorate, Graduate/Fellowship)* [1555]
Harvey Washington Banks Scholarships in Astronomy *(Undergraduate/Scholarship)* [6486]
M. Hildred Blewett Fellowships *(Postdoctorate/Scholarship)* [997]
William E. "Buck" Bragunier Scholarships *(Undergraduate/Scholarship)* [1556]
Charles F. Brandenburg Memorial Scholarships *(Undergraduate/Scholarship)* [2622]
Charles S. Brown Scholarships in Physics *(Graduate, Undergraduate/Scholarship)* [6487]
Lt. General Douglas D. Buchholz Memorial Scholarships *(Undergraduate/Scholarship)* [1557]
Burroughs Wellcome Fund Career Awards at the Scientific Interface *(Doctorate, Postdoctorate/Fellowship)* [2211]
Burroughs Wellcome Fund Collaborative Research Travel Grants *(Doctorate/Grant)* [2212]
Julian E. Carnes Scholarship Fund *(Undergraduate/Scholarship)* [3891]
CfA Postdoctoral Fellowships *(Postdoctorate/Fellowship)* [4471]
Clay Postdoctoral Fellowships *(Postdoctorate/Fellowship)* [4472]
SRC NRI Hans J. Coufal Fellowships *(Graduate/Fellowship)* [8086]
D&A Florida Scholarships *(Undergraduate/Scholarship)* [8597]
DEPS Graduate Scholarship Program *(Graduate/Scholarship)* [3455]
Disabled War Veterans Scholarships *(Undergraduate/Scholarship)* [1559]
Peggy Dixon Two-Year Scholarships *(Undergraduate/Scholarship)* [8438]
DOE Computational Science Graduate Fellowships (DOE CSGF) *(Doctorate, Graduate/Fellowship)* [5306]
Robert A. Ellis Scholarships in Physics *(Undergraduate/Scholarship)* [6488]
Frank Fong Scholarships *(Undergraduate/Scholarship)* [8290]
Glendale Latino Association Scholarships *(High School, Undergraduate/Scholarship)* [4161]
Helm Family Scholarships *(Undergraduate/Scholarship)* [7932]
Elmer S. Imes Scholarships in Physics *(Undergraduate/Scholarship)* [6489]
Robert C. and Judith L. Knapp Scholarships *(Graduate, Undergraduate/Scholarship)* [3867]
Imelda and Ralph LeMar Scholarship Program *(Undergraduate/Scholarship)* [3201]
Herbert Levy Memorial Endowment Fund Scholarships *(Undergraduate/Scholarship)* [8439]
Barbara Lotze Scholarships for Future Teachers *(Undergraduate/Scholarship)* [533]
Lockheed Martin Graduate Scholarships *(Graduate/Scholarship)* [1560]
Lockheed Martin IT Scholarships *(Undergraduate/Scholarship)* [1561]
Walter Samuel McAfee Scholarships in Space Physics *(Undergraduate/Scholarship)* [6490]
Ronald E. McNair Scholarships in Space and Optical Physics *(Undergraduate/Scholarship)* [6491]
Willie Hobbs Moore Scholarships *(Undergraduate/Scholarship)* [6492]
Harry L. Morrison Scholarships *(Undergraduate/Scholarship)* [6493]
National GEM Consortium - PhD Science Fellowships *(Doctorate, Graduate/Fellowship)* [6307]
NDSEG Fellowships *(Graduate/Fellowship)* [6239]
Nonproliferation Graduate Fellowships Program (NGFP) *(Graduate/Fellowship)* [7033]
Northampton County Medical Society Alliance Scholarships *(Undergraduate/Scholarship)* [6794]
NPSC Fellowships *(Graduate/Fellowship)* [6440]

AFCEA General Emmett Paige Scholarships *(Undergraduate/Scholarship)* [1562]
RSNA/AAPM Fellowships for Graduate Study in Medical Physics *(Graduate/Fellowship)* [531]
Rubber Division American Chemical Society Undergraduate Scholarships *(Undergraduate/Scholarship)* [7829]
Ralph W. Shrader Diversity Scholarships *(Graduate/Scholarship)* [1563]
Sigma Pi Sigma Undergraduate Research Awards *(Undergraduate/Grant)* [8440]
Julia Viola Simms Science Scholarships *(Postgraduate/Scholarship)* [2128]
Sloan Research Fellowships *(Doctorate/Fellowship)* [8235]
SPS Future Teacher Scholarships *(Undergraduate/Scholarship)* [8441]
SPS Leadership Scholarships *(Undergraduate/Scholarship)* [8442]
Graduate Fellowship Program - Peter Verhofstadt Fellowships (GFP) *(Graduate/Fellowship)* [8084]
Veterans of Enduring Freedom (Afghanistan) and Iraqi Freedom Scholarships *(Undergraduate/Scholarship)* [1565]
Arthur BC Walker Scholarships *(Undergraduate/Scholarship)* [6494]
Washington Higher Education Coordinating Board Health Professional Scholarships *(Graduate/Scholarship)* [9506]
AFCEA General John A. Wickham Scholarships *(Undergraduate/Scholarship)* [1566]
Marine Corps Sgt. Jeannette L. Winters Memorial Scholarships *(Undergraduate/Scholarship)* [1567]
Women In Defense HORIZONS Scholarships *(Graduate, Undergraduate/Scholarship)* [9696]
Women in Science and Technology Scholarships *(Doctorate, Graduate, Master's, Undergraduate/Scholarship)* [9442]
Xavier University Departmental Scholarships *(Undergraduate/Scholarship)* [9780]
Xerox Technical Minority Scholarships *(Graduate, Undergraduate/Scholarship)* [9787]

Physiology

Bruce and Betty Alberts Endowed Scholarships in Physiology *(Undergraduate/Scholarship)* [5611]
American Physiological Society Post-doctoral Fellowships in Physiological Genomics (APS) *(Postdoctorate/Fellowship)* [1003]
APS/NIDDK Minority Travel Fellowship Awards *(Graduate, Postdoctorate/Fellowship)* [1004]
Dominio of Canada Insurance Scholarships *(Graduate/Scholarship)* [7324]
Epilepsy Foundation Pre-doctoral Research Training Fellowships *(Graduate/Grant)* [3663]
Fellowships and Internships Program in Latin America *(Graduate/Fellowship, Internship)* [8269]
Heart and Stroke Foundation of Canada/Physiotherapy Foundation of Canada Scholarships in Physiotherapy Research *(Doctorate, Master's/Scholarship)* [7325]
Indiana State Alumni Association Rural Health Scholarships *(Undergraduate/Scholarship)* [4748]
Mountain Memorial Scholarships *(Undergraduate/Scholarship)* [5624]
Physiotherapy Foundation of Canada Research Grants *(Professional development/Grant)* [7326]
Porter Physiology Development Fellowship Awards *(Doctorate/Fellowship)* [1005]
B.E. Schnurr Memorial Fund Research Grants *(Professional development/Grant)* [7327]
Scholarships for Emigres in the Health Sciences *(Undergraduate/Scholarship)* [5157]
Short-Term Fellowships *(Undergraduate, Graduate, Postdoctorate/Fellowship)* [8271]
Caroline tum Suden Professional Opportunity Awards *(Postdoctorate, Professional development/Award)* [1006]
Earl S. Tupper 3-year Postdoctoral Fellowships in Tropical Biology *(Postdoctorate/Fellowship)* [8272]
Ann Collins Whitmore Memorial Scholarships (ACWMS) *(Graduate/Scholarship)* [7328]

Plastic surgery

American Association of Plastic Surgeons Academic Scholars Program *(Graduate/Grant)* [535]

Podiatry

Zelda Walling Vicha Memorial Scholarships *(Undergraduate, Vocational/Occupational/Scholarship)* [1319]

Polish studies (See also Area and ethnic studies)

Falcon Achievement Scholarships *(Undergraduate/Scholarship)* [7371]

Harriet Irsay Scholarships *(Graduate, Undergraduate/Scholarship)* [869]

Kosciuszko Foundation Graduate Study and Research in Poland Scholarships *(Graduate/Scholarship)* [5296]

Kosciuszko Foundation Tuition Scholarships *(Graduate/Scholarship)* [5297]

Kosciuszko Foundation Year Abroad Scholarships *(Graduate, Undergraduate/Scholarship)* [5298]

Massachusetts Federation of Polish Women's Clubs Scholarships *(Undergraduate/Scholarship)* [5299]

Polish American Club of North Jersey Scholarships *(Graduate, Undergraduate/Scholarship)* [5300]

Polish National Alliance of Brooklyn, USA Scholarships *(Undergraduate/Scholarship)* [5301]

Tadeusz Sendzimir Scholarships *(Undergraduate/Scholarship)* [4460]

Dr. Marie E. Zakrzewski Medical Scholarships *(Doctorate/Scholarship)* [5302]

Political science

American Enterprise Institute National Research Initiative Fellowships (NRI) *(Graduate/Fellowship)* [718]

American Institute for Economic Research Student Summer Fellowships *(Doctorate, Graduate, Undergraduate/Fellowship)* [854]

American Political Science Association Federal Executives Fellowships *(Professional development/Fellowship)* [1014]

American Political Science Association/MCI Scholarships *(Postdoctorate/Scholarship)* [1016]

American Political Science Association Political Scientists Fellowships *(Postdoctorate/Fellowship)* [1017]

APSA Congressional Fellowships *(Professional development/Fellowship)* [4131]

Avista Corporation Minds in Motion Scholarships *(Undergraduate/Scholarship)* [5412]

UAA Mark A. Beltz Scholarships *(Graduate, Undergraduate, Vocational/Occupational/Scholarship)* [9087]

UAA Pat Brakke Political Science Scholarships *(Undergraduate/Scholarship)* [9088]

Sam Bull Memorial Scholarships *(Undergraduate/Scholarship)* [227]

Cecil E. Burney Scholarships *(Undergraduate/Scholarship)* [2940]

CIGNA Healthcare Graduate Scholarships *(Graduate/Scholarship)* [6290]

CIGNA Healthcare Undergraduate Scholarships *(Undergraduate/Scholarship)* [6291]

D&A Florida Scholarships *(Undergraduate/Scholarship)* [8597]

Douglas-Coldwell Foundation Scholarships in Social Affairs *(Graduate/Scholarship)* [3474]

UAA Governor William A. Egan Scholarships *(Undergraduate/Scholarship)* [9091]

Garikian Scholarship Fund *(Undergraduate/Scholarship)* [1593]

Senator James Gladstone Memorial Scholarships *(Graduate, Undergraduate/Scholarship)* [228]

Randy Green Memorial Scholarship Fund *(High School/Scholarship)* [3318]

Enid Hall Griswold Memorial Scholarships *(Undergraduate/Scholarship)* [6499]

Harkness Fellowships in Health Care Policy and Practice *(Doctorate, Graduate/Fellowship)* [3020]

Hench Post-Dissertation Fellowships *(Postdoctorate/Fellowship)* [419]

John Peter Humphrey Student Fellowships *(Graduate/Fellowship)* [2443]

KSA Scholarships *(Undergraduate/Scholarship)* [5262]

Lazarian Graduate Scholarships *(Graduate/Scholarship)* [1578]

William P. McHugh Memorial Fund Award *(Doctorate, Graduate/Fellowship)* [1141]

Minorities in Government Finance Scholarships *(Graduate, Undergraduate/Scholarship)* [4199]

MPAC-DC Graduate Policy Fellowships *(Graduate/Fellowship)* [5960]

The National Endowment for the Humanities Fellowships *(Doctorate, Graduate/Fellowship)* [1142]

National Iranian American Council Fellowships *(Graduate, Undergraduate/Fellowship)* [6365]

Nonproliferation Graduate Fellowships Program (NGFP) *(Graduate/Fellowship)* [7033]

NPELRA Foundation Scholarships *(Graduate/Scholarship)* [6836]

Pi Gamma Mu Scholarships *(Graduate/Scholarship)* [7330]

Thomas R. Pickering Graduate Foreign Affairs Fellowships *(Graduate/Fellowship)* [9619]

Political Leadership Scholarships *(Undergraduate/Scholarship)* [7415]

Political Studies Scholarships *(Undergraduate, Graduate/Scholarship)* [9447]

Betty Rendel Scholarships *(Undergraduate/Scholarship)* [6288]

Bertha and Byron L. Reppert Scholarship Fund *(Undergraduate/Scholarship)* [3957]

Ameen Rihani Scholarship Program *(Undergraduate/Scholarship)* [1492]

Fauneil J. Rinn Scholarships *(Undergraduate/Scholarship)* [8206]

Charles and Ruth Ronin Memorial Scholarships *(Undergraduate/Scholarship)* [7709]

Donald Smiley Prize *(Professional development/Prize)* [2585]

John Streiff Memorial Scholarships *(Undergraduate/Scholarship)* [5467]

TCA Turkish American Scholarships *(Undergraduate/Scholarship)* [8978]

Texas Muslims Scholarship Fund (TMSF) *(Graduate, Undergraduate/Scholarship)* [4006]

The United States Department of State, Bureau of Educational & Cultural Affairs Fellowships *(Doctorate, Graduate/Fellowship)* [1143]

Jill Vickers Prize *(Professional development/Prize)* [2586]

Women In Defense HORIZONS Scholarships *(Graduate, Undergraduate/Scholarship)* [9696]

Urashi Zen Scholarships *(Undergraduate/Scholarship)* [7429]

Population studies

Phyllis P. Harris Scholarships *(Postgraduate/Award)* [2463]

Portuguese studies (See also Area and ethnic studies)

Luso-American Education Foundation G-1 Grants *(Professional development/Grant)* [5542]

Luso-American Education Foundation G-2 Grants *(Professional development/Grant)* [5543]

Luso-American Education Foundation G-3 Grants *(Postgraduate/Grant)* [5544]

Poultry science

Canadian Poultry Research Council Postgraduate Scholarships *(Postgraduate/Scholarship)* [2588]

National Poultry and Food Distributors Association Scholarships *(Undergraduate/Scholarship)* [6444]

Practical nursing (See Nursing)

Pre-Columbian studies

Alexander Graham Bell Canada Graduate Scholarship Program *(Doctorate, Master's/Scholarship)* [6571]

Dumbarton Oaks Fellowships *(Doctorate, Graduate/Fellowship)* [3549]

Dumbarton Oaks Junior Fellowships *(Graduate/Fellowship)* [3550]

Natural Sciences and Engineering Research Council Postgraduate Scholarships *(Doctorate/Scholarship)* [6572]

Post-Doctoral Teaching Fellowships *(Postdoctorate/Fellowship)* [3551]

Preservation

SPOOM Research Grants *(Graduate/Grant)* [8463]

Printing trades and industries

Don Bailey Scholarships *(Undergraduate/Scholarship)* [6309]

FIRST Operator Certification Scholarships *(Undergraduate/Scholarship)* [3812]

TCA Turkish American Scholarships *(Undergraduate/Scholarship)* [8978]

Xerox Technical Minority Scholarships *(Graduate, Undergraduate/Scholarship)* [9787]

Printing--History

Katharine Pantzer Fellowships in the British Book Trades *(Professional development/Fellowship)* [2085]

Printmaking

Gravure Publishing Council Scholarships *(Undergraduate, Graduate/Scholarship)* [4320]

Lewis-Clark State College Presidential Technical Out-of-State Scholarships *(Undergraduate/Scholarship)* [5447]

Harry V. Quadracci Memorial Scholarships *(Undergraduate, Graduate/Scholarship)* [4321]

Psychiatry

Associates in Behavioral Health Scholarships *(Graduate/Scholarship)* [7398]

Patricia Pownder Conolly Memorial Scholarships *(Undergraduate/Scholarship)* [5777]

Daland Fellowships in Clinical Investigation *(Doctorate/Fellowship)* [989]

Depression and ADHD Fellowships *(Postdoctorate/Fellowship)* [5268]

Epilepsy Foundation Research and Training Fellowships for Clinicians *(Doctorate, Professional development/Grant)* [3665]

Linda Lyons Memorial Scholarship Fund *(Undergraduate/Scholarship)* [5779]

Psychology

American Psychoanalytic Association Fellowships *(Doctorate, Postdoctorate, Professional development/Fellowship)* [1027]

American Psychology-Law Society Dissertation Awards *(Graduate/Award)* [1043]

American Psychology-Law Society Early Career Professional Grants-In-Aid *(Professional development/Grant)* [1044]

American Psychology-Law Society Student Grants-In-Aid *(Graduate/Grant)* [1045]

APAGS-CLGBTC Grant Program *(Graduate/Grant)* [1029]

APAGS' Committee on Ethic Minority Affairs (CEMA) Grant Program *(Graduate/Grant)* [1030]

APF/COGDOP Graduate Research Scholarships *(Doctorate, Graduate/Scholarship)* [1037]

Tara Lynne Arnold Scholarships *(Undergraduate/Scholarship)* [8716]

ASPPB Larry J. Bass Jr., PhD. Memorial Scholar-

ship Awards *(Graduate, Undergraduate/Grant)*
[1031]
Associated Women for Pepperdine Scholarships
(AWP) *(Undergraduate/Scholarship)* [7167]
Associates in Behavioral Health Scholarships
(Graduate/Scholarship) [7398]
Association for Psychological Science Student
Grants (APS) *(Graduate, Undergraduate/Grant)*
[1845]
Delores A. Auzenne Fellowships *(Postgraduate/Fellowship)* [3818]
UAA Dr. Jon Baker Memorial Scholarships *(Graduate, Undergraduate, Vocational/Occupational/Scholarship)* [9085]
Benton-Meier Neuropsychology Scholarships
(Graduate/Scholarship) [1038]
Bisexual Foundation Scholarships *(Graduate/Scholarship)* [8471]
Frances P. Bolton Fellowships *(Doctorate/Fellowship)* [7051]
Patricia Pownder Conolly Memorial Scholarships
(Undergraduate/Scholarship) [5777]
CPA-F Minority Scholarships *(Graduate/Scholarship)* [2267]
Meredith P. Crawford Fellowships in I/O Psychology
(Doctorate/Fellowship) [4632]
Diversity Dissertation Scholarships *(Doctorate/Fellowship)* [1032]
Epilepsy Foundation Pre-doctoral Research Training
Fellowships *(Graduate/Grant)* [3663]
ETS Postdoctoral Fellowships *(Postdoctorate/Fellowship)* [3609]
Nancy B. Forest and L. Michael Honaker Master's
Scholarships for Research *(Doctorate, Graduate/Scholarship)* [1033]
Violet and Cyril Franks Scholarships *(Graduate/Scholarship)* [1039]
Garikian Scholarship Fund *(Undergraduate/Scholarship)* [1593]
Harold Gulliksen Psychometric Research Fellowships *(Doctorate, Graduate/Fellowship)* [3610]
Lee Hakel Graduate Student Scholarships *(Doctorate/Scholarship)* [8354]
Sylvia Taylor Johnson Minority Fellowships in Educational Measurement *(Doctorate/Fellowship)*
[3611]
Leslie W. Joyce and Paul W. Thayer Graduate Fellowships in I-O Psychology *(Doctorate/Fellowship)* [8355]
UAA Chris L. Kleinke Scholarships *(Graduate, Undergraduate/Scholarship)* [9101]
Elizabeth Munsterberg Koppitz Child Psychology
Graduate Fellowships *(Graduate/Fellowship)*
[1040]
Linda Lyons Memorial Scholarship Fund *(Undergraduate/Scholarship)* [5779]
Malyon-Smith Scholarships *(Graduate/Scholarship)*
[8472]
Clara Mayo Grants *(Graduate/Grant)* [8474]
Scott Mesh Honorary Scholarships for Research in
Psychology *(Graduate/Fellowship)* [1034]
Minority Medical Student Fellowships in HIV Psychiatry *(Undergraduate/Fellowship)* [1025]
NAJA Scholarships *(Graduate/Scholarship)* [6086]
NASP-ERT Minority Scholarships for Graduate
Training in School Psychology *(Graduate/Scholarship)* [6113]
New Jersey Psychological Association Scholarships
for Minority Graduate Students *(Postgraduate/Scholarship)* [6655]
Pi Gamma Mu Scholarships *(Graduate/Scholarship)* [7330]
David Pilon Scholarships for Training in Professional
Psychology *(Doctorate, Graduate/Scholarship)*
[1035]
Esther Katz Rosen Fellowships *(Graduate/Fellowship)* [1041]
Saleem Shah Early Career Development Awards
(Doctorate/Award) [1046]
SPPSI Grants-In-Aid Program *(Graduate, Postdoctorate/Grant)* [8475]
Taylor Statten Memorial Fellowships *(Graduate/Scholarship)* [9342]
Charles T. and Judith A. Tart Student Incentive
Awards *(Graduate, Postdoctorate, Undergraduate/Grant)* [7053]

Mary L. Tenopyr Graduate Student Scholarships
(Doctorate/Scholarship) [8356]

Public administration

AGBU Scholarships *(Graduate/Loan)* [1573]
American Society of Military Comptrollers National
Scholarship Program *(Undergraduate/Scholarship)* [1305]
Marvin A. Andrews Scholarships/Internships *(Graduate/Internship, Scholarship)* [1517]
Association of Government Accountants Undergraduate/Graduate Scholarships for Community
Service Accomplishments *(Graduate, Undergraduate/Fellowship, Scholarship)* [1789]
Association of Government Accountants Undergraduate/Graduate Scholarships for Full-time
study *(Graduate, Undergraduate/Fellowship,
Scholarship)* [1790]
Association of Government Accountants Undergraduate/Graduate Scholarships for Part-time
study *(Graduate, Undergraduate/Fellowship,
Scholarship)* [1791]
Center for Congressional and Presidential Studies
Endowment (CPPS) *(Graduate, Undergraduate/Scholarship)* [1404]
CIGNA Healthcare Graduate Scholarships *(Graduate/Scholarship)* [6290]
CIGNA Healthcare Undergraduate Scholarships
(Undergraduate/Scholarship) [6291]
Charles A. Esser Memorial Scholarships *(Graduate/Scholarship)* [1518]
HAESF Professional Internship Program *(Doctorate/Internship)* [4641]
HAESF Senior Leaders and Scholars Fellowships
(Professional development/Fellowship) [4642]
Michael Koizumi APWA Scholarships *(Undergraduate/Scholarship)* [1061]
Sue A. Malone Scholarships *(Doctorate, Graduate/Scholarship)* [5188]
Minorities in Government Finance Scholarships
(Graduate, Undergraduate/Scholarship) [4199]
George A. Nielsen Public Investor Scholarships
(Graduate, Undergraduate/Scholarship) [4200]
George H. Nofer Scholarships for Law and Public
Policy *(Doctorate, Graduate/Scholarship)* [2049]
NPELRA Foundation Scholarships *(Graduate/Scholarship)* [6836]
Pi Gamma Mu Scholarships *(Graduate/Scholarship)* [7330]
Thomas R. Pickering Graduate Foreign Affairs Fellowships *(Graduate/Fellowship)* [9619]
Political Leadership Scholarships *(Undergraduate/Scholarship)* [7415]
Fauneil J. Rinn Scholarships *(Undergraduate/Scholarship)* [8206]
Washington City/County Management Association
Scholarships *(Graduate/Scholarship)* [9494]

Public affairs

UAA Elaine Atwood Scholarships *(Undergraduate/Scholarship)* [9084]
Cleveland Executive Fellowships (CEF) *(Professional development/Fellowship)* [2903]
Congressional Hispanic Caucus Institute Graduate
and Young Professional Fellowships *(Doctorate,
Graduate/Fellowship)* [3224]
Congressional Hispanic Caucus Institute Public
Policy Fellowships *(Graduate/Fellowship)* [3225]
Coro Fellows Program in Public Affairs *(Graduate/Fellowship)* [3255]
The Jennifer Curtis Byler Scholarships *(Undergraduate/Scholarship)* [6533]
Jane R. Glaser Scholarships *(Undergraduate/Scholarship)* [1405]
Bryce Harlow Fellowship Program *(Graduate/Fellowship)* [4395]
IWPR/GW Fellowships in Women's Public Policy
Research *(Graduate/Fellowship)* [4836]
MPAC-DC Graduate Policy Fellowships *(Graduate/Fellowship)* [5960]
Clifford Roberts Graduate Fellowships *(Doctorate/Fellowship)* [3614]
Stanley M. Schoenfeld Memorial Scholarships
(Postgraduate/Fellowship) [6673]

Theodore C. Sorensen Fellowships *(All/Fellowship)*
[5242]
TCA Turkish American Scholarships *(Undergraduate/Scholarship)* [8978]
UAA GCI, Inc. Scholarships *(Undergraduate/Scholarship)* [9121]

Public health

AAHD Scholarships *(Graduate, Undergraduate/Scholarship)* [481]
A&WMA-GWS Scholarships *(Graduate, Undergraduate/Scholarship)* [111]
A&WMA Louisiana Section Scholarships *(Graduate,
Undergraduate/Scholarship)* [113]
American Lung Association/AAAAI Allergic Respiratory Diseases Awards *(Doctorate/Grant)* [908]
American Lung Association Biomedical Research
Grants *(Doctorate/Grant)* [909]
American Lung Association Clinical Patient Care
Research Grants *(Doctorate/Grant)* [910]
American Lung Association Dalsemer Research
Grants *(Doctorate/Grant)* [911]
American Lung Association DeSousa Awards *(Doctorate/Grant)* [912]
American Lung Association Lung Cancer Discovery
Awards *(Doctorate/Grant)* [913]
American Lung Association Senior Research Training Fellowships *(Doctorate/Fellowship)* [914]
American Lung Association Social-Behavioral Research Grants *(Doctorate/Grant)* [915]
Arkansas Public Health Association Scholarships
(Undergraduate/Scholarship) [1546]
Elizabeth and Sherman Asche Memorial Scholarships *(Graduate, Undergraduate/Scholarship)*
[1695]
ASPH/CDC/PRC Minority Health Fellowships *(Doctorate/Fellowship)* [1862]
ASPH/CDC Public Health Fellowships *(Doctorate,
Graduate/Fellowship)* [1863]
ASPH/CDC Public Health Preparedness Fellowships *(Postdoctore/Fellowship)* [1864]
ASPH/EPA Environmental Health Fellowships *(Doctorate, Postdoctorate/Fellowship)* [1865]
ASPH/NHTSA Public Health Fellowships *(Postdoctorate/Fellowship)* [1866]
ASPH Public Health Policy Fellowships *(Doctorate,
Postdoctorate/Fellowship)* [1867]
CANFIT Scholarships *(Graduate, Undergraduate/Scholarship)* [2228]
Malcolm U. Dantzler Scholarships *(Professional development/Scholarship)* [8549]
Frank L. Dautriel Memorial Scholarships for Graduates *(Graduate/Scholarship)* [5519]
Frank L. Dautriel Memorial Scholarships for Undergraduates *(Undergraduate/Scholarship)* [5520]
Florida Public Health Association Public Health
Graduate Scholarships *(Graduate/Scholarship)*
[3846]
Florida Public Health Association Public Health Undergraduate Scholarships *(Undergraduate/Scholarship)* [3847]
The Gates Millennium Scholars *(Undergraduate/Scholarship)* [4569]
Great Lakes Commission Sea Grant Fellowships
(Graduate/Scholarship) [4328]
HAESF Professional Internship Program *(Doctorate/Internship)* [4641]
Health Outcomes Post Doctoral Fellowships *(Postdoctorate/Fellowship)* [7223]
Health Outcomes Pre Doctoral Fellowships *(Doctorate/Fellowship)* [7224]
Health Outcomes Research Starter Grants *(Doctorate/Grant)* [7225]
Health Outcomes Sabbatical Fellowships *(Postdoctorate/Fellowship)* [7226]
Institute for Health Metrics and Evaluation Post
Bachelor Fellowships *(Graduate/Fellowship)*
[4795]
Institute for Health Metrics and Evaluation Post
Graduate Fellowships *(Doctorate, Postdoctorate/Fellowship)* [4796]
Jewish Federation Academic Scholarships *(Graduate, Undergraduate/Scholarship)* [5161]
W.K. Kellogg Foundation Doctoral Fellowships in

Health Policy *(Professional development/Fellowship)* [6402]

LPHA Scholarships *(Graduate, Undergraduate/Scholarship)* [5525]

Lung Health Dissertation Grants *(Graduate/Grant)* [916]

Sue A. Malone Scholarships *(Doctorate, Graduate/Scholarship)* [5188]

National Biosafety and Biocontainment Training Program Fellowships *(Graduate/Fellowship)* [6141]

Catherine E. Philbin Scholarships *(Graduate, Undergraduate/Scholarship)* [4082]

ASPH/CDC Allan Rosenfield Global Health Fellowships *(Postdoctorate, Postgraduate/Fellowship)* [1868]

Lucille and Edward R. Roybal Foundation Public Health Scholarships *(Graduate, Undergraduate/Scholarship)* [7827]

Scholarships for Leadership Training and Coaching *(Professional development/Scholarship)* [3457]

South Carolina Public Health Association Scholarships *(Undergraduate/Scholarship)* [8550]

Louis Stokes Health Scholars Program *(Undergraduate, Vocational/Occupational/Scholarship)* [3221]

Public relations (See also Advertising)

Rick Brewer Scholarships *(Undergraduate/Scholarship)* [9261]

Louis M. Connor Jr. Scholarships *(Undergraduate/Scholarship)* [9264]

Randy Green Memorial Scholarship Fund *(High School/Scholarship)* [3318]

HSBC-North America Scholarship Program *(Undergraduate/Scholarship)* [4571]

International Foodservice Editorial Council Scholarships *(Graduate, Undergraduate/Scholarship)* [4935]

Harriet Irsay Scholarships *(Graduate, Undergraduate/Scholarship)* [869]

The Lagrant Foundation - Graduate Students Scholarships *(Graduate/Scholarship)* [5315]

The Lagrant Foundation - Undergraduate Students Scholarships *(Undergraduate/Scholarship)* [5316]

MillerCoors National Scholarships *(Undergraduate/Scholarship)* [48]

New York Women in Communications, Inc. Foundation Scholarships *(Graduate, Undergraduate/Scholarship)* [6690]

Stephen D. Pisinski Memorial Scholarships *(Undergraduate/Scholarship)* [7539]

Betsy Plank/PRSSA Scholarships *(Undergraduate/Scholarship)* [7540]

PRSSA Multicultural Affairs Scholarships *(Undergraduate/Scholarship)* [7541]

Richard J. Roth Journalism Fellowships *(Graduate/Fellowship)* [6679]

NASCAR/Wendell Scott Awards *(Graduate, Undergraduate/Scholarship)* [4550]

Jim Springer Memorial Scholarships *(Undergraduate/Scholarship)* [2959]

Jay A. Strassberg Memorial Scholarships *(Undergraduate/Scholarship)* [2324]

TCA Turkish American Scholarships *(Undergraduate/Scholarship)* [8978]

Gary Yoshimura Scholarships *(Undergraduate/Scholarship)* [7542]

Public service

Marc and Ruti Bell Foundation Scholarships *(Undergraduate/Scholarship)* [2052]

Willis W. and Ethel M. Clark Foundation Fellowships *(Graduate/Fellowship)* [2899]

Johnnie L. Cochran, Jr./MWH Scholarships *(Graduate, Undergraduate/Scholarship)* [6292]

Conference on Asian Pacific American Leadership Scholarships *(Graduate, Undergraduate/Scholarship)* [3211]

Alice Yuriko Endo Memorial Scholarships *(Undergraduate/Scholarship)* [5141]

John E. Fenton, Jr. Public Service Fellowships *(Postgraduate/Fellowship)* [7605]

The Future Colleagues Scholarships *(Undergraduate/Scholarship)* [6293]

John Gardner Fellowships *(Undergraduate/Fellowship)* [9195]

Charles David Hughes Scholarships *(Graduate/Scholarship)* [3028]

Land-Use Planning Scholarships *(Graduate/Scholarship)* [6294]

Lazarian Graduate Scholarships *(Graduate/Scholarship)* [1578]

Lewis-Clark State College Governor's Cup Scholarships *(Undergraduate/Scholarship)* [5443]

Willie T. Loud - CH2M Hill Scholarships *(Undergraduate/Scholarship)* [6295]

Walter Moran Farmer Scholarships *(Undergraduate/Scholarship)* [9531]

NFBPA/CDM Scholarships *(Graduate, Undergraduate/Scholarship)* [6296]

NUF Fellowships *(Graduate, Postgraduate, Professional development/Fellowship)* [6553]

Rotary Public Safety Scholarships *(Undergraduate/Scholarship)* [3920]

Donald A. Strauss Scholarships *(Undergraduate/Scholarship)* [9196]

Sheila Tarr-Smith Memorial Scholarships *(Undergraduate/Scholarship)* [7531]

Harry S. Truman Scholarships *(Postgraduate/Scholarship)* [8970]

UAA College of Business & Public Policy Scholarships *(Graduate, Undergraduate, Vocational/Occupational/Scholarship)* [9118]

UAA Pignalberi Public Policy Scholarships *(Graduate/Scholarship)* [9124]

Undergraduate Session Assistants Program *(Undergraduate/Other)* [6680]

Judith Warner Memorial Scholarships *(Undergraduate/Scholarship)* [7532]

Webster Society Scholarships *(Undergraduate/Scholarship)* [9534]

Richard A. Wiebe Public Service Fellowships *(Graduate/Fellowship)* [6681]

Publishing

Malcolm and Mildred Freidberg Fellowships *(Graduate, Doctorate/Fellowship)* [5670]

WNBA Eastman Grants *(Professional development/Grant)* [9731]

Purchasing

Canadian Purchasing Research Foundation Prize *(Doctorate, Graduate/Prize)* [2590]

Quality assurance and control

Ellis R. Ott Scholarships *(Graduate, Master's/Scholarship)* [1321]

Radio and television

American Radio Relay League Louisiana Memorial Scholarships *(Undergraduate/Scholarship)* [1067]

Earl I. Anderson Scholarships *(Undergraduate/Scholarship)* [1068]

ARRL Foundation General Fund Scholarships *(Undergraduate/Scholarship)* [1069]

ARRLF Mississippi Scholarships *(Undergraduate/Scholarship)* [1070]

Richard W. Bendicksen Memorial Scholarships *(Undergraduate/Scholarship)* [1071]

William Bennett W7PHO Memorial Scholarships *(Undergraduate/Scholarship)* [1072]

Henry Broughton, K2AE Memorial Scholarships *(Undergraduate/Scholarship)* [1073]

Mary Lou Brown Scholarships *(Undergraduate/Scholarship)* [1074]

John Cannon Memorial Scholarships *(Undergraduate/Scholarship)* [6009]

L.B. Cebik, W4RNL, and Jean Cebik, N4TZP, Memorial Scholarships *(Undergraduate/Scholarship)* [1075]

Central Arizona DX Association Scholarships *(Undergraduate/Scholarship)* [1076]

Challenge Met Scholarships *(Undergraduate/Scholarship)* [1077]

Chicago FM Club Scholarships *(Undergraduate/Scholarship)* [1078]

Tom and Judith Comstock Scholarships *(Undergraduate/Scholarship)* [1079]

Irvine W. Cook WA0CGS Scholarships *(Undergraduate/Scholarship)* [1080]

Charles Clarke Cordle Memorial Scholarships *(Undergraduate/Scholarship)* [1081]

Albuquerque ARC/Toby Cross Scholarships *(Undergraduate/Scholarship)* [1082]

Dayton Amateur Radio Association Scholarships *(Undergraduate/Scholarship)* [1083]

Charles N. Fisher Memorial Scholarships *(Undergraduate/Scholarship)* [1084]

Allison E. Fisher Scholarships *(Graduate, Undergraduate/Scholarship)* [3805]

William R. Goldfarb Memorial Scholarships *(Undergraduate/Scholarship)* [1085]

American Radio Relay League Scholarships Honoring Barry Goldwater, K7UGA *(Undergraduate/Scholarship)* [1086]

Paul and Helen L. Grauer Scholarships *(Undergraduate/Scholarship)* [1087]

K2TEO Martin J. Green, Sr. Memorial Scholarships *(Undergraduate/Scholarship)* [1088]

Perry F. Hadlock Memorial Scholarships *(Undergraduate/Scholarship)* [1089]

Albert H. Hix, W8AH Memorial Scholarships *(Undergraduate/Scholarship)* [1090]

Seth Horen, K1LOM Memorial Scholarships *(Undergraduate/Scholarship)* [1091]

Ken Kashiwahara Scholarships *(Undergraduate/Scholarship)* [7569]

Dr. James L. Lawson Memorial Scholarships *(Undergraduate/Scholarship)* [1092]

MANAA Media Scholarships *(Graduate, Undergraduate/Scholarship)* [5737]

Fred R. McDaniel Memorial Scholarships *(Undergraduate/Scholarship)* [1093]

Edmond A. Metzger Scholarships *(Undergraduate/Scholarship)* [1094]

David W. Misek, N8NPX Memorial Scholarships *(Undergraduate/Scholarship)* [1095]

Muddy Waters Scholarships *(Undergraduate/Scholarship)* [2155]

New England FEMARA Scholarships *(Undergraduate/Scholarship)* [1096]

Northern California DX Foundation Scholarships *(Undergraduate/Scholarship)* [1097]

Ray, NORP and Katie, WOKTE Pautz Scholarships *(Undergraduate/Scholarship)* [1098]

Peoria Area Amateur Radio Club Scholarships *(Undergraduate/Scholarship)* [1099]

PHD ARA Scholarships *(Doctorate, Undergraduate/Scholarship)* [1100]

Thomas W. Porter, W8KYZ Scholarships Honoring Michael Daugherty, W8LSE *(Undergraduate/Scholarship)* [1101]

Quarter Century Wireless Association Scholarships *(Undergraduate/Scholarship)* [7554]

Donald Riebhoff Memorial Scholarships *(Undergraduate/Scholarship)* [1102]

Fred Rogers Memorial Scholarships *(Graduate, Undergraduate/Scholarship)* [35]

IRARC Memorial Joseph P. Rubino WA4MMD Scholarships *(Undergraduate/Scholarship)* [1103]

Bill Salerno, W2ONV, Memorial Scholarships *(Undergraduate/Scholarship)* [1104]

Eugene Gene Sallee, W4YFR Memorial Scholarships *(Undergraduate/Scholarship)* [1105]

Abe Schechter Graduate Scholarships *(Graduate/Scholarship)* [7570]

Scholarships of the Morris Radio Club of New Jersey *(Undergraduate/Scholarship)* [1106]

SCMS Dissertation Awards *(Postdoctorate/Award)* [8311]

SCMS Student Writing Awards *(Graduate/Award)* [8312]

Six Meter Club of Chicago Scholarships *(Undergraduate/Scholarship)* [1107]

Zachary Taylor Stevens Memorial Scholarships *(Undergraduate/Scholarship)* [1108]

Carole J. Streeter, KB9JBR Scholarships *(Undergraduate/Scholarship)* [1109]

Norman E. Strohmeier, W2VRS Memorial Scholarships *(Undergraduate/Scholarship)* [1110]

Gary Wagner, K3OMI Scholarships *(Undergraduate/Scholarship)* [1111]

Francis Walton Memorial Scholarships *(Undergraduate/Scholarship)* [1112]

L. Phil Wicker Scholarships *(Undergraduate/Scholarship)* [1113]

Yankee Clipper Contest Club, Inc. Youth Scholarships *(Undergraduate/Scholarship)* [1114]

Yasme Foundation Scholarships *(Undergraduate/Scholarship)* [1115]

Radiology

American Roentgen Ray Society Scholarships *(Professional development/Scholarship)* [1159]

Anna Ames Clinical Excellence Student Grants *(Undergraduate/Grant)* [2281]

Richard J. Burk, Jr. Fellowships *(Graduate/Fellowship)* [4488]

Robert Gardner Memorial Fellowships *(Graduate/Fellowship)* [4489]

Jerman-Cahoon Student Scholarship Program *(Undergraduate/Scholarship)* [1324]

Stacy Kaiser Memorial Funds *(Undergraduate/Scholarship)* [8984]

Robert S. Landauer, Sr. Memorial Fellowships *(Graduate/Fellowship)* [4490]

Lewis-Clark State College Presidential Technical Out-of-State Scholarships *(Undergraduate/Scholarship)* [5447]

Ruth McMillan Student Grants *(Undergraduate/Grant)* [2282]

Monster Medical Imaging Educators Scholarship Program *(Postdoctorate/Scholarship)* [1325]

Burton J. Moyer Memorial Fellowships *(Graduate/Fellowship)* [4491]

Royce-Osborn Minority Scholarship Program *(Undergraduate/Scholarship)* [1326]

Siemens Clinical Advancement Scholarship Program *(Postgraduate/Scholarship)* [1327]

Society for Pediatric Radiology Research Fellows *(Graduate, Professional development/Fellowship)* [8429]

Society for Pediatric Radiology Seed Grants *(Graduate, Professional development/Grant)* [8430]

J. Newell Stannard Fellowships *(Graduate/Fellowship)* [4492]

Superior District Legislative Mentoring Student Grants RT to DC *(Undergraduate/Grant)* [2284]

Superior District Legislative Mentoring Student Grants *(Undergraduate/Grant)* [2283]

Varian Radiation Therapy Scholarship Program *(Postdoctorate/Scholarship)* [1328]

Reading

Jeanne S. Chall Research Fellowships *(Doctorate, Graduate/Grant)* [4975]

Malcolm and Mildred Freidberg Fellowships *(Graduate, Doctorate/Fellowship)* [5670]

Elva Knight Research Grants *(All/Grant)* [4976]

Helen M. Robinson Grants *(Doctorate/Grant)* [4977]

Steven A. Stahl Research Grants *(Graduate/Grant)* [4978]

Real estate

Appraisal Institute Education Trust Scholarships *(Graduate, Undergraduate/Scholarship)* [1488]

George M. Brooker Collegiate Scholarships for Minorities *(Graduate, Postgraduate, Undergraduate/Scholarship)* [4818]

Connecticut Mortgage Bankers Scholarships-Social Affairs Committee *(Undergraduate/Scholarship)* [4422]

The Rick Crane Group Real Estate Scholarship Fund *(Undergraduate/Scholarship)* [5422]

Mary Lou Fiala Fellowships *(Professional development/Fellowship)* [4907]

Donald M. Furbush Professional Development Grants *(Professional development/Grant)* [4819]

Kenneth M. Good Graduate Students Fellowship Program *(Undergraduate/Fellowship)* [9396]

Graduate Realtor Institute Scholarships *(Graduate/Scholarship)* [5244]

Charles Grossman Graduate Scholarships *(Graduate/Scholarship)* [4908]

Michigan Association of Realtors Scholarship Trust (MARST) *(Graduate, Undergraduate/Scholarship)* [5812]

Pension Real Estate Association Scholarships *(Undergraduate/Scholarship)* [7163]

Paul H. Rittle Sr. Professional Development Grants *(Professional development/Grant)* [4820]

Schurgin Family Foundation Scholarships *(Undergraduate/Scholarship)* [4910]

Recreational therapy

The Dave Family "Humor Studies" Scholarships *(Undergraduate/Scholarship)* [1703]

Ed Dunkelblau Scholarships *(All/Scholarship)* [1704]

Margie Klein "Paper Plate" Scholarships *(All/Scholarship)* [1705]

Lenny Ravich "Shalom" Scholarships *(All/Scholarship)* [1706]

Patty Wooten Scholarships *(Undergraduate/Scholarship)* [1707]

Rehabilitation, Physical/Psychological

Patricia Pownder Conolly Memorial Scholarships *(Undergraduate/Scholarship)* [5777]

Rudolph Dillman Memorial Scholarships *(Graduate, Undergraduate/Scholarship)* [750]

Delta Gamma Foundation Florence Margaret Harvey Memorial Scholarships *(Graduate, Undergraduate/Scholarship)* [752]

Linda Lyons Memorial Scholarship Fund *(Undergraduate/Scholarship)* [5779]

Religion

Ambrose-Ramsey Trust Scholarships *(Undergraduate/Scholarship)* [7059]

Martha and Robert Atherton Ministerial Scholarships *(Graduate, Master's/Scholarship)* [8993]

Lewis B. Barber Memorial Scholarships *(Undergraduate/Scholarship)* [8590]

TCDA Carroll Barnes Student Scholarships *(Graduate, Undergraduate/Scholarship)* [8846]

Olympia Brown and Max Kapp Awards *(Graduate/Scholarship)* [8994]

Pamfil and Maria Bujea Family Orthodox Christian Seminarian Scholarships *(Undergraduate/Scholarship)* [1163]

Richard D. and Sheppard R. Cooke Memorial Scholarships *(Graduate/Scholarship)* [4371]

CSBS Student Prize Competition *(Graduate/Prize)* [2598]

CSF Graduate Fellowships *(Graduate/Fellowship)* [2787]

CTRF Scholarships for Graduate Study in Transportation *(Graduate/Scholarship)* [2626]

David Eaton Scholarships *(Graduate, Master's/Scholarship)* [8997]

Doris W. Frey Memorial Scholarships *(Undergraduate/Scholarship)* [8603]

FTE Dissertation Fellowships *(Graduate/Fellowship)* [4020]

FTE Doctoral Fellowships *(Doctorate, Graduate/Fellowship)* [4021]

FTE North American Doctoral Fellowships *(Doctorate, Graduate/Fellowship)* [4023]

TCDA Bill Gorham Student Scholarships *(Graduate, Undergraduate/Scholarship)* [8848]

Joseph H. Fichter Research Grants *(Professional development/Grant)* [1874]

Magoichi & Shizuko Kato Memorial Scholarships *(Graduate/Scholarship)* [5143]

KCC-JEE Graduate Fellowships *(Graduate/Fellowship)* [5279]

David B. Larson Fellowships in Health and Spirituality *(Doctorate/Fellowship)* [5275]

Molly McKay Scholarships *(Undergraduate/Scholarship)* [9291]

William F. Miles Scholarships *(Undergraduate/Scholarship)* [4379]

Leonard M. Perryman Communications Scholar-

ships for Ethnic Minority Students *(Undergraduate/Scholarship)* [9013]

David Pohl Scholarships *(Graduate, Master's/Scholarship)* [8998]

Roy H. Pollack Scholarships *(Graduate, Master's/Scholarship)* [8999]

Robert J. McNamara Student Paper Awards *(Graduate/Award)* [1875]

Samuel Robinson Awards *(Undergraduate/Award)* [7388]

David W. Self Scholarships *(Undergraduate/Scholarship)* [9015]

John M. and Mary A. Shanley Memorial Scholarships *(Undergraduate/Scholarship)* [8622]

Hy Smith Endowment Fund *(Undergraduate/Scholarship)* [4382]

Richard S. Smith Scholarships *(Undergraduate/Scholarship)* [9016]

Iwalani Carpenter Sowa Scholarships *(Graduate/Scholarship)* [5222]

The Tabat Scholarship Fund *(Graduate/Scholarship)* [3738]

TCDA Gandy Ink Student Scholarships *(Graduate, Undergraduate/Scholarship)* [8850]

TCDA Past Presidents Student Scholarships *(Graduate, Undergraduate/Scholarship)* [8852]

Templeton-Cambridge Journalism Fellowships *(All/Fellowship)* [8839]

Rev. Chuck and Nancy Thomas Scholarships *(Graduate, Master's/Scholarship)* [9004]

Von Ogden Vogt Scholarships *(Graduate, Master's/Scholarship)* [9005]

TCDA Cloys Webb Student Scholarships *(Graduate, Undergraduate/Scholarship)* [8853]

Wexner Graduate Fellowships/Davidson Scholars *(Graduate/Fellowship)* [9589]

Remote sensing

Robert N. Colwell Memorial Fellowships *(Doctorate, Graduate/Fellowship)* [1666]

ERDAS Internships *(Graduate/Internship)* [1667]

William A. Fischer Memorial Scholarships *(Graduate/Scholarship)* [1668]

Ta Liang Memorial Awards *(Graduate/Grant)* [1669]

Francis H. Moffitt Memorial Scholarships *(Graduate, Undergraduate/Scholarship)* [1670]

Resource management

Alaska Support Industry Alliance Scholarships *(Undergraduate/Scholarship)* [9133]

Rheumatology (See Arthritis)

Risk management

Gongaware Scholarships *(Undergraduate/Scholarship)* [4743]

Insurance and Risk Management Scholarships - Grant MacEwan *(Undergraduate/Scholarship)* [7994]

William H. McGannon Foundation Scholarships *(Graduate, Undergraduate/Scholarship)* [5721]

Risk Management and Insurance Scholarships - University of Calgary *(Undergraduate/Scholarship)* [7995]

Thompson Scholarships for Women in Safety *(Graduate/Scholarship)* [1355]

Robotics

Tribeca Film Institute New Media Fellowships *(Professional development/Fellowship)* [8960]

Romanian studies (See Area and ethnic studies)

Russian studies

NEH Fellowships for Senior Scholars *(Doctorate/Fellowship)* [2695]

Prins Foundation Fellowship for Senior Scholars *(Doctorate/Fellowship)* [2696]

Prins Foundation Post-Doctoral and Early Career

Fellowship for Emigrating Scholars *(Professional development, Postdoctorate/Fellowship)* [2697]

Science

AAAS Science and Technology Policy Fellowships *(Postdoctorate/Fellowship)* [431]
Academic Promise Scholarships *(Undergraduate/Scholarship)* [4740]
Advanced Light Source Postdoctoral Fellowship Program *(Doctorate/Fellowship)* [5379]
AeA Scholarships *(Undergraduate/Scholarship)* [7904]
AFCEA Math and Science Teachers Scholarships *(Graduate, Undergraduate/Scholarship)* [1553]
African American Network - Carolinas Scholarship Fund *(Undergraduate/Scholarship)* [3882]
AHETEMS General Scholarships *(Graduate, Undergraduate/Scholarship)* [55]
AHETEMS Professional Scholarships *(Graduate/Scholarship)* [56]
Air Force Association Excellence Scholarships *(Graduate, Master's, Undergraduate/Scholarship)* [88]
Alberta Ingenuity Graduate Student Scholarships in Nanotechnology *(Doctorate, Graduate/Scholarship)* [231]
Alberta Ingenuity Graduate Student Scholarships *(Doctorate, Graduate/Scholarship)* [230]
Janet and Horace Allen Scholarships *(Undergraduate/Scholarship)* [238]
American Association of Family and Consumer Sciences Scholarships *(Undergraduate/Scholarship)* [477]
American Society of Crime Laboratory Directors Scholarships *(Graduate, Undergraduate/Scholarship)* [1217]
A.T. Anderson Memorial Scholarships *(Graduate, Undergraduate/Scholarship)* [834]
Hettie M. Anthony Fellowships *(Postdoctorate/Fellowship)* [5200]
Mike Ardaw Scholarships *(Undergraduate/Scholarship)* [9137]
ASBC Foundation Graduate Scholarships *(Doctorate, Graduate/Scholarship)* [1186]
Elizabeth and Sherman Asche Memorial Scholarships *(Graduate, Undergraduate/Scholarship)* [1695]
ASMS Research Awards *(Professional development/Grant)* [1293]
Astronaut Scholarship Foundation Scholarships *(Undergraduate/Scholarship)* [1916]
B&W Y-12 Scholarship Fund *(Undergraduate/Scholarship)* [3565]
Thomas J. Bardos Science Education Awards for Undergraduate Students *(Undergraduate/Award)* [451]
Bechtel Engineering and Science Scholarships *(High School/Scholarship)* [5645]
Bill & Nell Biggs Scholarships *(Undergraduate/Scholarship)* [9140]
Blow Molding Division Memorial Scholarships *(Graduate, Undergraduate/Scholarship)* [8444]
Rev. Andrew L. Bouwhuis Memorial Scholarship Program *(Graduate/Scholarship)* [2668]
Henry Broughton, K2AE Memorial Scholarships *(Undergraduate/Scholarship)* [1073]
Graduate Fellowship Program - Robert M Burger Fellowships (GFP) *(Doctorate, Graduate/Fellowship)* [8078]
Career Awards for Science and Mathematics Teachers *(Professional development/Award)* [2213]
Catching the Dream Scholarships *(Graduate, Undergraduate/Scholarship)* [817]
CERT College Scholarships *(Graduate, Undergraduate/Scholarship)* [3272]
Channabasappa Memorial Scholarships *(Graduate, Professional development/Scholarship)* [4918]
Charline Chilson Scholarships *(Undergraduate/Scholarship)* [3407]
Chrysler Foundation Scholarship Awards *(Undergraduate/Scholarship)* [4546]
Congressional Science Fellowships *(Postdoctorate/Fellowship)* [1302]
Robert E. Cramer Scholarships *(Graduate, Undergraduate/Scholarship)* [8445]

Critical Language Scholarships for Intensive Summer Institutes *(Graduate, Undergraduate/Scholarship)* [1145]
Robert G. Daily Scholarships *(Graduate, Undergraduate/Scholarship)* [8446]
Delta Gamma Scholarships *(Undergraduate/Scholarship)* [3398]
Development Fund for Black Students in Science and Technology Scholarships *(Undergraduate/Scholarship)* [3432]
Janusz & Roma Drzymala Scholarships *(Undergraduate/Scholarship)* [7760]
Lt. Colonel Romeo and Josephine Bass Ferretti Scholarships *(Undergraduate/Scholarship)* [92]
Dr. Mary Finegold Scholarships *(Undergraduate/Scholarship)* [8201]
Reuben H. Fleet Memorial Scholarships *(Undergraduate/Scholarship)* [7929]
Fleming/Blaszcak Scholarships *(Graduate, Undergraduate/Scholarship)* [8447]
Florida Education Fund McKnight Doctoral Fellowships *(Graduate/Fellowship)* [3822]
The Ginny Frankenthaler Memorial Scholarships *(Undergraduate/Scholarship)* [8567]
The Gates Millennium Scholars *(Undergraduate/Scholarship)* [4569]
Eloise Gerry Fellowships *(Graduate, Postdoctorate/Fellowship)* [8151]
Harold Giles Scholarships *(Graduate, Undergraduate/Scholarship)* [8448]
Benjamin A. Gilman International Scholarships *(Undergraduate/Scholarship)* [9096]
Glendale Latino Association Scholarships *(High School, Undergraduate/Scholarship)* [4161]
Dr. Robert H. Goddard Memorial Scholarships *(Graduate, Undergraduate/Scholarship)* [6523]
William R. Goldfarb Memorial Scholarships *(Undergraduate/Scholarship)* [1085]
Barry M. Goldwater Scholarships *(Undergraduate/Scholarship)* [9357]
Graduate Fellowship Program - Mahboob Khan/Advanced Micro Devices Fellowships (GFP) *(Doctorate, Graduate/Fellowship)* [8079]
Graduate Fellowship Program - Research Fellowships (GFP) *(Doctorate, Graduate/Fellowship)* [8080]
GREAT MINDS Collegiate Scholarship Program *(Undergraduate/Scholarship)* [340]
Great Minds in STEM Scholarships *(Graduate, Undergraduate/Scholarship)* [4331]
Gulf Coast Hurricane Scholarships *(Graduate, Undergraduate/Scholarship)* [8449]
Guntley-Lorimer Science and Arts Scholarships *(Undergraduate/Scholarship)* [2119]
Hertz Foundation's Graduate Fellowships *(Doctorate/Fellowship)* [6074]
Hinman-Jensen Endowed Scholarships *(Undergraduate/Scholarship)* [5433]
Jane Hood Memorial Fund *(Undergraduate/Scholarship)* [3776]
IDA Fellowship Awards *(Professional development/Fellowship)* [4919]
Injection Molding Division Scholarships *(Graduate, Undergraduate/Scholarship)* [8450]
Nancy Lorraine Jensen Memorial Scholarships *(Undergraduate/Scholarship)* [8531]
JSA/Jefferson Lab Graduate Fellowships *(Doctorate, Graduate/Fellowship)* [5155]
Lakselaget Foundation Scholarships *(Graduate, Undergraduate/Scholarship)* [5320]
Erwin Lew Memorial Scholarships *(Graduate, Undergraduate/Scholarship)* [8451]
Library Resident Research Fellowships *(Doctorate/Fellowship)* [993]
Carie and George Lyter Scholarship Fund *(Undergraduate/Scholarship)* [3951]
Thermoset Division/James I. Mackenzie and James H. Cunningham Scholarships *(Graduate, Undergraduate/Scholarship)* [8452]
Pat and John MacTavish Scholarship Fund *(Undergraduate/Scholarship)* [4229]
MAES Founders Scholarships *(Graduate, Undergraduate/Scholarship)* [5798]
MAES General Scholarships *(Graduate, Undergraduate/Scholarship)* [5799]

MAES Graduate Scholarships *(Graduate/Scholarship)* [5800]
MAES Padrino/Madrina Scholarships *(Graduate, Undergraduate/Scholarship)* [5801]
MAES Pipeline Scholarships *(Graduate, Undergraduate/Scholarship)* [5802]
MAES Presidential Scholarships *(Graduate, Undergraduate/Scholarship)* [5803]
Masonic-Range Science Scholarships *(Undergraduate/Scholarship)* [8484]
Master's Scholarships Program (MSP) *(Graduate, Master's/Scholarship)* [8081]
MESBEC Scholarships *(Undergraduate/Scholarship)* [2662]
Nell I. Mondy Fellowships *(Graduate, Postdoctorate/Fellowship)* [8152]
Robert E. and Judy More Scholarship Fund *(Undergraduate/Scholarship)* [3784]
John H. Moss Scholarships *(Undergraduate/Scholarship)* [9339]
NAAF Post-Secondary Education Scholarships *(Graduate, Undergraduate/Scholarship)* [5993]
National Co-op Scholarship Program *(Undergraduate/Scholarship)* [9750]
National GEM Consortium - MS Engineering Fellowships *(Graduate/Fellowship)* [6305]
National Security Technology Engineering and Science Scholarships *(Undergraduate/Scholarship)* [7510]
Ted and Ruth Neward Scholarships *(Graduate, Undergraduate/Scholarship)* [8453]
Virginia Nicklas Scholarships *(Undergraduate/Scholarship)* [3382]
Stuart L. Noderer Memorial Scholarships *(Undergraduate/Scholarship)* [7949]
Maureen E. Nolan-Cahill Memorial Scholarships *(Undergraduate/Scholarship)* [9165]
Vessa Notchev Fellowships *(Graduate, Postdoctorate/Fellowship)* [8153]
Robert Noyce Scholarship Program *(Undergraduate/Scholarship)* [7160]
Noyce Scholarships for Secondary Math and Science Education *(Undergraduate/Scholarship)* [4751]
Ocean Industries Student Research Awards *(Undergraduate, Graduate/Award)* [7736]
Ohio Space Grant Consortium Graduate Fellowships *(Doctorate, Graduate/Fellowship)* [6864]
Ohio Space Grant Consortium Special Minority Fellowships *(Doctorate, Graduate/Fellowship)* [6865]
Omicron Nu Research Fellowships *(Postdoctorate/Fellowship)* [5203]
L'Oreal USA Fellowships for Women in Science *(Postdoctorate/Fellowship)* [6926]
Phi Theta Kappa Scholarships *(Undergraduate/Scholarship)* [4752]
Plastics Pioneers Association Scholarships *(Graduate, Undergraduate/Scholarship)* [8454]
Polymer Modifiers and Additives Division Scholarships *(Graduate, Undergraduate/Scholarship)* [8455]
Graduate Fellowship Program - GRC/John L. Prince Fellowships (GFP) *(Graduate/Fellowship)* [8082]
Purdue Krannert School of Management SHPE Scholarships *(Undergraduate, Master's/Scholarship)* [8130]
RBC Royal Bank Scholarships for Undergraduates *(Undergraduate/Scholarship)* [7825]
Rechsteiner Family Scholarship Fund *(Undergraduate/Scholarship)* [3788]
UAA Jack & Martha Roderick Scholarships *(Graduate, Undergraduate/Scholarship)* [9108]
Leo S. Rowe Pan American Fund *(Graduate, Undergraduate/Loan)* [6967]
Charles A. Ryskamp Research Fellowships *(Doctorate/Fellowship)* [681]
Chester & Maria Sadowski Memorial Scholarships *(Undergraduate/Scholarship)* [7778]
SDF Community College Transfer Scholarships for Math and Science *(Undergraduate/Scholarship)* [7964]
Everett Oscar Shimp Memorial Scholarships *(Undergraduate/Scholarship)* [7113]
SHPE Foundation Dissertation Scholarships *(Doctorate/Scholarship)* [8131]
SHPE Foundation General Scholarships *(High*

Science technologies

Science--History

Scottish studies (See also British studies)

Sculpture

Secretarial sciences

Sexuality

Sleep and sleep disorders

Social sciences

Post-Doctoral Summer Travel-Research Grants *(Doctorate/Grant)* [4832]

Pre-doctoral Residential Research Fellowships *(Doctorate/Fellowship)* [9744]

Russell Sage Foundation Visiting Scholars *(Post-doctorate/Fellowship)* [7880]

Saskatchewan Government Insurance Graduate Student Traffic Safety Research Scholarhips *(Graduate/Scholarship)* [7999]

SFP Mid-Career/Mentor Awards for Family Planning *(Professional development/Grant)* [8323]

SHAFR Dissertation Completion Fellowships *(Doctorate/Fellowship)* [8342]

Short-term Senior Fellowships in Iranian Studies *(Doctorate, Graduate/Fellowship)* [858]

Social Sciences and Humanities Research Council of Canada Standard Research Grants *(Doctorate, Graduate/Grant)* [8287]

SSHRC Doctoral Fellowship Program *(Doctorate/Fellowship, Scholarship)* [8288]

Louis Stokes Urban Health Policy Fellows Program *(Graduate, Professional development/Fellowship)* [3222]

John Streiff Memorial Scholarships *(Undergraduate/Scholarship)* [5467]

Summer Language Study Grants in Turkey *(Graduate/Grant)* [4833]

Summer Research Diversity Fellowships in Law and Social Science *(Undergraduate/Fellowship)* [579]

The Rodney Thaxton Justice Fund *(Undergraduate/Scholarship)* [3322]

Trudeau Foundation Doctoral Scholarships *(Doctorate/Scholarship)* [8968]

Vanier Canada Graduate Scholarships *(Graduate/Scholarship)* [6573]

Social work

Emma and Meloid Algood Tuition Scholarships *(Graduate, Undergraduate/Scholarship)* [6039]

Associates in Behavioral Health Scholarships *(Graduate/Scholarship)* [7398]

Dr. Joyce Beckett Scholarships *(Graduate, Undergraduate/Scholarship)* [6040]

Eileen Blackey Doctoral Fellowships *(Doctorate/Fellowship)* [6121]

Mildred Cater Bradham Social Work Fellowships *(Graduate/Fellowship)* [9801]

Selena Danette Brown Book Scholarships *(Graduate, Undergraduate/Scholarship)* [6041]

Tropicana Community Services - Robert K. Brown Scholarships *(Undergraduate/Scholarship)* [2112]

Patricia Powder Conolly Memorial Scholarships *(Undergraduate/Scholarship)* [5777]

Council on Social Work Education Minority Fellowship Programs *(Postdoctorate/Fellowship)* [3282]

Council on Social Work Education Scholars Program *(Postdoctorate/Scholarship)* [3283]

Steve Dearduff Scholarships *(Graduate, Undergraduate/Scholarship)* [3075]

Douglas-Coldwell Foundation Scholarships in Social Affairs *(Graduate/Scholarship)* [3474]

Family and Children's Services of Lebanon County Fund *(Undergraduate/Scholarship)* [3942]

Consuelo W. Gosnell Memorial Scholarships *(Graduate/Fellowship)* [6122]

Randy Green Memorial Scholarship Fund *(High School/Scholarship)* [3318]

Guynn Family Foundation Scholarships *(Undergraduate/Scholarship)* [6042]

Hampton Roads Association of Social Workers Scholarships *(Graduate/Scholarship)* [4374]

International Scholarship Programs for Community Service *(All/Scholarship)* [5765]

Jewish Federation Academic Scholarships *(Graduate, Undergraduate/Scholarship)* [5161]

Maude Keisling/Cumberland County Extension Homemakers Scholarships *(Undergraduate/Scholarship)* [3112]

Linda Lyons Memorial Scholarship Fund *(Undergraduate/Scholarship)* [5779]

Verne LaMarr Lyons Memorial Scholarships *(Graduate/Fellowship)* [6123]

Joseph McCulley Educational Scholarships *(Graduate, Undergraduate/Scholarship)* [9337]

NAAF Post-Secondary Education Scholarships

(Graduate, Undergraduate/Scholarship) [5993]

Pi Gamma Mu Scholarships *(Graduate/Scholarship)* [7330]

Portuguese American Police Association Scholarships *(Undergraduate/Scholarship)* [7380]

Carl A. Scott Book Scholarships *(Undergraduate/Scholarship)* [3284]

Social Work Scholarships *(Undergraduate/Scholarship)* [7420]

Taylor Statten Memorial Fellowships *(Graduate/Scholarship)* [9342]

Philip F. Vineberg Travelling Fellowships in the Humanities *(Undergraduate/Scholarship)* [5726]

Washington University Law School Chancellor's Graduate Fellowships *(Graduate/Fellowship)* [9532]

Washington University Law School Olin Fellowships for Women *(Graduate/Fellowship)* [9533]

Wellstone Fellowships for Social Justice *(Graduate/Fellowship)* [3707]

Cenie Jomo Williams Tuition Scholarships *(Graduate, Undergraduate/Scholarship)* [6043]

Sociology (See also Aggression and violence)

UAA Michael Baring-Gould Memorial Scholarships *(Graduate, Undergraduate/Scholarship)* [9086]

Patricia Powder Conolly Memorial Scholarships *(Undergraduate/Scholarship)* [5777]

Dr. Feroz Ahmed Memorial Educational Post-Graduate Scholarships *(Doctorate, Postgraduate/Scholarship)* [8216]

Douglas-Coldwell Foundation Scholarships in Social Affairs *(Graduate/Scholarship)* [3474]

Garikian Scholarship Fund *(Undergraduate/Scholarship)* [1593]

Beth B. Hess Memorial Scholarships *(Doctorate, Graduate/Fellowship)* [8518]

Linda Lyons Memorial Scholarship Fund *(Undergraduate/Scholarship)* [5779]

Cheryl Allyn Miller Awards *(Doctorate, Graduate/Fellowship)* [8519]

Pi Gamma Mu Scholarships *(Graduate/Scholarship)* [7330]

Thomas R. Pickering Graduate Foreign Affairs Fellowships *(Graduate/Fellowship)* [9619]

UAA Eveline Schuster Memorial Award/Scholarships *(Graduate, Undergraduate/Scholarship)* [9110]

Minoru Yasui Memorial Scholarships *(Graduate/Scholarship)* [5147]

Soil science

Fellowships and Internships Program in Latin America *(Graduate/Fellowship, Internship)* [8269]

Dr. Karl C. Ivarson Scholarships *(Postgraduate/Scholarship)* [74]

Short-Term Fellowships *(Undergraduate, Graduate, Postdoctorate/Fellowship)* [8271]

Earl S. Tupper 3-year Postdoctoral Fellowships in Tropical Biology *(Postdoctorate/Fellowship)* [8272]

Space and planetary sciences (See Astronomy and astronomical sciences)

Spanish studies (See also Area and ethnic studies)

Jane Salanky-Onzik Scholarship Fund *(Undergraduate/Scholarship)* [3791]

Specific diseases

SCDAA Post-Doctoral Research Fellowships *(Doctorate/Fellowship)* [8138]

Speech, Debate, and Forensics

Gongoro Nakamura Memorial Scholarships *(Undergraduate/Scholarship)* [5145]

Speech and language pathology/Audiology

Acoustical Society of America Minority Fellowships *(Graduate/Fellowship)* [39]

AMBUCS Scholarships for Therapists Program *(Graduate, Undergraduate/Scholarship)* [371]

Fred Berg Awards *(All/Award)* [3594]

Zoe E. Collymore Page Scholarships *(Undergraduate/Scholarship)* [6145]

Communication Disorder/Speech Therapy Scholarships *(Graduate/Scholarship)* [4075]

Educational Audiology Association Doctoral Scholarships *(Doctorate/Scholarship)* [3595]

ETS Postdoctoral Fellowships *(Postdoctorate/Fellowship)* [3609]

Harold Gulliksen Psychometric Research Fellowships *(Doctorate, Graduate/Fellowship)* [3610]

Dwight A. Hamilton Scottish Rite Foundation of Colorado Graduate Scholarships *(Graduate/Scholarship)* [8063]

Houston/Nancy Holliman Scholarships *(Undergraduate/Scholarship)* [3413]

Frederick V. Hunt Postdoctoral Research Fellowships in Acoustics *(Postdoctorate/Fellowship)* [40]

Sylvia Taylor Johnson Minority Fellowships in Educational Measurement *(Doctorate/Fellowship)* [3611]

Maryland Speech Language Hearing Association Scholarships *(Graduate/Scholarship)* [5656]

Noel D. Matkin Awards *(Undergraduate/Award)* [3596]

NAJA Scholarships *(Graduate/Scholarship)* [6086]

Helen Woodruff Nolop Scholarships in Audiology and Allied Fields *(Graduate/Scholarship)* [3419]

OSHA Graduate Scholarships *(Graduate/Scholarship)* [6873]

Research Grants in Speech Science *(Doctorate/Grant)* [1389]

Raymond H. Stetson Scholarships in Phonetics and Speech Science *(Graduate/Scholarship)* [41]

Student Research Grants in Audiology *(Doctorate/Grant)* [1390]

Student Research Grants in Early Childhood Language Development *(Doctorate/Grant)* [1391]

Sports studies

Bernice Barabash Sports Scholarships *(Undergraduate, Vocational/Occupational/Scholarship)* [5090]

BCA Ethnic Minority Postgraduate Scholarships for Careers in Athletics *(Postgraduate/Scholarship)* [2135]

Walter Byers Postgraduate Scholarships *(Graduate, Postgraduate/Scholarship)* [6192]

Ethnic Minority and Women's Enhancement Postgraduate Scholarships *(Graduate/Scholarship)* [6193]

Evans Scholarships *(Undergraduate/Scholarship)* [5900]

Dorothy Harris Endowed Scholarships *(Graduate/Scholarship)* [9737]

Health, Sport, and Fitness SIG Student Research Awards *(Undergraduate/Award)* [1714]

Geordie Hilton Academic Scholarships *(Undergraduate/Scholarship)* [4184]

John McLendon Memorial Minority Postgraduate Scholarships *(Postdoctorate/Scholarship)* [6062]

Safer Athletic Field Environments Scholarships (SAFE) *(Graduate, Undergraduate/Scholarship)* [8649]

Saskatchewan Hockey Association Scholarships *(Undergraduate/Scholarship)* [8001]

Sports writing

Chuck Pezzano Scholarships *(Undergraduate, Vocational/Occupational/Scholarship)* [2166]

Statistics

AAUW Legal Advocacy Fund Selected Professions Fellowships *(Doctorate, Graduate/Fellowship)* [18]

ASA/NSF/BLS Fellowships (Graduate/Fellowship) [1393]

Avista Corporation Minds in Motion Scholarships (Undergraduate/Scholarship) [5412]

Edward C. Bryant Scholarships Trust Fund (Graduate/Fellowship) [1394]

Burroughs Wellcome Fund Career Awards at the Scientific Interface (Doctorate, Postdoctorate/Fellowship) [2211]

Burroughs Wellcome Fund Collaborative Research Travel Grants (Doctorate/Grant) [2212]

Mariam K. Chamberlain Fellowships in Women and Public Policy (Graduate/Fellowship) [4835]

Jorge Espejal Contreras Memorial Scholarships (Graduate, Undergraduate/Scholarship) [4873]

Gertrude M. Cox Scholarships (Doctorate, Graduate/Fellowship) [1395]

ETS Postdoctoral Fellowships (Postdoctorate/Fellowship) [3609]

Harold Gulliksen Psychometric Research Fellowships (Doctorate, Graduate/Fellowship) [3610]

Sylvia Taylor Johnson Minority Fellowships in Educational Measurement (Doctorate/Fellowship) [3611]

Ellis R. Ott Scholarships (Graduate, Master's/Scholarship) [1321]

Samuel S. Wilks Memorial Awards (Undergraduate/Award) [1396]

Substance abuse

ASA Minority Fellowship Program (Doctorate, Master's/Fellowship) [1377]

Suicide

AFSP - Distinguished Investigator Grants (Postgraduate/Grant) [766]

AFSP Postdoctoral Research Fellowships (Postgraduate/Fellowship) [767]

AFSP Standard Research Grants (Postgraduate/Grant) [768]

AFSP Young Investigator Grants (Postgraduate/Grant) [769]

American Foundation for Suicide and Prevention Pilot Grants (Postgraduate/Grant) [770]

Eleanor Bennett Scholarships (All/Scholarship) [8770]

Surgery

AAST/ACS/NIGMS Scholarships (Professional development/Scholarship) [554]

AAST/KCI Research Grants (All/Grant) [555]

AAST Medical Student Scholarships (All/Scholarship) [556]

American Association for Hand Surgery Annual Research Awards (Professional development/Award) [479]

American Pediatric Surgical Nurses Association Educational Grants (Professional development/Grant) [984]

American Society of Colon and Rectal Surgeons International Fellowships (Professional development/Fellowship) [1201]

American Society of Colon and Rectal Surgeons Travel Scholarships (Professional development/Scholarship) [1202]

AST National Honor Society Student Scholarships (Graduate/Scholarship) [1879]

Career Mobility Scholarship Awards (Doctorate, Undergraduate/Scholarship) [27]

Daland Fellowships in Clinical Investigation (Doctorate/Fellowship) [989]

Delmar Cengage Surgical Technology Scholarships (Graduate/Scholarship) [1880]

Foundation for Surgical Technology Advanced Education/Medical Mission Scholarships (Graduate/Scholarship) [1881]

Foundation for Surgical Technology Scholarships (Graduate/Scholarship) [1882]

Local Wound Haemostatics and Hemorrhage Control Scholarships (All/Scholarship) [557]

SUS Foundation Junior Faculty Grants (Professional development/Grant) [8511]

Wyeth-SUS Clinical Scholar Awards (Professional development/Award) [8512]

Surveying (See Cartography/Surveying)

Swedish studies

Lilly Lorenzen Scholarships (Undergraduate/Scholarship) [1400]

Malmberg Fellowships (Undergraduate/Fellowship) [1401]

Malmberg Scholarships (Undergraduate/Scholarship) [1402]

Systems engineering

Applied Physics Laboratory Alexander Kossiakoff Scholarships (Doctorate, Graduate/Scholarship) [4912]

ISA Aerospace Industries Division - William H. Atkinson Scholarships (Graduate, Undergraduate/Scholarship) [5052]

Norman E. Huston Scholarships (Graduate, Undergraduate/Scholarship) [5053]

ISA Educational Foundation Scholarships (Graduate, Undergraduate/Scholarship) [5054]

ISA Executive Board Scholarships (Graduate, Undergraduate/Scholarship) [5055]

ISA Section and District Scholarships - Birmingham (Graduate, Undergraduate/Scholarship) [5056]

ISA Section and District Scholarships - Houston (Graduate, Undergraduate/Scholarship) [5057]

ISA Section and District Scholarships - Lehigh Valley (Graduate, Undergraduate/Scholarship) [5058]

ISA Section and District Scholarships - New Jersey (Graduate, Undergraduate/Scholarship) [5059]

ISA Section and District Scholarships - Niagara Frontier (Graduate, Undergraduate/Scholarship) [5060]

ISA Section and District Scholarships - Northern California (Graduate, Undergraduate/Scholarship) [5061]

ISA Section and District Scholarships - Richmond Hopewell (Graduate, Undergraduate/Scholarship) [5062]

ISA Section and District Scholarships - Savannah River (Graduate, Undergraduate/Scholarship) [5063]

ISA Section and District Scholarships - Southwestern Wyoming (Graduate, Undergraduate/Scholarship) [5064]

ISA Section and District Scholarships - Texas, Louisiana and Mississippi (Graduate, Undergraduate/Scholarship) [5065]

ISA Section and District Scholarships - Wilmington (Graduate, Undergraduate/Scholarship) [5066]

ISA Technical Division Scholarships - Analysis Division (Graduate, Undergraduate/Scholarship) [5067]

ISA Technical Division Scholarships - Chemical and Petroleum Industries Division (Graduate, Undergraduate/Scholarship) [5068]

ISA Technical Division Scholarships - Computer Technology Division (Graduate, Undergraduate/Scholarship) [5069]

ISA Technical Division Scholarships - Food and Pharmaceutical Industries Division (Graduate, Undergraduate/Scholarship) [5070]

ISA Technical Division Scholarships - Power Industry Division (Graduate, Undergraduate/Scholarship) [5071]

ISA Technical Division Scholarships - Process Measurement and Control Division (Graduate, Undergraduate/Scholarship) [5072]

ISA Technical Division Scholarships - Pulp and Paper Industry Division (Graduate, Undergraduate/Scholarship) [5073]

ISA Technical Division Scholarships - Test Measurement Division (Graduate, Undergraduate/Scholarship) [5074]

ISA Technical Division Scholarships - Water and Wastewater Industries Division (Graduate, Undergraduate/Scholarship) [5075]

(ISC)2 Information Security Scholarships (Postgraduate/Scholarship) [4955]

Bob and Mary Ives Scholarships (Graduate, Undergraduate/Scholarship) [5076]

James E. Long Memorial Post Doctoral Fellowships (Postdoctorate/Fellowship) [4913]

Stevens Doctoral Awards (Doctorate/Award) [4914]

Taxonomy

Charlie Fleming Education Fund Scholarships (Undergraduate/Scholarship) [6542]

Teaching

AACTE Outstanding Book Awards (Professional development/Award) [463]

AACTE Outstanding Dissertation Awards (Doctorate/Award) [464]

AMS Teacher Education Scholarships (Undergraduate/Scholarship) [938]

Leon Bradley Scholarships (Undergraduate/Scholarship) [548]

Quincy Brown Memorial Scholarships (Undergraduate/Scholarship) [7634]

Jennifer Coulter Memorial Scholarships (Undergraduate/Scholarship) [7068]

David G. Imig Awards for Distinguished Achievement in Teacher Education (Professional development/Award) [465]

Patricia Ann Hughes Eastaugh Memorial Teaching Scholarships (Undergraduate/Scholarship) [9147]

Edward C. Pomeroy Awards for Outstanding Contributions to Teacher Education (Professional development/Award) [466]

ETS Postdoctoral Fellowships (Postdoctorate/Fellowship) [3609]

Jonathan Hastings Foster Scholarships (Undergraduate/Scholarship) [7930]

Harold Gulliksen Psychometric Research Fellowships (Doctorate, Graduate/Fellowship) [3610]

Ida L. Hartenberg Charitable Scholarships (Undergraduate/Scholarship) [4435]

Hartford County Retired Teachers Association Scholarships (Undergraduate/Scholarship) [4436]

Illinois Future Teacher Corps Scholarships (Undergraduate/Scholarship) [4695]

ITEEA FTE Scholarships (Undergraduate/Scholarship) [5010]

ITEEA Greer/FTE Grants (Professional development/Grant) [5011]

ITEEA Litherland/FTE Scholarships (Undergraduate/Scholarship) [5012]

Sylvia Taylor Johnson Minority Fellowships in Educational Measurement (Doctorate/Fellowship) [3611]

Johnson and Wales University Scholarships (Undergraduate/Scholarship) [5175]

KHEAA Teacher Scholarships (Undergraduate/Scholarship) [2091]

Doreen Legg Memorial Scholarships (Undergraduate/Scholarship) [7664]

James Madison Foundation - Junior Fellowships (Graduate/Fellowship) [5564]

James Madison Foundation - Senior Fellowships (Graduate/Fellowship) [5565]

Maley/FTE Scholarships (Graduate/Scholarship) [5013]

Margaret B. Lindsey Awards for Distinguished Research in Teacher Education (Professional development/Award) [467]

Minority Teachers of Illinois Scholarships (MTI) (Undergraduate/Scholarship) [4701]

Newtonville Woman's Club Scholarships (Undergraduate/Scholarship) [4079]

North Carolina Council of Epsilon Sigma Alpha Scholarships (Graduate, Professional development, Undergraduate/Scholarship) [6759]

Outlaw Student's Teacher Scholarships (Undergraduate/Scholarship) [8755]

Pitsco/Hearlihy/FTE Grants (Professional development/Grant) [5014]

Poundmaker Memorial Scholarships (Undergraduate/Scholarship) [6565]

Don Sahli-Kathy Woodall Graduate Scholarships (Graduate/Scholarship) [8841]

Sons and Daughters Don Sahli-Kathy Woodall Scholarships (Graduate, Undergraduate/Scholarship) [8842]

John M. and Mary A. Shanley Memorial Scholarships (Undergraduate/Scholarship) [8622]

John I. and Madeleine R. Taeni Scholarships (Undergraduate/Scholarship) [8627]

University of Hawaii at Manoa Graduate Assistantship Awards (Graduate/Award) [9207]

Wachovia/TELACU Excellence in Teaching Scholarships (Undergraduate/Scholarship) [8823]

Edwyna Wheadon Postgraduate Training Scholarship Fund (Professional development/Scholarship) [6219]

Technical communications

Alaska Aerospace Development Corporation Scholarships (Undergraduate/Scholarship) [9130]

Julia Broderick Scholarships (Undergraduate/Scholarship) [8498]

Mid-South STC Chapter Scholarships (Graduate, Undergraduate/Scholarship) [8502]

Marian Norby Scholarships (Professional development/Scholarship) [8495]

Melissa Pellegrin Memorial Scholarships (Graduate, Undergraduate/Scholarship) [8504]

STC-PSC Scholarships (Graduate, Undergraduate/Scholarship) [8506]

STC Scholarships (Graduate, Undergraduate/Scholarship) [8496]

Traditional Education Scholarships (Graduate, Undergraduate/Scholarship) [8500]

Youth Scholarships (Undergraduate/Scholarship) [8305]

Technology

Accenture American Indian Scholarship Program (Graduate, Undergraduate/Scholarship) [825]

AFFIRM University Scholarships (Undergraduate/Scholarship) [1775]

AHETEMS General Scholarships (Graduate, Undergraduate/Scholarship) [55]

AHETEMS Professional Scholarships (Graduate/Scholarship) [56]

Air Force Association Excellence Scholarships (Graduate, Master's, Undergraduate/Scholarship) [88]

Bank of America Junior Achievement Scholarship Fund (Undergraduate/Scholarship) [3885]

Kathi Bowles Scholarships for Women in Technology (Graduate, Undergraduate/Scholarship) [1898]

Graduate Fellowship Program - Robert M Burger Fellowships (GFP) (Doctorate, Graduate/Fellowship) [8078]

CBC Spouses Cheerios Brand Health Initiative Scholarships (Undergraduate/Scholarship) [3215]

Arthur and Gladys Cervenka Scholarships (Undergraduate/Scholarship) [8371]

Chapter 6 Fairfield County Scholarships (Undergraduate/Scholarship) [8379]

CN Scholarships for Women (Postgraduate/Scholarship) [8307]

Development Fund for Black Students in Science and Technology Scholarships (Undergraduate/Scholarship) [3432]

William P. Elrod Memorial Scholarships (Undergraduate, Vocational/Occupational/Scholarship) [8815]

Lt. Colonel Romeo and Josephine Bass Ferreti Scholarships (Undergraduate/Scholarship) [92]

Henry Ford Academy Scholarships (Undergraduate/Scholarship) [8384]

Graduate Fellowship Program - Mahboob Khan/Advanced Micro Devices Fellowships (GFP) (Doctorate, Graduate/Fellowship) [8079]

Graduate Fellowship Program - Research Fellowships (GFP) (Doctorate, Graduate/Fellowship) [8080]

GREAT MINDS Collegiate Scholarship Program (Undergraduate/Scholarship) [340]

Great Minds in STEM Scholarships (Graduate, Undergraduate/Scholarship) [4331]

Perry F. Hadlock Memorial Scholarships (Undergraduate/Scholarship) [1089]

Hamilton Industrial Environmental Association Bursaries-Mohawk College (Undergraduate/Scholarship) [4367]

Helm Family Scholarships (Undergraduate/Scholarship) [7932]

Hinman-Jensen Endowed Scholarships (Undergraduate/Scholarship) [5433]

ITEEA FTE Scholarships (Undergraduate/Scholarship) [5010]

ITEEA Greer/FTE Grants (Professional development/Grant) [5011]

ITEEA Litherland/FTE Scholarships (Undergraduate/Scholarship) [5012]

Johnson and Wales University Scholarships (Undergraduate/Scholarship) [5175]

Lucile B. Kaufman Women's Scholarships (Undergraduate/Scholarship) [8388]

Laser Technology, Engineering and Applications Scholarships (Graduate, Undergraduate/Scholarship) [8639]

Litherland/FTE Scholarships (Undergraduate/Scholarship) [5007]

MAES Founders Scholarships (Graduate, Undergraduate/Scholarship) [5798]

MAES General Scholarships (Graduate, Undergraduate/Scholarship) [5799]

MAES Graduate Scholarships (Graduate/Scholarship) [5800]

MAES Padrino/Madrina Scholarships (Graduate, Undergraduate/Scholarship) [5801]

MAES Pipeline Scholarships (Graduate, Undergraduate/Scholarship) [5802]

MAES Presidential Scholarships (Graduate, Undergraduate/Scholarship) [5803]

Malayalee Engineers Association Scholarships (Graduate/Fellowship) [5601]

Maley/FTE Scholarships (Graduate/Scholarship) [5013]

Maley/FTEE Teacher Scholarships (Graduate/Scholarship) [5008]

Master's Scholarships Program (MSP) (Graduate, Master's/Scholarship) [8081]

Giuliano Mazzetti Scholarships (Undergraduate/Scholarship) [8392]

NDIA Picatinny Chapter Scholarships (Undergraduate/Scholarship) [6237]

Nixon Family Scholarship Fund (Undergraduate/Scholarship) [9556]

Robert Noyce Scholarship Program (Undergraduate/Scholarship) [7160]

Ocean Industries Student Research Awards (Undergraduate, Graduate/Award) [7736]

Ohio Space Grant Consortium Graduate Fellowships (Doctorate, Graduate/Fellowship) [6864]

Ohio Space Grant Consortium Special Minority Fellowships (Doctorate, Graduate/Fellowship) [6865]

Rachael Patterson Memorial Scholarships (Undergraduate/Scholarship) [8987]

Pitsco/Hearlihy/FTE Grants (Professional development/Grant) [5014]

Portable Sanitation Association International Scholarship Fund (Undergraduate/Scholarship) [7375]

Graduate Fellowship Program - GRC/John L. Prince Fellowships (GFP) (Graduate/Fellowship) [8082]

Purdue Krannert School of Management SHPE Scholarships (Undergraduate, Master's/Scholarship) [8130]

NASCAR/Wendell Scott Awards (Graduate, Undergraduate/Scholarship) [4550]

SHPE Foundation Dissertation Scholarships (Doctorate/Scholarship) [8131]

SHPE Foundation General Scholarships (High School, Undergraduate, Graduate/Scholarship) [8132]

SHPE Foundation Northrop Grumman Scholarships (Undergraduate/Scholarship) [8133]

SHPE Foundation Professional Scholarships (Master's, Doctorate/Scholarship) [8134]

SMART Scholarships (Graduate, Undergraduate/Scholarship) [8056]

Society of Manufacturing Engineers Ford PAS Scholarships (SME) (Undergraduate/Scholarship) [8401]

SPEATBC Scholarships (Undergraduate/Scholarship) [8482]

SREB-State Doctoral Scholarships (Doctorate, Graduate/Scholarship) [8585]

Graduate Fellowship Program - GRC/Al Tasch Fellowships (GFP) (Graduate/Fellowship) [8083]

Eben Tisdale Fellowships (Graduate, Undergraduate/Fellowship) [4017]

TSA Teach Technology Scholarships (Undergraduate/Scholarship) [8816]

VEF Fellowship Program (Doctorate, Master's/Fellowship) [9424]

VEF Visiting Scholars Program (Doctorate/Scholarship) [9425]

Myrtle and Earl Walker Scholarships (Undergraduate/Scholarship) [8403]

William E. Weisel Scholarships (Undergraduate/Scholarship) [8405]

Wisconsin Laboratory Association Graduate Student Scholarships (Graduate/Scholarship) [9689]

Wisconsin Laboratory Association Technical Student Scholarships (Undergraduate/Scholarship) [9690]

Wisconsin Laboratory Association Undergraduate University Student Scholarships (Undergraduate/Scholarship) [9691]

Telecommunications systems

The Access Intelligence Scholarships (Graduate, Undergraduate/Scholarship) [8486]

APS/ASU Scholarships (Undergraduate/Scholarship) [7332]

Jim Bourque Scholarships (Postgraduate, Undergraduate/Scholarship) [1501]

Dickey Rural Networks College Scholarship Program (Undergraduate, Vocational/Occupational/Scholarship) [3438]

Richard Gregory Freeland, II Educational Scholarships (High School/Scholarship) [2147]

Future Leader in Radiocommunications Scholarships (Undergraduate/Scholarship) [7567]

The A.W. Perigard Fund (Graduate, Undergraduate/Scholarship) [8487]

The PSSC Legacy Fund (Graduate, Undergraduate/Scholarship) [8488]

Snodgrass Scholarships (Undergraduate/Scholarship) [9175]

The SSPI Mid-Atlantic Chapter Scholarships (Graduate, Undergraduate/Scholarship) [8489]

The SSPI Northeast Chapter Scholarships (Graduate, Undergraduate/Scholarship) [8490]

The SSPI Southern California Scholarships (Graduate, Undergraduate/Scholarship) [8491]

Television (See Radio and television)

Testing, educational/psychological

AERA-ETS Fellowship Program in Measurement (Postdoctorate/Fellowship) [715]

ASNT Fellowship Awards (Graduate/Fellowship) [1316]

Robert B. Oliver ASNT Scholarships (Undergraduate/Scholarship) [1317]

Textile science

California Association of Family and Consumer Sciences -San Diego Chapter Scholarships (CAFCS) (Graduate, Undergraduate, Vocational/Occupational/Scholarship) [7917]

S. Penny Chappell Scholarships (Undergraduate/Scholarship) [7279]

Charles H. Stone Scholarships (Undergraduate/Scholarship) [559]

Sutherland/Purdy Scholarships (Undergraduate/Scholarship) [7303]

Theater arts

Margaret M. Alkek Scholarships (Undergraduate/Scholarship) [3362]

Artistic Scholarship Awards (Undergraduate, Vocational/Occupational/Scholarship) [2023]

ASTR Research Fellowships (Professional development/Fellowship) [1359]

Charly Baker and Heath Merriwether Memorial Scholarships (Undergraduate/Scholarship) [7400]

Leighton M. Ballew Directing Scholarships (Under-

graduate/Scholarship) [8569]

Diane Basilone-Engle Memorial Scholarships (Undergraduate/Scholarship) [2329]

David Beltran Memorial Scholarships (Undergraduate/Scholarship) [7632]

Helen Krich Chinoy Dissertation Research Fellowships (Doctorate/Fellowship) [1360]

Cole Family Scholarships (Undergraduate/Scholarship) [7406]

The Drama Therapy Fund Graduate Research Grants (Graduate/Grant) [3518]

The Drama Therapy Fund Graduate Student Research Awards (Graduate/Grant) [3519]

William R. Durham/Theater Scholarships (Undergraduate/Scholarship) [3148]

S. Randolph Edmonds Young Scholars Competition (Graduate, Undergraduate/Scholarship) [2140]

Polly Holliday Scholarships (Undergraduate/Scholarship) [8570]

Indiana State Alumni Association Creative and Performing Arts Awards (Undergraduate/Scholarship) [4745]

Jerome Fellowships (Professional development/Fellowship) [7337]

Many Voices Fellowships (Professional development/Fellowship) [7338]

Heather McCallum Scholarships (Doctorate, Graduate, Professional development/Scholarship) [2413]

McKnight Advancement Grants (Professional development/Grant) [7339]

McKnight Theater Artist Fellowships (Professional development/Fellowship) [7340]

Montana Broadcasters Association Directors' Scholarships (Undergraduate/Scholarship) [5923]

Palo Verde High School Faculty Follies Scholarships (Undergraduate/Scholarship) [7513]

Robert Porterfield Graduate Scholarships (Graduate/Scholarship) [8571]

Stephen Schwartz Musical Theatre Scholarships (Undergraduate/Scholarship) [4630]

Anne Shaw Fellowships (Graduate/Fellowship) [8890]

Marian A. Smith Scholarships (Graduate/Scholarship) [8572]

Southeastern Theatre Conference Secondary School Scholarships (Undergraduate/Scholarship) [8573]

Theatre and Performance Art Project Grants (Professional development/Grant) [222]

Patricia Van Kirk Scholarships (Undergraduate/Scholarship) [7424]

Wilder Dimension Scholarships for Advanced Study in Theatre Arts (Graduate/Scholarship) [3520]

William E. Wilson Scholarships (Graduate/Scholarship) [8574]

Gwen Yarnell Theatre Scholarships (Undergraduate/Scholarship) [3751]

Theology (See also Religion)

Pamfil and Maria Bujea Family Orthodox Christian Seminarian Scholarships (Undergraduate/Scholarship) [1163]

CSF Graduate Fellowships (Graduate/Fellowship) [2787]

FTE Congregational Fellowships (Graduate/Fellowship) [4019]

FTE Dissertation Fellowships (Graduate/Fellowship) [4020]

FTE Doctoral Fellowships (Doctorate, Graduate/Fellowship) [4021]

FTE Ministry Fellowships (Graduate/Fellowship) [4022]

FTE North American Doctoral Fellowships (Doctorate, Graduate/Fellowship) [4023]

FTE Undergraduate Fellowships (Undergraduate/Fellowship) [4024]

FTE Volunteers Exploring Vocation Fellowships (Graduate/Fellowship) [4025]

Father Rutilio Grande Scholarships (Graduate, Undergraduate/Scholarship) [7893]

Rev. and Mrs. A.K. Jizmejian Educational Fund (Undergraduate/Scholarship) [1600]

J. Milton Richardson Theological Fellowships (Graduate/Fellowship) [369]

The Tabat Scholarship Fund (Graduate/Scholarship) [3738]

Toxicology

A&WMA-GWS Scholarships (Graduate, Undergraduate/Scholarship) [111]

Clinical Toxicology Fellowships (Doctorate/Fellowship) [537]

Pharmacology/Toxicology Post Doctoral Fellowships (Postdoctorate/Fellowship) [7235]

Pharmacology/Toxicology Pre Doctoral Fellowships (Doctorate/Fellowship) [7236]

Pharmacology/Toxicology Research Starter Grants (Doctorate/Grant) [7237]

Pharmacology/Toxicology Sabbatical Fellowships (Postdoctorate/Fellowship) [7238]

School of Pharmacy Continuing Student Scholarships (Undergraduate/Scholarship) [9370]

University of Wisconsin-Madison Pharmacy New Student Scholarships (Undergraduate/Scholarship) [9381]

Traffic management (See Transportation)

Transportation

ABA Diversity Scholarships (Undergraduate/Scholarship) [588]

ABA Members Scholarships for ABA Bus and Tour Operators Only (Undergraduate/Scholarship) [589]

ABA Members Scholarships for All ABA Member Companies (Undergraduate/Scholarship) [590]

Academic Scholarship Program A (Undergraduate/Scholarship) [6241]

Academic Scholarship Program B (Undergraduate/Scholarship) [6242]

Air Traffic Control Association Full-time Employee Student Scholarships (Professional development/Scholarship) [103]

American Bus Association Academic Merit Scholarships (Undergraduate/Scholarship) [591]

Sharon D. Banks Undergraduate Memorial Scholarships (Undergraduate/Scholarship) [9739]

Bison Transport Scholarships (Undergraduate/Scholarship) [6897]

Richard J. Bouchard Scholarships (Graduate, Undergraduate/Scholarship) [1050]

Parsons Brinckerhoff-Jim Lammie Scholarships (Graduate, Undergraduate/Scholarship) [1051]

Continuing Education Awards (All/Scholarship) [6109]

CTP Scholarship Program (Professional development/Scholarship) [6455]

Ginger and Fred Deines Canada Scholarships (Undergraduate, Vocational/Occupational/Scholarship) [8949]

Ginger and Fred Deines Mexico Scholarships (Undergraduate, Vocational/Occupational/Scholarship) [8950]

Delta Nu Alpha Foundation Scholarships (Undergraduate/Scholarship) [3400]

Florida Public Transportation Association Scholarships (FPTA) (Graduate, Undergraduate/Scholarship) [1052]

Jack R. Gilstrap Scholarships (Graduate, Undergraduate/Scholarship) [1053]

Harold F. Hammond Scholarships (Graduate/Scholarship) [4822]

Gabe A. Hartl Scholarships (Undergraduate/Scholarship) [105]

Hooper Memorial Scholarships (Undergraduate, Vocational/Occupational/Scholarship) [8951]

Institute of Transportation Engineers - Texas District Fellowships (Graduate/Fellowship) [4823]

Institute of Transportation Engineers - Western District Fellowships (Graduate/Fellowship) [4824]

ITE Transit Council Scholarships (Graduate/Scholarship) [4825]

Louis T. Klauder Scholarships (Graduate, Undergraduate/Scholarship) [1054]

Ann Koby Legacy Scholarships (Undergraduate/Scholarship) [9740]

Denny Lydic Scholarships (Undergraduate, Vocational/Occupational/Scholarship) [8952]

Reba Malone Scholarships (Graduate, Undergraduate/Scholarship) [1055]

Marathon Oil Corporation College Scholarship Program (Graduate, Undergraduate/Scholarship) [4578]

Burton W. Marsh Fellowships (Graduate/Fellowship) [4826]

Helene M. Overly Memorial Scholarships (Undergraduate/Scholarship) [9741]

Peter L. Picknelly Honorary Scholarships (Undergraduate/Scholarship) [592]

Dan M. Reichard, Jr. Scholarships (Graduate, Undergraduate/Scholarship) [1056]

Frank J. Richter Scholarships (Graduate, Undergraduate/Scholarship) [543]

SC and R Foundation Grant Program (Undergraduate, Vocational/Occupational/Grant) [8631]

SC and R Foundation Scholarships (Undergraduate/Scholarship) [8632]

E.J. Sierleja Memorial Fellowships (Graduate/Fellowship) [4809]

Dr. George M. Smerk Scholarships (Graduate, Undergraduate/Scholarship) [1057]

Snowmobile Association of Massachusetts Scholarships (Undergraduate, Vocational/Occupational/Scholarship) [8274]

TAC Foundation-Albert M. Stevens Scholarships (Postgraduate/Scholarship) [8931]

TAC Foundation-3M Canada Company Scholarships (Postgraduate, Undergraduate/Scholarship) [8932]

TAC Foundation-Armtec Scholarships (Undergraduate/Scholarship) [8933]

TAC Foundation-Cement Association of Canada Scholarships (Postgraduate, Undergraduate/Scholarship) [8934]

TAC Foundation-Delcan Corporation Scholarships (Postgraduate, Undergraduate/Scholarship) [8935]

TAC Foundation-Dillon Consulting Scholarships (Undergraduate/Scholarship) [8936]

TAC Foundation-EBA Engineering Consultants Ltd. Scholarships (Graduate, Postgraduate/Scholarship) [8937]

TAC Foundation-IBI Group Scholarships (Postgraduate, Undergraduate/Scholarship) [8938]

TAC Foundation-iTRANS Consulting Scholarships (Postgraduate/Scholarship) [8939]

TAC Foundation-McCormick Rankin Corporation Scholarships (Undergraduate/Scholarship) [8940]

TAC Foundation-MMM Group Limited Scholarships (Postgraduate, Undergraduate/Scholarship) [8941]

TAC Foundation-Municipalities Scholarships (Postgraduate, Undergraduate/Scholarship) [8942]

TAC Foundation-Provinces and Territories Scholarships (Postgraduate, Undergraduate/Scholarship) [8943]

TAC Foundation-Stantec Consulting Scholarships (Postgraduate/Scholarship) [8944]

TAC Foundation-UMA Engineering Ltd. Scholarships (Undergraduate/Scholarship) [8945]

TAC Foundation-Waterloo Alumni Scholarships (Postgraduate/Scholarship) [8946]

Texas Transportation Scholarships (Undergraduate, Vocational/Occupational/Scholarship) [8953]

Transoft Solutions, Inc. Ahead of the Curve Scholarships (AOTC) (Graduate, Undergraduate/Scholarship) [4827]

Transportation Association of Canada Foundation Scholarships (Postgraduate, Undergraduate/Scholarship) [8947]

Alice Glaisyer Warfield Scholarships (Undergraduate, Vocational/Occupational/Scholarship) [8954]

Travel and tourism

ABA Diversity Scholarships (Undergraduate/Scholarship) [588]

ABA Members Scholarships for ABA Bus and Tour Operators Only (Undergraduate/Scholarship) [589]

ABA Members Scholarships for All ABA Member Companies (Undergraduate/Scholarship) [590]

Alaska Airlines Scholarships (Undergraduate/Scholarship) [1362]

Alaska Visitors Association/Gomar Scholarships (Undergraduate/Scholarship) [9134]

American Bus Association Academic Merit Scholarships (Undergraduate/Scholarship) [591]

American Express Travel Scholarships (Undergraduate/Scholarship) [1363]

American Society of Travel Agents AVIS Scholarships (Graduate, Professional development, Undergraduate/Scholarship) [1364]

Applied Hospitality Degree Scholarships (Undergraduate/Scholarship) [2487]

Arizona Chapter Gold Scholarships (Undergraduate/Scholarship) [1365]

Canadian Hospitality Foundation College Entrance Scholarships (Undergraduate/Scholarship) [2488]

Canadian Hospitality Foundation University Entrance Scholarships (Undergraduate/Scholarship) [2489]

Sue and Ken Dyer Foundation Travel Scholarships (Undergraduate/Scholarship) [3941]

GLP Program Scholarships (Professional development/Scholarship) [4166]

David J. Hallissey Memorial Scholarships (Graduate, Undergraduate/Scholarship) [1366]

Healy Graduate Scholarships (Graduate/Scholarship) [1367]

Holland America Line-Westours Research Grants (Undergraduate/Grant) [1368]

Mike Kabo Global Scholarships (Professional development/Scholarship) [4167]

NC Hospitality Education Foundation Scholarships - Four Year College or University (Undergraduate/Scholarship) [6776]

NC Hospitality Education Foundation Scholarships - High School (Undergraduate, Vocational/Occupational/Scholarship) [6778]

NC Hospitality Education Foundation Scholarships - Two Year Community or Junior College (Undergraduate/Scholarship) [6779]

Peter L. Picknelly Honorary Scholarships (Undergraduate/Scholarship) [592]

Pleasant Hawaiian Holidays Scholarships (Undergraduate/Scholarship) [1369]

Stan and Leone Pollard Scholarships (Undergraduate/Scholarship) [1370]

George Reinke Scholarships (Professional development/Scholarship) [1371]

Thomas and Ruth River International Scholarships (Undergraduate, Graduate/Scholarship) [9756]

Ollie Rosenberg Scholarship Travel Fund (Undergraduate/Scholarship) [3959]

South Carolina Tourism and Hospitality Educational Foundation Scholarships (Undergraduate/Scholarship) [4603]

Nancy Stewart Scholarships (Undergraduate/Scholarship) [1372]

TIAC / Parks Canada Sustainable Tourism Scholarships (College, Undergraduate, Master's/Scholarship) [8921]

West Virginia Educational Foundation Hospitality Business Alliance Scholarships (Undergraduate/Scholarship) [9570]

West Virginia Hospitality and Travel Association General Scholarships (Undergraduate/Scholarship) [9571]

Youth for Understanding Scholarships (Undergraduate/Scholarship) [9797]

Turfgrass management

GCSAA Scholars Competition (Undergraduate/Scholarship) [4187]

GCSAA Student Essay Contest (Graduate, Undergraduate/Prize) [4188]

Dr. James Watson Fellowship Program (Doctorate, Graduate/Fellowship) [4189]

Turkish studies

Institute of Turkish Studies Dissertation Writing Grants (Doctorate/Grant) [4829]

Institute of Turkish Studies Sabbatical Research Grants (Professional development/Grant) [4830]

Post-Doctoral Summer Travel-Research Grants (Doctorate/Grant) [4832]

Summer Language Study Grants in Turkey (Graduate/Grant) [4833]

Ukrainian studies

Leo J. Krysa Family Undergraduate Scholarships (Undergraduate/Scholarship) [2504]

Ukrainian Canadian Professional and Business Club Scholarships in Education (Undergraduate/Scholarship) [2505]

United States studies

AAS-American Historical Print Collectors Society Fellowships (Doctorate/Fellowship) [410]

The Christoph Daniel Ebeling Fellowships (Doctorate/Fellowship) [418]

Ford Foundation Postdoctoral Fellowships (Postdoctorate/Fellowship) [6001]

Hench Post-Dissertation Fellowships (Postdoctorate/Fellowship) [419]

Institute-NEH Postdoctoral Fellowships (Doctorate, Professional development/Fellowship) [6882]

Kislak Fellowships in American Studies (Graduate, Postdoctorate/Fellowship) [5272]

Kislak Short Term Fellowships Opportunities in American Studies (All/Fellowship) [5273]

Marshall-Baruch Fellowships (Doctorate/Fellowship) [5649]

Institute Andrew W. Mellon Postdoctoral Research Fellowships (Doctorate/Fellowship) [6883]

The Reese Fellowships (Doctorate/Fellowship) [423]

Savatori Fellowships (Graduate/Fellowship) [4848]

United States Capitol Historical Society Fellowships (Graduate/Fellowship) [9037]

Urban affairs/design/planning

Charles Abrams Scholarships (Graduate/Scholarship) [1008]

Robert A. Catlin/David W. Long Memorial Scholarships (Graduate/Scholarship) [1009]

CIGNA Healthcare Graduate Scholarships (Graduate/Scholarship) [6290]

CIGNA Healthcare Undergraduate Scholarships (Undergraduate/Scholarship) [6291]

Economic Development Division Graduate Scholarships (Graduate/Scholarship) [1010]

Environment, Natural Resource and Energy Division Fellowships (ENRE) (Graduate/Fellowship) [1011]

Jewish Federation Academic Scholarships (Graduate, Undergraduate/Scholarship) [5161]

Judith McManus Price Scholarships (Graduate, Undergraduate/Scholarship) [1012]

Worldstudio AIGA Scholarships (Graduate, Undergraduate/Scholarship) [9761]

Urology

AUA Foundation/Astellas Rising Star in Urology Research Awards (Postdoctorate, Professional development/Fellowship) [1407]

AUA Foundation Bridge Awards (Postgraduate/Fellowship) [1408]

AUA Foundation - NIDDK/NCI Surgeon-Scientist Awards (Postgraduate/Fellowship) [1409]

AUA Foundation Ph.D. Post-Doctoral Fellowships (Postdoctorate/Fellowship) [1410]

Canadian Urological Association Community-based Research Awards (Doctorate/Award) [2628]

Canadian Urological Association Fellowships (Graduate/Fellowship) [2629]

Endourological Society Fellowships (Professional development/Fellowship) [3641]

KFOC Allied Health Scholarships (Graduate/Scholarship) [5256]

KFOC Biomedical Scholarships (Doctorate/Scholarship) [5258]

Vacuum science and technology

Society of Vacuum Coaters Foundation Scholarships (Vocational/Occupational, Two Year College, Undergraduate, Graduate/Scholarship) [8514]

Vegetarianism

Craig Johnson Family Scholarships (Undergraduate/Scholarship) [8884]

Veterinary science and medicine

AABP Amstutz Scholarships (Undergraduate/Scholarship) [443]

AABP Bovine Veterinary Student Recognition Awards (Undergraduate/Scholarship) [444]

AABP Education Grants (Undergraduate/Grant) [445]

AABP Research Assistantships (Doctorate/Scholarship) [446]

AABP Student Externship Program (Undergraduate/Scholarship) [447]

AAEP/ALSIC Scholarships (Undergraduate/Scholarship) [474]

AAEP Foundation Past Presidents' Research Fellowships (Doctorate/Scholarship) [475]

American Quarter Horse Foundation Scholarships (Undergraduate/Scholarship) [1063]

Association for Women Veterinarians Foundation Student Scholarships (Graduate/Scholarship) [1912]

Auburn University College of Veterinary Medicine Scholarships (Undergraduate/Scholarship) [177]

Diane Basilone-Engle Memorial Scholarships (Undergraduate/Scholarship) [2329]

DAAD Study Scholarship Awards (Graduate/Scholarship) [4116]

Downeast Feline Scholarships (Graduate/Scholarship) [5577]

Keith Gilmore Foundation - Postgraduate Scholarships (Postgraduate/Scholarship) [4154]

Keith Gilmore Foundation - Undergraduate Scholarships (Undergraduate/Scholarship) [4155]

Dr. M.G. "Doc" Headley Scholarships (Undergraduate/Scholarship) [8726]

Dr. Roger E. Meisner Veterinary Medicine Educational Scholarship Fund (Undergraduate/Scholarship) [6790]

Minority Presence Grant Program for Doctoral Study (Doctorate, Graduate/Grant) [9295]

NCF Fort Dodge Animal Health Legacy Scholarships for Veterinary Students (Undergraduate/Scholarship) [6178]

North Dakota Veterinary Medical Association Scholarships (Undergraduate/Scholarship) [6791]

Laurie Page-Peck Scholarship Fund (Undergraduate/Scholarship) [1914]

Stark County Dairy Promoters Scholarships (Undergraduate/Scholarship) [8701]

E.L. Stubbs Research Grants (Graduate/Grant) [5847]

Welder Wildlife Foundation Fellowships (Doctorate, Graduate/Fellowship) [9559]

Dr. William "Tim" Whalen Memorial Scholarships (Undergraduate/Scholarship) [6792]

Saul T. Wilson, Jr. Scholarships (Graduate, Undergraduate/Scholarship) [9403]

Video

UFVA Carole Fielding Student Grants (Graduate, Undergraduate/Grant) [9202]

Film and Video Arts Project Grants (Professional development/Grant) [219]

Vietnamese studies

Gamewarden Scholarship program (High School, Undergraduate, Vocational/Occupational/Scholarship) [4037]

BM1 James Elliott Williams and LCDR Jack Graf Memorial Scholarship Fund (Undergraduate/Scholarship) [7134]

Violence (See Aggression and violence)

Violin (See Music, Violin)

Visual arts

Artistic Scholarship Awards *(Undergraduate, Vocational/Occupational/Scholarship)* [2023]
William E. Barto Scholarships *(Undergraduate/Scholarship)* [3525]
Bill Bendiner and Doug Morgenson Scholarships *(Undergraduate/Scholarship)* [7402]
CBC Spouses Visual Arts Scholarships *(Undergraduate/Scholarship)* [3219]
Cintas Foundation Fellowships in Visual Arts *(Professional development/Fellowship)* [2882]
Sally Cole Visual Arts Scholarship Fund *(Undergraduate/Scholarship)* [3899]
College Art Association Professional Development Fellowships *(Graduate/Fellowship)* [2968]
College Art Association Wyeth Publication Grants *(Professional development/Grant)* [2969]
Constant Memorial Scholarship for Aquidneck Island Resident *(Undergraduate/Scholarship)* [7788]
Florida Education Fund McKnight Doctoral Fellowships *(Graduate/Fellowship)* [3822]
Jane Hood Memorial Fund *(Undergraduate/Scholarship)* [3776]
Manzer-Keener-Wefler Scholarships *(Undergraduate/Scholarship)* [8686]
Jack D. Motteler Scholarships *(Undergraduate/Scholarship)* [7413]
NAMTA - International Art Materials Trade Association Visual Arts Major Scholarships *(Graduate, Undergraduate/Scholarship)* [5981]
Native Hawaiian Visual Arts Scholarships *(Graduate, Undergraduate/Scholarship)* [5220]
Dr. Adolph Piotrowski Memorial Art Scholarships *(Undergraduate/Scholarship)* [7776]
RBC Royal Bank Scholarships for Undergraduates *(Undergraduate/Scholarship)* [7825]
Ric Ulrich and Chuck Pischke Scholarships *(Undergraduate/Scholarship)* [7423]
Patricia Van Kirk Scholarships *(Undergraduate/Scholarship)* [7424]
Virginia Museum of Fine Arts Visual Arts Fellowships *(Graduate, Professional development, Undergraduate/Fellowship)* [9457]
Visual Arts and New Media Project Grants *(Professional development/Grant)* [223]

Visual impairment

William and Dorothy Ferrell Scholarship Program *(Undergraduate/Scholarship)* [1759]

Viticulture

American Society for Enology and Viticulture Scholarships *(Graduate, Undergraduate/Scholarship)* [1243]
American Wine Society Educational Foundation Scholarships *(Graduate/Scholarship)* [1450]
Nancy Johnston Memorial Scholarships *(Graduate, Undergraduate/Scholarship)* [8837]

Waste management

A&WMA-GWS Scholarships *(Graduate, Undergraduate/Scholarship)* [111]
A&WMA Scholarships *(Graduate/Scholarship)* [107]
Environmental Research and Education Foundation Scholarships *(Doctorate, Postdoctorate/Scholarship)* [3658]
Ivanhoe Foundation Fellowships *(Master's/Fellowship)* [5086]
SSAWMA Scholarships *(Graduate/Scholarship)* [120]

Water resources

A&WMA-GWS Scholarships *(Graduate, Undergraduate/Scholarship)* [111]
Association of California Water Agencies Scholarships *(Undergraduate/Scholarship)* [1727]
Leo Bourassa Scholarships *(Undergraduate, Graduate/Scholarship)* [9455]
California Sea Grant State Fellowships *(Graduate/Fellowship)* [2277]
Thomas R. Camp Scholarships *(Graduate/Scholarship)* [1416]
Canadian Water Resources Association Scholarships *(All/Scholarship)* [2631]
Channabasappa Memorial Scholarships *(Graduate, Professional development/Scholarship)* [4918]
Holly A. Cornell Scholarships *(Graduate/Scholarship)* [1417]
Robert Esser Student Achievement Scholarships *(Graduate, Undergraduate/Fellowship, Scholarship)* [4685]
Stephen K. Hall ACWA Water Law and Policy Scholarships *(Graduate/Scholarship)* [1728]
B. Harper Bull Conservation Fellowships *(Graduate/Fellowship)* [8913]
Richard A. Herbert Memorial Scholarships *(Undergraduate/Scholarship)* [1412]
Clair A. Hill Scholarships *(Undergraduate/Scholarship)* [1729]
IDA Fellowship Awards *(Professional development/Fellowship)* [4919]
Illinois Lake Management Association Undergraduate/Graduate Scholarships *(Graduate, Undergraduate/Fellowship, Scholarship)* [4686]
Ivanhoe Foundation Fellowships *(Master's/Fellowship)* [5086]
John A. Knauss Marine Policy Fellowships *(Graduate/Fellowship)* [2278]
Larson Aquatic Research Support Scholarships (LARS) *(Doctorate, Graduate/Scholarship)* [1418]
Ken Thomson Scholarships *(Undergraduate/Scholarship)* [2632]
WEF Canham Graduate Studies Scholarships *(Graduate/Scholarship)* [9536]
West Coast Sea Grant Fellowships *(Graduate/Fellowship)* [2279]
Abel Wolman Fellowships *(Doctorate/Fellowship)* [1419]

Water supply industry

Len Assante Scholarship Fund *(Undergraduate/Scholarship)* [6311]
Thomas R. Camp Scholarships *(Graduate/Scholarship)* [1416]
Holly A. Cornell Scholarships *(Graduate/Scholarship)* [1417]
Larson Aquatic Research Support Scholarships (LARS) *(Doctorate, Graduate/Scholarship)* [1418]
Michigan Stormwater-Floodplain Association Scholarships *(Graduate, Undergraduate/Scholarship)* [5834]
Abel Wolman Fellowships *(Doctorate/Fellowship)* [1419]

Welding

Howard E. and Wilma J. Adkins Memorial Scholarships *(Undergraduate/Scholarship)* [1423]
American Welding Society District Scholarships *(Undergraduate/Scholarship)* [1424]
American Welding Society International Scholarships *(Undergraduate/Scholarship)* [1425]
American Welding Society National Scholarships *(Undergraduate/Scholarship)* [1426]
American Welding Society Past Presidents Scholarships *(Undergraduate/Scholarship)* [1427]
American Welding Society Research Fellowships *(Graduate/Scholarship)* [1428]
Arsham Amirikian Engineering Scholarships *(Undergraduate/Scholarship)* [1429]
Jerry Baker Scholarships *(Undergraduate/Scholarship)* [1430]
Jack R. Barckhoff Welding Management Scholarships *(Undergraduate/Scholarship)* [1431]
Edward J. Brady Memorial Scholarships *(Undergraduate/Scholarship)* [1432]
William A. and Ann M. Brothers Scholarships *(Undergraduate/Scholarship)* [1433]
Donald F. Hastings Scholarships *(Undergraduate/Scholarship)* [1434]
Donald and Shirley Hastings Scholarships *(Undergraduate/Scholarship)* [1435]
William B. Howell Scholarships *(Undergraduate/Scholarship)* [1436]
Hypertherm International HyTech Leadership Scholarships *(Graduate/Scholarship)* [1437]
ITW Welding Companies Scholarships *(Undergraduate/Scholarship)* [1438]
Terry Jarvis Memorial Scholarships *(Undergraduate/Scholarship)* [1439]
LCSC Welding Club Scholarships *(Undergraduate/Scholarship)* [5438]
John C. Lincoln Memorial Scholarships *(Undergraduate/Scholarship)* [1440]
Miller Electric International WorldSkills Competition Scholarships *(Undergraduate/Scholarship)* [1441]
Robert L. Peaslee-Detroit Brazing and Soldiering Division Scholarships *(Undergraduate/Scholarship)* [1442]
Ronald C. and Joyce Pierce Scholarships *(Undergraduate/Scholarship)* [1443]
Praxair International Scholarships *(Undergraduate/Scholarship)* [1444]
Resistance Welder Manufacturers' Association Scholarships *(Undergraduate/Scholarship)* [1445]
Jerry Robinson Inweld Corporation Scholarships *(Undergraduate/Scholarship)* [1446]
James A. Turner, Jr. Memorial Scholarships *(Undergraduate/Scholarship)* [1447]
Amos and Marilyn Winsand-Detroit Section Named Scholarships *(Undergraduate/Scholarship)* [1448]

Western European studies

Western Civilization Fellowships *(Graduate/Fellowship)* [4850]

Wildlife conservation, management, and science

Alaska Support Industry Alliance Scholarships *(Undergraduate/Scholarship)* [9133]
Lyle Carlson Wildlife Management Scholarships *(Undergraduate/Scholarship)* [9145]
CROW Fellowships *(All/Fellowship)* [2905]
Charles Dobbins FTA Scholarships *(Undergraduate, Vocational/Occupational/Scholarship)* [4033]
B. Harper Bull Conservation Fellowships *(Graduate/Fellowship)* [8913]
Dannie Jasmine Scholarships *(Undergraduate/Scholarship)* [5944]
Ben Meadows Natural Resource Scholarships - Academic Achievement Scholarships *(Undergraduate/Scholarship)* [2054]
Ben Meadows Natural Resource Scholarships - Leadership Scholarships *(Undergraduate/Scholarship)* [2055]
NGC College Scholarships *(Graduate, Undergraduate/Scholarship)* [6303]
Dennis Raveling Scholarships *(Undergraduate/Scholarship)* [2288]
Dr. Orrin J. Rongstad Wildlife Management Scholarships *(Undergraduate/Scholarship)* [9171]
Russian/Central Asian Student Scholarships *(Undergraduate/Scholarship)* [9172]
Welder Wildlife Foundation Fellowships *(Doctorate, Graduate/Fellowship)* [9559]
Wild Felid Legacy Scholarships *(Graduate/Scholarship)* [9599]

Women's studies

American Association of University Women Master's and First Professional Awards *(Professional development/Award)* [12]
Tara Lynne Arnold Scholarships *(Undergraduate/Scholarship)* [8716]
ASECS Women's Caucus Editing and Translation Fellowships *(Doctorate/Fellowship)* [1223]
Center for the Education of Women Student Research Grants *(Graduate, Undergraduate/Grant)* [2688]
Mariam K. Chamberlain Fellowships in Women and Public Policy *(Graduate/Fellowship)* [4835]
Emilie Du Chatelet Awards *(Doctorate/Award)* [1226]

City of Toronto Women's Studies Scholarships *(Graduate, Undergraduate/Scholarship)* [9329]

IWPR/GW Fellowships in Women's Public Policy Research *(Graduate/Fellowship)* [4836]

Joseph H. Fichter Research Grants *(Professional development/Grant)* [1874]

Catharine Macaulay Prize *(Graduate/Prize)* [1233]

Ruth R. and Alyson R. Miller Fellowships *(Graduate, Doctorate/Fellowship)* [5676]

Woodrow Wilson Dissertation Fellowships in Women's Studies *(Graduate/Fellowship)* [9620]

Women's Health Research Foundation of Canada Scholarship Program *(Graduate/Scholarship)* [9721]

Writing

AAS Fellowships for Creative and Performing Artists and Writers *(All/Fellowship)* [412]

Velma Shotwell Griffin Memorial Scholarship Fund *(Undergraduate/Scholarship)* [8671]

Bodie McDowell Scholarships *(Graduate, Undergraduate/Scholarship)* [7006]

McNamara Family Creative Arts Project Grants *(Graduate, Undergraduate/Grant)* [4579]

Mid-South STC Chapter Scholarships *(Graduate, Undergraduate/Scholarship)* [8502]

Melissa Pellegrin Memorial Scholarships *(Graduate, Undergraduate/Scholarship)* [8504]

Jim Poore Memorial Scholarships *(Undergraduate/Scholarship)* [4672]

Jack Shrader Memorial Awards *(Professional development/Scholarship)* [1744]

Zoology

Marion Breland-Bailey Awards *(Graduate, Undergraduate/Award)* [1713]

Margaret Dowell-Gravatt, M.D. Scholarships *(Undergraduate/Scholarship)* [2059]

Libbie H. Hyman Memorial Scholarships *(Graduate/Scholarship)* [8358]

Dennis Raveling Scholarships *(Undergraduate/Scholarship)* [2288]

This index lists awards that are restricted by the applicant's residence of legal record. Award citations are arranged alphabetically by country and subarranged by region, state or province. Each citation is followed by the study level and award type, which appear in parentheses. The numbers following the parenthetical information indicate book entry numbers for awards, not page numbers.

UNITED STATES

4th Infantry Division Association Scholarships *(All/Scholarship)* [5990]

AAA Leadership Mentoring/Shadow Award Program *(Graduate/Award)* [405]

AAA Minority Dissertation Fellowship Program *(Doctorate/Fellowship)* [406]

AAAA Operation Jumpstart III Scholarships *(Graduate/Scholarship)* [433]

AAAA Scholarship Program *(Undergraduate/Scholarship)* [1611]

AAACN Scholarships *(Undergraduate/Scholarship)* [437]

AAAS Mass Media Science and Engineering Fellowships *(Graduate, Postgraduate, Undergraduate/Fellowship)* [430]

AAAS Science and Technology Policy Fellowships *(Postdoctorate/Fellowship)* [431]

AABP Amstutz Scholarships *(Undergraduate/Scholarship)* [443]

AABP Bovine Veterinary Student Recognition Awards *(Undergraduate/Scholarship)* [444]

AABP Education Grants *(Undergraduate/Grant)* [445]

AABP Research Assistantships *(Doctorate/Scholarship)* [446]

AABP Student Externship Program *(Undergraduate/Scholarship)* [447]

AACE International Competitive Scholarships *(Undergraduate/Scholarship)* [4]

AACN Continuing Professional Development Scholarships *(Graduate, Professional development/Scholarship)* [469]

AACN Minority Nurse Faculty Scholarships *(Graduate/Scholarship)* [457]

AACOM Scholar in Residence Program *(Graduate, Undergraduate/Scholarship)* [461]

AACT Undergraduate Scholarships *(Undergraduate/Scholarship)* [7153]

AACTE Outstanding Book Awards *(Professional development/Award)* [463]

AACTE Outstanding Dissertation Awards *(Doctorate/Award)* [464]

AAEP/ALSIC Scholarships *(Undergraduate/Scholarship)* [474]

AAEP Foundation Past Presidents' Research Fellowships *(Doctorate/Scholarship)* [475]

AAFPE LEX Scholarships *(Undergraduate/Scholarship)* [526]

AAGS Graduate Fellowship Awards *(Undergraduate/Fellowship)* [641]

AAHD Scholarships *(Graduate, Undergraduate/Scholarship)* [481]

AAIB Scholarships *(Undergraduate/Scholarship)* [485]

AAJ Trial Advocacy Scholarships *(Undergraduate/Scholarship)* [489]

AAJA/CNN Scholar Program *(Graduate, Undergraduate/Scholarship)* [1640]

AAJA/COX Foundation Scholarships *(Graduate, Undergraduate/Scholarship)* [1641]

AAJUW Scholarships *(Graduate, Undergraduate/Scholarship)* [487]

AALL Leadership Academy Grants *(Professional development/Grant)* [507]

AALL Research Funds *(Professional development/Grant)* [495]

AALL Scholarships for Continuing Education Classes *(Postgraduate/Scholarship)* [496]

AALL Scholarships for Library School Graduates Seeking a Non-Law Degree *(Postgraduate/Scholarship)* [497]

AAMA Houston Chapter - Medical Student Scholarships *(Professional development/Scholarship)* [1494]

AAMFT Minority Fellowships *(Doctorate, Graduate/Fellowship)* [511]

A&WMA-GWS Scholarships *(Graduate, Undergraduate/Scholarship)* [111]

A&WMA Scholarships *(Graduate/Scholarship)* [107]

AANS Medical Student Summer Research Fellowships (MSSRF) *(Undergraduate/Fellowship)* [515]

AAOHN Professional Development Scholarships - Academic Study *(Graduate, Undergraduate/Scholarship)* [522]

AAOHN Professional Development Scholarships - Continuing Education *(Professional development/Scholarship)* [523]

AAPM Fellowships for Graduate Study in Medical Physics *(Graduate/Fellowship)* [528]

AAPM Minority Undergraduate Summer Experience Fellowships (MUSE) *(Undergraduate/Fellowship)* [529]

AAPM Summer Undergraduate Fellowships *(Undergraduate/Fellowship)* [530]

Leroy F. Aaron Scholarships *(Graduate, Undergraduate/Scholarship)* [6391]

AAS-American Historical Print Collectors Society Fellowships *(Doctorate/Fellowship)* [410]

AAS-American Society for Eighteenth Century Studies Fellowships *(Postdoctorate/Fellowship)* [411]

AAS CIAC Small Grants *(Graduate/Grant)* [1709]

AAS Fellowships for Creative and Performing Artists and Writers *(All/Fellowship)* [412]

AAS Korean Studies Scholarship Program *(Doctorate, Graduate/Scholarship)* [1710]

AAS National Endowment for the Humanities Long-Term Fellowships *(Postdoctorate/Fellowship)* [413]

AAS-Northeast Modern Language Association Fellowships *(All/Fellowship)* [414]

AAST/ACS/NIGMS Scholarships *(Professional development/Scholarship)* [554]

AAST/KCI Research Grants *(All/Grant)* [555]

AAST Medical Student Scholarships *(All/Scholarship)* [556]

AAUW Legal Advocacy Fund American Fellowships *(Doctorate/Fellowship)* [15]

AAUW Legal Advocacy Fund Career Development Grants *(Professional development/Grant)* [16]

AAUW Legal Advocacy Fund International Fellowships *(Doctorate, Graduate/Fellowship)* [17]

AAUW Legal Advocacy Fund Selected Professions Fellowships *(Doctorate, Graduate/Fellowship)* [18]

ABA Diversity Scholarships *(Undergraduate/Scholarship)* [588]

ABA Legal Opportunity Scholarship Funds *(Undergraduate/Scholarship)* [4566]

ABA Members Scholarships for ABA Bus and Tour Operators Only *(Undergraduate/Scholarship)* [589]

ABA Members Scholarships for All ABA Member Companies *(Undergraduate/Scholarship)* [590]

ABA Scholarships *(Undergraduate/Scholarship)* [581]

Anthony Abbene Scholarships *(Undergraduate/Scholarship)* [4650]

Clifford V. Abbott Memorial Scholarships *(Undergraduate/Scholarship)* [8714]

ABC-Clio Research Grants *(Graduate/Grant)* [8412]

Alejandro "Alex" Abecia Reaching High Scholarships *(Undergraduate, Vocational/Occupational/Scholarship)* [2932]

Abercrombie and Fitch Global Diversity Scholar Awards *(High School/Scholarship)* [6501]

ABF Doctoral Fellowships *(Doctorate, Graduate/Fellowship)* [577]

ABFSE National Scholarship Program *(Undergraduate/Scholarship)* [584]

Kyutaro & Yasuo Abiko Memorial Scholarships *(Undergraduate/Scholarship)* [5140]

Evelyn Abrams Memorial Scholarships *(Undergraduate/Scholarship)* [7462]

Charles Abrams Scholarships *(Graduate/Scholarship)* [1008]

The Frederick B. Abramson Public Interest Fellowships Awards *(All/Fellowship)* [23]

Academic Promise Scholarships *(Undergraduate/Scholarship)* [4740]

Academic Scholarship Program A *(Undergraduate/Scholarship)* [6241]

Academic Scholarship Program B *(Undergraduate/Scholarship)* [6242]

L'Academie de Cuisine Culinary Arts Scholarships *(All, Professional development/Scholarship)* [3305]

Academy of Motion Picture Arts and Sciences Student Academy Awards *(Undergraduate/Award)* [33]

Accenture American Indian Scholarship Program *(Graduate, Undergraduate/Scholarship)* [825]

The Access Intelligence Scholarships *(Graduate, Undergraduate/Scholarship)* [8486]

ACHE Junior and Community College Athletic Scholarships *(Undergraduate/Scholarship)* [157]

ACHE Junior and Community College Performing Arts Scholarships *(Undergraduate/Scholarship)* [158]

ACHE Two-Year College Academic Scholarships *(Undergraduate/Scholarship)* [161]

The Achieve Physical Therapy & Fitness Scholarships *(Doctorate/Scholarship)* [8737]

ACI BASF Construction Chemicals Student Fellowships *(Graduate, Undergraduate/Fellowship)* [628]

ACI Cagley ACI Student Fellowships *(Graduate, Master's, Undergraduate/Fellowship)* [629]

ACI President's Fellowships *(Doctorate, Master's/Fellowship)* [630]

ACI Scholarships *(Graduate/Scholarship)* [631]

Ken and Pat Ackerman Family Scholarship Fund *(Undergraduate/Scholarship)* [3755]

Wayne D. Ackerman Family Scholarship Fund *(Un-*

dergraduate/Scholarship) [8655]

ACLS Collaborative Research Fellowships (Doctorate/Fellowship) [671]

ACLS Digital Innovation Fellowships (Doctorate/Fellowship) [672]

ACMPE Scholarship Fund Program (Graduate, Undergraduate/Scholarship) [5739]

ACMS Faculty Research Fellowships (Professional development/Fellowship) [600]

ACMS Intensive Mongolian Language Fellowship Program (Undergraduate/Fellowship) [601]

ACMS Library Fellowships (Graduate, Professional development/Fellowship) [602]

ACMS Research Fellowships (Doctorate, Postdoctorate/Fellowship) [603]

ACMS U.S.-Mongolia Field Research Fellowship Program (Graduate, Undergraduate/Fellowship) [604]

ACNL Research Scholarships (Graduate/Scholarship) [1722]

ACNM Foundation, Inc. Fellowships for Graduate Education (Doctorate, Postdoctorate/Fellowship) [617]

ACNP Nurse Practitioner Student Scholarship Awards (Undergraduate/Scholarship) [621]

Acoustical Society of America Minority Fellowships (Graduate/Fellowship) [39]

ACS/ASA Health Policy and Management Scholarships (Professional development/Scholarship) [1398]

ACS Law Fellowships (Graduate/Fellowship) [654]

ACSUS Distinguished Dissertation Awards (Doctorate/Award) [1731]

ADAA Career Development Travel Awards (Professional development/Award) [1483]

ADAA Junior Faculty Research Grants (Professional development/Grant) [1484]

Nancy Ashley Adams/Ashley Adams Koetje Scholarships (Undergraduate/Scholarship) [3360]

Adams Family Scholarships (Undergraduate/Scholarship) [3361]

Ruth D. Adams Fund (Undergraduate/Scholarship) [3756]

Mamie Adams Memorial Awards (Undergraduate/Scholarship) [5410]

The Clarke B. Adams Memorial Foundation Lapeer County Community Foundation Fund (Undergraduate/Scholarship) [5347]

Ed Adams Memorial Scholarships (Professional development/Scholarship) [7753]

Lt. Holly Adams Memorial Scholarships (Undergraduate/Scholarship) [3091]

Ruth Adams Memorial Scholarships (Undergraduate/Scholarship) [7615]

Beaver Medical Clinic-Glen Adams Scholarship Awards (Undergraduate/Scholarship) [7616]

Henry Adams Scholarships (Undergraduate/Scholarship) [1262]

Adelante Fund Hope Scholarships, CPS Energy Dependents (Undergraduate/Scholarship) [43]

Adelante Fund Hope Scholarships, San Antonio, TX Students (Undergraduate/Scholarship) [44]

Adelante Fund UPS Scholarships (Undergraduate/Scholarship) [45]

Carl Joseph Adelhardt Memorial Scholarships (Undergraduate/Scholarship) [4050]

Adelson Family Scholarships (Undergraduate/Scholarship) [7463]

Adelson Scholarships (Undergraduate/Scholarship) [7464]

ADHA IOH Sigma Phi Alpha Graduate Scholarships (Graduate/Scholarship) [707]

Howard E. and Wilma J. Adkins Memorial Scholarships (Undergraduate/Scholarship) [1423]

Chris Nance Adler Scholarship Fund (High School/Scholarship) [2933]

Adolescent Literacy Pre-doctoral Fellowships (Doctorate/Fellowship) [6004]

Herb Adrian Memorial Scholarship Fund (Undergraduate/Scholarship) [3881]

Adult Students in Scholastic Transition Scholarships (ASIST) (All/Scholarship) [3693]

Advanced Cardiovascular Surgery Fellowships (Graduate, Postdoctorate/Fellowship) [561]

Advanced Light Source Postdoctoral Fellowship Program (Doctorate/Fellowship) [5379]

Advertising Production Club of New York High School Scholarships (APC) (Undergraduate/Scholarship) [58]

AE Flight Training Scholarships (Professional development/Scholarship) [6721]

AE Jet Type Rating Scholarships (Professional development/Scholarship) [6722]

AE Technical Training Scholarships (Professional development/Scholarship) [6723]

AECT Foundation Mentor Endowment Scholarships (Doctorate, Graduate/Scholarship) [1761]

AECT Legacy Scholarships (Graduate, Master's, Professional development/Scholarship) [1762]

AERA-AIR Fellows Program (Postdoctorate/Fellowship) [714]

AERA-ETS Fellowship Program in Measurement (Postdoctorate/Fellowship) [715]

AERA Minority Fellowship Program in Education Research (Postdoctorate/Fellowship) [716]

AESF Foundation Scholarships (Graduate, Undergraduate/Scholarship) [6127]

AfAA Graduate Student Paper Awards (Graduate/Award) [1688]

AfAA Undergraduate Student Paper Awards (Undergraduate/Award) [1689]

AFAR Scholarships (Graduate, Undergraduate/Scholarship) [746]

AFCEA Math and Science Teachers Scholarships (Graduate, Undergraduate/Scholarship) [1553]

AFCEA Scholarship for Working Professionals (Graduate/Scholarship) [1554]

AFFIRM University Scholarships (Undergraduate/Scholarship) [1775]

Affirmative Action Mini Grants and Student Scholarships (All/Grant) [25]

AFPPA Student Scholarships (Undergraduate/Scholarship) [1773]

African American Studies Fellowships (Graduate, Doctorate/Fellowship) [5668]

AFROTC Scholarships (Undergraduate/Scholarship) [87]

AFSA Chapter 155 Division 1 Scholarships - Category 1 (Undergraduate/Scholarship) [97]

AFSA Chapter 155 Division 1 Scholarships - Category 2 (Undergraduate/Scholarship) [98]

AFSA Chapter 155 Division 1 Scholarships - Category 3 (Undergraduate/Scholarship) [99]

AFSP - Distinguished Investigator Grants (Postgraduate/Grant) [766]

AFSP Postdoctoral Research Fellowships (Postgraduate/Fellowship) [767]

AFSP Standard Research Grants (Postgraduate/Grant) [768]

AFSP Young Investigator Grants (Postgraduate/Grant) [769]

AfterCollege/AACN Nursing Scholarships (Graduate, Undergraduate/Scholarship) [458]

AG BELL College Scholarship Awards (Undergraduate/Scholarship) [2048]

AGBU Scholarships (Graduate/Loan) [1573]

AGC Foundation Outstanding Educator Awards (Professional development/Award) [1675]

AGC New York State Chapter Scholarship Program (Undergraduate/Scholarship) [1677]

AGI Minority Participation Program Geoscience Student Scholarships (AGI-MPP) (Graduate, Undergraduate/Scholarship) [778]

Agriculture Future of America Community Scholarships (Undergraduate/Scholarship) [77]

Agriculture Future of America Scholarship Program (Undergraduate/Scholarship) [78]

Patty Ahearn Victoria Elementary Scholarships (Undergraduate/Scholarship) [7617]

Ahepa Buckeye Scholarship Awards (Undergraduate/Scholarship) [85]

Ahepa District No. 1 Scholarship Program (Graduate, Undergraduate/Scholarship) [790]

AHETEMS/ExxonMobil Scholarships (Undergraduate/Scholarship) [54]

AHETEMS General Scholarships (Graduate, Undergraduate/Scholarship) [55]

AHETEMS Professional Scholarships (Graduate/Scholarship) [56]

AHNS-ACS Career Development Awards (Professional development/Grant) [784]

AHNS Pilot Research Grants (Professional development/Grant) [785]

AHNS Young Investigator Awards (Professional development/Grant) [786]

Henry and Maria Ahrens Scholarships (Graduate/Scholarship) [4255]

AIA and the Global Automotive Aftermarket Symposium Scholarships (Undergraduate/Scholarship) [1955]

AIA/NEI Scholarships (Graduate, Undergraduate/Scholarship) [840]

AIAA Foundation Scholarship Program (Graduate, Undergraduate/Scholarship) [836]

AIBS Junior Fellowships (Doctorate/Fellowship) [843]

AIBS Senior Fellowships (Doctorate, Postdoctorate/Fellowship) [844]

AIDS Awareness Scholarships (Undergraduate/Scholarship) [7843]

AIGC Fellowships - Graduate (Graduate/Fellowship) [826]

AILA Scholarships (Graduate/Scholarship) [830]

AIMS Long-term Research Grants (Doctorate, Postdoctorate/Grant) [860]

AIMS Short-term Research Grants (Doctorate, Postdoctorate/Grant) [861]

AIPS Post-Doctoral Fellowships (Doctorate/Fellowship) [863]

AIPS Pre-Doctoral Fellowships (Doctorate, Graduate/Fellowship) [864]

Air Force Association Excellence Scholarships (Graduate, Master's, Undergraduate/Scholarship) [88]

Air Force Association/Grantham Scholarships (Undergraduate/Scholarship) [89]

Air Force Association Spouse Scholarships (Undergraduate/Scholarship) [90]

Air Force ROTC Enhanced HBCU Scholarships (Undergraduate/Scholarship) [9023]

Air Force Sergeants Association Scholarship Program (Undergraduate/Scholarship) [95]

Air Products and Chemicals, Inc. Scholarships (Undergraduate/Scholarship) [1793]

Air Traffic Control Association Full-time Employee Student Scholarships (Professional development/Scholarship) [103]

Air Traffic Control Association Non-employee Student Scholarships (Undergraduate/Scholarship) [104]

Aircraft Owners and Pilots Association Scholarships (Undergraduate/Scholarship) [122]

Airports Council International-North America Scholarships (Graduate, Undergraduate/Scholarship) [149]

AISC/Great Lakes Fabricators and Erectors Association Fellowships (Graduate/Fellowship) [871]

AISC/Rocky Mountain Steel Construction Association Fellowships (Graduate/Fellowship) [872]

AISC/Southern Association of Steel Fabricators Fellowships (Graduate/Fellowship) [873]

AISC/Southern Association of Steel Fabricators Scholarships (Undergraduate/Scholarship) [874]

AISC/US Steel Fellowships (Graduate/Fellowship) [876]

AISES Intel Scholarships (Graduate, Undergraduate/Scholarship) [832]

AISES Summer Internships (Graduate, Undergraduate/Internship) [833]

AIST Baltimore Chapter Scholarships (Undergraduate/Scholarship) [1799]

AIST Detroit Chapter Scholarships (Undergraduate/Scholarship) [1800]

AIST San Francisco Chapter Scholarships (Undergraduate/Scholarship) [1802]

AJL Convention Travel Grants (All/Grant) [1820]

AJL Scholarship Program (Graduate/Scholarship) [1821]

Akao Scholarships for QFD (Undergraduate/Scholarship) [7552]

Crown Prince Akihito Scholarship Foundation (Graduate/Scholarship) [5132]

Akron Bar Association Foundation Scholarships (Undergraduate/Scholarship) [151]

Al Muammar Scholarships for Journalism (Undergraduate/Scholarship) [1490]

Alabama Architectural Foundation Scholarships

(Postgraduate, Undergraduate/Scholarship) [153]

Alabama Horse Council Scholarships *(Undergraduate/Scholarship)* [175]

Alabama Power Scholarships *(Undergraduate/Scholarship)* [6809]

Jonathan Alan Scholarship Fund *(Undergraduate/Scholarship)* [9546]

Alaska Airlines Scholarships *(Undergraduate/Scholarship)* [1362]

Alaska Kidney Foundation-ASN Research Grants *(Doctorate/Grant)* [1311]

Alberta Holstein Association Scholarships *(Undergraduate/Scholarship)* [225]

Alberta Ingenuity Graduate Student Scholarships in Nanotechnology *(Doctorate, Graduate/Scholarship)* [231]

Alberta Ingenuity Graduate Student Scholarships *(Doctorate, Graduate/Scholarship)* [230]

Bruce and Betty Alberts Endowed Scholarships in Physiology *(Undergraduate/Scholarship)* [5611]

ALCOA Foundation Scholarships *(Undergraduate, Graduate/Scholarship)* [4317]

ALD Graduate Fellowships *(Graduate/Fellowship)* [6019]

Owen F. Aldis Scholarship Fund *(Graduate/Scholarship)* [4994]

Anne L. Alexander and Blaise Robert Alexander Memorial Scholarships *(Undergraduate/Scholarship)* [3757]

Neil Alexander Scholarships *(Undergraduate/Scholarship)* [6013]

Alex's Lemonade Stand Foundation Epidemiology Grants *(Doctorate, Professional development/Grant)* [292]

Alex's Lemonade Stand Foundation Innovation Grants *(Professional development/Grant)* [293]

Alex's Lemonade Stand Foundation Young Investigator Grants *(Doctorate, Professional development/Grant)* [294]

Floyd S. Alford Jr. Scholarships *(Undergraduate/Scholarship)* [9254]

Horatio Alger National Scholarships *(Undergraduate/Scholarship)* [312]

Emma and Meloid Algood Tuition Scholarships *(Graduate, Undergraduate/Scholarship)* [6039]

Margaret M. Alkek Scholarships *(Undergraduate/Scholarship)* [3362]

All-American Vector Marketing Scholarship Program *(Undergraduate/Scholarship)* [9416]

All-Ink Scholarships *(Graduate, Undergraduate/Scholarship)* [322]

ALL-SIS CONELL Grants *(Professional development/Grant)* [508]

Paul Shearman Allen and Associate Scholarships *(Undergraduate/Scholarship)* [9062]

Robinson G. Allen Athletic Memorial Scholarships *(Undergraduate/Scholarship)* [7618]

Peggy Allen Community Newspaper Internships *(Undergraduate/Internship)* [9255]

Frances C. Allen Fellowships *(Graduate/Fellowship)* [6692]

William A. Allen Memorial Metal Shop/Auto Body Scholarships *(Undergraduate/Scholarship)* [7619]

Dan Allen Memorial Scholarships *(Undergraduate/Scholarship)* [7844]

Alliance of Black Culinarians Scholarships *(Undergraduate/Scholarship)* [7465]

Alliance Defense Fund - Blackstone Legal Fellowships *(Undergraduate/Fellowship)* [333]

ALOA Scholarship Foundation *(Undergraduate/Scholarship)* [1679]

Tillie B. Alperin Scholarships *(Undergraduate/Scholarship)* [9220]

Harvey and Laura Alpert Scholarship Awards *(Undergraduate/Scholarship)* [4929]

ALPFA Scholarship Programs *(Postgraduate, Undergraduate/Scholarship)* [1824]

Alpha Chi Sigma Scholarship Awards *(Graduate, Undergraduate/Scholarship)* [348]

Alpha Delta Gamma Educational Foundation Scholarships (ADGEF) *(All/Scholarship)* [350]

Alpha Eta Scholarships *(Undergraduate/Scholarship)* [3363]

Alpha Kappa Alpha - Educational Advancement Foundation Financial Need-Based Scholarships *(Graduate, Undergraduate/Scholarship)* [352]

Alpha Kappa Alpha - Educational Advancement Foundation Merit Scholarships *(Graduate, Undergraduate/Scholarship)* [353]

Alpha Mu Tau Undergraduate Scholarships *(Undergraduate/Scholarship)* [1197]

Alpha Rho Leadership Scholarships *(Undergraduate/Scholarship)* [3364]

Alpha Tau Omega Graduate Scholarships *(Graduate/Scholarship)* [365]

Alpha Tau Omega Undergraduate Scholarships *(Undergraduate/Scholarship)* [366]

Justin Scot Alston Memorial Scholarships *(Undergraduate/Scholarship)* [4651]

Phillip Alston Scholarships *(Undergraduate/Scholarship)* [9256]

Robert E. Altenhofen Memorial Scholarships *(Graduate, Undergraduate/Scholarship)* [1665]

Luis W. Alvarez Postdoctoral Fellowships in Computational Science *(Doctorate/Fellowship)* [5380]

AMA Foundation Minority Scholars Awards *(Undergraduate/Scholarship)* [922]

AMA Foundation Physicians of Tomorrow Scholarships *(Undergraduate/Scholarship)* [923]

AMACESP Student Scholarships *(Undergraduate/Scholarship)* [147]

AMBUCS Scholarships for Therapists Program *(Graduate, Undergraduate/Scholarship)* [371]

Lou Amen Legacy Scholarships *(Undergraduate/Scholarship)* [2240]

America Responds Memorial Scholarships *(Undergraduate/Scholarship)* [1330]

American Academy of Periodontology Educator Scholarships *(Postdoctorate/Scholarship)* [392]

American Academy of Periodontology Foundation Education Fellowships *(Postdoctorate/Fellowship)* [393]

American Academy of Periodontology Teaching Fellowships *(Postdoctorate/Fellowship)* [394]

American Advertising Federation-Cleveland College Scholarships *(Undergraduate/Scholarship)* [402]

American Advertising Federation-Cleveland High School Scholarships *(Undergraduate/Scholarship)* [403]

American Art Therapy Association Anniversary Scholarships (AATA) *(Graduate/Scholarship)* [426]

American Association of Blacks in Energy Scholarships *(Undergraduate/Scholarship)* [441]

American Association for Cancer Research - GlaxoSmithKline Clinical Cancer Research Scholar Awards *(Graduate, Postdoctorate/Award)* [449]

American Association for Cancer Research Minority Scholar Awards *(Graduate/Award)* [450]

American Association of Cereal Chemists Graduate Fellowships *(Graduate/Fellowship)* [455]

American Association of Family and Consumer Sciences Scholarships *(Undergraduate/Scholarship)* [477]

American Association for Hand Surgery Annual Research Awards *(Professional development/Award)* [479]

American Association of Law Libraries Library School Scholarships *(Graduate, Postgraduate/Scholarship)* [498]

American Association of Plastic Surgeons Academic Scholars Program *(Graduate/Grant)* [535]

American Association of State Troopers Scholarship Foundation First Scholarships *(Undergraduate/Scholarship)* [550]

American Association of State Troopers Scholarship Foundation Second Scholarships *(Undergraduate/Scholarship)* [551]

American Association of Stratigraphic Palynologists Student Scholarships *(Graduate/Scholarship)* [6]

American Association of University Women American Fellowships *(Doctorate, Postdoctorate/Fellowship)* [9]

American Association of University Women Career Development Grants *(Postgraduate/Grant)* [10]

American Association of University Women Master's and First Professional Awards *(Professional development/Award)* [12]

American Association of University Women Selected Professions Fellowships *(Professional development/Fellowship)* [13]

American Association for Women in Community Col-

leges Regional Scholarships *(Undergraduate/Scholarship)* [565]

American Association for Women in Community Colleges Scholarship Leaders Institute *(Professional development/Scholarship)* [566]

American Astronomical Society Small Research Grants *(Doctorate/Grant)* [568]

The American Automobile Association Five Diamond Hospitality Scholarships (AAA) *(Undergraduate/Scholarship)* [795]

American Bus Association Academic Merit Scholarships *(Undergraduate/Scholarship)* [591]

American Business Women's Association Sarasota Sunrise Chapter Scholarships *(Undergraduate, Vocational/Occupational/Scholarship)* [3187]

American Cancer Society - Postdoctoral Fellowships *(Doctorate/Fellowship)* [594]

American Cancer Society - Research Scholar Grants *(Doctorate, Professional development/Grant)* [595]

American College of Radiation Oncology Resident Scholarships *(Graduate/Scholarship)* [623]

American Composites Manufacturers Association Scholarships *(Undergraduate/Scholarship)* [625]

American Composites Manufacturers Association Western Chapter Scholarships *(Undergraduate/Scholarship)* [626]

American Conifer Society Scholarships *(Undergraduate/Scholarship)* [652]

American Council of the Blind Scholarships *(Graduate, Undergraduate/Scholarship)* [658]

American Council of Engineering Companies of Illinois Scholarships *(Doctorate, Graduate, Undergraduate/Scholarship)* [660]

American Council of Independent Laboratories Scholarships *(Undergraduate/Scholarship)* [669]

American Council of Learned Societies Fellowships *(Postdoctorate/Fellowship)* [674]

American Counsel Association Scholarships *(Undergraduate/Scholarship)* [683]

American Criminal Justice Association Scholarships *(Graduate, Undergraduate/Scholarship)* [687]

American Culinary Federation Chair's Scholarship Grants *(All/Scholarship)* [689]

American Dental Association Dental Assisting Scholarship Program *(Undergraduate/Scholarship)* [701]

American Dental Association Dental Hygiene Scholarship Program *(Undergraduate/Scholarship)* [702]

American Dental Association Dental Laboratory Technology Scholarship Program *(Undergraduate/Scholarship)* [703]

American Dental Association Dental Student Scholarships *(Undergraduate/Scholarship)* [704]

American Dental Association Minority Dental Student Scholarships *(Undergraduate/Scholarship)* [705]

American Dental Hygienists' Association Institute for Oral Health Fellowships *(Master's/Fellowship)* [708]

American Division Veterans Association Scholarships *(Undergraduate, Vocational/Occupational/Scholarship)* [712]

American Dream Scholarship Program *(Undergraduate/Scholarship)* [7890]

American Enterprise Institute National Research Initiative Fellowships (NRI) *(Graduate/Fellowship)* [718]

American Express Professional Development Scholarships *(Professional development/Scholarship)* [796]

The American Express Scholarship Competition *(Undergraduate/Scholarship)* [797]

American Express Travel Scholarships *(Undergraduate/Scholarship)* [1363]

American Federation of Police and Concerned Citizen Scholarships *(Undergraduate, Vocational/Occupational/Scholarship)* [722]

American Foreign Service Association Scholarship Fund *(Undergraduate/Scholarship)* [744]

American Foundation for Pharmaceutical Education Gateway Research Scholarships *(Professional development/Scholarship)* [756]

American Foundation for Pharmaceutical Education Pre-Doctoral Fellowships in the Pharmaceutical

Anchor Scholarship Foundation *(Undergraduate/ Scholarship)* [8780]

William G. Anderson, DO, Minority Scholarships *(Undergraduate/Scholarship)* [969]

The Anderson Group Summer Institute Scholarships *(Professional development/Scholarship)* [1473]

Judge Isaac Anderson, Jr. Scholarships *(Undergraduate/Scholarship)* [8589]

A.T. Anderson Memorial Scholarships *(Graduate, Undergraduate/Scholarship)* [834]

Charles Lee Anderson Memorial Scholarships *(Undergraduate/Scholarship)* [3142]

Gladys C. Anderson Memorial Scholarships *(Graduate, Undergraduate/Scholarship)* [748]

Jane E. Anderson Scholarships *(Undergraduate/ Scholarship)* [3365]

Kathy D. and Stephen J. Anderson Scholarships *(Graduate/Scholarship)* [3092]

Redlands Rotary Club - Donald C. Anderson Scholarships *(Undergraduate/Scholarship)* [7620]

Michael P. Anderson Scholarships in Space Science *(Undergraduate/Scholarship)* [6484]

Warren M. Anderson Scholarships *(Undergraduate/ Scholarship)* [4741]

Margaret J. Andrew Memorial Scholarships *(Undergraduate/Scholarship)* [8156]

Cindy Andrews Educational Scholarships *(Undergraduate/Scholarship)* [7621]

William H. Andrews/HAWS Scholarships *(Undergraduate/Scholarship)* [9623]

Richard E. Andrews Memorial Scholarships *(Undergraduate/Scholarship)* [582]

Androscoggin County Chamber of Commerce Adult Scholarships *(Undergraduate/Scholarship)* [1475]

John D. Anello Sr. and Albert A. Silverman Memorial Scholarships *(Undergraduate/Scholarship)* [2887]

Angus Foundation General Undergraduate Student Scholarships *(High School, Undergraduate/Scholarship)* [1477]

Angus Foundation Graduate Student Degree Scholarship Program *(Graduate/Scholarship)* [1478]

Angus Foundation Scholarships *(Undergraduate/ Scholarship)* [6374]

Angus/Talon Youth Educational Learning Program Endowment Fund *(Graduate/Scholarship)* [1479]

Anheuser-Busch NAPABA Law Foundation Presidential Scholarships *(Undergraduate/Scholarship)* [6026]

Ann Arbor AWC Scholarships for Women in Computing *(Professional development, Undergraduate/ Scholarship)* [1896]

Anne Friedberg Innovative Scholarship Awards *(Professional development/Scholarship)* [8309]

Leonore Annenberg Teaching Fellowships *(Graduate/Fellowship)* [9614]

Anonymous Scholarship Fund *(Graduate/Scholarship)* [9547]

Jack Anson Fellowships *(Graduate/Fellowship)* [6738]

Hettie M. Anthony Fellowships *(Postdoctorate/Fellowship)* [5200]

AOA Research Grants *(Graduate/Grant)* [63]

AOFAS Research Grants Program *(Graduate/ Grant)* [966]

AORN Foundation Scholarship Program *(Undergraduate/Scholarship)* [1839]

AOS Research Training Fellowships *(Graduate/Fellowship)* [974]

AOSA Research Grants *(All/Grant)* [959]

AOSA Research Partnership Grants *(All/Grant)* [960]

APA Minority Fellowships Program *(Postdoctorate/ Fellowship)* [1646]

APAGS-CLGBTC Grant Program *(Graduate/Grant)* [1029]

APAGS' Committee on Ethic Minority Affairs (CEMA) Grant Program *(Graduate/Grant)* [1030]

APALA Scholarships *(Doctorate, Graduate/Scholarship)* [1648]

APBASV Scholarships *(All/Scholarship)* [1652]

APDA Postdoctoral Fellowships *(Professional development/Fellowship)* [979]

APDA Research Grants *(Professional development/ Grant)* [980]

APF/COGDOP Graduate Research Scholarships *(Doctorate, Graduate/Scholarship)* [1037]

APIASF Scholarships *(Undergraduate/Scholarship)* [1655]

Applied Physics Laboratory Alexander Kossiakoff Scholarships *(Doctorate, Graduate/Scholarship)* [4912]

Appraisal Institute Education Trust Scholarships *(Graduate, Undergraduate/Scholarship)* [1488]

APS/NIDDK Minority Travel Fellowship Awards *(Graduate, Postdoctorate/Fellowship)* [1004]

APS Scholarships for Minority Undergraduate Physics Majors *(Undergraduate/Scholarship)* [6485]

APT US&C Scholarships *(All/Scholarship)* [1847]

APTA Minority Scholarships - Faculty Development Scholarships *(Postdoctorate/Scholarship)* [999]

APTA Minority Scholarships - Physical Therapist Assistant Students *(All/Scholarship)* [1000]

APTA Minority Scholarships - Physical Therapist Students *(All/Scholarship)* [1001]

APTRA Scholarships *(Undergraduate/Scholarship)* [1684]

APWA Engineering Scholarships *(Undergraduate/ Scholarship)* [1059]

Aquatics Booster Club Scholarships *(Undergraduate/Scholarship)* [7622]

ARA Scholarship Awards *(Undergraduate/Scholarship)* [1961]

Frank G. Araujo Memorial Scholarships *(Undergraduate/Scholarship)* [7623]

Fred Archibald Communications Internships *(Undergraduate/Internship)* [8465]

Architecture, Design and Urban Design Prize *(Graduate, Undergraduate/Prize)* [8231]

AREMA Committee 18 - Light Density & Short Line Railways Scholarships *(Undergraduate/Scholarship)* [1118]

AREMA Committee 24 - Education and Training Scholarships *(Undergraduate/Scholarship)* [1119]

AREMA Committee 33 - Electric Energy Utilization Scholarships *(Undergraduate/Scholarship)* [1120]

AREMA Presidential Spouse Scholarships *(Undergraduate/Scholarship)* [1121]

Arent Fox Diversity Scholarships *(Undergraduate/ Scholarship)* [1503]

A.R.F.O.R.A. Undergraduate Scholarships for Women *(Undergraduate/Scholarship)* [1162]

Arizona Chapter Gold Scholarships *(Undergraduate/ Scholarship)* [1365]

Arizona Christian School Tuition Organization Scholarships *(Undergraduate/Scholarship)* [1515]

Arizona Hydrological Society Scholarships *(Graduate, Undergraduate/Scholarship)* [1522]

Arizona Nurses Foundation Scholarships *(Doctorate, Graduate, Undergraduate/Scholarship)* [1526]

Rick Arkans Eagle Scout Scholarships *(High School/Scholarship)* [6247]

Armed Forces Communications and Electronics Association Fellowships *(Doctorate, Graduate/Fellowship)* [1555]

Connie "Chelo" Armendariz Memorial Scholarships *(Undergraduate, Vocational/Occupational/Scholarship)* [7624]

Armenian American Medical Association Scholarships *(Undergraduate/Scholarship)* [1581]

Armenian American Pharmacists' Association Scholarships *(Doctorate, Graduate/Scholarship)* [1582]

Armenian Bar Association Graduate Scholarships in Law *(Graduate/Scholarship)* [1569]

Armenian General Athletic Union Scholarships *(Undergraduate/Scholarship)* [1583]

Armenian Professional Society Scholarship Fund *(Graduate/Scholarship)* [1575]

Armenian Relief Society Scholarships *(Graduate, Undergraduate/Scholarship)* [1584]

Louis Armstrong Scholarships *(High School/Scholarship)* [1206]

Tara Lynne Arnold Scholarships *(Undergraduate/ Scholarship)* [8716]

ARNOVA Emerging Scholar Awards *(Graduate, Undergraduate/Award)* [1858]

Jane B. Aron Doctoral Fellowships *(Doctorate/Fellowship)* [6120]

Judge Sidney M. Aronovitz Memorial Scholarships *(High School, Undergraduate/Scholarship)* [3314]

Merle Aronson Point Scholarships *(Graduate, Undergraduate/Scholarship)* [7354]

ARRL Foundation General Fund Scholarships *(Undergraduate/Scholarship)* [1069]

ARS Undergraduate Scholarships *(Undergraduate/ Scholarship)* [1577]

Art Institute of Colorado Scholarships *(Undergraduate/Scholarship)* [1624]

Art Institute's Best Teen Chef in America Culinary Scholarships *(Undergraduate/Prize, Scholarship)* [1625]

ARTC Glenn Moon Scholarships *(Undergraduate/ Scholarship)* [4409]

Arthritis Foundation Doctoral Dissertation Awards for Arthritis Health Professionals *(Professional development/Fellowship)* [1629]

Arthritis Foundation Postdoctoral Fellowships *(Doctorate/Fellowship)* [1630]

Arthur Lockwood Beneventi Law Scholarships *(Undergraduate/Scholarship)* [6497]

Artistic Scholarship Awards *(Undergraduate, Vocational/Occupational/Scholarship)* [2023]

David Arver Memorial Scholarships *(Undergraduate/ Scholarship)* [123]

Dutch and Ginger Arver Scholarships *(Undergraduate/Scholarship)* [124]

Chester Arzell and Helen Miller Montgomery Scholarships *(Undergraduate/Scholarship)* [9624]

ASA Graduate Scholarships *(Graduate/Scholarship)* [1182]

ASA Minority Fellowship Program *(Doctorate, Master's/Fellowship)* [1377]

ASA/NSF/BLS Fellowships *(Graduate/Fellowship)* [1393]

ASBA College Scholarship Program *(Undergraduate/Scholarship)* [1180]

ASBC Foundation Graduate Scholarships *(Doctorate, Graduate/Scholarship)* [1186]

ASBC Foundation Undergraduate Scholarships *(Undergraduate/Scholarship)* [1187]

ASBPE Young Leaders Scholarships *(All/Scholarship)* [1189]

ASC Graduate Fellowships for Ethnic Minorities *(Doctorate, Graduate/Fellowship)* [1219]

ASCEND/ING Scholarships *(Undergraduate/Scholarship)* [1635]

Elizabeth and Sherman Asche Memorial Scholarships *(Graduate, Undergraduate/Scholarship)* [1695]

ASECS Graduate Student Research Paper Awards *(Graduate/Award)* [1221]

ASECS Innovative Course Design Competition *(Undergraduate/Award)* [1222]

ASECS Women's Caucus Editing and Translation Fellowships *(Doctorate/Fellowship)* [1223]

ASET Educational Seminars, Courses and Program Scholarships *(All, Professional development/ Scholarship)* [1239]

ASG Scholar Awards *(Professional development/ Scholarship)* [1257]

ASHA Scholarships *(Graduate, Undergraduate/ Scholarship)* [1175]

ASHA Student Research Grants *(Graduate, Undergraduate/Scholarship)* [1176]

ASHFA Scholarships for Minority Students *(Graduate/Scholarship)* [1386]

ASHP Student Research Awards *(Doctorate/Award)* [1259]

ASHS Industry Division Student Travel Grants *(Graduate, Undergraduate/Grant)* [1273]

ASHS Scholars Awards *(Undergraduate/Scholarship)* [1274]

ASI Fellowships *(Doctorate/Fellowship)* [1481]

Asian American Lawyers Associations of Massachusetts Scholarships *(Undergraduate/Scholarship)* [1644]

Asian American Scholarships *(Undergraduate/Scholarship)* [9063]

ASIS Foundation Chapter Matching Scholarships *(Undergraduate/Scholarship)* [1657]

ASLA Council of Fellows Scholarships *(Undergraduate/Scholarship)* [5330]

ASM/CCID Program in Infectious Disease and Public Health Microbiology *(Postdoctorate/Fellowship)* [1299]

ASM Undergraduate Research Capstone Program *(Undergraduate/Fellowship)* [1300]

ASM Undergraduate Teaching Fellowships (ASM-

Birgit Baldwin Fellowships (Graduate/Fellowship) [5752]

Norman S. Baldwin Fishery Science Scholarships (Doctorate, Graduate/Scholarship) [4868]

Donald A. Baldwin Sr. Business Aviation Management Scholarships (All/Scholarship) [6161]

Balestreri/Cutino Scholarships (Undergraduate/ Scholarship) [690]

Lloyd G. Balfour Fellowships (Graduate/Fellowship) [6739]

Ball Horticultural Company Scholarships (Undergraduate/Scholarship) [724]

Vic and Margaret Ball Student Intern Scholarships (Undergraduate/Internship) [725]

Ballantyne Resident Research Grants (Professional development/Grant) [787]

B&W Y-12 Scholarship Fund (Undergraduate/Scholarship) [3565]

Bank of America Junior Achievement Scholarship Fund (Undergraduate/Scholarship) [3885]

Brenda S. Bank Educational Workshop Scholarships (Undergraduate/Scholarship) [8326]

Dr. Johnella Banks Memorial Scholarships (Undergraduate/Scholarship) [2137]

Harvey Washington Banks Scholarships in Astronomy (Undergraduate/Scholarship) [6486]

Sharon D. Banks Undergraduate Memorial Scholarships (Undergraduate/Scholarship) [9739]

Banner Bank Business Scholarships (Undergraduate/Scholarship) [5413]

Donald W. Banner Corporate Intern Scholarships (Undergraduate/Scholarship) [4844]

Donald W. Banner Diversity Scholarships for Law Students (Undergraduate/Scholarship) [2014]

Mark T. Banner Scholarships for Law Students (Graduate, Undergraduate/Scholarship) [7798]

Barakat Trust and Barakat Foundation Scholarships (Graduate/Scholarship) [1491]

Cynthia and Alan Baran Fine Arts and Music Scholarships (Undergraduate/Scholarship) [3093]

Leslie Baranowski Scholarships for Professional Excellence (All/Scholarship) [4764]

Barbri Scholarships for Bar Preparation (Undergraduate/Scholarship) [4561]

Jack R. Barckhoff Welding Management Scholarships (Undergraduate/Scholarship) [1431]

Janice K. Barden Aviation Scholarships (Undergraduate/Scholarship) [6162]

Thomas J. Bardos Science Education Awards for Undergraduate Students (Undergraduate/Award) [451]

Edgar Barge Memorial Scholarships (Undergraduate/Scholarship) [4256]

TCDA Carroll Barnes Student Scholarships (Graduate, Undergraduate/Scholarship) [8846]

Gina L. Barnhart Memorial Scholarship Fund (Undergraduate/Scholarship) [3759]

Robbie Baron Memorial Scholarships (Undergraduate/Scholarship) [3936]

Gloria Barron Wilderness Society Scholarships (Graduate/Scholarship) [9601]

Laura Beckley Barsotti Memorial Scholarships (Undergraduate/Scholarship) [4652]

Avery Bayle Barth Scholarships (Undergraduate/ Scholarship) [3367]

William E. Barto Scholarships (Undergraduate/ Scholarship) [3525]

Elsa Barton Educational Scholarship Fund (Undergraduate, Vocational/Occupational/Scholarship) [1023]

Bascom Hill Society Scholarships (Undergraduate/ Scholarship) [9349]

Basic Midwifery Student Scholarship Program (Undergraduate/Scholarship) [618]

Basic Research Fellowships (Postdoctorate/Fellowship) [586]

Diane Basilone-Engle Memorial Scholarships (Undergraduate/Scholarship) [2329]

Bat Conservation International Student Research Scholarships (Graduate, Undergraduate/Scholarship) [2028]

H. Burton Bates Jr. Scholarships (Graduate, Undergraduate/Scholarship) [9459]

Jim Batten Community Newspaper Internships (Undergraduate/Internship) [9258]

Hazel Reed Baumeister Scholarship Program (Undergraduate/Scholarship) [8197]

Jeannette Bautista Memorial Scholarships (Undergraduate/Scholarship) [7468]

Bob Baxter Scholarships (Graduate, Undergraduate/ Scholarship) [6448]

Timothy Baylink Good Fellowship Awards (Undergraduate/Fellowship) [7626]

John Bayliss Broadcast Foundation Internship Programs (Undergraduate/Internship) [2030]

John Bayliss Broadcast Foundation Scholarships (Undergraduate/Scholarship) [2031]

BCA Ethnic Minority Postgraduate Scholarships for Careers in Athletics (Postgraduate/Scholarship) [2135]

BCCC Foundation Scholarships (Undergraduate/ Scholarship) [2002]

BCEN Undergraduate Scholarships (Undergraduate/ Scholarship) [3633]

BDC Visiting Fellowships (Doctorate/Fellowship) [2196]

James Beard Foundation/Art Institute of Colorado Scholarships (Undergraduate/Scholarship) [1626]

Beard Scholarships (Master's/Scholarship) [4104]

Beatitudes Fellowships (Professional development/ Fellowship) [2037]

Catherine H. Beattie Fellowships (Graduate/Fellowship) [2705]

Beau Gunn Redlands Baseball For Youth Scholarships (Undergraduate/Scholarship) [7627]

Michael Beaudry Scholarships (Undergraduate/ Scholarship) [4054]

Beaver Medical Clinic-H.E.A.R.T. Scholarship Awards (Undergraduate/Scholarship) [7628]

Beaver Medical Clinic-Premed Scholarship Awards (Undergraduate/Scholarship) [7629]

Don C. Beaver Memorial Scholarships (Undergraduate/Scholarship) [2241]

BECA Foundation-CUSM Scholarships (Undergraduate/Scholarship) [2039]

BECA Foundation General Scholarships Fund (Undergraduate/Scholarship) [2040]

Bechtel Engineering and Science Scholarships (High School/Scholarship) [5645]

Bechtel Group Foundation Scholarships for Safety & Health (Undergraduate/Scholarship) [1333]

Stan Beck Fellowships (Graduate, Undergraduate/ Fellowship) [3652]

Dennis J. Beck Memorial Scholarships (Undergraduate, Vocational/Occupational/Scholarship) [5091]

Beck-Pfann Memorial Scholarships (Undergraduate/ Scholarship) [7168]

Garvin L. Beck Scholarships (Undergraduate/Scholarship) [7630]

Dr. Joyce Beckett Scholarships (Graduate, Undergraduate/Scholarship) [6040]

Beef Industry Scholarships (Undergraduate/Scholarship) [6174]

Raymond and Donald Beeler Memorial Scholarships (Undergraduate/Scholarship) [7631]

Notah Begay III Scholarship Program (Undergraduate/Scholarship) [278]

Behavioral Gerontology SIG Student Research Awards (Undergraduate/Award) [1712]

Behavioral Sciences Post-Doctoral Fellowships (Postdoctorate/Fellowship) [3660]

Behavioral Sciences Student Fellowships (Graduate, Undergraduate/Fellowship) [3661]

Norbert J. Beihoff Scholarships (Undergraduate/ Scholarship) [2888]

N.S. Beinstock Fellowships (Professional development/Fellowship) [7573]

Hannah Beiter Graduate Student Research Grants (Doctorate, Graduate/Grant) [2762]

Bel Canto Vocal Scholarship Foundation Vocal Competition (All/Award, Scholarship) [2046]

Belfer-Aptman Dissertation Research Awards (Doctorate/Grant) [5761]

Marc and Ruti Bell Foundation Scholarships (Undergraduate/Scholarship) [2052]

Alfred D. Bell Travel Grants (All/Grant) [3859]

Belmont University Commercial Music Scholarships (Undergraduate/Scholarship) [3094]

David Beltran Memorial Scholarships (Undergraduate/Scholarship) [7632]

Samuel Flagg Bemis Dissertation Research Grants

(Doctorate, Graduate/Grant) [8335]

Reckitt Benckiser Student Scholarships (Graduate/ Scholarship) [6105]

Richard W. Bendicksen Memorial Scholarships (Undergraduate/Scholarship) [1071]

H. Y. Benedict Fellowships (Graduate/Fellowship) [342]

Benign Essential Blepharospasm Research Foundation Research Grants (Doctorate, Postdoctorate/ Grant) [2057]

Jean Bennett Memorial Student Travel Grants (Graduate, Undergraduate/Grant) [6909]

Casey Bennett Scholarships (Undergraduate/Scholarship) [3740]

Eleanor Bennett Scholarships (All/Scholarship) [8770]

Reverend E.F. Bennett Scholarships (Undergraduate/Scholarship) [2937]

Elizabeth Benson Scholarship Awards (Undergraduate/Scholarship) [7727]

Benton-Meier Neuropsychology Scholarships (Graduate/Scholarship) [1038]

Linn Benton Scholarships (Undergraduate/Scholarship) [6952]

Lester G. Benz Memorial Scholarships for College Journalism Study (Professional development/ Scholarship) [7562]

Fred Berg Awards (All/Award) [3594]

Charlotte V. Bergen Scholarships (Undergraduate/ Scholarship) [1207]

Bergman Scholarships (Undergraduate/Scholarship) [6783]

The Joseph Berkman, and Michael and Sarah Chipkin Holocaust/Genocide Studies Awards (Graduate/Scholarship) [8738]

Berkowitz Fellowships (Professional development/ Fellowship) [8902]

ARRS/Leonard Berlin Scholarships in Medical Professionalism (Professional development/Scholarship) [1160]

Richard L. Bernardi Memorial Scholarships (Undergraduate/Scholarship) [3143]

Stuart L. Bernath Dissertation Grants (Doctorate, Graduate/Grant) [8336]

Myrna F. Bernath Fellowships (Doctorate, Graduate/ Fellowship) [8337]

Hon. Peggy Bernheim Memorial Scholarships (Undergraduate/Scholarship) [2190]

Donald H. Bernstein/John B. Talbert, Jr. Scholarships (Undergraduate/Scholarship) [3887]

The Berntsen International Scholarships in Surveying Technology (Undergraduate/Scholarship) [642]

Thomas M. Berry Jr. Scholarships (Graduate, Undergraduate/Scholarship) [9460]

Beta Gamma Memorial Scholarships (Undergraduate/Scholarship) [3368]

Beta Omega Scholarships (Undergraduate/Scholarship) [8158]

Beta Sigma Phi - Fine Arts Scholarships (Undergraduate/Scholarship) [8111]

Beta Sigma Scholarships (Undergraduate/Scholarship) [8159]

Bethune-Cookman University Excelsior Scholarships (Undergraduate/Scholarship) [2079]

Bethune-Cookman University Presidential Scholarships (Undergraduate/Scholarship) [2080]

Harold Bettinger Scholarships (Undergraduate/ Scholarship) [726]

Leonard Bettinger Vocational Scholarships (Undergraduate, Vocational/Occupational/Scholarship) [727]

Beverly Estate Scholarships (Undergraduate/Scholarship) [3480]

BIA Higher Education Grants (Graduate, Postgraduate, Undergraduate/Grant) [1509]

BIE-Loan for Service for Graduates (Graduate/ Loan) [827]

BIGALA Scholarships (Bisexual Gay and Lesbian Alliance) (Undergraduate/Scholarship) [7845]

James L. Biggane Fellowships in Finance (Graduate/Fellowship) [6677]

James Bilder Scholarships (Undergraduate, Vocational/Occupational/Scholarship) [8591]

Bill Bernbach Diversity Scholarships (Undergraduate/Scholarship) [434]

BioQuip Undergraduate Scholarships *(Undergraduate/Scholarship)* [3653]

BioRx/Hemophilia of North Carolina Educational Scholarships *(Undergraduate/Scholarship)* [6317]

Birmingham-Southern College Eagle Scout Scholarships *(Undergraduate/Scholarship)* [6248]

BISA's Scholarship Assistance Program *(High School/Scholarship)* [2146]

Bisexual Foundation Scholarships *(Graduate/Scholarship)* [8471]

Lebbeus F. Bissell Scholarships *(Undergraduate/Scholarship)* [4413]

Dr. Richard E. Bjork Memorial Graduate Study Awards *(Graduate/Scholarship)* [8739]

Ted Bjorn University of Idaho Graduate Student Scholarships *(Graduate/Scholarship)* [4661]

Ted Bjorn University of Idaho Undergraduate Student Scholarships *(Undergraduate/Scholarship)* [4662]

Black Student Fund *(High School/Scholarship)* [2107]

Reid Blackburn Scholarships *(Undergraduate/Scholarship)* [6449]

Eileen Blackey Doctoral Fellowships *(Doctorate/Fellowship)* [6121]

William T. Blackwell Scholarship Fund *(Undergraduate/Scholarship)* [6358]

Beatrice K. Blair Scholarships *(Undergraduate/Scholarship)* [2149]

Margaret Blanchard Dissertation Support Fund *(Postgraduate/Grant)* [9259]

Joan Blend Scholarship Fund *(Undergraduate/Scholarship)* [8657]

M. Hildred Blewett Fellowships *(Postdoctorate/Scholarship)* [997]

Bloch-Selinger Education Fund *(Undergraduate/Scholarship)* [3760]

F.A. and Charlotte Blount Scholarships *(Undergraduate/Scholarship)* [9625]

Blow Molding Division Memorial Scholarships *(Graduate, Undergraduate/Scholarship)* [8444]

Blues Ambassador Scholarships *(Undergraduate/Scholarship)* [7469]

Jordan ABDO/Michael Bluett Memorial Scholarships *(Undergraduate/Scholarship)* [8592]

Harry and Edith Blunt Scholarships *(Undergraduate/Scholarship)* [608]

BMES Graduate and Undergraduate Student Awards *(Graduate, Undergraduate/Award)* [2100]

David and Camille Boatwright Endowed Scholarships *(Undergraduate/Scholarship)* [7169]

Sandra Bobbitt Continuing Education Scholarships *(Undergraduate/Scholarship)* [1836]

Edith and Arnold N. Bodtker Grants *(All/Grant)* [3339]

Boeing Business Scholarships *(Undergraduate/Scholarship)* [4175]

Boeing Company Scholarships *(Undergraduate/Scholarship)* [8112]

Hagop Bogigian Scholarship Fund *(Undergraduate/Scholarship)* [1587]

Bohemian Lawyers Association of Chicago Scholarships *(Graduate/Scholarship)* [2162]

Frances P. Bolton Fellowships *(Doctorate/Fellowship)* [7051]

BOMA/NY Scholarships *(Undergraduate/Scholarship)* [2207]

Carol Bond Community College Scholarships *(Undergraduate/Scholarship)* [6748]

Carol Bond Environmental Educator Scholarships *(Professional development/Scholarship)* [6749]

Carol Bond University Scholarships *(Undergraduate/Scholarship)* [6750]

Barbara Bonnema Memorial Scholarships *(Undergraduate/Scholarship)* [7633]

Ellis J. Bonner Scholarships *(Doctorate, Graduate, Undergraduate/Scholarship)* [6080]

Scott Bonners Memorial Scholarships *(Undergraduate/Scholarship)* [2330]

Admiral Mike Boorda Scholarship Program *(Undergraduate, Vocational/Occupational/Scholarship)* [6592]

T. Frank Booth Memorial Scholarship Fund *(Undergraduate/Scholarship)* [3888]

Diane Booth Memorial Scholarships *(Undergraduate/Scholarship)* [3761]

Tom Boots Memorial Scholarships *(Undergraduate/Scholarship)* [6601]

National Security Education Program - David L. Boren Fellowships *(Undergraduate/Fellowship)* [9204]

David L. Boren Undergraduate Scholarships *(Graduate, Undergraduate/Scholarship)* [1784]

Dr. Anita Borg Memorial Scholarships - USA *(Graduate, Undergraduate/Scholarship)* [4193]

Maria Gonzales Borrero Scholarships *(Undergraduate/Scholarship)* [4414]

Tom Bost Scholarships *(Undergraduate/Scholarship)* [9260]

Stephen Botein Fellowships *(Doctorate/Fellowship)* [415]

Metropolitan Museum of Art Bothmer Fellowships *(Doctorate/Fellowship)* [5783]

Dr. George T. Bottomley Scholarships *(Undergraduate/Scholarship)* [5707]

Richard J. Bouchard Scholarships *(Graduate, Undergraduate/Scholarship)* [1050]

Miranda Bouldin General Scholarships *(Undergraduate/Scholarship)* [5513]

Bound to Stay Bound Books Scholarships (BTSB) *(Graduate/Scholarship)* [1826]

Rev. Andrew L. Bouwhuis Memorial Scholarship Program *(Graduate/Scholarship)* [2668]

William R. Bowen Scholarships *(Undergraduate/Scholarship)* [3052]

Billy Bowling Memorial Scholarships *(Undergraduate/Scholarship)* [6810]

Elizabeth W. Boyce Scholarships *(Undergraduate/Scholarship)* [2889]

Dr. Betty J. Boyd-Beu & Edwin G. Beu, Jr. Scholarships *(Undergraduate/Scholarship)* [9142]

W. Scott Boyd Group Grants *(All/Grant)* [4884]

Boyd N. Lyon Scholarships *(Doctorate, Graduate/Scholarship)* [5554]

Corris Boyd Scholarships *(Master's/Scholarship)* [1891]

Dody Boyd Scholarships *(Undergraduate/Scholarship)* [3096]

Verna Curry Boyer Scholarships *(Undergraduate/Scholarship)* [8718]

Mildred Cater Bradham Social Work Fellowships *(Graduate/Fellowship)* [9801]

Carol June Bradley Awards *(All/Grant)* [5955]

Charles Bradley Memorial Scholarships *(Undergraduate/Scholarship)* [4397]

Donald Franklin Bradley Memorial Scholarships *(Undergraduate/Scholarship)* [7470]

Ed Bradley Scholarships *(Undergraduate/Scholarship)* [7574]

Edward J. Brady Memorial Scholarships *(Undergraduate/Scholarship)* [1432]

Susan Brager Occupational Education Scholarships *(Undergraduate/Scholarship)* [7471]

William E. "Buck" Bragunier Scholarships *(Undergraduate/Scholarship)* [1556]

George and Mary Brammer Scholarships *(Undergraduate/Scholarship)* [3481]

The Helen and Edward Brancati Teacher Development Scholarships *(Professional development/Scholarship)* [2644]

Barbara Brantley Nursing Education Scholarships *(Graduate/Scholarship)* [1723]

Erika A. and George E. Brattain Sr. Scholarship Fund *(Undergraduate/Scholarship)* [9548]

Theodore E.D. Braun Research Travel Fellowships *(Professional development/Fellowship)* [1225]

Breakthrough to Nursing Scholarships *(Undergraduate/Scholarship)* [3976]

Ann Marie Bredefeld Scholarships *(Undergraduate/Scholarship)* [7170]

Kenneth H. Breeden Scholarships *(Undergraduate/Scholarship)* [5343]

The Lela Breitbart Memorial Scholarship Fund *(All/Scholarship)* [8892]

Marion Breland-Bailey Awards *(Graduate, Undergraduate/Award)* [1713]

Brenda Renee Horn Memorial Scholarship *(Undergraduate/Scholarship)* [4029]

Hilda E. Bretzlaff Foundation Scholarships *(Undergraduate/Grant)* [2173]

Rick Brewer Scholarships *(Undergraduate/Scholarship)* [9261]

Mary Ann Brichta Scholarships *(Undergraduate/Scholarship)* [9350]

James Bridenbaugh Memorial Scholarships *(Undergraduate/Scholarship)* [728]

Lloyd Bridges Scholarships *(Graduate, Professional development/Scholarship)* [2679]

Bridgestone Americas Fellowships *(Graduate/Fellowship)* [9414]

Bridging the GAP for Hispanic Success Awards *(Undergraduate/Scholarship)* [4545]

Parsons Brinckerhoff-Jim Lammie Scholarships *(Graduate, Undergraduate/Scholarship)* [1051]

Broadcast News Management Fellowships *(Professional development/Scholarship)* [7575]

Cathy L. Brock Memorial Scholarships *(Graduate/Scholarship)* [4787]

Margaret Martin Brock Scholarships in Law *(Undergraduate/Scholarship)* [7171]

Julia Broderick Scholarships *(Undergraduate/Scholarship)* [8498]

Ross P. Broesamle Educational Scholarship Fund *(Undergraduate/Scholarship)* [5348]

John G. Brokaw Scholarships *(Undergraduate/Scholarship)* [6585]

Brookdale Leadership in Aging Fellowships *(Professional development/Fellowship)* [2194]

Shirley J. Brooke Endowed Scholarships *(Undergraduate/Scholarship)* [7173]

George M. Brooker Collegiate Scholarships for Minorities *(Graduate, Postgraduate, Undergraduate/Scholarship)* [4818]

Seth R. and Corrine H. Brooks Memorial Scholarships *(All/Scholarship)* [2075]

Carl E. Brooks Scholarships *(Undergraduate/Scholarship)* [8593]

Dorothy B. Brothers Executive Scholarship Program *(High School/Scholarship)* [9717]

William A. and Ann M. Brothers Scholarships *(Undergraduate/Scholarship)* [1433]

Selena Danette Brown Book Scholarships *(Graduate, Undergraduate/Scholarship)* [6041]

Diana Brown Endowed Scholarships *(Undergraduate/Scholarship)* [5414]

Marjorie M. Brown Fellowship Program *(Postdoctorate/Fellowship)* [5201]

Brown Foundation College Scholarships *(Undergraduate/Scholarship)* [816]

Mary L. Brown High School Student Scholarships *(Undergraduate/Scholarship)* [5037]

The John Carter Brown Library Long-Term Fellowships *(All/Fellowship)* [2198]

The John Carter Brown Library Short-Term Fellowships *(Doctorate, Postdoctorate/Fellowship)* [2199]

Olympia Brown and Max Kapp Awards *(Graduate/Scholarship)* [8994]

Quincy Brown Memorial Scholarships *(Undergraduate/Scholarship)* [7634]

Jesse Brown Memorial Youth Scholarship Program *(All/Scholarship)* [3459]

JoAnn Brown-Nash Memorial Scholarships *(Undergraduate/Scholarship)* [3097]

Ron Brown Scholars Program *(Undergraduate/Scholarship)* [2201]

Jack H. Brown Scholarships *(Undergraduate/Scholarship)* [2242]

Charles S. Brown Scholarships in Physics *(Graduate, Undergraduate/Scholarship)* [6487]

VPPPA Stephen Brown Scholarships *(Graduate, Undergraduate/Scholarship)* [9474]

Warren K. Brown Scholarships *(Undergraduate/Scholarship)* [1334]

Richard A. Brown Student Scholarships *(Undergraduate/Scholarship)* [8855]

Regina Brown Undergraduate Student Fellowships *(Undergraduate/Fellowship)* [6212]

Peggy Browning Fund - Chicago School-Year Fellowships *(Graduate, Undergraduate/Fellowship)* [2203]

Sheriff W. Bruce Umpleby Law Enforcement Scholarship Fund *(Undergraduate/Scholarship)* [8658]

Gregory Brunk Scholarships *(Undergraduate/Scholarship)* [3482]

Bernard B. and Mary L. Brusin Scholarships *(Undergraduate/Scholarship)* [3526]

Edward C. Bryant Scholarships Trust Fund (Graduate/Fellowship) [1394]

BSA Educational Scholarships (Undergraduate/Scholarship) [2224]

BSF General Scholarship Awards (Undergraduate, Vocational/Occupational/Scholarship) [2024]

BSF Science and Medicine Research Grants (Professional development/Grant) [2026]

Patricia Buchanan Memorial Scholarships (Undergraduate/Scholarship) [9351]

Lt. General Douglas D. Buchholz Memorial Scholarships (Undergraduate/Scholarship) [1557]

John and Elisabeth Buck Endowed Scholarships (Graduate, Postdoctorate/Scholarship) [5612]

Buder Scholarships for American Indian Law Students (Undergraduate/Scholarship) [9530]

Gary L. Buffington Memorial Scholarships (Undergraduate/Scholarship) [4760]

Mike Buoncristiano Memorial Scholarship Fund (Undergraduate/Scholarship) [3445]

William T. Burbage Family Memorial Scholarships (Undergraduate/Scholarship) [3053]

C. Lalor Burdick Scholarships (Undergraduate/Scholarship) [5613]

George M. Burditt Scholarships (Undergraduate/Scholarship) [1781]

Max M. Burger Endowed Scholarships in Embryology (Undergraduate/Scholarship) [5614]

Graduate Fellowship Program - Robert M Burger Fellowships (GFP) (Doctorate, Graduate/Fellowship) [8078]

Burger King Employee Scholars Program (Undergraduate/Scholarship) [4474]

Burger King Scholars Program (Undergraduate/Scholarship) [4475]

Dorothy and Dick Burgess Scholarships (Undergraduate/Scholarship) [5092]

Richard J. Burk, Jr. Fellowships (Graduate/Fellowship) [4488]

Eleanor McWilliams Burke Fund (Undergraduate/Scholarship) [3762]

ACLS Frederick Burkhardt Residential Fellowships (Professional development/Fellowship) [416]

Ralph Burkhardt Scholarship Fund (Undergraduate/Scholarship) [9549]

Burroughs Wellcome Fund Career Awards at the Scientific Interface (Doctorate, Postdoctorate/Fellowship) [2211]

Burroughs Wellcome Fund Collaborative Research Travel Grants (Doctorate/Grant) [2212]

Ethel Beard Burstein Scholarship Program (Postgraduate/Scholarship) [951]

Bush Leadership Fellows Program (Professional development/Fellowship) [2218]

Kathy Bush Memorial Scholarships (Undergraduate/Scholarship) [7635]

Business and Transactional Law Center Scholarships (Undergraduate/Scholarship) [9485]

Lindsay Buster Memorial Scholarships (Undergraduate/Scholarship) [3144]

BWEL Law Student Scholarships (Undergraduate/Scholarship) [2142]

Walter Byers Postgraduate Scholarships (Graduate, Postgraduate/Scholarship) [6192]

Donald C. and Doris K. Byers Scholarships (Undergraduate/Scholarship) [3483]

Joe Bynum/Raymond James Investment Services Technical Excellence Scholarship Fund (Undergraduate/Scholarship) [3033]

Dr. F. Ross Byrd Scholarships (Graduate, Vocational/Occupational/Scholarship) [9523]

George J. Bysiewicz Scholarship Fund (Undergraduate/Scholarship) [3079]

C200 Scholar Awards (All/Scholarship) [3015]

Cabrillo Clubs of California Scholarships (Undergraduate/Scholarship) [7377]

Dr. Aurelio M. Caccomo Family Foundation Memorial Scholarships (Undergraduate/Scholarship) [1467]

Cadmus Communications Corporation Graphics Scholarship Endowment Fund (Undergraduate/Scholarship) [3889]

Edwin Anthony and Adelaine Bordeaux Cadogan Fellowships (Graduate/Fellowship) [7982]

Cal State San Macros Alumna Scholarships (Undergraduate/Scholarship) [2286]

Tese Caldarelli Memorial Scholarships (Graduate, Undergraduate/Scholarship) [6045]

J.E. Caldwell Centennial Scholarships (Undergraduate/Scholarship) [6498]

Calgary USAEE/IAEE North American Conference Registration Fee Scholarships (Undergraduate/Scholarship) [9034]

Calhoun County Auduburn University Scholarships (Undergraduate/Scholarship) [3034]

Hermione Grant Calhoun Scholarships (Undergraduate/Scholarship) [6273]

Calhoun Scholarships (Undergraduate/Scholarship) [2226]

California Sea Grant State Fellowships (Graduate/Fellowship) [2277]

California Shopping Cart Retrieval Corporation Inc. Scholarships (Undergraduate/Scholarship) [2243]

Calista Scholarships (Graduate, Undergraduate, Vocational/Occupational/Scholarship) [2290]

Jodi Callahan Memorial Scholarships (Undergraduate/Scholarship) [91]

W.L. Calvert Memorial Scholarships (Graduate/Scholarship) [4610]

Calvin Alumni Association-Black Alumni Chapter Scholarships (Undergraduate/Scholarship) [2293]

Calvin Alumni Association British Columbia Scholarships (Undergraduate/Scholarship) [2294]

Calvin Alumni Association Colorado Chapter Scholarships (Undergraduate/Scholarship) [2296]

Calvin Alumni Association-Washington, D.C. Scholarships (Undergraduate/Scholarship) [2311]

Camden County College Employee Memorial Scholarships (Undergraduate/Scholarship) [2331]

Camden County College Foundation Scholarships (Undergraduate/Scholarship) [2332]

Camden County Retired Educators Association Scholarships (Undergraduate/Scholarship) [2333]

Stuart Cameron and Margaret McLeod Memorial Scholarships (SCMS) (Graduate, Undergraduate/Scholarship loan) [4814]

Wesley C. Cameron Scholarships (Undergraduate/Scholarship) [6586]

Thomas R. Camp Scholarships (Graduate/Scholarship) [1416]

Lois Campbell Scholarship Awards (Undergraduate/Scholarship) [4930]

Lucille Campbell Scholarship Fund (Undergraduate/Scholarship) [9550]

Robert G. Campbell Scholarships (Undergraduate/Scholarship) [7636]

Campus Discovery Scholarships (Graduate, Undergraduate/Scholarship) [2352]

Cancer for College Scholarships (Graduate, Undergraduate/Scholarship) [2636]

Cancer Survivors' Fund Scholarships (Undergraduate/Scholarship) [2640]

Cancer Treatment Centers of America Post-Graduate Management Fellowships (Postgraduate/Fellowship) [2642]

CANFIT Nutrition, Physical Education and Culinary Arts Scholarships (Graduate, Undergraduate/Scholarship) [3026]

Annie J. Cannon Awards in Astronomy (Doctorate/Award) [569]

Therese A. Cannon Educational Scholarships (Professional development/Scholarship) [4971]

John Cannon Memorial Scholarships (Undergraduate/Scholarship) [6009]

Agustin C. Cano Memorial Scholarships (Undergraduate/Scholarship) [7472]

Commander Ronald J. Cantin Scholarships (Undergraduate/Scholarship) [2921]

CAODC Occupational Health and Safety Scholarships (Professional development/Scholarship) [2399]

CAODC Scholarship Program (Undergraduate/Scholarship) [2400]

John Caoile Memorial Scholarships (Undergraduate/Scholarship) [7473]

Cape Fear Community College Merit Scholarships (Undergraduate, Vocational/Occupational/Scholarship) [2647]

Lester J. Cappon Fellowships in Documentary Editing (Postdoctorate/Fellowship) [6694]

Daniel Cardillo Charitable Fund (All/Scholarship) [5573]

Career Advancement Scholarships (Undergraduate/Scholarship) [2220]

Career Awards for Science and Mathematics Teachers (Professional development/Award) [2213]

Career Colleges Scholarships (Undergraduate/Scholarship) [4706]

Career Development Scholarships (Postdoctorate, Postgraduate/Scholarship) [3855]

Career Fellowship Awards for Medical Scientists (Postdoctorate, Professional development/Fellowship) [2214]

Career Mobility Scholarship Awards (Doctorate, Undergraduate/Scholarship) [27]

Career Mobility Scholarships (Graduate, Undergraduate, Vocational/Occupational/Scholarship) [3977]

CareerFitter Scholarships (Graduate, Undergraduate/Scholarship) [2651]

Beth Carew Memorial Scholarships (Undergraduate/Scholarship) [6318]

John Carew Memorial Scholarships (Undergraduate/Scholarship) [729]

AABA Read Carlock Memorial Scholarship Fund (Professional development/Scholarship) [1507]

Glen and Babs Carlson Endowed Scholarships (Undergraduate/Scholarship) [5415]

Walta Wilkinson Carmichael Scholarships (Undergraduate/Scholarship) [8160]

Carnegie Observatories Graduate Research Fellowships (Doctorate, Graduate/Fellowship) [2655]

Carolinas-Virginias Retail Hardware Scholarships (Undergraduate/Scholarship) [3893]

Jeffrey Carollo Music Scholarships (Undergraduate/Scholarship) [6648]

Pete Carpenter Fellowships (All/Fellowship) [2157]

Carpenters' Company Scholarships (Undergraduate/Scholarship) [2657]

Walter & Elsie Carr Endowed Scholarships (Undergraduate/Scholarship) [5416]

Commander James Carr Forensic Science Scholarships (Undergraduate/Scholarship) [356]

Willis H. Carrier Scholarships (Undergraduate/Scholarship) [1265]

Karen D. Carsel Memorial Scholarships (Graduate/Scholarship) [749]

Rachel Carson Prize (Professional development/Prize) [1246]

Leigh Carter Scholarships (Undergraduate/Scholarship) [3099]

CASBS Residential Fellowships (Doctorate, Professional development/Fellowship) [2681]

Casey Family Scholars Scholarships (Undergraduate, Vocational/Occupational/Scholarship) [3871]

TCDA Jim and Glenda Casey Professional Scholarships (Graduate, Professional development/Scholarship) [8847]

Elton Casey Scholarships (Undergraduate/Scholarship) [9262]

Local 827 Peter J. Casey Scholarships (Undergraduate/Scholarship) [4888]

Carlos M. Castaneda Journalism Scholarships (Graduate/Scholarship) [4027]

Catching the Dream Scholarships (Graduate, Undergraduate/Scholarship) [817]

Caterpillar Scholars Award (Undergraduate/Scholarship) [8370]

Caterpillar Scholarships in Diesel Mechanics (Undergraduate/Scholarship) [5417]

Catholic Aid Association's Post-High School Tuition Scholarships (Undergraduate/Scholarship) [2670]

Catholic Biblical Association of America Scholarships (Undergraduate/Scholarship) [2666]

Robert A. Catlin/David W. Long Memorial Scholarships (Graduate/Scholarship) [1009]

Marshall Cavendish Scholarships (Graduate/Scholarship) [899]

Christine Kerr Cawthorne Scholarships (Undergraduate/Scholarship) [8161]

Llewellyn L. Cayvan String Instrument Scholarships (Undergraduate/Scholarship) [4275]

CBC Spouses Cheerios Brand Health Initiative Scholarships (Undergraduate/Scholarship) [3215]

CBC Spouses Education Scholarship Fund (Doctorate, Graduate, Undergraduate/Scholarship) [3216]

CBC Spouses Flexible Education Scholarships

(Graduate, Master's, Undergraduate/Scholarship) [3217]

CBC Spouses Heineken USA Performing Arts Scholarships (Undergraduate/Scholarship) [3218]

CBC Spouses Visual Arts Scholarships (Undergraduate/Scholarship) [3219]

CBCF Congressional Fellows Program (Professional development/Fellowship) [3220]

CCFA Career Development Awards (Doctorate, Graduate/Grant) [3292]

CCFA Research Fellowship Awards (Doctorate, Graduate/Fellowship) [3293]

CCFA Student Research Fellowship Awards (Graduate, Undergraduate/Grant) [3294]

CCSD School Counselors' Scholarships (Undergraduate/Scholarship) [7474]

CCU Alumni Endowed Scholarships (Undergraduate/Scholarship) [2986]

CCV Foundation Graduate and Undergraduate Fellowships (Doctorate, Graduate, Undergraduate/Fellowship) [2672]

CDA Foundation Allied Dental Student Scholarships (All/Scholarship) [2674]

CDA Foundation Dental Student Scholarships (All/Scholarship) [2675]

CDC Presidential Management Fellows Program (Graduate/Fellowship) [2711]

CDC Preventive Medicine Residency and Fellowships (Professional development/Fellowship) [2712]

CDC Public Health Informatics Fellowships (Graduate, Postdoctorate/Fellowship) [2713]

L.B. Cebik, W4RNL, and Jean Cebik, N4TZP, Memorial Scholarships (Undergraduate/Scholarship) [1075]

Betty J. Cecere Memorial Scholarship Endowment Fund (Undergraduate/Scholarship) [9551]

Cedarcrest Farms Scholarships (Graduate, Undergraduate/Scholarship) [884]

Delmar Cengage Learning-NAAE Upper Division Scholarships (Undergraduate/Scholarship) [6033]

Center for Congressional and Presidential Studies Endowment (CPPS) (Graduate, Undergraduate/Scholarship) [1404]

Center for the Education of Women Scholarships (Graduate, Undergraduate/Scholarship) [2687]

Center for the Education of Women Student Research Grants (Graduate, Undergraduate/Grant) [2688]

Center for Lesbian and Gay Studies Fellowships (Graduate/Fellowship) [2701]

Center for Women in Government and Civil Society Fellowships (Graduate/Fellowship) [2709]

Centerville-Abington Dollars for Scholars (Undergraduate/Scholarship) [9552]

CentraState Band Aid Open Committee Scholarships (Undergraduate/Scholarship) [2724]

CentraState Healthcare Foundation Health Professional Scholarships (Undergraduate/Scholarship) [2725]

CEPS-Tyco Scholarships (Undergraduate/Scholarship) [9250]

CERT College Scholarships (Graduate, Undergraduate/Scholarship) [3272]

Certified Municipal Clerk Scholarships (CMC) (Professional development/Scholarship) [4957]

Certified Neuroscience Registered Nurse Recertification Grant Program (CNRN) (Professional development/Grant) [518]

Cerutti Group Scholarships (Undergraduate, Graduate/Scholarship) [4318]

Arthur and Gladys Cervenka Scholarships (Undergraduate/Scholarship) [8371]

CES Conference Travel Grants (Graduate, Professional development/Grant) [3274]

CES Dissertation Completion Fellowships (Graduate/Fellowship) [3275]

CES Pre-Dissertation Research Fellowships (Graduate/Fellowship) [3276]

CfA Postdoctoral Fellowships (Postdoctorate/Fellowship) [4471]

CFERP Masters Fellowships (Graduate/Fellowship) [3030]

CFIDS Association of America NP Student Scholarships (Graduate/Scholarship) [376]

Rick Chace Foundation Scholarships (Graduate/Scholarship) [1829]

Chaine des Rotisseurs Scholarships (Undergraduate/Scholarship) [691]

Jeanne S. Chall Research Fellowships (Doctorate, Graduate/Grant) [4975]

Challenge Met Scholarships (Undergraduate/Scholarship) [1077]

Mariam K. Chamberlain Fellowships in Women and Public Policy (Graduate/Fellowship) [4835]

Logan S. Chambers Individual Scholarships (Professional development/Scholarship) [4885]

Chambersburg/Fannett-Metal School District Scholarship Fund (Undergraduate/Scholarship) [3937]

Chambliss Astronomy Achievement Student Awards (Undergraduate, Graduate/Award) [570]

Jason Chaney Memorial Scholarship Fund (Undergraduate/Scholarship) [9553]

Channabasappa Memorial Scholarships (Graduate, Professional development/Scholarship) [4918]

Harry H. and Floy B. Chapin Scholarships (Undergraduate/Scholarship) [3145]

Nancy J. Chapman Scholarships (Professional development/Scholarship) [1753]

S. Penny Chappell Scholarships (Undergraduate/Scholarship) [7279]

Chapter 31 - Peoria Endowed Scholarships (Undergraduate/Scholarship) [8375]

Chapter 52 - Wichita Scholarships (Graduate, Undergraduate/Scholarship) [8377]

Chapter 56 - Fort Wayne Scholarships (Graduate, Undergraduate/Scholarship) [8378]

Chapter 6 Fairfield County Scholarships (Undergraduate/Scholarship) [8379]

Chapter 67 - Phoenix Scholarships (Undergraduate/Scholarship) [8380]

Chapter One - Detroit Founding Chapter Scholarships (Graduate, Undergraduate/Scholarship) [8382]

Charles "Chuck" McAdams Memorial Scholarships (Graduate, Undergraduate/Scholarship) [8809]

Abram and Sylvia Chasens Teaching and Research Fellowships (Postdoctorate/Fellowship) [395]

Emilie Du Chatelet Awards (Doctorate/Award) [1226]

Chautauqua Scholarships Program (All/Scholarship) [4969]

Cesar E. Chavez Scholarships (Undergraduate/Scholarship) [7637]

Chemical Heritage Foundation Travel Grants (CHF) (All/Grant) [2740]

Cherokee Nation Pell Scholarships (Undergraduate/Scholarship) [2743]

Cherry Lane Foundation/Music Alive! Scholarships (Undergraduate/Scholarship) [1208]

Cheyenne High School Faculty Memorial Scholarships (Undergraduate/Scholarship) [7475]

Chi Chapter Undergraduate Scholarships (Undergraduate/Scholarship) [3369]

Melba Dawn Chiarenza Scholarship Fund (Undergraduate/Scholarship) [9554]

Chicago Division Scholarships (Undergraduate/Scholarship) [5858]

Child of Alumni Book Voucher Awards (Undergraduate/Scholarship) [4742]

Child and Family Advocacy Fellowships (Undergraduate/Scholarship) [9486]

Julia Child Memorial Scholarships (Undergraduate/Scholarship) [692]

Kevin Child Scholarships (Undergraduate/Scholarship) [6319]

Childbirth Educator Program Scholarships (All/Scholarship) [5326]

John and Ruth Childe Scholarships (Undergraduate/Scholarship) [8594]

Children of Evangeline Section Scholarships (Graduate, Undergraduate/Scholarship) [8435]

Children of Unitarian Universalist Ministers College Scholarships (Undergraduate/Scholarship) [8995]

Children's Memorial Hospital Postgraduate Administrative Fellowships (Postgraduate/Fellowship) [5539]

Jane Coffin Childs Memorial Fund - Medical Research Fellowships (Doctorate/Fellowship) [2764]

Charline Chilson Scholarships (Undergraduate/Scholarship) [3407]

Chinese American Medical Society Summer Research Fellowships Program (Undergraduate/Fellowship) [2766]

Helen Krich Chinoy Dissertation Research Fellowships (Doctorate/Fellowship) [1360]

Choose Your Future Scholarships (Undergraduate/Scholarship) [3101]

Chopin Foundation of the United States Scholarships (Undergraduate/Scholarship) [2777]

Chretien International Research Grants (Doctorate, Professional development/Grant) [571]

Frances N. Christian Memorial Endowment Nursing Scholarships (Graduate, Undergraduate/Scholarship) [8740]

Christian Pharmacist Fellowship International (All/Fellowship) [2783]

Christmas Tree Chapter Scholarship Awards (Undergraduate/Scholarship) [6933]

Commander Daniel J. Christovich Scholarship Fund (Undergraduate/Scholarship) [2922]

Chrysalis Scholarships (Graduate/Grant) [1901]

Chrysler Foundation Scholarship Awards (Undergraduate/Scholarship) [4546]

Church Family Scholarships (Undergraduate/Scholarship) [5418]

Edward D. Churchill Research Scholarships (Professional development/Scholarship) [562]

The Churchill Scholarships (Postgraduate/Scholarship) [2789]

CIA Undergraduate Scholarships (Undergraduate/Scholarship) [1785]

CIGNA Healthcare Graduate Scholarships (Graduate/Scholarship) [6290]

CIGNA Healthcare Undergraduate Scholarships (Undergraduate/Scholarship) [6291]

Cincinnati High School Scholarships (High School/Scholarship) [2799]

CISDL Associate Fellows (Graduate/Fellowship) [2730]

CISDL Legal Research Fellows (Graduate/Fellowship) [2731]

CISDL Senior Research Fellows (Professional development/Fellowship) [2732]

Carlos Enrique Cisneros Point Scholarships (Graduate, Undergraduate/Scholarship) [7356]

Citi Foundation Scholarship Program (Undergraduate/Scholarship) [805]

City of Sanibel Employee Dependent Scholarships (Undergraduate/Scholarship) [8595]

Civil Air Patrol Scholarships for School and Flying (Undergraduate/Scholarship) [2893]

Civitan Shropshire Scholarships (Undergraduate, Vocational/Occupational/Scholarship) [2895]

Clackamas Chapter Scholarship Awards (Undergraduate/Scholarship) [6934]

Claes Nobel Academic Scholarships for Members (High School/Scholarship) [6502]

Clan Ross Foundation Scholarships (Undergraduate/Scholarship) [2897]

Cecil Earl Clapp, Sr. Memorial Scholarships (Undergraduate/Scholarship) [6811]

Michelle Clark Fellowships (Undergraduate/Fellowship) [7576]

Vickie Clark-Flaherty Scholarships (Undergraduate, Vocational/Occupational/Scholarship) [6772]

Clark High School Academy of Finance Scholarships (Undergraduate/Scholarship) [7476]

Clark High School Alumni Leadership Circle Scholarships (Undergraduate/Scholarship) [7477]

Clark High School Teacher Education Academy Scholarships (Undergraduate/Scholarship) [7478]

Howard A. Clark Horticulture Scholarships (Undergraduate/Scholarship) [3102]

Robert A. Clark Memorial Educational Scholarships (Postgraduate/Scholarship) [6510]

Fisher Clark Memorial Endowed Scholarships (Undergraduate/Scholarship) [5419]

Thomas Arkle Clark Scholar-Leader of the Year Endowed Scholarships (Graduate, Undergraduate/Scholarship) [7254]

Athalie Clarke Endowed Scholarships (Undergraduate/Scholarship) [7174]

Lucy and Charles W.E. Clarke Scholarships (Undergraduate/Scholarship) [1660]

CLASS Fund Irrigation Scholarship Program (Graduate, Undergraduate/Scholarship) [5331]

Classic Wines of California Scholarships (Undergraduate/Scholarship) [2244]

J. Clawson Mills Scholarships (Doctorate/Scholarship) [5784]

Clay Postdoctoral Fellowships (Postdoctorate/Fellowship) [4472]

CLCA Landscape Educational Advancement Foundation Scholarships (Undergraduate/Scholarship) [2263]

Brian Dane Cleary Memorial Scholarships (Undergraduate/Scholarship) [7175]

Lula Faye Clegg Memorial Scholarship Fund (Undergraduate/Scholarship) [3897]

Cleveland Executive Fellowships (CEF) (Professional development/Fellowship) [2903]

Geraldine Clewell Fellowships - Doctoral Student (Graduate/Fellowship) [7280]

Geraldine Clewell Fellowships - Masteral (Graduate/Fellowship) [7281]

Geraldine Clewell Scholarships - Undergraduate (Undergraduate/Scholarship) [7282]

Justice Robert L. Clifford Fellowships (All/Fellowship) [5930]

James L. Clifford Prize (Professional development/Prize) [1227]

David H. Clift Scholarships (Graduate/Scholarship) [900]

Bryan Cline Memorial Soccer Scholarship Program (Undergraduate/Scholarship) [279]

Clinical Pharmacy Post-Pharm.D. Fellowships in the Biomedical Research Sciences (Postdoctorate/Fellowship) [758]

Clinical Research Fellowship for Medical Students (Graduate/Fellowship) [3522]

Clinical Research Training Fellowships (Professional development/Fellowship) [373]

Clinical Toxicology Fellowships (Doctorate/Fellowship) [537]

Clinician Scientist Development Awards (Postgraduate/Fellowship) [7127]

Closs/Parnitzke/Clarke Scholarships (Undergraduate/Scholarship) [7283]

Austin M. Cloyd, Matthew G. Gwaltney and Maxine S. Turner Doctoral Scholarships (Doctorate/Scholarship) [9461]

Club Managers Association of America Research Grants (CMAA) (All/Grant) [2910]

CMAA Student Conference Travel Grants (All/Grant) [2911]

CMSF Scholarships (Graduate, Undergraduate/Scholarship) [2781]

CNA Foundation Scholarships (Graduate, Undergraduate/Scholarship) [1335]

Coast Guard Foundation Enlisted Education Grants (All/Grant) [2923]

Coast Guard Foundation Scholarships (Undergraduate/Scholarship) [2924]

The Helena B. Cobb Annual Scholarships (Undergraduate, Vocational/Occupational/Scholarship) [9728]

The Helena B. Cobb Four-Year Higher Education Grants (Undergraduate, Vocational/Occupational/Scholarship) [9729]

J.C. and Rheba Cobb Memorial Scholarships (Undergraduate/Scholarship) [6198]

Gordon W. and Agnes P. Cobb Scholarships (Undergraduate/Scholarship) [3567]

John Coburn and Harold Winters Student Award in Plasma Science and Technology (Graduate/Award) [1980]

Coca-Cola First Generation Scholarships (Undergraduate/Scholarship) [806]

Coca-Cola Scholars Foundation Four-Year Awards for Seniors (Undergraduate/Scholarship) [2966]

Johnnie L. Cochran, Jr./MWH Scholarships (Graduate, Undergraduate/Scholarship) [6292]

Frank M. Coda Scholarships (Undergraduate/Scholarship) [1266]

CODY Foundation Fund (Undergraduate/Scholarship) [3938]

Coeur d'Alene Alumni Scholarships (Undergraduate/Scholarship) [5420]

Frank M. Coffin Family Law Fellowships (Graduate/Fellowship) [5569]

Claude T. Coffman Memorial Scholarships (Undergraduate/Scholarship) [9221]

Ruth M. Cogan Scholarship Fund (Undergraduate/Scholarship) [8661]

COHEAO Scholarships (Undergraduate/Scholarship) [2919]

Maurice and Marilyn Cohen Fund for Doctoral Dissertation Fellowships in Jewish Studies (Doctorate/Fellowship) [3974]

Ardis Cohoon Scholarships (Undergraduate/Scholarship) [9263]

Arthur H. Cole Grants in Aid (Doctorate/Grant) [3582]

Paul Cole Scholarships (Undergraduate/Scholarship) [8420]

Colgate-Palmolive/HDA Foundation Scholarships (Master's, Postgraduate/Scholarship) [4555]

College Art Association Professional Development Fellowships (Graduate/Fellowship) [2968]

College Art Association Wyeth Publication Grants (Professional development/Grant) [2969]

College of Marin Gay and Lesbian Student Scholarships (Undergraduate/Scholarship) [7847]

Jennet Colliflower Nursing Scholarships (Undergraduate/Scholarship) [3315]

Irene Culver Collins and Louis Franklin Collins Scholarships (Undergraduate/Scholarship) [3054]

Captain Winifred Quick Collins Scholarships (Undergraduate/Scholarship) [6587]

Elmer and Rosa Lee Collins Scholarships (Undergraduate/Scholarship) [9630]

Lloyd E. and Rachel S. Collins Scholarships (Undergraduate/Scholarship) [9631]

Zoe E. Collymore Page Scholarships (Undergraduate/Scholarship) [6145]

Colorado PROSTART/Art Institute of Colorado Art Scholarships for High School Seniors (Undergraduate/Scholarship) [1627]

ColorMasters Scholarships (Undergraduate/Scholarship) [4055]

Columbus Citizens Foundation High School Scholarships (High School/Scholarship) [3013]

Robert N. Colwell Memorial Fellowships (Doctorate, Graduate/Fellowship) [1666]

Committee 12 - Rail Transit Scholarships (Undergraduate/Scholarship) [1122]

Committee 27 - Maintenance-of-Way Work Equipment Scholarships (Undergraduate/Scholarship) [1123]

Commonwealth Fund/Harvard University Fellowships in Minority Health Policy (Professional development/Fellowship) [3019]

Commonwealth "Good Citizen" Scholarships (Undergraduate/Scholarship) [1795]

Communal Studies Association Research Fellowships (Graduate/Grant) [3022]

Communications Workers of America Scholarships (Undergraduate/Scholarship) [3024]

Community-based Natural Resource Management Assistantships (All/Internship) [3031]

The Community Foundation DBI Scholarships (Undergraduate, Vocational/Occupational/Scholarship) [3103]

Community Foundation of Sarasota County Adult Learner Scholarships (Undergraduate, Vocational/Occupational/Scholarship) [3189]

The Community Foundation Student Education Loans (Undergraduate/Loan) [3104]

Comparative Perspectives on Chinese Culture and Society Grants (Doctorate/Grant) [676]

Alan Compton and Bob Stanley Professional Scholarships (Undergraduate/Scholarship) [2016]

Richard G. Condon Prize (Doctorate, Graduate, Undergraduate/Prize) [8469]

Maridell Braham Condon Scholarships (Undergraduate/Scholarship) [8162]

Conference on Asian Pacific American Leadership Scholarships (Graduate, Undergraduate/Scholarship) [3211]

Conference of State Bank Supervisors Graduate School Scholarships (Graduate/Award) [3213]

Congressional Hispanic Caucus Institute Graduate and Young Professional Fellowships (Doctorate, Graduate/Fellowship) [3224]

Congressional Hispanic Caucus Institute Public Policy Fellowships (Graduate/Fellowship) [3225]

Congressional Hispanic Caucus Institute Scholarships (Community College, Graduate, Undergraduate/Scholarship) [3226]

Congressional Scholarship Awards (Undergraduate/Scholarship) [4016]

Congressional Science Fellowships (Postdoctorate/Fellowship) [1302]

Alan H. Conklin Business Aviation Management Scholarships (Undergraduate/Scholarship) [6163]

Cecilia Connelly Memorial Scholarships in Underwater Archaeology (Graduate, Undergraduate/Scholarship) [9698]

Louis M. Connor Jr. Scholarships (Undergraduate/Scholarship) [9264]

Patricia Pownder Conolly Memorial Scholarships (Undergraduate/Scholarship) [5777]

Conservation Department Program Fellowships (Graduate/Fellowship) [8258]

Conservation Guest Scholar Grants (Professional development/Grant) [4139]

Construction Trades Scholarships (Undergraduate/Scholarship) [6131]

Consumer Law Public Service Fellowships (All/Fellowship) [7603]

Contemporary Club Scholarships (Undergraduate/Scholarship) [7638]

The Continental Group Scholarship Fund (High School, Undergraduate/Scholarship) [3316]

Continuing Education Awards (All/Scholarship) [6109]

Continuing Education Awards (Graduate/Grant) [5741]

Jorge Espejal Contreras Memorial Scholarships (Graduate, Undergraduate/Scholarship) [4873]

Convergence Assistantship Grants (Undergraduate/Grant) [4386]

James & Maryetta Cook Scholarships (Undergraduate/Scholarship) [2334]

John Kent Cooke Foundation Graduate Scholarships (Graduate/Scholarship) [3245]

John Kent Cooke Foundation Undergraduate Transfer Scholarships (Undergraduate/Scholarship) [3246]

John Kent Cooke Foundation Young Scholars (High School/Scholarship) [3247]

Cooley's Anemia Foundation Research Fellowships (Postdoctorate/Fellowship) [3251]

Milton E. Cooper/Young AFCEAN Graduate Scholarships (Graduate/Scholarship) [1558]

Cope Middle School PTSA Scholarships (Undergraduate/Scholarship) [7639]

Rob Copeland Memorial Scholarships (Undergraduate/Scholarship) [5421]

Copper and Brass Servicenter Association Inc. Scholarship Program (Undergraduate/Scholarship) [3253]

Corbett-Porter Building Bridges Scholarships (Undergraduate/Scholarship) [7479]

Hazel Corbin/Childbirth Connection Grants for Evidence-based Midwifery Care (Professional development/Grant) [619]

Beta Nu/Caryl Cordis D'hondt Scholarships (Undergraduate/Scholarship) [8163]

Theta/Caryl Cordis D'hondt Scholarships (Undergraduate/Scholarship) [8164]

Bill Cormack Scholarships (Undergraduate/Scholarship) [8865]

Cornaro Scholarships for Graduate Studies (Graduate/Scholarship) [5191]

D.C. Cornelius Memorial Scholarships (Undergraduate/Scholarship) [9632]

Holly A. Cornell Scholarships (Graduate/Scholarship) [1417]

Corning Outstanding Student Paper Competition (Graduate, Undergraduate/Award) [6910]

Coro Fellows Program in Public Affairs (Graduate/Fellowship) [3255]

The Corp - Students of Georgetown Inc. Coke Scholarships (Undergraduate/Scholarship) [3257]

The Corp - Students of Georgetown Inc. Textbook Scholarships (Undergraduate/Scholarship) [3258]

The Corp - Students of Georgetown Inc.-Word Scholarships (Undergraduate/Scholarship) [3259]

Corporate Aviation Management Scholarships (Professional development/Scholarship) [6164]

Correctional Education Association Scholarships (Graduate, Undergraduate/Scholarship) [3266]

NSS Sara Corrie Memorial Grants *(All/Grant)* [6525]

Tom Cory Memorial Scholarships *(Undergraduate/Scholarship)* [1498]

Richard Cossette/Gale Memorial Scholarships *(All/Scholarship)* [1965]

James Costello Memorial Scholarships *(Undergraduate/Scholarship)* [5023]

Cotner Family Scholarships *(Undergraduate/Scholarship)* [3765]

George C. Cotzias, MD Memorial Fellowships *(Professional development/Fellowship)* [981]

SRC NRI Hans J. Coufal Fellowships *(Graduate/Fellowship)* [8086]

Council on Social Work Education Minority Fellowship Programs *(Postdoctorate/Fellowship)* [3282]

Council on Social Work Education Scholars Program *(Postdoctorate/Scholarship)* [3283]

Courage to Grow Scholarships *(Undergraduate/Scholarship)* [3286]

Soozie Courter Sharing a Brighter Tomorrow Hemophilia Scholarship Program *(Graduate, Undergraduate, Vocational/Occupational/Scholarship)* [6320]

Paul Courtland Scholarships *(Undergraduate/Scholarship)* [5332]

COUSE-Gram Scholarships *(Undergraduate/Scholarship)* [8596]

Richard P. Covert, Ph.D./FHIMSS Scholarships for Management Systems *(Graduate, Postgraduate, Undergraduate/Scholarship)* [4504]

The Joe E. Covington Awards for Research on Bar Admissions Testing *(Doctorate, Graduate/Award)* [6204]

Gertrude M. Cox Scholarships *(Doctorate, Graduate/Fellowship)* [1395]

CPA-F Minority Scholarships *(Graduate/Scholarship)* [2267]

CPCU Loman Education Foundation Scholarships *(Professional development/Scholarship)* [4838]

Craft Research Fund *(Professional development/Grant)* [2683]

Crafton Elementary School PTA Scholarships *(Undergraduate/Scholarship)* [7640]

Crafton Hills College Foundation Scholarships *(Undergraduate/Scholarship)* [7641]

Crain Educational Grant Program *(Undergraduate/Scholarship)* [8198]

Robert E. Cramer Scholarships *(Graduate, Undergraduate/Scholarship)* [8445]

The Rick Crane Group Real Estate Scholarship Fund *(Undergraduate/Scholarship)* [5422]

Meredith P. Crawford Fellowships in I/O Psychology *(Doctorate/Fellowship)* [4632]

AWG Maria Luisa Crawford Field Camp Scholarships *(Undergraduate/Scholarship)* [1902]

Creative Glass Center of America Fellowships *(All/Fellowship)* [3288]

Critical Language Scholarships for Intensive Summer Institutes *(Graduate, Undergraduate/Scholarship)* [1145]

CRMA Scholarships *(Graduate, Undergraduate/Scholarship)* [2748]

Crohn's and Colitis Foundation of America Senior Research Awards *(Doctorate, Graduate/Grant)* [3295]

Cromwell Fellowships *(Undergraduate/Fellowship)* [1291]

Redlands Rotary Club - Ernest L. Cronemeyer Memorial Scholarships *(Undergraduate/Scholarship)* [7642]

Kathryn M. Cronin Scholarships *(Graduate, Undergraduate/Scholarship)* [9265]

CrossLites Scholarships *(Graduate, High School, Undergraduate/Scholarship)* [3297]

R.G. and Ruth Crossno Memorial Scholarships *(Undergraduate/Scholarship)* [3569]

CROW Fellowships *(All/Fellowship)* [2905]

CRS Scholarships *(Undergraduate/Scholarship)* [2785]

Lydia Cruz and Sandra Maria Ramos Scholarships *(Undergraduate/Scholarship)* [3404]

The Crystal Green Blood Assurance Memorial Scholarships *(Undergraduate/Scholarship)* [2153]

CSA Fraternal Life Scholarships *(Undergraduate/Scholarship)* [3299]

CSCPA College Scholarships *(Graduate, Undergraduate/Scholarship)* [3005]

CSCPA High School Scholarships *(Undergraduate/Scholarship)* [3006]

CSCPA Sophomore Scholarships *(Undergraduate/Scholarship)* [3007]

CSF Graduate Fellowships *(Graduate/Fellowship)* [2787]

CSX Scholarships *(Undergraduate/Scholarship)* [1124]

CTFS Research Grants Program *(Graduate, Postdoctorate, Professional development/Grant)* [8268]

CTP Scholarship Program *(Professional development/Scholarship)* [6455]

Cuban American Bar Association Scholarships *(All/Scholarship)* [3301]

John P. Culhane Memorial Scholarships *(Undergraduate/Scholarship)* [191]

Linda Cullen Memorial Scholarships *(High School/Scholarship)* [693]

Murtha Cullina Scholarships *(Undergraduate/Scholarship)* [3080]

Brian Cummins Memorial Scholarships *(Undergraduate/Scholarship)* [4424]

Claire V. Cunningham Masonic Fund for Supporting Leadership in Nursing Scholarships *(Professional development/Scholarship)* [1724]

John J. Cunningham Memorial Scholarships *(Undergraduate/Scholarship)* [1125]

Tsutako Curo Scholarships *(Undergraduate/Scholarship)* [7480]

Nancy Curry Scholarships *(Postgraduate, Vocational/Occupational/Scholarship)* [8028]

Michael D. Curtin Renaissance Student Memorial Scholarships *(Undergraduate/Scholarship)* [3570]

The Jennifer Curtis Byler Scholarships *(Undergraduate/Scholarship)* [6533]

Don and Barbara Curtis Excellence Fund for Extra-curricular Student Activities *(Undergraduate/Grant)* [9266]

Dewey Lee Curtis Scholarships *(All/Scholarship)* [3356]

Cushing Academy Fellowships on Environmental History *(Graduate, Doctorate/Fellowship)* [5669]

CVS/All Kids Can Scholars Program *(Undergraduate, Vocational/Occupational/Scholarship)* [1935]

Cystic Fibrosis Cholestatic Liver Disease Liver Scholarships *(Doctorate/Award)* [905]

Cystic Fibrosis Scholarship Foundation *(Undergraduate, Vocational/Occupational/Scholarship)* [3312]

DAAD Study Scholarship Awards *(Graduate/Scholarship)* [4116]

DAAD Undergraduate Scholarship Program *(Undergraduate/Scholarship)* [4117]

Daggy Youth/Student Scholarships *(Professional development/Scholarship)* [5016]

Robert G. Daily Scholarships *(Graduate, Undergraduate/Scholarship)* [8446]

Dairy Farmers of America Scholarships *(Undergraduate/Scholarship)* [3331]

Dalai Lama Trust Graduate Scholarships *(Graduate/Scholarship)* [3333]

Daland Fellowships in Clinical Investigation *(Doctorate/Fellowship)* [989]

Dalcroze Society of America Memorial Scholarships *(Graduate/Scholarship)* [3335]

Chester Dale Fellowships *(Doctorate/Fellowship)* [5785]

Angela D. Dales Merit Scholarship Program *(Undergraduate/Scholarship)* [1486]

The John L. Dales Scholarship Fund *(Undergraduate, Vocational/Occupational/Scholarship)* [8069]

Dallas Hispanic Bar Association Scholarships *(Undergraduate/Scholarship)* [3337]

Marvin E. Daly Memorial Scholarships *(Undergraduate/Scholarship)* [6812]

June Danby and Pat Pearse Education Scholarships *(Undergraduate/Scholarship)* [5093]

Dance Education Scholarship Program *(High School/Scholarship)* [7985]

D&A Florida Scholarships *(Undergraduate/Scholarship)* [8597]

Robin M. Daniels Memorial Scholarships *(Undergraduate/Scholarship)* [7481]

Arthur H. Daniels Scholarships *(Undergraduate/Scholarship)* [7643]

Dante Prizes *(Undergraduate/Prize)* [3341]

Danville Education Association Scholarship Fund *(Undergraduate/Scholarship)* [3766]

Danville High School Class of 1963 Scholarship Fund *(Undergraduate/Scholarship)* [3767]

Danville Rotary Scholarships *(Undergraduate/Scholarship)* [3768]

Mary Mouzon Darby Undergraduate Scholarships *(Undergraduate/Scholarship)* [4627]

Hugh and Hazel Darling Dean Scholarships *(Undergraduate/Scholarship)* [7176]

Darling Foundation Endowed School of Law Scholarships *(Undergraduate/Scholarship)* [7177]

Daughters of the American Revolution American Indian Scholarships *(Undergraduate/Scholarship)* [818]

The Dave Family "Humor Studies" Scholarships *(Undergraduate/Scholarship)* [1703]

David G. Imig Awards for Distinguished Achievement in Teacher Education *(Professional development/Award)* [465]

David Library Fellowships *(Doctorate, Postdoctorate/Fellowship)* [3344]

Davis Educational Scholarship Fund *(Undergraduate, Vocational/Occupational/Scholarship)* [3190]

Kenneth and Kathleen Davis Endowed Scholarships *(Undergraduate/Scholarship)* [5424]

Davis Foundation Postdoctoral Fellowships *(Postdoctorate/Fellowship)* [4494]

The William H. Davis, Jr. Scholarship Fund *(Undergraduate/Scholarship)* [3086]

Davis Memorial Foundation Scholarship Awards Program *(Graduate, Undergraduate/Scholarship)* [3346]

Dwight F. Davis Memorial Scholarships *(Undergraduate/Scholarship)* [9408]

Johnny Davis Memorial Scholarships *(Undergraduate/Scholarship)* [125]

Arlene Davis Scholarships *(Undergraduate/Scholarship)* [3408]

Fran Morgenstern Davis Scholarships *(Undergraduate/Scholarship)* [1209]

IS&T Raymond Davis Scholarships *(Graduate, Undergraduate/Scholarship)* [8352]

James H. Davis Scholarships *(Undergraduate/Scholarship)* [3838]

Colonel Richard M. Dawson Scholarships *(Undergraduate/Scholarship)* [3105]

Dayton Amateur Radio Association Scholarships *(Undergraduate/Scholarship)* [1083]

DBA Law School Scholarship Program *(Undergraduate/Scholarship)* [3471]

DCH Freehold Toyota Scholarships *(Undergraduate/Scholarship)* [2726]

Edilia and Francois Auguste de Montequin Fellowships *(Doctorate/Fellowship)* [8295]

Elsie De Wolfe Point Scholarships *(Graduate, Undergraduate/Scholarship)* [7357]

Deafness Research Foundation Research Grants *(Doctorate/Grant)* [3350]

Alphonso Deal Scholarship Awards *(Undergraduate/Scholarship)* [6157]

Dean Prim Scholarships *(Undergraduate/Scholarship)* [9634]

DeBakey International Society Fellowship Awards *(Professional development/Award)* [3354]

Don Debolt Franchising Scholarship Program *(Undergraduate/Scholarship)* [4939]

Walter M. Decker Point Scholarships *(Graduate, Undergraduate/Scholarship)* [7358]

DEED Student Research Grant/Internships *(Graduate, Undergraduate/Grant)* [1048]

Anthony R. Dees Educational Workshop Scholarships *(Undergraduate/Scholarship)* [8327]

Jane Delano Student Nurse Scholarships *(Undergraduate/Scholarship)* [1135]

Jan DiMartino Delany Memorial Scholarships *(Undergraduate/Scholarship)* [3939]

Antonia Dellas Memorial Scholarships *(Undergraduate/Scholarship)* [5094]

Alexander A. Delle Cese Memorial Scholarships *(Undergraduate/Scholarship)* [2191]

Martha Delman and Milton Arthur Krug Endowed Scholarships *(Undergraduate/Scholarship)* [7178]

Delmar Cengage Surgical Technology Scholarships *(Graduate/Scholarship)* [1880]

Vine Deloria Jr. Memorial Scholarships *(Graduate/Scholarship)* [807]

Eric Delson Memorial Scholarships *(High School, Undergraduate, Vocational/Occupational/Scholarship)* [6321]

Delta Chi Alumnae Memorial Scholarships *(Undergraduate/Scholarship)* [8165]

Delta Epsilon Sigma Graduate Fellowships *(Graduate/Fellowship)* [3395]

Delta Epsilon Sigma Undergraduate Scholarships *(Undergraduate/Scholarship)* [3396]

Delta Faucet Scholarships *(Undergraduate/Scholarship)* [7345]

Delta Gamma Scholarships *(Undergraduate/Scholarship)* [3398]

Delta Iota Alumni Scholarships *(Undergraduate/Scholarship)* [8218]

Delta Nu Alpha Foundation Scholarships *(Undergraduate/Scholarship)* [3400]

Delta Phi Epsilon Educational Foundation Scholarships *(Undergraduate/Scholarship)* [3402]

Delta/VPPPA Safety, Health and Environmental Scholarships *(Undergraduate, Vocational/Occupational, Graduate/Scholarship)* [9475]

Delta Zeta Undergraduate Scholarships *(Undergraduate/Scholarship)* [3409]

Law Offices of Michael A. DeMayo Scholarships *(Undergraduate/Scholarship)* [5364]

DEMCO New Leaders Travel Grants *(All/Grant)* [7536]

Christopher Demetris Scholarships *(Undergraduate/Scholarship)* [4513]

Inez Demonet Scholarships *(Graduate/Scholarship)* [9421]

Michael Denton Scholarships *(Undergraduate/Scholarship)* [6813]

John Denver Music Scholarships *(Undergraduate/Scholarship)* [1210]

Denver Scholarship Foundation Scholarships *(Undergraduate/Scholarship)* [3428]

Tommy Depaola Scholarship Awards *(Undergraduate/Scholarship)* [4931]

Dick Depaolis Memorial Scholarships *(Undergraduate/Scholarship)* [3196]

Depression and ADHD Fellowships *(Postdoctorate/Fellowship)* [5268]

DEPS Graduate Scholarship Program *(Graduate/Scholarship)* [3455]

Karekin DerAvedision Memorial Endowment Fund *(Undergraduate/Scholarship)* [1590]

Pat Dermargosian Memorial Scholarships *(Undergraduate/Scholarship)* [7644]

Descendant Scholarships *(Undergraduate/Scholarship)* [3326]

Libby Deschenes Prize for Applied Research *(Undergraduate/Prize)* [9581]

Development Fund for Black Students in Science and Technology Scholarships *(Undergraduate/Scholarship)* [3432]

DHCC Board Scholarships *(Graduate, Professional development, Undergraduate/Scholarship)* [3442]

Edward D. Di Loreto-Odell S. McConnell Scholarships *(Undergraduate/Scholarship)* [7179]

William Diaz Fellowships *(Professional development/Fellowship)* [6729]

Julio C. Diaz Memorial Scholarship Fund *(High School/Scholarship)* [8662]

Jean Dearth Dickerscheid Fellowships *(Graduate/Fellowship)* [7284]

Dickey Rural Networks College Scholarship Program *(Undergraduate, Vocational/Occupational/Scholarship)* [3438]

Bill Dickey Scholarship Association Scholarships *(Undergraduate/Scholarship)* [3440]

Harold Dieckmann Draper, Sr. Scholarships *(Undergraduate/Scholarship)* [1938]

Rudolph Dillman Memorial Scholarships *(Graduate, Undergraduate/Scholarship)* [750]

Carol DiMaiti Scholarship Awards *(Undergraduate/Scholarship)* [5662]

Gretchen Dimico Memorial Scholarships *(Undergraduate/Scholarship)* [5425]

Raymond DiPaglia Endowment Scholarships *(Undergraduate/Scholarship)* [3484]

Disabled War Veterans Scholarships *(Undergraduate/Scholarship)* [1559]

Walt Disney Company Foundation Scholarships *(Undergraduate/Scholarship)* [5173]

Dissertation Fellowships in East European Studies *(Doctorate/Fellowship)* [677]

Dissertation Proposal Development Fellowships *(Doctorate/Fellowship)* [8282]

Distinguished Flying Cross Society Scholarships *(Undergraduate/Scholarship)* [3461]

Distinguished Young Women Scholarships *(Undergraduate/Scholarship)* [3463]

LaRue A. Ditmore Music Scholarships *(Undergraduate/Scholarship)* [9706]

Diversified Investment Advisors Leaders in Healthcare Scholarships *(Graduate/Scholarship)* [4788]

Diversity Dissertation Scholarships *(Doctorate/Fellowship)* [1032]

Diversity Executive Leadership Program Scholarships *(Professional development/Scholarship)* [1184]

Diversity Fellowship Program (DFP) *(Undergraduate/Fellowship)* [5928]

Diversity Scholars Awards *(Graduate/Award)* [3239]

Robert A. and Barbara Divine Graduate Student Travel Grants *(Graduate/Grant)* [8338]

Dixon Hughes Goodman LLP Annual Scholarship *(Undergraduate/Scholarship)* [3465]

Daniel B. Dixon Scholarships *(Undergraduate/Scholarship)* [326]

Peggy Dixon Two-Year Scholarships *(Undergraduate/Scholarship)* [8438]

Mychajlo Dmytrenko Fine Arts Foundation Scholarships *(Undergraduate/Scholarship)* [9074]

Charles Dobbins FTA Scholarships *(Undergraduate, Vocational/Occupational/Scholarship)* [4033]

Dr. Feroz Ahmed Memorial Educational Post-Graduate Scholarships *(Doctorate, Postgraduate/Scholarship)* [8216]

Doctoral Degree Scholarships in Cancer Nursing *(Doctorate/Scholarship)* [596]

Doctoral Fellowships - Dissertation *(Doctorate/Fellowship)* [4779]

Doctoral Fellowships - Graduate *(Doctorate/Fellowship)* [4780]

Document Management and Graphic Communications Industry Scholarships *(Undergraduate/Scholarship)* [3627]

Doddridge County Promise Scholarships *(Undergraduate/Scholarship)* [7072]

F. Atlee Dodge Maintenance Scholarships *(Undergraduate/Scholarship)* [192]

Robert Winchester Dodson Scholarships *(Undergraduate/Scholarship)* [9268]

DOE Computational Science Graduate Fellowships (DOE CSGF) *(Doctorate, Graduate/Fellowship)* [5306]

Emmett J. Doerr Memorial Distinguished Scout Scholarships *(High School/Scholarship)* [6249]

Dofflemyer Scholarships *(Undergraduate/Scholarship)* [6250]

Dollar-A-Day Academic Scholarships *(Graduate, Undergraduate/Scholarship)* [3467]

Dolphin Scholarships *(Undergraduate/Scholarship)* [3469]

Scott Dominguez - Craters of the Moon Chapter Scholarships *(Graduate, Undergraduate/Scholarship)* [1336]

Don Aron Scholarships *(Undergraduate/Scholarship)* [6208]

Marian Jones Donaldson Scholarship Fund *(Undergraduate/Scholarship)* [3769]

Harvey N. Dondero Communication and Journalism Excellence Scholarships *(Undergraduate/Scholarship)* [7482]

Hon. Ralph W.E. Donges Memorial Scholarships *(Undergraduate/Award)* [2317]

Mickey Donnelly Memorial Scholarships *(Undergraduate/Scholarship)* [7483]

Jim Doogan Memorial Scholarships *(Undergraduate/Scholarship)* [9185]

Doraine Pursuit of Educational Excellence Scholarships *(Undergraduate/Scholarship)* [2944]

Joseph M. Dorgan Scholarships *(Undergraduate/Scholarship)* [3486]

Dr. Michael Dorizas Memorial Scholarships *(Under-*

graduate/Scholarship)* [4514]

Pauly D'Orlando Memorial Art Scholarships *(Graduate, Undergraduate/Scholarship)* [8996]

Dosatron International Inc. Scholarships *(Undergraduate/Scholarship)* [731]

Eric Dostie Memorial College Scholarships *(Undergraduate/Scholarship)* [6322]

Father Connie Dougherty Scholarships *(Undergraduate, Vocational/Occupational/Scholarship)* [3191]

Sergeant Douglas and Charlotte DeHorse Scholarships *(Graduate, Undergraduate/Scholarship)* [2661]

Douglass Foundation Fellowships in American Art *(Graduate/Fellowship)* [5786]

Harold K. Douthit Regional Scholarships *(Undergraduate/Scholarship)* [6857]

Dow Chemical Company Fellowships *(Graduate/Fellowship)* [6427]

Margaret Dowell-Gravatt, M.D. Scholarships *(Undergraduate/Scholarship)* [2059]

Downeast Energy Scholarships *(Undergraduate/Scholarship)* [3477]

Rodger Doxsey Travel Prizes *(Graduate, Postdoctorate/Prize)* [572]

Nettie Dracup Memorial Scholarships *(Undergraduate/Scholarship)* [643]

AAGS Joseph F. Dracup Scholarship Awards *(Undergraduate/Scholarship)* [644]

Drake University Law School Law Opportunity Scholarships - Disadvantage *(Undergraduate/Scholarship)* [3487]

Drake University Law School Law Opportunity Scholarships - Diversity *(Undergraduate/Scholarship)* [3488]

Drake University Law School Public Service Scholarships *(Undergraduate/Scholarship)* [3489]

The Drama Therapy Fund Graduate Research Grants *(Graduate/Grant)* [3518]

The Drama Therapy Fund Graduate Student Research Awards *(Graduate/Grant)* [3519]

The "Drawn to Art" Fellowships *(Doctorate/Fellowship)* [417]

Vivian Drenckhahn Student Scholarships *(Graduate, Undergraduate/Scholarship)* [8477]

Cleveland Drennon, Jr. Memorial Scholarships *(Undergraduate/Scholarship)* [9222]

Wilma Sackett Dressel Scholarships *(Undergraduate/Scholarship)* [8166]

Margaret Drew Alpha Fellowships *(Graduate/Fellowship)* [7285]

Charles Drew Scholarships *(Professional development/Scholarship)* [1754]

Louis Dreyfus Warner-Chappell City College Scholarships *(Undergraduate/Scholarship)* [1211]

DRI Law Student Diversity Scholarships *(Undergraduate/Scholarship)* [2144]

Thomas J. Drinan Memorial Fellowships *(All/Fellowship)* [7604]

Lillian Cooper Droke Memorial Scholarships *(Undergraduate/Scholarship)* [5778]

Richard Drukker Memorial Scholarships *(Undergraduate/Scholarship)* [6651]

Drum Major Institute Scholars *(Undergraduate/Scholarship)* [8144]

Sergeant Major Douglas R. Drum Memorial Scholarship Fund *(Undergraduate/Scholarship)* [936]

W.E.B. Du Bois Fellowships *(Doctorate/Fellowship)* [6355]

Martin Duberman Fellowships *(Professional development/Fellowship)* [2702]

Lee Dubin Scholarship Fund *(Undergraduate/Scholarship)* [7848]

John W. Duckett Jr., AFUD Pediatric Research Scholarships *(Undergraduate/Scholarship)* [8432]

Mark Duda Scholarship Fund *(Graduate, Undergraduate/Scholarship)* [3446]

Deborah Gandee Dudding Memorial Scholarships *(Undergraduate/Scholarship)* [7073]

Doris Duke Conservation Fellows Program *(Graduate/Fellowship)* [9615]

Edward J. Dulis Scholarships *(Undergraduate/Scholarship)* [5690]

Duluth Building and Construction Trades Council Scholarships *(Undergraduate, Vocational/Occupational/Scholarship)* [3527]

Duluth Central High School Alumni Scholarships *(Undergraduate/Scholarship)* [3528]

Dumbarton Oaks Fellowships *(Doctorate, Graduate/Fellowship)* [3549]

Dumbarton Oaks Junior Fellowships *(Graduate/Fellowship)* [3550]

Dunbar Heritage Scholarships *(Undergraduate/Scholarship)* [8599]

Duncan Aviation Scholarships *(Undergraduate/Scholarship)* [126]

Wade and Marcelene Duncan Scholarships *(Undergraduate/Scholarship)* [9635]

Ed Dunkelblau Scholarships *(All/Scholarship)* [1704]

Travis Dunning Memorial Scholarships *(Undergraduate/Scholarship)* [7484]

Bus and Mary Ellen Durant Timberline High School Endowed Scholarships *(Undergraduate/Scholarship)* [5426]

Durning Sisters Scholarships *(Graduate/Scholarship)* [3370]

Joe Durso Memorial Scholarships *(Undergraduate/Scholarship)* [5921]

Roger C. Duvoisin, MD Research Grants *(Professional development/Grant)* [982]

Sue and Ken Dyer Foundation Travel Scholarships *(Undergraduate/Scholarship)* [3941]

Dystonia Medical Research Foundation Fellowships *(Postdoctorate/Fellowship)* [3557]

Josephine P. White Eagle Graduate Fellowships *(Graduate, Master's, Doctorate/Fellowship)* [4591]

Eagles Fly for Leukemia Scholarships *(Undergraduate/Scholarship)* [2755]

EAIA Research Grants *(Professional development/Grant)* [3561]

Howard G. and Gladys A. Eakes Memorial Scholarships *(Undergraduate/Scholarship)* [4259]

EAPSI Fellowships *(Doctorate, Graduate/Fellowship)* [6467]

Amelia Earhart Fellowship Program *(Postdoctorate/Fellowship)* [9811]

Amelia Earhart Memorial Academic Scholarships *(Undergraduate/Scholarship)* [6724]

Early Career Postdoctoral Fellowships in East European Studies *(Postdoctorate/Fellowship)* [678]

Robert E. Early Memorial Scholarships *(Undergraduate/Scholarship)* [3490]

Bob East Scholarships *(Graduate, Undergraduate/Scholarship)* [6450]

East Tennessee Foundation Scholarships *(Undergraduate/Scholarship)* [9223]

Eastern Orthodox Scouting Scholarships *(High School/Scholarship)* [6251]

Eastern Shore Building Industry Association Scholarships *(Undergraduate/Scholarship)* [3055]

David Eaton Scholarships *(Graduate, Master's/Scholarship)* [8997]

The Christoph Daniel Ebeling Fellowships *(Doctorate/Fellowship)* [418]

ECA Applied Urban Communication Research Grants *(Professional development/Grant)* [3575]

ECA Centennial Scholarships *(Master's, Doctorate/Scholarship)* [3576]

John E. Echlin Memorial Scholarships *(Undergraduate/Scholarship)* [1939]

ECMS Scholarships *(Undergraduate/Scholarship)* [3578]

Economic Development Division Graduate Scholarships *(Graduate/Scholarship)* [1010]

ECT Foundation Master Scholarships *(Graduate, Master's/Scholarship)* [1763]

Edgecliff Alumni Awards *(Undergraduate/Scholarship)* [9768]

Edgecliff McAuley Art Scholarships *(Undergraduate/Scholarship)* [9769]

Edgecliff McAuley Music Scholarships *(Undergraduate/Scholarship)* [9770]

Vivian Edmonds Scholarships *(Undergraduate/Scholarship)* [9269]

S. Randolph Edmonds Young Scholars Competition *(Graduate, Undergraduate/Scholarship)* [2140]

Melanie and Todd Edmonson Memorial Scholarships *(Undergraduate/Scholarship)* [3035]

Edon Farmers Cooperative Scholarships *(Undergraduate/Scholarship)* [3592]

Education Factor Scholarships *(Graduate, Under-*

graduate/Scholarship) [5735]

Education is Power Scholarships *(Undergraduate, Vocational/Occupational/Scholarship)* [6323]

Education Resource Center Scholarships (ERC) *(Undergraduate, Vocational/Occupational/Scholarship)* [8211]

Educational Administration Scholarship Awards *(Postgraduate/Scholarship)* [545]

Educational Audiology Association Doctoral Scholarships *(Doctorate/Scholarship)* [3595]

Educational and Cultural Affairs Alumni Small Grants Program (ECA) *(Professional development/Grant)* [4980]

Educational Enrichment Awards *(Undergraduate/Scholarship)* [1510]

Educational Leadership Foundation Grants *(Undergraduate/Grant)* [2973]

Educational Portal of the Americas Graduate Scholarships *(Postgraduate/Scholarship)* [3604]

Educational Portal of the Americas Undergraduate Scholarships *(Undergraduate/Scholarship)* [3605]

Educational and Professional Achievement Scholarships *(Undergraduate, Vocational/Occupational/Scholarship)* [1933]

Edward C. Pomeroy Awards for Outstanding Contributions to Teacher Education *(Professional development/Award)* [466]

Palo Verde High School - Barbara Edwards Memorial Scholarships *(Undergraduate/Scholarship)* [7485]

Jimmy Edwards Scholarships *(Undergraduate/Scholarship)* [3107]

EERI/FEMA Graduate Fellowships *(Graduate/Scholarship)* [3563]

EFWA Moss Adams Foundation Scholarships *(Graduate, Undergraduate/Scholarship)* [3598]

John and Alice Egan Multi-Year Mentioning Scholarships *(Undergraduate/Scholarship)* [3327]

Bill Egan Scholarship Program *(Undergraduate/Scholarship)* [6935]

EHA Exploratory Travel and Data Grants *(Doctorate/Grant)* [3583]

EHA Graduate Dissertation Fellowships *(Doctorate/Fellowship)* [3584]

E.I. DuPont Fellowships *(Graduate/Fellowship)* [6428]

Mike Eidson Scholarships *(Graduate, Undergraduate/Scholarship)* [490]

Eight and Forty Lung and Respiratory Disease Nursing Scholarships *(Professional development/Scholarship)* [896]

Hillel Einhorn New Investigator Awards *(Doctorate/Award)* [8363]

Albert Einstein Distinguished Educator Fellowships *(Graduate, Professional development/Fellowship)* [8956]

Harold E. Eisenberg Foundation Scholarships *(Professional development/Scholarship)* [4906]

Farouk El-Baz Student Research Grants *(Doctorate, Graduate, Undergraduate/Grant)* [4087]

El Dorado County Mineral and Gem Society Scholarships *(Graduate, Undergraduate/Scholarship)* [3620]

George & Isabelle Elanjian Scholarships *(Undergraduate/Scholarship)* [1591]

W. Eldridge and Emily Lowe Scholarships *(Undergraduate/Scholarship)* [8219]

Electric Cooperative Pioneer Trust Fund Scholarships *(Undergraduate/Scholarship)* [3491]

Electronic Materials and Processing Division - Postdoctoral Award *(Postdoctorate/Award)* [1981]

Herman E. Elgar Memorial Scholarships *(Undergraduate/Scholarship)* [3492]

Elks National Foundation Scholarships *(Undergraduate/Scholarship)* [3629]

Dr. Robert Elliott Memorial Scholarships *(Undergraduate/Scholarship)* [5708]

Pauline Elliott Scholarships *(Undergraduate/Scholarship)* [5709]

Robert A. Ellis Scholarships in Physics *(Undergraduate/Scholarship)* [6488]

William P. Elrod Memorial Scholarships *(Undergraduate, Vocational/Occupational/Scholarship)* [8815]

Emerald Empire Chapter Scholarship Awards *(Undergraduate/Scholarship)* [6936]

Emergency Medicine Physician Scholarships for Health Information Management Program *(Undergraduate/Scholarship)* [8664]

Emergency Nurses Association Undergraduate Scholarships *(Undergraduate/Scholarship)* [3634]

Emerging Teacher-Leaders in Elementary School Mathematics Grants for Grades K-5 Teachers *(Professional development/Grant)* [6221]

EMLF Law Student Scholarships *(Undergraduate/Scholarship)* [3643]

Emmanuel Bible College Scholarships *(Undergraduate/Scholarship)* [1592]

Thomas O. Enders Graduate Fellowships *(Graduate/Fellowship)* [1732]

Alice Yuriko Endo Memorial Scholarships *(Undergraduate/Scholarship)* [5141]

Endodontic Educator Fellowship Awards *(Graduate/Fellowship)* [471]

Endodontic Research Grants *(Graduate/Grant)* [472]

Endourological Society Fellowships *(Professional development/Fellowship)* [3641]

Endowment Fund for Education Grants (EFFE) *(Undergraduate/Grant)* [2093]

Endowment Fund for Education, Loans/Grants for Educational Materials *(Undergraduate/Grant)* [2095]

Endowment Fund for Education, Loans/Grants for Equipment *(Undergraduate/Grant)* [2096]

Endowment Fund for Education, Loans *(Undergraduate/Loan)* [2094]

The Eneslow Pedorthic Institute Scholarships *(Undergraduate/Scholarship)* [7139]

Vice Admiral Donald D. Engen Scholarships *(Undergraduate/Scholarship)* [6577]

Engineering Diversity Affairs Scholarships *(All/Scholarship)* [9353]

Engineers for Tomorrow Scholarship Program *(Undergraduate/Scholarship)* [5915]

Don English Memorial Scholarships *(Undergraduate/Scholarship)* [7486]

Harold E. Ennes Scholarships *(Graduate, Professional development/Scholarship)* [8303]

Irene Winifred Eno Grants *(All/Grant)* [1277]

Enterprise Rent-A-Car Scholarships *(Graduate, Undergraduate/Scholarship)* [7265]

Lindsay M. Entz Memorial Scholarships *(Undergraduate/Scholarship)* [3770]

Environment, Natural Resource and Energy Division Fellowships (ENRE) *(Graduate/Fellowship)* [1011]

Environmental Research and Education Foundation Scholarships *(Doctorate, Postdoctorate/Scholarship)* [3658]

Epicurean Charitable Foundation Scholarships *(Undergraduate/Scholarship)* [7487]

Epilepsy Foundation Post-doctoral Research Fellowships *(Postdoctorate, Professional development/Fellowship)* [3662]

Epilepsy Foundation Pre-doctoral Research Training Fellowships *(Graduate/Grant)* [3663]

Epilepsy Foundation Research Grants *(All/Grant)* [3664]

Epilepsy Foundation Research and Training Fellowships for Clinicians *(Doctorate, Professional development/Grant)* [3665]

Epsilon Epsilon Scholarships *(Undergraduate/Scholarship)* [8167]

Epsilon Tau Pi's Soaring Eagle Scholarships *(Undergraduate/Scholarship)* [6252]

Epsilon Tau Scholarships *(Undergraduate/Scholarship)* [8168]

Dena Epstein Awards for Archival and Library Research in American Music *(All/Grant)* [5956]

Alan R. Epstein "Reach for the Stars" Scholarships *(Undergraduate/Scholarship)* [3317]

Lee Epstein Scholarship Fund *(Graduate, Undergraduate/Scholarship)* [3447]

Equal Access to Justice Scholarships *(Undergraduate/Scholarship)* [6134]

Equal Justice Works Fellowship Program *(Graduate, Undergraduate/Fellowship)* [3675]

eQuality Scholarships *(Undergraduate/Scholarship)* [7849]

Robert C. Erb Sr. Scholarships *(Undergraduate/Scholarship)* [5710]

ERCA Community Contribution Scholarships *(Un-*

graduate/Scholarship) [7489]

Dave Florence Scholarship Fund (Undergraduate/Scholarship) [3448]

Florida Atlantic Planning Society Graduate Fellowships for Academic Excellence (Postgraduate/Fellowship) [3819]

Florida Automotive Industry Scholarships (Undergraduate/Scholarship) [1966]

Florida Education Fund McKnight Doctoral Fellowships (Graduate/Fellowship) [3822]

Florida Fertilizer and Agrichemical Association Scholarships (Graduate, Undergraduate/Scholarship) [3834]

Florida Nurses Foundation Scholarships (All/Scholarship) [3840]

Florida Outdoor Writers Association Scholarships (Undergraduate/Scholarship) [3842]

Florida Public Health Association Public Health Graduate Scholarships (Graduate/Scholarship) [3846]

Florida Public Health Association Public Health Undergraduate Scholarships (Undergraduate/Scholarship) [3847]

John Flynn Memorial Scholarships (Undergraduate/Scholarship) [3150]

Paul B. & Aline Flynn Scholarships (Undergraduate/Scholarship) [8601]

FMA-FEEA Scholarship Program (Undergraduate/Scholarship) [3729]

Frank Fong Scholarships (Undergraduate/Scholarship) [8290]

For the Love of Chocolate Foundation Scholarships (Graduate, Professional development, Undergraduate/Scholarship) [3857]

Henry Ford Academy Scholarships (Undergraduate/Scholarship) [8384]

Ford Foundation Dissertation Fellowships (Doctorate/Fellowship) [5999]

Ford Foundation Diversity Fellowships (Doctorate/Fellowship) [6000]

Ford Foundation Postdoctoral Fellowships (Postdoctorate/Fellowship) [6001]

Ford Foundation Predoctoral Fellowships (Postgraduate/Fellowship) [6002]

Ford Motor Company Scholarship Program (Undergraduate/Scholarship) [4568]

Anne Ford Scholarships (Undergraduate/Scholarship) [6186]

Foreign, Comparative & International Law - Schaffer Grants for Foreign Law Librarians (Professional development/Grant) [499]

George Foreman Tribute to Lyndon B. Johnson Scholarships (Undergraduate/Scholarship) [7577]

Nancy B. Forest and L. Michael Honaker Master's Scholarships for Research (Doctorate, Graduate/Scholarship) [1033]

Leland Stanford Forrest Scholarships (Undergraduate/Scholarship) [3494]

Genevieve Forthun Scholarships (Undergraduate/Scholarship) [7286]

Barbara Palo Foster Memorial Scholarships (Graduate, Undergraduate/Scholarship) [2756]

Andrew Foster Scholarships (Undergraduate/Scholarship) [6146]

Dr. Nancy Foster Scholarships (Doctorate, Graduate/Scholarship) [3873]

Foundation of American Institute for Conservation Lecture Grants (Professional development/Grant) [852]

Foundation for the Carolinas Rotary Scholarship Fund (Undergraduate/Scholarship) [3904]

Foundation of the Federal Bar Association Public Service Scholarships (Undergraduate/Scholarship) [3966]

The Foundation of the National Student Nurses' Association Scholarships (Graduate, Undergraduate/Scholarship) [6536]

Foundation for Neonatal Research and Education Scholarships (Doctorate, Graduate, Postgraduate, Undergraduate/Scholarship) [3981]

Foundation for the Preservation of Honey Bees Graduate Scholarships (Graduate/Scholarship) [3990]

Foundation Scholarships (Undergraduate/Scholarship) [5231]

Foundation for Surgical Technology Advanced Education/Medical Mission Scholarships (Graduate/Scholarship) [1881]

Foundation for Surgical Technology Scholarships (Graduate/Scholarship) [1882]

Founders Circle Professional Scholarships (Professional development/Scholarship) [4839]

Founding Fathers Leadership Scholarships (Undergraduate/Scholarship) [9676]

Captain Ernest Fox Perpetual Scholarships (Undergraduate/Scholarship) [2926]

FPA Aviation Scholarships (Graduate, Undergraduate/Scholarship) [3851]

Paris Fracasso Production Floriculture Scholarships (Undergraduate/Scholarship) [732]

William A. Fraker Student Heritage Awards (Graduate, Undergraduate/Award) [1195]

Franchise Law Diversity Scholarship Awards (Undergraduate/Scholarship) [4940]

Joe Francis Haircare Scholarships (Undergraduate/Scholarship) [3996]

Aracelis Francis Minority Scholarships in Gerontology (Master's/Scholarship) [1787]

Parker B. Francis Respiratory Research Grants (Professional development/Grant) [1155]

Joey and Florence Franco Legacy Scholarships (Undergraduate/Scholarship) [2245]

Joe Francomano Scholarships (Undergraduate/Scholarship) [5174]

Mayme and Herb Frank Scholarship Program (Graduate, Undergraduate/Scholarship) [1638]

Michael W. and Jean D. Franke Family Foundation Scholarships (Graduate, Undergraduate/Scholarship) [1127]

Loren Frankel Memorial Scholarships (Undergraduate, Graduate/Scholarship) [926]

Mary Weiking Franken Scholarships (Undergraduate/Scholarship) [7287]

The Ginny Frankenthaler Memorial Scholarships (Undergraduate/Scholarship) [8567]

John Hope Franklin Dissertation Fellowships (Doctorate/Fellowship) [990]

Franklin Elementary School PTA Scholarships (Undergraduate/Scholarship) [7647]

Denise Franklin Journalism Scholarships (Undergraduate/Scholarship) [9637]

John Hope Franklin Prize (Professional development/Prize) [5366]

Franklin Research Grants (Postgraduate/Grant) [991]

Violet and Cyril Franks Scholarships (Graduate/Scholarship) [1039]

Joseph Frasca Excellence in Aviation Scholarships (Undergraduate/Scholarship) [9191]

Fraser Family Scholarships (Undergraduate/Scholarship) [7490]

Fraser Stryker Diversity Scholarships (Undergraduate/Scholarship) [3998]

Carlyle Fraser/Wilton Looney Scholarships (Undergraduate/Scholarship) [1940]

FRAXA Postdoctoral Fellowships (Postdoctorate/Fellowship) [4000]

Fredrikson and Byron Foundation Minority Scholarships (Undergraduate/Scholarship) [4002]

Emanuel R. Freedman Scholarships (Graduate, Undergraduate/Scholarship) [7012]

Freedom Alliance Scholarships (Undergraduate/Scholarship) [4004]

Belknap Freeman Carnegie Mellon Scholarships (Undergraduate/Scholarship) [1128]

Kevin Freeman Travel Grants (Graduate, Professional development/Grant) [5957]

Freepali Scholarships (Graduate, Undergraduate/Scholarship) [4008]

Malcolm and Mildred Freidberg Fellowships (Graduate, Doctorate/Fellowship) [5670]

The French Culinary Institute Classic Pastry Arts Scholarships (Professional development, Undergraduate/Scholarship) [3306]

The French Culinary Institute Culinary Arts Scholarships (All, Professional development/Scholarship) [3307]

Ruth M. French Graduate or Undergraduate Scholarships (Doctorate, Graduate, Undergraduate/Scholarship) [1198]

Ludo Frevel Crystallography Scholarships (Graduate/Scholarship) [4896]

Doris W. Frey Memorial Scholarships (Undergraduate/Scholarship) [8603]

Carleton A. Friday Memorial Scholarships (Undergraduate/Scholarship) [5867]

Dale E. Fridell Memorial Scholarships (Undergraduate, Vocational/Occupational/Scholarship) [8750]

Fried, Frank, Harris, Shriver and Jacobson Fellowships (Graduate/Fellowship) [4010]

Marc Friedlaender Fellowships (Graduate, Doctorate/Fellowship) [5671]

A.E. Robert Friedman Scholarships (Undergraduate/Scholarship) [7035]

Phil Friel Scholarships (Undergraduate/Scholarship) [5711]

Kennedy T. Friend Scholarships (Graduate, Undergraduate/Scholarship) [327]

Friends of Mary Automotive Scholarships (Undergraduate/Scholarship) [8115]

Friends of Megan Bolton Memorial Fund (Undergraduate/Scholarship) [3944]

Froberg-Suess JD/MBA Scholarships (Undergraduate/Scholarship) [7182]

Dean A. Froehlich Endowed Scholarships (Undergraduate/Scholarship) [5428]

Fruits and Vegetable Industries Scholarships (Undergraduate/Scholarship) [5831]

Marian Johnson Frutiger Scholarships (Undergraduate/Scholarship) [8169]

William and Francis Fry Honorary Fellowships for Contributions to Therapeutic Ultrasound (Professional development/Fellowship) [5003]

FTE Congregational Fellowships (Graduate/Fellowship) [4019]

FTE Dissertation Fellowships (Graduate/Fellowship) [4020]

FTE Doctoral Fellowships (Doctorate, Graduate/Fellowship) [4021]

FTE Ministry Fellowships (Graduate/Fellowship) [4022]

FTE North American Doctoral Fellowships (Doctorate, Graduate/Fellowship) [4023]

FTE Undergraduate Fellowships (Undergraduate/Fellowship) [4024]

FTE Volunteers Exploring Vocation Fellowships (Graduate/Fellowship) [4025]

Gerard Swartz Fudge Memorial Scholarships (Undergraduate/Scholarship) [4653]

Keiko Fukuda Scholarships (Undergraduate/Scholarship) [9056]

Kathryn Fuller Science for Nature Post-Doctoral Fellowships (Graduate, Postdoctorate/Fellowship) [9759]

Don and Eileen Fulton Nursing Scholarships (Undergraduate/Scholarship) [8722]

Daniel G. and Helen I. Fultz Scholarship Fund (Undergraduate/Scholarship) [3772]

Arkansas Nursing Foundation - Dorothea Fund Scholarships (Professional development/Scholarship) [1543]

Donald M. Furbush Professional Development Grants (Professional development/Grant) [4819]

Furman-Tikvah Scholarships (Graduate/Scholarship) [8903]

The Future Colleagues Scholarships (Undergraduate/Scholarship) [6293]

Future Leaders of Manufacturing Scholarships (Graduate, Undergraduate/Scholarship) [8385]

Mearl K. Gable II Memorial Grants (Professional development/Grant) [4387]

Gaddy Student Scholarships (Undergraduate/Scholarship) [9638]

Gadsden State/McClellan Campus Nursing Scholarship Awards (Undergraduate/Scholarship) [3036]

Gaebe Eagle Scout Awards (Undergraduate/Scholarship) [6253]

Farley Moody Galbraith Scholarship Fund (Undergraduate/Scholarship) [3037]

Thomas W. Gallagher Scholarships Fund (Undergraduate/Scholarship) [8667]

Louise Bales Gallagher Scholarships (Undergraduate/Scholarship) [3372]

Whitney Laine Gallahar Memorial Scholarship Fund (Undergraduate/Scholarship) [3038]

Sam Gallant Memorial Scholarships (Graduate, Undergraduate/Scholarship) [1530]

The Gallery Collection's Greeting Card Scholarships

(Undergraduate/Scholarship) [4035]

Gamewarden Scholarship program (High School, Undergraduate, Vocational/Occupational/Scholarship) [4037]

Gamma Iota Scholarships - Gamma Tau (Undergraduate/Scholarship) [8170]

Gamma Iota Scholarships - Kappa Eta (Undergraduate/Scholarship) [8171]

Gamma Iota Scholarships - Zeta Kappa (Undergraduate/Scholarship) [8172]

Gamma Iota Scholarships - Zeta Nu (Undergraduate/Scholarship) [8173]

Gamma Sigma Alpha Graduate Scholarships (Graduate/Scholarship) [4039]

Veronica Gantt Memorial Scholarships (Undergraduate/Scholarship) [7491]

GAPA Scholarships (Undergraduate/Scholarship) [4048]

Joel Garcia Memorial Scholarships (Undergraduate/Scholarship) [2237]

Michael and Gina Garcia Rail Engineering Scholarships (Undergraduate/Scholarship) [1129]

William R. Gard Memorial Scholarships (Undergraduate/Scholarship) [6091]

Garden Club of America Awards in Tropical Botany (GCA) (Doctorate/Award) [4041]

Garden Club Council of Winston-Salem and Forsyth County Council (Undergraduate/Scholarship) [9639]

Garden State Rotary Club of Cherry Hill Scholarships (Undergraduate/Scholarship) [2335]

Jewels Gardiner Scholarships (Undergraduate/Scholarship) [2270]

John Gardner Fellowships (Undergraduate/Fellowship) [9195]

Gardner Foundation Infusion Nurses Society Education Scholarships (All/Scholarship) [4765]

Robert Gardner Memorial Fellowships (Graduate/Fellowship) [4489]

Dwight D. Gardner Scholarships (Undergraduate/Scholarship) [4801]

Victoria M. Gardner Scholarships (Undergraduate/Scholarship) [9272]

Eugene Garfield Doctoral Dissertation Fellowships (Doctorate, Graduate/Fellowship) [2070]

Peter M. Gargano Scholarship Fund (Undergraduate/Scholarship) [3529]

Garikian Scholarship Fund (Undergraduate/Scholarship) [1593]

Garmin Scholarships (Undergraduate/Scholarship) [128]

Gerald Garner Memorial Scholarships (Undergraduate/Scholarship) [7183]

Gail Garner R.I.S.E. Memorial Scholarships (Undergraduate/Scholarship) [7648]

Eileen J. Garrett Scholarships (Undergraduate/Scholarship) [7052]

Kays Gary Scholarships (Undergraduate/Scholarship) [9273]

Edwin W. Gaston Scholarships (Undergraduate/Scholarship) [343]

Gates Cambridge Scholarships (Doctorate, Postgraduate/Scholarship) [6072]

The Gates Millennium Scholars (Undergraduate/Scholarship) [4569]

William H. Gates Public Service Law Scholarships (Undergraduate/Scholarship) [4046]

Stephen Gates Scholarships (Undergraduate/Scholarship) [9274]

Raffin Gathercole Scholarships (Undergraduate/Scholarship) [4051]

A.R.F.O.R.A. Martha Gavrila Scholarships for Women (Postgraduate/Scholarship) [1164]

GAWP Graduate Scholarships (Graduate/Fellowship) [4099]

Gay, Lesbian, Bisexual, Transgender Alumni Council Scholarships (Undergraduate/Scholarship) [9356]

Lowell Gaylor Memorial Scholarships (Undergraduate/Scholarship) [129]

Florence S. Gaynor Scholarships (Doctorate, Graduate, Undergraduate/Scholarship) [6081]

GCSAA Scholars Competition (Undergraduate/Scholarship) [4187]

GCSAA Student Essay Contest (Graduate, Undergraduate/Prize) [4188]

GE Healthcare Management Scholarship Program

(Graduate/Scholarship) [1323]

GED Jump Start Scholarships (Undergraduate/Scholarship) [8029]

GEF Scholarship Program (Undergraduate, Graduate/Scholarship) [4319]

Lawrence Gelfand - Armin Rappaport Fellowships (Doctorate, Graduate/Fellowship, Grant) [8339]

Irma Gelhausen Scholarship Fund (Undergraduate/Scholarship) [5349]

Elaine Gelman Scholarship Awards (Undergraduate/Scholarship) [6106]

The Gene and John Athletic Scholarships (Undergraduate/Scholarship) [8746]

General Falcon Scholarships (Undergraduate/Scholarship) [7372]

General Mills Foundation Scholarships (Undergraduate/Scholarship) [808]

Geological Society of America Graduate Student Research Grants (Doctorate, Graduate/Grant) [4088]

Georgia Engineering Foundation Scholarships (Graduate/Scholarship) [4102]

Gerber Fellowships in Pediatric Nutrition (Undergraduate/Fellowship) [6091]

Doris Y. and John J. Gerber Scholarships (Undergraduate/Scholarship) [9524]

Daniel Gerber, Sr. Medallion Scholarships (Undergraduate/Scholarship) [4113]

Walter Gerboth Awards (Professional development/Grant) [5958]

German Historical Institute Doctoral and Postdoctoral Fellowships (Doctorate, Postgraduate/Fellowship) [4126]

German Historical Institute Fellowships at the Horner Library (Doctorate/Fellowship) [4127]

German Studies Research Grants (Undergraduate/Grant) [4119]

Eloise Gerry Fellowships (Graduate, Postdoctorate/Fellowship) [8151]

Getty GRI-NEH Postdoctoral Fellowships (Postdoctorate/Fellowship) [4140]

Getty Postdoctoral Fellowships (Postdoctorate/Fellowship) [4141]

Getty Predoctoral Fellowships (Doctorate/Fellowship) [4142]

Getty Scholar Grants (Professional development/Grant) [4143]

GFLC-A&WMA Scholarships (Graduate, Undergraduate/Scholarship) [109]

Mary Ghezzi Nursing Scholarships (Undergraduate/Scholarship) [8983]

GIA Endowment Scholarships - Distance Education (Graduate/Scholarship) [4056]

GIA Endowment Scholarships - On Campus (Graduate/Scholarship) [4057]

IDSA Gianninoto Graduate Scholarships (Graduate/Scholarship) [4758]

John J. Gibbons Fellowships in Public Interest and Constitutional Law (All/Fellowship) [4149]

Joy Gibson Scholarships (Undergraduate/Scholarship) [9275]

L.C. Gifford Distinguished Journalism Scholarships (Undergraduate/Scholarship) [9276]

Dr. Virginia Gilbert Memorial Scholarships (Undergraduate/Scholarship) [7492]

Margaret S. Gilbert Scholarship Fund (Undergraduate/Scholarship) [8669]

Gilbreth Memorial Fellowships (Graduate/Scholarship) [4802]

Gilder Lehrman Short-Term Fellowships (Graduate, Postdoctorate/Fellowship) [4151]

Terry M. Giles Honor Scholarships (Undergraduate/Scholarship) [7184]

Harold Giles Scholarships (Graduate, Undergraduate/Scholarship) [8448]

William Harrison Gill Education Fund (Undergraduate/Scholarship) [2061]

R.L. Gillette Scholarships (Undergraduate/Scholarship) [751]

Gilliam Fellowships for Advanced Study (Doctorate/Fellowship) [4621]

Benjamin A. Gilman International Scholarships (Undergraduate/Scholarship) [9096]

Ethel Z. Gilman Scholarships (Professional development/Scholarship) [8804]

Leo Gilmartin Scholarships (High School/Scholarship) [7352]

Susan Kay Munson Gilmore Memorial Scholarships (Undergraduate, Vocational/Occupational/Scholarship) [3151]

Jack R. Gilstrap Scholarships (Graduate, Undergraduate/Scholarship) [1053]

Lawrence Ginocchio Aviation Scholarships (Undergraduate/Scholarship) [6168]

Nick Giorgione Hope for Hearts Scholarships (Undergraduate/Scholarship) [7493]

Alex Gissler Memorial Scholarships (Undergraduate/Scholarship) [5712]

Jane R. Glaser Scholarships (Undergraduate/Scholarship) [1405]

John Glaser Scholarships (Undergraduate/Scholarship) [2971]

Elizabeth Glaser Scientist Awards (Professional development/Award) [4157]

Ann and Brad Glassco Scholarships (Undergraduate/Scholarship) [7649]

GLATA Living Memorial Doctorate Scholarships (Doctorate, Graduate/Fellowship) [4325]

GLATA Living Memorial Undergraduate/Graduate Scholarships (Graduate, Undergraduate/Fellowship, Scholarship) [4326]

Gleaner Life Insurance Scholarship Foundation (Undergraduate/Scholarship) [4159]

Glendale Latino Association Scholarships (High School, Undergraduate/Scholarship) [4161]

Global Volcanism Program for Visiting Scientist/Postdoctoral Fellowships (Postdoctorate/Fellowship) [8261]

Globe-Trotters Chapter Scholarships (Undergraduate/Scholarship) [1805]

Northeastern Ohio Chapter Scholarships - Alfred B. Glossbrenner and John Klusch Scholarships (Undergraduate/Scholarship) [1806]

Bud Glover Memorial Scholarships (Undergraduate/Scholarship) [130]

GLP Program Scholarships (Professional development/Scholarship) [4166]

Irene Carlson Gnaedinger Memorial Scholarships (Undergraduate/Scholarship) [5429]

Dr. Robert H. Goddard Memorial Scholarships (Graduate, Undergraduate/Scholarship) [6523]

Glenn Godfrey Memorial Scholarships (Graduate, Undergraduate, Vocational/Occupational/Scholarship) [5283]

Max Godwin Endowed Scholarships (Undergraduate/Scholarship) [8880]

John Goerlich Memorial Scholarships (Undergraduate/Scholarship) [1941]

Gogos Scholarships (Undergraduate/Scholarship) [2980]

Gold Key Scholarships (Undergraduate/Scholarship) [5232]

William Goldberg Diamond Corp. Scholarships (Undergraduate/Scholarship) [4058]

Daniel B. Goldberg Scholarships (Graduate/Scholarship) [4197]

Golden Key Graduate Scholar Awards (Postgraduate, Professional development/Fellowship) [6073]

Golden Key International Honour Society Study Abroad Scholarships (Undergraduate/Scholarship) [4176]

Golden Key Math Scholarships (Undergraduate/Scholarship) [4177]

William R. Goldfarb Memorial Scholarships (Undergraduate/Scholarship) [1085]

Dr. Guido Goldman Fellowships (Doctorate, Postdoctorate/Fellowship) [666]

Alois and Marie Goldmann Scholarship Fund (Undergraduate/Scholarship) [4669]

American Radio Relay League Scholarships Honoring Barry Goldwater, K7UGA (Undergraduate/Scholarship) [1086]

Barry M. Goldwater Scholarships (Undergraduate/Scholarship) [9357]

Joshua Gomes Memorial Scholarship Fund (Graduate, Undergraduate/Scholarship) [6324]

Gongaware Scholarships (Undergraduate/Scholarship) [4743]

Millie Gonzalez Memorial Scholarships (Undergraduate, Vocational/Occupational/Scholarship) [6325]

Kenneth M. Good Graduate Students Fellowship Program *(Undergraduate/Fellowship)* [9396]

Goodman & Company Scholarships *(Undergraduate/Scholarship)* [9463]

Victor and Ruth N. Goodman Memorial Scholarships *(Graduate/Scholarship)* [4373]

David B. Goodstein Point Scholarships *(Graduate, Undergraduate/Scholarship)* [7360]

Google-American Indian Science and Engineering Society Scholarships *(Graduate, Undergraduate/Scholarship)* [4194]

Google Hispanic College Fund Scholarships *(Graduate, Undergraduate/Scholarship)* [4195]

Richard Goolsby Scholarship Fund *(Graduate, Undergraduate/Scholarship)* [3905]

Richard C. Gorecki Scholarships *(Undergraduate/Scholarship)* [7373]

TCDA Bill Gorham Student Scholarships *(Graduate, Undergraduate/Scholarship)* [8848]

Nettie and Jesse Gorov Scholarships *(Undergraduate/Scholarship)* [3152]

Consuelo W. Gosnell Memorial Scholarships *(Graduate/Fellowship)* [6122]

Louis Gottschalk Prize *(Professional development/Prize)* [1228]

Carl W. Gottschalk Research Scholar Grants *(Doctorate/Grant)* [1312]

Norma Gotwalt Scholarship Fund *(Undergraduate/Scholarship)* [3945]

Government Documents Special Interest Section - Veronica Maclay Student Grants *(Master's/Grant)* [509]

Wilford Hayes Gowen Scholarships *(Undergraduate/Scholarship)* [9226]

ACI W.R. Grace Scholarships *(Graduate/Scholarship)* [634]

Graduate Fellowship Program - Mahboob Khan/Advanced Micro Devices Fellowships (GFP) *(Doctorate, Graduate/Fellowship)* [8079]

Graduate Fellowship Program - Research Fellowships (GFP) *(Doctorate, Graduate/Fellowship)* [8080]

Graduate Fellowships in Alternatives in Scientific Research *(Doctorate, Graduate/Fellowship)* [4937]

Graduate Research Fellowships *(Doctorate/Fellowship)* [2694]

Graduate Scholarships in Cancer Nursing Practice *(Master's, Doctorate/Scholarship)* [597]

Graduate Student Travel Grants *(Graduate, Professional development/Grant)* [8314]

Graham & Dunn 1L Diversity Fellowships *(Graduate/Fellowship)* [4203]

Rachel Graham Memorial Scholarships *(Undergraduate/Scholarship)* [7650]

Jim Graham Scholarships *(Undergraduate/Scholarship)* [6781]

Grand Canyon Historical Society Scholarships *(Graduate/Scholarship)* [4205]

Charles Hall Grandgent Awards *(Graduate/Award)* [3342]

AMA/Charles H. Grant Scholarships *(Undergraduate/Scholarship)* [29]

Nicholas J. Grant Scholarships *(Undergraduate/Scholarship)* [5691]

Grass Fellowships *(Doctorate, Postdoctorate/Fellowship)* [4315]

Lucile Cheever Graubart/Lambda Scholarships *(Undergraduate/Scholarship)* [8174]

Thomas B. Grave and Elizabeth F. Grave Scholarships *(Undergraduate/Scholarship)* [5615]

Caswell Grave Scholarships *(Undergraduate/Scholarship)* [5616]

Gravure Publishing Council Scholarships *(Undergraduate, Graduate/Scholarship)* [4320]

Alexander G. Gray, Jr. Scholarships *(Graduate/Scholarship)* [5682]

Arkansas Nursing Foundation - Mary Gray Scholarships *(Professional development/Scholarship)* [1544]

Great Falls Broadcasters Association Scholarships *(Undergraduate/Scholarship)* [5922]

Great Lakes Commission Sea Grant Fellowships *(Graduate/Scholarship)* [4328]

GREAT MINDS Collegiate Scholarship Program *(Undergraduate/Scholarship)* [340]

Great Minds in STEM Scholarships *(Graduate, Undergraduate/Scholarship)* [4331]

Greater Research Opportunities Undergraduate Fellowships (GRO) *(Undergraduate/Fellowship)* [9041]

Frank L. Greathouse Government Accounting Scholarships *(Graduate, Undergraduate/Scholarship)* [4198]

Bishop Charles P. Greco Graduate Fellowships *(Graduate/Fellowship)* [5277]

Greek Orthodox Archdiocese of America Paleologos Graduate Scholarships *(Graduate/Scholarship)* [4345]

Green Hill Yacht and Country Club Scholarships *(Undergraduate, Vocational/Occupational/Scholarship)* [3058]

James H. and Shirley L. Green Scholarship Fund *(Undergraduate/Scholarship)* [8670]

William G. and Mayme J. Green Scholarships *(Undergraduate/Scholarship)* [4434]

K2TEO Martin J. Green, Sr. Memorial Scholarships *(Undergraduate/Scholarship)* [1088]

Helen R. Greenamyer Memorial Scholarships *(Undergraduate/Scholarship)* [8723]

Robert D. Greenberg Scholarships *(Graduate, Professional development/Scholarship)* [8304]

Michael Greenberg Student Writing Competition *(Graduate/Prize, Scholarship)* [6394]

Curt Greene Memorial Scholarships *(Undergraduate/Scholarship)* [4399]

Elizabeth Greenhalgh Memorial Scholarships in Journalism, Graphic Arts, or Photography *(Graduate, Undergraduate/Scholarship)* [9699]

Greenlining Institute Fellowships *(Graduate/Fellowship)* [4349]

Guy P. Greenwald Jr. Endowed Scholarships *(Undergraduate/Scholarship)* [7185]

Frances Harris Gresham Scholarships *(Undergraduate/Scholarship)* [8606]

Lily H. Gridley Memorial Scholarships *(Undergraduate/Scholarship)* [9707]

Griffin Foundation Scholarships *(Undergraduate/Scholarship)* [4353]

Velma Shotwell Griffin Memorial Scholarship Fund *(Undergraduate/Scholarship)* [8671]

Homajean Grisham Memorial Scholarships *(Undergraduate/Scholarship)* [6814]

Enid Hall Griswold Memorial Scholarships *(Undergraduate/Scholarship)* [6499]

Andrew Gronholdt Arts Scholarship Awards *(Undergraduate, Vocational/Occupational, Graduate, Master's/Scholarship)* [288]

Charles Grossman Graduate Scholarships *(Graduate/Scholarship)* [4908]

F.C. Grote Fund Scholarships *(Graduate, Undergraduate/Scholarship)* [328]

Grow Your Own Your Library Institutional Scholarships *(Graduate, Professional development/Scholarship)* [7537]

Katherin F. Gruber Scholarship Program *(All/Scholarship)* [2151]

Elizabeth M. Gruber Scholarships *(Graduate/Scholarship)* [3410]

Jack & Mary Lou Gruber Scholarships *(Undergraduate/Scholarship)* [5430]

Harry Frank Guggenheim Fellowships *(Doctorate/Fellowship)* [4357]

Guggenheim Fellowships *(Doctorate/Fellowship)* [8251]

Harry Frank Guggenheim Foundation Research Grants *(All/Grant)* [4358]

John Simon Guggenheim Memorial Fellowships - U.S. and Canadian Competition *(Advanced Professional/Fellowship)* [4360]

Community Bank - Lee Guggisberg Foundation Memorial Scholarships *(Undergraduate/Scholarship)* [7651]

Bobette Bibo Gugliotta Memorial Scholarships for Creative Writing *(Undergraduate/Scholarship)* [8202]

Guide Dogs for the Blind Dorothea and Roland Bohde Leadership Scholarships *(Postgraduate/Scholarship)* [6275]

Jimmy Guild Memorial Scholarships *(Undergraduate/Scholarship)* [5431]

GuildScholar Awards *(Undergraduate/Scholarship)* [5159]

Guin-Stanford Scholarships *(Professional development/Scholarship)* [3039]

Calouste Gulbenkian Foundation Scholarships *(Graduate, Undergraduate/Scholarship)* [1595]

Gulf Coast Past President's Scholarships *(Undergraduate/Scholarship)* [1338]

Larry Gulley Scholarships *(Undergraduate/Scholarship)* [8328]

Harold Gulliksen Psychometric Research Fellowships *(Doctorate, Graduate/Fellowship)* [3610]

Warren and Rosalie Gummow Endowed Scholarships *(Undergraduate/Scholarship)* [7186]

Connie and Robert T. Gunter Scholarships *(Undergraduate/Scholarship)* [8386]

Patricia S. Gustafson '56 Memorial Scholarships *(Undergraduate/Scholarship)* [3530]

Woody Guthrie Fellowships *(All/Fellowship)* [2158]

Guynn Family Foundation Scholarships *(Undergraduate/Scholarship)* [6042]

Guzkowski Family Scholarships *(Undergraduate/Scholarship)* [7652]

GWSCPA Scholarships *(Undergraduate/Scholarship)* [4343]

Wesley R. Habley NACADA Summer Institute Scholarships *(Professional development/Scholarship)* [5996]

Louise Wallace Hackney Fellowships for the Study of Chinese Art *(Doctorate, Postdoctorate/Fellowship)* [964]

HACU/Wal-Mart Achievers Scholarships *(Undergraduate/Scholarship)* [4547]

Jaye Haddad Memorial Fund *(Undergraduate/Scholarship)* [7851]

Perry F. Hadlock Memorial Scholarships *(Undergraduate/Scholarship)* [1089]

Joseph E. Hagan Memorial Scholarships *(Undergraduate/Scholarship)* [4030]

Charles V. Hagler Scholarships *(Undergraduate/Scholarship)* [1942]

Sophia Hagopian Memorial Fund *(Undergraduate/Scholarship)* [1596]

The Richard D. Hailey AAJ Law Student Scholarships *(Undergraduate/Scholarship)* [491]

Lee Hakel Graduate Student Scholarships *(Doctorate/Scholarship)* [8354]

Marion H. Halfacre Scholarships *(Graduate/Scholarship)* [4059]

Hall of Achievement Scholarships *(Undergraduate/Scholarship)* [2246]

Stephen K. Hall ACWA Water Law and Policy Scholarships *(Graduate/Scholarship)* [1728]

Joyce C. Hall College Scholarships *(Undergraduate/Scholarship)* [7165]

Hall County Medical Society Scholarships *(Graduate/Scholarship)* [4260]

Anna E. Hall Memorial Scholarships *(Undergraduate/Scholarship)* [7251]

Chappie Hall Scholarship Program *(Graduate, Postgraduate, Undergraduate/Scholarship)* [2]

David J. Hallissey Memorial Scholarships *(Graduate, Undergraduate/Scholarship)* [1366]

Alice Hamilton Prize *(Professional development/Prize)* [1247]

TIAA-CREF Ruth Simms Hamilton Research Fellowships *(Graduate/Fellowship)* [8811]

Richard A. Hammill Scholarship Fund *(Undergraduate/Scholarship)* [918]

Jay Hammond Memorial Scholarships *(Undergraduate/Scholarship)* [9187]

Harold F. Hammond Scholarships *(Graduate/Scholarship)* [4822]

Tommie J. Hamner Scholarships *(Undergraduate/Scholarship)* [7288]

Adam Hampton Memorial Scholarship Fund *(Undergraduate/Scholarship)* [3773]

Morris Hanauer Scholarships *(Undergraduate/Scholarship)* [4060]

Robert Hancock Memorial Scholarship Awards *(Undergraduate/Scholarship)* [5836]

Handweavers Guild of America and Dendel Scholarships *(Graduate, Undergraduate/Scholarship)* [4388]

Ilse and George Hanfmann Fellowships *(Doctorate/Fellowship)* [1150]

John M. Haniak Scholarships *(Undergraduate/Scholarship)* [5692]

Byron Hanke Fellowships *(Doctorate, Graduate, Undergraduate/Fellowship)* [3933]

Zenon C.R. Hansen Leadership Scholarships *(Undergraduate/Scholarship)* [6255]

Martha and Oliver Hansen Memorial Scholarships *(Undergraduate/Scholarship)* [5098]

Zenon C.R. Hansen Memorial Scholarships *(Undergraduate/Scholarship)* [1943]

Penelope Hanshaw Scholarships *(Graduate, Undergraduate/Scholarship)* [1903]

Clem T. Hanson Scholarship Fund *(Undergraduate/Scholarship)* [5916]

Duane Hanson Scholarships *(Undergraduate/Scholarship)* [1267]

Haraldson Foundation Scholarships *(Graduate, Undergraduate/Scholarship)* [4391]

Isaac and Mary Harbottle Scholarships *(Graduate, Undergraduate/Scholarship)* [5212]

Bob and Dawn Hardy Automotive Scholarships *(Undergraduate/Scholarship)* [5099]

Bryce Harlow Fellowship Program *(Graduate/Fellowship)* [4395]

Matt Harmon Memorial Scholarships *(Undergraduate/Scholarship)* [8607]

North Las Vegas Firefighters - William J. Harnedy Memorial Scholarships *(Undergraduate/Scholarship)* [7495]

Harness Tracks of America Scholarship Fund *(Undergraduate/Scholarship)* [4401]

Walter and Lucille Harper Scholarships *(Undergraduate/Scholarship)* [5233]

Harris Corporation Merit Scholarships *(Undergraduate/Scholarship)* [4403]

Dorothy Harris Endowed Scholarships *(Graduate/Scholarship)* [9737]

H.H. Harris Foundation Scholarships *(Undergraduate/Scholarship)* [772]

Leon Harris/Les Nichols Memorial Scholarships to Spartan College of Aeronautics & Technology *(Undergraduate/Scholarship)* [131]

William H. Harris Memorial Scholarships *(Graduate, Undergraduate/Scholarship)* [7267]

Frank and Charlene Harris Scholarships *(Undergraduate/Scholarship)* [3109]

Peg Hart Harrison Memorial Scholarships *(Undergraduate/Scholarship)* [3373]

Evelyn W. Harrison Point Scholarships *(Graduate, Undergraduate/Scholarship)* [7361]

Lullelia W. Harrison Scholarships in Counseling *(Graduate, Undergraduate/Scholarship)* [9802]

Claude B. Hart Memorial Scholarships *(Undergraduate/Scholarship)* [9641]

Carroll Hart Scholarships *(Graduate/Scholarship)* [8329]

Mollie Harter Memorial Fund *(Undergraduate/Scholarship)* [3775]

Karen Harter Recruitment Scholarship Grants *(Undergraduate/Scholarship)* [3153]

Hartford Geriatrics Health Outcomes Research Scholars Award Program *(Professional development/Grant)* [80]

Hartford Grammar School Scholarships *(Undergraduate/Scholarship)* [4438]

Gabe A. Hartl Scholarships *(Undergraduate/Scholarship)* [105]

William T. Hartzell Memorial Scholarships *(Undergraduate/Scholarship)* [7653]

James J. Harvey Dissertation Fellowships *(Doctorate/Fellowship)* [7852]

Delta Gamma Foundation Florence Margaret Harvey Memorial Scholarships *(Graduate, Undergraduate/Scholarship)* [752]

Donald F. Hastings Scholarships *(Undergraduate/Scholarship)* [1434]

Donald and Shirley Hastings Scholarships *(Undergraduate/Scholarship)* [1435]

Gretchen Hauff Memorial Scholarships *(Undergraduate/Scholarship)* [7496]

Charles Hauser Scholarships *(Undergraduate/Scholarship)* [9277]

AISC/Fred R. Havens Fellowships *(Graduate, Undergraduate/Fellowship)* [877]

Lex and Scott Hawkins Endowed Scholarships *(Undergraduate/Scholarship)* [3495]

Don C. Hawkins Memorial Scholarships *(Undergraduate/Scholarship)* [132]

Thomas T. Hayashi Memorial Scholarships *(Graduate, Undergraduate/Scholarship)* [5142]

R. Garn Haycock Memorial Scholarships *(Undergraduate/Scholarship)* [7654]

Edward and Cora Hayes Scholarships *(Undergraduate/Scholarship)* [3496]

Samuel P. Hays Research Fellowships *(Professional development/Fellowship)* [1248]

HBO Point Scholarships *(Graduate, Undergraduate/Scholarship)* [7362]

HDR Engineering, Inc. Scholarships for Diversity in Engineering *(Undergraduate/Scholarship)* [1796]

HDSA Research Grants *(Professional development/Grant)* [4644]

Edith Head Scholarships *(Undergraduate/Scholarship)* [3411]

Dr. M.G. "Doc" Headley Scholarships *(Undergraduate/Scholarship)* [8726]

Health and Aging Policy Fellows *(Professional development/Fellowship)* [1018]

Health Outcomes Post Doctoral Fellowships *(Postdoctorate/Fellowship)* [7223]

Health Outcomes Pre Doctoral Fellowships *(Doctorate/Fellowship)* [7224]

Health Outcomes Research Starter Grants *(Doctorate/Grant)* [7225]

Health Outcomes Sabbatical Fellowships *(Postdoctorate/Fellowship)* [7226]

Health Sciences Student Fellowships *(Doctorate, Graduate/Fellowship)* [3666]

Health, Sport, and Fitness SIG Student Research Awards *(Undergraduate/Award)* [1714]

Healthcare Information Management Systems Scholarships *(Graduate, Postgraduate, Undergraduate/Scholarship)* [4505]

Healy Graduate Scholarships *(Graduate/Scholarship)* [1367]

Annamae Heaps Law Scholarships *(Undergraduate/Scholarship)* [3497]

Erin Kumelos Heard Memorial Scholarships *(Undergraduate/Scholarship)* [3374]

William Randolph Hearst Educational Endowments *(Undergraduate/Scholarship)* [5617]

Dr. James H. Heckaman Memorial Scholarship Fund *(Undergraduate/Scholarship)* [8672]

Professor Ulla Hedner Scholarships *(Undergraduate, Vocational/Occupational/Scholarship)* [6326]

Howell Heflin Memorial Scholarships *(Undergraduate/Scholarship)* [6815]

Lavonne Heghinian Scholarships *(Undergraduate/Scholarship)* [3412]

Barbara and Nicole Heicox Foreign Travel and Study Scholarship Fund *(Undergraduate/Scholarship)* [4220]

Dale O. Heimberger CRNA Memorial Scholarship Fund *(Graduate/Scholarship)* [8673]

Helicopter Foundation International Commercial Helicopter Rating Scholarships *(Professional development/Scholarship)* [4508]

Helicopter Foundation International Maintenance Technician Certificate Scholarships *(Professional development/Scholarship)* [4509]

Hellenic University Club of Philadelphia Founders Scholarships *(Undergraduate/Scholarship)* [4515]

Joan Heller-Diane Bernard Fellowships *(Graduate, Undergraduate/Fellowship)* [2703]

Joseph T. Helling Scholarship Fund *(Undergraduate/Scholarship)* [4730]

Helm Family Scholarships *(Undergraduate/Scholarship)* [7932]

PPQ William F. Helms Student Scholarships *(Undergraduate/Scholarship)* [9402]

ASIL Arthur C. Helton Fellowship Program *(All/Fellowship)* [1280]

Clinton J. Helton Manufacturing Scholarships *(Undergraduate/Scholarship)* [8387]

Hemlow Prize in Burney Studies *(Graduate/Prize)* [1229]

Jeanne H. Hemmingway Scholarships *(Undergraduate/Scholarship)* [3531]

Hemophilia Federation of America Educational Scholarships *(Undergraduate/Scholarship)* [4528]

Hemophilia Health Services Memorial Scholarship

Program *(Graduate, Undergraduate/Scholarship)* [6327]

Hench Post-Dissertation Fellowships *(Postdoctorate/Fellowship)* [419]

Henderson Memorial Endowed Scholarships *(Undergraduate/Scholarship)* [5432]

Edith H. Henderson Scholarships *(Undergraduate/Scholarship)* [1283]

Doris Hendren Memorial Scholarships *(Undergraduate/Scholarship)* [7933]

Marjorie M. Hendricks Environmental Education Scholarship Fund *(Undergraduate/Scholarship)* [4221]

Henigson Human Rights Fellowships *(Graduate/Fellowship)* [4467]

Herb Kohl Educational Foundation Excellence Scholarships *(Undergraduate/Scholarship)* [4530]

Herb Kohl Educational Foundation Initiative Scholarships *(High School/Scholarship)* [4532]

Richard A. Herbert Memorial Scholarships *(Undergraduate/Scholarship)* [1412]

Hereditary Disease Foundation Research Grants *(Postdoctorate/Grant)* [4540]

Herbert Herff Presidential Law Scholarships *(Undergraduate/Scholarship)* [9227]

Catarino and Evangelina Hernandez Research Fellowships in Latino History *(Professional development/Fellowship)* [8874]

Alia Herrera Memorial Scholarships *(Undergraduate/Scholarship)* [492]

Ella Beren Hersch Scholarships *(Undergraduate/Scholarship)* [7090]

Isabel M. Herson Scholarships in Education *(Graduate, Undergraduate/Scholarship)* [9803]

Hertz Foundation's Graduate Fellowships *(Doctorate/Fellowship)* [6074]

Darrel Hess Community College Geography Scholarships *(Undergraduate/Scholarship)* [1693]

Beth A. Hess Memorial Scholarships *(Doctorate, Graduate/Fellowship)* [8518]

Peter Hess Scholarships *(Undergraduate/Scholarship)* [4061]

Nicholas S. Hetos, DDS, Memorial Graduate Scholarships *(Graduate/Scholarship)* [4516]

Caroline M. Hewins Scholarships *(Graduate/Scholarship)* [4465]

HFMA Connecticut Chapter Scholarships *(Graduate, Undergraduate/Scholarship)* [4501]

HGS Foundation Scholarships *(Undergraduate/Scholarship)* [4611]

HHMI Medical Research Fellowships *(Undergraduate/Fellowship)* [4623]

HHS Memorial Scholarships *(Graduate, Undergraduate/Scholarship)* [37]

HIAA Graduate Student Travel Grants *(Graduate/Grant)* [4588]

Mark and Michelle Hiepler Endowed Scholarships *(Undergraduate/Scholarship)* [7187]

Regina Higdon Scholarships *(Undergraduate/Scholarship)* [3110]

High School Councilors Scholarships *(Undergraduate/Scholarship)* [4707]

Hilb, Rogal and Hobbs Scholarships *(Undergraduate/Scholarship)* [9449]

Robert S. Hilbert Memorial Student Travel Grants *(Graduate, Undergraduate/Grant)* [6911]

Gus and Henrietta Hill Scholarships *(Undergraduate/Scholarship)* [3532]

Judge Delmas C. Hill Scholarships *(Undergraduate/Scholarship)* [9487]

Conrad N. Hilton Scholarships *(Undergraduate/Scholarship)* [3613]

D. Glenn Hilts Scholarships *(Graduate, Undergraduate/Scholarship)* [1872]

Lucy Hilty Research Grants *(All/Grant)* [1065]

Brooke Hindle Postdoctoral Fellowships *(Postdoctorate/Fellowship)* [8344]

Jim & Nancy Hinkle Travel Grants *(Postdoctorate/Grant)* [4525]

Hinman-Jensen Endowed Scholarships *(Undergraduate/Scholarship)* [5433]

HIPLA Judicial Fellowships *(Undergraduate/Fellowship)* [4613]

HIPLA Scholarships for University of Houston Law Center Students *(Graduate, Undergraduate/Scholarship)* [4614]

Hispanic Association of Colleges and Universities Scholarships *(Undergraduate/Scholarship)* [4548]

Hispanic Association on Corporate Responsibility Scholarship Program *(Undergraduate/Scholarship)* [4553]

Hispanic Scholarship Fund College Scholarship Program (HSF) *(Graduate, Undergraduate/Scholarship)* [4570]

Hispanic Serving Institution Scholarships (HSIS) *(Undergraduate/Scholarship)* [9024]

Historically Black College or University Scholarships (HBCUS) *(Undergraduate/Scholarship)* [9025]

HLS/MLA Professional Development Grants *(Professional development/Grant)* [5742]

James E. Hoff, S.J. Scholars *(Undergraduate/Scholarship)* [9771]

Dorothy M. and Earl S. Hoffman Awards *(Graduate/Award)* [1982]

Henry Hoffman Memorial Scholarship Fund *(Undergraduate/Scholarship)* [6064]

Robert and Elaine Hoffman Memorial Scholarships *(Undergraduate/Scholarship)* [9228]

Electronics Division Lewis C. Hoffman Scholarships *(Undergraduate/Scholarship)* [606]

Michael J. Hogan Fellowships *(Graduate/Fellowship)* [8340]

The Thelma S. Hoge Memorial Scholarship Fund *(Undergraduate/Scholarship)* [3087]

Raymond T. Hoge Scholarship Fund *(Undergraduate/Scholarship)* [8674]

Michael J. Hoggard Memorial Scholarships *(Undergraduate/Scholarship)* [7497]

Holland America Line-Westours Research Grants *(Undergraduate/Grant)* [1368]

Houston/Nancy Holliman Scholarships *(Undergraduate/Scholarship)* [3413]

Ernest F. Hollings Undergraduate Scholarships *(Undergraduate/Scholarship)* [6417]

Cleve Holloway Memorial Scholarship Fund *(Undergraduate/Scholarship)* [3040]

Joseph A. Holmes Safety Association Scholarships *(Graduate, Undergraduate/Scholarship)* [4593]

Robert Holmes Scholarships *(Undergraduate/Scholarship)* [3198]

Alan Holoch Memorial Grants *(Professional development/Grant)* [500]

W. Stull Holt Dissertation Fellowships *(Doctorate, Graduate/Fellowship, Grant)* [8341]

Caroline Holt Nursing Scholarships *(Undergraduate/Scholarship)* [4441]

The Homeland Security Undergraduate Scholarships *(Undergraduate/Scholarship)* [9039]

Honeywell Avionics Scholarships *(Undergraduate, Vocational/Occupational/Scholarship)* [133]

Jane Hood Memorial Fund *(Undergraduate/Scholarship)* [3776]

Kathryn Hookanson Law Fellowships *(Undergraduate/Scholarship)* [9229]

Hooper Memorial Scholarships *(Undergraduate, Vocational/Occupational/Scholarship)* [8951]

Lillie Hope-McGarvey Health Scholarship Awards *(Undergraduate, Vocational/Occupational, Graduate, Master's/Scholarship)* [289]

Hope for the Warriors Spouses Scholarships *(Graduate, Master's, Undergraduate, Vocational/Occupational/Scholarship)* [4599]

Hopi Education Awards *(Doctorate, Undergraduate/Award)* [1511]

Minnie Hopkins Memorial Scholarship Fund of Lathrop/Compton School *(Undergraduate/Scholarship)* [8675]

Sam J. Hord Memorial Scholarships *(Undergraduate/Scholarship)* [8563]

Seth Horen, K1LOM Memorial Scholarships *(Undergraduate/Scholarship)* [1091]

Hormel Foods Charitable Trust Scholarships *(Undergraduate/Scholarship)* [4601]

Edward L. Horne, Jr. Scholarships *(All/Scholarship)* [6969]

Judge and Mrs. Robert D. Horowitz Legal Scholarship Fund *(Graduate/Scholarship)* [8676]

Detroit Tigers Willie Horton Scholarships *(Undergraduate/Scholarship)* [3199]

Hospitality Food Service Scholarships *(Undergraduate/Scholarship)* [6621]

John C. "Jack" Hough Memorial Law Scholarships

(Undergraduate/Scholarship) [9230]

Max and Julia Houghton Duluth Central Scholarships *(Undergraduate/Scholarship)* [3533]

Paul Green Houston Scholarships *(Undergraduate/Scholarship)* [9278]

Sarah Jane Houston Scholarships *(Undergraduate/Scholarship)* [3414]

Houtan Scholarships *(Graduate/Scholarship)* [4616]

Kaspar Hovannisian Memorial Scholarships *(Graduate/Scholarship)* [1597]

Hirair and Anna Hovnanian Foundation Presidential Scholarships *(Undergraduate/Scholarship)* [1598]

Hirair and Anna Hovnanian Foundation Scholarships *(Undergraduate/Scholarship)* [1599]

NORDAM Dee Howard/Etienne Fage Scholarships *(Undergraduate/Scholarship)* [6169]

C.D. Howard Scholarships *(Undergraduate/Scholarship)* [4898]

William B. Howell Scholarships *(Undergraduate/Scholarship)* [1436]

Christopher Hoy/ERT Scholarships *(Graduate, Master's/Scholarship)* [901]

Carol Hoy Scholarship Fund *(Undergraduate/Scholarship)* [3947]

HRH Prince Alwaleed Bin Talal ISNA Fellowships *(Graduate/Fellowship)* [5080]

HRP Global Human Rights Fellowships *(Graduate/Fellowship)* [4468]

HSBC-North America Scholarship Program *(Undergraduate/Scholarship)* [4571]

HSF/Atrisco Heritage Foundation Scholarship Program *(Graduate, Undergraduate/Scholarship)* [4572]

HSF/Citi Fellows Program *(Undergraduate/Scholarship)* [4573]

HSF/General Motors Scholarship Program *(Undergraduate/Scholarship)* [4574]

HSF/IDT Hope High School Scholarship Program *(Undergraduate/Scholarship)* [4575]

HSF/Nissan Community College Transfer Scholarship Program *(Undergraduate/Scholarship)* [4576]

HSF/Wal-Mart Stores Inc. Scholarship Program *(Graduate, Undergraduate/Scholarship)* [4577]

Hubbard Scholarships *(Master's/Scholarship)* [4105]

Amber Huber Memorial Scholarships *(Undergraduate/Scholarship)* [3154]

Hudson River Graduate Fellowships *(Doctorate, Master's/Fellowship)* [4618]

Huenefeld/Denton Scholarships *(Undergraduate/Scholarship)* [3415]

Roger K. Hughes Legacy Scholarships *(Undergraduate/Scholarship)* [2247]

Howard Hughes Medical Institute Predoctoral Fellowships *(Graduate/Fellowship)* [6075]

Paul A. Hughes Memorial Scholarships *(Undergraduate/Scholarship)* [2248]

Mary M. Hughes Research Fellowships in Texas History *(Professional development/Fellowship)* [8875]

Huguenot Society of South Carolina Graduate Scholarships *(Graduate/Scholarship)* [4628]

Human Ecology Continuing Undergraduate Student Scholarships *(Undergraduate/Scholarship)* [9358]

Humane Studies Fellowships *(Graduate/Fellowship)* [4798]

Humanism in Medicine Scholarships *(Undergraduate/Scholarship)* [8766]

Kevin Hummer Point Scholarships *(Graduate, Undergraduate/Scholarship)* [7363]

Cecil C. Humphreys Law Fellowships *(Undergraduate/Fellowship)* [9231]

Dr. Richard M. Hunt Fellowships *(Doctorate, Postdoctorate/Fellowship)* [667]

Hunt Postdoctoral Fellowships *(Doctorate/Fellowship)* [9561]

Frederick V. Hunt Postdoctoral Research Fellowships in Acoustics *(Postdoctorate/Fellowship)* [40]

Michael A. Hunter Memorial Scholarships *(Undergraduate/Scholarship)* [2757]

Clay Huntington Sports Communications Scholarships *(Undergraduate/Scholarship)* [4338]

Huntington's Disease Society of America Research Fellowships *(Postdoctorate/Fellowship)* [4645]

James F. Hurley III Bicentennial Merit Scholarships *(Undergraduate/Scholarship)* [9279]

Doc Hurley Scholarships *(Undergraduate/Scholarship)* [4442]

Zora Neale Hurston Scholarships *(Graduate/Scholarship)* [9804]

Norman E. Huston Scholarships *(Graduate, Undergraduate/Scholarship)* [5053]

Dr. James L. Hutchinson and Evelyn Ribbs Hutchinson Medical School Scholarship Fund *(Undergraduate/Scholarship)* [8203]

Fred Hutchison Travel Scholarships *(Undergraduate/Scholarship)* [9280]

The Hyatt Hotels Fund For Minority Lodging Management Students *(Undergraduate/Scholarship)* [798]

Hydro Research Foundation Fellowships *(Master's/Fellowship)* [4648]

Mike Hylton and Ron Niederman Memorial Scholarships *(Undergraduate/Scholarship)* [6328]

Libbie H. Hyman Memorial Scholarships *(Graduate/Scholarship)* [8358]

The Steve Hymans Extended Stay Scholarship Program *(Undergraduate/Scholarship)* [799]

Hypertherm International HyTech Leadership Scholarships *(Graduate/Scholarship)* [1437]

IADR David B. Ste. Scott Fellowships *(Undergraduate/Fellowship)* [4860]

IADR John Ste. Clarkson Fellowships *(Postdoctorate/Fellowship)* [4861]

IADR John Ste. Gray Fellowships *(Professional development/Fellowship)* [4862]

IADR Norton Ste. Ross Fellowships *(Postgraduate/Fellowship)* [4863]

IADR Toshio Ste. Nakao Fellowships *(Professional development/Fellowship)* [4864]

IAESTE United States Scholarships *(Undergraduate/Scholarship)* [3309]

IAHCSMM - Purdue University Scholarship Awards *(Professional development/Scholarship)* [4870]

IALD Education Trust Scholarship Program *(Graduate, Undergraduate/Scholarship)* [4878]

IAWP International Recognition and Scholarship Awards *(Professional development/Scholarship)* [4882]

IBEA Undergraduate Scholarships *(Undergraduate/Scholarship)* [4683]

ICAFS Idaho Graduate Student Scholarships *(Graduate/Scholarship)* [4663]

ICAFS Idaho High School Student Scholarships *(Undergraduate/Scholarship)* [4664]

ICAFS Idaho Undergraduate Student Scholarships *(Undergraduate/Scholarship)* [4665]

ICDA Graduate Scholarships *(Graduate/Scholarship)* [5034]

ICDA Research Grants *(Graduate/Grant)* [5035]

Ice Skating Institute of America Education Foundation Scholarships *(Undergraduate/Scholarship)* [4657]

iCORE ICT Graduate Student Scholarships *(Doctorate, Graduate, Master's/Scholarship)* [232]

IDA Fellowship Awards *(Professional development/Fellowship)* [4919]

Idaho Attorney General Scholarships *(Undergraduate/Scholarship)* [5435]

Idaho Nursing Scholarships *(Undergraduate/Scholarship)* [4670]

David Iden Memorial Safety Scholarships *(Undergraduate/Scholarship)* [1340]

IFMA Foundation Certificate Program Scholarships *(Graduate/Scholarship)* [4926]

IFMA Foundation Graduate/Undergraduate Scholarships *(Graduate, Undergraduate/Scholarship)* [4927]

IFSEA Worthy Goal Scholarships *(Four Year College, Two Year College, Undergraduate, Vocational/Occupational/Scholarship)* [4933]

IIE Council of Fellows Undergraduate Scholarships *(Undergraduate/Scholarship)* [4803]

Illinois Association of Chamber of Commerce Executives Scholarships *(Postdoctorate/Scholarship)* [4680]

Illuminator Educational Foundation Scholarships *(Undergraduate/Scholarship)* [2249]

IMA Memorial Education Fund Scholarships (MEF) *(Graduate, Undergraduate/Scholarship loan)* [4815]

ment Division *(Graduate, Undergraduate/Scholarship)* [5074]

ISA Technical Division Scholarships - Water and Wastewater Industries Division *(Graduate, Undergraduate/Scholarship)* [5075]

ISBA General Scholarships *(Undergraduate/Scholarship)* [4678]

Hazel D. Isbell Fellowships *(Graduate/Fellowship)* [3376]

(ISC)2 Information Security Scholarships *(Postgraduate/Scholarship)* [4955]

ISDS Graduate Student Scholarships *(Doctorate, Graduate/Scholarship)* [4990]

ISF Excellence in Community Service Scholarships *(Undergraduate/Scholarship)* [5048]

ISF Undergraduate Scholarships *(Undergraduate/Scholarship)* [5049]

Islamic Scholarship Fund Scholarships (ISF) *(Postgraduate, Undergraduate/Scholarship)* [5078]

Broughton Isom Memorial Scholarships *(Undergraduate/Scholarship)* [6816]

ISOPE Offshore Mechanics Scholarships for Outstanding Students *(Graduate/Scholarship)* [4999]

ISPE Advantage Award/Foundation Scholarships *(Undergraduate/Scholarship)* [4691]

ISRS Graduate Fellowships *(Doctorate, Graduate/Fellowship)* [5001]

ISTU Student Prize *(All/Prize)* [5004]

Italian American Lawyers Association Annual Scholarships *(Undergraduate/Scholarship)* [5084]

Italian Language Scholarships *(Undergraduate/Scholarship)* [6922]

ITE Transit Council Scholarships *(Graduate/Scholarship)* [4825]

ITEEA FTE Scholarships *(Undergraduate/Scholarship)* [5010]

ITEEA Greer/FTE Grants *(Professional development/Grant)* [5011]

ITEEA Litherland/FTE Scholarships *(Undergraduate/Scholarship)* [5012]

ITNS Research Grants *(Professional development/Grant)* [5021]

ITW Welding Companies Scholarships *(Undergraduate/Scholarship)* [1438]

Ivanhoe Foundation Fellowships *(Master's/Fellowship)* [5086]

Bob and Mary Ives Scholarships *(Graduate, Undergraduate/Scholarship)* [5076]

IWPR/GW Fellowships in Women's Public Policy Research *(Graduate/Fellowship)* [4836]

Jackman Scholarships *(Undergraduate/Scholarship)* [7289]

Jackson High School Alumni Scholarship Fund *(Undergraduate/Scholarship)* [8678]

Gene Jackson Scholarships *(Undergraduate/Scholarship)* [9282]

Ruth K. Jacobs Memorial Scholarships *(Graduate, Undergraduate/Scholarship)* [2779]

Freddy L. Jacobs Scholarships *(Undergraduate/Scholarship)* [4886]

Eric L. Jacobson Memorial Scholarships *(Undergraduate/Scholarship)* [7655]

Karl A. Jacobson Scholarships *(Undergraduate/Scholarship)* [1341]

Peter Lars Jacobson Scholarships *(Undergraduate/Scholarship)* [9283]

Jacque Placette Chapman Master's Fellowships *(Graduate/Fellowship)* [6918]

Louis I. Jaffe Memorial Scholarships-ODU *(Graduate/Scholarship)* [4377]

Cory Jam Awards *(Undergraduate/Scholarship)* [3536]

Jamail/Long Challenge Grant Scholarships *(Graduate, Undergraduate/Scholarship)* [4559]

The J. Franklin Jameson Fellowships in American History *(Doctorate/Fellowship)* [793]

Jan Jancin Competition Awards *(Undergraduate/Award)* [881]

The Dawn Janisse Scholarships *(Undergraduate/Scholarship)* [7140]

Japan Foundation, New York Doctoral Fellowship Program *(Doctorate/Fellowship)* [5134]

Japan Foundation, New York Research Fellowship Program *(Undergraduate/Fellowship)* [5135]

Japan Foundation, New York Short-Term Fellowship Program *(Doctorate/Fellowship)* [5136]

Japanese American Bar Association Scholarships *(Graduate, Undergraduate/Scholarship)* [5138]

Dr. Ali Jarrahi Merit Scholarships *(Undergraduate/Scholarship)* [5050]

Carl and Lucille Jarrett Scholarship Fund *(Graduate, Undergraduate/Scholarship)* [3778]

Terry Jarvis Memorial Scholarships *(Undergraduate/Scholarship)* [1439]

Dannie Jasmine Scholarships *(Undergraduate/Scholarship)* [5944]

Jacob K. Javits Fellowships *(Doctorate, Master's/Fellowship)* [6076]

JCC Association Graduate Education Scholarships *(Graduate/Scholarship)* [5151]

J.D. Graduate Tikvah Scholarships *(Graduate/Scholarship)* [8904]

J.D. or LL.M. Tikvah Scholarships *(Graduate/Scholarship)* [8905]

JD/MBA Scholarships *(Undergraduate/Scholarship)* [7188]

Sister Rita Jeanne Scholarships *(Undergraduate/Scholarship)* [5169]

Jefferson Graduate Fellowships *(Doctorate, Graduate/Fellowship)* [5153]

Elise Reed Jenkins Memorial Scholarships - Gamma Lambda *(Undergraduate/Scholarship)* [8175]

Elise Reed Jenkins Memorial Scholarships - Gamma Psi *(Undergraduate/Scholarship)* [8176]

John H. Jenkins Research Fellowships in Texas History *(Professional development/Fellowship)* [8876]

Martha Combs Jenkins Scholarships *(Undergraduate/Scholarship)* [7290]

Gaynold Jensen Education Stipends *(Postdoctorate, Professional development/Scholarship)* [3443]

Walter J. Jensen Fellowships *(Professional development/Fellowship)* [7248]

Nancy Lorraine Jensen Memorial Scholarships *(Undergraduate/Scholarship)* [8531]

Mike Jensen R.I.S.E. Memorial Scholarships *(Undergraduate/Scholarship)* [7656]

Stanley "Doc" Jensen Scholarships *(High School/Scholarship)* [694]

Jerman-Cahoon Student Scholarship Program *(Undergraduate/Scholarship)* [1324]

Kenneth Jernigan Scholarships *(Undergraduate/Scholarship)* [6276]

Jerome Fellowships *(Professional development/Fellowship)* [7337]

James Jesinski Scholarships *(Undergraduate/Scholarship)* [9359]

Jewish Caucus Scholarships *(Undergraduate/Scholarship)* [6559]

Brian Jimenez Memorial Scholarships *(Undergraduate/Scholarship)* [7657]

Rev. and Mrs. A.K. Jizmejian Educational Fund *(Undergraduate/Scholarship)* [1600]

JMA Architecture Studios Scholarships *(Undergraduate/Scholarship)* [7498]

John W. Webb Lecture Awards *(Professional development/Award)* [1260]

Alvin H. Johnson AMS Dissertation Fellowships *(Graduate/Fellowship)* [940]

Robert Wood Johnson Clinical Scholarships *(Graduate/Scholarship)* [5165]

Craig Johnson Family Scholarships *(Undergraduate/Scholarship)* [8884]

The Robert Wood Johnson Health Policy Fellowship Program *(All/Fellowship)* [1019]

MCCA Lloyd M. Johnson, Jr. Scholarships *(Undergraduate/Scholarship)* [5904]

Joseph C. Johnson Memorial Grants *(Undergraduate/Scholarship)* [1191]

Fred Johnson Memorial Scholarships *(Doctorate, Graduate, Master's/Scholarship)* [6176]

Gregory D. Johnson Memorial Scholarships *(Doctorate, Graduate, Master's/Scholarship)* [6378]

Sylvia Taylor Johnson Minority Fellowships in Educational Measurement *(Doctorate/Fellowship)* [3611]

Dr. Bill Johnson Scholarships *(Undergraduate/Scholarship)* [8116]

Johnson and Wales University Scholarships *(Undergraduate/Scholarship)* [5175]

Nancy Johnston Memorial Scholarships *(Graduate, Undergraduate/Scholarship)* [8837]

OOIDA Mary Johnston Scholarships *(Undergraduate/Scholarship)* [7025]

George E. Jonas Scholarships *(Graduate, Undergraduate/Scholarship)* [5167]

Greater Baton Rouge Chapter - Don Jones Excellence in Safety Scholarships *(Undergraduate/Scholarship)* [1342]

Edward H. Jones Scholarships *(Undergraduate/Scholarship)* [3500]

Barbara Jordan Memorial Scholarships *(Graduate, Undergraduate/Scholarship)* [1884]

Joseph H. Fichter Research Grants *(Professional development/Grant)* [1874]

E.J. Josey Scholarships *(Graduate/Scholarship)* [2133]

Journyx Scholarships *(Graduate, Undergraduate/Scholarship)* [5171]

Leslie W. Joyce and Paul W. Thayer Graduate Fellowships in I-O Psychology *(Doctorate/Fellowship)* [8355]

JSA/Jefferson Lab Graduate Fellowships *(Doctorate, Graduate/Fellowship)* [5155]

JSR Foundation Endowed School of Law Scholarships *(Undergraduate/Scholarship)* [7189]

George E. Judd Scholarships *(Undergraduate/Scholarship)* [8609]

Woodrow Judkins Endowed Scholarships *(Undergraduate/Scholarship)* [7190]

Junior Achievement of East Central Ohio, Inc. Scholarship Fund *(Undergraduate/Scholarship)* [8679]

Junior Firefighter Scholarships *(Undergraduate/Scholarship)* [6555]

Junior Women of the Contemporary Club Scholarships *(Undergraduate/Scholarship)* [7658]

George W. Juno Memorial Scholarships *(Graduate/Scholarship)* [4062]

Juvenile Arthritis Scholarships *(Undergraduate/Scholarship)* [4444]

K-12 Edu-Grants *(Other/Grant)* [6329]

Mike Kabo Global Scholarships *(Professional development/Scholarship)* [4167]

Annette Kade Fellowships *(Graduate/Fellowship)* [5787]

Kade-Heideking Fellowships *(Doctorate/Fellowship)* [4128]

Daniel Kahikina and Millie Akaka Scholarships *(Graduate, Undergraduate/Scholarship)* [5213]

Kaiser Media Fellowships in Health *(Advanced Professional/Fellowship)* [5180]

David A. Kaiser Memorial Scholarship Fund *(Undergraduate/Scholarship)* [8680]

Kamehameha Schools Class of 1968 "Ka Poli O Kaiona" Scholarships *(Graduate, Undergraduate/Scholarship)* [5214]

Kamehameha Schools Class of 1972 Scholarships *(Graduate, Undergraduate/Scholarship)* [5215]

Benjamin Kaminer Endowed Scholarships in Physiology *(Undergraduate/Scholarship)* [5618]

Martin S. Kane Memorial Community Service Award Scholarships *(Undergraduate/Scholarship)* [3062]

Kansas City Division Scholarships *(All/Scholarship)* [5860]

Walter Kapala Scholarships *(Undergraduate/Scholarship)* [4445]

Don Kaplan Legacy Scholarships *(Undergraduate/Scholarship)* [2250]

Kaplan Scholarships *(Undergraduate/Scholarship)* [4562]

Kaplan Test Prep and Admission Scholarships for NSHSS Members *(High School/Scholarship)* [6503]

Steve Kaplan TV and Film Studies Scholarships *(Professional development/Scholarship)* [1212]

Kappa Chapter Centennial Scholarships *(Undergraduate/Scholarship)* [3377]

Kappa Kappa Gamma Graduate Scholarships *(Graduate/Scholarship)* [5193]

Kappa Kappa Gamma Undergraduate Scholarships *(Undergraduate/Scholarship)* [5194]

Kappa Omicron Nu National Alumni Fellowships *(Graduate/Fellowship)* [5196]

Kappa Omicron Nu Undergraduate Scholarships *(Undergraduate/Scholarship)* [5197]

Don Kuhn Memorial Scholarship Fund *(Graduate/ Scholarship)* [3449]

Irene Corbally Kuhn Scholarships *(Graduate, Undergraduate/Scholarship)* [7014]

Kumin Scholars Program *(Undergraduate/Scholarship)* [8204]

Kris M. Kunze Memorial Scholarships *(Undergraduate/Scholarship)* [645]

Charles Kuralt Fellowships in International Broadcasting *(Postgraduate/Scholarship)* [9285]

Chris Kurzweil Scholarships *(Undergraduate/Scholarship)* [3200]

Sam S. Kuwahara Memorial Scholarships *(Undergraduate/Scholarship)* [5144]

Julia Kwan Endowed Scholarships *(Graduate/Scholarship)* [7193]

L-3 Avionics Systems Scholarships *(Undergraduate, Vocational/Occupational/Scholarship)* [134]

Gretchen Laatsch Scholarships *(Graduate/Scholarship)* [1740]

The Labor Law Scholarships *(Undergraduate/Scholarship)* [6660]

LAF/Class Fund AILA/YAMAGAMI/Hope Fellowships *(Postgraduate/Fellowship)* [1284]

Ken LaFountaine First Nations Scholarships *(Undergraduate/Scholarship)* [8118]

Ron LaFreniere Business Scholarships *(Undergraduate/Scholarship)* [8119]

The Lagrant Foundation - Graduate Students Scholarships *(Graduate/Scholarship)* [5315]

The Lagrant Foundation - Undergraduate Students Scholarships *(Undergraduate/Scholarship)* [5316]

Casey Laine Armed Forces Scholarships *(Undergraduate/Scholarship)* [2951]

Lake George Dollars for Scholars Awards *(Undergraduate/Scholarship)* [5318]

Lalor Foundation Post-Doctoral Fellowships *(Postdoctorate/Fellowship)* [5322]

Lam Research Corporation Core Values Scholarships *(Undergraduate/Scholarship)* [5324]

Lamar University College of Engineering Scholarships *(Undergraduate/Scholarship)* [6257]

Lambda Alumni, UCLA Lesbian & Gay Alumni Association Scholarships Program *(Undergraduate/Scholarship)* [7854]

Frank S. Land Scholarships *(Undergraduate/Scholarship)* [3425]

Robert S. Landauer, Sr. Memorial Fellowships *(Graduate/Fellowship)* [4490]

Landscape Forms Design for People Scholarships *(Undergraduate/Scholarship)* [5334]

The Lanford Family Highway Worker Memorial Scholarship Program *(Undergraduate/Scholarship)* [1157]

Frank H. Lang Merit Scholarships *(Undergraduate/Scholarship)* [5341]

The Otis and Florence Lapham Memorial Scholarships *(Undergraduate/Scholarship)* [5101]

Christian Larew Memorial Scholarships *(Graduate/Scholarship)* [5484]

Peter and Jody Larkin Legacy Scholarships *(Undergraduate/Scholarship)* [2251]

Arnold Les Larsen, FAIA, Memorial Scholarships *(Graduate, Master's/Scholarship)* [841]

Larson Aquatic Research Support Scholarships (LARS) *(Doctorate, Graduate/Scholarship)* [1418]

David B. Larson Fellowships in Health and Spirituality *(Doctorate/Fellowship)* [5275]

Las Vegas Chinatown Scholarships *(Undergraduate/Scholarship)* [7500]

Las Vegas Elks Scholarships for the Physically Challenged *(Undergraduate, Vocational/Occupational/Scholarship)* [7502]

Las Vegas Elks Scholarships *(Undergraduate, Vocational/Occupational/Scholarship)* [7501]

Laser Technology, Engineering and Applications Scholarships *(Graduate, Undergraduate/Scholarship)* [8639]

Jay and Deborah Last Fellowships *(Doctorate/Fellowship)* [420]

Latham Diversity Scholars *(Undergraduate/Scholarship)* [5354]

Latinos for Dental Careers Scholarships *(All/Scholarship)* [2676]

Robert J. Lavidge Nonprofit Marketing Research

Scholarships *(Professional development/Scholarship)* [919]

Law Enforcement Memorial Scholarship Fund *(Undergraduate/Scholarship)* [3911]

Law Foundation of Ontario Community Leadership in Justice Fellowships *(Professional development/Fellowship)* [5362]

Law and Social Science Dissertation Fellowship and Mentoring Program *(Doctorate, Graduate/Fellowship)* [578]

Law and Society Association Article Prize *(Professional development/Prize)* [5367]

Law and Society Association Dissertation Prize *(Professional development/Prize)* [5368]

Law and Society Association Student Paper Prize *(Graduate, Undergraduate/Prize)* [5370]

Willie D. Lawson, Jr. Memorial Scholarships *(Doctorate, Graduate, Professional development/Scholarship)* [6150]

Verne Lawyer Scholarships *(Undergraduate/Scholarship)* [3503]

Lazarian Graduate Scholarships *(Graduate/Scholarship)* [1578]

Richard J. Lazzara Fellowships in Advanced Implant Surgery *(Postdoctorate/Fellowship)* [396]

LCSC Welding Club Scholarships *(Undergraduate/Scholarship)* [5438]

Betsy B. and Garold A. Leach Scholarships for Museum Studies *(Undergraduate/Scholarship)* [3416]

LeaderShape Institute Scholarships *(Undergraduate/Grant)* [5202]

Leadership Development Scholarships *(Professional development/Scholarship)* [524]

League of Attorneys' Wives Scholarships *(Undergraduate/Scholarship)* [3504]

LEAGUE Foundation Scholarships *(Undergraduate/Scholarship)* [7855]

League of Latin American Citizens General Electric Scholarships *(Undergraduate, Vocational/Occupational/Scholarship)* [5386]

Leakey Foundation Research Grants *(Doctorate/Grant)* [5391]

Learn German in Germany Grants *(Doctorate/Grant)* [4122]

William C. Leary Memorial Emergency Services Scholarships *(Undergraduate/Scholarship)* [8985]

Albert J. and Mae Lee Memorial Scholarships *(Undergraduate/Scholarship)* [7194]

Bruce Lee Scholarships *(Undergraduate/Scholarship)* [9064]

Harold Leeming Memorial Scholarships *(Undergraduate/Scholarship)* [7663]

The Leesfield/AAJ Law Student Scholarships *(Undergraduate/Scholarship)* [493]

Judge William B. Leffler Scholarships *(Undergraduate/Scholarship)* [9232]

The Legacy Fellowships *(Doctorate/Fellowship)* [421]

Legacy Scholarship Program *(Undergraduate/Scholarship)* [8870]

Legacy Scholarships for Graduate Students *(Graduate/Scholarship)* [1278]

Legal Research Service Scholarships *(Undergraduate/Scholarship)* [3505]

Doreen Legg Memorial Scholarships *(Undergraduate/Scholarship)* [7664]

Jay C. and B. Nadine Leggett Charitable Scholarship Fund *(Undergraduate/Scholarship)* [8684]

Herbert Lehman Education Scholarships *(Undergraduate/Scholarship)* [5971]

PCH Architects/Steven J. Lehnhof Memorial Architectural Scholarships *(Undergraduate/Scholarship)* [7665]

Leiber and Stoller Music Scholarships *(Undergraduate/Scholarship)* [1213]

Imelda and Ralph LeMar Scholarship Program *(Undergraduate/Scholarship)* [3201]

Lemelson Center Travel to Collections Awards *(Graduate, Professional development/Award)* [8256]

Stan Lencki Scholarships *(Undergraduate/Scholarship)* [5713]

John Lennon Scholarships *(All/Prize, Scholarship)* [2159]

Craig Lensch Memorial Scholarships *(Undergraduate/Scholarship)* [2192]

Franklin A. Lentesty Scholarships *(Undergraduate/Scholarship)* [6817]

V.A. Leonard Scholarships *(Graduate, Undergraduate/Scholarship)* [357]

Leopold Education Project Scholarships *(Undergraduate/Scholarship)* [3158]

Lerner-Scott Dissertation Prizes *(Doctorate/Prize)* [6959]

Irwin S. Lerner Student Scholarships *(Undergraduate/Scholarship)* [6513]

The Irving Leuchter Memorial Scholarships *(All/Scholarship)* [6714]

Gerald J. Levandoski Memorial Scholarship Fund *(Undergraduate/Scholarship)* [3779]

Myra Levick Scholarships *(Graduate/Scholarship)* [427]

Harold A. Levin Scholarships *(Undergraduate/Scholarship)* [2890]

Jack A. and Louise S. Levine Memorial Scholarships *(Undergraduate/Scholarship)* [7666]

Herbert Levy Memorial Endowment Fund Scholarships *(Undergraduate/Scholarship)* [8439]

Erwin Lew Memorial Scholarships *(Graduate, Undergraduate/Scholarship)* [8451]

Lewis-Clark Coin Club Endowed Scholarships *(Undergraduate/Scholarship)* [5439]

Lewis and Clark Fund for Exploration and Field Research *(Doctorate/Grant)* [992]

Lewis-Clark State College/American Chemical Society Scholars Program *(Undergraduate/Scholarship)* [5440]

Lewis-Clark State College Non-Traditional Student Scholarships *(Undergraduate/Scholarship)* [5445]

Lewis-Clark State College Presidential Out-of-State Scholarships *(Undergraduate/Scholarship)* [5446]

Lewis-Clark State College Presidential Technical Out-of-State Scholarships *(Undergraduate/Scholarship)* [5447]

Lewis-Clark State College Transfer Scholarships *(Undergraduate/Scholarship)* [5449]

Lloyd Lewis Fellowships in American History *(Postdoctorate/Fellowship)* [6696]

George T. Lewis, Jr. Academic Scholarship Fund *(Undergraduate/Scholarship)* [3912]

Frederick D. Lewis Jr. Scholarships *(Undergraduate/Scholarship)* [3506]

Flora Lewis Memorial Scholarships *(Graduate, Undergraduate/Scholarship)* [7015]

S. Evelyn Lewis Memorial Scholarships in Medical Health Sciences *(Graduate, Undergraduate/Scholarship)* [9805]

Jonathan D. Lewis Point Scholarships *(Graduate, Undergraduate/Scholarship)* [7365]

Lewiston Service League Memorial Scholarships *(Undergraduate/Scholarship)* [5452]

Lexington Alumni Scholarships *(Undergraduate/Scholarship)* [5473]

Lexington Community Foundation Annual Scholarships *(Undergraduate/Scholarship)* [5474]

Lexington Community Foundation/CCC Scholarships *(Undergraduate/Scholarship)* [5475]

LGBT HEART Scholarships *(Graduate/Scholarship)* [5407]

Ta Liang Memorial Awards *(Graduate/Grant)* [1669]

Liberace Scholarship Fund *(Undergraduate/Scholarship)* [5482]

Liberty Bell Award Law Scholarships *(Graduate/Scholarship)* [2736]

Liberty Mutual Scholarships *(Undergraduate/Scholarship)* [1346]

Richard T. Liddicoat Scholarships *(Graduate/Scholarship)* [4063]

Dolores Zohrab Liebmann Fund - Graduate School Fellowships *(Graduate/Fellowship)* [5488]

Dolores Zohrab Liebmann Fund - Independent Research/Study Grants *(Graduate/Grant)* [5489]

Dolores Zohrab Liebmann Fund - Publication Grants *(Graduate/Grant)* [5490]

LIFE Lessons Scholarship Program *(Undergraduate/Scholarship)* [5492]

Life Sciences Research Foundation Postdoctoral Fellowship Program *(Graduate, Doctorate/Fellowship)* [5494]

Frank R. Lillie Fellowships and Scholarships *(Under-

graduate/Scholarship) [5620]

Eli Lilly and Company/Black Data Processing Associates Scholarships (High School/Scholarship) [2033]

Lilly Endocrine Scholars Fellowship Awards (Doctorate, Professional development/Fellowship) [3638]

Lilly Reintegration Scholarships (All, Vocational/Occupational/Scholarship) [2707]

Lily Scholarships in Religion for Journalists (Professional development/Scholarship) [7732]

Esther Lim Memorial Scholarships (Undergraduate/Scholarship) [2767]

Lim, Ruger and Kim Scholarships (Undergraduate/Scholarship) [6027]

LIN Media Minority Scholarships and Training Program (Undergraduate/Scholarship) [5501]

AIST Ronald E. Lincoln Memorial Scholarships (Undergraduate/Scholarship) [1808]

John C. Lincoln Memorial Scholarships (Undergraduate/Scholarship) [1440]

Linda's Scholarships (All/Scholarship) [5882]

Donald A.B. Lindberg Research Fellowships (Doctorate, Graduate/Fellowship) [5744]

Charles A. Lindbergh Fellowships (Graduate/Fellowship) [8252]

Lindenwood University Scouting Scholarships (Undergraduate/Scholarship) [6258]

George N. Lindsay Civil Rights Legal Fellowships (Graduate/Fellowship) [5384]

Johnny Lineberry Memorial Scholarships (Undergraduate, Vocational/Occupational/Scholarship) [9645]

Link Foundation/Smithsonian Graduate Fellowships in Marine Science (Graduate/Fellowship) [8262]

F. Maynard Lipe Scholarship Awards (Postdoctorate, Postgraduate/Scholarship) [615]

Lawrence Lipking Fellowships at the Newberry Library (Graduate/Fellowship) [6697]

LIT Scholarships (Graduate, Undergraduate/Scholarship) [5328]

LITA and LSSI Minority Scholarships (Graduate/Scholarship) [5485]

LITA/OCLC Minority Scholarships (Graduate/Scholarship) [5486]

Litherland/FTE Scholarships (Undergraduate/Scholarship) [5007]

Ruth Liu Memorial Scholarships (Undergraduate/Scholarship) [2768]

Live Out Loud Annual Scholarships (Undergraduate/Scholarship) [7856]

Lawrence Livermore National Laboratory Fellowships (Doctorate/Fellowship) [5382]

LLN Scholarships (Community College/Scholarship) [5358]

E.C. Lloyd and J.C.U. Johnson Scholarship Fund (Undergraduate/Scholarship) [3042]

Loan Forgiveness Scholarships (Graduate, Undergraduate/Loan, Scholarship) [8634]

Virgil K. Lobring Scholarships (Undergraduate/Scholarship) [3202]

Local Wound Haemostatics and Hemorrhage Control Scholarships (All/Scholarship) [557]

Leon I. Lock and Barbara R. Lock Scholarship Fund (Undergraduate/Scholarship) [3950]

William J. Locklin Scholarships (Undergraduate/Scholarship) [1285]

Lodging Management Program Scholarships (LMP) (Undergraduate/Scholarship) [800]

Audrey Loftus Memorial Scholarships (Undergraduate/Scholarship) [9188]

Stephen Logan Memorial Scholarships (Undergraduate/Scholarship) [4052]

Abram D. and Maxine H. Londa Scholarships (Undergraduate/Scholarship) [6661]

Lone Star GIA Associate and Alumni Scholarships (Undergraduate/Scholarship) [4064]

Lawrence A. Long Memorial Law Scholarships (Undergraduate/Scholarship) [368]

James E. Long Memorial Post Doctoral Fellowships (Postdoctorate/Fellowship) [4913]

Long-Term Research Fellowship Programs (Professional development/Fellowship) [5672]

Kay Longscope Scholarships (Graduate, Undergraduate/Scholarship) [6392]

Audre Lord Scholarships (Graduate, Undergraduate/Scholarship) [7857]

Suzanne and Caleb Loring Research Fellowships (Graduate, Doctorate/Fellowship) [5673]

Barbara Lotze Scholarships for Future Teachers (Undergraduate/Scholarship) [533]

Willie T. Loud - CH2M Hill Scholarships (Undergraduate/Scholarship) [6295]

Louisiana Agricultural Consultants Association Scholarships (Graduate, Undergraduate/Scholarship) [5517]

Louisville Institute Dissertation Fellowships (Doctorate/Fellowship) [5527]

Louisville Institute First Book Grants for Minority Scholars (Doctorate/Grant) [5528]

Louisville Institute Project Grants for Researchers (Doctorate/Grant) [5529]

Louisville Institute Sabbatical Grants for Researchers (Doctorate/Grant) [5530]

First Lieutenant Scott McClean Love Memorial Scholarship - Children of Soldiers (Undergraduate, Vocational/Occupational/Scholarship) [1615]

First Lieutenant Scott McClean Love Memorial Scholarship - Spouses of Soldiers (Undergraduate, Vocational/Occupational/Scholarship) [1616]

D.J. Lovell Scholarships (Graduate, Undergraduate/Scholarship) [8640]

The Lowell H. and Dorothy Loving Undergraduate Scholarships (Undergraduate/Scholarship) [646]

Gertie S. Lowe Nursing Scholarship Awards (Undergraduate/Scholarship) [3043]

LPHA Scholarships (Graduate, Undergraduate/Scholarship) [5525]

LRF Post-Doctoral Fellowships (Doctorate, Graduate/Fellowship) [5552]

Henry Luce Foundation Dissertation Fellowships in American Art (Doctorate/Fellowship) [679]

Elsa Ludeke Graduate Scholarships (Graduate/Scholarship) [3417]

David F. Ludovici Scholarships (Undergraduate/Scholarship) [3829]

Lugonia Alumni/Harrison Lightfoot Scholarships (Undergraduate/Scholarship) [7667]

LULAC GM Scholarships (Graduate, High School, Undergraduate, Vocational/Occupational/Award) [5387]

LULAC National Scholarship Fund (Graduate, High School, Undergraduate, Vocational/Occupational/Scholarship) [5388]

Audrey Lumsden-Kouvel Fellowships (Postdoctorate/Fellowship) [6698]

Lung Health Dissertation Grants (Graduate/Grant) [916]

Luso-American Fraternal Federation B-2 Scholarships (Postgraduate/Scholarship) [5545]

Luso-American Fraternal Federation B-3 Scholarships (All, Vocational/Occupational/Scholarship) [5546]

Luso-American Fraternal Federation B-4 Scholarships (All/Scholarship) [5547]

Norval Neil Luxon Prize for Scholarships to Juniors (Undergraduate/Scholarship) [9286]

Denny Lydic Scholarships (Undergraduate, Vocational/Occupational/Scholarship) [8952]

The C. Lyons Fellowship Program (All/Fellowship) [6389]

Linda Lyons Memorial Scholarship Fund (Undergraduate/Scholarship) [5779]

Verne LaMarr Lyons Memorial Scholarships (Graduate/Fellowship) [6123]

Carie and George Lyter Scholarship Fund (Undergraduate/Scholarship) [3951]

John Mabry Forestry Scholarships (Undergraduate/Scholarship) [7587]

Dr. Mac Scholarships (Undergraduate/Scholarship) [3118]

Bill MacAloney Legacy Scholarships (Undergraduate/Scholarship) [2252]

Catharine Macaulay Prize (Graduate/Prize) [1233]

MACC Scholarships (Professional development/Scholarship) [5796]

Katie MacDonald Memorial Scholarships (Graduate, Undergraduate/Scholarship) [9018]

Irene and Daisy MacGregor Memorial Scholarships (Graduate/Scholarship) [4448]

Nate Mack/Cindi Turner Scholarships (Undergraduate/Scholarship) [7504]

Robert Mack Scholarships (Graduate, Undergraduate/Scholarship) [5556]

James Mackenzie Fallows Scholarships Honoring William Cunningham (Undergraduate/Scholarship) [7668]

Thermoset Division/James I. Mackenzie and James H. Cunningham Scholarships (Graduate, Undergraduate/Scholarship) [8452]

Mackey-Byars Scholarships for Communication Excellence (Undergraduate/Scholarship) [9287]

Carol E. Macpherson Memorial Scholarship and Alumnae Society Scholarships (Graduate, Undergraduate/Scholarship) [9244]

Andrew Macrina Scholarships (High School/Scholarship) [695]

Eileen C. Maddex Fellowships (Graduate/Fellowship) [5198]

Lawrence Madeiros Scholarships (Undergraduate/Scholarship) [6330]

James Madison Foundation - Junior Fellowships (Graduate/Fellowship) [5564]

James Madison Foundation - Senior Fellowships (Graduate/Fellowship) [5565]

Gordon and Delores Madson Scholarships (Undergraduate/Scholarship) [3507]

MAES Founders Scholarships (Graduate, Undergraduate/Scholarship) [5798]

MAES General Scholarships (Graduate, Undergraduate/Scholarship) [5799]

MAES Graduate Scholarships (Graduate/Scholarship) [5800]

MAES Padrino/Madrina Scholarships (Graduate, Undergraduate/Scholarship) [5801]

MAES Pipeline Scholarships (Graduate, Undergraduate/Scholarship) [5802]

MAES Presidential Scholarships (Graduate, Undergraduate/Scholarship) [5803]

Jay Magazine Memorial Fund College Scholarships (JMMF) (Graduate, Undergraduate/Scholarship) [5759]

Magnetic Interfaces and Nanostructures Division - The Leo M. Falicov Student Award (Graduate/Award) [1983]

Dr. Edward May Magruder Medical Scholarships (Undergraduate/Scholarship) [609]

Dan and Rachel Mahi Educational Scholarships (Graduate, Undergraduate/Scholarship) [5216]

Maiman Student Paper Competition (Graduate, Undergraduate/Award) [6912]

Maine Graphic Arts Association Scholarships (Undergraduate/Scholarship) [5597]

Maintenance Technical Reward and Career Scholarships (Undergraduate/Scholarship) [6170]

Malayalee Engineers Association Scholarships (Graduate/Scholarship) [5601]

MALDEF Dream Act Student Activist Scholarships (Undergraduate, Graduate/Scholarship) [5805]

Maley/FTE Scholarships (Graduate/Scholarship) [5013]

Maley/FTEE Teacher Scholarships (Graduate/Scholarship) [5008]

Mallet Nursing Scholarships (Undergraduate/Scholarship) [8120]

Malmberg Fellowships (Undergraduate/Fellowship) [1401]

Malmberg Scholarships (Undergraduate/Scholarship) [1402]

Joseph J. Malone Fellowships in Arab and Islamic Studies (Professional development/Fellowship) [6227]

Reba Malone Scholarships (Graduate, Undergraduate/Scholarship) [1055]

Sue A. Malone Scholarships (Doctorate, Graduate/Scholarship) [5188]

David C. Maloney Scholarships (Undergraduate/Scholarship) [6423]

Dr. Julianne Malveaux Scholarships (Undergraduate/Scholarship) [6093]

Malyon-Smith Scholarships (Graduate/Scholarship) [8472]

Lyle Mamer Fellowships (Graduate/Fellowship) [9724]

MANAA Media Scholarships (Graduate, Undergraduate/Scholarship) [5737]

Mangasar M. Mangasarian Scholarship Fund (Graduate/Scholarship) [1602]

Norm Manly - YMTA Maritime Educational Scholarships *(Undergraduate/Scholarship)* [9795]

Horace Mann Insurance Scholarships *(High School/Scholarship)* [6878]

Raleigh Mann Scholarships *(Undergraduate/Scholarship)* [9288]

Mansfield Soccer Association Scholarships *(Undergraduate/Scholarship)* [5603]

Honorable Carol Los Mansmann Memorial Scholarships *(Graduate, Undergraduate/Scholarship)* [329]

Paul Mansur Scholarships *(Undergraduate/Scholarship)* [4952]

Marathon Oil Corporation College Scholarship Program *(Graduate, Undergraduate/Scholarship)* [4578]

March of Dimes Graduate Nursing Scholarships *(Graduate/Scholarship)* [5607]

Harold and Inge Marcus Scholarships *(Undergraduate/Scholarship)* [4805]

The Eric Marder Scholarships *(Undergraduate/Scholarship)* [4710]

American Turkish Society Arif Mardin Music Fellowships *(Professional development/Fellowship)* [8976]

Margaret B. Lindsey Awards for Distinguished Research in Teacher Education *(Professional development/Award)* [467]

Marine Biological Laboratory Pioneers Fund *(Undergraduate/Scholarship)* [5621]

Marine Corps Engineer Association Assistance Fund *(Graduate, High School, Undergraduate/Scholarship)* [5635]

Marine Corps League National Scholarships *(Undergraduate/Scholarship)* [5637]

Marine Technology Society ROV Scholarships *(Graduate, Undergraduate/Scholarship)* [5639]

Marine Technology Society Scholarships for Graduate and Undergraduate Students *(Graduate, Undergraduate/Scholarship)* [5640]

Marine Technology Society Student Scholarships for Graduating High School Seniors *(Undergraduate/Scholarship)* [5641]

Marine Technology Society Student Scholarships for Two-year Technical, Engineering and Community College Students *(Community College, Two Year College, Undergraduate/Scholarship)* [5642]

Dr. Frank and Florence Marino Scholarships *(Undergraduate/Scholarship)* [4451]

Mariposa Elementary School PTA Scholarships *(Undergraduate, Vocational/Occupational/Scholarship)* [7669]

Howard T. Markey Memorial Scholarships *(Undergraduate/Scholarship)* [3717]

Ed Markham International Scholarships *(Undergraduate/Scholarship)* [733]

Markley Family Scholarship Fund *(Undergraduate/Scholarship)* [8687]

Markley Scholarships *(Graduate, Undergraduate/Scholarship)* [6046]

Markowski-Leach Scholarship Fund *(Graduate, Undergraduate/Scholarship)* [7858]

Richard Marks Educational Fund *(Graduate/Scholarship)* [5217]

Kaia Lynn Markwalter Endowed Scholarships *(Undergraduate/Scholarship)* [5453]

Marliave Scholarship Fund *(Undergraduate/Scholarship)* [1768]

Marmot Leadership Scholarships *(Postgraduate, Professional development, Undergraduate/Scholarship)* [7008]

Abraham Lincoln Marovitz Public Interest Law Scholarships *(Undergraduate/Scholarship)* [2746]

Carl J. Marrara Memorial Scholarship Fund *(Undergraduate/Scholarship)* [3780]

Marsh College Scholarships *(Undergraduate/Scholarship)* [4842]

Burton W. Marsh Fellowships *(Graduate/Fellowship)* [4826]

George Perkins Marsh Prize *(Professional development/Prize)* [1249]

Marsh Risk Consulting Scholarships *(Undergraduate/Scholarship)* [1347]

Barry H. Marshal Scholarships *(Undergraduate/Scholarship)* [7859]

Marshall-Baruch Fellowships *(Doctorate/Fellowship)* [5649]

Marshall Memorial Fellowships *(Professional development/Fellowship)* [4132]

Ray and Gertrude Marshall Scholarships *(Undergraduate/Scholarship)* [696]

Ron Marshall Scholarships *(Undergraduate/Scholarship)* [1138]

Sarah Shinn Marshall Scholarships *(Undergraduate/Scholarship)* [3379]

Lockheed Martin Graduate Scholarships *(Graduate/Scholarship)* [1560]

Lockheed Martin IT Scholarships *(Undergraduate/Scholarship)* [1561]

Susan B. Martin Memorial Scholarships *(Graduate/Scholarship)* [4666]

Edna Martin Scholarships *(Undergraduate/Scholarship)* [3119]

Martin Sisters Scholarships *(Undergraduate/Scholarship)* [3380]

Dottie Martin Teacher Scholarships *(Graduate, Undergraduate/Scholarship)* [6765]

John S. Martinez and Family Scholarship Fund *(Undergraduate/Scholarship)* [3081]

Eric Martinez Memorial Scholarships *(Graduate, Undergraduate/Scholarship)* [9019]

Corporal Joseph Martinez U.S. Army Memorial Scholarships *(Undergraduate/Scholarship)* [7505]

Michael Marucci Memorial Scholarships *(Undergraduate/Scholarship)* [6278]

Michael L. Marx and Donald K. Marshall Scholarships *(Undergraduate/Scholarship)* [7860]

Maryland Poison Center Clinical Toxicology Fellowships *(Doctorate, Graduate/Fellowship)* [5654]

Maryland Speech Language Hearing Association Scholarships *(Graduate/Scholarship)* [5656]

Mas Family Scholarships *(Graduate, Undergraduate/Scholarship)* [5658]

The Maschhoffs Pork Production Scholarships *(Undergraduate/Scholarship)* [6379]

Masonic-Range Science Scholarships *(Undergraduate/Scholarship)* [8484]

Massachusetts Bar Foundation Legal Intern Fellowship Program (LIFP) *(All/Fellowship)* [5664]

Massachusetts Society of the Cincinnati Fellowships *(Graduate, Doctorate/Fellowship)* [5674]

S.O. Mast Founder's Scholarships *(Undergraduate/Scholarship)* [5622]

The Master Gardeners of Pierce County Scholarships *(Undergraduate/Scholarship)* [4339]

Master Municipal Clerks Academy Scholarships *(Professional development/Scholarship)* [4958]

Master's Degree with a Major in Nursing Academic Scholarships *(Graduate/Scholarship)* [6100]

Master's Scholarships Program (MSP) *(Graduate, Master's/Scholarship)* [8081]

Matching Scholarships Program *(Undergraduate/Scholarship)* [3328]

Material Handling Education Foundation Scholarships *(Doctorate, Graduate, Undergraduate/Scholarship)* [5688]

Materials Information Society National Merit Scholarships *(Undergraduate/Scholarship)* [5693]

Larry Matfay Scholarships *(Graduate, Undergraduate/Scholarship)* [5287]

Katharine & Bryant Mather Scholarships *(Graduate/Scholarship)* [635]

Noel D. Matkin Awards *(Undergraduate/Award)* [3596]

Rene Matos Memorial Scholarships *(Undergraduate, Vocational/Occupational/Scholarship)* [6338]

The Renardo A. Matteucci Scholarship Fund *(Undergraduate/Scholarship)* [3088]

Greg Matthews Memorial Scholarships *(Undergraduate/Scholarship)* [7195]

Donald Mauer Scholarships *(Undergraduate/Scholarship)* [9289]

Maxwell Graduate Scholarships in Medical Journalism *(Postgraduate/Scholarship)* [9290]

Juliann and Joseph Maxwell Scholarships *(Undergraduate/Scholarship)* [3120]

Juliann King Maxwell Scholarships for Riverview High School Students *(Undergraduate, Vocational/Occupational/Scholarship)* [3121]

May-Cassioppi Scholarships *(Undergraduate/Scholarship)* [3159]

Howard Mayer Brown Fellowships *(Graduate/Fellowship)* [941]

John E. Mayfield ABLE Scholarships *(Undergraduate/Scholarship)* [3122]

Clara Mayo Grants *(Graduate/Grant)* [8474]

Charles D. Mayo Student Scholarships *(Undergraduate/Scholarship)* [4944]

Giuliano Mazzetti Scholarships *(Undergraduate/Scholarship)* [8392]

Bill McAdam Scholarships *(Undergraduate/Scholarship)* [6331]

Walter Samuel McAfee Scholarships in Space Physics *(Undergraduate/Scholarship)* [6490]

Durwood McAlister Scholarships *(Undergraduate/Scholarship)* [4107]

McBurney Disability Scholarships *(Undergraduate/Scholarship)* [9363]

Bill McCarthy Scout Scholarship Fund *(Undergraduate/Scholarship)* [8688]

McCaughan Heritage Scholarships *(Undergraduate/Scholarship)* [970]

McClatchy Scholarships *(Undergraduate/Scholarship)* [8552]

McCleary Law Fellows Program *(Graduate, Undergraduate/Fellowship)* [4634]

McColl Family Fellowships *(Professional development/Fellowship)* [776]

Anne O'Hare McCormick Scholarship Fund *(Graduate/Scholarship)* [6716]

Niqui McCown Honor and Memorial Scholarship Fund *(Undergraduate/Scholarship)* [9555]

McDaniel College Eagle Scout Scholarships *(Undergraduate/Scholarship)* [6259]

Ronald McDonald House Charities African American Future Achievers Scholarships *(Undergraduate/Scholarship)* [5700]

Ronald McDonald House Charities of Hispanic Heritage *(Undergraduate/Scholarship)* [5701]

Ronald McDonald House Charities of Las Vegas Scholarships *(Undergraduate/Scholarship)* [7507]

Ronald McDonald House Charities Scholarships in Asia *(Undergraduate/Scholarship)* [5702]

Ronald McDonald House Charities Scholarships *(Undergraduate/Scholarship)* [5703]

J. McDonald and Judy Williams School of Law Scholarships *(Undergraduate/Scholarship)* [7196]

Larry McDonald Scholarships *(Undergraduate/Scholarship)* [3680]

Michele L. McDonald Scholarships *(Undergraduate/Scholarship)* [3599]

McDonald's USA National Employee Scholarship Program *(Undergraduate/Scholarship)* [5705]

Bodie McDowell Scholarships *(Graduate, Undergraduate/Scholarship)* [7006]

Nancy B. Woolridge McGee Graduate Fellowships *(Graduate/Fellowship)* [9806]

Senator Patricia K. McGee Nursing Faculty Scholarships *(Doctorate, Graduate/Scholarship)* [6675]

Lucile E. McGee Scholarships *(Undergraduate/Scholarship)* [5102]

Lee Kimche McGrath Worldwide Fellowships *(Professional development/Fellowship)* [1870]

William P. McHugh Memorial Fund Award *(Doctorate, Graduate/Fellowship)* [1141]

Brouwer D. McIntyre Memorial Scholarships *(Undergraduate/Scholarship)* [1946]

McJulien Minority Graduate Scholarships *(Graduate/Scholarship)* [1764]

Molly McKay Scholarships *(Undergraduate/Scholarship)* [9291]

McKelvey Foundation Entrepreneurial Scholarships *(Undergraduate/Scholarship)* [5728]

McKelvey Scholarships *(Undergraduate/Scholarship)* [5729]

McKesson Scholarships *(Undergraduate/Scholarship)* [3978]

John J. McKetta Undergraduate Scholarships *(Undergraduate/Scholarship)* [846]

Arthur Patch McKinlay Scholarships *(Graduate, Undergraduate/Scholarship)* [612]

McKinley Elementary School PTA Scholarships *(Undergraduate, Vocational/Occupational/Scholarship)* [7670]

John L. and Eleanore I. Mckinley Scholarships *(Undergraduate/Scholarship)* [3418]

Elizabeth McKissick Memorial Scholarships *(Under-*

graduate/Scholarship) [5454]

H.H. McKnight Memorial Scholarships (Undergraduate/Scholarship) [9233]

C.A. "Pete" McKnight Scholarships (Undergraduate/Scholarship) [9292]

Paul R. McLaughlin Fellowships (All/Fellowship) [7606]

McLean Scholarships (Undergraduate/Scholarship) [1797]

John McLendon Memorial Minority Postgraduate Scholarships (Postdoctorate/Scholarship) [6062]

Charles McMahon Memorial Construction Management/Engineering Scholarship Awards (Undergraduate/Scholarship) [1632]

Ruth McMillan Student Grants (Undergraduate/Grant) [2282]

Ronald E. McNair Scholarships in Space and Optical Physics (Undergraduate/Scholarship) [6491]

McNamara Family Creative Arts Project Grants (Graduate, Undergraduate/Grant) [4579]

McNeil Dissertation Fellowships (All/Fellowship) [9667]

National Association of Pediatric Nurse Practitioners McNeil Rural and Underserved Scholarships (Graduate/Scholarship) [6107]

Joan Reagin McNeill Scholarships - Alpha Theta (Undergraduate/Scholarship) [8178]

Joan Reagin McNeill Scholarships - Theta Phi (Undergraduate/Scholarship) [8179]

MDA Development Grants (Doctorate/Grant) [5952]

MDA Research Grants (Doctorate/Grant) [5953]

MDF Post-Doctoral Fellowships (Postdoctorate/Fellowship) [5969]

Margaret Mead Awards (Professional development/Award) [407]

Mead Leadership Fellows Program (Professional development/Fellowship) [6796]

David Meador Student Scholarships (Undergraduate/Scholarship) [6622]

Ben Meadows Natural Resource Scholarships - Academic Achievement Scholarships (Undergraduate/Scholarship) [2054]

Ben Meadows Natural Resource Scholarships - Leadership Scholarships (Undergraduate/Scholarship) [2055]

Jerry Medforth Nursing Scholarship Awards (Undergraduate/Scholarship) [3044]

Medical Library Association Scholarships for Minority Students (Graduate/Scholarship) [5745]

Medical Professionals of Tomorrow Scholarships (Undergraduate, Graduate/Scholarship) [9060]

Medical Student Summer Research Scholarships (Undergraduate/Scholarship) [374]

Medicus Student Exchange Scholarships (Graduate, Undergraduate/Scholarship) [8783]

Medieval Academy Dissertation Grants (Graduate/Grant) [5753]

Rixio Medina and Associates Hispanics in Safety Scholarships (Graduate, Undergraduate/Scholarship) [1348]

Augustine and Sandra Medina Memorial Scholarships (Undergraduate/Scholarship) [7671]

Edward Heywood Megson Scholarships (Undergraduate/Scholarship) [9293]

Karl Mehlman Scholarships (Undergraduate/Scholarship) [2988]

Kumar Mehta Scholarships (Graduate/Scholarship) [636]

Dr. Roger E. Meisner Veterinary Medicine Educational Scholarship Fund (Undergraduate/Scholarship) [6790]

Frederic G. Melcher Scholarships (Graduate/Scholarship) [1827]

Andrew W. Mellon Dissertation Completion Fellowships (Doctorate/Fellowship) [680]

Andrew W. Mellon Fellowships (Graduate, Doctorate/Fellowship) [5675]

Mellon Fellowships (Doctorate, Graduate/Fellowship) [3279]

Andrew W. Mellon Foundation Fellowships (Graduate/Fellowship) [6983]

Institute Andrew W. Mellon Postdoctoral Research Fellowships (Doctorate/Fellowship) [6883]

E.V. and Nancy Melosi Travel Grants (Graduate, Professional development/Grant) [1250]

Joseph C. Menezes Scholarships (Undergraduate/Scholarship) [5571]

Mensa Education and Research Foundation U.S. Scholarships (Graduate, Undergraduate, Vocational/Occupational/Scholarship) [5775]

Mentored Research Scholar Grant in Applied and Clinical Research (Doctorate, Professional development/Grant) [598]

Mentoring Travel Grants for Women (Postdoctorate/Scholarship) [1907]

Benchwarmers of Redlands-Jess Mercado Football Scholarships (Undergraduate/Scholarship) [7672]

John Merrick Law Scholarships (Undergraduate/Scholarship) [7197]

William J. Merriman American Council on Exercise Educational Scholarships (Undergraduate/Scholarship) [663]

VISTAKON George Mertz and Sheldon Wechsler Residency Awards (All/Award) [387]

MESA Graduate Student Paper Prize (Graduate/Prize) [5851]

MESA Student Travel Fund (Undergraduate/Grant) [5852]

MESBEC Scholarships (Undergraduate/Scholarship) [2662]

Scott Mesh Honorary Scholarships for Research in Psychology (Graduate/Fellowship) [1034]

Christopher Mesi Memorial Music Scholarships (Undergraduate/Scholarship) [2659]

Mesothelioma Memorial Scholarships (Undergraduate, Vocational/Occupational/Scholarship) [8751]

Mesquite Club Evening Chapter Scholarships (Undergraduate/Scholarship) [7508]

Messenger-Anderson Journalism Scholarships and Internships Program (Undergraduate/Scholarship) [7861]

Ruth Messmer Memorial Scholarships (Undergraduate/Scholarship) [8614]

MetroPCS Community Scholars Program (Undergraduate/Scholarship) [5781]

Metropolitan Museum of Art Conservation and Scientific Research Fellowships (Graduate/Fellowship) [5788]

Metropolitan Museum of Art Research Scholarships in Photograph Conservation (Graduate/Scholarship) [5789]

Mexican American Alumni Association Scholarships (Graduate, Undergraduate/Scholarship) [9400]

Mexican American Legal Defense and Educational Fund Law School Scholarships (Undergraduate/Scholarship) [5806]

MHS Health Career Scholarships (Undergraduate/Scholarship) [5750]

Michigan Accountancy Foundation Fifth/Graduate Year Scholarships (MAF) (Graduate/Scholarship) [5808]

Michigan Association of Realtors Scholarship Trust (MARST) (Graduate, Undergraduate/Scholarship) [5812]

Michigan Council of Women in Technology High School Scholarship Program (Undergraduate/Scholarship) [5816]

Michigan Education Association Scholarships (Undergraduate/Scholarship) [5819]

Michigan League for Nursing Scholarships (Undergraduate/Scholarship) [5821]

Michigan Nursery and Landscape Association Scholarships (Undergraduate/Scholarship) [5823]

Michigan Society of Fellows Three-Year Fellowships (Postdoctorate/Fellowship) [5827]

Michigan Society of Professional Engineers Scholarships (Undergraduate/Scholarship) [5829]

Michigan Stormwater-Floodplain Association Scholarships (Graduate, Undergraduate/Scholarship) [5834]

Michigan Tech Alumni Scholarships (Graduate, Undergraduate/Scholarship) [1130]

John G. and Betty J. Mick Scholarship Fund (Undergraduate/Scholarship) [8691]

Microsoft Research Graduate Women's Scholarships (Graduate/Scholarship) [5844]

Microsoft Research PhD Fellowships (Doctorate/Fellowship) [5845]

Mid-Continent Instrument Scholarships (Undergraduate/Scholarship) [135]

Mid-South STC Chapter Scholarships (Graduate,

Undergraduate/Scholarship) [8502]

Beth Middleton Memorial Scholarships (Undergraduate/Scholarship) [3709]

Midwest Modern Language Association Fellowships (Doctorate/Fellowship) [6699]

Albert and Eloise Midyette Memorial Scholarship Fund (Undergraduate/Scholarship) [3913]

Keith Miffioli Scholarships (Undergraduate/Scholarship) [3160]

Migrant Health Scholarships (Professional development/Scholarship) [6182]

Mihaly Russin Scholarship Awards (Graduate/Scholarship) [7837]

Mikimoto Scholarships (Graduate/Scholarship) [4065]

Mary Ann Mikulic Scholarships (Professional development/Scholarship) [1856]

Milan Getting Scholarships (Undergraduate/Scholarship) [8522]

Milbank Diversity Scholarships (Undergraduate/Scholarship) [5870]

Mildred Colodny Diversity Scholarships for Graduate Study in Historic Preservation (Graduate/Scholarship) [6546]

Eunice Miles Scholarships (Undergraduate/Scholarship) [4066]

William F. Miles Scholarships (Undergraduate/Scholarship) [4379]

Military Intelligence Corps Association Scholarships (Undergraduate, Vocational/Occupational/Scholarship) [5872]

Military Order of the Purple Heart Foundation Scholarships (Undergraduate/Scholarship) [5455]

Cheryl Allyn Miller Awards (Doctorate, Graduate/Fellowship) [8519]

Miller Electric International WorldSkills Competition Scholarships (Undergraduate/Scholarship) [1441]

Ruth R. and Alyson R. Miller Fellowships (Graduate, Doctorate/Fellowship) [5676]

Robbie Miller Memorial Scholarships (Undergraduate/Scholarship) [5456]

Raymond W. Miller, PE and Alice E. Miller Scholarships (Undergraduate/Scholarship) [3830]

Raymond W. Miller, PE Scholarships (Undergraduate/Scholarship) [3831]

Glenn Miller Scholarships (Undergraduate/Scholarship) [5880]

MillerCoors Chicago Scholarships (Community College, Undergraduate/Scholarship) [46]

MillerCoors Engineering and Sciences Scholarships (Undergraduate/Scholarship) [47]

MillerCoors National Scholarships (Undergraduate/Scholarship) [48]

Dolphus E. Milligan Graduate Fellowships (Graduate/Fellowship) [6429]

George Hi'ilani Mills Perpetual Fellowships (Graduate/Fellowship) [5218]

Quincy Sharpe Mills Scholarships (Undergraduate/Scholarship) [9294]

Milton Center Fellowships (Graduate/Fellowship) [4703]

Mined Land Reclamation Educational Grant Program (Undergraduate/Grant) [6125]

Mary Minglen Scholarship Program (Postgraduate/Scholarship) [953]

Minnesota Association County Probation Officers Scholarships (Undergraduate/Scholarship) [5890]

Minnesota Association of Township Scholarships (Undergraduate, Vocational/Occupational/Scholarship) [5894]

Minnesota Division Scholarships (Undergraduate/Scholarship) [5861]

Minnesota State Archery Association Scholarships Program (Undergraduate/Scholarship) [5902]

Jacque I. Minnotte Health Reporting Fellowships (Professional development/Fellowship) [7579]

Minorities in Government Finance Scholarships (Graduate, Undergraduate/Scholarship) [4199]

Minority Leadership Development Awards (Graduate/Award) [503]

Minority Medical Student Fellowships in HIV Psychiatry (Undergraduate/Fellowship) [1025]

Minority Pharmacy Faculty New Investigator Grants (Professional development/Grant) [759]

Minority Scholarship Awards for College Students (Undergraduate/Scholarship) [847]

Minority Scholarship Awards for Incoming College Freshmen (Undergraduate/Scholarship) [848]

Minority-Serving Institution Faculty Scholar Awards (Doctorate/Award) [452]

Minority Student Gateway to Research Scholarships (Professional development/Scholarship) [760]

Minority Student Pre-Doctoral Fellowship Program (Doctorate, Graduate/Fellowship) [761]

Minority Visiting Students Awards (Undergraduate, Graduate/Award, Internship) [8241]

MiraCosta College Two-Year Colleges Scholarships (Undergraduate/Scholarship) [5906]

The Aristotle Mirones Scholarships (Undergraduate/Scholarship) [7141]

Molly Ann Mishler Memorial Scholarships (Undergraduate/Scholarship) [9163]

Joseph and Catherine Missigman Memorial Nursing Scholarships (Undergraduate/Scholarship) [3782]

Missigman Scholarship Fund (Undergraduate/Scholarship) [3783]

Joshua Esch Mitchell Aviation Scholarships (Undergraduate/Scholarship) [4293]

George J. Mitchell Postgraduate Scholarships (Postgraduate/Scholarship) [6077]

Dorothy Mitchell Scholarships (Undergraduate/Scholarship) [7673]

George J. Mitchell Scholarships (Undergraduate/Scholarship) [9398]

Sam Mizrahi Memorial Scholarships (Undergraduate/Scholarship) [3952]

MJSA Education Foundation Scholarship Fund (Undergraduate/Scholarship) [5605]

MJSA Educational Foundation Jewelry Scholarships (Undergraduate/Scholarship) [7792]

MLA/NLM Spectrum Scholarship Program (Undergraduate/Scholarship) [5746]

MLA Research, Development, and Demonstration Project Grants (Graduate/Grant) [5747]

MMUF Dissertation Grants (Doctorate/Grant) [9616]

MMUF Travel and Research Grants (Doctorate/Grant) [9617]

MOAA American Patriot Scholarships (Undergraduate/Scholarship) [5874]

MOAA Base/Post Scholarships (Undergraduate/Scholarship) [5875]

Modern Woodmen of America Scholarships (Undergraduate/Scholarship) [3538]

Ralph Modjeski Scholarships (Graduate, Undergraduate/Scholarship) [7369]

MODNA Nursing Education Scholarships (Doctorate, Graduate/Fellowship) [5849]

Francis H. Moffitt Memorial Scholarships (Graduate, Undergraduate/Scholarship) [1670]

Donald and Idabelle Mohr Scholarships (Undergraduate/Scholarship) [2891]

Molecular Evolution Fellowships (Doctorate/Fellowship) [8242]

Antoinette M. Molinari Memorial Scholarships (Doctorate/Scholarship) [388]

Momeni Foundation Scholarships (Undergraduate/Scholarship) [6364]

Nell I. Mondy Fellowships (Graduate, Postdoctorate/Fellowship) [8152]

Monster Medical Imaging Educators Scholarship Program (Postdoctorate/Scholarship) [1325]

Montana Broadcasters Association Directors' Scholarships (Undergraduate/Scholarship) [5923]

Montana Broadcasters Association Engineers' Scholarships (Undergraduate/Scholarship) [5924]

Letitia Moore Art Scholarships (Undergraduate/Scholarship) [9789]

Cary Moore Memorial Scholarship Fund (Undergraduate/Scholarship) [3203]

Moore Middle School PTA Scholarships (Undergraduate/Scholarship) [7674]

Farmers Union Marketing and Processing Foundation Stanley Moore Scholarships (Undergraduate, Vocational/Occupational/Scholarship) [6784]

Stanley Moore Scholarships (Undergraduate, Vocational/Occupational/Scholarship) [6785]

Willie Hobbs Moore Scholarships (Undergraduate/Scholarship) [6492]

Walter Moran Farmer Scholarships (Undergraduate/Scholarship) [9531]

Jim Moran Scholarships (Undergraduate/Scholarship) [1947]

Dan Mordecai Educational Scholarships (Graduate, Undergraduate/Scholarship) [6619]

Jake S. More Scholarships (Undergraduate/Scholarship) [3508]

Thomas More Scholarships (Undergraduate/Scholarship) [4191]

More Uncommon Grounds Scholarships (MUG) (Undergraduate/Scholarship) [3260]

Thomas S. Morgan Memorial Scholarships (Graduate, Master's/Scholarship) [7241]

Sonia Morgan Scholarships (Undergraduate/Scholarship) [6662]

Alexander Morisey Scholarships (Undergraduate/Scholarship) [9296]

Robert S. Morison Fellowships (Doctorate, Graduate/Fellowship) [720]

Leo F. Moro Baseball Memorial Scholarships (Undergraduate/Scholarship) [3953]

Frank Morrell Endowed Memorial Scholarships (Undergraduate/Scholarship) [5623]

Morris County Psychological Association Scholarships (Undergraduate/Scholarship) [5933]

Morris Newspaper Corp. Scholarships (Undergraduate/Scholarship) [4108]

June Morrison Scholarship Fund (Undergraduate/Scholarship) [9582]

Harry L. Morrison Scholarships (Undergraduate/Scholarship) [6493]

Dorothy Morrison Undergraduate Scholarships (Undergraduate/Scholarship) [1199]

Mortar Board National Foundation Fellowships (Postdoctorate/Fellowship) [5937]

Dwight Mosley Scholarships (Undergraduate/Scholarship) [9410]

John R. Mott Scholarships (Undergraduate/Scholarship) [5939]

Mt. Hood Chapter Scholarship Awards (Undergraduate/Scholarship) [6938]

Dorothy Mountain Memorial Scholarships (Graduate/Scholarship) [5532]

Mountain Memorial Scholarships (Undergraduate/Scholarship) [5624]

Burton J. Moyer Memorial Fellowships (Graduate/Fellowship) [4491]

MPAC-DC Graduate Policy Fellowships (Graduate/Fellowship) [5960]

MPAEA Memorial Scholarships (Graduate/Scholarship) [5941]

MPAEA Student Scholarships (Other/Scholarship) [5942]

MPI CRV Scholarships (Professional development/Scholarship) [5757]

MPower Scholarships (Graduate, Undergraduate/Scholarship) [7269]

MSPT Sports Medicine Scholarships (Undergraduate/Scholarship) [7509]

Ruth Mu-Lan and James S.C. Chao Scholarships (Undergraduate/Scholarship) [9065]

Muddy Waters Scholarships (Graduate/Scholarship) [2155]

Brittany Mueller Memorial Scholarships (High School/Scholarship) [6603]

Mueller Undergraduate Scholarships (Undergraduate/Scholarship) [9677]

Ryan Mullaly Second Chance Fund Scholarships (Undergraduate, Vocational/Occupational/Scholarship) [5946]

Barbara H. Mullin Memorial Scholarships (Graduate, Undergraduate/Scholarship) [9573]

Multi-Country Research Fellowships (Doctorate/Fellowship) [3270]

Multicultural Advertising Intern Program (Graduate, Undergraduate/Internship) [435]

Muncy Rotary Club Scholarship Fund (Undergraduate/Scholarship) [3785]

Muncy Scholars Award Fund (Undergraduate/Award) [3786]

Marvin Mundel Memorial Scholarships (Undergraduate/Scholarship) [4806]

Harry Munoz Memorial Scholarships (Undergraduate/Scholarship) [7675]

Rick Munoz Memorial Scholarships (Undergraduate/Scholarship) [7676]

Jack and Gertrude Murphy Fellowships (Graduate/Fellowship) [7983]

Linda J. Murphy Scholarships (Undergraduate/Scholarship) [9704]

NACCED Annual John C. Murphy Scholarships (Graduate, Undergraduate/Scholarship) [6066]

Carolyn Murray Memorial Scholarships (Undergraduate/Scholarship) [2337]

Muscle Shoals Kiwanis/Wal-Mart Scholarships (Undergraduate/Scholarship) [6818]

Muslim Sister Scholarships (Undergraduate/Scholarship) [8224]

My Life As A Lawyer Scholarships (Graduate, Undergraduate/Scholarship) [3262]

MyApartmentMap Housing Scholarships (Undergraduate/Scholarship) [5962]

Sam A. Myar Jr. Law Scholarships (Undergraduate/Scholarship) [9235]

Myasthenia Gravis Foundation of America Nursing Fellowships (Undergraduate/Fellowship) [5964]

Myasthenia Gravis Foundation of America Student Fellowships (Graduate, Undergraduate/Fellowship) [5965]

Clarence and Josephine Myers Scholarships (Graduate, Undergraduate/Scholarship) [8394]

Mary Fran Myers Scholarships (All/Grant) [6569]

NAAMA Scholarships (Undergraduate/Scholarship) [6024]

NABA National Scholarship Program (Graduate, Undergraduate/Scholarship) [6037]

NACA East Coast Graduate Student Scholarships (Graduate, Postdoctorate/Scholarship) [6047]

NACA East Coast Higher Education Research Scholarships (Postgraduate/Scholarship) [6048]

NACA East Coast Undergraduate Scholarships for Student Leaders (Undergraduate/Scholarship) [6049]

NACA Foundation Graduate Scholarships (Graduate, Master's, Postdoctorate/Scholarship) [6050]

NACA Regional Council Student Leadership Scholarships (Undergraduate/Scholarship) [6051]

NACA Southeast Student Leadership Scholarships (Undergraduate/Scholarship) [6052]

NACADA Scholarships (Doctorate, Graduate/Scholarship) [5997]

NAED/Spencer Dissertation Fellowship Program (Doctorate/Fellowship) [6005]

NAFA International Dissertation Research Fellowships (Doctorate/Fellowship) [6078]

NAFEO Internship Program (Undergraduate/Internship) [6068]

Jack Nagasaka Memorial Scholarships (Undergraduate/Scholarship) [7677]

Gongoro Nakamura Memorial Scholarships (Undergraduate/Scholarship) [5145]

NALS of Detroit Scholarships (Undergraduate/Scholarship) [5977]

NAMTA - International Art Materials Trade Association Visual Arts Major Scholarships (Graduate, Undergraduate/Scholarship) [5981]

NANBPWC National Scholarships (Undergraduate/Scholarship) [6095]

Robyn Nance Memorial Scholarships (Undergraduate/Scholarship) [7678]

Nanometer-Scale Science and Technology Division Graduate Award (Graduate/Award) [1984]

NAPABA Law Foundation Scholarships (Undergraduate/Scholarship) [6028]

NARFE-FEEA Scholarship Awards Program (Undergraduate/Scholarship) [6011]

NARRP Student Conference Scholarships (Graduate, Undergraduate/Scholarship) [6111]

NASA Aeronautics Scholarships - Undergraduate Program (Undergraduate/Scholarship) [1241]

NASCOE Scholarships (Undergraduate/Scholarship) [6070]

NASE Future Entrepreneur Scholarships (Undergraduate/Scholarship) [6117]

Kermit B. Nash Academic Scholarships (Undergraduate/Scholarship) [8137]

Elizabeth Nash Foundation Scholarships (Graduate, Undergraduate/Scholarship) [5983]

Archie Hartwell Nash Memorial Scholarships (Graduate, Undergraduate/Scholarship) [3127]

Mike Nash Memorial Scholarships (Undergraduate/Scholarship) [9427]

NASIG Conference Student Grants (Graduate, Postdoctorate/Grant) [6743]

NEMLA Summer Fellowships *(Graduate, Professional development/Fellowship)* [6799]

NEMRA Educational Scholarship Foundation *(Undergraduate, Vocational/Occupational/Scholarship)* [6267]

Nephrology Nurse Researcher Awards *(Doctorate, Graduate/Award)* [945]

NERRS Graduate Research Fellowships (GRF) *(Graduate, Master's/Fellowship)* [6271]

NESCPA Fifth-Year Scholarships *(Graduate/Scholarship)* [6612]

NESCPA General Scholarships *(Graduate, Undergraduate/Scholarship)* [6613]

Amelia and Emanuel Nessell Scholarships *(Undergraduate/Scholarship)* [3540]

Netherlands-Florida Scholarship Foundation Scholarships *(Doctorate, Graduate/Scholarship)* [6615]

Reverend John S. Nettled Scholarships *(Undergraduate/Scholarship)* [3045]

Networks Scholarships College of Business *(Undergraduate/Scholarship)* [4750]

Elizabeth Neuffer Fellowships *(Professional development/Fellowship)* [5030]

Nevada Black Police Association Scholarships *(Undergraduate/Scholarship)* [7511]

Nevada Parent Teacher Association Scholarships *(Undergraduate/Scholarship)* [7512]

New Century Scholars Doctoral Scholarships *(Postdoctorate/Scholarship)* [1387]

New Century Scholars Research Grants *(Doctorate/Grant)* [1388]

New Hampshire Snowmobile Association Scholarships *(Undergraduate, Vocational/Occupational/Scholarship)* [6633]

New Jersey Psychological Association Scholarships for Minority Graduate Students *(Postgraduate/Scholarship)* [6655]

New Mexico Association for Bilingual Education Scholarships *(Undergraduate/Scholarship)* [6665]

New York Financial Writers' Associations Scholarships *(Graduate, Undergraduate/Scholarship)* [6667]

New York State Senate - Legislative Fellowships *(Graduate, Postgraduate/Fellowship)* [6678]

The New York Times College Scholarships *(Undergraduate/Scholarship)* [6685]

New York Water Environment Association Scholarships *(Undergraduate/Scholarship)* [6688]

Ted and Ruth Neward Scholarships *(Graduate, Undergraduate/Scholarship)* [8453]

Newberry Consortium on American Indian Studies Faculty Fellowships *(Professional development/Fellowship)* [6701]

Newberry Consortium on American Indian Studies Graduate Student Fellowships *(Doctorate/Fellowship)* [6702]

Newberry Library ACM/GLCA Faculty Fellowships *(Professional development/Fellowship)* [6703]

Newberry Library/British Academy Fellowships for Study in Great Britain *(Doctorate/Fellowship)* [6704]

Newberry Library/Ecole Nationale des Chartes Exchange Fellowships *(Graduate/Fellowship)* [6705]

Newberry Library Short-Term Fellowships in the History of Cartography *(Doctorate/Fellowship)* [6706]

Newberry Library Short-Term Resident Fellowships for Individual Research *(Postdoctorate/Fellowship)* [6707]

The Shanon Newberry Physical Therapy Scholarship Endowment *(Doctorate/Scholarship)* [8741]

Charlotte W. Newcombe Doctoral Dissertation Fellowships *(Doctorate/Fellowship)* [9618]

Newcomer Supply Student Scholarships *(Undergraduate/Scholarship)* [6514]

AAJA/S.I. Newhouse Foundation Scholarships *(Graduate, Undergraduate/Scholarship)* [1642]

Newkirk Center for Science and Society Graduate Student Fellowships *(Doctorate, Graduate/Fellowship)* [6712]

Frank Newman Leadership Awards *(Undergraduate/Scholarship)* [2350]

Edsel Newman Scholarships *(Undergraduate/Scholarship)* [5476]

Newman University Scouting Scholarships *(Undergraduate/Scholarship)* [6260]

Alwin B. Newton Scholarships *(Undergraduate/Scholarship)* [1268]

NFBPA/CDM Scholarships *(Graduate, Undergraduate/Scholarship)* [6296]

NFDA Professional Women's Conference Scholarships *(Undergraduate/Scholarship)* [4031]

NFID Advanced Vaccinology Course Travel Grants *(Postdoctorate/Grant)* [6301]

NFPA/PACE Scholarships *(Professional development/Scholarship)* [6284]

NFPA and Thomson West Scholarships *(Undergraduate/Scholarship)* [6285]

NFPA Youth Scholarships *(Undergraduate, Vocational/Occupational/Scholarship)* [6299]

NGAT Educational Scholarships *(Graduate, Undergraduate/Scholarship)* [6313]

NGC College Scholarships *(Graduate, Undergraduate/Scholarship)* [6303]

NHAEOP Member Scholarships *(Undergraduate/Scholarship)* [6626]

NHFA Scholarships *(Graduate/Scholarship)* [6340]

NHLBI Individual Pre-Doctoral Fellowships *(Doctorate, Graduate/Fellowship)* [6315]

NHPGA Apprentice Scholarships *(Undergraduate/Scholarship)* [5715]

NHS National Scholarships *(Undergraduate/Scholarship)* [6342]

NIAF Scholarships - General Category I *(Undergraduate/Scholarship)* [6369]

NIAF Scholarships - General Category II *(Undergraduate/Scholarship)* [6370]

NIBA Presidential Scholarships *(Undergraduate/Scholarship)* [6351]

Donald E. Nichols Scholarships *(Undergraduate/Scholarship)* [1269]

Gunnar Nicholson Endowed Scholarships *(Undergraduate/Scholarship)* [7199]

Herbert W. Nickens Medical Student Scholarships *(Undergraduate/Scholarship)* [1701]

Virginia Nicklas Scholarships *(Undergraduate/Scholarship)* [3382]

George A. Nielsen Public Investor Scholarships *(Graduate, Undergraduate/Scholarship)* [4200]

Mike Niemeyer Memorial Football Scholarships *(Undergraduate/Scholarship)* [7679]

Eric Niemitalo Scholarships in Earth and Environmental Science *(Undergraduate/Scholarship)* [8121]

Helen W. Nies Memorial Scholarships *(Undergraduate/Scholarship)* [3718]

NIJ Visiting Fellowships *(Professional development/Fellowship)* [6356]

Evelyn S. Nish Scholarships *(Undergraduate/Scholarship)* [8180]

Anderson Niskanen Scholarships *(Undergraduate/Scholarship)* [3541]

Nissan North America, Inc. Scholarships *(Undergraduate/Scholarship)* [809]

Nixon Family Scholarship Fund *(Undergraduate/Scholarship)* [9556]

NJCBIR Individual Research Grants *(Professional development/Grant)* [6639]

NJCBIR Pilot Research Grants *(Professional development/Grant)* [6640]

NJCBIR Postdoctoral and Graduate Student Fellowships *(Graduate, Postdoctorate/Fellowship)* [6641]

NJLA Scholarships *(Graduate, Postgraduate/Scholarship)* [6646]

NJSA Visionary Leader Scholarships *(Graduate/Scholarship)* [6381]

NLBRA/Wrangler Academic Scholarships *(Undergraduate/Scholarship)* [6398]

NLM Associate Fellowships *(Graduate, Postgraduate/Fellowship)* [6396]

NMCRS Gold Star Scholarship Program *(Undergraduate, Vocational/Occupational/Scholarship)* [6593]

NMIA Scholarship Program *(Undergraduate/Scholarship)* [6415]

NMSC College and University Sponsorship of Merit Scholarship Awards *(Undergraduate/Scholarship)* [6406]

NMSC Corporate-Sponsored Achievement Scholarship Awards *(Undergraduate/Scholarship)* [6407]

NMSC National Achievement Scholarship Program *(Undergraduate/Scholarship)* [6408]

NMSC Special Scholarships *(Undergraduate/Scholarship)* [6409]

NNF Scholarship Program *(Graduate, Undergraduate/Scholarship)* [520]

NOAA Graduate Sciences Scholarships *(Graduate/Scholarship)* [6418]

NOAA Undergraduate Scholarships *(Undergraduate/Scholarship)* [6419]

NOBCChE Procter and Gamble Fellowships *(Graduate/Fellowship)* [6430]

Leonard Noble Educational Scholarships *(Postgraduate/Scholarship)* [6515]

George H. Nofer Scholarships for Law and Public Policy *(Doctorate, Graduate/Scholarship)* [2049]

NOHIMSS Student Scholarship Program *(Undergraduate, Master's, Doctorate/Scholarship)* [6805]

Alfred H. Nolle Scholarships *(Undergraduate/Scholarship)* [344]

Helen Woodruff Nolop Scholarships in Audiology and Allied Fields *(Graduate/Scholarship)* [3419]

Non Commissioned Officers Association Scholarships *(Undergraduate/Scholarship)* [6726]

Nonproliferation Graduate Fellowships Program (NGFP) *(Graduate/Fellowship)* [7033]

Nor' Easters Scholarships - Four-year Program *(Undergraduate/Scholarship)* [6732]

Nor' Easters Scholarships - Two-year Program *(Undergraduate/Scholarship)* [6733]

Norall Scholarship Trust *(Undergraduate/Scholarship)* [5477]

Arthur L. Norberg Travel Grants *(All/Grant)* [1991]

Marian Norby Scholarships *(Professional development/Scholarship)* [8495]

Norfolk Southern Foundation Scholarships *(Undergraduate/Scholarship)* [1131]

Norfolk Southern Scholarships *(Undergraduate/Scholarship)* [9450]

Norkus Charitable Foundation Scholarships *(Undergraduate/Scholarship)* [2727]

North American Conference on British Studies Dissertation Year Fellowships *(Doctorate, Postdoctorate/Fellowship)* [6735]

North American Conference on British Studies-Huntington Library Fellowships *(Doctorate, Postdoctorate/Fellowship)* [6736]

North Carolina Association of Health Care Recruiters Scholarships *(Undergraduate/Scholarship)* [6755]

North Carolina Commercial Flower Growers Association Floriculture Scholarships *(Graduate, Undergraduate/Scholarship)* [6757]

North Carolina Council of Epsilon Sigma Alpha Scholarships *(Graduate, Professional development, Undergraduate/Scholarship)* [6763]

North Carolina Nursery and Landscape Association Horticulture Scholarships *(Undergraduate/Scholarship)* [6769]

North Central, Region 9 Scholarships *(Undergraduate/Scholarship)* [8395]

North Dakota Division Scholarships *(Undergraduate/Scholarship)* [5862]

North Dakota Farmers Union Co-op House Scholarships *(Undergraduate/Scholarship)* [6786]

North Dakota Farmers Union Scholarships *(Undergraduate/Scholarship)* [6787]

North Florida Chapter Safety Education Scholarships *(Graduate, Undergraduate/Scholarship)* [1349]

North Mecklenburg Teachers' Memorial Scholarships *(Undergraduate/Scholarship)* [3916]

Michelle North Scholarships for Safety *(Professional development/Scholarship)* [4510]

North Texas GIA Alumni Association Scholarships *(Undergraduate/Scholarship)* [4067]

NorthCoast Medical Scholarship Program *(Postgraduate/Scholarship)* [954]

Northeastern Illinois Chapter Scholarships *(Graduate, Undergraduate/Scholarship)* [1350]

Northern Arizona Native-American Foundation Scholarships *(Undergraduate, Vocational/Occupational/Scholarship)* [6801]

Northern California Chapter of HIMSS Scholarships *(Graduate, Postgraduate, Undergraduate/Scholarship)* [4506]

Northern California DX Foundation Scholarships

(Undergraduate/Scholarship) [1097]

Northern Virginia Alumnae Chapter Scholarships *(Undergraduate/Scholarship)* [3383]

Eugene Northrup Scholarships *(Undergraduate/Scholarship)* [5457]

Northwest-Shoals Community College Academic Scholarships *(Undergraduate/Scholarship)* [6819]

Northwest-Shoals Community College Applied Technology Scholarships *(Undergraduate, Vocational/Occupational/Scholarship)* [6820]

Northwest-Shoals Community College Athletic Scholarships *(Undergraduate/Scholarship)* [6821]

Northwest-Shoals Community College Bank Independent Scholarships *(Undergraduate/Scholarship)* [6822]

Northwest-Shoals Community College Fine Arts Scholarships - Art *(Undergraduate/Scholarship)* [6823]

Northwest-Shoals Community College Fine Arts Scholarships - Drama *(Undergraduate/Scholarship)* [6824]

Northwest-Shoals Community College Fine Arts Scholarships - Music *(Undergraduate/Scholarship)* [6825]

Northwest-Shoals Community College High School Academic Scholarships *(Undergraduate/Scholarship)* [6826]

Northwest-Shoals Community College Independent Computer Scholarships *(Undergraduate/Scholarship)* [6827]

Northwest-Shoals Community College Student Activities Scholarships *(Undergraduate/Scholarship)* [6828]

Northwestern Mutual Financial Network Scholarships *(Graduate, Undergraduate/Scholarship)* [7270]

Vessa Notchev Fellowships *(Graduate, Postdoctorate/Fellowship)* [8153]

Notre Dame Club of Canton Scholarships *(Undergraduate/Scholarship)* [8693]

NOVA Foundation Scholarships *(Doctorate, Graduate, Undergraduate/Scholarship)* [6840]

Mike and Flo Novovesky Scholarships *(Undergraduate/Scholarship)* [735]

Robert Noyce Scholarship Program *(Undergraduate/Scholarship)* [7160]

Noyce Scholarships for Secondary Math and Science Education *(Undergraduate/Scholarship)* [4751]

NPC Scholarships *(Graduate/Scholarship)* [6442]

NPELRA Foundation Scholarships *(Graduate/Scholarship)* [6836]

NPM Program Scholarships *(Undergraduate/Scholarship)* [6103]

NPPF Still and Multimedia Scholarships *(Undergraduate/Scholarship)* [6452]

NPSC Fellowships *(Graduate/Fellowship)* [6440]

NRL Postdoctoral Fellowships *(Postdoctorate/Fellowship)* [6581]

NSCLC Post-Graduate Fellowships *(Postgraduate/Fellowship)* [6472]

NSF Pickwick Postdoctoral Research Fellowships *(Postdoctorate/Fellowship)* [6476]

NSHMBA Scholarships *(Graduate/Scholarship)* [6508]

NSHSS Academic Paper Awards *(High School/Scholarship)* [6504]

NSHSS National Scholar Awards *(High School/Scholarship)* [6505]

NSPS Board of Governors Scholarships *(Undergraduate/Scholarship)* [648]

The NSPS Scholarships *(Undergraduate/Scholarship)* [649]

NSS Conservation Grants *(All/Grant)* [6526]

NSS Education Grants *(All/Grant)* [6527]

NSSA/NSCA Collegiate Scholarships *(Undergraduate/Scholarship)* [6531]

NTHS/HOSA Scholarships *(Undergraduate/Scholarship)* [6544]

NUF Fellowships *(Graduate, Postgraduate, Professional development/Fellowship)* [6553]

Nurseries Foundation Scholarship Awards *(Undergraduate/Scholarship)* [6939]

Nurseries Memorial Scholarship Awards *(Graduate/Scholarship)* [6940]

Nursing Scholarship Program *(Undergraduate/Scholarship)* [4498]

Nuts, Bolts and Thingamajigs Scholarships *(Undergraduate, Vocational/Occupational/Scholarship)* [6842]

NVIDIA Graduate Fellowships *(Doctorate/Fellowship)* [6844]

NWF Campus Ecology Fellowships *(Graduate, Undergraduate/Fellowship)* [6557]

NWF's Women for Sustainable Development Scholarships (WSD) *(Undergraduate/Scholarship)* [8145]

NWSA Distinguished Fellowships *(All/Fellowship)* [6561]

NWSA Graduate Scholarships *(Graduate/Scholarship)* [6562]

OAH-IEHS Huggins-Quarles Dissertation Awards *(Doctorate/Grant)* [6960]

OBAP Fellowships - Airline Transport (ATP) *(Professional development/Fellowship)* [6970]

OBAP Fellowships - Commercial *(Professional development/Fellowship)* [6971]

OBAP Fellowships - Instructor Rating CFI/CFII/MEI *(Professional development/Fellowship)* [6972]

OBAP Fellowships - Multi-Engine *(Professional development/Fellowship)* [6973]

Dennis J. O'Brien USAEE/IAEE Best Student Paper Awards *(Undergraduate/Award)* [9035]

Katharine H. Obye Scholarship Awards *(Undergraduate/Scholarship)* [3163]

Oceanic Research Group Scholarships *(Graduate, Undergraduate/Scholarship)* [6850]

Edward A. O'Connor Founder's Scholarships *(Undergraduate/Scholarship)* [68]

Odd Fellows Lodge No. 8 Endowed Scholarships *(Undergraduate/Scholarship)* [5458]

Captain Jennifer Shafer Odom Memorial Scholarships - Children of Soldiers *(Undergraduate, Vocational/Occupational/Scholarship)* [1617]

Captain Jennifer Shafer Odom Memorial Scholarships - Spouses of Soldiers *(Undergraduate, Vocational/Occupational/Scholarship)* [1618]

Office Depot Scholarships *(Undergraduate/Scholarship)* [4549]

Ohio Association of Broadcaster's Kids Scholarships *(Undergraduate/Scholarship)* [6852]

Ohio Newspaper Association Minority Scholarships *(Undergraduate/Scholarship)* [6858]

Ohio Newspaper Association University Journalism Scholarships *(Undergraduate/Scholarship)* [6859]

Ohio Newspaper Association Women's Scholarships *(Undergraduate/Scholarship)* [6860]

Ohio Space Grant Consortium Graduate Fellowships *(Doctorate, Graduate/Fellowship)* [6864]

Ohio Space Grant Consortium Special Minority Fellowships *(Doctorate, Graduate/Fellowship)* [6865]

Ohio Valley Chapter Scholarships *(Undergraduate/Scholarship)* [1815]

Ohio War Orphan Scholarships *(Undergraduate/Scholarship)* [9773]

Lawrence "Bud" Ohlman Memorial Scholarships *(Undergraduate/Scholarship)* [736]

Oklahoma City University Merit Scholarships *(Undergraduate/Scholarship)* [6868]

Oklahoma Restaurant Association Scholarships *(Graduate, Undergraduate/Scholarship)* [6871]

Olin/Searle Fellows in Law *(Professional development/Fellowship)* [3731]

Jeff Oliphant Memorial Post-Graduate Scholarships *(Postgraduate/Scholarship)* [9678]

Robert B. Oliver ASNT Scholarships *(Undergraduate/Scholarship)* [1317]

Andrew Oliver Research Fellowships *(Graduate, Doctorate/Fellowship)* [5677]

Frank del Olmo Memorial Scholarships *(Undergraduate/Scholarship)* [2238]

Roy C. and Dorothy Jean Olson Memorial Scholarships *(Undergraduate/Scholarship)* [4961]

Charlie O'Meilia Scholarships *(Undergraduate/Scholarship)* [4901]

Omicron Delta Kappa Foundation Scholarships *(Graduate/Scholarship)* [6880]

Omicron Nu Research Fellowships *(Postdoctorate/Fellowship)* [5203]

Eloise Pitts O'More Scholarships *(Undergraduate/Scholarship)* [3129]

Oncology Nursing Society Foundation - Doctoral Scholarships *(Doctorate/Scholarship)* [6885]

Oncology Nursing Society Foundation - Master's and Post-Master's NP Certificate Scholarships *(Master's/Scholarship)* [6886]

Oncology Nursing Society Foundation - Non-RN Bachelors Scholarships *(Graduate/Scholarship)* [6887]

Oncology Nursing Society Foundation - Non-RNHS Bachelors Scholarships *(Undergraduate/Scholarship)* [6888]

Oncology Nursing Society Foundation - RN Bachelors Scholarships *(Graduate/Scholarship)* [6889]

Open Society Fellowships *(Professional development/Fellowship)* [6903]

Opera Foundation Scholarships *(Professional development/Scholarship)* [6905]

Operation Homefront Scholarships *(Undergraduate, Vocational/Occupational/Scholarship)* [6907]

Sheldon Oppenheim Memorial Scholarships *(Undergraduate/Scholarship)* [7863]

Frank Oppenheimer Scholarship Program *(Postgraduate/Scholarship)* [955]

Dwight D. Opperman Scholarships *(Undergraduate/Scholarship)* [3509]

OPSF Scholarships *(Graduate/Scholarship)* [6846]

Optical Design and Engineering Scholarships *(Graduate, Undergraduate/Scholarship)* [8641]

Optimist Club Of Redlands - Ralph Maloof Scholarships *(Undergraduate/Scholarship)* [7680]

Optimist Club of Redlands - Virginia Elliott Scholarships *(Undergraduate/Scholarship)* [7681]

Order of Omega Doctoral Fellowships *(Doctorate, Graduate/Fellowship)* [6919]

Order Sons of Italy Foundation General Scholarships *(Graduate, Undergraduate/Scholarship)* [6923]

L'Oreal USA Fellowships for Women in Science *(Postdoctorate/Fellowship)* [6926]

Oregon Association of Nurseries Scholarship Program *(Undergraduate/Scholarship)* [6941]

Oregon Farm Bureau Memorial Scholarships *(Undergraduate/Scholarship)* [6947]

Oregon Logging Conference Scholarships *(Undergraduate/Scholarship)* [5459]

Doris Orenstein Memorial Convention Travel Grants *(All/Grant)* [1822]

Organization of American States Academic Scholarships *(Undergraduate/Scholarship)* [6963]

Organization of American States AOS-Placed Scholarships *(Graduate, Undergraduate/Scholarship)* [6964]

Organization of American States Graduate Scholarships *(Doctorate, Graduate/Scholarship)* [6965]

Organization of American States Self-Placed Scholarships *(Doctorate, Graduate/Scholarship)* [6966]

Organization of Black Aerospace Professionals General Scholarships *(All/Scholarship)* [6974]

Organization of Chinese Americans Scholarships *(Undergraduate/Scholarship)* [6976]

Oronzio de Nora Industrial Electrochemistry Fellowships *(Postdoctorate/Fellowship)* [3624]

Orthopaedic Trauma Association Research Grants *(Professional development/Grant)* [6990]

Orthopedic Foot and Ankle Fellowships *(Graduate/Fellowship)* [967]

The Kenneth J. Osborn Memorial Scholarships *(Undergraduate/Scholarship)* [1671]

OSCA Graduate Student Scholarship Program *(Graduate/Scholarship)* [6862]

OSHA Graduate Scholarships *(Graduate/Scholarship)* [6873]

OSU Gay, Lesbian, Bisexual and Transgender Alumni Society PFLAG Scholarships *(Undergraduate/Scholarship)* [7864]

AIChE/Donald F. and Mildred Topp Othmer National Scholarship Awards *(Undergraduate/Scholarship)* [849]

Ellis R. Ott Scholarships *(Graduate, Master's/Scholarship)* [1321]

Ottawa Police 150th Anniversary Scholarships *(Undergraduate/Scholarship)* [2168]

Outlaw Student's Medical Professions Scholarships *(Undergraduate/Scholarship)* [8752]

Outlaw Student's Minority Scholarships *(Undergraduate/Scholarship)* [8753]

Outlaw Student's Nursing School Scholarships *(Undergraduate/Scholarship)* [8754]

Outlaw Student's Teacher Scholarships *(Undergraduate/Scholarship)* [8755]

Outstanding Undergraduate Scholarships, Student Organization for Alumni Relations (SOAR) *(Undergraduate/Scholarship)* [9217]

Outward Bound Leadership Scholarships for Educators *(Professional development/Scholarship)* [7009]

Outward Bound Wilderness Leadership Awards for Youth *(High School, Professional development/Award)* [7010]

Helene M. Overly Memorial Scholarships *(Undergraduate/Scholarship)* [9741]

Overseas Press Club Foundation Harper's Magazine Scholarships *(Graduate, Undergraduate/Scholarship)* [7016]

Overseas Press Club Foundation Reuters Scholarships *(Graduate, Undergraduate/Scholarship)* [7017]

Charles and Melva T. Owen Memorial Scholarships *(Undergraduate/Scholarship)* [6280]

Ozarks Division Scholarships *(Undergraduate/Scholarship)* [5863]

The Pac-10 Postgraduate Scholarships *(Graduate/Scholarship)* [7027]

PACE/Columbian Lawyers Association of Westchester County Endowed Scholarships *(Undergraduate/Scholarship)* [3010]

Pacific Legal Foundation Faculty Grants *(All/Grant)* [7031]

The Arthur J. Packard Memorial Scholarship Competition *(Undergraduate/Scholarship)* [801]

Dr. Nicholas Padis Memorial Graduate Scholarships *(Graduate/Scholarship)* [4517]

Laurie Page-Peck Scholarship Fund *(Undergraduate/Scholarship)* [1914]

Raymond E. Page Scholarships *(Undergraduate/Scholarship)* [1286]

AFCEA General Emmett Paige Scholarships *(Undergraduate/Scholarship)* [1562]

Paleontological Society Student Research Grants *(Graduate, Undergraduate/Grant)* [7]

Robert R. Palmer Research Travel Fellowships *(Professional development/Fellowship)* [1234]

Palo Verde High School Faculty Follies Scholarships *(Undergraduate/Scholarship)* [7513]

PAMA Foundation Scholarship Program *(Graduate, Undergraduate/Scholarship)* [7437]

Pan-Macedonian National Scholarships *(Undergraduate/Scholarship)* [7039]

Pan Pacific Law Enforcement Scholarships *(Undergraduate/Scholarship)* [7978]

The PanHellenic Scholarships *(Undergraduate/Scholarship)* [7041]

ACI Charles Pankow Foundation ACI Student Fellowships *(Graduate, Undergraduate/Fellowship)* [637]

Panther Cafe Scholarships *(Undergraduate/Scholarship)* [7514]

Katharine Pantzer Fellowships in the British Book Trades *(Professional development/Fellowship)* [2085]

Paper Stock Industries Chapter of ISRI Scholarship Program *(Undergraduate/Scholarship)* [7047]

Paper Stock Industries/RRF Scholarships *(Undergraduate/Scholarship)* [7045]

Parapsychological Association Research Endowments *(All/Grant)* [7049]

Pardee Community Building Scholarships *(Undergraduate/Scholarship)* [7515]

Joseph M. Parish Memorial Grants *(Undergraduate/Scholarship)* [1192]

William Park Woodside Founder's Scholarships *(Undergraduate/Scholarship)* [5694]

Cissy McDaniel Parker Scholarships *(Undergraduate/Scholarship)* [3384]

E.U. Parker Scholarships *(Undergraduate/Scholarship)* [6281]

Parking Industry Institute Scholarship Program *(Undergraduate/Scholarship)* [6436]

Parkinson's Disease Foundation International Research Grants Program *(Postdoctorate/Grant)* [7128]

PARMA Scholarships *(Undergraduate/Scholarship)* [7460]

The Paros-Digiquartz Scholarships *(Graduate, Undergraduate/Scholarship)* [5643]

William E. Parrish Scholarships *(Graduate, Master's/Scholarship)* [7242]

Elizabeth M. and Winchell M. Parson Scholarships *(Doctorate/Scholarship)* [1661]

Partnership for Pediatric Epilepsy Research *(Doctorate/Grant)* [3667]

Pasteur Foundation Postdoctoral Fellowships *(Graduate/Fellowship)* [7130]

PATCH Early Childhood Education Scholarships *(Professional development/Scholarship)* [7132]

James H. Patrenos Memorial Scholarships *(Undergraduate/Scholarship)* [8220]

Gail Patrick Charitable Trust Scholarships *(Undergraduate/Scholarship)* [3420]

Alice Conger Patterson Scholarships *(Undergraduate/Scholarship)* [9649]

Walter S. Patterson Scholarships *(All/Scholarship)* [2183]

Patterson Trust Postdoctoral Fellowships in Brain Circuitry *(Postdoctorate/Fellowship)* [4496]

Joanne Holbrook Patton Military Spouse Scholarships *(Graduate, Undergraduate/Scholarship)* [6411]

Joanne Holbrook Patton Military Spouse Scholarships for Spouses of the Fallen *(Graduate, Undergraduate/Scholarship)* [6412]

Joanne Holbrook Patton Military Spouse Scholarships for Spouses of the Wounded *(Graduate, Undergraduate/Scholarship)* [6413]

Paul and Inger Friend 4-H Scholarships *(Undergraduate/Scholarship)* [8731]

Kenyon T. Payne Outstanding Student Awards *(Undergraduate/Award)* [5838]

PB Rail Engineering Scholarships *(Undergraduate/Scholarship)* [1132]

PDC Scholarships *(Undergraduate/Scholarship)* [1351]

Chuck Peacock Memorial Scholarships *(Undergraduate/Scholarship)* [137]

Charles S. Pearce Scholarships *(Undergraduate/Prize, Scholarship)* [9365]

Scott Pearlman Field Awards for Science and Exploration *(Professional development/Award)* [3698]

Robert L. Peaslee-Detroit Brazing and Soldiering Division Scholarships *(Undergraduate/Scholarship)* [1442]

Laura Ann Peck Memorial Endowed Scholarships *(Undergraduate/Scholarship)* [5460]

Pediatric Endocrinology Nursing Society Academic Education Scholarships *(Undergraduate/Scholarship)* [7136]

Pediatric Endocrinology Nursing Society Convention Reimbursement Awards *(Undergraduate/Award)* [7137]

Mario Pedrozzi Scholarships *(Graduate, Undergraduate, Vocational/Occupational/Scholarship)* [7145]

Peermusic Latin Scholarships *(All/Prize, Scholarship)* [2160]

Melissa Pellegrin Memorial Scholarships *(Graduate, Undergraduate/Scholarship)* [8504]

Adolph Van Pelt Special Fund for Indians Scholarships *(Undergraduate/Scholarship)* [1696]

Louis Pelzer Memorial Awards *(Graduate/Award)* [6961]

Margaret Pemberton Scholarships *(Undergraduate/Scholarship)* [2138]

Robert B. and Dorothy Pence Scholarships *(Undergraduate/Scholarship)* [8616]

Penn-Bird Family Memorial Scholarships *(Undergraduate/Scholarship)* [7516]

Penndelphia Scholarship Foundation *(Undergraduate, Vocational/Occupational/Scholarship)* [7147]

Pension Real Estate Association Scholarships *(Undergraduate/Scholarship)* [7163]

PEO Educational Loan Funds *(Graduate, Undergraduate, Vocational/Occupational/Loan)* [7306]

Pepperdine University Armenian Student Scholarships *(Undergraduate/Scholarship)* [7200]

Pepperdine University Dean's Scholarships *(Doctorate, Graduate/Scholarship)* [7201]

Pepperdine University Diversity Scholarships *(Doctorate, Graduate/Scholarship)* [7202]

Pepperdine University Faculty Scholarships *(Doctorate, Graduate/Scholarship)* [7203]

Pepsi Scholarships *(Undergraduate/Scholarship)* [802]

Pepsico Scholarships *(Undergraduate/Scholarship)* [9066]

Joe Perdue Scholarships *(Undergraduate/Scholarship)* [2913]

Joaquin Pereira Memorial Scholarships *(Undergraduate/Scholarship)* [5549]

Rudy Perez Songwriting Scholarships *(Undergraduate/Scholarship)* [1214]

Peridian International, Inc./Rae L. Price, FASLA Scholarships *(Undergraduate/Scholarship)* [5335]

The A.W. Perigard Fund *(Graduate, Undergraduate/Scholarship)* [8487]

Sanky Perlowin Memorial Scholarships *(Undergraduate/Scholarship)* [3453]

Zoe Gore Perrin Scholarships *(Undergraduate/Scholarship)* [3385]

Eleanor Perry Memorial Endowed Scholarships *(Undergraduate/Scholarship)* [5461]

Chet and Jannett Perry Scholarships *(Undergraduate/Scholarship)* [8617]

Jim Perry Vocational Scholarships *(Undergraduate, Vocational/Occupational/Scholarship)* [737]

Leonard M. Perryman Communications Scholarships for Ethnic Minority Students *(Undergraduate/Scholarship)* [9013]

Persian Language Study in Tehran Scholarships *(Doctorate, Graduate/Fellowship)* [856]

Dr. Connell Persico Scholarships *(Undergraduate/Scholarship)* [7865]

Gilberto and Lennetta Pesquera Medical School Scholarships *(Graduate/Scholarship)* [4163]

Peter Buck Fellowships Program - Graduate *(Graduate/Fellowship)* [8263]

Peter Buck Fellowships Program - Postdoctoral *(Postdoctorate/Fellowship)* [8264]

Peter R. Weitz Prize *(Professional development/Prize)* [4133]

Kate B. and Hall J. Peterson Fellowships *(Doctorate/Fellowship)* [422]

Lizette Peterson Homer Injury Prevention Grant Awards *(Professional development, Undergraduate/Grant)* [8426]

Silvio and Eugenio Petrini Grants *(Professional development/Grant)* [4389]

Petroleum Engineering Scholarships *(Graduate, Undergraduate/Scholarship)* [8436]

Petroleum Packaging Council Scholarships *(Undergraduate/Scholarship)* [7217]

Jerome S. Petz, S.J., Scholarships *(Undergraduate/Scholarship)* [3510]

Chuck Pezzano Scholarships *(Undergraduate, Vocational/Occupational/Scholarship)* [2166]

Dr. Harry V. Pfautz Memorial Scholarship Fund *(Undergraduate/Scholarship)* [3955]

Ruth Cook Pfautz Memorial Scholarship Fund *(Undergraduate/Scholarship)* [3956]

Pfizer Epilepsy Scholarships *(Graduate, Undergraduate/Scholarship)* [7221]

Pfizer Inc. Endowed Scholarships *(Undergraduate/Scholarship)* [5625]

Pfizer Inc. NP Student Scholarships *(Graduate/Scholarship)* [378]

Pfizer Minority Medical Journalism Scholarships *(Postgraduate/Scholarship)* [9298]

Carl H. Pforzheimer, Jr. Research Grants *(Graduate, Professional development/Grant)* [5225]

Pharmaceutics Post Doctoral Fellowships *(Postdoctorate/Fellowship)* [7231]

Pharmaceutics Pre Doctoral Fellowships *(Doctorate/Fellowship)* [7232]

Pharmaceutics Research Starter Grants *(Doctorate/Grant)* [7233]

Pharmaceutics Sabbatical Fellowships *(Postdoctorate/Fellowship)* [7234]

Pharmacology/Toxicology Post Doctoral Fellowships *(Postdoctorate/Fellowship)* [7235]

Pharmacology/Toxicology Pre Doctoral Fellowships *(Doctorate/Fellowship)* [7236]

Pharmacology/Toxicology Research Starter Grants *(Doctorate/Grant)* [7237]

Pharmacology/Toxicology Sabbatical Fellowships

(Postdoctorate/Fellowship) [7238]

Pharmacy Faculty Fellowships in Community Pharmacy Practice *(Postdoctorate/Fellowship)* [762]

Pharmacy Faculty Fellowships in Geriatric Pharmacy/Geriatric Pharmaceutical Science *(Postdoctorate/Fellowship)* [763]

Pharmacy Faculty New Investigator Grants Program *(Doctorate/Grant)* [764]

Pharmacy Student Scholarship Program *(Postdoctorate/Scholarship)* [6060]

Pharmavite LLC NP Doctoral Education Scholarships *(Doctorate/Scholarship)* [379]

Marshall Phelps Athletic Memorial Scholarships *(Undergraduate/Scholarship)* [7682]

Phi Alpha Theta Doctoral Scholarships *(Doctorate/Scholarship)* [7243]

Phi Eta Sigma Distinguished Member Scholarships (Graduate or Professional) *(Graduate, Professional development/Scholarship)* [7255]

Phi Eta Sigma Distinguished Member Scholarships (Undergraduate) *(Undergraduate/Scholarship)* [7256]

Phi Eta Sigma Undergraduate Scholarship Awards *(Undergraduate/Scholarship)* [7257]

Phi Kappa Phi Fellowships *(Graduate, Undergraduate/Fellowship)* [7259]

Phi Kappa Sigma Need-Based Scholarships *(Undergraduate/Scholarship)* [7261]

Phi Kappa Sigma Participation-Based Scholarships *(Undergraduate/Scholarship)* [7262]

Phi Sigma Epsilon Past National President Scholarships *(Graduate, Undergraduate/Scholarship)* [7271]

Phi Theta Kappa Scholarships *(Undergraduate/Scholarship)* [4752]

Phi Upsilon Omicron Candle Fellowships *(Graduate/Fellowship)* [7292]

Phi Upsilon Omicron Challenge Scholarships *(Undergraduate/Scholarship)* [7293]

Phi Upsilon Omicron Diamond Anniversary Fellowships *(Graduate/Fellowship)* [7294]

Phi Upsilon Omicron Founders Fellowships *(Graduate/Fellowship)* [7295]

Phi Upsilon Omicron Golden Anniversary Scholarships *(Undergraduate/Scholarship)* [7296]

Phi Upsilon Omicron Past Presidents Scholarships *(Undergraduate/Scholarship)* [7297]

Phi Upsilon Omicron Presidents Research Fellowships *(Graduate/Fellowship)* [7298]

Philip Morris USA Scholarships *(Undergraduate/Scholarship)* [9067]

Walter T. Philippy Scholarships *(Undergraduate/Scholarship)* [5716]

Jamie Phillips Endowed Scholarships *(Undergraduate/Scholarship)* [7204]

Phillips Fund Grants for Native American Research *(Graduate/Grant)* [994]

William Philpott Scholarships *(All/Scholarship)* [2098]

Ed Phinney Commemorative Scholarships *(Graduate, Undergraduate/Scholarship)* [613]

Howard and Mildred Phoenix Scholarships *(Undergraduate/Scholarship)* [7683]

The Physical Therapy Faculty Scholarship Endowment *(Graduate/Scholarship)* [8742]

Pi Gamma Mu Scholarships *(Graduate/Scholarship)* [7330]

Thomas R. Pickering Graduate Foreign Affairs Fellowships *(Graduate/Fellowship)* [9619]

Mary Pickford Scholarships *(Graduate/Scholarship)* [1831]

Peter L. Picknelly Honorary Scholarships *(Undergraduate/Scholarship)* [592]

Ronald C. and Joyce Pierce Scholarships *(Undergraduate/Scholarship)* [1443]

William Pigott Memorial Scholarships *(Undergraduate/Scholarship)* [3164]

David Pilon Scholarships for Training in Professional Psychology *(Doctorate, Graduate/Scholarship)* [1035]

John Pine Memorial Scholarships *(Doctorate/Scholarship)* [7244]

Julia T. Pingree Student Scholarships *(Undergraduate/Scholarship)* [6627]

Pioneer Hi-Bred International Graduate Student Fellowships *(Graduate/Fellowship)* [3654]

Stephen D. Pisinski Memorial Scholarships *(Undergraduate/Scholarship)* [7539]

Christopher Pitkin Memorial Scholarships *(Undergraduate, Vocational/Occupational/Scholarship)* [6332]

Day Pitney LLP Scholarships *(Undergraduate/Scholarship)* [4456]

Peter George Pitsakis Memorial Scholarships *(Undergraduate/Scholarship)* [4518]

Pitsco/Hearlihy/FTE Grants *(Professional development/Grant)* [5014]

Pitsenbarger Awards *(Undergraduate/Scholarship)* [93]

Robert Pittman Scholarships *(Undergraduate/Scholarship)* [9299]

Pittsburg State University Distinguished Graduate Scholarships *(Undergraduate/Scholarship)* [9489]

PKD Foundation Fellowships *(Doctorate, Graduate/Fellowship)* [7335]

Al Plamann Legacy Scholarships *(Undergraduate/Scholarship)* [2253]

TFC Edward A. Plank, Jr. Memorial Scholarships *(Undergraduate/Scholarship)* [3063]

Betsy Plank/PRSSA Scholarships *(Undergraduate/Scholarship)* [7540]

Plastics Pioneers Association Scholarships *(Graduate, Undergraduate/Scholarship)* [8454]

Katherine Barton Platt Excavation Fellowships *(Professional development, Undergraduate/Fellowship)* [1178]

Platt Family Scholarship Prize Essay Contest *(Graduate, Undergraduate/Prize, Scholarship)* [5503]

Pleasant Hawaiian Holidays Scholarships *(Undergraduate/Scholarship)* [1369]

PLSCA Scholarships *(Undergraduate/Scholarship)* [5505]

Harold and Harriet Plum Memorial Scholarships *(Undergraduate/Scholarship)* [2320]

Plumbing-Heating-Cooling Contractors Association Educational Foundation Need-Based Scholarships *(Undergraduate/Scholarship)* [7347]

Plumbing-Heating-Cooling Contractors Association Educational Foundation Scholarships *(Undergraduate/Scholarship)* [7348]

PMCA Graduate Fellowships for Confectionery Research at Pennsylvania State University *(Graduate/Fellowship)* [7154]

David Pohl Scholarships *(Graduate, Master's/Scholarship)* [8998]

Point Foundation Scholarships *(Graduate, Postgraduate, Undergraduate/Scholarship)* [7866]

Daniel H. Pokorny Memorial Scholarship Awards *(Undergraduate/Scholarship)* [7728]

Pokross/Curhan Family Fund Prize *(Graduate, Undergraduate/Prize)* [888]

Donald and Susie Polden Dean's Scholarships *(Undergraduate/Scholarship)* [9236]

Tibor T. Polgar Fellowships *(Graduate, Undergraduate/Fellowship)* [4619]

Police Explorer Scholarships Program *(Undergraduate/Scholarship)* [3844]

Polish American Club of North Jersey Scholarships *(Graduate, Undergraduate/Scholarship)* [5300]

Polish National Alliance of Brooklyn, USA Scholarships *(Undergraduate/Scholarship)* [5301]

Political Studies Scholarships *(Undergraduate, Graduate/Scholarship)* [9447]

Roy H. Pollack Scholarships *(Graduate, Master's/Scholarship)* [8999]

Stan and Leone Pollard Scholarships *(Undergraduate/Scholarship)* [1370]

Harvey M. Pollicove Memorial Scholarships *(Undergraduate/Scholarship)* [6913]

David J. Pollini Scholarships *(Undergraduate/Scholarship)* [5717]

Justice Stewart G. Pollock Fellowships *(All/Fellowship)* [5931]

The Sidney M. Pols Scholarships *(Undergraduate/Scholarship)* [7142]

Polsinelli Diversity Scholarships *(Undergraduate/Scholarship)* [9490]

Harold F. Polston Scholarships *(Graduate, Undergraduate/Scholarship)* [1352]

Polymer Modifiers and Additives Division Scholar-

ships *(Graduate, Undergraduate/Scholarship)* [8455]

Henry Belin du Pont Dissertation Fellowships *(Doctorate, Graduate/Fellowship)* [4364]

Henry Belin du Pont Fellowships *(Graduate/Fellowship)* [4365]

Buster Pool Memorial Scholarships *(Undergraduate/Scholarship)* [3130]

Pope Scholarship Awards *(Undergraduate/Scholarship)* [5718]

Portable Sanitation Association International Scholarship Fund *(Undergraduate/Scholarship)* [7375]

Porter Physiology Development Fellowship Awards *(Doctorate/Fellowship)* [1005]

Gail Porterfield Memorial Scholarships *(Undergraduate/Scholarship)* [7684]

Portland Area Business Association Scholarships *(Undergraduate/Scholarship)* [3681]

Portuguese-American Scholarship Foundation *(Undergraduate/Scholarship)* [7378]

Post-doctoral Residential Research and Teaching Fellowships *(Postdoctorate/Fellowship)* [9743]

Post-Doctoral or Sabbatical Fellowships *(Doctorate/Fellowship)* [9248]

Post-Doctoral Summer Travel-Research Grants *(Doctorate/Grant)* [4832]

Post-Doctoral Teaching Fellowships *(Postdoctorate/Fellowship)* [3551]

Post-Doctoral Tikvah Scholarships *(Postdoctorate/Scholarship)* [8906]

Postdoctoral Fellowships in Conservation Science *(Doctorate/Fellowship)* [4145]

Postdoctoral Fellowships *(Postdoctorate/Fellowship)* [4781]

Postdoctoral Research Fellowships *(Postdoctorate/Award)* [906]

Poteet Strawberry Festival Association Scholarships *(Graduate, Undergraduate/Scholarship)* [7382]

Terry Linda Potter Scholarship Fund *(Undergraduate/Scholarship)* [4234]

Barbara Potter Scholarships *(All/Scholarship)* [961]

Erwin Potts Scholarships *(Undergraduate/Scholarship)* [9300]

George V. Powell Diversity Scholarships *(Undergraduate/Scholarship)* [5339]

Gerald Powell Scholarships *(Undergraduate/Scholarship)* [3046]

The Power to Continue Learning Scholarships *(Undergraduate, Vocational/Occupational/Scholarship)* [7685]

Susan Kelly Power and Helen Hornbeck Tanner Fellowships *(Doctorate, Postdoctorate/Fellowship)* [6708]

Powers-Knapp Scholarships *(Undergraduate/Scholarship)* [9367]

Master Sergeant Neal E. Powers Memorial Scholarships *(Undergraduate/Scholarship)* [100]

Practising Law Institute Law Student Scholarships *(Undergraduate/Scholarship)* [7384]

Lou and Carole Prato Sports Reporting Scholarships *(Undergraduate/Scholarship)* [7580]

Praxair International Scholarships *(Undergraduate/Scholarship)* [1444]

Pre-doctoral Residential Research Fellowships *(Doctorate/Fellowship)* [9744]

Presbyterian Association of Musicians Scholarships *(All/Scholarship)* [7386]

Presidents Scholarships *(Undergraduate/Scholarship)* [4807]

Prevent Cancer Foundation Fellowships *(Doctorate, Graduate/Fellowship)* [7394]

Jim and Dee Price Scholarships *(Undergraduate/Scholarship)* [4262]

Judith McManus Price Scholarships *(Graduate, Undergraduate/Scholarship)* [1012]

Rae L. Price Scholarships *(Undergraduate/Scholarship)* [1287]

Pride Foundation Scholarships *(Undergraduate/Scholarship)* [7867]

Lendon N. Pridgen, GlaxoSmithKline - NOBCChE Fellowships *(Graduate/Fellowship)* [6431]

Eric Primavera Memorial Scholarships *(Undergraduate/Scholarship)* [3832]

Josef Princ Memorial Scholarships *(Undergraduate/Scholarship)* [7517]

R.M. Princ Scholarships (Undergraduate/Scholarship) [7518]

Graduate Fellowship Program - GRC/John L. Prince Fellowships (GFP) (Graduate/Fellowship) [8082]

Print Graphics Scholarship Foundation (PGSF) (Graduate, Undergraduate/Fellowship, Scholarship) [7435]

Private High School Awards (Undergraduate/Award) [1512]

Miguel Pro Scholarships (Undergraduate/Scholarship) [9774]

Procida Tile Importers Scholarships (Undergraduate/Scholarship) [7519]

Procter and Gamble Complex PE Scholars Grant (Undergraduate/Award) [971]

Procter & Gamble Professional Oral Health/HDA Foundation Scholarships (Undergraduate/Scholarship) [4556]

Producers Academy Scholarships (All/Scholarship) [3264]

Professional Association Leadership Alumni Scholarships (PAL) (Graduate/Scholarship) [8805]

Professional Women in Pest Management Scholarships (PWIPM) (Graduate, Professional development/Scholarship) [6438]

Progress Lane Scholarships (Undergraduate/Scholarship) [3064]

Progressive Dairy Producer Awards (All/Grant) [6233]

Project Red Flag Academic Scholarships for Women with Bleeding Disorders (Undergraduate/Scholarship) [6333]

Project10 - Models of Excellence Scholarships (Undergraduate/Scholarship) [7448]

Property and Environment Research Center Graduate Fellowships (Graduate/Fellowship) [7452]

Property and Environment Research Center Lone Mountain Fellowships (Professional development/Fellowship) [7453]

Property and Environment Research Center Media Fellowships (Professional development/Fellowship) [7454]

Prospective Secondary Teacher Course Work Scholarships (Postgraduate/Scholarship) [6222]

Providence Alaska Medical Center Auxiliary Scholarships (Undergraduate/Scholarship) [9106]

Barbara F. Prowant Nursing Research Grants (Graduate/Grant) [946]

ProWorld Study Abroad Scholarships (Undergraduate/Scholarship) [4178]

PRSSA Multicultural Affairs Scholarships (Undergraduate/Scholarship) [7541]

Peter DeWitt Pruden and Phyliss Harrill Pruden Scholarships (Undergraduate/Scholarship) [9301]

Neil Pruitt, Sr. Memorial Scholarships (Undergraduate/Scholarship) [6201]

Pryor Graduate Fellowships (Graduate/Fellowship) [345]

Cheryl White Pryor Memorial Scholarships (Undergraduate/Scholarship) [3386]

PSHF Good Idea Grants (Professional development/Grant) [7544]

The PSSC Legacy Fund (Graduate, Undergraduate/Scholarship) [8488]

Public Agency Training Council Criminal Justice Scholarships (Undergraduate/Scholarship) [358]

Public Education Foundation Opportunity Scholarships (Undergraduate/Scholarship) [7520]

Public Employee Retirement Research and Administration Scholarships (Graduate/Scholarship) [4201]

Public Interest Environmental Law Fellowships (Postgraduate/Fellowship) [3656]

Public Interest Scholarships (Undergraduate/Scholarship) [2234]

Public Service International Law Fellowships (All/Fellowship) [7607]

Puget Sound LGBT Leadership Scholarships Fund (Undergraduate/Scholarship) [7868]

Eugene C. Pulliam Fellowships for Editorial Writing (Professional development/Fellowship) [8149]

Pulliam/Kilgore Freedom of Information Internships (Undergraduate/Internship) [8466]

Purdue Krannert School of Management SHPE Scholarships (Undergraduate, Master's/Scholarship) [8130]

John Purfield Endowed Scholarships (Undergraduate/Scholarship) [7205]

Elizabeth Pusey Scholarships (Undergraduate/Scholarship) [3066]

A.O. Putnam Memorial Scholarships (Undergraduate/Scholarship) [4808]

The Henley Putnam University Scholarships (Professional development/Scholarship) [4874]

Davis Putter Scholarships Fund (Undergraduate/Scholarship) [7869]

Harry V. Quadracci Memorial Scholarships (Undergraduate, Graduate/Scholarship) [4321]

Quarter Century Wireless Association Scholarships (Undergraduate/Scholarship) [7554]

Queer Foundation Effective Writing and Scholarships (Undergraduate/Prize, Scholarship) [7560]

Michael J. Quill Scholarships (Undergraduate/Scholarship) [8929]

Salvatore E. Quinci Foundation Scholarships (Undergraduate, Vocational/Occupational/Scholarship) [6334]

Bob Quincy Scholarships (Undergraduate/Scholarship) [9302]

Chips Quinn Scholarships (Graduate, Undergraduate/Scholarship) [7565]

Dr. Sidney Rafal Memorial Scholarships (Undergraduate/Scholarship) [4457]

Marjorie Usher Ragan Scholarships (Undergraduate/Scholarship) [9303]

Rain Bird Intelligent Use of Water Scholarships (Undergraduate/Scholarship) [5336]

Rainwater Family Scholarships (Undergraduate/Scholarship) [6399]

Tom D. Ralls Memorial Scholarships (Professional development/Scholarship) [3849]

The NASSCO Jeffrey D. Ralston Memorial Scholarships (Undergraduate/Scholarship) [5988]

Rama Scholarships for the American Dream (Graduate, Undergraduate/Scholarship) [803]

RAMEF Co-Branded Scholarships for High School Seniors (Undergraduate/Scholarship) [7747]

Raul Ramirez Memorial Scholarships (Undergraduate/Scholarship) [7686]

A. Stanley Rand Fellowships Program (Undergraduate, Doctorate, Postdoctorate/Fellowship) [8270]

Herbert W. Rand Fellowships and Scholarships (Undergraduate/Scholarship) [5626]

Ayn Rand Institute Anthem Essay Contest (High School, Undergraduate/Prize) [7592]

Ayn Rand Institute Former Participants' Essay Contest (High School, Undergraduate/Prize) [7593]

Ayn Rand Institute Fountainhead Essay Contest (High School, Undergraduate/Prize) [7594]

Ayn Rand Institute We the Living Essay Contest (High School, Undergraduate/Prize) [7595]

Newell S. Rand Jr. Memorial Scholarships (Undergraduate/Scholarship) [7055]

Helen F. "Jerri" Rand Memorial Scholarships (Undergraduate, Vocational/Occupational/Scholarship) [3193]

James Randi Educational Foundation Scholarships (Graduate, Undergraduate/Scholarship) [7597]

The Jennings Randolph Peace Scholar Dissertation Program (Doctorate/Scholarship) [9081]

United States Institute of Peace Jennings Randolph Senior Fellowship Program (All/Fellowship) [9082]

Rangel Graduate Fellowships (Graduate/Fellowship) [7599]

Jeannette Rankin Scholarships (Undergraduate, Vocational/Occupational/Scholarship) [7601]

Rappaport Fellows Program in Law and Public Policy (All/Fellowship) [7608]

General John Paul Ratay Educational Grants (Undergraduate/Grant) [5876]

Dr. Mark Rathke Family Scholarships (Undergraduate/Scholarship) [3542]

James K. Rathmell Jr. Scholarships (Undergraduate/Scholarship) [738]

Ratner and Sugarmon Scholarships (Undergraduate/Scholarship) [9237]

Carol A. Ratza Memorial Scholarships (Undergraduate/Scholarship) [4329]

Dennis Raveling Scholarships (Undergraduate/Scholarship) [2288]

Lenny Ravich "Shalom" Scholarships (All/Scholarship) [1706]

Rawley Silver Awards for Excellence (Graduate/Scholarship) [428]

Raytheon Scholarship Program (Undergraduate/Scholarship) [7611]

RBPA Scholarships (All/Scholarship) [7589]

RCSA Cottrell Scholarships (Graduate/Scholarship) [7734]

Ronald Reagan College Leaders Scholarship Program (Undergraduate/Scholarship) [7313]

Carl C. and Abbie Rebman Trust Scholarships (Undergraduate/Scholarship) [4263]

Rechsteiner Family Scholarship Fund (Undergraduate/Scholarship) [3788]

Redlands Area Interfaith Council Scholarships (Undergraduate/Scholarship) [7687]

Redlands Community Scholarship Foundation Scholarships (Undergraduate/Scholarship) [7688]

Redlands Council PTA - Dorathy Jolley Memorial Scholarships (Undergraduate/Scholarship) [7689]

Redlands High School Academic Decathalon Scholarships (Undergraduate/Scholarship) [7690]

Redlands High School Boy's Varsity Volleyball Scholarships (Undergraduate/Scholarship) [7691]

Redlands High School Drama Boosters Awards (Undergraduate/Scholarship) [7692]

Redlands High School Girls' Volleyball Boosters Scholarship Awards (Undergraduate/Scholarship) [7693]

Redlands High School Mock Trial Scholarships (Undergraduate/Scholarship) [7694]

Redlands High School-PTSA Scholarships (Undergraduate, Vocational/Occupational/Scholarship) [7695]

Redlands High School Soccer Boosters Scholarship Awards (Undergraduate/Scholarship) [7696]

Redlands High School Softball Booster Scholarship Awards (Undergraduate/Scholarship) [7697]

Redlands High School Speech Boosters Scholarship Awards (Undergraduate/Scholarship) [7698]

Redlands High School Spiritleaders Scholarships (Undergraduate/Scholarship) [7699]

Redlands High School Terrier Band Boosters Club Scholarships (Undergraduate/Scholarship) [7700]

Redlands High School Vocal Music Boosters Scholarship Awards (Undergraduate/Scholarship) [7701]

Redlands Morning Kiwanis Club Foundation Scholarships (Undergraduate, Vocational/Occupational/Scholarship) [7702]

Redlands Noon Kiwanis Club Foundation Scholarships (Undergraduate/Scholarship) [7703]

Redlands Noon Kiwanis Club - Martin and Dorothy Munz Scholarships (Undergraduate/Scholarship) [7704]

Redlands Rotary Club Foundation Discretionary Scholarships (Undergraduate/Scholarship) [7705]

Redlands Teachers Association Scholarships (Undergraduate/Scholarship) [7706]

Sarah Rebecca Reed Scholarships (Graduate/Scholarship) [2071]

The Reese Fellowships (Doctorate/Fellowship) [423]

Bob Reeve Aviation Management Scholarships (Undergraduate/Scholarship) [193]

REFORMA Scholarship Program (Doctorate, Graduate, Professional development/Scholarship) [7721]

Dan M. Reichard, Jr. Scholarships (Graduate, Undergraduate/Scholarship) [1056]

Mark A. Reid Memorial Scholarship Grants (Undergraduate/Scholarship) [3165]

Henry J. Reilly Memorial Scholarships - For Freshmen in College (Undergraduate/Scholarship) [7738]

Henry J. Reilly Memorial Scholarships - For Graduating High School Seniors (Undergraduate/Scholarship) [7739]

Henry J. Reilly Memorial Scholarships - For Sophomores and Juniors in College (Undergraduate/Scholarship) [7740]

Henry J. Reilly Memorial Scholarships - Graduate Program (Graduate, Professional development/Scholarship) [7741]

George Reinke Scholarships (Professional development/Scholarship) [1371]

REMSA Scholarships (Undergraduate/Scholarship) [1133]

Betty Rendel Scholarships (Undergraduate/Scholarship) [6288]

Bertha and Byron L. Reppert Scholarship Fund (Undergraduate/Scholarship) [3957]

Republic Services Environmental Studies Scholarships (Undergraduate/Scholarship) [7521]

Research Fellowships in Iranian Studies, Resident Director-Tehran (Doctorate, Graduate/Fellowship) [857]

Research Grants in Speech Science (Doctorate/Grant) [1389]

Reserve Officers Training Corps Scholarships (ROTC) (Undergraduate/Scholarship) [9368]

Resistance Welder Manufacturers' Association Scholarships (Undergraduate/Scholarship) [1445]

Paul Resnick and Bruce Donnelly Scholarships (Undergraduate/Scholarship) [2928]

Retail Chapter Scholarship Awards (Undergraduate/Scholarship) [6942]

Retail Packaging Association Scholarships (RPA) (Undergraduate/Scholarship) [7751]

Retired League Postmasters Scholarship Program (Undergraduate/Scholarship) [7755]

Mike Reynolds Journalism Scholarships (Undergraduate/Scholarship) [7581]

Janet Reynoldson Memorial Scholarships (Undergraduate/Scholarship) [3511]

RFDF MBA Preparation Fellowships (Graduate, Undergraduate/Fellowship) [7800]

RFDF Pre-MBA Fellowships (Graduate/Fellowship) [7801]

Lori Rhett Memorial Scholarships (Graduate, Undergraduate/Scholarship) [6055]

Rho Chi, AFPE First Year Graduate Fellowships (Doctorate, Graduate/Fellowship) [7781]

Rho Chi Society Clinical Research Scholarships (Postdoctorate/Scholarship) [7782]

Haynes Rice Scholarships (Doctorate, Graduate, Undergraduate/Scholarship) [6082]

Barbara Hagan Richards Scholarships (Undergraduate/Scholarship) [3131]

James Edward "Bill" Richards Scholarships (Undergraduate/Scholarship) [3132]

Ellen Swallow Richards Travel Grants (Graduate, Professional development/Grant) [1251]

Phillip Guy Richardson Memorial Scholarships (Undergraduate/Scholarship) [5103]

J. Milton Richardson Theological Fellowships (Graduate/Fellowship) [369]

Frank J. Richter Scholarships (Graduate, Undergraduate/Scholarship) [543]

Howard Brown Rickard Scholarships (Undergraduate/Scholarship) [6282]

Honorable Joseph H. Ridge Memorial Scholarships (Undergraduate/Scholarship) [330]

Jasper Ridge Restoration Fellowships Jasper Ridge Biological Preserve (Graduate, Postdoctorate/Fellowship) [3580]

Donald Riebhoff Memorial Scholarships (Undergraduate/Scholarship) [1102]

Rieser Fellowships (Undergraduate/Fellowship) [2209]

Ameen Rihani Scholarship Program (Undergraduate/Scholarship) [1492]

RA Consulting Service/Maria Riley Scholarships (Graduate, Undergraduate/Scholarship) [6297]

Susan E. Riley Scholarships (Undergraduate/Scholarship) [3387]

Fauneil J. Rinn Scholarships (Undergraduate/Scholarship) [8206]

John T. Riordan Professional Education Scholarships (Professional development/Scholarship) [4909]

Ritchie-Jennings Memorial Scholarships (Graduate, Undergraduate/Scholarship) [1738]

Paul H. Rittle Sr. Professional Development Grants (Professional development/Grant) [4820]

Thomas and Ruth River International Scholarships (Undergraduate, Graduate/Scholarship) [9756]

Riverside Sheriffs Association Member Scholarship Program (Graduate, Undergraduate/Scholarship) [7803]

Jean Wiggin Roach Scholarships (Undergraduate/Scholarship) [3388]

Robert J. McNamara Student Paper Awards (Graduate/Award) [1875]

Clifford Roberts Graduate Fellowships (Doctorate/Fellowship) [3614]

Eugene L. Roberts Jr. Prize (Undergraduate/Prize) [9304]

Liz Roberts Memorial Scholarships (Undergraduate/Scholarship) [7707]

Smiley Elementary School PTA - Beverly Roberts Memorial Scholarships (Undergraduate/Scholarship) [7708]

Elliott C. Roberts Scholarships (Graduate/Scholarship) [4789]

George A. Roberts Scholarships (Undergraduate/Scholarship) [5695]

Lola Ellis Robertson Scholarships (Undergraduate/Scholarship) [5627]

David G. Robinson Arts Scholarships (Undergraduate/Scholarship) [8619]

Samuel Robinson Awards (Undergraduate/Award) [7388]

Isador M. Robinson Endowment Scholarships (Undergraduate/Scholarship) [3512]

Jackie Robinson Foundation Minority Scholarships (Undergraduate/Scholarship) [822]

Helen M. Robinson Grants (Doctorate/Grant) [4977]

Jerry Robinson Inweld Corporation Scholarships (Undergraduate/Scholarship) [1446]

Claude Robinson Scholarships (Undergraduate/Scholarship) [6382]

Jackie Robinson Scholarships (Undergraduate/Scholarship) [7808]

Nell Bryant Robinson Scholarships (Undergraduate/Scholarship) [7299]

Paul S. Robinson Scholarships (Undergraduate/Scholarship) [8318]

August M. Rocco Scholarship Fund (Undergraduate/Scholarship) [8696]

Rockin' Christmas Fund Scholarships (Undergraduate/Scholarship) [8620]

Rockwell Collins Scholarships (Undergraduate/Scholarship) [138]

Rocky Mountain Research Fellowships (Graduate/Fellowship) [7815]

R.O.E.A. Dumitru Golea Goldy-Gemu Scholarships (Undergraduate/Scholarship) [1165]

ROFY Scholarships (Undergraduate/Scholarship) [7613]

Kimberly Marie Rogers Memorial Scholarship Fund (Undergraduate, Vocational/Occupational/Scholarship) [3789]

Fred Rogers Memorial Scholarships (Graduate, Undergraduate/Scholarship) [35]

Joseph Wood Rogers Memorial Scholarships (Undergraduate/Scholarship) [8122]

Kenneth Rogers Memorial Scholarships (Undergraduate/Scholarship) [5462]

Mary Stuart Rogers Scholarships (Undergraduate/Scholarship) [9606]

Mary Louise Roller Pan-Hellenic Scholarships (Undergraduate/Scholarship) [6741]

Rome Prize (Doctorate, Graduate/Prize) [400]

Charles and Ruth Ronin Memorial Scholarships (Undergraduate/Scholarship) [7709]

Dorothy Worden Ronken Scholarships (Graduate/Scholarship) [3421]

Alice W. Rooke Scholarships (Undergraduate/Scholarship) [4459]

Roothbert Fund Scholarships (Undergraduate/Scholarship) [7819]

ROP - Rob Bruce Memorial Scholarships (Undergraduate/Scholarship) [7710]

Barnes W. Rose, Jr. and Eva Rose Nichol Scholarship Fund (Undergraduate/Scholarship) [282]

Florence C. Rose and S. Meryl Rose Scholarships (Undergraduate/Scholarship) [5628]

Dr. Wayne F. Rose Scholarship Fund (Undergraduate/Scholarship) [3790]

David Rose Scholarships (Undergraduate/Scholarship) [1215]

Esther Katz Rosen Fellowships (Graduate/Fellowship) [1041]

Ollie Rosenberg Educational Trust (Undergraduate/Scholarship) [3958]

Ollie Rosenberg Scholarship Travel Fund (Undergraduate/Scholarship) [3959]

Mandell and Lester Rosenblatt and Robert N. Herbert Undergraduate Scholarships (Undergraduate/Scholarship) [8417]

Barbara Rosenblum Cancer Dissertation Scholarships (Doctorate, Graduate/Fellowship) [8520]

ASPH/CDC Allan Rosenfield Global Health Fellowships (Postdoctorate, Postgraduate/Fellowship) [1868]

Rosenthal Bar Exam Scholarships (Undergraduate/Scholarship) [2235]

Jean and Tom Rosenthal Scholarship Program (Undergraduate/Scholarship) [3204]

Marty Rosness Student Scholarships (Undergraduate/Scholarship) [1505]

Bettsy Ross Educational Fund (All, Professional development/Scholarship) [6727]

Ross-Fahey Scholarships (Graduate, Postgraduate/Scholarship) [6056]

Dorothy M. Ross Memorial Scholarships (Undergraduate/Scholarship) [1948]

The Bea and Harry Ross Scholarship Endowment (Graduate/Scholarship) [8743]

Ross Trust Graduate Student Scholarships (Graduate, Postdoctorate/Scholarship) [685]

Hon. Rudolph J. Rossetti Memorial Scholarships (Undergraduate/Award) [2322]

The Rotary Foundation Ambassadorial Scholarships (Undergraduate/Scholarship) [7821]

Bernard Rotberg Memorial Scholarships (Undergraduate/Scholarship) [5163]

Richard J. Roth Journalism Fellowships (Graduate/Fellowship) [6679]

Edward S. Roth Manufacturing Engineering Scholarships (Graduate, Undergraduate/Scholarship) [8396]

Isaac Roth Newspaper Carrier Scholarship Program (Undergraduate/Scholarship) [6653]

Marjorie Roy Rothermel Scholarships (Graduate/Scholarship) [1663]

Hal Rothman Dissertation Fellowships (Doctorate/Fellowship) [1252]

Theodore Rousseau Fellowships (Graduate/Fellowship) [5790]

Marion and Donald Routh Student Research Grants (Undergraduate/Grant) [8427]

Roy Rowan Scholarships (Graduate, Undergraduate/Scholarship) [7018]

Rowe Family Fellowships (Graduate/Fellowship) [6985]

Royal Palm Audubon Society Environmental Fellowships (Postgraduate/Fellowship) [3820]

Lucille and Edward R. Roybal Foundation Public Health Scholarships (Graduate, Undergraduate/Scholarship) [7827]

Royce-Osborn Minority Scholarship Program (Undergraduate/Scholarship) [1326]

RSDSA Research Grants (Postdoctorate, Professional development/Grant) [7719]

RSNA/AAPM Fellowships for Graduate Study in Medical Physics (Graduate/Fellowship) [531]

Rubber Division American Chemical Society Undergraduate Scholarships (Undergraduate/Scholarship) [7829]

Mike Ruben Scholarships (Undergraduate/Scholarship) [7111]

William Rucker Greenwood Scholarships (Graduate, Undergraduate/Scholarship) [1904]

Paul and Ellen Ruckes Scholarships (Graduate, Undergraduate/Scholarship) [753]

Lawrence E. & Mabel Jackson Rudberg Scholarships (Undergraduate/Scholarship) [3543]

Joe Rudd Scholarships (Undergraduate/Scholarship) [7813]

Anna M. Rundquist Memorial Scholarships (Undergraduate/Scholarship) [4340]

Damon Runyon Cancer Research Foundation Fellowships (Doctorate, Graduate, Postdoctorate/Fellowship) [7831]

Damon Runyon Clinical Investigator Awards (Doctorate, Graduate, Postdoctorate/Fellowship) [7832]

Damon Runyon-Rachleff Innovation Awards (Postdoctorate/Fellowship) [7833]

Ruppert Educational Grant Program (Undergraduate/Grant) [8207]

Rural Telephone Company Scholarships (Undergraduate/Scholarship) [7835]

Hermann G. Rusch Scholarships (Professional development/Scholarship) [697]

Norman K. Russell Scholarships (Doctorate, Graduate/Scholarship) [6434]

Michael A. Russo Memorial Scholarships (Undergraduate/Scholarship) [7711]

The Anthony C. Russo Scholarships (Graduate/Scholarship) [6457]

Lucile Rust Scholarships (Undergraduate/Scholarship) [7300]

Deborah Jean Rydberg Memorial Scholarships (Undergraduate/Scholarship) [3168]

Jeanne Graves Ryland Scholarships (Undergraduate/Scholarship) [3389]

Charles A. Ryskamp Research Fellowships (Doctorate/Fellowship) [681]

SAA Native American Scholarships (Graduate, Professional development, Undergraduate/Scholarship) [8293]

SABA Foundation Fellowships (Undergraduate/Fellowship) [8538]

Sacks For CF Scholarships (All/Scholarship) [3687]

Julie Anne Sadlier Memorial Scholarships (Undergraduate/Scholarship) [3390]

Safer Athletic Field Environments Scholarships (SAFE) (Graduate, Undergraduate/Scholarship) [8649]

Russell Sage Foundation Visiting Scholars (Postdoctorate/Fellowship) [7880]

Ruth Sager Scholarships (Undergraduate/Scholarship) [5629]

SAH Study Tour Fellowships (Doctorate/Fellowship) [8297]

Virginia Hartford Saharov Memorial Scholarships (Undergraduate/Scholarship) [3391]

Don Sahli-Kathy Woodall Graduate Scholarships (Graduate/Scholarship) [8841]

Sons and Daughters Don Sahli-Kathy Woodall Scholarships (Graduate, Undergraduate/Scholarship) [8842]

St. Francis Xavier Scholarships (Undergraduate/Scholarship) [9775]

St. James Armenian Church Memorial Scholarships (All/Scholarship) [1604]

St. Louis Division Scholarships (Undergraduate/Scholarship) [5864]

St. Louis Paralegal Association Student Scholarships (Undergraduate/Scholarship) [7884]

Saint Vincent College Eagle Scout Scholarships (Undergraduate/Scholarship) [6261]

Saints Cyril and Methodius Scholarships (Undergraduate/Scholarship) [7838]

SAJA Journalism Scholarships (Graduate, Undergraduate/Scholarship) [8540]

Casey Sakir Point Scholarships (Graduate, Undergraduate/Scholarship) [7366]

Joseph and Amelia Saks Scholarship Fund (Undergraduate/Scholarship) [3047]

Jane Salanky-Onzik Scholarship Fund (Undergraduate/Scholarship) [3791]

Bill Salerno, W2ONV, Memorial Scholarships (Undergraduate/Scholarship) [1104]

The Sallie Mae 911 Education Fund (Undergraduate/Scholarship) [7891]

Sally Beauty Scholarships for High School Graduates (Undergraduate/Scholarship) [7439]

Henry Salvatori Scholarships (Undergraduate/Scholarship) [6924]

The Walter Samek III Memorial Scholarship Fund (Undergraduate/Scholarship) [3089]

SAMFund Scholarships (Graduate, Undergraduate/Scholarship) [7897]

Margaret Jerome Sampson Scholarships (Undergraduate/Scholarship) [7301]

Samsung American Legion Scholarships (Undergraduate/Scholarship) [897]

The San Diego Foundation Community Scholarships II (Undergraduate/Scholarship) [7959]

Barbara Sanchez Scholarships (Undergraduate/Scholarship) [8348]

Sand Hill Scholars Program (Undergraduate/Scholarship) [8209]

Major General Jerry Sanders Scholarship Program (High School, Undergraduate/Scholarship) [1461]

Bill Sanderson Aviation Maintenance Technician Scholarships (Postgraduate/Scholarship) [4511]

Bert Saperstein Communication Scholarships (Undergraduate/Scholarship) [7987]

Saskatchewan Trucking Association Scholarships (Undergraduate/Scholarship) [8010]

Satter Human Rights Fellowships (Graduate/Fellowship) [4469]

Dave Sauer Memorial College Scholarships (Undergraduate/Scholarship) [116]

Curtis M. Saulsbury Scholarship Fund (Undergraduate/Scholarship) [3082]

Dr. William A. and Marcelein J. Sautter Hanover-Horton High School Youth of Promise Scholarships (Undergraduate/Scholarship) [5104]

Savatori Fellowships (Graduate/Fellowship) [4848]

Save Mart Legacy Scholarships (Undergraduate/Scholarship) [2254]

John A. Savoy Scholarship Fund (Undergraduate/Scholarship) [3792]

Bill Sawyer Memorial Scholarships (Undergraduate/Scholarship) [5463]

SBA Four-Year Scholarships Program (Undergraduate/Scholarship) [8644]

SBA One-Year Scholarship Program (Undergraduate, Vocational/Occupational/Scholarship) [8645]

SC and R Foundation Grant Program (Undergraduate, Vocational/Occupational/Grant) [8631]

SC and R Foundation Scholarships (Undergraduate/Scholarship) [8632]

Leslie and Mary Ella Scales Memorial Scholarships (Undergraduate/Scholarship) [3048]

Edith Scandlyn/Sammie Lynn Scandlyn Puett Memorial Scholarships (Undergraduate/Scholarship) [3392]

SCCLA Fellowships (All/Fellowship) [8578]

SCCLA Scholarships (All/Scholarship) [8579]

SCDAA Post-Doctoral Research Fellowships (Doctorate/Fellowship) [8138]

Mary Turnbull Schacht Memorial Scholarships (Undergraduate/Scholarship) [8181]

David W. Schacht Native American Student Scholarships (Undergraduate/Scholarship) [2064]

Schaible Health Care Services Scholarships (Undergraduate/Scholarship) [8988]

Schallek Awards (Graduate/Award) [5754]

Schallek Fellowships (Graduate/Fellowship) [5755]

Schatz Energy Fellowships for Graduate Studies (Graduate/Fellowship) [8016]

Abe Schechter Graduate Scholarships (Graduate/Scholarship) [7570]

Abe Schecter Graduate Scholarships (Postgraduate/Scholarship) [7582]

Scheduler and Dispatchers Scholarships (Professional development/Scholarship) [6171]

Leopold Schepp Foundation Scholarships (Doctorate, Graduate, Undergraduate/Scholarship) [8018]

Robert C. and Margaret A. Schikora Scholarships (Undergraduate/Scholarship) [8621]

Victor E. Schimmel Memorial Nursing Scholarships (Doctorate, Graduate, Master's/Scholarship) [1725]

Arthur M. Schlesinger, Jr. Fellowships (All/Fellowship) [5240]

Esther Schlundt Memorial Scholarships (Graduate/Scholarship) [4737]

Julie Schmid Research Scholarships (All/Scholarship) [1837]

Ronald L. Schmied Scholarships (Professional development, Undergraduate/Scholarship) [4362]

David M. Schneider Awards (Doctorate/Award) [408]

Prof. George Schneider, Jr. Manufacturing Technology Education Scholarships (Undergraduate/Scholarship) [8397]

Richard J. Schnell Memorial Scholarships (Postdoctorate/Scholarship) [3169]

Stanley M. Schoenfeld Memorial Scholarships (Postgraduate/Fellowship) [6673]

Lillian P. Schoephoerster Scholarships (Undergraduate/Scholarship) [7302]

The Scholarship Foundation of St. Louis Scholarships (Graduate, Undergraduate/Scholarship) [8022]

Scholarship Foundation of Santa Barbara Art Scholarship Program (Undergraduate/Scholarship) [8024]

Scholarship for Junior PHS Commissioned Officers (Undergraduate, Vocational/Occupational/Scholarship) [7315]

Scholarships of the Arts (Graduate, Undergraduate/Scholarship) [3688]

Scholarships for Disadvantaged Students (Undergraduate/Scholarship) [4499]

Scholarships for Leadership Training and Coaching (Professional development/Scholarship) [3457]

Scholarships for Lutheran College Students (Undergraduate/Scholarship) [2077]

Scholarships of the Morris Radio Club of New Jersey (Undergraduate/Scholarship) [1106]

The Dr. William M. Scholl College of Podiatric Medicine Scholarships (Undergraduate/Scholarship) [7143]

The Schonstedt Scholarships in Surveying (Undergraduate/Scholarship) [650]

School Age Financial Aid Program (Undergraduate/Scholarship) [2050]

School In-Service Training Grants for Grades 6-8 Teachers (High School/Grant) [6223]

School In-Service Training Grants for Grades 9-12 Teachers (High School/Grant) [6224]

School In-Service Training Grants for Grades K-5 Teachers (High School/Grant) [6225]

School of Pharmacy Continuing Student Scholarships (Undergraduate/Scholarship) [9370]

Schoolsfirst Federal Credit Union Scholarships (Undergraduate/Scholarship) [7712]

Susan P. Schroeder Memorial Scholarships (Undergraduate/Scholarship) [5464]

Kurt H. and Donna M. Schuler Cash Grants (Undergraduate/Scholarship) [1193]

Alice Southworth Schulman Simmons Scholarships for UU Women (Undergraduate/Scholarship) [9000]

Richard E. Schultes Research Awards (Graduate/Grant) [8316]

Al Schuman Ecolab Undergraduate Entrepreneurial Scholarships (Undergraduate/Scholarship) [6463]

Schurgin Family Foundation Scholarships (Undergraduate/Scholarship) [4910]

Karen Schuvie Scholarships (Undergraduate/Scholarship) [5189]

AIST William E. Schwabe Memorial Scholarships (Undergraduate/Scholarship) [1817]

Schwan's Food Service Scholarships (Undergraduate, Vocational/Occupational/Scholarship) [8030]

Marla Schwartz Grants (Professional development, Graduate/Grant) [504]

Abba P. Schwartz Research Fellowships (All/Fellowship) [5241]

Fritz Schwartz Serials Education Scholarships (Graduate, Professional development/Scholarship) [6744]

Evalee C. Schwarz Educational Loans (Graduate, Undergraduate/Loan) [8052]

David R. Schweisberg Memorial Scholarships (Graduate, Undergraduate/Scholarship) [7019]

Science to Achieve Results Fellowships (STAR) (Graduate/Fellowship) [9042]

Science Foundation Arizona Graduate Research Fellowships (GRF) (Graduate/Fellowship) [8054]

Scleroderma Foundation Established Investigator Grants (Doctorate/Grant) [8058]

Scleroderma Foundation New Investigator Grants (Doctorate/Grant) [8059]

SCMS Dissertation Awards (Postdoctorate/Award) [8311]

SCMS Student Writing Awards (Graduate/Award) [8312]

NASCAR/Wendell Scott Awards (Graduate, Undergraduate/Scholarship) [4550]

Carl A. Scott Book Scholarships (Undergraduate/Scholarship) [3284]

Herbert Scoville Jr. Peace Fellowships (Graduate/Fellowship) [8067]

Bonnie Sorenson Scudder Scholarships (Undergraduate/Scholarship) [3170]

Lewis L. Seaman Junior Enlisted Awards for Outstanding Operational Support *(Professional development/Award)* [1462]

Seaspace Scholarships *(Graduate, Undergraduate/Scholarship)* [8073]

Seattle Chapter ASWA Scholarships *(Undergraduate/Scholarship)* [3600]

SEE Education Foundation Scholarships *(Doctorate, Graduate, Undergraduate/Scholarship)* [4992]

Seed Companies Scholarships *(Undergraduate/Scholarship)* [739]

Elisabeth Seegmiller Recruitment Scholarship Grants *(Undergraduate/Scholarship)* [3171]

Aaron Seesan Memorial Scholarship Fund *(Undergraduate/Scholarship)* [8697]

Detective Cheryl Seiden Memorial Scholarships *(Undergraduate/Scholarship)* [359]

D. Mitchell Self Memorial Scholarships *(Undergraduate/Scholarship)* [6829]

David W. Self Scholarships *(Undergraduate/Scholarship)* [9015]

Walter and Rita Selvy Scholarships *(Undergraduate/Scholarship)* [3513]

June M. Seneca Scholarships *(Graduate/Scholarship)* [8088]

Senior Memorial Scholarships *(Undergraduate/Scholarship)* [3172]

Sentinels of Freedom "Life Scholarships" *(All/Scholarship)* [8090]

William "Buddy" Sentner Scholarship Awards *(Undergraduate/Scholarship)* [539]

Felix R. Sepulveda Memorial Scholarships - Northside Booster Club *(Undergraduate/Scholarship)* [7713]

Serbian Bar Association of America Scholarships *(Undergraduate/Scholarship)* [8092]

Sertoma Communicative Disorders Scholarships *(Graduate/Scholarship)* [8094]

Sertoma Hard of Hearing and Deaf Scholarships *(Undergraduate/Scholarship)* [8095]

Captain Anthony D. Sesow Scholarships *(Undergraduate/Scholarship)* [6578]

Frank B. Sessa Scholarships for Continuing Professional Education *(Professional development/Scholarship)* [2072]

Seton Hall Law School's Merit Scholarship Program *(Undergraduate/Scholarship)* [8097]

Margaret B. Sevcenko Prize in Islamic Art and Culture *(Doctorate/Prize)* [4589]

Hubert K. Seymour Scholarships *(Undergraduate/Scholarship)* [6788]

SFFS Education Colleges & Universities Scholarship Program *(Undergraduate, Graduate/Scholarship)* [7980]

SFP Junior Investigator's Career Development Awards *(Professional development/Grant)* [8322]

SFP Mid-Career/Mentor Awards for Family Planning *(Professional development/Grant)* [8323]

SFP Student and Resident Research Grants *(Graduate/Grant)* [8324]

Al Shackleford and Dan Martin Professional Scholarships *(Undergraduate/Scholarship)* [2017]

Barbara A. Shacochis Scholarships *(Undergraduate/Scholarship)* [7206]

Charles Shafae' Scholarships *(Undergraduate/Prize, Scholarship)* [7043]

Elizabeth Shafer Memorial Scholarships *(Undergraduate/Scholarship)* [7522]

SHAFR Dissertation Completion Fellowships *(Doctorate/Fellowship)* [8342]

Saleem Shah Early Career Development Awards *(Doctorate/Award)* [1046]

Shamberg Scholarships *(Undergraduate/Scholarship)* [9491]

William Shannon American Council on Exercise Certification Scholarships *(Professional development, Undergraduate/Scholarship)* [664]

William H. Shannon Fellowships *(Graduate, Undergraduate/Fellowship)* [5017]

Commander Dan F. Shanower Scholarships *(Undergraduate/Scholarship)* [6579]

W.L. Shattuck Scholarships *(Undergraduate/Scholarship)* [4674]

Benjamin G. Shatz Scholarships *(Undergraduate/Scholarship)* [7207]

Anne Shaw Fellowships *(Graduate/Fellowship)* [8890]

Luci Shaw Fellowships *(Undergraduate/Fellowship)* [4704]

Regina B. Shearn Scholarships *(Graduate, Undergraduate/Scholarship)* [360]

Dezna C. Sheehan Memorial Educational Scholarships *(Postgraduate/Scholarship)* [6516]

Jim Sheerin Scholarships *(Undergraduate/Scholarship)* [5719]

Sheet Metal And Air Conditioning Contractors' National Association College of Fellows Scholarships *(Undergraduate/Scholarship)* [8101]

Nettie and Edward Shelah Scholarships *(Undergraduate/Scholarship)* [8733]

Shell Incentive Scholarship Fund *(Undergraduate/Scholarship)* [8103]

Shell Process Technology Scholarships *(Undergraduate/Scholarship)* [8104]

Shell Technical Scholarships *(Undergraduate/Scholarship)* [8105]

Bruce Shelton Scholarships *(Undergraduate/Scholarship)* [9654]

Matthew Shepard Scholarships *(Undergraduate/Scholarship)* [7870]

Bill and Ann Sheperd Legal Scholarship Fund *(Undergraduate/Scholarship)* [3683]

Joseph Henry Shepherd Scholarships *(Undergraduate/Scholarship)* [9238]

Robert P. Sheppard Leadership Awards *(High School/Scholarship)* [6506]

Marion A. and Ruth Sherwood Family Fund Education Scholarships *(Undergraduate/Scholarship)* [4243]

Morgan and Jeanie Sherwood Travel Grants *(Graduate, Professional development/Grant)* [1253]

Shields-Gillespie Scholarships *(All, Professional development/Scholarship)* [962]

Drs. Poh Shien and Judy Young Scholarships *(Undergraduate/Scholarship)* [9068]

Milton L. Shifman Endowed Scholarships *(Undergraduate/Scholarship)* [5630]

The Shincho Graduate Fellowships for Study in Japan *(Graduate/Fellowship)* [5227]

Ethel Shinn Alumni-Vocational Scholarships *(Undergraduate/Scholarship)* [5465]

Joseph Shinoda Memorial Scholarships *(Undergraduate/Scholarship)* [8109]

Jason Shipley Memorial Scholarships *(Undergraduate/Scholarship)* [6383]

Shohet Scholars Program *(Postdoctorate/Fellowship)* [4890]

Shoreline Community College Academic Excellence Scholarships for Graduating High School Seniors *(Undergraduate/Scholarship)* [8123]

Shoreline Community College Academic Improvement Scholarships for Graduating High School Seniors *(Undergraduate/Scholarship)* [8124]

Shoreline Community College Continuing Students Scholarships *(Undergraduate/Scholarship)* [8125]

Shoreline Community College Part-Time Students Scholarships *(Undergraduate/Scholarship)* [8126]

Short-Term Fellowships *(Undergraduate, Graduate, Postdoctorate/Fellowship)* [8271]

Short-term Senior Fellowships in Iranian Studies *(Doctorate, Graduate/Fellowship)* [858]

SHOT-NASA Fellowships *(Doctorate, Postdoctorate/Fellowship)* [8346]

SHPE Foundation Dissertation Scholarships *(Doctorate/Scholarship)* [8131]

SHPE Foundation General Scholarships *(High School, Undergraduate, Graduate/Scholarship)* [8132]

SHPE Foundation Northrop Grumman Scholarships *(Undergraduate/Scholarship)* [8133]

SHPE Foundation Professional Scholarships *(Master's, Doctorate/Scholarship)* [8134]

SHPE Foundation Verizon Scholarships *(Undergraduate/Scholarship)* [8135]

Ralph W. Shrader Diversity Scholarships *(Graduate/Scholarship)* [1563]

Jack Shrader Memorial Awards *(Professional development/Scholarship)* [1744]

SHRM Certification Scholarships - Individual *(Graduate/Scholarship)* [8349]

SHRM Foundation Regional Academic Scholarships *(Graduate, Undergraduate/Scholarship)* [8350]

Phil Shykes Memorial Scholarships *(Undergraduate, Vocational/Occupational/Scholarship)* [3544]

Mary Isabel Sibley Fellowships *(Doctorate/Fellowship)* [7249]

SICB Fellowships of Graduate Student Travel (FGST) *(Graduate/Fellowship)* [8359]

SICB Grants-in-Aid of Research Program (GIAR) *(Graduate/Grant)* [8360]

Sidley Prelaw Scholars Initiative *(Undergraduate/Scholarship)* [8140]

Norman Siegel Research Scholar Grants *(Doctorate/Grant)* [1313]

Jeff Siegel Scholarships *(Undergraduate/Scholarship)* [6669]

Siemens Clinical Advancement Scholarship Program *(Postgraduate/Scholarship)* [1327]

Siemens Teacher Scholarships *(Graduate, Undergraduate/Scholarship)* [8142]

E.J. Sierleja Memorial Fellowships *(Graduate/Fellowship)* [4809]

Sig Memorial Scholarships *(Undergraduate/Scholarship)* [30]

Sigma Delta Epsilon Fellowships *(Graduate, Postdoctorate/Fellowship)* [8154]

Sigma Diagnostics Student Scholarships *(Undergraduate/Scholarship)* [6517]

Sigma Kappa Foundation Alumnae Continuing Education Scholarships *(Undergraduate/Scholarship)* [8182]

Sigma Kappa Foundation Alzheimer's/Gerontology Scholarships *(Undergraduate/Scholarship)* [8183]

Sigma Kappa Foundation Founders' Scholarships *(Undergraduate/Scholarship)* [8184]

Sigma Kappa Foundation Gerontology Scholarships *(Undergraduate/Scholarship)* [8185]

Sigma Pi Sigma Undergraduate Research Awards *(Undergraduate/Grant)* [8440]

Silver Nugget Family Scholarships *(Undergraduate/Scholarship)* [7523]

Silver Nugget Gaming Ambassadors Scholarships *(Undergraduate/Scholarship)* [7524]

Meyer and Dorothy Silverman Scholarships *(Undergraduate/Scholarship)* [3133]

Stuart Silverman Scholarships *(Undergraduate/Scholarship)* [7208]

Willard B. Simmons Sr. Memorial Scholarships *(Undergraduate/Scholarship)* [6202]

Julian Simon Fellowships *(Professional development/Fellowship)* [7455]

Simon Youth Foundation Community Scholarships *(Undergraduate, Vocational/Occupational/Scholarship)* [8212]

Simonton Windows Scholarships *(Undergraduate, Vocational/Occupational/Scholarship)* [7115]

DW Simpson Actuarial Science Scholarship Program *(Undergraduate/Scholarship)* [8214]

Carole Simpson Scholarships *(Undergraduate/Scholarship)* [7583]

Aaron B. Singleton Memorial Scholarships *(Undergraduate/Scholarship)* [6830]

Sino-American Pharmaceutical Professionals Association Scholarships *(Undergraduate/Scholarship)* [8222]

Helen J. Sioussat/Fay Wells Scholarships *(All/Scholarship)* [2184]

Wiggsy Sivertsen Scholarships *(Undergraduate/Scholarship)* [7871]

Leif and Inger Sjoberg Awards *(Professional development/Award)* [1173]

Skadden Fellowships *(Graduate/Fellowship)* [8229]

R. Skeeles Memorial Scholarship Fund *(Undergraduate/Scholarship)* [8699]

Francelene Skinner Memorial Scholarships *(Undergraduate/Scholarship)* [5478]

Allogan Slagle Memorial Scholarships *(All/Scholarship)* [1697]

Robert W. Sledge Fellowships *(Graduate/Fellowship)* [346]

Slifka Foundation Interdisciplinary Fellowships *(Doctorate/Fellowship)* [5791]

Sloan Northwood University Heavy-Duty Scholarships *(Undergraduate/Scholarship)* [1968]

Sloan Research Fellowships *(Doctorate/Fellowship)* [8235]

Thomas J. Slocum Memorial Scholarships to Westwood College of Aviation Technology *(Under-

graduate/Scholarship) [139]

The Aaron and Rita Slom Scholarships (Undergraduate/Scholarship) [8923]

SMART Scholarships (Graduate, Undergraduate/Scholarship) [8056]

SME Coal and Energy Division Scholarships (Undergraduate/Scholarship) [8414]

SME Directors Scholarships (Undergraduate/Scholarship) [8398]

SME Education Foundation Family Scholarships (Undergraduate/Scholarship) [8399]

SME Environmental Division Scholarships (Undergraduate/Scholarship) [8415]

Dr. George M. Smerk Scholarships (Graduate, Undergraduate/Scholarship) [1057]

SMFM/AAOGF Scholarship Awards (Graduate/Scholarship) [8410]

Hy Smith Endowment Fund (Undergraduate/Scholarship) [4382]

Ryan and Jamie Smith Essay Contest (Graduate, Postgraduate/Scholarship) [8237]

Stanley Smith Horticultural Fellowships (Graduate, Undergraduate/Fellowship) [6987]

James I. Smith, III Notre Dame Law School Scholarship Fund (Graduate, Undergraduate/Scholarship) [331]

Charles Smith Memorial Scholarship Awards (Undergraduate/Scholarship) [1633]

Boy Scouts of America Troop 3 Scholarships - Art Till/Nathan E. Smith Memorial Scholarships (Undergraduate, Vocational/Occupational/Scholarship) [7714]

Colonel Nate Smith Memorial Scholarships (Graduate, Undergraduate/Scholarship) [5731]

Tacy Ana Smith Memorial Scholarships (Undergraduate/Scholarship) [3921]

Smith-Reynolds Founder Fellowships (Graduate/Fellowship) [4526]

The Eileen J. Smith, R.N. Memorial Scholarships (Undergraduate/Scholarship) [5105]

Ralph and Josephine Smith Scholarship Fund (Undergraduate/Scholarship) [3793]

A.O. Smith Scholarships (Undergraduate/Scholarship) [7349]

Esther M. Smith Scholarships (Undergraduate/Scholarship) [3069]

Helen J. and Harold Gilman Smith Scholarships (Graduate, Undergraduate/Scholarship) [2065]

Joseph Sumner Smith Scholarships (All/Scholarship) [9001]

Richard S. Smith Scholarships (Undergraduate/Scholarship) [9016]

William E. Smith Scholarships (Graduate/Scholarship) [171]

Drue Smith/Society of Professional Journalists Scholarships (Undergraduate/Scholarship) [3134]

Nadine Barrie Smith Student Awards (All/Award) [5005]

Smith's Personal Best Scholarships (Undergraduate/Scholarship) [7525]

Smithsonian Fellowships in Museum Practice (Professional development/Fellowship) [8266]

Smithsonian Institution Graduate Student Fellowships (Graduate/Fellowship) [8245]

Smithsonian Institution Postdoctoral Fellowships (Doctorate/Fellowship) [8246]

Smithsonian Institution Predoctoral Fellowships (Doctorate/Fellowship) [8247]

Smithsonian Institution Senior Fellowships (Doctorate/Fellowship) [8248]

Smithsonian Postgraduate Fellowships in Conservation of Museum Collection Program (Postgraduate/Fellowship) [8249]

Gladys Snauble Scholarships (Undergraduate/Scholarship) [4299]

SNF Professional Growth Scholarships (Graduate, Undergraduate/Scholarship) [8031]

SNMTS Bachelor's Degree Completion Scholarships (Undergraduate/Scholarship) [8421]

SNMTS Clinical Advancement Scholarships (Professional development/Scholarship) [8422]

Helen D. Snow Memorial Scholarships (Undergraduate/Scholarship) [7252]

A.C. Snow Scholarships (Undergraduate/Scholarship) [9305]

Snowmobile Association of Massachusetts Scholar-

ships (Undergraduate, Vocational/Occupational/Scholarship) [8274]

Stuart H. Snyder Memorial Scholarships (Undergraduate/Scholarship) [1949]

Arnold Sobel Scholarships (Undergraduate/Scholarship) [2929]

Social Equity Venture Fund Teaching Fellowships (Professional development/Fellowship) [8280]

Society of Allied Weight Engineers Scholarships (Undergraduate/Scholarship) [8291]

Society for the Arts in Healthcare Environmental Research Grants (Professional development/Grant) [8300]

Society for the Arts in Healthcare Student Scholarships (Doctorate, Graduate, Undergraduate/Scholarship) [8301]

Society of Exploration Geophysicists Foundation Scholarships (Graduate, Undergraduate/Scholarship) [8320]

Society for Linguistic Anthropology Student Essay Prize (Graduate, Undergraduate/Prize) [8365]

Society of Manufacturing Engineers Ford PAS Scholarships (SME) (Undergraduate/Scholarship) [8401]

Society of Marine Port Engineers Scholarship Loans (Undergraduate/Scholarship loan, Loan) [8408]

Society of Naval Architects and Marine Engineers Undergraduate Scholarships (Undergraduate/Scholarship) [8418]

Society of Pediatric Nurses Educational Scholarships (Graduate, Professional development/Scholarship) [8424]

Society for Pediatric Radiology Research Fellows (Graduate, Professional development/Fellowship) [8429]

Society for Pediatric Radiology Seed Grants (Graduate, Professional development/Grant) [8430]

Society for Pediatric Urology Research Grant Program (Undergraduate/Grant) [8433]

Society of Plastics Engineers General Scholarships (Graduate, Undergraduate/Scholarship) [8456]

Society of Plastics Engineers Pittsburgh Section Scholarships (Graduate, Undergraduate/Scholarship) [8457]

Society for the Scientific Study of Sexuality Student Research Grants (Undergraduate/Grant) [8493]

Society of Vacuum Coaters Foundation Scholarships (Vocational/Occupational, Two Year College, Undergraduate, Graduate/Scholarship) [8514]

Society of Women Engineers Scholarships (Undergraduate/Scholarship) [8516]

Louis B. Sohn Fellowships in Human Rights and Environment (Graduate/Fellowship) [2692]

CFI Sid Solow Scholarships (Graduate/Scholarship) [1832]

Dr. Kiyoshi Sonoda Memorial Scholarships (Graduate/Scholarship) [5146]

Sons of Norway Foundation Scholarships to Oslo International School (Undergraduate/Scholarship) [8532]

Sons of Union Veterans of the Civil War Scholarships (Undergraduate/Scholarship) [8534]

Sony Pictures Scholarships (Graduate/Scholarship) [1833]

SOPHE/ATSDR Student Fellowships in Environmental Health or Emergency Preparedness (Doctorate, Graduate, Master's/Fellowship) [8478]

SOPHE/CDC Student Fellowships in Child, Adolescent and School Health (Doctorate, Graduate, Master's/Fellowship) [8479]

SOPHE/CDC Student Fellowships in Injury Prevention (Graduate/Fellowship) [8480]

Theodore C. Sorensen Fellowships (All/Fellowship) [5242]

Soroptimist International of Chambersburg Scholarship Fund (Undergraduate/Scholarship) [3961]

Soroptimist International of Redlands Scholarships (Undergraduate/Scholarship) [7715]

Paul and Daisy Soros Fellowships (Graduate/Fellowship) [8536]

Eastman Kodak Dr. Theophilus Sorrell Fellowships (Graduate/Fellowship) [6432]

South Carolina Association for Financial Professionals Certified Treasury Professional Scholarships (Professional development/Scholarship) [8544]

South Carolina Scholastic Press Association Scholarships (Undergraduate/Scholarship) [8553]

South Carolina Scholastic Press Association Yearbook Scholarships (Undergraduate/Scholarship) [8554]

South Carolina Tourism and Hospitality Educational Foundation Scholarships (Undergraduate/Scholarship) [4603]

South Carolina Undergraduate Scholarships (Undergraduate/Scholarship) [4604]

South Central Modern Language Association Fellowships (Doctorate/Fellowship) [6709]

South Central Power Scholarships (Undergraduate, Vocational/Occupational/Scholarship) [8556]

South Dakota Division Scholarships (Undergraduate/Scholarship) [5865]

South Jersey Golf Association Scholarships (Undergraduate/Scholarship) [8561]

Southeast Aerospace Inc. Scholarships (Undergraduate/Scholarship) [140]

Southern Nevada Sports Hall of Fame Athletic Scholarships (Undergraduate/Scholarship) [7526]

Southern Scholarship Foundation Scholarships (Undergraduate/Scholarship) [8587]

Southwest Movers Association Scholarships (Undergraduate/Scholarship) [8629]

Sovereign Nations Scholarships (Undergraduate/Scholarship) [810]

Iwalani Carpenter Sowa Scholarships (Graduate/Scholarship) [5222]

Master Sergeant William Sowers Memorial Scholarships (Undergraduate/Scholarship) [101]

SPA Certified Legal Assistant Scholarships (Professional development/Scholarship) [7885]

Willard and Spackman Scholarship Program (Postgraduate/Scholarship) [956]

Amy E. Spain Memorial Scholarships (Undergraduate/Scholarship) [9239]

Nathan Sparks Memorial Scholarships (Undergraduate/Scholarship) [3049]

Spartan Staff Scholarships (Undergraduate/Scholarship) [7527]

Special Education Scholarships (Graduate, Undergraduate/Scholarship) [362]

Special Law School Scholarships (Undergraduate/Scholarship) [7209]

Specialty Equipment Market Association Scholarships (Graduate, Undergraduate, Vocational/Occupational/Scholarship) [8635]

Specialty Nursing Scholarships (Undergraduate/Scholarship) [3979]

Faith Speckhard Scholarships (Undergraduate, Vocational/Occupational/Scholarship) [5106]

Spencer Foundation Research Grants (All/Grant) [6007]

Spice Box Grants (Professional development/Grant) [698]

Patrick Spielman Memorial Scholarship Program (Undergraduate, Vocational/Occupational/Scholarship) [8071]

Spirit of Allison Graduation Awards (Undergraduate/Award) [3806]

The Spirit Square Center for Arts and Education Scholarship Fund (Undergraduate/Scholarship) [3922]

SPOOM Research Grants (Graduate/Grant) [8463]

Sporty's Pilot Shop/Cincinnati Avionics Scholarships (Undergraduate, Vocational/Occupational/Scholarship) [141]

Spotlight on Nursing Graduate Nursing Scholarships (Graduate/Scholarship) [8651]

Spouse Tuition Aids Program (STAP) (Graduate, Undergraduate/Loan) [6594]

SPPSI Grants-In-Aid Program (Graduate, Postdoctorate/Grant) [8475]

James F. and Donna Springfield Scholarships (Undergraduate/Scholarship) [9240]

SPS Future Teacher Scholarships (Undergraduate/Scholarship) [8441]

SPS Leadership Scholarships (Undergraduate/Scholarship) [8442]

SPSmedical CS Scholarships (Professional development/Scholarship) [4871]

SREB-State Doctoral Scholarships (Doctorate, Graduate/Scholarship) [8585]

Kei Takemoto Memorial Scholarships *(Undergraduate/Scholarship)* [142]

Tall Awareness Scholarships *(Undergraduate/Scholarship)* [7529]

Tall Clubs International Student Scholarships *(Undergraduate/Scholarship)* [8802]

Janet Cullen Tanaka Scholarships *(Undergraduate/Scholarship)* [1905]

Tanana Valley Campus Culinary Arts Scholarships *(Undergraduate/Scholarship)* [8989]

Alexander M. Tanger Scholarships *(All/Scholarship)* [2185]

William J. Tangye Scholarships *(Undergraduate/Scholarship)* [4902]

Hal Tanner Jr. Scholarships *(Undergraduate/Scholarship)* [9306]

Alex Tanous Scholarship Awards *(Undergraduate/Scholarship)* [8807]

Lee Tarbox Memorial Scholarships *(Undergraduate/Scholarship)* [143]

Targeted Research Initiative for Health Outcomes *(Doctorate/Grant)* [3668]

Targeted Research Initiative for Mood Disorders *(Doctorate/Grant)* [3669]

Targeted Research Initiative for Seniors *(Doctorate/Grant)* [3670]

Tarkanian Teacher Education Academy at Clark High School Scholarships (TEACH) *(Undergraduate/Scholarship)* [7530]

Sheila Tarr-Smith Memorial Scholarships *(Undergraduate/Scholarship)* [7531]

Bud and Linda Tarrson Fellowships *(Postdoctorate/Fellowship)* [397]

Tarrson Regeneration Scholarships *(Postdoctorate/Scholarship)* [398]

Charles T. and Judith A. Tart Student Incentive Awards *(Graduate, Postdoctorate, Undergraduate/Grant)* [7053]

Graduate Fellowship Program - GRC/AI Tasch Fellowships (GFP) *(Graduate/Fellowship)* [8083]

Jack Tate/ThinkCOLLEGE Scholarship Fund *(Undergraduate/Scholarship)* [3924]

Jordan B. Tatter Scholarships *(Undergraduate/Scholarship)* [5832]

Taylor/Blakeslee University Fellowships *(Professional development, Undergraduate/Fellowship)* [3268]

Charles "Buck" and Dora Taylor Endowed Law Scholarships *(Undergraduate/Scholarship)* [3514]

Tom Taylor Memorial Scholarships to Spartan College of Aeronautics and Technology *(Undergraduate/Scholarship)* [144]

TCA-BAACBH Scholarships *(Undergraduate/Scholarship)* [8977]

TCA Outstanding Graduate Student Awards *(Graduate/Award)* [8859]

TCA Turkish American Scholarships *(Undergraduate/Scholarship)* [8978]

TCA-UMD Scholarships *(Undergraduate/Scholarship)* [8979]

TCATA College Scholarship Program *(Undergraduate/Scholarship)* [8886]

TCDA Abbott IPCO Professional Scholarships *(Graduate, Professional development/Scholarship)* [8849]

TCDA Gandy Ink Student Scholarships *(Graduate, Undergraduate/Scholarship)* [8850]

TCDA General Fund Scholarships *(Graduate, Undergraduate/Scholarship)* [8851]

TCDA Past Presidents Student Scholarships *(Graduate, Undergraduate/Scholarship)* [8852]

TDKF Scholarships *(Undergraduate/Scholarship)* [5237]

Teammates Mentoring Scholarship Program *(Undergraduate/Scholarship)* [4264]

Technical Services Special Interest Section Grants *(Professional development/Grant)* [506]

Technical Women's Organization Scholarship Program (TWO) *(Undergraduate/Scholarship)* [8813]

Dwight Teed Scholarships *(Undergraduate/Scholarship)* [8772]

Marvin H. and Kathleen G. Teget Leadership Scholarships *(Undergraduate/Scholarship)* [8768]

Paul Tejada Memorial Scholarships *(Undergraduate/Scholarship)* [5107]

Telecommunications Association of Michigan Scholarship Fund *(Undergraduate/Scholarship)* [8825]

Television News Scholarships *(Undergraduate/Scholarship)* [6453]

Telford Scholarships *(Undergraduate/Scholarship)* [31]

Telluride Association Summer Program Scholarships *(High School/Scholarship)* [8827]

Templeton-Cambridge Journalism Fellowships *(All/Fellowship)* [8839]

Mary L. Tenopyr Graduate Student Scholarships *(Doctorate/Scholarship)* [8356]

Charles L. Terrell/New Haven Savings Bank Scholarship Fund *(Undergraduate/Scholarship)* [3083]

Steven M. Teutsch Prevention Effectiveness Fellowships *(Doctorate/Fellowship)* [2715]

Texas Computer Education Association Professional Educator Grants *(Professional development/Grant)* [8857]

Texas Elks State Association Eagle Scout Scholarships *(High School/Scholarship)* [8861]

Texas Elks State Association Girl Scout Gold Award Scholarships *(High School, Undergraduate/Scholarship)* [8862]

Texas Music Educators Association Past-Presidents Memorial Scholarships *(Undergraduate/Scholarship)* [8866]

Texas Muslims Scholarship Fund (TMSF) *(Graduate, Undergraduate/Scholarship)* [4006]

Texas Mutual Scholarship Program *(Undergraduate, Vocational/Occupational/Scholarship)* [8868]

Texas Society of Professional Engineers Scholarships *(Undergraduate/Scholarship)* [8872]

Texas State Technical College Scholarships *(Undergraduate/Scholarship)* [145]

Texas Telephone Association Foundation Scholarships *(Undergraduate/Scholarship)* [8882]

Texas Transportation Scholarships *(Undergraduate, Vocational/Occupational/Scholarship)* [8953]

Jim and Pat Thacker Sports Communication Internships *(Undergraduate/Internship)* [9307]

ThanksUSA Scholarships *(Undergraduate, Vocational/Occupational/Scholarship)* [8888]

Dr. Peter A. Theodos Memorial Graduate Scholarships *(Graduate/Scholarship)* [4519]

Thermo Scientific Educational Scholarships *(Postgraduate/Scholarship)* [6518]

Thermoforming Division Memorial Scholarships *(Graduate, Undergraduate/Scholarship)* [8458]

Thermoplastic Materials and Foams Division Scholarships *(Graduate, Undergraduate/Scholarship)* [8459]

Thermoplastics Elastomers Special Interest Group Scholarships *(Graduate, Undergraduate/Scholarship)* [8460]

Thesaurus Linguae Latinae Fellowships (TTL) *(Doctorate/Fellowship)* [987]

Theta Tau Scholarships *(Undergraduate/Scholarship)* [8189]

Dean James Thomas Memorial Scholarships *(Undergraduate/Scholarship)* [9680]

E.D. Thomas Post Doctoral Fellowships *(Postdoctorate/Fellowship)* [4014]

Barber Owen Thomas Scholarships *(Undergraduate/Scholarship)* [8190]

Elizabeth R. Thomas Scholarships *(Undergraduate/Scholarship)* [8128]

Rev. Chuck and Nancy Thomas Scholarships *(Graduate, Master's/Scholarship)* [9004]

Honorable Raymond Thompson Endowed Scholarships *(Undergraduate/Scholarship)* [7210]

Barbara and Howard Thompson Scholarships *(Undergraduate/Scholarship)* [5108]

Marjorie Anderson Thompson Scholarships *(Graduate, Undergraduate/Scholarship)* [363]

Thompson Scholarships for Women in Safety *(Graduate/Scholarship)* [1355]

Thomson Reuters/MLA Doctoral Fellowships *(Doctorate/Fellowship)* [5748]

Thornberg/Havens Scholarships *(Undergraduate/Scholarship)* [3423]

Thyssen-Heideking Fellowships *(Postdoctorate/Fellowship)* [4129]

Tikvah Fellowships *(Graduate, Professional development/Fellowship)* [8909]

Jack E. Tillson Scholarships *(Graduate/Scholarship)* [5040]

Time Warner Point Scholarships *(Graduate, Undergraduate/Scholarship)* [7367]

Time Warner Tribal Scholars Program *(Undergraduate/Scholarship)* [812]

Eben Tisdale Fellowships *(Graduate, Undergraduate/Fellowship)* [4017]

TMA Research Fellowships *(Graduate, Postdoctorate/Grant)* [5967]

TMCF Scholarships *(Undergraduate/Scholarship)* [5647]

Star and Barry Tobias Scholarships *(Undergraduate/Scholarship)* [2728]

Mario J. Tocco Hydrocephalus Foundation Scholarships *(Undergraduate/Scholarship)* [4654]

Richard Cecil Todd and Clauda Pennock Todd Tripod Scholarships *(Graduate, Undergraduate/Scholarship)* [7276]

Robert Toigo Foundation Fellowships *(Master's/Fellowship)* [8911]

William Tomar Memorial Scholarships *(Undergraduate/Scholarship)* [2326]

The Adelle and Erwin Tomash Fellowships *(Doctorate/Fellowship)* [1992]

John Tomasovic, Sr. Scholarships *(Undergraduate/Scholarship)* [740]

Tomato Fest Scholarship Grants *(Undergraduate/Scholarship)* [699]

George Torkildsen Literary Awards *(Professional development/Award)* [9757]

Aram Torossian Memorial Scholarships *(Undergraduate/Scholarship)* [1606]

Ferdinand Torres Scholarships *(Graduate, Undergraduate/Scholarship)* [754]

Touchstone Special Achievement Scholarships *(Undergraduate, Vocational/Occupational/Scholarship)* [8557]

Judith A. Towle Environmental Studies Fund *(Undergraduate/Fellowship)* [5082]

Toyota Community Scholars *(Undergraduate/Scholarship)* [8927]

Toyota High School Scholarship Program *(Undergraduate/Scholarship)* [4581]

The Joyce Tracy Fellowships *(Doctorate/Fellowship)* [424]

Traditional Student Scholarships *(Undergraduate/Scholarship)* [3194]

TRALA Scholarship Program *(Undergraduate/Scholarship)* [8964]

Reuben Trane Scholarships *(Undergraduate/Scholarship)* [1270]

Transatlantic Fellows Program *(Professional development/Fellowship)* [4134]

Transoft Solutions, Inc. Ahead of the Curve Scholarships (AOTC) *(Graduate, Undergraduate/Scholarship)* [4827]

Traub-Dicker Rainbow Scholarships *(Undergraduate/Scholarship)* [8747]

Morton M. Traum Surface Science Student Awards *(Graduate, Doctorate/Award)* [1986]

Travel Fellowships in Architecture, Design and Urban Design *(Graduate, Undergraduate/Fellowship)* [8233]

Travel Grants for Women Researchers *(Postdoctorate/Grant)* [1908]

Trelut Family Legacy Scholarships *(Undergraduate/Scholarship)* [2255]

Davis Wright Tremaine 1L Diversity Scholarships *(Undergraduate/Scholarship)* [3348]

Tribal Business Management Program Scholarships (TBM) *(Undergraduate/Scholarship)* [2664]

Tribeca Film Institute Film and Video Fellowships *(Professional development/Fellowship)* [8958]

Tribeca Film Institute New Media Fellowships *(Professional development/Fellowship)* [8960]

Thomas and Glenna Trimble Endowed Scholarships *(Undergraduate/Scholarship)* [7211]

Tim Triner Letter Carriers Scholarship Fund *(Undergraduate/Scholarship)* [8704]

J.P. and Madeline Trinkaus Endowed Scholarships in Embryology *(Undergraduate/Scholarship)* [5632]

Jo Anne J. Trow Scholarships *(Undergraduate/Scholarship)* [6020]

Troy University Rodeo Team Scholarships *(Graduate/Scholarship)* [181]

Truckload Carriers Association Scholarships *(Under-*

graduate/Scholarship) [8966]

Harry S. Truman Scholarships (Postgraduate/Scholarship) [8970]

Trustee, Schawe, and Presidential Scholarships (Undergraduate/Scholarship) [9776]

Trustee Scholarships (Undergraduate/Scholarship) [5235]

Trustees College Scholarships (Undergraduate/Scholarship) [5561]

Trustees Law School Scholarships (Undergraduate/Scholarship) [5562]

TSA Teach Technology Scholarships (Undergraduate/Scholarship) [8816]

Norman J. Tschantz/Walter C. Deuble Scholarships (Undergraduate/Scholarship) [8705]

TUUT HSF College Scholarship Program (Undergraduate/Scholarship) [4582]

Tucker Family Scholarships (Undergraduate/Scholarship) [9308]

Barry Tuckwell Scholarships (All/Scholarship) [4953]

Richard R. Tufenkian Memorial Scholarships (Undergraduate/Scholarship) [1571]

Edward Tuinier Memorial Scholarships (Undergraduate/Scholarship) [741]

Graydon A. Tunstall Undergraduate Student Scholarships (Undergraduate/Scholarship) [7245]

Earl S. Tupper 3-year Postdoctoral Fellowships in Tropical Biology (Postdoctorate/Fellowship) [8272]

Turf and Ornamental Communicators Association Scholarship Program (Undergraduate/Scholarship) [8974]

Hans Turley Prize in Queer Eighteenth-Century Studies (Graduate, Professional development/Prize) [1235]

Jeff Turner-Forsyth Audubon Society Scholarships (Undergraduate/Scholarship) [9658]

James A. Turner, Jr. Memorial Scholarships (Undergraduate/Scholarship) [1447]

Mark and Vera Turner Memorial Scholarships (Undergraduate/Scholarship) [5479]

Emmett H. Turner Scholarships (Undergraduate/Scholarship) [3137]

Ira G. Turpin Scholars Fund (Undergraduate/Scholarship) [8706]

Tuscumbia Kiwanis Scholarships (Undergraduate/Scholarship) [6831]

Lydia Donaldson Tutt-Jones Memorial Research Grant (Graduate, Professional development/Grant) [72]

Vice Adm. Jerry O. Tuttle, USN (Ret.) and Mrs. Barbara A. Tuttle Science and Technology Scholarships (Undergraduate/Scholarship) [1564]

Two Year/Community Broadcast Education Association Scholarship Awards (All/Scholarship) [2186]

UAF Alumni Association Scholarships (Undergraduate/Scholarship) [9189]

UAL/UABT Scholarship Program (Undergraduate/Scholarship) [9007]

UC MEXUS Grants for Dissertation Research (Graduate/Grant) [9199]

UC MEXUS Short-Term Projects (Master's, Doctorate, Postdoctorate/Grant) [9200]

UCB, Inc. NP Student Scholarships (Graduate/Scholarship) [380]

Morris K. Udall Scholarships (Undergraduate/Scholarship) [8991]

Udall Scholarships (Undergraduate/Scholarship) [9197]

UFCW Scholarships (Undergraduate/Scholarship) [9011]

Sandy Ulm Scholarships (Undergraduate/Scholarship) [3816]

Undergraduate and Medical/Graduate General Scholarships and Loans Program (Undergraduate, Vocational/Occupational/Scholarship) [8026]

Undergraduate Session Assistants Program (Undergraduate/Other) [6680]

Bettie Underwood Dental Assisting Scholarships (All/Scholarship) [2677]

UNESCO-L'Oreal for Women in Science International Fellowships (Doctorate, Postdoctorate/Fellowship) [6927]

Union of Marash Armenian Scholarships (Graduate, Undergraduate/Scholarship) [1607]

Union Plus Scholarship Program (Undergraduate/Scholarship) [5025]

United Engineering Foundation Grants (All/Grant) [9009]

United Health Foundation National Association of Hispanic Nurses Scholarships (Graduate, Undergraduate/Scholarship) [6084]

United Parcel Service Scholarships for Female Students (Undergraduate/Scholarship) [4810]

United Parcel Service Scholarships for Minority Students (Undergraduate/Scholarship) [4811]

United South and Eastern Tribes Scholarship Fund (Undergraduate/Scholarship) [9021]

U.S. Air Force ROTC Enhanced HSI Scholarships (Undergraduate/Scholarship) [9026]

U.S. Air Force ROTC Express Scholarships (Undergraduate/Scholarship) [9027]

U.S. Air Force ROTC High School Scholarships (Undergraduate/Scholarship) [9028]

U.S. Air Force ROTC In-College Scholarships (Undergraduate/Scholarship) [9029]

U.S. Aircraft Insurance Group Professional Development Program (USAIG PDP) Scholarships (Undergraduate/Scholarship) [6172]

U.S. Bates Scholarship Program (Undergraduate/Scholarship) [5026]

U.S. BIA Indian Higher Education Grants (Undergraduate/Grant) [823]

United States Capitol Historical Society Fellowships (Graduate/Fellowship) [9037]

The United States Department of State, Bureau of Educational & Cultural Affairs Fellowships (Doctorate, Graduate/Fellowship) [1143]

United States Geospatial Intelligence Foundation Graduate Scholarships (Postgraduate/Scholarship) [9044]

United States Geospatial Intelligence Foundation High School Scholarships (Undergraduate/Scholarship) [9045]

United States Geospatial Intelligence Foundation Undergraduate Scholarships (Undergraduate/Scholarship) [9046]

United States Golf Association Fellowship Program (All/Fellowship) [9048]

United States Golf Association Scholarship Program (Undergraduate/Scholarship) [9049]

U.S. Pan Asian American Chamber of Commerce McDonald's Scholarships (Undergraduate/Scholarship) [9069]

U.S. Pan Asian American Chamber of Commerce UPS Scholarships (Undergraduate/Scholarship) [9070]

United States Society on Dams Scholarships (Graduate/Scholarship) [9072]

United Teachers Los Angeles Stonewall Scholarship Fund (Undergraduate/Scholarship) [7873]

Universal Studios Preservation Scholarships (Graduate/Scholarship) [1834]

University Alliance HSF/UGA College Scholarship Program (Undergraduate/Scholarship) [4583]

University of California LGBT Alumni Scholarships (UCGALA) (Undergraduate/Scholarship) [7874]

University of Hawaii at Manoa East-West Center Graduate Fellowships (Graduate, Postdoctorate/Fellowship) [9206]

University of Hawaii at Manoa Graduate Assistantship Awards (Graduate/Award) [9207]

University of Hawaii at Manoa Graduate Student Organization Travel Funds (Graduate/Grant) [9208]

University of Hawaii at Manoa Japan Travel Bureau Scholarships (Graduate, Undergraduate/Scholarship) [9209]

University Junior Standing Scholarships (Undergraduate/Scholarship) [1531]

University of Minnesota Women Student Travel Grants (Graduate, Undergraduate/Grant) [9245]

University of New Hampshire Alumni Association Legacy Scholarships (Undergraduate/Scholarship) [9251]

University of New Hampshire Parent's Association Endowment Scholarship Fund (Undergraduate/Scholarship) [9252]

University of Oregon Dean's Scholarships (Undergraduate/Scholarship) [9315]

University of Oregon Diversity Excellence Scholar-

ships (Graduate, Undergraduate/Scholarship) [9316]

University of Oregon General University Scholarships (Undergraduate/Scholarship) [9317]

University Senior and Master's Program Scholarships (Graduate/Scholarship) [1532]

University Summer Course Grants (Undergraduate/Grant) [4124]

University of West Alabama Rodeo Team Scholarships (Graduate/Scholarship) [182]

University of Wisconsin-Madison African American Alumni Scholarships (Undergraduate/Scholarship) [9372]

University of Wisconsin-Madison American Indian Alumni Scholarships (Undergraduate/Scholarship) [9373]

University of Wisconsin-Madison/CALS Continuing Student Scholarships (Undergraduate/Scholarship) [9374]

University of Wisconsin-Madison/CALS Minority Scholarships (Undergraduate/Scholarship) [9375]

University of Wisconsin-Madison Chancellor's Scholarships (Undergraduate/Scholarship) [9376]

University of Wisconsin-Madison Hispanic/Latino Alumni Scholarships (Undergraduate/Scholarship) [9377]

University of Wisconsin-Madison Music Scholarships (Undergraduate/Scholarship) [9379]

University of Wisconsin-Madison National Merit Scholarships (Undergraduate/Scholarship) [9380]

University of Wisconsin-Madison Pharmacy New Student Scholarships (Undergraduate/Scholarship) [9381]

University of Wisconsin-Madison Single Parent and Adult Scholarships (Undergraduate/Scholarship) [9382]

Upakar Indian-American Scholarships (Undergraduate/Scholarship) [9389]

Samuel Upchurch Memorial Scholarships (Undergraduate/Scholarship) [183]

UPE/ACM Scholarship Awards (Graduate, Undergraduate/Award) [9391]

UPE Scholarship Awards (Graduate, Undergraduate/Award) [9392]

UPS Diversity Scholarships (Undergraduate/Scholarship) [1356]

Urban and Regional Policy (Comparative Domestic Policy) Fellowships (Professional development/Fellowship) [4135]

The Urban Scholarship Fund (Undergraduate/Scholarship) [8844]

CASFM-Ben Urbonas Scholarships (Graduate/Scholarship) [2982]

USA Funds Access to Education Scholarships (Graduate, Undergraduate, Vocational/Occupational/Scholarship) [9079]

USAWOASF/Grantham University On-Line Scholarships (Graduate, Undergraduate, Vocational/Occupational/Scholarship) [9031]

USAWOASF Regular Scholarships (Undergraduate, Vocational/Occupational/Scholarship) [9032]

USHJA General Scholarships (Undergraduate/Scholarship) [9051]

USHJA Postgraduate Scholarships (Postgraduate/Scholarship) [9052]

USS Coral Sea Remembrance Scholarships (Undergraduate/Scholarship) [9405]

USS Tennessee Scholarship Fund (Undergraduate, Vocational/Occupational/Scholarship) [6595]

USTA Serves College Education Scholarships (Undergraduate/Scholarship) [9411]

USTA Tennis and Education Foundation College Textbook Scholarships (Undergraduate/Scholarship) [9412]

Utility Workers Union of America Scholarship Program (Undergraduate/Scholarship) [70]

John D. Utterback Scholarship Program (Undergraduate/Scholarship) [324]

Uva Faculty Fellowships (Professional development/Fellowship) [4782]

VABANC Scholarships (Graduate, Undergraduate/Scholarship) [9429]

Wallace Vail Scholarships (Undergraduate/Scholarship) [6663]

Valley Alliance of Mentors for Opportunities and

Scholarship Program (VAMOS) *(Undergraduate/ Scholarship)* [4584]

Valpak Scholarships *(Graduate, Undergraduate/ Scholarship)* [7272]

Valuing Diversity PhD Scholarships *(Doctorate/ Scholarship)* [920]

Hurad Van Der Bedrosian Memorial Scholarships *(Graduate/Scholarship)* [1608]

William P. Van Wagenen Fellowships *(Undergraduate/Fellowship)* [516]

The Vander Putten Family Scholarships *(All/Scholarship)* [2930]

Jacob VanNamen-Vans Marketing Scholarships *(Undergraduate/Scholarship)* [742]

Russell and Sigurd Varian Award *(Graduate/Award)* [1987]

Varian Radiation Therapy Scholarship Program *(Postdoctorate/Scholarship)* [1328]

Vector Marketing Canadian Scholarship Awards *(Undergraduate/Scholarship)* [9417]

Vector Marketing Scholarships *(Graduate, Undergraduate/Scholarship)* [7273]

Ventana Medical Systems In Situ Hybridization Awards *(Professional development/Award)* [6519]

Veolia ES Waste-to-Energy/Terrence L. Guest Memorial Awards *(Graduate/Scholarship)* [8527]

Helen Veress-Mitchell Scholarship Fund *(Graduate, Undergraduate/Scholarship)* [2649]

Graduate Fellowship Program - Peter Verhofstadt Fellowships (GFP) *(Graduate/Fellowship)* [8084]

Vermont Paralegal Organization Scholarships *(Undergraduate/Scholarship)* [9419]

Chester M. Vernon Memorial Eagle Scout Scholarships *(High School/Scholarship)* [6263]

Dimitri J. Ververelli Memorial Scholarships *(Undergraduate/Scholarship)* [4520]

A. Verville Fellowships *(All/Fellowship)* [8253]

Vesalius Trust Student Scholarships *(Graduate, Undergraduate/Scholarship)* [9422]

Veterans of Enduring Freedom (Afghanistan) and Iraqi Freedom Scholarships *(Undergraduate/ Scholarship)* [1565]

Veterans of Foreign Wars Scout of the Year *(High School/Scholarship)* [6264]

Zelda Walling Vicha Memorial Scholarships *(Undergraduate, Vocational/Occupational/Scholarship)* [1319]

Vilas Equity Scholarships *(Undergraduate/Scholarship)* [9383]

William F. Vilas Scholarships *(Undergraduate/Scholarship)* [9384]

Dr. Juan D. Villarreal/HDA Foundation Scholarships *(Undergraduate/Scholarship)* [4557]

Villers Fellowships for Health Care Justice *(Graduate/Fellowship)* [3706]

Vinyl Plastics Division Scholarships *(Graduate, Undergraduate/Scholarship)* [8461]

Violin Society of America Scholarships *(Undergraduate/Scholarship)* [9436]

Virginia Historical Society Research Fellowships *(Doctorate/Fellowship)* [9453]

Visiting Doctoral Tikvah Scholarships *(Doctorate/ Scholarship)* [8907]

Visiting Fellowships *(Professional development/Fellowship)* [4783]

Visiting Scholars Fellowships *(Postdoctorate/Fellowship)* [2043]

Visiting Scholars Program *(Doctorate/Fellowship)* [2699]

VISTAKON Research Grants *(All/Grant)* [389]

John D. Voelker Foundation Native American Scholarships *(Undergraduate/Scholarship)* [9470]

Von Ogden Vogt Scholarships *(Graduate, Master's/ Scholarship)* [9005]

Miki Vohryzek-Bolden Student Paper Awards *(Undergraduate/Award)* [9583]

Irma E. Voigt Memorial Scholarships *(Undergraduate/Scholarship)* [8191]

Vorgin-Bell Scholarships *(Graduate, Master's, Undergraduate/Scholarship)* [6848]

The Sibyl Jennings Vorheis Memorial Undergraduate Scholarships *(Undergraduate/Scholarship)* [3926]

Abe Voron Scholarships *(All/Scholarship)* [2187]

VPPPA June Brothers Scholarships *(Graduate, Undergraduate/Scholarship)* [9477]

VSCPA Educational Foundation Graduate Scholarships *(Graduate/Scholarship)* [9464]

VSCPA Educational Foundation Minority Scholarships *(Graduate, Undergraduate/Scholarship)* [9465]

VSCPA Educational Foundation Undergraduate Scholarships *(Undergraduate/Scholarship)* [9466]

VSCPA PhD Accounting Scholarships *(Doctorate, Graduate/Scholarship)* [9467]

VSP Research Grants *(All/Grant)* [390]

Wachovia Scholars Program *(Undergraduate/Scholarship)* [4551]

Bruce Wade Memorial Scholarships for Lesbian, Gay and Bisexual *(Undergraduate/Scholarship)* [7875]

Mercedes Laurie Wade Scholarships *(Undergraduate/Scholarship)* [2341]

Robert & Barbara Wade Scholarships *(Undergraduate/Scholarship)* [5480]

Wadsworth International Fellowships *(Graduate/Fellowship)* [9562]

WAEPA Scholarship Program *(Undergraduate, Vocational/Occupational/Scholarship)* [9763]

Jack H. Wagner Scholarships *(Graduate, Undergraduate/Scholarship)* [5842]

Selman A. Waksman Endowed Scholarships in Microbial Diversity *(Undergraduate/Scholarship)* [5633]

Jane C. Waldbaum Archaeological Field School Scholarships *(Undergraduate/Scholarship)* [1496]

Margaret E. Waldron Scholarship Fund *(Undergraduate/Scholarship)* [3794]

Gary Walker Memorial Scholarships *(Professional development/Scholarship)* [3972]

Arthur BC Walker Scholarships *(Undergraduate/ Scholarship)* [6494]

Myrtle and Earl Walker Scholarships *(Undergraduate/Scholarship)* [8403]

Walmart Associate Scholarships *(Undergraduate/ Scholarship)* [9479]

Sam Walton Community Scholarships *(Undergraduate/Scholarship)* [9480]

Walton Family Foundation Scholarships *(Undergraduate/Scholarship)* [9481]

Harry Walts Memorial Graduate Scholarships *(Graduate/Scholarship)* [5533]

Imogene Ward Nursing Scholarships *(Undergraduate/Scholarship)* [3814]

Alice Glaisyer Warfield Scholarships *(Undergraduate, Vocational/Occupational/Scholarship)* [8954]

Judith Warner Memorial Scholarships *(Undergraduate/Scholarship)* [7532]

Rachel Warner Memorial Scholarships *(Graduate, Undergraduate/Scholarship)* [6336]

Earl Warren Civil Rights Training Scholarships *(Graduate/Scholarship)* [5972]

Earl Warren Shearman and Sterling Scholarships *(Graduate/Scholarship)* [5973]

Washington College Bound Scholarships *(Undergraduate/Scholarship)* [9504]

Washington County Farm Bureau Scholarships *(Undergraduate/Scholarship)* [6948]

Washington CPA Foundation Scholarships *(Graduate, Undergraduate/Scholarship)* [9514]

Washington Group International Safety Scholarships *(Undergraduate/Scholarship)* [1357]

Washington Higher Education Coordinating Board Health Professional Scholarships *(Graduate/ Scholarship)* [9506]

Washington Reciprocity Out-of-State Scholarships *(Undergraduate/Scholarship)* [5469]

Washington University Law School Chancellor's Graduate Fellowships *(Graduate/Fellowship)* [9532]

Washington University Law School Olin Fellowships for Women *(Graduate/Fellowship)* [9533]

Vincent T. Wasilewski Scholarships *(All/Scholarship)* [2188]

John J. Wasmuth Postdoctoral Fellowships *(Postdoctorate/Fellowship)* [4541]

George Waterman Memorial Scholarships *(Graduate, Undergraduate/Scholarship)* [9515]

Stand Watie Scholarships *(Undergraduate/Scholarship)* [8529]

Robert D. Watkins Graduate Research Fellowships *(Postdoctorate/Fellowship)* [1303]

Dr. James Watson Fellowship Program *(Doctorate, Graduate/Fellowship)* [4189]

Jeannette K. Watson Fellowships *(Undergraduate/ Fellowship)* [9542]

Thomas J. Watson Fellowships *(Graduate/Fellowship)* [9544]

Watsontown Volunteer Fire Company Scholarships *(Undergraduate/Scholarship)* [2342]

The Wax Company Scholarships *(Undergraduate/ Scholarship)* [185]

Wayne County Bank Scholarships *(Undergraduate/ Scholarship)* [6832]

Kurt Wayne Scholarships *(Graduate/Scholarship)* [4069]

W.B.H. Dowse Fellowships *(Graduate, Doctorate/ Fellowship)* [5680]

WDHOF Scholarships in Marine Conservation *(Graduate, Undergraduate/Scholarship)* [9700]

Richard M. Weaver Fellowships *(Graduate/Fellowship)* [4849]

Faye and Rendell Webb Scholarships *(Undergraduate/Scholarship)* [2962]

TCDA Cloys Webb Student Scholarships *(Graduate, Undergraduate/Scholarship)* [8853]

Allen and Loureena Weber Scholarships *(Undergraduate/Scholarship)* [8404]

Jerome P. Webster Fellowships *(Professional development/Fellowship)* [7749]

Webster Society Scholarships *(Undergraduate/ Scholarship)* [9534]

Kenneth G. Weckel Scholarships *(Undergraduate/ Scholarship)* [5868]

WEF Canham Graduate Studies Scholarships *(Graduate/Scholarship)* [9536]

Frank L. Weil Memorial Eagle Scout Scholarships *(Undergraduate/Scholarship)* [6265]

Arthur Weinberg Fellowships for Independent Scholars *(Professional development/Fellowship)* [6710]

ACI Bertold E. Weinberg Scholarships *(Graduate/ Scholarship)* [638]

Edith Weingarten Scholarship Program *(Postgraduate/Scholarship)* [957]

The Bee Winkler Weinstein Scholarship Fund *(All, Vocational/Occupational/Scholarship)* [8748]

William E. Weisel Scholarships *(Undergraduate/ Scholarship)* [8405]

Polaire Weissman Funds *(Graduate/Fellowship)* [5793]

Edward Kent Welch Memorial Scholarships *(Undergraduate/Scholarship)* [9661]

Welch Scholars Grants *(Undergraduate/Grant)* [972]

Welder Wildlife Foundation Fellowships *(Doctorate, Graduate/Fellowship)* [9559]

Sue Marsh Weller Memorial Scholarships *(Graduate, Postgraduate, Undergraduate/Scholarship)* [4738]

Wells Fargo American Indian Scholarships - Graduate *(Graduate/Scholarship)* [828]

Wells Fargo Scholarship Program *(Graduate, Undergraduate/Scholarship)* [4585]

Donald M. Wells Scholarships *(Undergraduate/ Scholarship)* [4307]

Wellstone Fellowships for Social Justice *(Graduate/ Fellowship)* [3707]

Francis X. Weninger Scholarships *(Undergraduate/ Scholarship)* [9777]

Wenner-Gren Foundation Dissertation Fieldwork Grants *(Doctorate/Grant)* [9563]

Wenner-Gren Foundation Post-PhD Research Grants *(Doctorate/Grant)* [9564]

John R. and Joan F. Werren Scholarships Fund *(Undergraduate/Scholarship)* [8708]

Lucille and Charles A. Wert Scholarships *(Undergraduate/Scholarship)* [5696]

West Coast Sea Grant Fellowships *(Graduate/Fellowship)* [2279]

West Virginia Hospitality and Travel Association General Scholarships *(Undergraduate/Scholarship)* [9571]

West Virginia PTA Scholarships *(Undergraduate/ Scholarship)* [9568]

Redlands Evening Lions Club - Barbara Westen Scholarships *(Undergraduate/Scholarship)* [7716]

Western Civilization Fellowships *(Graduate/Fellowship)* [4850]

Western Governors University Scholarship Program *(Undergraduate/Scholarship)* [4586]

Robert B. Westover Scholarships *(Undergraduate/Scholarship)* [4070]

Frederick K. Weyerhaeuser Forest History Fellowships *(Graduate/Fellowship)* [3860]

WFI International Fellowships *(Undergraduate/Fellowship)* [9754]

J. Irving Whalley Memorial Scholarships *(Undergraduate/Scholarship)* [1952]

Whan Memorial Scholarships *(Graduate, Undergraduate/Scholarship)* [7274]

Edwyna Wheadon Postgraduate Training Scholarship Fund *(Professional development/Scholarship)* [6219]

Haemer Wheatcraft Scholarships *(Undergraduate/Scholarship)* [3515]

Stan Wheeler Mentorship Awards *(Professional development/Award)* [5371]

Seitlin Franklin E. Wheeler Scholarship Fund *(Undergraduate/Scholarship)* [3324]

Paul A. Whelan Aviation Scholarships *(Undergraduate, Graduate/Scholarship)* [9193]

Brian J. White Endowed Law Scholarships *(Undergraduate/Scholarship)* [7212]

Howard A. White Endowed Scholarships *(Undergraduate/Scholarship)* [7213]

Richard S. White Fellowships *(Undergraduate/Fellowship)* [4522]

White House Fellows *(Professional development/Fellowship)* [7392]

Mary Kean White Memorial Scholarship Fund *(Undergraduate/Scholarship)* [8709]

White Rose Scholarships *(Undergraduate/Scholarship)* [7876]

Bradford White Scholarships *(Undergraduate/Scholarship)* [7350]

Paul D. White Scholarships *(Undergraduate/Award)* [2000]

ACI Richard N. White Student Fellowships *(Master's/Fellowship)* [639]

Robert B. and Sophia Whiteside Scholarships *(Undergraduate/Scholarship)* [3547]

Ann Cook Whitman Scholarships for Perry High School *(Undergraduate/Scholarship)* [3615]

Ann Cook Whitman Washington, DC Scholarships *(Undergraduate/Scholarship)* [3616]

Jane and Morgan Whitney Fellowships *(Graduate/Fellowship)* [5794]

Helen Hay Whitney Foundation Fellowships *(Doctorate, Graduate/Fellowship)* [9595]

Donna Axum Whitworth Scholarships *(Undergraduate/Scholarship)* [3393]

Why Get Your Blue On? Video Scholarships *(Graduate, Undergraduate/Award, Scholarship)* [9587]

Louise Wachter Wichman Scholarship Fund *(Undergraduate/Scholarship)* [4250]

Alice Hersey Wick Scholarships *(Undergraduate/Scholarship)* [8192]

Tom Wicker Scholarships *(Undergraduate/Scholarship)* [9310]

AFCEA General John A. Wickham Scholarships *(Undergraduate/Scholarship)* [1566]

Wicomico High School Class of '55 Scholarships *(Undergraduate/Scholarship)* [3070]

Lois Widley Student Scholarships *(Graduate, Undergraduate/Scholarship)* [4967]

Richard A. Wiebe Public Service Fellowships *(Graduate/Fellowship)* [6681]

Ethyl and Armin Wiebke Memorial Scholarships *(Undergraduate/Scholarship)* [9708]

Barbara Wiedner and Dorothy Vandercook Memorial Peace Scholarships *(Undergraduate/Scholarship)* [4311]

Edwin F. Wiegand Science and Technology Scholarships *(Undergraduate/Scholarship)* [7533]

Elie Wiesel Prize in Ethics *(Undergraduate/Prize)* [9597]

Fred Wiesner Educational Excellence Scholarships *(Graduate, Undergraduate/Scholarship)* [1885]

The WIFLE Scholarship Fund *(Graduate, Postdoctorate, Undergraduate/Scholarship)* [9702]

Fred C. Wikoff, Jr. Scholarships *(Undergraduate, Vocational/Occupational/Scholarship)* [3928]

Teddy Wilburn Scholarships *(Undergraduate/Scholarship)* [3138]

Wild Felid Legacy Scholarships *(Graduate/Scholarship)* [9599]

Wilder Dimension Scholarships for Advanced Study in Theatre Arts *(Graduate/Scholarship)* [3520]

Wiley Publishing Inc. Scholarships *(Undergraduate/Scholarship)* [3711]

Samuel S. Wilks Memorial Awards *(Undergraduate/Award)* [1396]

Andrea Will Memorial Scholarships *(Undergraduate/Scholarship)* [8193]

Willamette Chapter Scholarship Awards *(Undergraduate/Scholarship)* [6943]

Willamette Valley AG Association Scholarships *(Undergraduate/Scholarship)* [6949]

M. William and Frances J. Tilghman Scholarships *(Undergraduate/Scholarship)* [3071]

William J. Brennan Graduate Assistant Fellowships *(Graduate/Fellowship)* [6920]

Williams Chorale Bacardi Fallon Performing Arts Scholarships *(Undergraduate/Award, Scholarship)* [9608]

Williams Foundation Scholarships *(Undergraduate/Scholarship)* [7534]

Sidney B. Williams, Jr. Scholarships *(Undergraduate/Scholarship)* [882]

BM1 James Elliott Williams and LCDR Jack Graf Memorial Scholarship Fund *(Undergraduate/Scholarship)* [7134]

Rodney Williams Legacy Scholarships *(Undergraduate/Grant)* [9218]

T. Franklin Williams Research Scholars Award Program *(Professional development/Grant)* [81]

CSM Virgil R. Williams Scholarships *(Undergraduate/Scholarship)* [3645]

Elizabeth T. Williams Scholarships *(Undergraduate/Scholarship)* [9662]

Maxine Williams Scholarships *(Postdoctorate/Scholarship)* [513]

Redlands Footlighters, Inc. - Merle and Peggy Williams Scholarships *(Undergraduate/Scholarship)* [7717]

Cenie Jomo Williams Tuition Scholarships *(Graduate, Undergraduate/Scholarship)* [6043]

Edwin H. and Louise N. Williamson Endowed Scholarships *(Undergraduate/Scholarship)* [9663]

Williamsport-Lycoming Community Foundation - Benjamin Franklin Scholarships *(Undergraduate, Vocational/Occupational/Scholarship)* [3796]

Beverly Willis Architecture Foundation Dissertation Fellowships *(Doctorate/Fellowship)* [8298]

Gary S. Wilmer RAMI Music Scholarships *(Undergraduate/Scholarship)* [3174]

Woodrow Wilson Dissertation Fellowships in Women's Studies *(Graduate/Fellowship)* [9620]

Pete Wilson Graduate Scholarships *(Graduate, Undergraduate/Scholarship)* [7584]

Woodrow Wilson International Center for Scholars Fellowships *(Doctorate/Fellowship)* [9612]

Pete Wilson Journalism Scholarships *(Graduate, Undergraduate/Scholarship)* [7585]

Saul T. Wilson, Jr. Scholarships *(Graduate, Undergraduate/Scholarship)* [9403]

Bob Wilson Legacy Scholarships *(Undergraduate/Scholarship)* [2256]

The Arthur N. Wilson, MD, Scholarships *(Undergraduate/Scholarship)* [924]

Woodrow Wilson-Rockefeller Brothers Fund Fellowships for Aspiring Teachers of Color *(Graduate/Fellowship)* [9621]

John Charles Wilson Scholarships *(Undergraduate/Scholarship)* [4856]

Theo Wilson Scholarships *(Graduate, Undergraduate/Scholarship)* [7023]

Harriet Barnhart Wimmer Scholarships *(Undergraduate/Scholarship)* [1288]

David A. Winston Health Policy Scholarships *(Graduate/Scholarship)* [1892]

Winston-Salem Foundation Scholarships *(Undergraduate/Scholarship)* [9664]

Winston Scholarships *(Graduate, Undergraduate, Vocational/Occupational/Scholarship)* [8032]

Marine Corps Sgt. Jeannette L. Winters Memorial Scholarships *(Undergraduate/Scholarship)* [1567]

Winterthur Research Fellowships *(All/Fellowship)* [9668]

Wisconsin Broadcasters Association Scholarships *(Undergraduate/Scholarship)* [9682]

Wisconsin Laboratory Association Graduate Student Scholarships *(Graduate/Scholarship)* [9689]

Wisconsin Laboratory Association Technical Student Scholarships *(Undergraduate/Scholarship)* [9690]

Wisconsin Laboratory Association Undergraduate University Student Scholarships *(Undergraduate/Scholarship)* [9691]

Wisconsin-Madison Journalism Scholarships *(Undergraduate/Scholarship)* [9386]

Wisconsin-Madison Music Clinic Scholarships *(Undergraduate/Scholarship)* [9387]

Wisconsin Region Student Leadership Scholarships *(Graduate, Undergraduate/Scholarship)* [6057]

Witt Mares Scholarships *(Undergraduate/Scholarship)* [9451]

WKIX Alumni Association Scholarships *(Undergraduate/Scholarship)* [9311]

WMA Memorial Scholarships *(Undergraduate/Scholarship)* [9709]

WNBA Eastman Grants *(Professional development/Grant)* [9731]

WOCN Accredited Nursing Education Scholarships *(Graduate, Undergraduate/Scholarship)* [9765]

WOCN Advanced Education Scholarships *(Doctorate, Graduate, Undergraduate/Scholarship)* [9766]

Woksape Oyate: "Wisdom of the People" Distinguished Scholars Awards *(Undergraduate/Scholarship)* [813]

Paul R. Wolf Memorial Scholarships *(Graduate/Scholarship)* [1672]

Emil Wolf Outstanding Student Paper Competition *(Graduate, Undergraduate/Award)* [6914]

Wolf Trap Foundation Scholarship Program for Performing Arts Teachers *(Professional development/Scholarship)* [9693]

The Wolf Trap Internship Program *(Graduate, Professional development, Undergraduate/Internship)* [9694]

Deborah Partridge Wolfe International Fellowships *(Graduate, Undergraduate/Fellowship)* [9807]

Tim Wolfred Scholarships *(Undergraduate/Scholarship)* [7877]

Eleanor M. Wolfson Memorial Scholarship Fund *(Undergraduate/Scholarship)* [3797]

Wendy Y. Wolfson Memorial Scholarship Fund *(Undergraduate/Scholarship)* [3798]

Abel Wolman Fellowships *(Doctorate/Fellowship)* [1419]

Woman's Club of Grand Haven Scholarships Fund *(Undergraduate/Scholarship)* [4251]

Women in Cancer Research Scholar Awards *(Graduate, Postdoctorate/Award)* [453]

Women In Defense HORIZONS Scholarships *(Graduate, Undergraduate/Scholarship)* [9696]

Women In Need Scholarships *(Undergraduate/Scholarship)* [3601]

Women In Transition Scholarships *(Undergraduate/Scholarship)* [3602]

Women of WSAJ Bar Preparation Scholarships *(Undergraduate/Scholarship)* [9518]

Women's Army Corps Veterans Association Scholarships *(Undergraduate/Scholarship)* [9711]

Women's Independence Scholarship Programs *(Undergraduate/Scholarship)* [8774]

Women's Jewelry Association Member Grants *(All/Grant)* [9726]

Women's Leadership in Agriculture Scholarship Program *(Undergraduate/Scholarship)* [6855]

Women's Overseas and Service League Scholarships for Women *(Undergraduate/Scholarship)* [9733]

Carolyn Wones Recruitment Scholarship Grants *(Undergraduate/Scholarship)* [3176]

Dennis Wong and Associates Scholarships *(Graduate, Undergraduate/Scholarship)* [5223]

Dr. Harold S. Wood Awards for Excellence *(Undergraduate/Award)* [4072]

Wood County Bar Association Memorial Scholarships *(Undergraduate/Scholarship)* [7125]

Mary and Elliot Wood Foundation Graduate Scholarship Fund *(Graduate/Scholarship)* [3930]

Wood Fruitticher Grocery Company, Inc. Scholarships *(Graduate, Undergraduate/Scholarship)* [173]

Rolla F. Wood Graduate Scholarships *(Graduate/ Scholarship)* [7277]

Ed Wood Memorial Scholarship Awards *(Undergraduate/Scholarship)* [6944]

Irene Woodall Graduate Scholarships *(Master's/ Scholarship)* [710]

Woodcock Family Education Scholarship Program *(Undergraduate/Scholarship)* [284]

Betsy B. Woodward Scholarships *(Undergraduate/ Scholarship)* [1782]

Woodyard Family Scholarships *(Undergraduate/ Scholarship)* [4265]

Blance E. Woolls Scholarships *(Graduate/Scholarship)* [2073]

Patty Wooten Scholarships *(Undergraduate/Scholarship)* [1707]

John W. Work III Memorial Foundation Scholarships *(Undergraduate/Scholarship)* [3140]

Working for Farmers' Success Scholarships *(Undergraduate/Scholarship)* [9748]

The Working Press Internships *(Undergraduate/Internship)* [8467]

World Book Graduate Scholarships in Library and Information Science *(Graduate/Scholarship)* [2521]

Worldstudio AIGA Scholarships *(Graduate, Undergraduate/Scholarship)* [9761]

Donald Worster Travel Grants *(Graduate, Professional development/Grant)* [1255]

WREI Congressional Fellows on Women and Public Policy *(Doctorate, Graduate, Master's/Fellowship)* [9735]

WRI Education Foundation Scholarships - Graduate *(Graduate/Scholarship)* [9670]

WRI Education Foundation Scholarships - High School Seniors *(Undergraduate/Scholarship)* [9671]

WRI Education Foundation Scholarships - Undergraduate *(Undergraduate/Scholarship)* [9672]

WSAJ Diversity Bar Preparation Scholarships *(Undergraduate/Scholarship)* [9520]

WSCPA Chapter Scholarships *(Graduate, Undergraduate/Scholarship)* [9516]

WSSA Students Paper Competition *(Undergraduate/ Award)* [9579]

WYCUP Scholarships *(Professional development/ Scholarship)* [9752]

Wyeth-SUS Clinical Scholar Awards *(Professional development/Award)* [8512]

Xavier Community-Engaged Fellowships *(Undergraduate/Fellowship)* [9778]

Xavier University Chancellor Scholarships *(Undergraduate/Scholarship)* [9779]

Xavier University Departmental Scholarships *(Undergraduate/Scholarship)* [9780]

Xavier University Honors Bachelor of Arts Scholarships *(Undergraduate/Scholarship)* [9781]

Xavier University Legacy Scholarships *(Undergraduate/Scholarship)* [9782]

Xavier University ROTC Scholarships - Air Force ROTC *(Undergraduate/Scholarship)* [9783]

Xavier University ROTC Scholarships - Army ROTC *(Undergraduate/Scholarship)* [9784]

Xavier University Williams Scholarships *(Undergraduate/Scholarship)* [9785]

Xerox Technical Minority Scholarships *(Graduate, Undergraduate/Scholarship)* [9787]

M.H. Yager Memorial Scholarships *(Undergraduate/ Scholarship)* [1953]

Yale Graduate and Professional Students Research Fellowships *(Graduate, Professional development/ Fellowship)* [2044]

Yamhill County Farm Bureau Scholarships *(Undergraduate/Scholarship)* [6950]

William J. Yankee Memorial Scholarships *(Undergraduate/Scholarship)* [1021]

Gwen Yarnell Theatre Scholarships *(Undergraduate/ Scholarship)* [3751]

Yasme Foundation Scholarships *(Undergraduate/ Scholarship)* [1115]

Minoru Yasui Memorial Scholarships *(Graduate/ Scholarship)* [5147]

Willa Yeck Memorial Scholarship Fund *(Undergraduate/Scholarship)* [3450]

Marilyn Yetso Memorial Scholarships *(Undergraduate, Vocational/Occupational/Scholarship)* [2759]

Vera Yip Memorial Scholarships *(Undergraduate, Vocational/Occupational/Scholarship)* [2760]

York Rite Grand Chapter Royal Arch Masons Scholarships *(Undergraduate/Scholarship)* [3426]

Gary Yoshimura Scholarships *(Undergraduate/ Scholarship)* [7542]

Jack and Edna May Yost Scholarships *(Undergraduate/Scholarship)* [3964]

Alma H. Young Emerging Scholar Awards *(Doctorate/Scholarship)* [9394]

Young Investigator Grants *(Undergraduate/Grant)* [6529]

Searle Young Legal Scholars Research Fellowships *(Professional development/Fellowship)* [3732]

Young People For Fellowships (YP4) *(Undergraduate/Fellowship)* [8147]

Donnell B. Young Scholarships *(Undergraduate/ Scholarship)* [286]

Elmer Cooke Young - Taylor Young Scholarships *(Undergraduate/Scholarship)* [4463]

Yount, Hyde & Barbour Scholarships *(Undergraduate/Scholarship)* [9468]

Youth Empowerment Summit Scholarships *(Undergraduate/Scholarship)* [6148]

Youth Partners Accessing Capital (PAC) *(Graduate, Undergraduate/Scholarship)* [354]

The Youth Scholarship Program *(Undergraduate/ Scholarship)* [2719]

Youth Scholarships *(Undergraduate/Scholarship)* [8305]

Youth for Understanding Scholarships *(Undergraduate/Scholarship)* [9797]

Diane Yu Loan Repayment Assistance Program *(Undergraduate/Loan)* [6029]

YWA Foundation Scholarships *(Graduate, Undergraduate/Scholarship)* [9793]

Z/I Imaging Scholarships *(Graduate/Scholarship)* [1673]

Zagunis Student Leader Scholarships *(Graduate, Undergraduate/Scholarship)* [6058]

Lisa Zaken Awards For Excellence *(Graduate, Undergraduate/Award)* [4812]

Michael A. Zamperini/W. Clay Burchell Scholarships *(Undergraduate/Scholarship)* [7878]

James and Joy Zana Memorial Scholarships *(Undergraduate/Scholarship)* [4266]

Zarley, McKee, Thomte, Voorhees, Sease Law Scholarships *(Undergraduate/Scholarship)* [3516]

Urashi Zen Scholarships *(Undergraduate/Scholarship)* [7429]

Harry and Angel Zerigian Scholarships *(Undergraduate/Scholarship)* [1609]

Zeta Chapter Memorial Scholarship Awards *(Undergraduate/Scholarship)* [3178]

Zeta Phi Beta Sorority General Graduate Scholarships *(Graduate, Postdoctorate/Scholarship)* [9808]

Zeta Phi Beta Sorority General Undergraduate Scholarships *(Undergraduate/Scholarship)* [9809]

A.F. Zimmerman Scholarships *(Graduate, Master's/ Scholarship)* [7246]

Blanche Raper Zimmerman Scholarships *(Professional development/Scholarship)* [9665]

A.R. Zipf Fellowships *(Graduate/Fellowship)* [3280]

Morris L. and Rebecca Ziskind Memorial Scholarships *(Undergraduate/Scholarship)* [4655]

Ruth and Sherman Zudekoff Scholarships *(Undergraduate/Scholarship)* [3084]

Leo Zupin Memorial Scholarship Fund *(Undergraduate, Vocational/Occupational/Scholarship)* [4253]

Francis Sylvia Zverina Scholarships *(Undergraduate/Scholarship)* [4538]

UNITED STATES (BY REGION)

Midwestern states

Midwest Chapter Scholarships - Jack Gill *(Undergraduate/Scholarship)* [1804]

MAC Emeritus Scholarships for First-Time Meeting Attendees *(All/Scholarship)* [5855]

Midwest Chapter Scholarships - Betty McKern *(Undergraduate/Scholarship)* [1809]

Midwest Chapter Scholarships - Engineering *(Undergraduate/Scholarship)* [1810]

Midwest Chapter Scholarships - Non-Engineering *(Undergraduate/Scholarship)* [1811]

Midwest Chapter Scholarships - Western States Awards *(Undergraduate/Scholarship)* [1812]

Archie Motley Memorial Scholarships for Minority Students *(Graduate/Scholarship)* [5856]

Midwest Chapter Scholarships - Don Nelson *(Undergraduate/Scholarship)* [1813]

Midwest Chapter Scholarships - Mel Nickel *(Undergraduate/Scholarship)* [1814]

New England states

Dvora Brodie Scholarships *(Graduate, Postgraduate, Undergraduate/Scholarship)* [4503]

NELA Scholarships *(Graduate, Master's/Scholarship)* [6624]

Shaw-Worth Memorial Scholarships *(Undergraduate/Scholarship)* [4636]

Northeastern states

The SSPI Northeast Chapter Scholarships *(Graduate, Undergraduate/Scholarship)* [8490]

Northwestern states

AIST Northwest Chapter Scholarships *(Undergraduate/Scholarship)* [1801]

William Bennett W7PHO Memorial Scholarships *(Undergraduate/Scholarship)* [1072]

Earl Deadman Memorial Scholarships *(Undergraduate/Scholarship)* [730]

Out of the United States

C.V. Starr Scholarships *(Undergraduate, Graduate/Scholarship)* [2690]

Southeastern states

Leighton M. Ballew Directing Scholarships *(Undergraduate/Scholarship)* [8569]

Polly Holliday Scholarships *(Undergraduate/Scholarship)* [8570]

Robert Porterfield Graduate Scholarships *(Graduate/Scholarship)* [8571]

Marian A. Smith Scholarships *(Graduate/Scholarship)* [8572]

Southeast Member Chapter Scholarships *(Undergraduate/Scholarship)* [1818]

Southeastern Theatre Conference Secondary School Scholarships *(Undergraduate/Scholarship)* [8573]

William E. Wilson Scholarships *(Graduate/Scholarship)* [8574]

Southern states

The SSPI Southern California Scholarships *(Graduate, Undergraduate/Scholarship)* [8491]

Western states

Institute of Transportation Engineers - Western District Fellowships *(Graduate/Fellowship)* [4824]

Western Society of Weed Science Outstanding Student Scholarship Program *(Doctorate, Graduate, Undergraduate/Scholarship)* [9585]

UNITED STATES (BY STATE)

Insurance and Risk Management Scholarships - Grant MacEwan *(Undergraduate/Scholarship)* [7994]

Alabama

ACHE/American Legion Auxiliary Scholarships *(Undergraduate/Scholarship)* [155]

ACHE/American Legion Scholarships *(Undergraduate/Scholarship)* [156]

ACHE Police Officers and Firefighters Survivors' Educational Assistance Programs *(Undergraduate/Scholarship)* [159]

ACHE Senior Adult Scholarships (Undergraduate/ Scholarship) [160]
Alabama Gi Dependents Educational Benefit Program (Undergraduate/Scholarship) [162]
Alabama National Guard Educational Assistance Program (Undergraduate/Scholarship) [163]
Alabama Scholarships for Dependents of Blind Parents (Undergraduate/Scholarship) [164]
Alabama Student Assistance Programs (Undergraduate/Scholarship) [165]
Alabama Student Grant Programs (Undergraduate, Vocational/Occupational/Grant) [166]
Paul Arnold Memorial Scholarships (Undergraduate/Scholarship) [7396]
Asian and Pacific Islander Queers Sisters Scholarships (Undergraduate/Scholarship) [7397]
Associates in Behavioral Health Scholarships (Graduate/Scholarship) [7398]
Barbara Bailey Scholarships (Undergraduate/ Scholarship) [7399]
Charly Baker and Heath Merriwether Memorial Scholarships (Undergraduate/Scholarship) [7400]
Bellevue PFLAG Scholarships (Undergraduate/ Scholarship) [7401]
Bill Bendiner and Doug Morgenson Scholarships (Undergraduate/Scholarship) [7402]
Birmingham District Alabama Dietetic Association Scholarships (Graduate, Undergraduate/Scholarship) [168]
William Verbon Black Scholarships (Undergraduate/Scholarship) [187]
Robert Browning Scholarships (Undergraduate/ Scholarship) [7403]
Johnston Cabaniss Scholarships (Undergraduate/ Scholarship) [188]
Deloris Carter Hampton Scholarships (Undergraduate/Scholarship) [7404]
Donald O. Coffman Scholarships (Undergraduate/ Scholarship) [7405]
Cole Family Scholarships (Undergraduate/Scholarship) [7406]
Dennis Coleman Choral Conducting Scholarships (Undergraduate/Scholarship) [7407]
Compassionate Care Scholarships (Undergraduate/Scholarship) [7408]
Charles Clarke Cordle Memorial Scholarships (Undergraduate/Scholarship) [1081]
J. Craig and Page T. Smith Scholarships (Undergraduate/Scholarship) [8239]
Brian M. Day Scholarships (Undergraduate/Scholarship) [7409]
Gulf Coast Hurricane Scholarships (Graduate, Undergraduate/Scholarship) [8449]
Cecil Lane Family Scholarships (Undergraduate/ Scholarship) [178]
Legacy Inc. College Undergraduate and Graduate Scholarships (Graduate, Undergraduate/Scholarship) [5400]
McFarffels Scholarships (Undergraduate/Scholarship) [7412]
Jack D. Motteler Scholarships (Undergraduate/ Scholarship) [7413]
NAJA Scholarships (Graduate/Scholarship) [6086]
North Alabama Dietetic Association Scholarships (Graduate, Undergraduate/Scholarship) [169]
Northeast Alabama District Dietetic Association Scholarships (Graduate, Undergraduate/Scholarship) [170]
Obrzut Ling Scholarships (Undergraduate, Vocational/Occupational/Scholarship) [7414]
Political Leadership Scholarships (Undergraduate/ Scholarship) [7415]
Ina E. Powell Memorial Scholarships (Undergraduate/Scholarship) [179]
Pride Foundation Regional Scholarships (Undergraduate/Scholarship) [7416]
Rosenberg-Ibarra Scholarships (Undergraduate/ Scholarship) [7419]
Justice Janie L. Shores Scholarships (Undergraduate/Scholarship) [189]
Social Work Scholarships (Undergraduate/Scholarship) [7420]
Southeast Alabama Dietetic Association Scholarships (Graduate, Undergraduate/Scholarship) [172]
Kathy Spadoni Memorial Scholarships (Undergraduate/Scholarship) [7421]
Ric Ulrich and Chuck Pischke Scholarships (Undergraduate/Scholarship) [7423]
Patricia Van Kirk Scholarships (Undergraduate/ Scholarship) [7424]
Ed Wadsworth Memorial Scholarships (Undergraduate/Scholarship) [184]
Wells Fargo Scholarships (Undergraduate/Scholarship) [7425]
Mary Katherine "Kathy" Williamson Scholarship Fund (Undergraduate/Scholarship) [3050]
James and Colin Lee Wozumi Scholarships (Undergraduate/Scholarship) [7427]
You Go Girl! Scholarships (Undergraduate/Scholarship) [7428]
Urashi Zen Scholarships (Undergraduate/Scholarship) [7429]

Alaska

AIA Alaska Scholarships (Graduate, Undergraduate/Scholarship) [838]
Alaska Aerospace Development Corporation Scholarships (Undergraduate/Scholarship) [9130]
Alaska Native Medical Center Auxiliary Scholarships (Undergraduate/Scholarship) [9131]
Alaska Press Club Scholarships (Undergraduate/ Scholarship) [9132]
Alaska Support Industry Alliance Scholarships (Undergraduate/Scholarship) [9133]
Alaska Visitors Association/Gomar Scholarships (Undergraduate/Scholarship) [9134]
Alaska Yukon Pioneer Memorial Scholarships (Undergraduate/Scholarship) [9135]
Amos Joe Alter ASCE Section Alaska Section Scholarships (Undergraduate/Scholarship) [9136]
Mike Ardaw Scholarships (Undergraduate/Scholarship) [9137]
UAA Elaine Atwood Scholarships (Undergraduate/ Scholarship) [9084]
UAA Dr. Jon Baker Memorial Scholarships (Graduate, Undergraduate, Vocational/Occupational/Scholarship) [9085]
UAA Michael Baring-Gould Memorial Scholarships (Graduate, Undergraduate/Scholarship) [9086]
Lawrence Bayer Business Administration Scholarships (Undergraduate/Scholarship) [9138]
Charles E. Behlke Engineering Memorial Scholarships (Undergraduate/Scholarship) [9139]
UAA Mark A. Beltz Scholarships (Graduate, Undergraduate, Vocational/Occupational/Scholarship) [9087]
Bill & Nell Biggs Scholarships (Undergraduate/ Scholarship) [9140]
Bolick Foreign Student Scholarships (Undergraduate/Scholarship) [9141]
UAA Pat Brakke Political Science Scholarships (Undergraduate/Scholarship) [9088]
Mary Lou Brown Scholarships (Undergraduate/ Scholarship) [1074]
Charles E. Bunnell Scholarships (Undergraduate/ Scholarship) [9143]
Loyal D. Burkett Memorial Scholarships (Undergraduate/Scholarship) [9144]
Lyle Carlson Wildlife Management Scholarships (Undergraduate/Scholarship) [9145]
Chugach Gem & Mineral Society Scholarships (Undergraduate/Scholarship) [9089]
UAA Edward Rollin Clinton Memorial for Music (Undergraduate/Scholarship) [9090]
Mable B. Crawford Memorial Scholarships (Undergraduate/Scholarship) [9146]
Patricia Ann Hughes Eastaugh Memorial Teaching Scholarships (Undergraduate/Scholarship) [9147]
UAA Governor William A. Egan Scholarships (Undergraduate/Scholarship) [9091]
Alaska Community Foundation Sven E. & Lorraine Eriksson Scholarships (Undergraduate/Scholarship) [9092]
Excellence in Geographic Information Systems Scholarships (Undergraduate/Scholarship) [9148]
Lydia Fohn-Hansen/Lola Hill Memorial Scholarships (Undergraduate/Scholarship) [9149]
UAA Michael D. Ford Memorial Scholarships (Graduate, Undergraduate/Scholarship) [9093]
Johnny and Sarah Frank Scholarships (Undergraduate/Scholarship) [9150]
UAA Jan & Glenn Fredericks Scholarships (Graduate, Undergraduate/Scholarship) [9094]
UAA Ardell French Memorial Scholarships (Undergraduate/Scholarship) [9095]
Charles F. Gould Endowment Scholarships (Undergraduate/Scholarship) [9151]
UAA Ken Gray Endowment Scholarships (Undergraduate/Scholarship) [9097]
Patty Hamilton Early Childhood Development Scholarships (Undergraduate/Scholarship) [9152]
UAA Muriel Hannah Scholarships in Art (Undergraduate, Vocational/Occupational/Scholarship) [9098]
Lenore & George Hedla Accounting Scholarships (Undergraduate/Scholarship) [9099]
John B. Henderson Scholarships (Undergraduate/ Scholarship) [9153]
Donald Wills Jacobs Scholarships (Undergraduate/Scholarship) [9154]
Stacy Kaiser Memorial Funds (Undergraduate/ Scholarship) [8984]
UAA Chris L. Kleinke Scholarships (Graduate, Undergraduate/Scholarship) [9101]
Iver & Cora Knapstad Scholarships (Undergraduate/Scholarship) [9155]
UAA Kris Knudson Memorial Scholarships (Graduate, Undergraduate/Scholarship) [9102]
Robert Wade Korn Endowed Scholarships (Undergraduate/Scholarship) [9156]
Arlene Kuhner Memorial Scholarships (Undergraduate/Scholarship) [9103]
UAA Paul G. Landis Scholarships (Undergraduate/Scholarship) [9104]
Austin E. Lathrop Scholarships (Undergraduate/ Scholarship) [9157]
Franklin M. Leach Scholarships (Undergraduate/ Scholarship) [9158]
Ruth Lister Scholarships (Undergraduate, Vocational/Occupational/Scholarship) [8986]
Mat-Su Health Foundation Scholarships (Undergraduate/Scholarship) [9159]
Matanuska-Susitna College Regent's Scholarships (Undergraduate/Scholarship) [9160]
Dave McCloud Aviation Memorial Scholarships (Undergraduate/Scholarship) [9161]
The Cady McDonnell Memorial Scholarships (Undergraduate/Scholarship) [647]
Richard Mellon Endowment Scholarships (Undergraduate/Scholarship) [9162]
Andrew Nerland Endowment Scholarships (Undergraduate/Scholarship) [9164]
Maureen E. Nolan-Cahill Memorial Scholarships (Undergraduate/Scholarship) [9165]
Nordic Ski Association of Anchorage Scholarships (Undergraduate/Scholarship) [197]
Don & Jan O'Dowd/SWAA Scholarships (Undergraduate/Scholarship) [9166]
UAA Diane Olsen Memorial Scholarships (Undergraduate/Scholarship) [9105]
Alvin G. Ott Fish and Wildlife Scholarships (Undergraduate/Scholarship) [9167]
Rachael Patterson Memorial Scholarships (Undergraduate/Scholarship) [8987]
Point Lay Memorial Scholarships (Undergraduate/ Scholarship) [9168]
UAA April Relyea Scholarships (Graduate, Undergraduate, Vocational/Occupational/Scholarship) [9107]
A.D. 'Al' Robertson Memorial Scholarships (Undergraduate/Scholarship) [9169]
UAA Jack & Martha Roderick Scholarships (Graduate, Undergraduate/Scholarship) [9108]
Pat and Cliff Rogers Nursing Scholarships (Undergraduate/Scholarship) [9170]
Dr. Orrin J. Rongstad Wildlife Management Scholarships (Undergraduate/Scholarship) [9171]
UAA Brown Schoenheit Memorial Scholarships

(Undergraduate/Scholarship) [9109]

UAA Eveline Schuster Memorial Award/Scholarships *(Graduate, Undergraduate/Scholarship)* [9110]

Seldovia Native Association Achievement Scholarships *(Undergraduate, Graduate/Scholarship)* [8075]

Seldovia Native Association General Scholarships *(Undergraduate, Graduate/Scholarship)* [8076]

Clair Shirey Scholarships *(Undergraduate/Scholarship)* [9173]

Linda Simmons Memorial Scholarships *(Undergraduate/Scholarship)* [195]

Ward Sims Memorial Scholarships *(Undergraduate/Scholarship)* [9174]

Single Parent Scholarships *(Graduate, Undergraduate/Scholarship)* [1549]

Lillian Smith Scholarship for Teaching Students *(Graduate, Undergraduate/Scholarship)* [9111]

Snodgrass Scholarships *(Undergraduate/Scholarship)* [9175]

Sourdough Reunion Memorial Scholarships *(Undergraduate/Scholarship)* [9176]

Sheri Stears Education Scholarships *(Undergraduate/Scholarship)* [9112]

Sturgulewski Family Scholarships *(Graduate, Undergraduate, Vocational/Occupational/Scholarship)* [9113]

UAA Accounting Club Scholarships *(Undergraduate/Scholarship)* [9114]

UAA Alaska Kidney Foundation Scholarships *(Graduate, Undergraduate/Scholarship)* [9115]

UAA Alumni Association Scholarships *(Undergraduate/Scholarship)* [9116]

UAA Anchorage Daily News Journalism Scholarships *(Undergraduate/Scholarship)* [9117]

UAA College of Business & Public Policy Scholarships *(Graduate, Undergraduate, Vocational/Occupational/Scholarship)* [9118]

UAA Emi Chance Memorial Scholarships *(Undergraduate/Scholarship)* [9119]

UAA Friends of the Performing Arts Scholarships *(Undergraduate/Scholarship)* [9120]

UAA GCI, Inc. Scholarships *(Undergraduate/Scholarship)* [9121]

UAA Kimura Scholarship Fund Illustration Scholarships *(Undergraduate/Scholarship)* [9122]

UAA Kimura Scholarship Fund Photography Scholarships *(Undergraduate/Scholarship)* [9123]

UAA Pignalberi Public Policy Scholarships *(Graduate/Scholarship)* [9124]

UAA Quanterra Scholarships *(Undergraduate/Scholarship)* [9125]

UAA RRANN Program Scholarships *(Undergraduate/Scholarship)* [9126]

UAA Wells Fargo Career Scholarships *(Graduate/Scholarship)* [9127]

Umialik Scholarships *(Undergraduate/Scholarship)* [9177]

University of Alaska Scholars Program *(Undergraduate/Scholarship)* [9178]

William S. Wilson Memorial Scholarships *(Undergraduate/Scholarship)* [9179]

UAA Melissa J. Wolf Scholarships *(Undergraduate/Scholarship)* [9128]

Guy A. Woodings Scholarships *(Undergraduate/Scholarship)* [9180]

Ralph Yetka Memorial Scholarships *(Undergraduate/Scholarship)* [9181]

Joan C. Yoder Memorial Nursing Scholarships *(Undergraduate/Scholarship)* [9182]

Yukon Delta Fisheries Development Association Scholarships *(Undergraduate/Scholarship)* [9183]

Arizona

ACSO Scholarships *(Undergraduate/Scholarship)* [1520]

Marvin A. Andrews Scholarships/Internships *(Graduate/Internship, Scholarship)* [1517]

APS/ASU Scholarships *(Undergraduate/Scholarship)* [7332]

APS/Maricopa County Community Colleges

Scholarships *(Undergraduate/Scholarship)* [7333]

Arizona Nursery Association Scholarships *(Undergraduate/Scholarship)* [1524]

ASCPA High School Scholarships *(Undergraduate/Scholarship)* [1528]

Walt Bartram Memorial Education Award, Region 12 and Chapter 119 *(Undergraduate/Scholarship)* [8369]

Calvin Alumni Association Arizona Central Chapter Scholarships *(Undergraduate/Scholarship)* [2292]

Central Arizona DX Association Scholarships *(Undergraduate/Scholarship)* [1076]

Charles N. Fisher Memorial Scholarships *(Undergraduate/Scholarship)* [1084]

Gail Goodell Folsom Memorial Scholarships *(Undergraduate/Award)* [5975]

Future CPA Scholarships *(Community College, Graduate, Undergraduate/Scholarship)* [1529]

Gold Country Section & Region II Scholarships *(Graduate, Undergraduate/Scholarship)* [1337]

HSBC-North America Scholarship Program *(Undergraduate/Scholarship)* [4571]

Kappa Delta Phi Scholarship Program *(Postgraduate/Scholarship)* [952]

Stephen T. Marchello Scholarships *(Undergraduate/Scholarship)* [5609]

The Cady McDonnell Memorial Scholarships *(Undergraduate/Scholarship)* [647]

Prescott Fine Arts Association Scholarship Program *(Undergraduate/Scholarship)* [7390]

William C. Ray, CIH, CSP Arizona Scholarships *(Graduate, Undergraduate/Scholarship)* [1353]

Rocky Mountain Coal Mining Institute Engineering/Geology Scholarships *(Undergraduate/Scholarship)* [7810]

Rocky Mountain Coal Mining Institute Technical Scholarships *(Undergraduate, Vocational/Occupational/Scholarship)* [7811]

Tribal Priority Scholarships *(Graduate, Professional development, Undergraduate/Scholarship)* [1513]

Arkansas

ARAFCS Doctoral Scholarships *(Doctorate/Scholarship)* [1534]

ARAFCS Masters Scholarships *(Graduate/Scholarship)* [1535]

Arkansas Public Health Association Scholarships *(Undergraduate/Scholarship)* [1546]

Arkansas Society of Professional Sanitarians Scholarships *(Undergraduate/Scholarship)* [1547]

Arkansas State University Mountain Home Scholarships *(Undergraduate/Scholarship)* [1551]

ArLA Scholarships *(Graduate, Master's/Scholarship)* [1541]

Cherokee Nation Graduate Scholarships *(Graduate/Scholarship)* [2742]

Cherokee Nation Scholarships *(Undergraduate/Scholarship)* [2744]

Lone Star GIA Associate and Alumni Scholarships *(Undergraduate/Scholarship)* [4064]

Randall Matthis for Environmental Studies Scholarships *(Graduate, Undergraduate/Scholarship)* [1537]

Fred R. McDaniel Memorial Scholarships *(Undergraduate/Scholarship)* [1093]

NAJA Scholarships *(Graduate/Scholarship)* [6086]

Hatton W. Sumners Scholarships *(Undergraduate/Scholarship)* [6869]

Larry Wilson for Environmental Studies Scholarships *(Graduate, Undergraduate/Scholarship)* [1538]

Larry Wilson Scholarships for Undergraduate Civil Engineering Students *(Undergraduate/Scholarship)* [1539]

California

92109 Community Fund-Mark and Karla Stuart Family Scholarships *(Undergraduate, Vocational/Occupational/Scholarship)* [7903]

Above and Beyond Scholarships *(Graduate/Scholarship)* [2269]

AeA Scholarships *(Undergraduate/Scholarship)* [7904]

After-the-Fires Scholarships *(Undergraduate, Vocational/Occupational/Scholarship)* [7905]

AISC/Structural Steel Education Council Fellowships *(Graduate/Fellowship)* [875]

Armenian American Citizen's League Scholarships *(Undergraduate/Scholarship)* [1580]

Marvin Arnold and Irene Jaquetta Heye Scholarships *(Undergraduate/Scholarship)* [7906]

ARREOLA/CBSPM Scholarships *(Undergraduate, Vocational/Occupational/Scholarship)* [7907]

Asian/Pacific Bar Association of Sacramento Law Foundation Scholarships *(Graduate, Postgraduate/Scholarship)* [1650]

Association of California Water Agencies Scholarships *(Undergraduate/Scholarship)* [1727]

Association for Women in Architecture Scholarships *(Undergraduate/Scholarship)* [1894]

Frank H. Ault Scholarships *(Undergraduate/Scholarship)* [7908]

Ballard Family Foundation Scholarships *(Undergraduate, Vocational/Occupational/Scholarship)* [7909]

Barta-Lehman Musical Scholarships *(Undergraduate/Scholarship)* [7910]

Walt Bartram Memorial Education Award, Region 12 and Chapter 119 *(Undergraduate/Scholarship)* [8369]

Bay Area Minority Law Student Scholarships *(Graduate, Undergraduate/Scholarship)* [2019]

Beacon of Hope Scholarships *(Undergraduate/Scholarship)* [2035]

Ray and Mary Bell Memorial Scholarships *(Undergraduate/Scholarship)* [7911]

James R. and Geraldine F. Bertelsen Scholarships *(Undergraduate/Scholarship)* [7912]

Biocom Scholarships *(Undergraduate/Scholarship)* [7913]

Norman Blachford Point Scholarships *(Graduate, Undergraduate/Scholarship)* [7355]

Dorothy M. Bolyard Memorial Scholarships *(Undergraduate/Scholarship)* [7914]

Breslauer Family Scholarships *(Undergraduate/Scholarship)* [7915]

Louise A. Broderick San Diego County Scholarships *(Undergraduate, Vocational/Occupational/Scholarship)* [7916]

California Association of Family and Consumer Sciences -San Diego Chapter Scholarships (CAFCS) *(Graduate, Undergraduate, Vocational/Occupational/Scholarship)* [7917]

California Association of Private Postsecondary Schools Scholarships *(Undergraduate/Scholarship)* [2232]

The California Endowment and AACN Minority Nurse Faculty Scholarships *(Graduate/Scholarship)* [459]

California Groundwater Association Scholarships *(Undergraduate/Scholarship)* [2258]

California Scottish Rite Foundation Scholarships *(Undergraduate/Scholarship)* [2275]

Calvin Alumni Association Southern California Chapter Scholarships *(Undergraduate/Scholarship)* [2309]

CANFIT Scholarships *(Graduate, Undergraduate/Scholarship)* [2228]

CHEA Undergraduate Scholarship Program for Students with Disabilities *(High School, Undergraduate/Scholarship)* [2260]

CHEA Vocational Grants *(High School/Grant)* [2261]

Cheerful Giver Scholarships *(Undergraduate/Scholarship)* [7918]

Chicana Latina Scholarship Fund *(Graduate, Undergraduate/Scholarship)* [2750]

Citi/TELACU Scholarships *(Undergraduate/Scholarship)* [8820]

Willis W. and Ethel M. Clark Foundation Fellowships *(Graduate/Fellowship)* [2899]

The Club at Morningside Scholarships *(Undergraduate, Vocational/Occupational/Scholarship)* [7919]

Madison and Edith Cooper Scholarships *(Under-

Colorado

(Graduate, Undergraduate/Scholarship) [1337]

Dwight A. Hamilton Scottish Rite Foundation of Colorado Graduate Scholarships (Graduate/Scholarship) [8063]

Johnson and Johnson: Nightingale Scholarships (Graduate, Undergraduate/Scholarship) [2997]

Kaiser Permanente: Nightingale Scholarships (Graduate, Undergraduate/Scholarship) [2998]

Latin American Educational Foundation Scholarships (Undergraduate, Vocational/Occupational/Scholarship) [5356]

Stephen T. Marchello Scholarships (Undergraduate/Scholarship) [5609]

The Cady McDonnell Memorial Scholarships (Undergraduate/Scholarship) [647]

H.M. Muffly Memorial Scholarships (Graduate, Undergraduate/Scholarship) [2999]

Colorado Nurses Association: Virginia Paulson Memorial Scholarships (Graduate, Undergraduate/Scholarship) [3000]

Peierls Rising Star Scholarship Program (Undergraduate/Scholarship) [4580]

Poudre Valley Health System, Fort Collins: Nightingale Scholarships (Graduate, Undergraduate/Scholarship) [3001]

Rocky Mountain Coal Mining Institute Engineering/Geology Scholarships (Undergraduate/Scholarship) [7810]

Rocky Mountain Coal Mining Institute Technical Scholarships (Undergraduate, Vocational/Occupational/Scholarship) [7811]

SACHS Foundation Graduate Scholarships (Graduate/Scholarship) [7840]

SACHS Foundation Undergraduate Scholarships for Colorado Black Students (High School/Scholarship) [7841]

St. Anthony's Hospitals, Denver: Nightingale Scholarships (Graduate, Undergraduate/Scholarship) [3002]

Patty Walter Memorial Scholarships (Graduate, Undergraduate/Scholarship) [3003]

Connecticut

Frederick G. Adams Scholarships (Undergraduate/Scholarship) [4405]

Alliance Francaise of Hartford Harpin/Rohinsky Scholarships (Undergraduate/Scholarship) [4406]

American Fire Sprinkler Association Scholarships (Undergraduate/Scholarship) [4407]

American Marketing Association-Connecticut Chapter, Anna C. Klune Memorial Scholarships (Graduate/Scholarship) [4408]

Officer Brian A. Aselton Memorial Scholarships (Undergraduate/Scholarship) [4410]

Malcolm Baldrige Scholarships (Undergraduate/Scholarship) [4411]

John Bell and Lawrence Thornton Scholarship Fund (Undergraduate/Scholarship) [4412]

Thomas M. Blake Memorial Scholarships (Undergraduate/Scholarship) [3230]

Leon Bradley Scholarships (Undergraduate/Scholarship) [548]

W. Philip Braender and Nancy Coleman Braender Scholarships (Undergraduate/Scholarship) [4415]

Gail Burns-Smith "Dare to Dream" Fund (Undergraduate/Scholarship) [4416]

Rhea Sourifman Caplin Memorial Scholarships (Undergraduate/Scholarship) [4417]

CLN Scholarships (Graduate, Undergraduate/Scholarship) [3237]

The College Club of Hartford Scholarships (Undergraduate/Scholarship) [4418]

Columbus Citizens Foundation College Scholarships (Undergraduate/Scholarship) [3012]

Connecticut Association of Land Surveyors Memorial Scholarships (Undergraduate/Scholarship) [3228]

Connecticut Association of Latinos in Higher Education Scholarships (Undergraduate/Scholarship) [4419]

Connecticut Building Congress Scholarships (Undergraduate/Scholarship) [4420]

Connecticut Capitol Scholarship Program (Under-

graduate/Scholarship) [4421]

Connecticut Mortgage Bankers Scholarships-Social Affairs Committee (Undergraduate/Scholarship) [4422]

Connecticut Nurserymen's Foundation Scholarships (Undergraduate/Scholarship) [4423]

C. Rodney Demarest Memorial Scholarships (Undergraduate/Scholarship) [4425]

Albert and Jane Dewey Scholarships (Undergraduate/Scholarship) [4426]

Harry A. Donn Scholarships (Undergraduate/Scholarship) [4427]

Charles Dubose Scholarships (Undergraduate/Scholarship) [4428]

Christine H. Eide Memorial Scholarships (Graduate, Undergraduate/Scholarship) [5496]

Priscilla Maxwell Endicott Scholarships (Undergraduate/Scholarship) [4429]

Farmington UNICO Scholarships (Undergraduate/Scholarship) [4430]

Symee Ruth Feinburg Memorial Scholarships (Undergraduate/Scholarship) [4431]

James L. and Genevieve H. Goodwin Scholarships (Undergraduate/Scholarship) [4433]

Greenwich Scholarship Association Scholarships (GSA) (Undergraduate/Scholarship) [4351]

Ida L. Hartenberg Charitable Scholarships (Undergraduate/Scholarship) [4435]

Hartford County Retired Teachers Association Scholarships (Undergraduate/Scholarship) [4436]

Hartford Foundation College Scholarship Program (Undergraduate/Scholarship) [4437]

Hartford Jazz Society Scholarships (Undergraduate/Scholarship) [4439]

Hartford Whalers Booster Club Scholarships (Undergraduate/Scholarship) [4440]

Interracial Scholarship Fund of Greater Hartford (Undergraduate/Scholarship) [4443]

Killingworth Foundation Scholarships (Undergraduate/Scholarship) [5260]

Herman P. Kopplemann Scholarships (Undergraduate/Scholarship) [4446]

KSA Scholarships (Undergraduate/Scholarship) [5262]

Dr. James L. Lawson Memorial Scholarships (Undergraduate/Scholarship) [1092]

Les Dames D'Escoffier New York Scholarships (Undergraduate/Scholarship) [5405]

Lighthouse International Scholarships - College-bound Awards (High School, Undergraduate/Scholarship) [5497]

Lighthouse International Scholarships - Graduate Awards (Graduate/Scholarship) [5498]

Lighthouse International Scholarships - Undergraduate Awards (Undergraduate/Scholarship) [5499]

H.B. Paul Lowenberg Lions Scholarships (Undergraduate/Scholarship) [4447]

Sonia S. Maguire Outstanding Scholastic Achievement Awards (Graduate, Undergraduate/Scholarship) [8782]

Mary Main Memorial Scholarships (Undergraduate/Scholarship) [4449]

Manchester Scholarship Foundation Scholarships (Undergraduate/Scholarship) [4450]

Michaels Jewelers Foundation Scholarships for Athletes (Undergraduate/Scholarship) [4452]

New England FEMARA Scholarships (Undergraduate/Scholarship) [1096]

New York Women in Communications, Inc. Foundation Scholarships (Graduate, Undergraduate/Scholarship) [6690]

Sylvia Parkinson Scholarships (Undergraduate/Scholarship) [4453]

Pellegrini Scholarships (Graduate, Undergraduate, Vocational/Occupational/Scholarship) [8784]

Dorothy E. Hofmann Pembroke Scholarships (Undergraduate/Scholarship) [4454]

Nicholas J. Piergrossi Scholarships (Undergraduate/Scholarship) [4455]

Rosa Quezada Memorial Education Scholarships (Undergraduate/Scholarship) [3231]

Mary C. Rawlins Scholarships (Undergraduate/Scholarship) [4458]

Tadeusz Sendzimir Scholarships (Undergraduate/Scholarship) [4460]

John Soto Scholarships (Undergraduate/Scholarship) [3232]

Town and County Club Scholarships (Undergraduate/Scholarship) [4462]

Marta Vallin Memorial Scholarships (Undergraduate/Scholarship) [3233]

Yankee Clipper Contest Club, Inc. Youth Scholarships (Undergraduate/Scholarship) [1114]

Zimmermann Scholarships (Graduate/Scholarship) [8785]

Delaware

Horatio Alger Delaware Scholarships (Undergraduate/Scholarship) [298]

Leon Bradley Scholarships (Undergraduate/Scholarship) [548]

Chrysler Technical Scholarship Fund (Undergraduate/Scholarship) [3358]

Columbus Citizens Foundation College Scholarships (Undergraduate/Scholarship) [3012]

Generation III Scholarships (Undergraduate/Scholarship) [3586]

German Society Scholarships (Undergraduate/Scholarship) [4137]

Gruwell Scholarships (Undergraduate/Scholarship) [3059]

Lighthouse International Scholarships - College-bound Awards (High School, Undergraduate/Scholarship) [5497]

Lighthouse International Scholarships - Graduate Awards (Graduate/Scholarship) [5498]

Lighthouse International Scholarships - Undergraduate Awards (Undergraduate/Scholarship) [5499]

Sonia S. Maguire Outstanding Scholastic Achievement Awards (Graduate, Undergraduate/Scholarship) [8782]

Pellegrini Scholarships (Graduate, Undergraduate, Vocational/Occupational/Scholarship) [8784]

Drew Smith Memorial Scholarships (Undergraduate/Scholarship) [3068]

The SSPI Mid-Atlantic Chapter Scholarships (Graduate, Undergraduate/Scholarship) [8489]

Zimmermann Scholarships (Graduate/Scholarship) [8785]

District of Columbia

The Frederick B. Abramson Memorial Foundation Scholarships (Undergraduate/Scholarship) [22]

Horatio Alger District of Columbia, Maryland and Virginia Scholarships (Undergraduate/Scholarship) [299]

Cocke, Szpanka and Taylor Scholarships (Undergraduate/Scholarship) [9462]

Columbus Citizens Foundation College Scholarships (Undergraduate/Scholarship) [3012]

Richard Gregory Freeland, II Educational Scholarships (High School/Scholarship) [2147]

HSBC-North America Scholarship Program (Undergraduate/Scholarship) [4571]

Dwight P. Jacobus Scholarships (Undergraduate/Scholarship) [1860]

Lighthouse International Scholarships - College-bound Awards (High School, Undergraduate/Scholarship) [5497]

Lighthouse International Scholarships - Graduate Awards (Graduate/Scholarship) [5498]

Lighthouse International Scholarships - Undergraduate Awards (Undergraduate/Scholarship) [5499]

Spring Internships in International Civil Society Law (Undergraduate/Internship) [4894]

The SSPI Mid-Atlantic Chapter Scholarships (Graduate, Undergraduate/Scholarship) [8489]

Florida

Horatio Alger Florida Scholarships (Undergraduate/Scholarship) [300]

Earl I. Anderson Scholarships (Undergraduate/Scholarship) [1068]

Lewis B. Barber Memorial Scholarships (Undergraduate/Scholarship) [8590]

byourself Scholarship Fund *(Undergraduate, Vocational/Occupational/Scholarship)* [3188]

Cesar A. Calas/FES Miami Chapter Scholarships *(Undergraduate/Scholarship)* [3824]

Calvin Alumni Association Florida-Gulf Coast Scholarships *(Undergraduate/Scholarship)* [2297]

Calvin Alumni Association-South Florida Scholarships *(Undergraduate/Scholarship)* [2305]

Calvin Alumni Association-South Florida Sophomore Scholarships *(Undergraduate/Scholarship)* [2306]

Central Florida Jazz Society Scholarships *(Undergraduate/Award, Scholarship)* [2717]

Reuben R. Cowles Youth Awards *(Undergraduate/Award)* [885]

DBPR Division of CPA - BOA Minority Scholarships *(Undergraduate/Scholarship)* [3430]

Doctors IRA & UDAYA Nursing Scholarships *(Undergraduate/Scholarship)* [8598]

FICPA Educational Foundation 1040K Race Scholarships *(Undergraduate/Scholarship)* [3836]

Florida Engineering Society Junior College Scholarships *(Undergraduate/Scholarship)* [3827]

Florida Engineering Society University Scholarships *(Undergraduate/Scholarship)* [3828]

Florida Public Transportation Association Scholarships (FPTA) *(Graduate, Undergraduate/Scholarship)* [1052]

Charles and Margaret Foster Scholarships *(Undergraduate/Scholarship)* [8602]

James Franklin and Dorothy J. Warnell Scholarship Fund *(Undergraduate, Vocational/Occupational/Scholarship)* [3192]

American Association of University Women-Mary Sue Gottcent Memorial Scholarships *(Undergraduate/Scholarship)* [8604]

William L. Graddy Law School Scholarships *(Undergraduate/Scholarship)* [8605]

Randy Green Memorial Scholarship Fund *(High School/Scholarship)* [3318]

Gulf Coast Hurricane Scholarships *(Graduate, Undergraduate/Scholarship)* [8449]

HSBC-North America Scholarship Program *(Undergraduate/Scholarship)* [4571]

HSF/Citi Fellows Program *(Undergraduate/Scholarship)* [4573]

IAAP Wings Chapter Scholarships *(Undergraduate, Vocational/Occupational/Scholarship)* [4854]

V.J. Johnson Memorial Scholarships *(Undergraduate/Scholarship)* [552]

Chip Johnson Scholarships *(Undergraduate/Scholarship)* [8608]

Kappa Delta Phi Scholarship Program *(Postgraduate/Scholarship)* [952]

Michael Kidger Memorial Scholarships in Optical Design *(Graduate/Scholarship)* [8638]

Robert A. Kleckner Scholarships *(Undergraduate/Scholarship)* [8612]

Lighthouse International Scholarships - College-bound Awards *(High School, Undergraduate/Scholarship)* [5497]

Lighthouse International Scholarships - Graduate Awards *(Graduate/Scholarship)* [5498]

Lighthouse International Scholarships - Undergraduate Awards *(Undergraduate/Scholarship)* [5499]

Love of Bonita Empowerment Scholarships *(Undergraduate/Scholarship)* [8613]

Robert V. McKenna Scholarships *(Undergraduate/Scholarship)* [8818]

NAJA Scholarships *(Graduate/Scholarship)* [6086]

Judge William J. Nelson Scholarships *(Undergraduate/Scholarship)* [8615]

Dr. Felix H. Reyler Memorial Scholarships *(Undergraduate/Scholarship)* [3319]

Faye Lynn Roberts Educational Scholarships *(Undergraduate/Scholarship)* [8618]

The Rotary Club of Cape Coral Goldcoast Scholarship Fund *(Undergraduate/Scholarship)* [2645]

IRARC Memorial Joseph P. Rubino WA4MMD

Scholarships *(Undergraduate/Scholarship)* [1103]

Samalot - Sebastian Scholarship Fund *(High School/Scholarship)* [3320]

John M. and Mary A. Shanley Memorial Scholarships *(Undergraduate/Scholarship)* [8622]

Southwest Florida Community Foundation College Assistance Scholarships *(Undergraduate/Scholarship)* [8623]

John I. and Madeleine R. Taeni Scholarships *(Undergraduate/Scholarship)* [8627]

The Rodney Thaxton Justice Fund *(Undergraduate/Scholarship)* [3322]

Jacki Tuckfield Memorial Graduate Business Scholarship Fund *(Doctorate, Graduate, Master's/Scholarship)* [3323]

Ted C. Wilson Memorial Scholarships *(Undergraduate/Scholarship)* [7441]

Georgia

Horatio Alger Georgia Scholarships *(Undergraduate/Scholarship)* [302]

Charles Clarke Cordle Memorial Scholarships *(Undergraduate/Scholarship)* [1081]

Reuben R. Cowles Youth Awards *(Undergraduate/Award)* [885]

Larry Dean Davis Scholarship Program *(Undergraduate, Vocational/Occupational/Scholarship)* [2171]

Steve Dearduff Scholarships *(Graduate, Undergraduate/Scholarship)* [3075]

E. Lanier Finch Scholarships *(Undergraduate/Scholarship)* [4097]

Forsyth County United Way Scholarships *(Undergraduate/Scholarship)* [5344]

Gene Henson Scholarships *(High School, Undergraduate/Scholarship)* [1922]

HSF/Nissan Community College Transfer Scholarship Program *(Undergraduate/Scholarship)* [4576]

Philip R. Karr, III Scholarship Fund *(Graduate/Fellowship)* [4100]

Lighthouse International Scholarships - College-bound Awards *(High School, Undergraduate/Scholarship)* [5497]

Lighthouse International Scholarships - Graduate Awards *(Graduate/Scholarship)* [5498]

Lighthouse International Scholarships - Undergraduate Awards *(Undergraduate/Scholarship)* [5499]

Mollie Lukken Memorial Scholarships *(Graduate, Professional development/Scholarship)* [5178]

Edna A. Noblin Dawsonville Lions Club Scholarships *(Undergraduate/Scholarship)* [5345]

NWAG Georgia, USA Scholarships *(High School/Scholarship)* [6718]

William C. Rogers Scholarships *(Undergraduate/Scholarship)* [4109]

Eugene Gene Sallee, W4YFR Memorial Scholarships *(Undergraduate/Scholarship)* [1105]

George and Pearl Strickland Scholarships *(Graduate, Undergraduate/Scholarship)* [3076]

Kirk Sutlive Scholarships *(Undergraduate/Scholarship)* [4110]

University Alliance HSF/UGA College Scholarship Program *(Undergraduate/Scholarship)* [4583]

Watson-Brown Scholarships *(Undergraduate/Scholarship)* [9540]

Ted C. Wilson Memorial Scholarships *(Undergraduate/Scholarship)* [7441]

Hawaii

Gladys Kamakakuokalani 'Ainoa Brandt Scholarships *(Graduate, Undergraduate/Scholarship)* [5209]

CHEA Undergraduate Scholarship Program for Students with Disabilities *(High School, Undergraduate/Scholarship)* [2260]

CHEA Vocational Grants *(High School/Grant)* [2261]

Tommy Crabb Scholarship Fund *(Undergraduate/Scholarship)* [4480]

Victoria S. and Bradley L. Geist Scholarships *(Undergraduate/Scholarship)* [4477]

Goldman Sachs/Matsuo Takabuki Commemorative Scholarships *(Graduate/Scholarship)* [5211]

Hawaii Community Foundation Scholarships *(Undergraduate, Graduate/Scholarship)* [4478]

R.W. "Bob" Holden Memorial Scholarships *(Undergraduate/Scholarship)* [4482]

HPGS/ALOH Graduate Scholarships *(Graduate/Scholarship)* [4485]

HPGS Undergraduate Scholarships *(Undergraduate/Scholarship)* [4486]

Clem Judd Jr. Memorial Scholarships *(Undergraduate/Scholarship)* [4483]

Ka'u Chamber of Commerce College Scholarships *(Undergraduate/Scholarship)* [5207]

Lamaku Post-Secondary Scholarships *(Undergraduate/Scholarship)* [83]

The Cady McDonnell Memorial Scholarships *(Undergraduate/Scholarship)* [647]

William S. Richardson Commemorative Scholarships *(Graduate/Scholarship)* [5221]

David T. Woolsey Scholarships *(Undergraduate/Scholarship)* [1289]

Hawaii Chapter/David T. Woolsey Scholarships *(Graduate, Undergraduate/Scholarship)* [5337]

Idaho

The "21" Endowed Scholarships *(Undergraduate/Scholarship)* [5409]

Horatio Alger Idaho University Scholarships *(Undergraduate/Scholarship)* [303]

Horatio Alger Lola and Duane Hagadone Idaho Scholarships *(Undergraduate/Scholarship)* [307]

American Legion Boys/Girls State Scholarships *(Undergraduate/Scholarship)* [5411]

Paul Arnold Memorial Scholarships *(Undergraduate/Scholarship)* [7396]

Asian and Pacific Islander Queers Sisters Scholarships *(Undergraduate/Scholarship)* [7397]

Associates in Behavioral Health Scholarships *(Graduate/Scholarship)* [7398]

Barbara Bailey Scholarships *(Undergraduate/Scholarship)* [7399]

Charly Baker and Heath Merriwether Memorial Scholarships *(Undergraduate/Scholarship)* [7400]

Bellevue PFLAG Scholarships *(Undergraduate/Scholarship)* [7401]

Bill Bendiner and Doug Morgenson Scholarships *(Undergraduate/Scholarship)* [7402]

Mary Lou Brown Scholarships *(Undergraduate/Scholarship)* [1074]

Robert Browning Scholarships *(Undergraduate/Scholarship)* [7403]

Deloris Carter Hampton Scholarships *(Undergraduate/Scholarship)* [7404]

Donald O. Coffman Scholarships *(Undergraduate/Scholarship)* [7405]

Cole Family Scholarships *(Undergraduate/Scholarship)* [7406]

Dennis Coleman Choral Conducting Scholarships *(Undergraduate/Scholarship)* [7407]

Compassionate Care Scholarships *(Undergraduate/Scholarship)* [7408]

Mike Crapo Math and Science Scholarship Fund *(Undergraduate/Scholarship)* [4668]

Laura Moore Cunningham Foundation General Scholarships *(Undergraduate/Scholarship)* [5423]

Brian M. Day Scholarships *(Undergraduate/Scholarship)* [7409]

Gold Country Section & Region II Scholarships *(Graduate, Undergraduate/Scholarship)* [1337]

Frank and Gladys Hopkins Endowed Scholarships *(Undergraduate/Scholarship)* [5434]

Idaho Nursery and Landscape Association Scholarships *(Undergraduate/Scholarship)* [4676]

Idaho Promise Category B Scholarships *(Undergraduate/Scholarship)* [5436]

Idaho Society of CPA's Scholarships *(Undergraduate/Scholarship)* [4671]

Inland Northwest Business Alliance Scholarships (INBA) *(Undergraduate/Scholarship)* [7411]

Margaret G. Johnson and Marge J. Stout Scholarships *(Undergraduate, Vocational/Occupational/ Scholarship)* [5437]

Lewis-Clark State College Foundation Scholars Scholarships *(Undergraduate/Scholarship)* [5441]

Lewis-Clark State College Freshman Scholarships *(Undergraduate/Scholarship)* [5442]

Lewis-Clark State College Governor's Cup Scholarships *(Undergraduate/Scholarship)* [5443]

Lewis-Clark State College/Idaho Society of CPAs Scholarships Fund *(Undergraduate/Scholarship)* [5444]

Lewis-Clark State College Provost Scholarships *(Undergraduate/Scholarship)* [5448]

Lewis-Clark State College Valley Scholarships *(Undergraduate/Scholarship)* [5450]

Lewiston Clarkston Kiwanis Club Scholarships *(Undergraduate/Scholarship)* [5451]

Monna Mawson Scholarships *(Undergraduate/ Scholarship)* [4659]

The Cady McDonnell Memorial Scholarships *(Undergraduate/Scholarship)* [647]

McFarffels Scholarships *(Undergraduate/Scholarship)* [7412]

Jack D. Motteler Scholarships *(Undergraduate/ Scholarship)* [7413]

Obrzut Ling Scholarships *(Undergraduate, Vocational/Occupational/Scholarship)* [7414]

Political Leadership Scholarships *(Undergraduate/ Scholarship)* [7415]

Jim Poore Memorial Scholarships *(Undergraduate/Scholarship)* [4672]

Pride Foundation Regional Scholarships *(Undergraduate/Scholarship)* [7416]

Rosenberg-Ibarra Scholarships *(Undergraduate/ Scholarship)* [7419]

Roger C. Sathre Memorial Scholarship Fund *(Undergraduate/Scholarship)* [4673]

Social Work Scholarships *(Undergraduate/Scholarship)* [7420]

Kathy Spadoni Memorial Scholarships *(Undergraduate/Scholarship)* [7421]

State of Idaho Scholarships Category A *(Undergraduate, Vocational/Occupational/Scholarship)* [5466]

Tschudy Family Scholarships *(Undergraduate/ Scholarship)* [5468]

Ric Ulrich and Chuck Pischke Scholarships *(Undergraduate/Scholarship)* [7423]

Patricia Van Kirk Scholarships *(Undergraduate/ Scholarship)* [7424]

Wells Fargo Scholarships *(Undergraduate/Scholarship)* [7425]

James and Colin Lee Wozumi Scholarships *(Undergraduate/Scholarship)* [7427]

You Go Girl! Scholarships *(Undergraduate/Scholarship)* [7428]

Urashi Zen Scholarships *(Undergraduate/Scholarship)* [7429]

Illinois

Horatio Alger Illinois Scholarships *(Undergraduate/ Scholarship)* [304]

Allied Health Care Professional Scholarships *(Undergraduate/Scholarship)* [4693]

Earl I. Anderson Scholarships *(Undergraduate/ Scholarship)* [1068]

MAC Louisa Bowen Memorial Scholarships for Graduate Students in Archival Administration *(Graduate/Scholarship)* [5854]

Robert C. Byrd Honors Scholarships *(Undergraduate/Scholarship)* [4694]

Calvin Alumni Association-Illinois Scholarships *(Undergraduate/Scholarship)* [2298]

Chapter 23 - Quad Cities Iowa/Illinois Scholarships *(Undergraduate/Scholarship)* [8374]

Chicago FM Club Scholarships *(Undergraduate/ Scholarship)* [1078]

Community Foundation of the Fox River Valley Scholarships *(Undergraduate/Scholarship)* [3073]

Community Foundation Scholarships *(Undergraduate/Scholarship)* [3146]

Margaret T. Craig Community Service Scholarships *(Undergraduate/Scholarship)* [3147]

Felicia De Bow Memorial Scholarships *(All/Scholarship)* [7037]

William R. Durham/Theater Scholarships *(Undergraduate/Scholarship)* [3148]

Robert Esser Student Achievement Scholarships *(Graduate, Undergraduate/Fellowship, Scholarship)* [4685]

Field Museum Graduate Student Fellowships *(Graduate/Fellowship)* [3742]

HSBC-North America Scholarship Program *(Undergraduate/Scholarship)* [4571]

HSF/Nissan Community College Transfer Scholarship Program *(Undergraduate/Scholarship)* [4576]

Charles David Hughes Scholarships *(Graduate/ Scholarship)* [3028]

IBEA Graduate Scholarships *(Graduate/Scholarship)* [4682]

Illinois Future Teacher Corps Scholarships *(Undergraduate/Scholarship)* [4695]

Illinois Lake Management Association Undergraduate/Graduate Scholarships *(Graduate, Undergraduate/Fellowship, Scholarship)* [4686]

Illinois Landscape Contractors Association Scholarships *(Undergraduate/Scholarship)* [4688]

Illinois Special Education Teacher Tuition Waiver Scholarships (SETTW) *(Undergraduate/Scholarship)* [4696]

Illinois Student Assistance Commission Medical Student Scholarships *(Undergraduate/Scholarship)* [4697]

Illinois Student Assistance Commission Merit Recognition Scholarships (MRS) *(Undergraduate/ Scholarship)* [4698]

Illinois Student Assistance Commission Nurse Educator Scholarships (NESP) *(Undergraduate/ Scholarship)* [4699]

Illinois Student Assistance Commission Nursing Education Scholarships *(Undergraduate/Scholarship)* [4700]

International Management Council Scholarships (IMC) *(Undergraduate/Scholarship)* [3155]

Jewish Federation Academic Scholarships *(Graduate, Undergraduate/Scholarship)* [5161]

La Voz Latina Scholarships *(Undergraduate/ Scholarship)* [3157]

Edmond A. Metzger Scholarships *(Undergraduate/ Scholarship)* [1094]

Minority Teachers of Illinois Scholarships (MTI) *(Undergraduate/Scholarship)* [4701]

Daniel Murphy Scholarships *(High School/Scholarship)* [5950]

Northwest Community Center Scholarships *(Undergraduate/Scholarship)* [3162]

Peoria Area Amateur Radio Club Scholarships *(Undergraduate/Scholarship)* [1099]

Rockford Area Habitat for Humanity College Scholarships *(Undergraduate/Scholarship)* [3166]

Rockford Chapter Daughters of the American Revolution Memorial Scholarships *(Undergraduate/Scholarship)* [3167]

APSAIL's Ralph Silverman Memorial Scholarships *(Undergraduate/Scholarship)* [1967]

Six Meter Club of Chicago Scholarships *(Undergraduate/Scholarship)* [1107]

Ernest and Charlene Stachowiak Memorial Scholarships *(Undergraduate/Scholarship)* [3173]

Hartman E. Stime Scholarships *(Undergraduate/ Scholarship)* [3553]

Charlie Trotters's Culinary Education Foundation Culinary Study Scholarships *(Professional development, Undergraduate/Scholarship)* [8962]

Francis Walton Memorial Scholarships *(Undergraduate/Scholarship)* [1112]

Lee Womack Scholarship Fund *(Undergraduate/ Scholarship)* [5917]

Women of Today's Manufacturing Scholarships *(Undergraduate/Scholarship)* [3175]

Margaret Wyeth Scholarships *(Undergraduate/ Scholarship)* [3177]

Indiana

Mandel & Lauretta Abrahamer Scholarships *(Undergraduate/Scholarship)* [8715]

Horatio Alger Indiana Scholarships *(Undergraduate/Scholarship)* [305]

Earl I. Anderson Scholarships *(Undergraduate/ Scholarship)* [1068]

Richard L. Baker Memorial Scholarships *(Undergraduate/Scholarship)* [8717]

MAC Louisa Bowen Memorial Scholarships for Graduate Students in Archival Administration *(Graduate/Scholarship)* [5854]

Builders Association of Northeast Indiana Scholarships (BANI) *(Undergraduate/Scholarship)* [8719]

Chicago FM Club Scholarships *(Undergraduate/ Scholarship)* [1078]

Ellen Eberhardt Memorial Scholarships *(Undergraduate/Scholarship)* [8720]

Farmers State Bank Scholarships *(Undergraduate, Vocational/Occupational/Scholarship)* [8721]

Granger Business Association College Scholarships *(Undergraduate/Scholarship)* [4313]

Katherine M. Grosscup Scholarships *(Graduate, Undergraduate/Scholarship)* [4042]

Ed Haas Memorial Scholarships *(Undergraduate/ Scholarship)* [8724]

H. Pauline Hand Memorial Scholarships *(Undergraduate/Scholarship)* [8725]

Dale Hughes, Jr. Memorial Scholarships *(Undergraduate/Scholarship)* [8727]

Indiana Alumni Scholarships *(Undergraduate/ Scholarship)* [9772]

Indiana Broadcasters Association College Scholarship Program *(Undergraduate/Scholarship)* [4733]

Indiana Broadcasters Association High School Scholarship Program *(Undergraduate/Scholarship)* [4734]

Indiana State Alumni Association Rural Health Scholarships *(Undergraduate/Scholarship)* [4748]

Sylvia E. Jackson Scholarships *(Undergraduate/ Scholarship)* [8728]

Jewish Federation Academic Scholarships *(Graduate, Undergraduate/Scholarship)* [5161]

Kappa Delta Phi Scholarship Program *(Postgraduate/Scholarship)* [952]

John W. Kelley Memorial Scholarships *(Undergraduate/Scholarship)* [8729]

Las Limas Community Scholarships *(Undergraduate/Scholarship)* [8730]

Edmond A. Metzger Scholarships *(Undergraduate/ Scholarship)* [1094]

Anthony Munoz Scholarships *(Undergraduate/ Scholarship)* [5948]

Dr. J. Glenn Radcliffe Memorial Scholarships *(Undergraduate/Scholarship)* [8732]

Frederick Rakestraw Law Scholarships *(Graduate/ Scholarship)* [6803]

Reid Hospital Graduate Student Scholarships *(Graduate/Scholarship)* [9557]

Six Meter Club of Chicago Scholarships *(Undergraduate/Scholarship)* [1107]

University of Louisville Eagle Scout Scholarships *(Undergraduate/Scholarship)* [6262]

Francis Walton Memorial Scholarships *(Undergraduate/Scholarship)* [1112]

Iowa

Ak-Sar-Ben Scholarships *(Undergraduate/Scholarship)* [296]

Horatio Alger Ak-Sar-Ben Scholarships *(Undergraduate/Scholarship)* [297]

MAC Louisa Bowen Memorial Scholarships for Graduate Students in Archival Administration *(Graduate/Scholarship)* [5854]

Chapter 23 - Quad Cities Iowa/Illinois Scholarships *(Undergraduate/Scholarship)* [8374]

Grace O. Doane Scholarships *(Undergraduate/ Scholarship)* [3485]

Paul and Helen L. Grauer Scholarships *(Undergraduate/Scholarship)* [1087]

John M. Helmick Law Scholarships *(Undergraduate/Scholarship)* [3498]

Herbert Hoover Uncommon Student Awards *(Undergraduate/Scholarship)* [4597]

INF Scholarships (Undergraduate/Scholarship) [5042]

James P. Irish Scholarships (Undergraduate/Scholarship) [3499]

Kappa Delta Phi Scholarship Program (Postgraduate/Scholarship) [952]

James B. Morris Scholarships (Undergraduate/Scholarship) [5935]

Ray, NORP and Katie, WOKTE Pautz Scholarships (Undergraduate/Scholarship) [1098]

PHD ARA Scholarships (Doctorate, Undergraduate/Scholarship) [1100]

Carter Pitts Scholarships (Undergraduate/Scholarship) [5044]

Kansas

MAC Louisa Bowen Memorial Scholarships for Graduate Students in Archival Administration (Graduate/Scholarship) [5854]

Cherokee Nation Graduate Scholarships (Graduate/Scholarship) [2742]

Cherokee Nation Scholarships (Undergraduate/Scholarship) [2744]

Irvine W. Cook WA0CGS Scholarships (Undergraduate/Scholarship) [1080]

Paul and Helen L. Grauer Scholarships (Undergraduate/Scholarship) [1087]

Kansas Association of Broadcasters Scholarships (Undergraduate/Scholarship) [5182]

Kansas Optometry Service Scholarships (Graduate, Undergraduate/Scholarship) [5184]

Kansas Osteopathic Medical Service Scholarships (Graduate, Professional development/Scholarship) [5185]

John J. Mingenback Memorial Scholarships (Graduate, Undergraduate/Scholarship) [4173]

Ray, NORP and Katie, WOKTE Pautz Scholarships (Undergraduate/Scholarship) [1098]

PHD ARA Scholarships (Doctorate, Undergraduate/Scholarship) [1100]

Hatton W. Sumners Scholarships (Undergraduate/Scholarship) [6869]

J.L. Weigand, Jr. Legal Education Trust Scholarships (Undergraduate/Scholarship) [9492]

Kentucky

Horatio Alger Kentucky Scholarships (Undergraduate/Scholarship) [306]

MAC Louisa Bowen Memorial Scholarships for Graduate Students in Archival Administration (Graduate/Scholarship) [5854]

Graduate Realtor Institute Scholarships (Graduate/Scholarship) [5244]

Katherine M. Grosscup Scholarships (Graduate, Undergraduate/Scholarship) [4042]

Kappa Delta Phi Scholarship Program (Postgraduate/Scholarship) [952]

KATS Graduate Scholarships (Graduate/Scholarship) [5246]

KATS Undergraduate Scholarships (Undergraduate/Scholarship) [5247]

Kentucky Alumni Club Scholarships - Capital Region Alumni Club (Undergraduate/Scholarship) [9213]

Kentucky Alumni Club Scholarships - Central Kentucky Alumni Club (Undergraduate/Scholarship) [9214]

Kentucky Alumni Club Scholarships - Lake Cumberland Alumni Club (Undergraduate/Scholarship) [9215]

Kentucky Alumni Club Scholarships - Northern Kentucky Alumni Club (Undergraduate/Scholarship) [9216]

Kentucky Educational Excellence Scholarships (Graduate, Undergraduate/Scholarship) [2090]

KHEAA Teacher Scholarships (Undergraduate/Scholarship) [2091]

KYCPA Scholarships (Undergraduate/Scholarship) [5253]

Anthony Munoz Scholarships (Undergraduate/Scholarship) [5948]

South Kentucky RECC High School Senior Scholarships (Undergraduate/Scholarship) [8564]

University of Louisville Eagle Scout Scholarships (Undergraduate/Scholarship) [6262]

Woman In Rural Electrification Scholarships (WIRE) (Undergraduate/Scholarship) [8565]

Wyatt, Tarrant and Combs, LLP Scholarships (Undergraduate/Scholarship) [9242]

Louisiana

A&WMA Louisiana Section Scholarships (Graduate, Undergraduate/Scholarship) [113]

Horatio Alger Louisiana Scholarships (Undergraduate/Scholarship) [308]

American Radio Relay League Louisiana Memorial Scholarships (Undergraduate/Scholarship) [1067]

Frank L. Dautriel Memorial Scholarships for Graduates (Undergraduate/Scholarship) [5519]

Frank L. Dautriel Memorial Scholarships for Undergraduates (Undergraduate/Scholarship) [5520]

Gulf Coast Hurricane Scholarships (Graduate, Undergraduate/Scholarship) [8449]

Lone Star GIA Associate and Alumni Scholarships (Undergraduate/Scholarship) [4064]

Louisiana Library Association Scholarships (Graduate, Master's/Scholarship) [5522]

Fred R. McDaniel Memorial Scholarships (Undergraduate/Scholarship) [1093]

Mary Moore Mitchell Scholarships (Graduate, Master's/Scholarship) [5523]

NAJA Scholarships (Graduate/Scholarship) [6086]

Society of Louisiana Certified Public Accountants Scholarships (Undergraduate/Scholarship) [8367]

Hatton W. Sumners Scholarships (Undergraduate/Scholarship) [6869]

Maine

Leon Bradley Scholarships (Undergraduate/Scholarship) [548]

Central Maine Power Scholarship Fund (Undergraduate/Scholarship) [5574]

Churchill Family Scholarships (Undergraduate/Scholarship) [5575]

Clinical Laboratory Management Association High School Senior Scholarships (High School/Scholarship) [2907]

Clinical Laboratory Management Association Undergraduate Scholarships (Undergraduate/Scholarship) [2908]

Columbus Citizens Foundation College Scholarships (Undergraduate/Scholarship) [3012]

John S. and Marjoria R. Cunningham Camp Scholarships (All/Scholarship) [5576]

Downeast Feline Scholarships (Graduate/Scholarship) [5577]

Foundation for Seacoast Health Scholarships (Graduate, Undergraduate/Scholarship) [3992]

Guy P. Gannett Scholarships (Undergraduate/Scholarship) [5578]

Georgetown Working League Scholarships (Undergraduate/Scholarship) [4090]

Ronald P. Guerrette Future Farmers of America Scholarship Fund (Undergraduate/Scholarship) [5579]

Ella R. Ifill Fund (Undergraduate/Scholarship) [5580]

Island Institute Scholarship Fund (Undergraduate/Scholarship) [5581]

Edward G. Kaelber Scholarships (Undergraduate/Scholarship) [5582]

Dr. James L. Lawson Memorial Scholarships (Undergraduate/Scholarship) [1092]

Lighthouse International Scholarships - Collegebound Awards (High School, Undergraduate/Scholarship) [5497]

Lighthouse International Scholarships - Graduate Awards (Graduate/Scholarship) [5498]

Lighthouse International Scholarships - Undergraduate Awards (Undergraduate/Scholarship) [5499]

Maine Community Foundation - CWG Scholarship Fund (Graduate/Scholarship) [5584]

Maine Community Foundation - Rice Scholarships (Undergraduate/Scholarship) [5585]

Maine Nutrition Council Scholarships (Undergraduate/Scholarship) [5599]

Maine Vietnam Veterans Scholarships (All/Scholarship) [5586]

Joseph W. Mayo ALS Scholarships (Undergraduate/Scholarship) [5587]

Gary Merrill Memorial Scholarships (Undergraduate/Scholarship) [5588]

Ruth Milan-Altrusa Scholarships (Undergraduate/Scholarship) [5589]

Hugh and Elizabeth Montgomery Scholarships (Undergraduate/Scholarship) [5590]

New England FEMARA Scholarships (Undergraduate/Scholarship) [1096]

Patriot Education Scholarships (Undergraduate/Scholarship) [5591]

Jerome Peters Family Scholarships (Undergraduate/Scholarship) [5592]

Riggs Cove Foundation Scholarships (Undergraduate/Scholarship) [4091]

Benjamin Riggs Scholarships (Undergraduate/Scholarship) [4092]

Lawrence and Louise Robbins Scholarships (Undergraduate/Scholarship) [5593]

Robinhood Marine Center Scholarships (Undergraduate/Scholarship) [4093]

James and Marilyn Rockfeller Scholarships (Undergraduate/Scholarship) [5594]

Henry L.P. Schmelzer College Transitions Scholarships (Undergraduate/Scholarship) [5595]

Josephine Hooker Shain Scholarships (Undergraduate/Scholarship) [4094]

Southern Maine Women's Golf Association Scholarships (All/Scholarship) [8583]

Lawrence Alan Spiegel Remembrance Scholarships (Undergraduate/Scholarship) [4595]

Woodex Bearing Company Scholarships (Undergraduate/Scholarship) [4095]

Yankee Clipper Contest Club, Inc. Youth Scholarships (Undergraduate/Scholarship) [1114]

Maryland

Horatio Alger District of Columbia, Maryland and Virginia Scholarships (Undergraduate/Scholarship) [299]

BCCC Foundation Workforce Scholarships (Undergraduate/Scholarship) [2003]

Letitia B. Carter Scholarships (All/Scholarship) [7745]

Columbus Citizens Foundation College Scholarships (Undergraduate/Scholarship) [3012]

Richard Gregory Freeland, II Educational Scholarships (High School/Scholarship) [2147]

Hancock Family Snow Hill High School Scholarships (Undergraduate/Scholarship) [3060]

Marcia S. Harris Legacy Fund Scholarships (Undergraduate/Scholarship) [7746]

Dick and Pat Hazel Minority Scholarships (Professional development/Scholarship) [3061]

Dwight P. Jacobus Scholarships (Undergraduate/Scholarship) [1860]

Land-Use Planning Scholarships (Graduate/Scholarship) [6294]

Lighthouse International Scholarships - Collegebound Awards (High School, Undergraduate/Scholarship) [5497]

Lighthouse International Scholarships - Graduate Awards (Graduate/Scholarship) [5498]

Lighthouse International Scholarships - Undergraduate Awards (Undergraduate/Scholarship) [5499]

MACPA Scholarships (Graduate, Undergraduate/Scholarship) [5652]

Duane V. Puerde Memorial Scholarships (Undergraduate, Vocational/Occupational/Scholarship) [3065]

Lana K. Rinehart Scholarships (Undergraduate/Scholarship) [3067]

Drew Smith Memorial Scholarships (Undergraduate/Scholarship) [3068]

The SSPI Mid-Atlantic Chapter Scholarships (Graduate, Undergraduate/Scholarship) [8489]

Gary Wagner, K3OMI Scholarships (Undergraduate/Scholarship) [1111]

Massachusetts

Adler Pollock & Sheehan Diversity Scholarships *(Undergraduate/Scholarship)* [50]

Boston City Federation "Return to School" Scholarships *(Graduate, Undergraduate/Scholarship)* [4074]

Leon Bradley Scholarships *(Undergraduate/Scholarship)* [548]

Sgt. Michael F. Cherven Memorial Scholarships *(Undergraduate/Scholarship)* [5666]

Citizens' Scholarship Foundation of Wakefield Scholarships *(All/Scholarship)* [2885]

Columbus Citizens Foundation College Scholarships *(Undergraduate/Scholarship)* [3012]

Communication Disorder/Speech Therapy Scholarships *(Graduate/Scholarship)* [4075]

Community Foundation of Western Massachusetts Community Scholarship Program *(Undergraduate/Scholarship)* [3207]

Dorchester Woman's Club Scholarships *(Undergraduate/Scholarship)* [4076]

Early Childhood Educators Scholarship Program *(Undergraduate/Scholarship)* [5684]

Mark Jonathan Elliot Scholarship Fund *(Graduate, Undergraduate/Scholarship)* [4722]

Gehring Memorial Foundation Scholarships *(Graduate, Undergraduate/Scholarship)* [4723]

Barnett D. Gordon Scholarships *(Graduate, Undergraduate/Scholarship)* [4724]

Hai Guin Scholarships Association *(Undergraduate/Scholarship)* [1594]

Ann L. Holland Memorial Scholarships *(Graduate, Undergraduate/Scholarship)* [4077]

Independent University Alumni Association Scholarships *(Graduate, Undergraduate/Scholarship)* [4725]

International Study Abroad Scholarships *(Graduate, Undergraduate/Scholarship)* [4078]

Joseph Kaplan Fund *(Graduate, Undergraduate/Scholarship)* [4726]

Lighthouse International Scholarships - Collegebound Awards *(High School, Undergraduate/Scholarship)* [5497]

Lighthouse International Scholarships - Graduate Awards *(Graduate/Scholarship)* [5498]

Lighthouse International Scholarships - Undergraduate Awards *(Undergraduate/Scholarship)* [5499]

MALSCE Scholarships *(Undergraduate/Scholarship)* [5660]

Massachusetts Federation of Polish Women's Clubs Scholarships *(Undergraduate/Scholarship)* [5299]

Newtonville Woman's Club Scholarships *(Undergraduate/Scholarship)* [4079]

"Nickels for Notes" Scholarships *(Undergraduate/Scholarship)* [4080]

Pennies for Art Scholarships *(Undergraduate/Scholarship)* [4081]

Catherine E. Philbin Scholarships *(Graduate, Undergraduate/Scholarship)* [4082]

Plumbing-Heating-Cooling Contractors Association Educational Foundation Massachusetts Auxiliary Scholarships *(Undergraduate/Scholarship)* [7346]

Portuguese American Police Association Scholarships *(Undergraduate/Scholarship)* [7380]

Prince Henry Society Scholarships *(Undergraduate/Scholarship)* [7433]

University of Lowell Bookstore Associates Scholarships *(Graduate, Undergraduate/Scholarship)* [4727]

Women's Italian Club of Boston Scholarships *(Undergraduate/Scholarship)* [4083]

Worcester District Medical Society Scholarship Fund *(Undergraduate/Scholarship)* [9746]

Yankee Clipper Contest Club, Inc. Youth Scholarships *(Undergraduate/Scholarship)* [1114]

Dr. Marie E. Zakrzewski Medical Scholarships *(Doctorate/Scholarship)* [5302]

Jacob Ziskind Memorial Fund for Upperclassmen *(Graduate, Undergraduate/Scholarship)* [4728]

Michigan

Altrusa International of Grand Rapids Scholarships *(Undergraduate/Scholarship)* [4270]

Earl I. Anderson Scholarships *(Undergraduate/Scholarship)* [1068]

Dr. Noyes L. Avery, Jr. & Ann E. Avery Scholarships *(Undergraduate/Scholarship)* [4271]

Bernice Barabash Sports Scholarships *(Undergraduate, Vocational/Occupational/Scholarship)* [5090]

Charles A. Bassett Endowed Memorial Scholarship Fund *(Undergraduate/Scholarship)* [4207]

Birmingham Student Scholarship Fund Association *(Undergraduate/Scholarship)* [2102]

Geraldine Geistert Boss Scholarships *(Undergraduate/Scholarship)* [4272]

MAC Louisa Bowen Memorial Scholarships for Graduate Students in Archival Administration *(Graduate/Scholarship)* [5854]

James W. Jr. and Jane T. Brown Scholarship Fund *(Undergraduate/Scholarship)* [4208]

Harry and Lucille Brown Scholarships *(Undergraduate/Scholarship)* [4273]

Calvin Alumni Association California- Bay Area Scholarships *(Undergraduate/Scholarship)* [2295]

Calvin Alumni Association-Iowa/Pella Scholarships *(Undergraduate/Scholarship)* [2299]

Calvin Alumni Association-Maryland/Baltimore Scholarships *(Undergraduate/Scholarship)* [2300]

Calvin Alumni Association-Michigan Lakeshore Scholarships *(Undergraduate/Scholarship)* [2301]

Calvin Alumni Association-Michigan, Lansing Scholarships *(Undergraduate/Scholarship)* [2302]

Calvin Alumni Association-New York, Rochester Scholarships *(Undergraduate/Scholarship)* [2304]

Calvin Alumni Association-Southeast Michigan Scholarships *(Undergraduate/Scholarship)* [2307]

Calvin Alumni Association-Southwest Michigan, Kalamazoo Scholarships *(Undergraduate/Scholarship)* [2310]

Calvin Alumni Association-Washington, Lynden Scholarships *(Undergraduate/Scholarship)* [2312]

Orrie & Dorothy Cassada Scholarships *(Undergraduate/Scholarship)* [4274]

Chapter 198 - Downriver Detroit Scholarships *(Graduate, Undergraduate/Scholarship)* [8373]

Chapter 311 - Tri City Scholarships *(Undergraduate/Scholarship)* [8376]

Geri Coccodrilli Culinary Scholarship Fund *(Undergraduate/Scholarship)* [4209]

Thomas D. Coffield Scholarships *(Undergraduate/Scholarship)* [4276]

Paul Collins Scholarships *(Undergraduate/Scholarship)* [4277]

Dake Community Manufacturing Scholarships *(Undergraduate/Scholarship)* [4210]

Antenore C. "Butch" Davanzo Scholarships *(Graduate, Undergraduate/Scholarship)* [5840]

Achille & Irene Despres, William & Andre Scholarships *(Undergraduate/Scholarship)* [4278]

Detroit Economic Club Scholarships *(Undergraduate/Scholarship)* [3197]

Chapter 116 - Kalamazoo - Roscoe Douglas Scholarships *(Undergraduate/Scholarship)* [8383]

E.V. Erickson Field of Interest Education Scholarship Fund *(Undergraduate/Scholarship)* [4211]

Melissa Eleonor Ernest Scholarships *(Undergraduate/Scholarship)* [5096]

Bertha M. Fase Memorial Scholarship Fund *(Undergraduate/Scholarship)* [4213]

Virginia Valk Fehsenfeld Scholarships *(Undergraduate/Scholarship)* [4279]

Floto-Peel Family Scholarship Fund *(Undergraduate, Vocational/Occupational/Scholarship)* [4215]

John and Victory E. Frantz Scholarship Fund *(Undergraduate/Scholarship)* [4216]

Melbourne & Alice E. Frontjes Scholarships *(Undergraduate/Scholarship)* [4280]

Carolyn Gallmeyer Scholarships *(Undergraduate/Scholarship)* [4281]

Mathilda & Carolyn Gallmeyer Scholarships *(Undergraduate/Scholarship)* [4282]

Gauthier Family Scholarship Fund *(Undergraduate/Scholarship)* [4217]

Gerber Foundation Merit Scholarships *(Undergraduate/Scholarship)* [4112]

Tom Gifford Scholarships *(Undergraduate/Scholarship)* [4218]

Grand Haven Offshore Challenge Scholarship Fund *(Undergraduate/Scholarship)* [4219]

Grand Rapids Scholarship Association *(Undergraduate/Scholarship)* [4283]

Philip F. Greco Memorial Scholarships *(Undergraduate/Scholarship)* [5560]

Katherine M. Grosscup Scholarships *(Graduate, Undergraduate/Scholarship)* [4042]

Guy D. & Mary Edith Halladay Graduate Scholarships *(Undergraduate/Scholarship)* [4284]

Guy D. & Mary Edith Halladay Music Scholarships *(Graduate, Undergraduate/Scholarship)* [4285]

John P. Hennessey Scholarships *(Graduate, Undergraduate/Scholarship)* [5841]

Michael Herman Memorial Scholarship Fund *(Undergraduate, Vocational/Occupational/Scholarship)* [4222]

Hierholzer-Fojtik Scholarship Fund *(Undergraduate/Scholarship)* [4223]

Wayne Hildebrant Police Scholarship Fund *(Undergraduate/Scholarship)* [5350]

Hoffman Family Scholarship Fund *(Undergraduate/Scholarship)* [4224]

Donald & Florence Hunting Scholarships *(Undergraduate/Scholarship)* [4286]

Jack Family Scholarships *(Undergraduate/Scholarship)* [4287]

Camilla C. Johnson Scholarships *(Undergraduate/Scholarship)* [4288]

Kellogg Company Career Scholarships *(Undergraduate/Scholarship)* [5234]

Seth Koehler Central High School Scholarship Fund *(Undergraduate, Vocational/Occupational/Scholarship)* [4225]

Lavina Laible Scholarships *(Undergraduate/Scholarship)* [4289]

Paul J. Laninga Memorial Scholarship Fund *(Undergraduate/Scholarship)* [4226]

Stephen Lankester Scholarships *(Undergraduate/Scholarship)* [4290]

Lapeer County Medical Scholarship Fund *(Undergraduate/Scholarship)* [5351]

Rick and Beverly Lattin Education Scholarship Fund *(Undergraduate/Scholarship)* [4227]

Law Student Diversity Scholarships *(Undergraduate/Scholarship)* [5814]

Jack W. Leatherman Family Scholarship Fund *(Graduate/Scholarship)* [4228]

Sherman L. & Mabel C. Lepard Scholarships *(Undergraduate/Scholarship)* [4291]

Pat and John MacTavish Scholarship Fund *(Undergraduate/Scholarship)* [4229]

John T. & Frances Maghielse Scholarships *(Undergraduate/Scholarship)* [4292]

Michigan Council of Women in Technology Undergraduate Scholarship Program *(Graduate, Undergraduate/Scholarship)* [5817]

Michigan Nurses Foundation Scholarships *(Doctorate, Undergraduate/Scholarship)* [5825]

Robert L. & Hilda Treasure Mitchell Scholarships *(Undergraduate/Scholarship)* [4294]

Kyle Moreland Memorial Endowment Scholarship Fund *(Undergraduate/Scholarship)* [4230]

NALS of Michigan Scholarships *(Undergraduate/Award)* [5979]

North Ottawa Hospital Auxiliary Scholarship Fund *(Undergraduate/Scholarship)* [4231]

Peggy Kommer Novosad Scholarships *(Graduate, Postgraduate/Scholarship)* [4295]

Patricia & Armen Oumedian Scholarships *(Undergraduate/Scholarship)* [4296]

Carl Parsell Scholarship Fund *(Undergraduate/Scholarship)* [5810]

Marvin R. and Pearl E. Patterson Family Scholarships Fund *(Undergraduate/Scholarship)* [4232]

P.E.O. Chapter Scholarship Fund (Undergraduate, Vocational/Occupational/Scholarship) [4233]

Jacob L. Reinecke Memorial Scholarship Fund (Undergraduate/Scholarship) [4235]

Daniel L. Reiss Memorial Scholarship Fund (Undergraduate/Scholarship) [4236]

Harold and Eleonor Ringelberg Scholarship Fund (Undergraduate/Scholarship) [4237]

Josephine Ringold Scholarships (Undergraduate/ Scholarship) [4297]

Charles and Eleonor Rycenga Education Scholarship Fund (Undergraduate/Scholarship) [4238]

Millicent M. Schaffner Endowed Memorial Scholarships (Undergraduate/Scholarship) [4239]

David and Ginny Schultz Family Scholarship Fund (Undergraduate/Scholarship) [4240]

Jeptha Wade Schureman Scholarship Program (Undergraduate/Scholarship) [3205]

David and Sharon Seaver Family Scholarship Fund (Undergraduate/Scholarship) [4241]

Margery J. Seeger Scholarships (Undergraduate/ Scholarship) [4298]

Ken and Sandy Sharkey Family Scholarship Fund (Undergraduate/Scholarship) [4242]

Marion A. and Ruth K. Sherwood Family Fund Engineering Scholarships (Undergraduate/ Scholarship) [4244]

Miller G. Sherwood Family Scholarship Fund (Undergraduate/Scholarship) [4245]

Sigma Kappa Foundation Michigan Scholarships (Undergraduate/Scholarship) [8186]

Hazel Simms Nursing Scholarships (Professional development/Scholarship) [5352]

Christine Soper Scholarships (Undergraduate/ Scholarship) [4300]

Dr. William E. & Norma Sprague Scholarships (Undergraduate/Scholarship) [4301]

Zachary Taylor Stevens Memorial Scholarships (Undergraduate/Scholarship) [1108]

Edward P. Suchecki Family Scholarship Fund (Undergraduate/Scholarship) [4246]

Henry D. and Ruth G. Swartz Family Scholarship Fund (Undergraduate/Scholarship) [4247]

Dorothy B. & Charles E. Thomas Scholarships (Undergraduate/Scholarship) [4302]

Dorothy J. Thurston Graduate Scholarships (Undergraduate/Scholarship) [4303]

Mildred E. Troske Music Scholarships (Undergraduate/Scholarship) [4304]

TRW Foundation Scholarships (Undergraduate/ Scholarship) [1951]

H. Wayne Van Agtmael Cosmetology Scholarship Fund (Undergraduate/Scholarship) [4248]

Keith C. Vanderhyde Scholarships (Undergraduate/Scholarship) [4305]

Jacob R. & Mary M. VanLoo & Lenore K. VanLoo Scholarships (Undergraduate/Scholarship) [4306]

Sue Walicki Nursing Scholarships (Undergraduate/Scholarship) [5109]

Warner Norcross & Judd LLP Minorty Scholarships (Undergraduate/Scholarship) [9483]

West Michigan Nursery and Landscape Association Scholarship Fund (Undergraduate/Scholarship) [4249]

Western Michigan Society of Health-System Pharmacists Scholarships (Undergraduate/Scholarship) [9577]

Elmo Wierenga Alumni Scholarships (Undergraduate/Scholarship) [4308]

Amos and Marilyn Winsand-Detroit Section Named Scholarships (Undergraduate/Scholarship) [1448]

Audrey L. Wright Scholarships (Undergraduate/ Scholarship) [4309]

Zenko Family Scholarship Fund (Undergraduate/ Scholarship) [4252]

Minnesota

Horatio Alger Minnesota Scholarships (Undergraduate/Scholarship) [309]

MAC Louisa Bowen Memorial Scholarships for Graduate Students in Archival Administration (Graduate/Scholarship) [5854]

Bush Artist Fellowships (All/Fellowship) [2217]

Gunnar Isberg Student Scholarships (Undergraduate/Scholarship) [5896]

The Jackson Club Scholarships (Undergraduate/ Scholarship) [3535]

Lakselaget Foundation Scholarships (Graduate, Undergraduate/Scholarship) [5320]

Lawton Minority Retention Grants (Undergraduate/ Scholarship) [9362]

Lilly Lorenzen Scholarships (Undergraduate/ Scholarship) [1400]

Many Voices Fellowships (Professional development/Fellowship) [7338]

McKnight Advancement Grants (Professional development/Grant) [7339]

McKnight Theater Artist Fellowships (Professional development/Fellowship) [7340]

Minneapolis Camp Scholarships (Undergraduate/ Scholarship) [5888]

Minnesota Association of Public Accountant Scholarships (Undergraduate/Scholarship) [5892]

Minnesota GLBT Educational Fund (Undergraduate/Scholarship) [7862]

Minnesota Health Information Management Association Scholarships (Undergraduate/Scholarship) [5898]

Minnesota Power Community Involvement Scholarships (Undergraduate/Scholarship) [3537]

Dale and Betty George Sola Scholarships (Undergraduate/Scholarship) [3545]

Upper Midwest Human Rights Fellowship Program (Professional development/Fellowship) [9246]

Mississippi

ARRLF Mississippi Scholarships (Undergraduate/ Scholarship) [1070]

Beacon of Hope Scholarships (Undergraduate/ Scholarship) [2035]

Gold Award/Eagle Scout Scholarships (Undergraduate/Scholarship) [6254]

Gulf Coast Hurricane Scholarships (Graduate, Undergraduate/Scholarship) [8449]

HSF/Nissan Community College Transfer Scholarship Program (Undergraduate/Scholarship) [4576]

Fred R. McDaniel Memorial Scholarships (Undergraduate/Scholarship) [1093]

MSCPA Undergraduate Scholarships (Undergraduate/Scholarship) [5910]

NAJA Scholarships (Graduate/Scholarship) [6086]

Ross/Nickey Scholarships and Gary E. Thornton Memorial Scholarships (Graduate/Scholarship) [5911]

Missouri

Horatio Alger Missouri Scholarships (Undergraduate/Scholarship) [310]

Paul Arnold Memorial Scholarships (Undergraduate/Scholarship) [7396]

Asian and Pacific Islander Queers Sisters Scholarships (Undergraduate/Scholarship) [7397]

Associates in Behavioral Health Scholarships (Graduate/Scholarship) [7398]

Barbara Bailey Scholarships (Undergraduate/ Scholarship) [7399]

Charly Baker and Heath Merriwether Memorial Scholarships (Undergraduate/Scholarship) [7400]

Bellevue PFLAG Scholarships (Undergraduate/ Scholarship) [7401]

Bill Bendiner and Doug Morgenson Scholarships (Undergraduate/Scholarship) [7402]

MAC Louisa Bowen Memorial Scholarships for Graduate Students in Archival Administration (Graduate/Scholarship) [5854]

Robert Browning Scholarships (Undergraduate/ Scholarship) [7403]

Deloris Carter Hampton Scholarships (Undergraduate/Scholarship) [7404]

Chapter 17 - St. Louis Scholarships (Undergraduate/Scholarship) [8372]

Cherokee Nation Graduate Scholarships (Graduate/Scholarship) [2742]

Cherokee Nation Scholarships (Undergraduate/ Scholarship) [2744]

Donald O. Coffman Scholarships (Undergraduate/ Scholarship) [7405]

Cole Family Scholarships (Undergraduate/Scholarship) [7406]

Dennis Coleman Choral Conducting Scholarships (Undergraduate/Scholarship) [7407]

Compassionate Care Scholarships (Undergraduate/Scholarship) [7408]

Brian M. Day Scholarships (Undergraduate/Scholarship) [7409]

Paul and Helen L. Grauer Scholarships (Undergraduate/Scholarship) [1087]

Kappa Delta Phi Scholarship Program (Postgraduate/Scholarship) [952]

Samuel C. Kraus, Jr. Memorial Scholarships (Undergraduate/Scholarship) [6534]

McFarffels Scholarships (Undergraduate/Scholarship) [7412]

Jack D. Motteler Scholarships (Undergraduate/ Scholarship) [7413]

MPTA Doctoral Scholarships (Doctorate/Scholarship) [5913]

NAJA Scholarships (Graduate/Scholarship) [6086]

Obrzut Ling Scholarships (Undergraduate, Vocational/Occupational/Scholarship) [7414]

Ray, NORP and Katie, WOKTE Pautz Scholarships (Undergraduate/Scholarship) [1098]

PHD ARA Scholarships (Doctorate, Undergraduate/Scholarship) [1100]

Political Leadership Scholarships (Undergraduate/ Scholarship) [7415]

Pride Foundation Regional Scholarships (Undergraduate/Scholarship) [7416]

Rosenberg-Ibarra Scholarships (Undergraduate/ Scholarship) [7419]

Social Work Scholarships (Undergraduate/Scholarship) [7420]

Kathy Spadoni Memorial Scholarships (Undergraduate/Scholarship) [7421]

Hatton W. Sumners Scholarships (Undergraduate/ Scholarship) [6869]

Ric Ulrich and Chuck Pischke Scholarships (Undergraduate/Scholarship) [7423]

Patricia Van Kirk Scholarships (Undergraduate/ Scholarship) [7424]

Wells Fargo Scholarships (Undergraduate/Scholarship) [7425]

James and Colin Lee Wozumi Scholarships (Undergraduate/Scholarship) [7427]

You Go Girl! Scholarships (Undergraduate/Scholarship) [7428]

Urashi Zen Scholarships (Undergraduate/Scholarship) [7429]

Montana

Horatio Alger Montana Scholarships (Undergraduate/Scholarship) [311]

Mary Lou Brown Scholarships (Undergraduate/ Scholarship) [1074]

EAA Tuition Scholarships (College, Vocational/ Occupational/Scholarship) [3647]

EAA Workshop Scholarships (College, Vocational/ Occupational/Scholarship) [3648]

Gold Country Section & Region II Scholarships (Graduate, Undergraduate/Scholarship) [1337]

Inland Northwest Business Alliance Scholarships (INBA) (Undergraduate/Scholarship) [7411]

Stephen T. Marchello Scholarships (Undergraduate/Scholarship) [5609]

The Cady McDonnell Memorial Scholarships (Undergraduate/Scholarship) [647]

Donald E. Pizzini Memorial Nurse Scholarships (Professional development/Scholarship) [5926]

Rocky Mountain Coal Mining Institute Engineering/Geology Scholarships (Undergraduate/ Scholarship) [7810]

Rocky Mountain Coal Mining Institute Technical Scholarships (Undergraduate, Vocational/Occupational/Scholarship) [7811]

Upper Midwest Human Rights Fellowship Program *(Professional development/Fellowship)* [9246]

Nebraska

Horatio Alger Ak-Sar-Ben Scholarships *(Undergraduate/Scholarship)* [297]

MAC Louisa Bowen Memorial Scholarships for Graduate Students in Archival Administration *(Graduate/Scholarship)* [5854]

Susan Thompson Buffett Foundation Scholarships *(Undergraduate/Scholarship)* [2205]

Karen Connick Memorial Scholarships *(Undergraduate/Scholarship)* [4257]

Doniphan Community Foundation Scholarships *(Undergraduate/Scholarship)* [4258]

Paul and Helen L. Grauer Scholarships *(Undergraduate/Scholarship)* [1087]

Nebraska Farm Bureau Young Farmers and Ranchers Greater Horizon Scholarships *(Undergraduate/Scholarship)* [6599]

Nebraska Paralegal Association Student Scholarships *(Undergraduate/Scholarship)* [6610]

Louise A. Nixon Scholarships *(Graduate/Scholarship)* [6608]

Ray, NORP and Katie, WOKTE Pautz Scholarships *(Undergraduate/Scholarship)* [1098]

PHD ARA Scholarships *(Doctorate, Undergraduate/Scholarship)* [1100]

Pleasantview Public Schools Fund *(Undergraduate/Scholarship)* [4261]

Hatton W. Sumners Scholarships *(Undergraduate/Scholarship)* [6869]

Nevada

AISC/Structural Steel Education Council Fellowships *(Graduate/Fellowship)* [875]

Aaron Edward Arnoldsen Memorial Scholarships *(Undergraduate/Scholarship)* [1620]

Fraser Family Scholarships *(Undergraduate/Scholarship)* [7490]

Glazing Industry Scholarships *(Undergraduate/Scholarship)* [7494]

Gold Country Section & Region II Scholarships *(Graduate, Undergraduate/Scholarship)* [1337]

HSBC-North America Scholarship Program *(Undergraduate/Scholarship)* [4571]

Michael Koizumi APWA Scholarships *(Undergraduate/Scholarship)* [1061]

Las Vegas Elks Scholarships for the Physically Challenged *(Undergraduate, Vocational/Occupational/Scholarship)* [7502]

Las Vegas Elks Scholarships *(Undergraduate, Vocational/Occupational/Scholarship)* [7501]

Melissa A. Lyles Memorial Scholarships *(Undergraduate/Scholarship)* [7503]

Aaron Matusek Memorial Scholarships *(Undergraduate/Scholarship)* [7506]

The Cady McDonnell Memorial Scholarships *(Undergraduate/Scholarship)* [647]

SON Scholarships *(Undergraduate/Scholarship)* [7899]

New Hampshire

Leon Bradley Scholarships *(Undergraduate/Scholarship)* [548]

Bruce Clement Post-Secondary Education Scholarships *(Undergraduate/Scholarship)* [6631]

Columbus Citizens Foundation College Scholarships *(Undergraduate/Scholarship)* [3012]

Foundation for Seacoast Health Scholarships *(Graduate, Undergraduate/Scholarship)* [3992]

Dr. James L. Lawson Memorial Scholarships *(Undergraduate/Scholarship)* [1092]

Lighthouse International Scholarships - College-bound Awards *(High School, Undergraduate/Scholarship)* [5497]

Lighthouse International Scholarships - Graduate Awards *(Graduate/Scholarship)* [5498]

Lighthouse International Scholarships - Undergraduate Awards *(Undergraduate/Scholarship)* [5499]

Rick Mahoney Scholarships *(Undergraduate/Scholarship)* [5714]

The Medallion Fund Scholarships *(Undergraduate,*

Vocational/Occupational/Scholarship) [6629]

New England FEMARA Scholarships *(Undergraduate/Scholarship)* [1096]

NHSCPA Scholarships *(Graduate, Undergraduate/Scholarship)* [6635]

Johnny Trombly Scholarships *(Undergraduate/Scholarship)* [5919]

Yankee Clipper Contest Club, Inc. Youth Scholarships *(Undergraduate/Scholarship)* [1114]

New Jersey

A&WMA NCNJ Chapter Scholarships *(Graduate, Undergraduate/Scholarship)* [118]

Benjamin Asbell Memorial Scholarships *(Undergraduate/Scholarship)* [2315]

Leon Bradley Scholarships *(Undergraduate/Scholarship)* [548]

Armen H. Bululian Scholarships *(Undergraduate/Scholarship)* [1588]

Calvin Alumni Association-New Jersey Scholarships *(Undergraduate/Scholarship)* [2303]

CentraState Associated Auxiliaries Scholarships *(Undergraduate/Scholarship)* [2723]

Columbus Citizens Foundation College Scholarships *(Undergraduate/Scholarship)* [3012]

Constantinople Armenian Relief Society Scholarships (CARS) *(Undergraduate/Scholarship)* [1589]

Hon. Joseph W. Cowgill Memorial Scholarships *(Undergraduate/Scholarship)* [2316]

DuBois Brothers Scholarships *(Undergraduate/Scholarship)* [2318]

Christine H. Eide Memorial Scholarships *(Graduate, Undergraduate/Scholarship)* [5496]

Gallo Blue Chip Scholarships *(Undergraduate/Scholarship)* [4398]

Vincent S. Haneman-Joseph B. Perskie Memorial Foundation Scholarships *(Graduate, Undergraduate/Scholarship)* [1924]

HRET Health Career Scholarships *(Graduate, Undergraduate/Scholarship)* [6644]

HSBC-North America Scholarship Program *(Undergraduate/Scholarship)* [4571]

HSF/Nissan Community College Transfer Scholarship Program *(Undergraduate/Scholarship)* [4576]

Bernadine Johnson-Marshall and Martha Bell Williams Scholarships *(Undergraduate/Award)* [1718]

Les Dames D'Escoffier New York Scholarships *(Undergraduate/Scholarship)* [5405]

Lighthouse International Scholarships - College-bound Awards *(High School, Undergraduate/Scholarship)* [5497]

Lighthouse International Scholarships - Graduate Awards *(Graduate/Scholarship)* [5498]

Lighthouse International Scholarships - Undergraduate Awards *(Undergraduate/Scholarship)* [5499]

Sonia S. Maguire Outstanding Scholastic Achievement Awards *(Graduate, Undergraduate/Scholarship)* [8782]

New Jersey Association of Osteopathic Physicians and Surgeons Scholarships *(Undergraduate/Scholarship)* [6637]

New York Women in Communications, Inc. Foundation Scholarships *(Graduate, Undergraduate/Scholarship)* [6690]

NJCBIR Programmatic Multi-Investigator Project Grants *(Professional development/Grant)* [6642]

NJSCPA College Scholarships *(Graduate, Undergraduate/Scholarship)* [6657]

NJSCPA High School Scholarships *(Undergraduate/Scholarship)* [6658]

Pellegrini Scholarships *(Graduate, Undergraduate, Vocational/Occupational/Scholarship)* [8784]

Louis C. Portella Memorial Scholarships *(Graduate/Scholarship)* [2321]

Jerrothia Allenfonzo Riggs & Anna & Dorothy Mae Barnes Scholarships *(Undergraduate/Scholarship)* [2339]

Ann S. Salsberg Scholarship Awards *(Undergraduate/Award, Scholarship)* [2323]

Star-Ledger Scholarships for the Performing Arts

(Undergraduate/Scholarship) [6649]

Walter W. Stillman Scholarships *(Undergraduate/Scholarship)* [1950]

Jay A. Strassberg Memorial Scholarships *(Undergraduate/Scholarship)* [2324]

Madlyn D. Thompson Memorial Scholarships *(Undergraduate/Scholarship)* [2340]

Daniel B. Toll Memorial Scholarships *(Undergraduate/Scholarship)* [2325]

Bruce A. Wallace Memorial Scholarships *(Undergraduate/Scholarship)* [2327]

Zimmermann Scholarships *(Graduate/Scholarship)* [8785]

New Mexico

Walt Bartram Memorial Education Award, Region 12 and Chapter 119 *(Undergraduate/Scholarship)* [8369]

Chapter 93 - Albuquerque Scholarships *(Undergraduate/Scholarship)* [8381]

Albuquerque ARC/Toby Cross Scholarships *(Undergraduate/Scholarship)* [1082]

Excel Staffing Companies Scholarships for Excellence in Continuing Education *(Undergraduate/Scholarship)* [280]

Gold Country Section & Region II Scholarships *(Graduate, Undergraduate/Scholarship)* [1337]

Lone Star GIA Associate and Alumni Scholarships *(Undergraduate/Scholarship)* [4064]

Fred R. McDaniel Memorial Scholarships *(Undergraduate/Scholarship)* [1093]

The Cady McDonnell Memorial Scholarships *(Undergraduate/Scholarship)* [647]

New Mexico Manufactured Housing Association Scholarship Program *(Undergraduate/Scholarship)* [281]

Rocky Mountain Coal Mining Institute Engineering/Geology Scholarships *(Undergraduate/Scholarship)* [7810]

Rocky Mountain Coal Mining Institute Technical Scholarships *(Undergraduate, Vocational/Occupational/Scholarship)* [7811]

Hatton W. Sumners Scholarships *(Undergraduate/Scholarship)* [6869]

New York

Advertising Production Club Scholarship Awards *(Graduate, Undergraduate/Scholarship)* [59]

APC Tuition-Assist Scholarship Awards *(Graduate, Undergraduate/Scholarship)* [60]

Leon Bradley Scholarships *(Undergraduate/Scholarship)* [548]

Henry Broughton, K2AE Memorial Scholarships *(Undergraduate/Scholarship)* [1073]

Calvin Alumni Association-New Jersey Scholarships *(Undergraduate/Scholarship)* [2303]

Columbian Lawyers Association of Westchester County Scholarships *(Undergraduate/Scholarship)* [3009]

Columbus Citizens Foundation College Scholarships *(Undergraduate/Scholarship)* [3012]

Constantinople Armenian Relief Society Scholarships (CARS) *(Undergraduate/Scholarship)* [1589]

Christine H. Eide Memorial Scholarships *(Graduate, Undergraduate/Scholarship)* [5496]

Gallo Blue Chip Scholarships *(Undergraduate/Scholarship)* [4398]

Joseph H. Gellert/Dutchess County Bar Association Scholarships *(Undergraduate/Scholarship)* [3555]

HSBC-North America Scholarship Program *(Undergraduate/Scholarship)* [4571]

HSF/Citi Fellows Program *(Undergraduate/Scholarship)* [4573]

HSF/Nissan Community College Transfer Scholarship Program *(Undergraduate/Scholarship)* [4576]

Bryan L. Knapp Point Scholarships *(Graduate, Undergraduate/Scholarship)* [7364]

Dr. James L. Lawson Memorial Scholarships *(Undergraduate/Scholarship)* [1092]

Les Dames D'Escoffier New York Scholarships *(Undergraduate/Scholarship)* [5405]

Lighthouse International Scholarships - College-bound Awards (*High School, Undergraduate/Scholarship*) [5497]

Lighthouse International Scholarships - Graduate Awards (*Graduate/Scholarship*) [5498]

Lighthouse International Scholarships - Undergraduate Awards (*Undergraduate/Scholarship*) [5499]

Sonia S. Maguire Outstanding Scholastic Achievement Awards (*Graduate, Undergraduate/Scholarship*) [8782]

New York State Association of Agricultural Fairs Scholarships (*Undergraduate/Scholarship*) [6671]

New York Women in Communications, Inc. Foundation Scholarships (*Graduate, Undergraduate/Scholarship*) [6690]

NYSSCPA - FAE Excellence in Accounting Scholarships (*Undergraduate/Scholarship*) [6683]

Faith E. O'Neal Scholarships (*Undergraduate/Scholarship*) [7558]

Victoria Ovis Memorial Scholarships (*Undergraduate/Scholarship*) [6387]

Pellegrini Scholarships (*Graduate, Undergraduate, Vocational/Occupational/Scholarship*) [8784]

PGSF-GATF Scholarships (*Graduate, Undergraduate/Scholarship*) [61]

Harry B. Pulver Scholarships (*Undergraduate/Scholarship*) [4164]

Saint Andrews Scholarships (*Undergraduate/Scholarship*) [7882]

Saratoga County Bar Association Law Student Scholarships (*All/Scholarship*) [7989]

Scholarships for Emigres in the Health Sciences (*Undergraduate/Scholarship*) [5157]

Norman E. Strohmeier, W2VRS Memorial Scholarships (*Undergraduate/Scholarship*) [1110]

Albert E. Wischmeyer Memorial Scholarships (*Undergraduate/Scholarship*) [8406]

Yankee Clipper Contest Club, Inc. Youth Scholarships (*Undergraduate/Scholarship*) [1114]

Zimmermann Scholarships (*Graduate/Scholarship*) [8785]

Lorraine Zitone Memorial Scholarship Fund (*Undergraduate/Scholarship*) [3451]

North Carolina

Henry S. and Carolyn Adams Scholarship Fund (*Undergraduate/Scholarship*) [3880]

African American Network - Carolinas Scholarship Fund (*Undergraduate/Scholarship*) [3882]

William Tasse Alexander Scholarship Fund (*Undergraduate/Scholarship*) [3883]

Andersen Nontraditional Scholarships for Women's Education and Retraining (*Undergraduate/Scholarship*) [3884]

AT&T Business Internship Awards (*Postgraduate/Internship*) [9257]

Pete and Ellen Bensley Memorial Scholarship Fund (*Undergraduate/Scholarship*) [3886]

Sam L. Booke, Sr. Scholarships (*Undergraduate/Scholarship*) [9626]

Tien Bui Memorial Scholarships (*Undergraduate/Scholarship*) [9627]

Wes Burton Memorial Scholarships (*Undergraduate/Scholarship*) [9628]

Kasie Ford Capling Memorial Scholarship Endowment Fund (*Undergraduate/Scholarship*) [3890]

William F. Carl Scholarships (*Undergraduate, Vocational/Occupational/Scholarship*) [6771]

Julian E. Carnes Scholarship Fund (*Undergraduate/Scholarship*) [3891]

Carolina Panthers Scholarship Fund (*Graduate/Scholarship*) [3892]

Carolina's Gay & Lesbian Scholarships (*Undergraduate/Scholarship*) [7846]

Charlotte Housing Authority Scholarship Fund (CHASF) (*Undergraduate, Vocational/Occupational/Scholarship*) [3894]

Charlotte-Mecklenburg Schools Scholarship Incentive Program (*Undergraduate/Scholarship*) [3895]

Children's Scholarship Fund of Charlotte (*Undergraduate/Scholarship*) [3896]

Andrew Blake Clark Memorial Scholarships (*Undergraduate/Scholarship*) [9629]

Cole Foundation Undergraduate Scholarship Program (*Undergraduate/Scholarship*) [3898]

Sally Cole Visual Arts Scholarship Fund (*Undergraduate/Scholarship*) [3899]

Reuben R. Cowles Youth Awards (*Undergraduate/Award*) [885]

Crowder Scholarships (*Undergraduate/Scholarship*) [9631]

Serena D. Dalton Scholarships (*Undergraduate/Scholarship*) [9633]

James Davis Scholarships (*Undergraduate/Scholarship*) [9267]

The E.R. and Lilian B. Dimmette Scholarship Fund (*Undergraduate/Scholarship*) [3902]

Jack Ervin EDI Scholarships (*Professional development/Scholarship*) [6761]

Forsyth County Nursing Scholarships (*Undergraduate/Scholarship*) [9636]

Golden Corral Scholarships (*Undergraduate/Scholarship*) [6773]

L. Gordon, Jr. and June D. Pfefferkorn Scholarships (*Undergraduate/Scholarship*) [9640]

Governor James E. Holshouser Professional Development Scholarships (*Professional development/Scholarship*) [6762]

Hughes Memorial Foundation Scholarships (*Graduate/Scholarship*) [4625]

IFH Foodservice Distribution Scholarships (*Undergraduate/Scholarship*) [6774]

Edward Jackson International Scholarships (*Undergraduate/Scholarship*) [9281]

Oliver Joel and Ellen Pell Denny Healthcare Scholarship Fund (*Undergraduate/Scholarship*) [9642]

James V. Johnson Scholarship Fund (*Undergraduate/Scholarship*) [3908]

Stella B. Johnson Scholarships (*Undergraduate/Scholarship*) [9643]

Annabel Lambeth Jones Scholarships (*Undergraduate/Scholarship*) [3909]

K & W Cafeterias Scholarships (*Undergraduate/Scholarship*) [6775]

Glenn Keever Scholarships (*Undergraduate/Scholarship*) [9284]

Mary and Millard Kiker Scholarships (*Undergraduate/Scholarship*) [3910]

Douglas Gray Kimel Scholarships (*Undergraduate/Scholarship*) [9644]

Lighthouse International Scholarships - College-bound Awards (*High School, Undergraduate/Scholarship*) [5497]

Lighthouse International Scholarships - Graduate Awards (*Graduate/Scholarship*) [5498]

Lighthouse International Scholarships - Undergraduate Awards (*Undergraduate/Scholarship*) [5499]

L.D. and Elsie Long Memorial Scholarships (*Graduate/Scholarship*) [9646]

Carolina Panthers Players Sam Mills Memorial Scholarship Fund (*Undergraduate/Scholarship*) [3914]

Minority Presence Grant Program for Doctoral Study (*Doctorate, Graduate/Grant*) [9295]

N.W. Mitchell-Piedmont Federal Savings and Loans Endowed Scholarships (*Undergraduate/Scholarship*) [9647]

Dr. Blanca Moore-Velez Woman of Substance Scholarships (*Undergraduate/Scholarship*) [6094]

NC Hospitality Education Foundation Scholarships - Four Year College or University (*Undergraduate/Scholarship*) [6776]

NC Hospitality Education Foundation Scholarships - Graduate (*Graduate/Scholarship*) [6777]

NC Hospitality Education Foundation Scholarships - High School (*Undergraduate, Vocational/Occupational/Scholarship*) [6778]

NC Hospitality Education Foundation Scholarships - Two Year Community or Junior College (*Undergraduate/Scholarship*) [6779]

North Carolina CPA Foundation Scholarships (*Undergraduate/Scholarship*) [6752]

North Carolina Heroes Fund Scholarships (*All/Scholarship*) [6767]

North Carolina League for Nursing Academic

Scholarships (*Graduate/Scholarship*) [3915]

Orthopaedic Specialists Nursing Scholarships (*Undergraduate/Scholarship*) [9648]

Ted H. Ousley Scholarship Fund (*Undergraduate/Scholarship*) [3917]

Outstanding Minority Accounting Student Scholarships (*All/Scholarship*) [6753]

William H. and Lena M. Petree Scholarships (*Undergraduate/Scholarship*) [9650]

Pfafftown Jaycees/Lynn Canada Memorial Scholarships (*Undergraduate/Scholarship*) [9651]

John S. and Jacqueline P. Rider Scholarships (*Undergraduate/Scholarship*) [9652]

Ben Robinette Scholarship Endowment Fund (*Undergraduate/Scholarship*) [3919]

Rotary Public Safety Scholarships (*Undergraduate/Scholarship*) [3920]

Ray and Pearl Sams Scholarships (*Undergraduate/Scholarship*) [9653]

Tom Shown Scholarships (*Undergraduate/Scholarship*) [9655]

The Dan Stewart Scholarships (*Professional development/Scholarship*) [6763]

Mary Stewart and William T. Covington, Jr. Scholarship Fund (*Undergraduate/Scholarship*) [3923]

Charles H. Stone Scholarships (*Undergraduate/Scholarship*) [559]

Stultz Scholarships (*Undergraduate/Scholarship*) [9656]

Virginia Elizabeth and Alma Vane Taylor Student Nurse Scholarships (*Undergraduate/Scholarship*) [9657]

Turner Family Scholarships (*Undergraduate, Vocational/Occupational/Scholarship*) [3925]

Nell and Spencer Waggoner Scholarships (*Undergraduate/Scholarship*) [9659]

Gary Wagner, K3OMI Scholarships (*Undergraduate/Scholarship*) [1111]

Laramie Walden Memorial Fund (*Undergraduate/Scholarship*) [3927]

Art and Dannie Weber Scholarships (*Undergraduate/Scholarship*) [9660]

David Julian Wichard Scholarships (*Undergraduate/Scholarship*) [9309]

L. Phil Wicker Scholarships (*Undergraduate/Scholarship*) [1113]

The Wilmore Scholarship Fund (*Undergraduate, Vocational/Occupational/Scholarship*) [3929]

Ted C. Wilson Memorial Scholarships (*Undergraduate/Scholarship*) [7441]

Mary and Elliot Wood Foundation Undergraduate Scholarship Fund (*Undergraduate/Scholarship*) [3931]

WTVD Endowment Scholarships (*Undergraduate/Scholarship*) [9312]

North Dakota

Horatio Alger North Dakota Scholarships (*Undergraduate/Scholarship*) [313]

MAC Louisa Bowen Memorial Scholarships for Graduate Students in Archival Administration (*Graduate/Scholarship*) [5854]

Bush Artist Fellowships (*All/Fellowship*) [2217]

North Dakota Veterinary Medical Association Scholarships (*Undergraduate/Scholarship*) [6791]

Rocky Mountain Coal Mining Institute Engineering/Geology Scholarships (*Undergraduate/Scholarship*) [7810]

Rocky Mountain Coal Mining Institute Technical Scholarships (*Undergraduate, Vocational/Occupational/Scholarship*) [7811]

Upper Midwest Human Rights Fellowship Program (*Professional development/Fellowship*) [9246]

Dr. William "Tim" Whalen Memorial Scholarships (*Undergraduate/Scholarship*) [6792]

Ohio

American Advertising Federation-Cleveland College Scholarships (*Undergraduate/Scholarship*) [402]

American Guild of Organists, Canton Chapter

Charitable Fund (Undergraduate/Scholarship) [8656]

Ora E. Anderson Scholarships (Undergraduate/Scholarship) [3875]

CSF Michael Bany Memorial Scholarships (Undergraduate/Scholarship) [2793]

CSF Walter and Marilyn Bartlett Scholarships (Undergraduate/Scholarship) [2794]

CSF Johnny Bench Scholarships (Undergraduate/Scholarship) [2795]

MAC Louisa Bowen Memorial Scholarships for Graduate Students in Archival Administration (Graduate/Scholarship) [5854]

CSF M. and E. Brown Scholarships (Undergraduate/Scholarship) [2796]

Harry D. Callahan Educational Trust (Undergraduate/Scholarship) [8659]

CSF Eugene Carroll Scholarships (Undergraduate/Scholarship) [2797]

George H. and Anna Casper Fund (Undergraduate/Scholarship) [8660]

CFT/ACPSOP Scholarships (Undergraduate/Scholarship) [2798]

CSF T.L. Conlan Memorial Scholarships (Undergraduate/Scholarship) [2800]

Dave Couch Memorial Scholarships (Undergraduate/Scholarship) [7067]

CSF Ach Family Scholarships (Undergraduate/Scholarship) [2801]

CSF Barr Foundation Scholarships (Undergraduate/Scholarship) [2802]

CSF Barrett Family Scholarships (Undergraduate/Scholarship) [2803]

CSF Bigg's/Curtis Breeden Scholarships (Undergraduate/Scholarship) [2804]

CSF Borden Inc. Scholarships (Undergraduate/Scholarship) [2805]

CSF Castellini Foundation Scholarships (Undergraduate/Scholarship) [2806]

CSF Cincinnati Bell Scholarships (Undergraduate/Scholarship) [2807]

CSF Cincinnati Financial Corporation Scholarships (Undergraduate/Scholarship) [2808]

CSF Cincinnati Milacron Scholarships (Undergraduate/Scholarship) [2809]

CSF Crosset Family Scholarships (Undergraduate/Scholarship) [2810]

CSF Dater Foundation Scholarships (Undergraduate/Scholarship) [2811]

CSF Duke Energy Scholarships (Undergraduate/Scholarship) [2812]

CSF Farmer Family Foundation Scholarships (Undergraduate/Scholarship) [2813]

CSF Fifth Third Bank Combined Scholarships (Undergraduate/Scholarship) [2814]

CSF Fletemeyer Family Scholarships (Undergraduate/Scholarship) [2815]

CSF Gardner Foundation Scholarships (Undergraduate/Scholarship) [2816]

CSF G.E. Aircraft Engines Scholarships (Undergraduate/Scholarship) [2817]

CSF Goldman, Sachs and Company Scholarships (Undergraduate/Scholarship) [2818]

CSF Greater Cincinnati Scholarships Association (Undergraduate/Scholarship) [2819]

CSF Heidelberg Distributing Co. Scholarships (Undergraduate/Scholarship) [2820]

CSF Heinz Pet Products Scholarships (Undergraduate/Scholarship) [2821]

CSF Juilfs Foundation Scholarships (Undergraduate/Scholarship) [2822]

CSF Kroger Cincinnati/Dayton Scholarships (Undergraduate/Scholarship) [2823]

CSF Lazarus/Federated Scholarships (Undergraduate/Scholarship) [2824]

CSF McCall Educational Scholarships (Undergraduate/Scholarship) [2825]

CSF Midland Company Scholarships (Undergraduate/Scholarship) [2826]

CSF Nethercott Family Scholarships (Undergraduate/Scholarship) [2827]

CSF Ohio National Foundation Scholarships (Undergraduate/Scholarship) [2828]

CSF Pepper Family Scholarships (Undergraduate/Scholarship) [2829]

CSF Pichler Family Scholarships (Undergraduate/Scholarship) [2830]

CSF PNC Bank Scholarships (Undergraduate/Scholarship) [2831]

CSF Procter and Gamble Scholarships (Undergraduate/Scholarship) [2832]

CSF SC Johnson, A Family Company Scholarships (Undergraduate/Scholarship) [2833]

CSF Scripps Headliners Scholarships (Undergraduate/Scholarship) [2834]

CSF Semple Foundation Scholarships (Undergraduate/Scholarship) [2835]

CSF Union Central 135th Anniversary Scholarships (Undergraduate/Scholarship) [2836]

CSF U.S. Bank N.A. Scholarships (Undergraduate/Scholarship) [2837]

CSF Western-Southern Foundation Scholarships (Undergraduate/Scholarship) [2838]

CSF Woodward Trustees Scholarships (Undergraduate/Scholarship) [2839]

CSF Wynne Family Memorial Scholarships (Undergraduate/Scholarship) [2840]

CSF Estelle Davis Memorial Scholarships (Undergraduate/Scholarship) [2841]

Rob Digiacomo Scholarship Fund (Undergraduate/Scholarship) [8663]

CSF Thomas J. Emery Memorial Scholarships (Undergraduate/Scholarship) [2842]

CSF Lyle and Arlene Everingham Scholarships (Undergraduate/Scholarship) [2844]

CSF Lyle Everingham Scholarships (Undergraduate/Scholarship) [2843]

Fine Arts Association Minority Scholarships (Undergraduate/Scholarship) [3749]

Fine Arts Association United Way Scholarships (Undergraduate/Scholarship) [3750]

Alice J. Foit Scholarships (Undergraduate/Scholarship) [8666]

CSF William A. Friedlander Scholarships (Undergraduate/Scholarship) [2845]

CSF Priscilla Gamble Scholarships (Undergraduate/Scholarship) [2846]

David A. and Pamela A. Gault Charitable Fund (Undergraduate/Scholarship) [8668]

Laverne L. Gibson Memorial Scholarships (Undergraduate/Scholarship) [7077]

Zelma Gray Medical School Scholarships (Doctorate/Fellowship) [3876]

Katherine M. Grosscup Scholarships (Graduate, Undergraduate/Scholarship) [4042]

CSF Richard Heekin Scholarships (Undergraduate/Scholarship) [2847]

CSF Dwight Hibbard Scholarships (Undergraduate/Scholarship) [2848]

CSF Florette B. Hoffheimer Scholarships (Undergraduate/Scholarship) [2849]

CSF Roger and Joyce Howe Family Scholarships (Undergraduate/Scholarship) [2850]

Virginia C. Jack and Ralph L. Jack Scholarships (Undergraduate, Vocational/Occupational/Scholarship) [8677]

CSF Ella Wilson Johnson Scholarships (Undergraduate/Scholarship) [2851]

CSF David J. Joseph Company Scholarships (Undergraduate/Scholarship) [2852]

CSF M. Kantor and Brothers Scholarships (Undergraduate/Scholarship) [2853]

Kappa Delta Phi Scholarship Program (Postgraduate/Scholarship) [952]

CSF Raymond and Augusta Klink Scholarships (Undergraduate/Scholarship) [2854]

CSF Bob and Linda Kohlhepp Scholarships (Undergraduate/Scholarship) [2855]

Samuel Krugliak Legal Scholarship Fund (Undergraduate/Scholarship) [8682]

Lake Dollars for Scholars Endowment Fund (Undergraduate, Vocational/Occupational/Scholarship) [8683]

Marvin Lewis Scholarships (Undergraduate/Scholarship) [5471]

CSF Carl H. Lindner Family Scholarships (Undergraduate/Scholarship) [2856]

Lillian Grace Mahan Scholarship Fund (Graduate/Scholarship) [8685]

Manzer-Keener-Wefler Scholarships (Undergraduate/Scholarship) [8686]

Sanders J. Mestel Legal Scholarship Fund (Undergraduate/Scholarship) [8689]

Harry Mestel Memorial Accounting Scholarship Fund (Undergraduate/Scholarship) [8690]

David W. Misek, N8NPX Memorial Scholarships (Undergraduate/Scholarship) [1095]

Lt. Colonel Robert G. Moreland Vocational/Technical Fund (Undergraduate, Vocational/Occupational/Scholarship) [8692]

Anthony Munoz Scholarships (Undergraduate/Scholarship) [5948]

CSF Corwin Nixon Scholarships (Undergraduate/Scholarship) [2857]

Ohio Association of Broadcasters Scholarships (Undergraduate/Scholarship) [6853]

Ohio Valley Chapter Scholarships (Undergraduate/Scholarship) [1815]

O'Jays Scholarship Fund (Undergraduate, Vocational/Occupational/Scholarship) [8694]

Perry Township School Memorial Scholarship Fund (Undergraduate/Scholarship) [8695]

CSF Charles and Claire Phillips Scholarships (Undergraduate/Scholarship) [2858]

CSF George and Amy Polley Scholarships (Undergraduate/Scholarship) [2859]

Thomas W. Porter, W8KYZ Scholarships Honoring Michael Daugherty, W8LSE (Undergraduate/Scholarship) [1101]

CSF Marvin Rammelsberg Memorial Scholarships (Undergraduate/Scholarship) [2860]

CSF Robert H. Reakirt Foundation Scholarships (Undergraduate/Scholarship) [2861]

Reid Hospital Graduate Student Scholarships (Graduate/Scholarship) [9557]

CSF William J. Rielly/MCURC Scholarships (Undergraduate/Scholarship) [2862]

CSF Mary Roberts Scholarships (Undergraduate/Scholarship) [2863]

Thomas Warren Roberts Scholarships (Undergraduate/Scholarship) [7107]

St. Joseph's Hospital School of Nursing Alumnae Scholarships (Undergraduate/Scholarship) [7112]

CSF Charlotte R. Schmidlapp Scholarships (Undergraduate/Scholarship) [2864]

CSF H.C. Schott Foundation Scholarships (Undergraduate/Scholarship) [2865]

CSF Nelson Schwab Jr. Family Scholarships (Undergraduate/Scholarship) [2866]

Stephen Schwartz Musical Theatre Scholarships (Undergraduate/Scholarship) [4630]

CSF Judge Benjamin Schwartz Scholarships (Undergraduate/Scholarship) [2867]

CSF E.W. Scripps Scholarships (Undergraduate/Scholarship) [2868]

CSF S. David Shor Scholarships (Undergraduate/Scholarship) [2869]

Don and Madalyn Sickafoose Educational Trust (Undergraduate/Scholarship) [8698]

CSF Lowe Simpson Scholarships (Undergraduate/Scholarship) [2870]

CSF Frank Foster Skillman Scholarships (Undergraduate/Scholarship) [2871]

SSOC Scholarships (Undergraduate/Scholarship) [8014]

Stark County Bar Association Fund (Undergraduate/Scholarship) [8700]

Stark County Dairy Promoters Scholarships (Undergraduate/Scholarship) [8701]

CSF Helen Steiner Rice Scholarships (Undergraduate/Scholarship) [2872]

CSF Joseph S. Stern, Jr. Scholarships (Undergraduate/Scholarship) [2873]

Zachary Taylor Stevens Memorial Scholarships (Undergraduate/Scholarship) [1108]

Jeffery Tyler Sweitzer Wrestling Memorial Scholarship Fund (Undergraduate/Scholarship) [8702]

CSF Martha W. Tanner Memorial Scholarships (Undergraduate/Scholarship) [2874]

CSF Christopher Todd Grant Memorial Scholarships (Undergraduate/Scholarship) [2875]

CSF Dee Wacksman Memorial Scholarships (Undergraduate/Scholarship) [2876]

Lester and Eleanor Webster Charitable Trust Fund (Undergraduate/Scholarship) [8707]

Western Reserve Herb Society Scholarships (Un-

ships *(Undergraduate/Scholarship)* [1114]
Zimmermann Scholarships *(Graduate/Scholarship)* [8785]

Rhode Island

Adler Pollock & Sheehan Diversity Scholarships *(Undergraduate/Scholarship)* [50]
Bach Organ and Keyboard Music Scholarships *(Undergraduate/Scholarship)* [7786]
Thomas F. Black, Jr. Memorial Scholarships *(Undergraduate/Scholarship)* [7784]
Leon Bradley Scholarships *(Undergraduate/Scholarship)* [548]
Antonio Cirino Memorial Art Education Fellowships *(Undergraduate/Fellowship)* [7787]
Columbus Citizens Foundation College Scholarships *(Undergraduate/Scholarship)* [3012]
Constant Memorial Scholarship for Aquidneck Island Resident *(Undergraduate/Scholarship)* [7788]
Edward Leon Duhamel Freemasons Scholarships *(Undergraduate/Scholarship)* [7789]
GFWC Women's Club of South County Scholarships *(Undergraduate/Scholarship)* [7790]
Rhode Island Commission on Women/Freda H. Goldman Education Awards *(Undergraduate/Award)* [7791]
Dr. James L. Lawson Memorial Scholarships *(Undergraduate/Scholarship)* [1092]
Lighthouse International Scholarships - College-bound Awards *(High School, Undergraduate/Scholarship)* [5497]
Lighthouse International Scholarships - Graduate Awards *(Graduate/Scholarship)* [5498]
Lighthouse International Scholarships - Undergraduate Awards *(Undergraduate/Scholarship)* [5499]
New England FEMARA Scholarships *(Undergraduate/Scholarship)* [1096]
Rhode Island Association of Former Legislators Scholarships *(Undergraduate/Scholarship)* [7793]
Lily and Catello Sorrentino Memorial Scholarships *(Undergraduate/Scholarship)* [7794]
Bruce and Marjorie Sundlun Scholarships *(Undergraduate/Scholarship)* [7795]
Patricia Tillinghast Memorial Scholarships *(Graduate, Undergraduate/Scholarship)* [879]
Marilyn Graboys Wool Scholarships *(Undergraduate/Scholarship)* [7796]
Yankee Clipper Contest Club, Inc. Youth Scholarships *(Undergraduate/Scholarship)* [1114]

South Carolina

African American Network - Carolinas Scholarship Fund *(Undergraduate/Scholarship)* [3882]
Andersen Nontraditional Scholarships for Women's Education and Retraining *(Undergraduate/Scholarship)* [3884]
Julian E. Carnes Scholarship Fund *(Undergraduate/Scholarship)* [3891]
Carolina Panthers Scholarship Fund *(Graduate/Scholarship)* [3892]
Carolina's Gay & Lesbian Scholarships *(Undergraduate/Scholarship)* [7846]
Reuben R. Cowles Youth Awards *(Undergraduate/Award)* [885]
Judy Crocker Memorial Scholarship Fund *(Undergraduate/Scholarship)* [3900]
Howard B. Higgins South Carolina Dental Scholarships *(Undergraduate/Scholarship)* [3906]
Wilbert L. and Zora F. Holmes Scholarship Endowment Fund *(Undergraduate, Vocational/Occupational/Scholarship)* [3907]
Lighthouse International Scholarships - College-bound Awards *(High School, Undergraduate/Scholarship)* [5497]
Lighthouse International Scholarships - Graduate Awards *(Graduate/Scholarship)* [5498]
Lighthouse International Scholarships - Undergraduate Awards *(Undergraduate/Scholarship)* [5499]
Carolina Panthers Players Sam Mills Memorial

Scholarship Fund *(Undergraduate/Scholarship)* [3914]
Henry DeWitt Plyler Scholarship Fund *(Undergraduate/Scholarship)* [3918]
SCACPA Educational Foundation Scholarships *(Graduate, Undergraduate/Scholarship)* [8542]
SCLEOA Scholarships *(Undergraduate/Scholarship)* [8547]
South Carolina Association for Financial Professionals College Education Scholarships *(Undergraduate/Scholarship)* [8545]
Charles H. Stone Scholarships *(Undergraduate/Scholarship)* [559]
Watson-Brown Scholarships *(Undergraduate/Scholarship)* [9540]
L. Phil Wicker Scholarships *(Undergraduate/Scholarship)* [1113]
Ted C. Wilson Memorial Scholarships *(Undergraduate/Scholarship)* [7441]
YMF Scholarships *(All/Scholarship)* [9791]

South Dakota

Horatio Alger South Dakota Scholarships *(Undergraduate/Scholarship)* [315]
MAC Louisa Bowen Memorial Scholarships for Graduate Students in Archival Administration *(Graduate/Scholarship)* [5854]
Bush Artist Fellowships *(All/Fellowship)* [2217]
Upper Midwest Human Rights Fellowship Program *(Professional development/Fellowship)* [9246]
Jerry Wheeler Scholarships *(Undergraduate/Scholarship)* [8559]

Tennessee

George Oliver Benton Memorial Scholarships *(Undergraduate/Scholarship)* [3095]
Ruby A. Brown Memorial Scholarships *(Undergraduate/Scholarship)* [3566]
William and Clara Bryan Scholarships *(Undergraduate/Scholarship)* [3098]
Cheatham County Scholarships *(Undergraduate/Scholarship)* [3100]
Steven L. Coffey Memorial Scholarships *(Undergraduate/Scholarship)* [3568]
Reuben R. Cowles Youth Awards *(Undergraduate/Award)* [885]
B.J. Dean Scholarships *(Undergraduate/Scholarship)* [3106]
Federal Court Bench and Bar Scholarships *(Undergraduate/Scholarship)* [9225]
Pauline LaFon Gore Scholarships *(Undergraduate/Scholarship)* [3108]
HSF/Nissan Community College Transfer Scholarship Program *(Undergraduate/Scholarship)* [4576]
Maude Keisling/Cumberland County Extension Homemakers Scholarships *(Undergraduate/Scholarship)* [3112]
Senator Carl O. Koella, Jr. Memorial Scholarships *(Undergraduate/Scholarship)* [3114]
Michael B. Kruse Scholarships *(Graduate, Undergraduate/Scholarship)* [3115]
Heloise Werthan Kuhn Scholarships *(Undergraduate/Scholarship)* [3116]
Diane G. Lowe and John Gomez, IV Scholarships *(Undergraduate/Scholarship)* [3117]
Aurella Varallo Mariani Scholarship Program *(Undergraduate/Scholarship)* [5985]
John E. Mayfield Scholarships for Cheatham County Central High School *(Undergraduate/Scholarship)* [3123]
John E. Mayfield Scholarships for Harpeth High School *(Undergraduate/Scholarship)* [3124]
John E. Mayfield Scholarships Pleasant View Christian School *(Undergraduate/Scholarship)* [3125]
John E. Mayfield Scholarships for Sycamore High School *(Undergraduate/Scholarship)* [3126]
Memphis Access and Diversity Law Scholarships *(Undergraduate/Scholarship)* [9234]
NAJA Scholarships *(Graduate/Scholarship)* [6086]

Nashville Unit Scholarships *(Undergraduate/Scholarship)* [4534]
Jerry Newson Scholarships *(Undergraduate/Scholarship)* [3128]
Tennessee Bar Foundation IOLTA Law School Scholarships *(Undergraduate/Scholarship)* [9241]
Tennessee Trucking Association Scholarships *(Undergraduate/Scholarship)* [3136]
Gary Wagner, K3OMI Scholarships *(Undergraduate/Scholarship)* [1111]
The Woman's Club of Nashville Scholarships *(Undergraduate/Scholarship)* [3139]
Wyatt, Tarrant and Combs, LLP Scholarships *(Undergraduate/Scholarship)* [9242]

Texas

Horatio Alger Texas - Fort Worth Scholarships *(Undergraduate/Scholarship)* [316]
Horatio Alger Texas Scholarships *(Undergraduate/Scholarship)* [317]
Allen - Marty Allen Scholarships *(High School, Undergraduate, Vocational/Occupational/Scholarship)* [2934]
BAFTX Early Starters Awards *(Undergraduate/Scholarship)* [2175]
BAFTX Graduate Awards *(Undergraduate/Scholarship)* [2176]
BAFTX Junior Achievers Awards *(Undergraduate/Scholarship)* [2177]
BAFTX Undergraduate Awards *(Undergraduate/Scholarship)* [2178]
Zachary Barriger Memorial Scholarships *(Undergraduate/Scholarship)* [2935]
Willa Beach-Porter Music Scholarships *(Undergraduate/Scholarship)* [2721]
O.J. Beck, Jr. Memorial Scholarships *(Undergraduate/Scholarship)* [2936]
Mary E. Bivins Foundation Religious Scholarship Program *(Graduate, Undergraduate/Scholarship)* [2104]
Kathi Bowles Scholarships for Women in Technology *(Graduate, Undergraduate/Scholarship)* [1898]
Marion Luna Brem/Pat McNeil Health and Education Scholarships *(Undergraduate/Scholarship)* [2938]
Kae and Kay Brockermeyer Endowed Scholarships *(Undergraduate/Scholarship)* [7172]
D.C. and Virginia Brown Scholarships *(High School, Undergraduate/Scholarship)* [2939]
Cecil E. Burney Scholarships *(Undergraduate/Scholarship)* [2940]
C.C.H.R.M.A. Scholarships *(High School, Undergraduate/Scholarship)* [2941]
Tom and Judith Comstock Scholarships *(Undergraduate/Scholarship)* [1079]
Justin Forrest Cox "Beat the Odds" Memorial Scholarships *(Undergraduate/Scholarship)* [2942]
B.J. Dean Scholarships *(Undergraduate/Scholarship)* [3106]
Derek Lee Dean Soccer Scholarships *(High School/Scholarship)* [2943]
Cindy P. Dennis Scholarship Fund *(Undergraduate/Scholarship)* [3241]
Jay Downes Memorial Scholarships *(Undergraduate/Scholarship)* [2945]
John R. Eidson Jr., Scholarships *(Undergraduate/Scholarship)* [2946]
Barney Flynn Memorial Scholarships *(High School/Scholarship)* [2947]
Melissa Guerra Scholarships *(Undergraduate/Scholarship)* [2948]
Gulf Coast Hurricane Scholarships *(Graduate, Undergraduate/Scholarship)* [8449]
George Gustafson HSE Memorial Scholarships *(Graduate, Undergraduate/Scholarship)* [1339]
George and Mary Josephine Hamman Foundation Scholarships *(Undergraduate/Scholarship)* [4369]
Manuel Hernandez, Jr. Foundation Scholarships *(Undergraduate, Vocational/Occupational/Scholarship)* [2949]
Hill Country Master Gardeners Horticulture Schol-

arships *(Graduate, Undergraduate/Scholarship)* [4543]

Houston Alumnae Chapter Graduate Fellowships *(Graduate/Fellowship)* [3375]

HSF/Citi Fellows Program *(Undergraduate/Scholarship)* [4573]

HSF/Nissan Community College Transfer Scholarship Program *(Undergraduate/Scholarship)* [4576]

Puedo Scholarships - Joseph Huerta *(Undergraduate/Scholarship)* [2950]

Institute of Transportation Engineers - Texas District Fellowships *(Graduate/Fellowship)* [4823]

JLTLA Scholarships *(Undergraduate/Scholarship)* [8981]

Mary Jon and J. P. Bryan Leadership in Education Awards *(Professional development/Award)* [8877]

Sue Kay Lay Memorial Scholarships *(Undergraduate/Scholarship)* [2952]

Danny T. Le Memorial Scholarships *(High School, Undergraduate/Scholarship)* [9431]

Lone Star GIA Associate and Alumni Scholarships *(Undergraduate/Scholarship)* [4064]

Fred R. McDaniel Memorial Scholarships *(Undergraduate/Scholarship)* [1093]

McKinney Sisters Undergraduate Scholarships *(Undergraduate/Scholarship)* [3381]

Brian and Colleen Miller Scholarships *(Undergraduate/Scholarship)* [2953]

NAJA Scholarships *(Graduate/Scholarship)* [6086]

Le Hoang Nguyen College Scholarships (LHN) *(High School/Scholarship)* [9432]

The Thuy Nguyen Scholarships *(High School/Scholarship)* [9433]

North Texas GIA Alumni Association Scholarships *(Undergraduate/Scholarship)* [4067]

Peierls Rising Star Scholarship Program *(Undergraduate/Scholarship)* [4580]

J.J. Rains Memorial Scholarships *(High School/Scholarship)* [2954]

W.B. Ray HS Class of '56 Averill Johnson Scholarships *(Undergraduate/Scholarship)* [2955]

Rocky Mountain Coal Mining Institute Engineering/Geology Scholarships *(Undergraduate/Scholarship)* [7810]

Rocky Mountain Coal Mining Institute Technical Scholarships *(Undergraduate, Vocational/Occupational/Scholarship)* [7811]

Rotary Club of Corpus Christi Scholarships *(Undergraduate/Scholarship)* [2956]

San Angelo Area Foundation Scholarships *(All/Scholarship)* [7901]

Seaman Family Scholarships *(Undergraduate/Scholarship)* [2957]

Judge Terry Shamsie Scholarships *(High School/Scholarship)* [2958]

SLEAMC Scholarships *(Graduate, Undergraduate/Scholarship)* [8107]

Herman J. Smith Scholarships *(Undergraduate/Scholarship)* [6345]

South Texas Unit Scholarships *(Undergraduate/Scholarship)* [4536]

Jim Springer Memorial Scholarships *(Undergraduate/Scholarship)* [2959]

Stewart Title Firefighters Scholarships *(High School, Undergraduate/Scholarship)* [2960]

Hatton W. Sumners Scholarships *(Undergraduate/Scholarship)* [6869]

Talbert Family Memorial Accounting and Financial Management Scholarships *(Undergraduate/Scholarship)* [2961]

Texas Elks State Association Scholarships *(Undergraduate/Scholarship)* [8863]

Traditional Education Scholarships *(Graduate, Undergraduate/Scholarship)* [8500]

Vera Tran Memorial Scholarships *(Undergraduate/Scholarship)* [9434]

TSHP R&E Foundation Scholarship Program *(Undergraduate, Graduate/Scholarship)* [8972]

Valley Alliance of Mentors for Opportunities and Scholarship Program (VAMOS) *(Undergraduate/Scholarship)* [4584]

WBSN Foundation Scholarships *(Graduate, Professional development/Scholarship)* [9719]

Wheelchair Success Foundation Scholarships *(Undergraduate/Scholarship)* [2963]

Dr. Dana Williams Scholarships *(Undergraduate/Scholarship)* [2964]

Utah

Horatio Alger Utah Scholarships *(Undergraduate/Scholarship)* [318]

Gold Country Section & Region II Scholarships *(Graduate, Undergraduate/Scholarship)* [1337]

The Cady McDonnell Memorial Scholarships *(Undergraduate/Scholarship)* [647]

Rocky Mountain Coal Mining Institute Engineering/Geology Scholarships *(Undergraduate/Scholarship)* [7810]

Rocky Mountain Coal Mining Institute Technical Scholarships *(Undergraduate, Vocational/Occupational/Scholarship)* [7811]

Vermont

Leon Bradley Scholarships *(Undergraduate/Scholarship)* [548]

Columbus Citizens Foundation College Scholarships *(Undergraduate/Scholarship)* [3012]

Dr. James L. Lawson Memorial Scholarships *(Undergraduate/Scholarship)* [1092]

Lighthouse International Scholarships - College-bound Awards *(High School, Undergraduate/Scholarship)* [5497]

Lighthouse International Scholarships - Graduate Awards *(Graduate/Scholarship)* [5498]

Lighthouse International Scholarships - Undergraduate Awards *(Undergraduate/Scholarship)* [5499]

New England FEMARA Scholarships *(Undergraduate/Scholarship)* [1096]

Johnny Trombly Scholarships *(Undergraduate/Scholarship)* [5919]

Yankee Clipper Contest Club, Inc. Youth Scholarships *(Undergraduate/Scholarship)* [1114]

Virginia

Horatio Alger District of Columbia, Maryland and Virginia Scholarships *(Undergraduate/Scholarship)* [299]

Leo Bourassa Scholarships *(Undergraduate, Graduate/Scholarship)* [9455]

Buena M. Chesshir Memorial Women's Educational Scholarships *(Graduate, Master's, Undergraduate/Scholarship)* [9440]

Richard D. and Sheppard R. Cooke Memorial Scholarships *(Graduate/Scholarship)* [4371]

Reuben R. Cowles Youth Awards *(Undergraduate/Award)* [885]

Richard Gregory Freeland, II Educational Scholarships *(High School/Scholarship)* [2147]

Friends of Coal Scholarships *(Undergraduate/Scholarship)* [9566]

Jane S. Glenn Memorial Endowed Scholarships *(Undergraduate/Scholarship)* [7805]

Hampton Roads Association of Social Workers Scholarships *(Graduate/Scholarship)* [4374]

Hampton Roads Sanitation District Environmental Scholarships *(Graduate/Scholarship)* [4375]

HSBC-North America Scholarship Program *(Undergraduate/Scholarship)* [4571]

Hughes Memorial Foundation Scholarships *(Graduate/Scholarship)* [4625]

Louis I. Jaffe Memorial Scholarships-NSU Alumni *(Graduate/Scholarship)* [4376]

James N. Kincanon Scholarships *(Undergraduate/Scholarship)* [7806]

Karen B. Lewis Career Education Scholarships *(Undergraduate/Scholarship)* [9441]

Lighthouse International Scholarships - College-bound Awards *(High School, Undergraduate/Scholarship)* [5497]

Lighthouse International Scholarships - Graduate Awards *(Graduate/Scholarship)* [5498]

Lighthouse International Scholarships - Undergraduate Awards *(Undergraduate/Scholarship)* [5499]

Marshall Undergraduate Scholars Program *(Undergraduate/Award)* [5650]

Lewis K. Martin II, M.D. and Cheryl Rose Martin Scholarship Fund *(Graduate/Scholarship)* [4378]

Ellis W. Rowe Scholarships *(Undergraduate/Scholarship)* [4380]

Drs. Kirkland Ruffin & Willcox Ruffin Scholarships *(Graduate/Scholarship)* [4381]

Florence L. Smith Medical Scholarships *(Graduate/Scholarship)* [4383]

Drew Smith Memorial Scholarships *(Undergraduate/Scholarship)* [3068]

Enid W. and Bernard B. Spigel Architectural Scholarships *(Graduate, Undergraduate/Scholarship)* [4384]

The SSPI Mid-Atlantic Chapter Scholarships *(Graduate, Undergraduate/Scholarship)* [8489]

Charles H. Stone Scholarships *(Undergraduate/Scholarship)* [559]

Tidewater Builders Association Scholarships *(Undergraduate/Scholarship)* [8900]

Virginia Museum of Fine Arts Visual Arts Fellowships *(Graduate, Professional development, Undergraduate/Fellowship)* [9457]

Gary Wagner, K3OMI Scholarships *(Undergraduate/Scholarship)* [1111]

L. Phil Wicker Scholarships *(Undergraduate/Scholarship)* [1113]

Alice Hinchcliffe Williams, RDH, MS Graduate Scholarships *(Graduate/Scholarship)* [9445]

Ted C. Wilson Memorial Scholarships *(Undergraduate/Scholarship)* [7441]

Women in Science and Technology Scholarships *(Doctorate, Graduate, Master's, Undergraduate/Scholarship)* [9442]

Nettie Tucker Yowell Scholarships *(Undergraduate/Scholarship)* [9443]

Washington

Horatio Alger Washington Scholarships *(Undergraduate/Scholarship)* [319]

American Indian Endowed Scholarships *(Graduate, Undergraduate/Scholarship)* [9503]

Paul Arnold Memorial Scholarships *(Undergraduate/Scholarship)* [7396]

Asian and Pacific Islander Queers Sisters Scholarships *(Undergraduate/Scholarship)* [7397]

Associates in Behavioral Health Scholarships *(Graduate/Scholarship)* [7398]

Barbara Bailey Scholarships *(Undergraduate/Scholarship)* [7399]

Charly Baker and Heath Merriwether Memorial Scholarships *(Undergraduate/Scholarship)* [7400]

Bellevue PFLAG Scholarships *(Undergraduate/Scholarship)* [7401]

Bill Bendiner and Doug Morgenson Scholarships *(Undergraduate/Scholarship)* [7402]

Mary Lou Brown Scholarships *(Undergraduate/Scholarship)* [1074]

Robert Browning Scholarships *(Undergraduate/Scholarship)* [7403]

Calvin Alumni Association-Washington-Seattle/Tacoma Scholarships *(Undergraduate/Scholarship)* [2313]

Deloris Carter Hampton Scholarships *(Undergraduate/Scholarship)* [7404]

Chateau Ste. Michelle Scholarship Fund *(Undergraduate/Scholarship)* [2975]

Dr. Princeton L. Co Emergency Fund for Dental Hygiene Scholarships *(Undergraduate/Scholarship)* [8113]

Donald O. Coffman Scholarships *(Undergraduate/Scholarship)* [7405]

Cole Family Scholarships *(Undergraduate/Scholarship)* [7406]

Dennis Coleman Choral Conducting Scholarships *(Undergraduate/Scholarship)* [7407]

Compassionate Care Scholarships *(Undergraduate/Scholarship)* [7408]

Brian M. Day Scholarships *(Undergraduate/Scholarship)* [7409]

Derivative Duo Scholarships *(Undergraduate/Scholarship)* [7410]

Carli Edwards Memorial Scholarships *(Undergraduate/Scholarship)* [8114]

Richard Gregory Freeland, II Educational Scholarships *(High School/Scholarship)* [2147]

Fuchs-Harden Educational Scholarships Fund *(Undergraduate/Scholarship)* [4337]

Grays Harbor Community Foundation Scholarships *(Graduate, Undergraduate/Scholarship)* [4323]

Greater Seattle Business Association Scholarships *(Undergraduate/Scholarship)* [4333]

Inland Northwest Business Alliance Scholarships (INBA) *(Undergraduate/Scholarship)* [7411]

Gregori Jakovina Endowment Scholarships *(Undergraduate/Scholarship)* [3677]

JQSOW Scholarships *(Undergraduate/Scholarship)* [5149]

Just Out Scholarship Fund *(Undergraduate/Scholarship)* [3678]

Kaiser Permanente Northwest Pride Scholarships *(Undergraduate/Scholarship)* [3679]

Leadership 1000 Scholarships *(Undergraduate/Scholarship)* [2976]

Lemelson Center Fellowships *(Doctorate, Postdoctorate, Professional development/Fellowship)* [8255]

Edmund F. Maxwell Scholarships *(Undergraduate/Scholarship)* [5698]

The Cady McDonnell Memorial Scholarships *(Undergraduate/Scholarship)* [647]

McFarffels Scholarships *(Undergraduate/Scholarship)* [7412]

Mill Creek Business Association Scholarships *(Undergraduate/Scholarship)* [5878]

Chapter 63 - Portland James E. Morrow Scholarships *(Graduate, Undergraduate/Scholarship)* [8393]

Jack D. Motteler Scholarships *(Undergraduate/Scholarship)* [7413]

Obrzut Ling Scholarships *(Undergraduate, Vocational/Occupational/Scholarship)* [7414]

Olympia Tumwater Foundation Traditional Scholarships *(Undergraduate/Scholarship)* [6875]

Olympia Tumwater Foundation Transitional (nontraditional) Scholarships *(Undergraduate/Scholarship)* [6876]

Political Leadership Scholarships *(Undergraduate/Scholarship)* [7415]

Pride Foundation Regional Scholarships *(Undergraduate/Scholarship)* [7416]

Pride of the Rose Scholarship Fund *(Undergraduate/Scholarship)* [3682]

Realize the Dream Scholarships *(Undergraduate/Scholarship)* [2977]

Don Renschler Scholarships *(Graduate/Scholarship)* [7417]

Richard C. Rolfs Scholarships *(Undergraduate/Scholarship)* [7418]

Rosenberg-Ibarra Scholarships *(Undergraduate/Scholarship)* [7419]

Chapter 63 - Portland Uncle Bud Smith Scholarships *(Graduate, Undergraduate/Scholarship)* [8400]

Social Work Scholarships *(Undergraduate/Scholarship)* [7420]

Kathy Spadoni Memorial Scholarships *(Undergraduate/Scholarship)* [7421]

Ric Ulrich and Chuck Pischke Scholarships *(Undergraduate/Scholarship)* [7423]

Patricia Van Kirk Scholarships *(Undergraduate/Scholarship)* [7424]

WALPA Lake Scholarships *(Graduate, Undergraduate/Scholarship)* [9526]

Washington City/County Management Association Scholarships *(Graduate/Scholarship)* [9494]

Washington Higher Education Coordinating Board Educational Opportunity Grants *(Undergraduate/Grant)* [9505]

Washington Higher Education Coordinating Board - State Need Grants (SNG) *(Undergraduate/Grant)* [9507]

Washington State Governors' Scholarship for Foster Youth *(Undergraduate/Scholarship)* [2978]

Washington State Nurses Association Foundation Scholarships (WSNF) *(Graduate, Undergraduate/Scholarship)* [9528]

Wells Fargo Scholarships *(Undergraduate/Scholarship)* [7425]

Whidbey Island Giving Circle Scholarships *(Undergraduate/Scholarship)* [7426]

WIGA Scholarships *(Postgraduate, Professional development, Undergraduate/Scholarship)* [9512]

James and Colin Lee Wozumi Scholarships *(Undergraduate/Scholarship)* [7427]

WSAJ American Justice Essay Scholarships *(Undergraduate/Scholarship)* [9519]

WSAJ Presidents' Scholarships *(Undergraduate/Scholarship)* [9521]

You Go Girl! Scholarships *(Undergraduate/Scholarship)* [7428]

Urashi Zen Scholarships *(Undergraduate/Scholarship)* [7429]

West Virginia

Bob Adkins Memorial Scholarships *(Undergraduate/Scholarship)* [7057]

Martin K. Alsup Scholarships *(Undergraduate/Scholarship)* [7058]

Ambrose-Ramsey Trust Scholarships *(Undergraduate/Scholarship)* [7059]

Joe Barbarow Memorial Scholarships *(Undergraduate/Scholarship)* [7060]

Lewis and Gurry Batten/Sand Plains Educational Trust Scholarships *(Undergraduate/Scholarship)* [7061]

William (Billbo) Boston Scholarships *(Undergraduate/Scholarship)* [7062]

Leon Bradley Scholarships *(Undergraduate/Scholarship)* [548]

Chester H. Bruce Memorial Scholarships *(Undergraduate, Vocational/Occupational/Scholarship)* [7063]

Freda Burge Scholarships *(Undergraduate/Scholarship)* [7064]

George H. Clinton Scholarship Fund *(Undergraduate/Scholarship)* [7065]

Dwight O. Conner and Ellen Conner Lepp/Danhart Scholarships *(Undergraduate/Scholarship)* [7066]

Dave Couch Memorial Scholarships *(Undergraduate/Scholarship)* [7067]

Jennifer Coulter Memorial Scholarships *(Undergraduate/Scholarship)* [7068]

Cindy Curry Memorial Scholarships *(Undergraduate/Scholarship)* [7069]

Kenneth D. and Katherine D. Davis Scholarships *(Undergraduate/Scholarship)* [7070]

Lawrence E. Davis Scholarships *(Undergraduate/Scholarship)* [7071]

Fostering Hope Scholarships Fund *(Undergraduate/Scholarship)* [7075]

William E. "Bill" Gallagher Scholarships *(Undergraduate/Scholarship)* [7076]

Laverne L. Gibson Memorial Scholarships *(Undergraduate/Scholarship)* [7077]

Shane Gilbert Memorial Scholarships *(Undergraduate/Scholarship)* [7078]

Russ Grant Memorial Scholarship for Tennis *(Undergraduate/Scholarship)* [7079]

Katherine M. Grosscup Scholarships *(Graduate, Undergraduate/Scholarship)* [4042]

Sara Gwisdalla Memorial Scholarships *(Undergraduate/Scholarship)* [7080]

Nathaniel Hafer Memorial Scholarships *(Undergraduate/Scholarship)* [7081]

Clayburn and Garnet R. Hanna Scholarships *(Undergraduate/Scholarship)* [7082]

H.G. Hardbarger Science and Mathematics Awards *(Undergraduate/Award)* [7083]

Ruth Harris Memorial Scholarships *(Undergraduate/Scholarship)* [7084]

Harrisville Lions Club Scholarships *(Undergraduate, Vocational/Occupational/Scholarship)* [7085]

Harry C. Hartleben III. Scholarships *(Undergraduate/Scholarship)* [7086]

Gail Hartshorn Scholarships *(Undergraduate/Scholarship)* [7087]

Gregory Lynn Haught Citizenship Awards *(Undergraduate/Award)* [7088]

Dorcas Edmonson Haught Scholarships *(Undergraduate/Scholarship)* [7089]

Albert H. Hix, W8AH Memorial Scholarships *(Undergraduate/Scholarship)* [1090]

Holly Jackson-Wuller Memorial Scholarships *(Undergraduate/Scholarship)* [7091]

K.A.S.A Memorial Scholarships *(Undergraduate/Scholarship)* [7092]

Dr. Charles Kelly Memorial Scholarships *(Undergraduate/Scholarship)* [7093]

Judge Oliver Kessel Memorial Scholarships - Ripley Rotary *(Graduate/Scholarship)* [7094]

Rhonda Knopp Memorial Scholarships *(Undergraduate/Scholarship)* [7095]

Harold Knopp Scholarships *(Undergraduate/Scholarship)* [7096]

Langfitt-Ambrose Trust Funds *(Undergraduate/Scholarship)* [7097]

Lighthouse International Scholarships - Collegebound Awards *(High School, Undergraduate/Scholarship)* [5497]

Lighthouse International Scholarships - Graduate Awards *(Graduate/Scholarship)* [5498]

Lighthouse International Scholarships - Undergraduate Awards *(Undergraduate/Scholarship)* [5499]

Megan Nicole Longwell Scholarships *(Undergraduate/Scholarship)* [7098]

Bryce-Lietzke Martin Scholarships *(Undergraduate/Scholarship)* [7099]

Dudley Mullins/Cabot Corporation Scholarships *(Undergraduate/Scholarship)* [7100]

Pennsboro Alumni Scholarship Fund *(Undergraduate/Scholarship)* [7101]

Pepsi Wood County Technical/Caperton Center Scholarship Fund *(Undergraduate/Scholarship)* [7102]

William R. Pfalzgraf Scholarships *(Undergraduate/Scholarship)* [7103]

Herschel Pifer Memorial Scholarships *(Undergraduate/Scholarship)* [7104]

Thomas W. Porter, W8KYZ Scholarships Honoring Michael Daugherty, W8LSE *(Undergraduate/Scholarship)* [1101]

William Reaser Scholarships *(Undergraduate, Vocational/Occupational/Scholarship)* [7105]

James H. Roberts Athletic Scholarships *(Undergraduate/Scholarship)* [7106]

James Robinson Memorial Scholarships *(Undergraduate/Scholarship)* [7108]

Carl M. Rose Memorial Scholarship Fund *(Undergraduate/Scholarship)* [7109]

S. Byrl Ross Memorial Scholarship Fund *(Undergraduate/Scholarship)* [7110]

St. Joseph's Hospital School of Nursing Alumnae Scholarships *(Undergraduate/Scholarship)* [7112]

Everett Oscar Shimp Memorial Scholarships *(Undergraduate/Scholarship)* [7113]

Pat Shimp Memorial Scholarships *(Undergraduate/Scholarship)* [7114]

Bill Six Memorial Scholarship Fund *(Undergraduate/Scholarship)* [7116]

Mary K. Smith Rector Scholarships *(Undergraduate, Vocational/Occupational/Scholarship)* [7117]

The SSPI Mid-Atlantic Chapter Scholarships *(Graduate, Undergraduate/Scholarship)* [8489]

Zachary Taylor Stevens Memorial Scholarships *(Undergraduate/Scholarship)* [1108]

Charles H. Stone Scholarships *(Undergraduate/Scholarship)* [559]

C.R. Thomas Scholarships *(Undergraduate/Scholarship)* [7118]

Charles A. Townsend Scholarships *(Undergraduate/Scholarship)* [7119]

Gary Wagner, K3OMI Scholarships *(Undergraduate/Scholarship)* [1111]

Wayne-Meador-Elliott Scholarships *(Undergraduate/Scholarship)* [7120]

West Virginia Educational Foundation Hospitality Business Alliance Scholarships *(Undergraduate/Scholarship)* [9570]

West Virginia Nurses Association District No. 3 Scholarships *(Undergraduate/Scholarship)* [7121]

Whitaker-Minard Memorial Scholarships *(Undergraduate/Scholarship)* [7122]

L. Phil Wicker Scholarships (Undergraduate/Scholarship) [1113]

S. William & Martha R. Goff Educational Scholarships (Undergraduate/Scholarship) [7123]

Glenn Wilson Broadcast Journalism Scholarships (Undergraduate/Scholarship) [7124]

Wisconsin

Victor Albright Scholarships-Dane County (Undergraduate/Scholarship) [9347]

Victor Albright Scholarships (Undergraduate/Scholarship) [9348]

MAC Louisa Bowen Memorial Scholarships for Graduate Students in Archival Administration (Graduate/Scholarship) [5854]

Walter and Louise Buell Graduate Scholarships (Graduate/Scholarship) [3862]

Calvin Alumni Association-Southeastern Wisconsin Scholarships (Undergraduate/Scholarship) [2308]

Chicago FM Club Scholarships (Undergraduate/Scholarship) [1078]

Jason Dahnert Memorial Scholarships (Graduate, Undergraduate/Scholarship) [3863]

Engineering Departmental Scholarships (Undergraduate/Scholarship) [9352]

Jerome Hake Engineering Scholarships (Graduate, Undergraduate/Scholarship) [3864]

Gene Halker Memorial Scholarships (Graduate, Undergraduate/Scholarship) [3865]

Eileen Harrison Education Scholarships (Graduate, Undergraduate/Scholarship) [3866]

Herb Kohl Educational Foundation Fellowships (Professional development/Fellowship) [4531]

Kemper K. Knapp Scholarships (Undergraduate/Scholarship) [9360]

Robert C. and Judith L. Knapp Scholarships (Graduate, Undergraduate/Scholarship) [3867]

Jane Shaw Knox Graduate Scholarships (Graduate/Scholarship) [3868]

George Koeppel and Roland W. Zinns Scholarships (Undergraduate/Scholarship) [9361]

Lawton Minority Retention Grants (Undergraduate/Scholarship) [9362]

E.H. Marth Food and Environmental Scholarships (Undergraduate/Scholarship) [9674]

Menominee Tribal Scholarships (Graduate, Undergraduate/Scholarship) [5769]

Edmond A. Metzger Scholarships (Undergraduate/Scholarship) [1094]

John P. and Tashia F. Morgridge Scholarships (Undergraduate/Scholarship) [9364]

Pi Lambda Theta Scholarships (Undergraduate/Scholarship) [9366]

Ralph and Clara Rutledge Memorial Scholarships (Graduate/Scholarship) [3869]

School of Education Scholarships for Students from Underrepresented Groups (Undergraduate/Scholarship) [9369]

Six Meter Club of Chicago Scholarships (Undergraduate/Scholarship) [1107]

University of Wisconsin-Madison Academic Excellence Scholarships (Undergraduate/Scholarship) [9371]

University of Wisconsin-Madison Minority Teacher Loans (Professional development, Undergraduate/Loan, Scholarship) [9378]

Upper Midwest Human Rights Fellowship Program (Professional development/Fellowship) [9246]

Chapter 4 - Lawrence A. Wacker Memorial Awards (Undergraduate/Scholarship) [8402]

Francis Walton Memorial Scholarships (Undergraduate/Scholarship) [1112]

WDA Full-Time Graduate Scholarships (Graduate/Scholarship) [9684]

WDA Part-Time Graduate Scholarships (Graduate/Scholarship) [9685]

WIEA Scholarships (Doctorate, Graduate, Undergraduate, Vocational/Occupational/Scholarship) [9687]

Wisconsin High School Scholarships (Undergraduate/Scholarship) [9385]

Wyoming

Horatio Alger Wyoming Scholarships (Undergraduate/Scholarship) [320]

Gold Country Section & Region II Scholarships (Graduate, Undergraduate/Scholarship) [1337]

The Cady McDonnell Memorial Scholarships (Undergraduate/Scholarship) [647]

Rocky Mountain Coal Mining Institute Engineering/Geology Scholarships (Undergraduate/Scholarship) [7810]

Rocky Mountain Coal Mining Institute Technical Scholarships (Undergraduate, Vocational/Occupational/Scholarship) [7811]

CANADA

AABP Amstutz Scholarships (Undergraduate/Scholarship) [443]

AANS Medical Student Summer Research Fellowships (MSSRF) (Undergraduate/Fellowship) [515]

Dr. Anderson Abbott Awards (Undergraduate/Scholarship) [9320]

Jack Ackroyd Scholarships (Professional development/Scholarship) [2372]

ACMS Research Fellowships (Doctorate, Postdoctorate/Fellowship) [603]

ADAC Foundation Scholarships (Undergraduate/Scholarship) [1622]

AHNS Pilot Research Grants (Professional development/Grant) [785]

Airports Council International-North America Scholarships (Graduate, Undergraduate/Scholarship) [149]

Alaska Airlines Scholarships (Undergraduate/Scholarship) [1362]

Alberta Agricultural Economics Association Masters Scholarships (Graduate/Scholarship) [203]

Alberta Agricultural Economics Association Undergraduate Scholarships (Undergraduate/Scholarship) [204]

Alberta Association of Gerontology Student Awards - Edmonton Chapter (Graduate, Undergraduate/Award) [207]

Alberta Association of Gerontology Student Awards (Graduate/Award) [206]

Alberta Award for the Study of Canadian Human Rights and Multiculturalism (Doctorate, Graduate/Award) [236]

Alberta Child Care Association Professional Development Grants (Professional development/Grant) [213]

Alberta Ingenuity Graduate Student Scholarships in Nanotechnology (Doctorate, Graduate/Scholarship) [231]

Alberta Ingenuity Graduate Student Scholarships (Doctorate, Graduate/Scholarship) [230]

Alberta Teachers Association Doctoral Fellowships in Education (Doctorate/Fellowship) [272]

Alberta Teachers Association Educational Research Awards (Professional development/Grant) [273]

Alexander Graham Bell Canada Graduate Scholarship Program (Doctorate, Master's/Scholarship) [6571]

Hon. Lincoln Alexander Scholarships (Undergraduate/Scholarship) [2109]

Stephanie Ali Memorial Scholarships (Undergraduate/Scholarship) [9321]

Lorraine Allison Scholarships (Graduate/Scholarship) [1500]

AMEC Aboriginal Undergraduate Scholarships (Undergraduate/Scholarship) [2453]

AMEC Masters Scholarships (Graduate, Master's/Scholarship) [2454]

American Association for Cancer Research Minority Scholar Awards (Graduate/Award) [450]

American College of Radiation Oncology Resident Scholarships (Graduate/Scholarship) [623]

American Express Travel Scholarships (Undergraduate/Scholarship) [1363]

American Judges Association Law Student Essay Competition (Undergraduate/Prize) [890]

American Society of Comparative Law TransCoop Programs (All/Fellowship) [1204]

American Standard Scholarships (Undergraduate/Scholarship) [7344]

Bernard Amtmann Fellowships (Postgraduate, Professional development/Fellowship) [2087]

Dr. Andy Anderson Young Professional Awards (Professional development/Award) [7317]

APALA Scholarships (Doctorate, Graduate/Scholarship) [1648]

Aplastic Anemia and Myelosdysplasia Scholarships (Graduate/Scholarship) [2533]

Applied Hospitality Degree Scholarships (Undergraduate/Scholarship) [2487]

Architects Association of PEI Scholarships (Undergraduate/Scholarship) [3180]

Arizona Chapter Gold Scholarships (Undergraduate/Scholarship) [1365]

Robin P. Armstrong Memorial Prize for Excellence in Native Studies Awards (Doctorate, Graduate/Award) [2377]

ASA Graduate Scholarships (Graduate/Scholarship) [1182]

ASAC-CJAS PhD Research Grant Awards (Doctorate/Grant) [52]

Association of Desk and Derrick Clubs Education Trust Scholarships (Undergraduate/Scholarship) [1749]

Association of Universities and Colleges of Canada Public Scholarships (Undergraduate/Scholarship) [1889]

Association for Women Veterinarians Foundation Student Scholarships (Graduate/Scholarship) [1912]

AstraZeneca RURAL Scholarships (Doctorate/Scholarship) [2534]

Martha and Robert Atherton Ministerial Scholarships (Graduate, Master's/Scholarship) [8993]

Atkinson Fellowships in Public Policy (Professional development/Fellowship) [1920]

Atlantic Provinces Library Association Memorial Awards (Professional development/Scholarship) [1926]

Atlantic Salmon Federation Olin Fellowships (All/Fellowship) [1929]

Auto Body Technician Certificate Scholarships (Undergraduate/Scholarship) [7991]

Jerry Baker Scholarships (Undergraduate/Scholarship) [1430]

Lynn Ann Baldwin Scholarships (Master's/Scholarship) [2395]

Ballantyne Resident Research Grants (Professional development/Grant) [787]

Bank of Canada Fellowships (Doctorate, Professional development/Fellowship) [2011]

Bank of Canada Governor's Awards (Doctorate, Professional development/Award) [2012]

Helen Bassett Commemorative Scholarships (Undergraduate/Scholarship) [6567]

Baxter Corporation Canadian Research Awards in Anesthesia (Professional development/Award) [2356]

BBM Canada Scholarships (Undergraduate/Scholarship) [2365]

BCPA Bursaries (Undergraduate/Scholarship) [2180]

Suzanne Beauregard Scholarships (Undergraduate/Scholarship) [4180]

Beaverbrook Media at McGill Student Paper Prize (Graduate/Prize) [2435]

Stan Beck Fellowships (Graduate, Undergraduate/Fellowship) [3652]

Anne Beckingham Scholarships (Graduate, Professional development/Scholarship) [2474]

Dr. Ann C. Beckingham Scholarships (Doctorate/Scholarship) [2535]

Harvey Bell Memorial Prize (Graduate/Prize) [6564]

Beverlee Bell Scholarships in Human Rights and Democracy (Graduate/Scholarship) [3473]

Louise Bennett-Coverley Scholarships (Undergraduate/Scholarship) [2110]

The Viscount Bennett Fellowships (Graduate/Fellowship) [2419]

Dr. Noorali & Sabiya Bharwani Endowment (Undergraduate/Scholarship) [2082]

Hussein Jina Bharwani Memorial Endowment (Undergraduate/Scholarship) [2083]

J.P. Bickell Mining Scholarships (Undergraduate/Scholarship) [9322]

Dr. Biljan Memorial Awards *(Graduate/Award)* [2466]

BioQuip Undergraduate Scholarships *(Undergraduate/Scholarship)* [3653]

Birks Family Foundation Scholarships *(Undergraduate/Scholarship)* [2536]

Bison Transport Scholarships *(Undergraduate/Scholarship)* [6897]

Black Canadian Scholarships *(Undergraduate/Scholarship)* [6994]

Lucie and Thornton Blackburn Scholarships *(Undergraduate/Scholarship)* [2363]

Alex Blaski Memorial Scholarships *(Undergraduate/Scholarship)* [7757]

M. Hildred Blewett Fellowships *(Postdoctorate/Scholarship)* [997]

Lawrence Bloomberg Entrance Awards *(Postgraduate/Award)* [8034]

BMO Financial Group Scholarships *(Undergraduate/Scholarship)* [2111]

Edith and Arnold N. Bodtker Grants *(All/Grant)* [3339]

Steve Bonk Scholarships *(Postgraduate/Scholarship)* [2634]

Lorne and Ruby Bonnell Scholarships *(Undergraduate/Scholarship)* [3182]

Anne-Marie Bonner Scholarships *(Undergraduate/Scholarship)* [5115]

Maria and Czeslaw Borek Scholarships *(Undergraduate/Scholarship)* [7758]

Bound to Stay Bound Books Scholarships (BTSB) *(Graduate/Scholarship)* [1826]

Jim Bourque Scholarships *(Postgraduate, Undergraduate/Scholarship)* [1501]

CAG Margery Boyce Bursary Awards *(Postgraduate/Award)* [2381]

Charles F. Brandenburg Memorial Scholarships *(Undergraduate/Scholarship)* [2622]

Louis J. Brody Q.C. Entrance Scholarships *(Postgraduate/Scholarship)* [8035]

Peter F. Bronfman Entrance Awards *(Postgraduate/Award)* [8036]

Peter F. Bronfman Scholarships of Merit *(Postgraduate/Scholarship)* [8037]

Randall Brown and Associates Awards *(Postgraduate/Award)* [2468]

Brown Dental Scholarships *(Undergraduate/Scholarship)* [5116]

Olympia Brown and Max Kapp Awards *(Graduate/Scholarship)* [8994]

Tropicana Community Services - Robert K. Brown Scholarships *(Undergraduate/Scholarship)* [2112]

Pamfil and Maria Bujea Family Orthodox Christian Seminarian Scholarships *(Undergraduate/Scholarship)* [1163]

Burger King Scholars Program *(Undergraduate/Scholarship)* [4475]

Burroughs Wellcome Fund Career Awards at the Scientific Interface *(Doctorate, Postdoctorate/Fellowship)* [2211]

Business, Education and Technology Scholarships *(Graduate, Undergraduate, Vocational/Occupational/Scholarship)* [336]

Business Insurance Diploma Scholarships *(Undergraduate/Scholarship)* [7992]

Peter Butler III - Rose Fortune Scholarship Program *(Undergraduate/Scholarship)* [1716]

Leon C. Bynoe Memorial Scholarships *(Undergraduate/Scholarship)* [9323]

CADE Bursary *(Undergraduate/Scholarship)* [2374]

CADE Scholarships *(Undergraduate/Scholarship)* [2375]

CAG Health and Health Care Study Group Awards *(Graduate/Award)* [2378]

CAHR Master's Level Scholarships *(Master's/Scholarship)* [2384]

CALL/ACBD Education Reserve Fund Grants *(Graduate/Grant)* [2388]

Cameco Corporation Scholarships in the Geological Sciences - Continuing Students *(Undergraduate/Scholarship)* [2344]

Cameco Corporation Scholarships in the Geological Sciences - Entering Students *(Undergraduate/Scholarship)* [2345]

Dalton Camp Awards *(All/Prize)* [4012]

Canada Graduate Scholarship Program *(Graduate/Scholarship)* [8285]

Canadian Anesthesiologists' Society Research Awards *(Professional development/Award)* [2357]

Canadian Association of Cardiac Rehabilitation Graduate Scholarship Awards *(Graduate/Scholarship)* [2370]

Canadian Association of Geographers Historical Geography Study Group Awards *(Doctorate, Graduate, Undergraduate/Award)* [2379]

Canadian Association of Law Libraries CALL Research Grants *(Graduate/Grant)* [2389]

Canadian Association of Law Teachers Award for Academic Excellence *(Professional development/Award)* [2393]

Canadian Association for the Practical Study of Law in Education Fellowships *(Graduate/Fellowship)* [2402]

Canadian Association for Studies in Co-operation Scholarships Lemaire Co-operative Studies Awards (CASC) *(Graduate, Undergraduate/Scholarship)* [2431]

Canadian Blood Services Graduate Fellowships *(Graduate/Fellowship)* [2421]

Canadian Blood Services Postdoctoral Fellowships *(Postdoctorate/Fellowship)* [2422]

Canadian Council of Technicians and Technologists Scholarships for Technology Students *(Postgraduate/Scholarship)* [2445]

Canadian Evaluation Society Educational Fund Scholarships *(Graduate/Scholarship)* [2459]

Canadian Evaluation Society Memorial Scholarships *(Graduate, Professional development/Scholarship)* [2475]

Canadian Federation of Independent Grocers National Scholarships *(Undergraduate/Scholarship)* [2461]

Canadian Federation of University Women Etobicoke Bursary *(Undergraduate/Scholarship)* [9324]

Canadian Hard of Hearing Association Scholarships *(Undergraduate/Scholarship)* [2481]

Canadian Hospitality Foundation College Entrance Scholarships *(Undergraduate/Scholarship)* [2488]

Canadian Hospitality Foundation University Entrance Scholarships *(Undergraduate/Scholarship)* [2489]

Canadian Hydrographic Association Student Awards *(Undergraduate/Award)* [2492]

Canadian Identification Society Essay Scholarship Awards *(Professional development/Prize)* [2494]

Canadian Iranian Foundation Scholarships *(Undergraduate/Scholarship)* [2509]

Canadian IT Law Association Student Writing Contest *(Doctorate/Prize)* [2511]

Canadian Japanese-Mennonite Scholarships *(Graduate/Scholarship)* [5767]

Canadian Nurses Foundation - Baxter Corporation Scholarships *(Graduate/Scholarship)* [2537]

Canadian Nurses Foundation Northern Scholarships *(Undergraduate/Scholarship)* [2538]

Canadian Nurses Foundation Scholarships *(Undergraduate/Scholarship)* [2539]

Canadian Occupational Therapy Foundation Graduate Scholarships *(Graduate/Scholarship)* [2558]

Canadian Occupational Therapy Foundation Invacare Master's Scholarships *(Graduate/Scholarship)* [2559]

Canadian Pain Society Post-Doctoral Fellowship Awards *(Doctorate/Fellowship)* [2567]

Canadian Parking Association Scholarships *(Undergraduate/Scholarship)* [2581]

Canadian Picture Pioneers Scholarships *(Undergraduate/Scholarship)* [2583]

Canadian Polar Commission Scholarships *(Doctorate, Graduate/Scholarship)* [1734]

Canadian Poultry Research Council Postgraduate Scholarships *(Postgraduate/Scholarship)* [2588]

Canadian Purchasing Research Foundation Prize *(Doctorate, Graduate/Prize)* [2590]

Canadian Sanitation Supply Association Scholarships *(Undergraduate/Scholarship)* [2592]

Canadian Seniors' Golf Association Scholarships *(Undergraduate/Scholarship)* [4181]

Canadian Society for the Study of Education Mentorship Awards *(Professional development/Award)* [2615]

Canadian Society for the Study of Education New Scholar Fellowships (CSSE) *(Professional development/Fellowship)* [2616]

Canadian Technical Asphalt Association Scholarships *(Undergraduate/Scholarship)* [2624]

Canadian Urological Association Community-based Research Awards *(Doctorate/Award)* [2628]

Canadian Urological Association Fellowships *(Graduate/Fellowship)* [2629]

Canadian Water Resources Association Scholarships *(All/Scholarship)* [2631]

Dr. John Big Canoe Memorial Scholarships *(Undergraduate/Scholarship)* [2523]

Thelma Cardwell Scholarships *(Graduate/Scholarship)* [2560]

Career Development Scholarships *(Postdoctorate, Postgraduate/Scholarship)* [3855]

Career Fellowship Awards for Medical Scientists *(Postdoctorate, Professional development/Fellowship)* [2214]

Herb Carnegie Scholarships *(Undergraduate/Scholarship)* [2113]

CARO-ELEKTA Research Fellowship Program *(Professional development/Fellowship)* [2404]

Orin Carver Scholarships *(Undergraduate/Scholarship)* [3183]

CAS/GE Healthcare Canada Inc. Research Awards *(Professional development/Award)* [2358]

CAS/Vitaid-LMA Residents' Research Grant Competition *(Professional development/Award)* [2359]

CASAA Leaders of Distinction Scholarships *(Professional development/Scholarship)* [2409]

CASAA Scholarships *(Undergraduate/Scholarship)* [2410]

Fraser Milner Casgrain LLP Scholarships *(Undergraduate/Scholarship)* [2114]

Caterpillar Scholars Award *(Undergraduate/Scholarship)* [8370]

Catzman Awards for Professionalism and Civility *(Professional development/Award)* [65]

Marshall Cavendish Scholarships *(Graduate/Scholarship)* [899]

CAWEE International Student Fellowships *(Postgraduate/Fellowship)* [8038]

CC Times Scholarships *(Undergraduate/Scholarship)* [2770]

CCFF Clinical Fellowships *(Doctorate, Graduate/Fellowship)* [2447]

CCFF Fellowships *(Doctorate, Graduate/Fellowship)* [2448]

CCFF Scholarships *(Doctorate, Graduate/Scholarship)* [2449]

CCLA Summer Legal Internships *(Undergraduate, Graduate/Internship)* [2428]

CEMF Undergraduate Engineering Scholarships *(Undergraduate/Scholarship)* [2455]

CGPF Endowments Conference Scholarships *(Professional development/Scholarship)* [2478]

Mary Anne Chambers Scholarships *(Undergraduate/Scholarship)* [5117]

Chapter 6 Fairfield County Scholarships *(Undergraduate/Scholarship)* [8379]

Chernos Essay Competition *(High School/Prize)* [2429]

Childhood Cancer Foundation Scholarships *(Undergraduate/Scholarship)* [2752]

Childhood Cancer Survivor Scholarships *(All/Scholarship)* [2753]

Chinese Professionals Association of Canada BMO Diversity Scholarships *(Undergraduate/Scholarship)* [2771]

Chinese Professionals Association of Canada Education Foundation Awards *(High School/Award)* [2772]

Chinese Professionals Association of Canada Journalism Scholarships *(Undergraduate/Scholarship)* [2773]

Chinese Professionals Association of Canada Professional Achievement Awards *(Professional development/Award)* [2774]

Patricia Smith Christensen Scholarships *(Postdoctorate/Scholarship)* [8195]

CHS - Bursary Program Scholarships *(Undergraduate/Scholarship)* [2483]

CHS - Mature Student Bursary Program Scholarships *(Professional development/Scholarship)* [2484]

CHS Scholarships *(Undergraduate, Vocational/Occupational/Scholarship)* [2485]

CIBC Scholarships *(Undergraduate/Scholarship)* [2115]

CIHR Health Law and Policy Fellowships *(Graduate/Fellowship)* [2791]

CIP Fellow's Travel Scholarships *(Postgraduate/Scholarship)* [2502]

CISDL Associate Fellows *(Graduate/Fellowship)* [2730]

CISDL Legal Research Fellows *(Graduate/Fellowship)* [2731]

CISDL Senior Research Fellows *(Professional development/Fellowship)* [2732]

City of Toronto Graduate Scholarships for Women in Mathematics *(Graduate/Scholarship)* [9325]

City of Toronto Queen Elizabeth II Sesquicentennial Scholarships in Community Health Nursing for Graduates *(Graduate/Scholarship)* [9326]

City of Toronto Queen Elizabeth II Sesquicentennial Scholarships in Community Health Nursing for Undergraduates *(Undergraduate/Scholarship)* [9327]

City of Toronto Scholarships for Aboriginal Students *(Graduate, Undergraduate/Scholarship)* [9328]

City of Toronto Women's Studies Scholarships *(Graduate, Undergraduate/Scholarship)* [9329]

CJF Canadian Journalism Fellowships *(Graduate, Professional development, Undergraduate/Fellowship)* [2513]

CLA Student Summer Internship Program *(Undergraduate/Internship)* [2517]

Greg Clerk Awards *(Professional development/Award)* [2514]

David H. Clift Scholarships *(Graduate/Scholarship)* [900]

Clinical Pain Management Fellowship Awards *(Postgraduate/Fellowship)* [2568]

CN Scholarships for Women *(Postgraduate/Scholarship)* [8307]

CNST Scholarships *(Doctorate, Graduate/Scholarship)* [1735]

Marshall A. Cohen Entrance Awards *(Postgraduate/Award)* [8039]

Erma Collins Scholarships *(Undergraduate/Scholarship)* [2116]

Desmond Conacher Scholarships *(Graduate/Scholarship)* [2901]

Connor/Spafford Scholarships *(Undergraduate/Scholarship)* [4182]

Continuing Education Awards *(Graduate/Grant)* [5741]

Roy Cooper Scholarships *(Undergraduate/Scholarship)* [5397]

COPA Scholarship Fund *(Undergraduate/Scholarship)* [2563]

Copnick/Hilliard Scholarships *(Professional development/Scholarship)* [2578]

Steve Cowan Memorial Scholarships *(Undergraduate/Scholarship)* [3290]

Gertrude M. Cox Scholarships *(Doctorate, Graduate/Fellowship)* [1395]

CPS Excellence in Interprofessional Pain Education Awards *(Professional development/Award)* [2569]

CPS Interprofessional Nursing Project Awards *(Professional development/Award)* [2570]

CPS Knowledge Translation Research Awards *(Professional development/Grant)* [2571]

CPS Nursing Excellence in Pain Management Awards *(Professional development/Award)* [2572]

CPS Nursing Research and Education Awards *(Professional development/Grant)* [2573]

CPS Outstanding Pain Mentorship Awards *(Professional development/Award)* [2574]

CPS Toronto Poly Clinic - ROD Inter-Disciplinary Pain Education Grants *(Professional development/Grant)* [2575]

CPS Trainee Research Awards *(Doctorate/Grant)* [2576]

CRM-ISM Postdoctoral Fellowships *(Postdoctorate/Fellowship)* [2734]

CSBS Student Prize Competition *(Graduate/Prize)* [2598]

CSCI Distinguished Scientist Lectures and Awards *(Doctorate/Award)* [2600]

CSEG Scholarship Trust Fund *(Graduate, Undergraduate/Scholarship)* [2607]

CSMLS Student Scholarship Awards *(Postgraduate/Scholarship)* [2609]

CSOHNS Fellowships *(Graduate/Fellowship)* [2611]

CSSE ARTS Graduate Research Awards *(Graduate/Award)* [2617]

CSSHE Masters Thesis/Project Awards *(Master's/Award)* [2619]

CSSHE Research Awards *(Professional development/Award)* [2620]

CTRF Scholarships for Graduate Study in Transportation *(Graduate/Scholarship)* [2626]

Culinary (1-Year Program) Scholarships *(Undergraduate/Scholarship)* [2490]

CWEDA Scholarship Program *(Undergraduate/Scholarship)* [2354]

DAAD Study Scholarship Awards *(Graduate/Scholarship)* [4116]

DAAD Undergraduate Scholarship Program *(Undergraduate/Scholarship)* [4117]

CLA/ACB Dafoe Scholarships *(Graduate/Scholarship)* [2519]

Roger Daley Postdoctoral Publication Awards *(Postdoctorate/Award)* [2525]

D&R Sobey Scholarships *(Undergraduate/Scholarship)* [8276]

Dante Prizes *(Undergraduate/Prize)* [3341]

Canadian Association for Studies in Co-operation Scholarships - Amy and Tim Dauphinee Scholarships (CASC) *(Graduate/Scholarship)* [2432]

Ginger and Fred Deines Canada Scholarships *(Undergraduate, Vocational/Occupational/Scholarship)* [8949]

Delta Faucet Scholarships *(Undergraduate/Scholarship)* [7345]

Helen L. Dewar Scholarships *(Undergraduate/Scholarship)* [8894]

Diabetes Hope Foundation Scholarships *(Undergraduate/Scholarship)* [3434]

Dr. Allan A. Dixon Memorial Scholarships *(Postgraduate/Scholarship)* [2596]

William Donald Dixon Research Grants *(Graduate/Grant)* [2495]

Julian Dobranowski Memorial Scholarships *(Undergraduate/Scholarship)* [7759]

Dominio of Canada Insurance Scholarships *(Graduate/Scholarship)* [7324]

Douglas-Coldwell Foundation Scholarships in Social Affairs *(Graduate/Scholarship)* [3474]

Tommy Douglas Scholarships *(Undergraduate/Scholarship)* [6548]

Janusz & Roma Drzymala Scholarships *(Undergraduate/Scholarship)* [7760]

Aleksander & Stefania Dulemba Scholarships *(Undergraduate/Scholarship)* [7761]

Joshua Dyke Family Scholarships *(Undergraduate/Scholarship)* [8895]

Fernandez Earle Undergraduate Entrance Scholarships *(Undergraduate/Scholarship)* [3559]

David Eaton Scholarships *(Graduate, Master's/Scholarship)* [8997]

Edmonton Epilepsy Continuing Education Scholarships *(Undergraduate/Scholarship)* [3590]

EJLB Foundation's Scholar Research Programme *(Graduate, Postgraduate/Scholarship)* [3618]

Clay Elliott Scholarship Foundation Scholarships *(Undergraduate/Scholarship)* [3631]

Environmental History of Quebec Scholarships *(Postdoctorate, Postgraduate/Scholarship)* [6617]

Erb Group Companies Service to Community Scholarships *(Undergraduate/Scholarship)* [6898]

Extendicare Scholarships in Gerontology *(Graduate/Scholarship)* [2540]

Faculty Research Visit Grants *(Doctorate/Grant)* [4118]

Fellowships in the Humanities and Social Sciences in Turkey *(Postdoctorate/Fellowship)* [1147]

Fellowships in the PMAC-AGPC *(Professional development/Fellowship)* [7450]

FFB-C Postdoctoral Fellowships *(Postdoctorate/Fellowship)* [3968]

Fields Research Immersion Fellowships *(Postdoctorate/Fellowship)* [3744]

Fire Safety Awards *(Postgraduate/Award)* [2469]

Martin Fischer Awards *(All/Award)* [2479]

Flamenco Student Scholarships *(Undergraduate/Scholarship)* [3808]

Walter & Anna Flis Memorial Scholarships *(Undergraduate/Scholarship)* [7762]

Foresters Scholarships *(Undergraduate/Scholarship)* [4714]

Edward Foster Awards *(All/Award)* [2496]

Foundation for the Advancement of Aboriginal Youth Bursary Program *(Undergraduate/Scholarship)* [2440]

Foundation for the Advancement of Aboriginal Youth Scholarships *(Undergraduate/Scholarship)* [2441]

Terry Fox Memorial Scholarships *(Undergraduate/Scholarship)* [6549]

Fraser Milner Casgrain Scholarships *(Professional development/Scholarship)* [2006]

Henry Friesen Awards and Lectures *(Doctorate/Award)* [2601]

Future Leader in Radiocommunications Scholarships *(Undergraduate/Scholarship)* [7567]

FXRFC Medical Research Postdoctoral Fellowships *(Postdoctorate/Fellowship)* [3994]

Franciszek Gadzala Memorial Scholarships *(Undergraduate/Scholarship)* [7763]

Harry Gairey Scholarships *(Undergraduate/Scholarship)* [2117]

Marcus Mosiah Garvey Scholarships *(Undergraduate/Scholarship)* [5118]

GCABS Youth Scholarship Awards *(High School, Undergraduate/Scholarship)* [4147]

Geological Association of Canada Student Prizes *(Undergraduate/Award)* [4085]

Geological Society of America Graduate Student Research Grants *(Doctorate, Graduate/Grant)* [4088]

Keith Gilmore Foundation - Diploma Scholarships *(Professional development/Scholarship)* [4153]

Keith Gilmore Foundation - Postgraduate Scholarships *(Postgraduate/Scholarship)* [4154]

Keith Gilmore Foundation - Undergraduate Scholarships *(Undergraduate/Scholarship)* [4155]

Dr. Helen Preston Glass Fellowships *(Doctorate/Fellowship)* [2541]

Franciszek Glogowski Memorial Scholarships *(Undergraduate/Scholarship)* [7764]

Daniel B. Goldberg Scholarships *(Graduate/Scholarship)* [4197]

Charles D. Gonthier Research Fellowships *(Graduate, Professional development/Fellowship)* [2498]

Goodfellow Professional Development Fund *(Professional development/Scholarship)* [5508]

J.O. Goodman Scholarship Awards *(Undergraduate/Scholarship)* [6899]

Baxter Corporation - Jean Goodwill Scholarships *(Postgraduate/Scholarship)* [20]

Lucille May Gopie Scholarships *(Undergraduate/Scholarship)* [2118]

Graduate Fellowship Program - Research Fellowships (GFP) *(Doctorate, Graduate/Fellowship)* [8080]

Graduate Student Scholarships *(Graduate/Scholarship)* [246]

Charles Hall Grandgent Awards *(Graduate/Award)* [3342]

Frank L. Greathouse Government Accounting Scholarships *(Graduate, Undergraduate/Scholarship)* [4198]

Reginald K. Groome Memorial Scholarships *(Undergraduate/Scholarship)* [8065]

John Simon Guggenheim Memorial Fellowships - U.S. and Canadian Competition *(Advanced Professional/Fellowship)* [4360]

Guntley-Lorimer Science and Arts Scholarships *(Undergraduate/Scholarship)* [2119]

David J. Hallissey Memorial Scholarships *(Graduate, Undergraduate/Scholarship)* [1366]

Hamilton Industrial Environmental Association Bursaries-Mohawk College *(Undergraduate/Scholarship)* [4367]

Al Hamilton Scholarships *(Undergraduate/Scholarship)* [2120]

Stan Hamilton Scholarships *(Undergraduate/Scholarship)* [7993]

Ruth Hancock Scholarships *(Undergraduate/Scholarship)* [2366]

Handweavers Guild of America and Dendel Scholarships *(Graduate, Undergraduate/Scholarship)* [4388]

Hannah Junior General Scholarships *(Graduate/Scholarship)* [1681]

Hannah Senior General Scholarships *(Graduate/Scholarship)* [1682]

Tom Hanson Photojournalism Awards *(Professional development/Internship)* [2515]

B. Harper Bull Conservation Fellowships *(Graduate/Fellowship)* [8913]

Phyllis P. Harris Scholarships *(Postgraduate/Award)* [2463]

Healy Graduate Scholarships *(Graduate/Scholarship)* [1367]

Heart and Stroke Foundation of Canada/Physiotherapy Foundation of Canada Scholarships in Physiotherapy Research *(Doctorate, Master's/Scholarship)* [7325]

Riva Heft Hecht Scholarships *(Undergraduate/Scholarship)* [7556]

Mary Jane Hendrie Memorial Scholarships *(Graduate, Undergraduate/Scholarship)* [9330]

Judy Hill Scholarships *(Undergraduate/Scholarship)* [2542]

Geordie Hilton Academic Scholarships *(Undergraduate/Scholarship)* [4184]

D. Glenn Hilts Scholarships *(Graduate, Undergraduate/Scholarship)* [1872]

Hispanic Serving Institution Scholarships (HSIS) *(Undergraduate/Scholarship)* [9024]

C.V. Hoar Scholarship Awards *(Undergraduate/Scholarship)* [6900]

C.H.(Chuck) Hodgson Scholarships *(Undergraduate/Scholarship)* [9591]

Irving J. Hoffman Memorial Scholarships *(Undergraduate/Scholarship)* [9331]

Lois Hole Humanities and Social Sciences Scholarships *(Undergraduate/Scholarship)* [247]

Holland America Line-Westours Research Grants *(Undergraduate/Grant)* [1368]

Norm Hollend Fellowships in Oncology *(Postdoctorate/Fellowship)* [5535]

Hosinec Family Scholarships *(Graduate, Undergraduate/Scholarship)* [9332]

Lloyd Houlden Research Fellowships *(Professional development/Fellowship)* [2386]

Goldwin Howland Scholarships *(Graduate/Scholarship)* [2561]

Christopher Hoy/ERT Scholarships *(Graduate, Master's/Scholarship)* [901]

William Peyton Hubbard Scholarships *(Undergraduate/Scholarship)* [2121]

Steven Huesing Scholarships *(Graduate, Undergraduate/Scholarship)* [2915]

Tertia M.C. Hughes Memorial Graduate Student Prizes *(Graduate/Prize)* [2526]

Humber College Institute of Technology and Advanced Learning Scholarships *(Undergraduate/Scholarship)* [5119]

John Peter Humphrey Student Fellowships *(Graduate/Fellowship)* [2443]

I Have a Dream Scholarships *(Undergraduate/Scholarship)* [5120]

IBA Law Student Scholarship Foundation Scholarships *(Undergraduate/Scholarship)* [4754]

iCORE ICT Graduate Student Scholarships *(Doctorate, Graduate, Master's/Scholarship)* [232]

IIE Council of Fellows Undergraduate Scholarships *(Undergraduate/Scholarship)* [4803]

In-course Scholarships - Chinese Dance Workshop Scholarships *(Undergraduate/Scholarship)* [9333]

Informatics Circle of Research Excellence Scholarships *(Doctorate, Graduate/Scholarship)* [248]

Barbara Ingram, Janet W. McCarthy and W.J.P. Jack Robertson Memorial Scholarships *(Undergraduate/Scholarship)* [6998]

Institute Community Support Publication Prizes *(Doctorate, Graduate, Undergraduate/Prize)* [2507]

Intensive Language Course Grants *(Doctorate/Grant)* [4120]

Inter American Press Association Scholarships *(Undergraduate/Scholarship)* [4846]

International Association of Black Actuaries Scholarships *(Undergraduate/Scholarship)* [4858]

International Association of Foundation Drilling Scholarships for Civil Engineering Students *(Postgraduate/Scholarship)* [1756]

International Association of Foundation Drilling Scholarships for Part-time Civil Engineering Graduate School Students *(Postgraduate/Scholarship)* [1757]

International Association of Law Libraries Scholarship Program *(Professional development/Scholarship)* [4876]

International Council for Canadian Studies Graduate Student Scholarships *(Postgraduate/Scholarship)* [4904]

International Education Awards - Ukraine *(Undergraduate/Scholarship)* [249]

International Grenfell Association Bursary *(Undergraduate/Scholarship)* [4946]

International Grenfell Association Secondary/High School Scholarships *(Undergraduate/Scholarship)* [4947]

International Grenfell Association University/College Scholarships *(Undergraduate/Scholarship)* [4948]

International Municipal Lawyers Association Canadian Scholarships *(Professional development/Scholarship)* [4963]

Investigators in the Pathogenesis of Infectious Disease Awards *(Doctorate, Postdoctorate/Grant)* [2215]

Investors Group Scholarships for Not-For-Profit Leaders *(Professional development/Scholarship)* [2007]

ISM Doctoral Fellowships *(Doctorate/Fellowship)* [4775]

ISM Scholarships for Graduate Studies *(Graduate/Scholarship)* [4776]

Dr. Karl C. Ivarson Scholarships *(Postgraduate/Scholarship)* [74]

Jamaica Day Basil Duncan Memorial Scholarships *(Undergraduate/Scholarship)* [5121]

Jamaica National Building Society Scholarships *(Undergraduate/Scholarship)* [5122]

Jamaican Canadian Association Alberta Scholarship Program *(Undergraduate/Scholarship)* [5130]

Terry Jarvis Memorial Scholarships *(Undergraduate/Scholarship)* [1439]

Right Hon. Michaelle Jean Legacy Scholarships *(Undergraduate/Scholarship)* [2122]

Harry Jerome Scholarships *(Undergraduate/Scholarship)* [2123]

Johnson & Johnson Scholarships *(Undergraduate/Scholarship)* [2543]

Robert V.A. Jones Canadians Corporate Counsel Awards *(Professional development/Award)* [2438]

E.J. Josey Scholarships *(Graduate/Scholarship)* [2133]

Kazimiera Juchniewicz Memorial Scholarships *(Undergraduate/Scholarship)* [7765]

Stefan & Weronika Kacperski Memorial Scholarships *(Undergraduate/Scholarship)* [7766]

Kalmen Kaplansky Scholarships in Economic and Social Rights *(Graduate/Scholarship)* [3475]

Lucile B. Kaufman Women's Scholarships *(Undergraduate/Scholarship)* [8388]

E. Wayne Kay Community College Scholarships *(Undergraduate/Scholarship)* [8390]

Gunild Keetman Scholarships *(Professional development, Undergraduate/Scholarship)* [6957]

Dr. Dorothy J. Kergin Scholarships *(Doctorate/Scholarship)* [2544]

Edgar Kerstan Memorial Scholarships *(Undergraduate/Scholarship)* [5771]

KFOC Allied Health Fellowships *(Doctorate/Fellowship)* [5255]

KFOC Allied Health Scholarships *(Graduate/Scholarship)* [5256]

KFOC Biomedical Fellowships *(Postdoctorate/Fellowship)* [5257]

KFOC Biomedical Scholarships *(Doctorate/Scholarship)* [5258]

Khaki University and Y.M.C.A. Memorial Scholarships *(Undergraduate/Scholarship)* [9334]

Killam Fellowships Program *(Undergraduate/Fellowship)* [9100]

Mackenzie King Open Scholarships *(Graduate/Scholarship)* [5723]

Mackenzie King Travelling Scholarships *(Graduate/Scholarship)* [5724]

Annie Kirshenblatt Memorial Scholarships *(Graduate, Undergraduate/Scholarship)* [8915]

Stefan & Janina Klimt Scholarships *(Undergraduate/Scholarship)* [7767]

George Kokocinski Memorial Scholarships *(Undergraduate/Scholarship)* [7768]

Bernie Kom Memorial Awards *(Postgraduate/Award)* [8040]

Korean Studies Dissertation Workshop Funds *(Graduate/Fellowship, Grant)* [8283]

Krawczyk-Krane Family Scholarships *(Undergraduate/Scholarship)* [7769]

Robert Krembil Scholarships of Merit *(Postgraduate/Scholarship)* [8041]

Kress Pre-Doctoral Fellowships in the History of Art and Archeology in Turkey *(Postdoctorate/Fellowship)* [1151]

David A. Kronick Travelling Fellowships *(Doctorate/Fellowship)* [5743]

Leo J. Krysa Family Undergraduate Scholarships *(Undergraduate/Scholarship)* [2504]

Jan Kuropas Memorial Scholarships *(Undergraduate/Scholarship)* [7770]

Lafarge Community Leaders Scholarships *(Professional development/Scholarship)* [2008]

Canadian Association for Studies in Co-operation Scholarships Alexander Fraser Laidlaw Fellowships (CASC) *(Graduate/Fellowship)* [2433]

Allen T. Lambert Scholarships *(Postgraduate/Scholarship)* [8042]

John and Lois Lamont Graduate Scholarships *(Postgraduate/Award)* [2464]

James D. Lang Memorial Scholarships *(Graduate/Scholarship)* [2390]

Jason Lang Scholarships *(Undergraduate/Scholarship)* [252]

Stanislaw & Aniela Lasek Scholarships *(Undergraduate/Scholarship)* [7771]

Kenneth Laundy Entrance Scholarships *(Postgraduate/Scholarship)* [8043]

Law Society of British Columbia Scholarships *(Graduate, Undergraduate/Scholarship)* [5373]

Robert G. Lawrence Prize *(Doctorate, Graduate, Professional development/Prize)* [2412]

The Leaders of Tomorrow Scholarships *(Undergraduate, Vocational/Occupational/Scholarship)* [3572]

Leber Rubes Inc. Awards *(Postgraduate/Award)* [2470]

Carol Anne Letheren Entrance Awards *(Postgraduate/Award)* [8044]

Eli Lilly Graduate Scholarships *(Graduate/Scholarship)* [2451]

Tecla Lin & Nelia Laroza Memorial Scholarships *(Undergraduate/Scholarship)* [2545]

Linda's Scholarships *(All/Scholarship)* [5882]

Donald A.B. Lindberg Research Fellowships *(Doctorate, Graduate/Fellowship)* [5744]

LITA and LSSI Minority Scholarships *(Graduate/Scholarship)* [5485]

LITA/OCLC Minority Scholarships *(Graduate/Scholarship)* [5486]

Ian Lithgow Memorial Awards *(Postgraduate/Award)* [8045]

Nancy Llewellyn, RN Pediatric Nursing Bursaries *(Graduate, Professional development/Scholarship)* [1849]

Lo Family Scholarships *(Undergraduate/Scholarship)* [9335]

London Goodenough Association of Canada Scholarships *(Graduate/Scholarship)* [5515]

Pat Lyon Nursing Fellowships *(Graduate/Fellowship)* [8916]

John Macara, Barrister of Goderich, Scholarships *(Undergraduate/Scholarship)* [9336]

CEMF Claudette MacKay-Lassonde Graduate Scholarships *(Doctorate, Postdoctorate/Scholarship)* [2456]

R. Tait Mackenzie Awards *(Professional development/Award)* [7318]

MAF Canada Scholarship Fund *(Undergraduate/Scholarship)* [5908]

Major Collaborative Research Initiatives Grants *(Graduate/Grant)* [8286]

Dick Martin Scholarships *(Postgraduate/Scholarship)* [2426]

Eleanor Jean Martin Scholarships *(Graduate/Scholarship)* [2546]

Right Honourable Paul Martin Sr. Scholarships *(Graduate/Scholarship)* [2500]

Beverly Mascoll Scholarships *(Undergraduate/Scholarship)* [2124]

Val Mason Scholarships *(Postgraduate/Scholarship)* [2603]

Tadeusz Maziarz Scholarships *(Undergraduate/Scholarship)* [7772]

John Mazurek Memorial-Morgex Insurance Scholarships *(Professional development/Scholarship)* [274]

Heather McCallum Scholarships *(Doctorate, Graduate, Professional development/Scholarship)* [2413]

David McColm Fellowships in Lung Cancer Research *(Postdoctorate/Fellowship)* [5536]

Hans McCorriston Motive Power Machinist Grant Programs *(Undergraduate, Vocational/Occupational/Scholarship)* [1956]

Joseph McCulley Educational Scholarships *(Graduate, Undergraduate/Scholarship)* [9337]

William H. McGannon Foundation Scholarships *(Graduate, Undergraduate/Scholarship)* [5721]

McGill University Scholarships for Research Trips to Europe *(Graduate/Scholarship)* [5725]

James H. McLaughlin Scholarships *(Undergraduate/Scholarship)* [6740]

John Alexander McLean Scholarships *(Undergraduate/Scholarship)* [8896]

R. Roy McMurty Fellowships in Legal History *(Doctorate, Graduate/Fellowship)* [6992]

Douglas McRorie Memorial Scholarships *(Postgraduate/Scholarship)* [75]

Medical Library Association Scholarships for Minority Students *(Graduate/Scholarship)* [5745]

Medical Student Summer Research Scholarships *(Undergraduate/Scholarship)* [374]

Dr. Ernest and Minnie Mehl Scholarships *(Undergraduate/Scholarship)* [257]

Frederic G. Melcher Scholarships *(Graduate/Scholarship)* [1827]

Mensa Canada General Scholarships *(Undergraduate/Scholarship)* [5772]

CAG Donald Menzies Bursary Awards *(Postgraduate/Award)* [2382]

Merck Frosst Canada Ltd. Postgraduate Pharmacy Fellowships *(Doctorate, Postgraduate/Fellowship)* [1771]

Al Mercury Scholarships *(Undergraduate/Scholarship)* [9338]

Bernard Michel Scholarships *(Undergraduate/Scholarship)* [2348]

Bronislaw Michno Memorial Scholarships *(Undergraduate/Scholarship)* [7773]

Military Nurses Association Scholarships *(Graduate, Master's/Scholarship)* [2547]

Miller Thomson Foundation Scholarships *(Undergraduate/Scholarship)* [5884]

Mineralogical Association of Canada Scholarships *(Doctorate, Postgraduate/Scholarship)* [5886]

Minerva Scholarships *(Undergraduate/Scholarship)* [2125]

Minorities in Government Finance Scholarships *(Graduate, Undergraduate/Scholarship)* [4199]

Minority-Serving Institution Faculty Scholar Awards *(Doctorate/Award)* [452]

MLA Research, Development, and Demonstration Project Grants *(Graduate/Grant)* [5747]

Murray Montague Memorial Scholarships *(Undergraduate/Scholarship)* [4268]

Thomas More Scholarships *(Undergraduate/Scholarship)* [4191]

John H. Moss Scholarships *(Undergraduate/Scholarship)* [9339]

Marvin Mundel Memorial Scholarships *(Undergraduate/Scholarship)* [4806]

Margaret Munro Scholarships *(Undergraduate/Scholarship)* [2548]

Dr. Helen K. Mussallem Fellowships *(Graduate/Scholarship)* [2549]

NAAF Aboriginal Health Careers Bursary and Scholarships *(Graduate, Undergraduate/Scholarship)* [5992]

NAAF Post-Secondary Education Scholarships *(Graduate, Undergraduate/Scholarship)* [5993]

NAAMA Scholarships *(Undergraduate/Scholarship)* [6024]

Irwin Allen Nadal Entrance Awards *(Postgraduate/Award)* [8046]

Miles Spencer Nadal Entrance Awards *(Postgraduate/Award)* [8047]

Nadine International Inc. Awards *(Postgraduate/Award)* [2471]

The National Board Technical Scholarships *(Undergraduate/Scholarship)* [6159]

National Society of Accountants Scholarship Program *(Undergraduate/Scholarship)* [6481]

Natural Sciences and Engineering Research Council Postgraduate Scholarships *(Doctorate/Scholarship)* [6572]

Marek Nawrot Memorial Scholarships *(Undergraduate/Scholarship)* [7774]

NCLEJ Law School Graduate Fellows and Volunteers *(Graduate/Fellowship)* [6184]

Dr. Ezra Nesbeth Scholarships *(Undergraduate/Scholarship)* [5123]

Alan H. Neville Memorial Scholarships *(Graduate, Undergraduate, Vocational/Occupational/Scholarship)* [337]

New Brunswick Law Foundation Graduate Scholarships in Law *(Graduate/Scholarship)* [5375]

Newberry Library/Ecole Nationale des Chartes Exchange Fellowships *(Graduate/Fellowship)* [6705]

Norman Nicholson Scholarships *(Undergraduate/Scholarship)* [2424]

Sharon Nield Memorial Scholarships *(Undergraduate/Scholarship)* [2551]

George A. Nielsen Public Investor Scholarships *(Graduate, Undergraduate/Scholarship)* [4200]

NLM Associate Fellowships *(Graduate, Postgraduate/Fellowship)* [6396]

Norfolk Southern Foundation Scholarships *(Undergraduate/Scholarship)* [1131]

North American Conference on British Studies Dissertation Year Fellowships *(Doctorate, Postdoctorate/Fellowship)* [6735]

North American Conference on British Studies-Huntington Library Fellowships *(Doctorate, Postdoctorate/Fellowship)* [6736]

North American Society Fellowships *(Professional development/Fellowship)* [7319]

Northern Resident Scholarships *(Doctorate, Graduate/Scholarship)* [1736]

Nova Scotia Salmon Association Scholarships *(All/Scholarship)* [6834]

NRC-HIA Plaskett Fellowships *(Doctorate/Fellowship)* [6461]

Nueroscience Certification Bursary Awards *(Professional development/Award)* [2396]

Nuffield Canada Farming Scholarships *(Undergraduate/Scholarship)* [6838]

AEBC Rick Oakes Scholarships for the Arts *(Graduate, Undergraduate, Vocational/Occupational/Scholarship)* [338]

OHTN Postdoctoral Fellowships *(Doctorate/Fellowship)* [6893]

OMHF Postdoctoral Fellowships *(Postdoctorate/Fellowship)* [6895]

Ontario Hockey Association War Memorial Scholarships *(Undergraduate/Scholarship)* [9341]

OTA Education Foundation Scholarships *(Undergraduate/Scholarship)* [6901]

Senator Norman Paterson Fellowships *(Doctorate/Fellowship)* [2552]

Q.O.(Quint) Patrick Scholarships *(Undergraduate/Scholarship)* [9592]

Arthur Paulin Automotive Aftermarket Scholarship Awards *(Postgraduate, Undergraduate/Scholarship)* [1957]

PEA Bursaries *(Undergraduate/Scholarship)* [7443]

PEA Scholarships *(Undergraduate/Scholarship)* [7444]

Florrie Penney, RN Rehabilitation Nursing Bursaries *(Graduate, Professional development/Scholarship)* [1850]

PEO Educational Loan Funds *(Graduate, Undergraduate, Vocational/Occupational/Loan)* [7306]

Mary Perlmutter Scholarships *(Postgraduate/Award)* [2565]

Petroleum History Society Graduate Scholarships *(Graduate/Scholarship)* [7215]

PHE Canada Health Educator Awards *(Professional development/Award)* [7320]

PHE Canada Student Awards *(Undergraduate/Award)* [7321]

Shoshana Philipp (Kirshenblatt) R.N. Memorial Scholarships *(Graduate, Undergraduate/Scholarship)* [8917]

Physical Education Teaching Excellence (PETE) Awards *(Professional development/Award)* [7322]

Physiotherapy Foundation of Canada Research Grants *(Professional development/Grant)* [7326]

Eleonora Pidperyhora Scholarship *(Undergraduate/Scholarship)* [7775]

PIMS Postdoctoral Fellowships *(Doctorate/Fellowship)* [7029]

Dr. Adolph Piotrowski Memorial Art Scholarships *(Undergraduate/Scholarship)* [7776]

Pleasant Hawaiian Holidays Scholarships *(Undergraduate/Scholarship)* [1369]

D.F. Plett Graduate Fellowships *(Graduate/Fellowship)* [7342]

Plumbing-Heating-Cooling Contractors Association Educational Foundation Need-Based Scholarships *(Undergraduate/Scholarship)* [7347]

Plumbing-Heating-Cooling Contractors Association Educational Foundation Scholarships *(Undergraduate/Scholarship)* [7348]

David Pohl Scholarships *(Graduate, Master's/Scholarship)* [8998]

Roy H. Pollack Scholarships *(Graduate, Master's/Scholarship)* [8999]

Stan and Leone Pollard Scholarships *(Undergraduate/Scholarship)* [1370]

Gail Posluns Fellowships in Hematology *(Postdoctorate/Fellowship)* [5537]

Post Basic Course Bursaries *(Graduate, Professional development/Scholarship)* [1851]

Postdoctoral Fellowships at the Fields Institute *(Postdoctorate/Fellowship)* [3745]

J.R. (Joe) Power National Scholarships *(Postgraduate/Scholarship)* [7546]

Gerald Pratley Awards *(Doctorate, Graduate/Award)* [3747]

President's Prize *(Professional development/Prize)* [2527]

Diana M. Priestly Memorial Scholarships *(Undergraduate/Scholarship)* [2391]

Prince Edward Island Law Student Scholarships *(Undergraduate/Scholarship)* [5377]

Dennis R. Prince Scholarships *(Undergraduate/Scholarship)* [7457]

Professional Institute of the Public Service of Canada Expanded Scholarships *(Undergraduate/Scholarship)* [7446]

Provincial and Regional 4-H Scholarships *(Undergraduate/Scholarship)* [200]

ProWorld Study Abroad Scholarships *(Undergraduate/Scholarship)* [4178]

PSAC - Coughlin National Scholarships *(Postgraduate/Scholarship)* [7547]

PSAC - Groulx National Scholarships *(Postgraduate/Scholarship)* [7548]

PSAC National Scholarships *(Postgraduate/Scholarship)* [7549]

PSAC Regional Scholarships *(Postgraduate/Scholarship)* [7550]

Public Employee Retirement Research and Administration Scholarships *(Graduate/Scholarship)* [4201]

Doug Purvis Prize *(Professional development/Prize)* [2368]

Queen Elizabeth II Graduate Scholarship Program *(Doctorate, Graduate/Scholarship)* [263]

RBC Financial Group Scholarships *(Graduate/Scholarship)* [2126]

RBC Royal Bank Scholarships for First Year Medical & Dental Students *(Undergraduate/Scholarship)* [7823]

RBC Royal Bank Scholarships for New Canadians *(Undergraduate/Scholarship)* [7824]

RBC Royal Bank Scholarships for Undergraduates *(Undergraduate/Scholarship)* [7825]

J.H. Stewart Reid Memorial Fellowship Trust *(Doctorate/Fellowship)* [2415]

J.H. Stewart Reid Memorial Fellowships *(Doctorate, Graduate/Fellowship)* [7730]

Siobhan Isabella Reid Memorial Scholarships *(Graduate, Undergraduate/Scholarship)* [5393]

George Reinke Scholarships *(Professional development/Scholarship)* [1371]

W. Reymonta Scholarships *(Undergraduate/Scholarship)* [7777]

Marion Roberts Memorial Scholarships *(Undergraduate/Scholarship)* [1958]

Gertrude J. Robinson Book Prize *(Professional development/Prize)* [2436]

R.O.E.A. Dumitru Golea Goldy-Gemu Scholarships *(Undergraduate/Scholarship)* [1165]

Geraldine Ruth Rogers Scholarships *(Undergraduate/Scholarship)* [8897]

Mandell and Lester Rosenblatt and Robert N. Herbert Undergraduate Scholarships *(Undergraduate/Scholarship)* [8417]

Robert Roy Awards *(Professional development/Award)* [2406]

RPNAS Baccalaureate Level Program Scholarships *(Graduate/Scholarship)* [7723]

RPNAS Doctorate Level Program Scholarships *(Doctorate/Scholarship)* [7724]

RPNAS Master's Level Program Scholarships *(Graduate, Master's/Scholarship)* [7725]

Glen Ruby Memorial Scholarships *(Undergraduate/Scholarship)* [2613]

Violet D. Ruelokke Primary Health Care Awards *(Graduate, Professional development/Scholarship)* [1852]

Rutherford Scholars *(Undergraduate/Scholarship)* [265]

Ryerson Scholarships *(Undergraduate/Scholarship)* [5124]

Chester & Maria Sadowski Memorial Scholarships *(Undergraduate/Scholarship)* [7778]

Saint Paul University Excellence Scholarships *(Undergraduate/Scholarship)* [7887]

Saint Paul University Financial Aid Bursaries *(Undergraduate/Scholarship)* [7888]

AIST David H. Samson Scholarships *(Undergraduate/Scholarship)* [1816]

Sanofi Pasteur Scholarships *(Graduate/Scholarship)* [2553]

Saskatchewan Government Insurance Actuarial Science Scholarships *(Undergraduate/Scholarship)* [7996]

Saskatchewan Government Insurance Anniversary Scholarships *(Undergraduate/Scholarship)* [7997]

Saskatchewan Government Insurance Graduate Student Traffic Safety Research Scholarhips *(Graduate/Scholarship)* [7999]

Saskatchewan Hockey Association Scholarships *(Undergraduate/Scholarship)* [8001]

Saskatchewan Pulse Growers Undergraduate Scholarships *(Undergraduate/Scholarship)* [8004]

Saskatchewan School Boards Association Education Scholarships *(Undergraduate/Scholarship)* [8007]

Saskatchewan School Boards Association Graduate Student Awards *(Graduate, Doctorate/Award)* [8008]

Francois J. Saucier Prize in Applied Oceanography *(Professional development/Prize)* [2528]

Savoy Foundation Postdoctoral and Clinical Research Fellowships *(Postdoctorate/Fellowship)* [8012]

SCA Nursing Scholarships *(Graduate, Professional development/Scholarship)* [2476]

Richard J. Schmeelk Fellowships *(Graduate/Fellowship)* [8020]

B.E. Schnurr Memorial Fund Research Grants *(Professional development/Grant)* [7327]

Scholarships for Aboriginal Canadians *(Undergraduate/Scholarship)* [6550]

Scholarships for Visible Minorities *(Undergraduate/Scholarship)* [6551]

School Age Financial Aid Program *(Undergraduate/Scholarship)* [2050]

Tanna H. Schulich MBA Entrance Scholarships *(Postgraduate/Scholarship)* [8048]

Fritz Schwartz Serials Education Scholarships

(Graduate, Professional development/Scholarship) [6744]

Scotiabank Scholarship for Business Studies *(Graduate/Scholarship)* [2127]

SEMA Memorial Scholarships *(Graduate, Undergraduate, Vocational/Occupational/Scholarship)* [1959]

Lal Bahadur Shastri Student Prize *(Graduate, Undergraduate/Prize)* [8099]

David S. Sheridan Canadian Research Awards *(Professional development/Award)* [2360]

Sigma Theta Tau International Scholarships *(Doctorate/Scholarship)* [2554]

Julia Viola Simms Science Scholarships *(Postgraduate/Scholarship)* [2128]

Sloan Research Fellowships *(Doctorate/Fellowship)* [8235]

SME Education Foundation Family Scholarships *(Undergraduate/Scholarship)* [8399]

Donald Smiley Prize *(Professional development/Prize)* [2585]

Eva Smith Bursary *(Undergraduate/Scholarship)* [5125]

David W. Smith Fellowships *(Postdoctorate/Fellowship)* [2605]

A.O. Smith Scholarships *(Undergraduate/Scholarship)* [7349]

Brian Smith Scholarships *(Undergraduate/Scholarship)* [2169]

Smiths Medical Canada Ltd. Research Awards *(Professional development/Award)* [2361]

Boleslaw & Irena Sobczak Scholarships *(Undergraduate/Scholarship)* [7779]

Frank H. Sobey Awards for Excellence in Business Studies *(Undergraduate/Award)* [8277]

Sobeys & Empire Work Experience & Scholarship Program - Future Leaders Awards *(Professional development/Award)* [8278]

Social Sciences and Humanities Research Council of Canada Standard Research Grants *(Doctorate, Graduate/Grant)* [8287]

Society of Graphic Designers of Canada Adobe Scholarships *(Undergraduate/Scholarship)* [8331]

Society of Graphic Designers of Canada Applied Arts Scholarships *(Undergraduate/Scholarship)* [8332]

Society of Graphic Designers of Canada Veer Scholarships *(Undergraduate/Scholarship)* [8333]

Society of Naval Architects and Marine Engineers Undergraduate Scholarships *(Undergraduate/Scholarship)* [8418]

Carin Alma E. Somers Scholarship Trust *(Undergraduate/Scholarship)* [1927]

SPEATBC Scholarships *(Undergraduate/Scholarship)* [8482]

Patrick Spielman Memorial Scholarship Program *(Undergraduate, Vocational/Occupational/Scholarship)* [8071]

SSHRC Doctoral Fellowship Program *(Doctorate/Fellowship, Scholarship)* [8288]

Taylor Statten Memorial Fellowships *(Graduate/Scholarship)* [9342]

The Stanley H. Stearman Awards *(Undergraduate/Scholarship)* [6482]

Harry Steele Entrance Awards *(Postgraduate/Award)* [8049]

H.H. Stern Grant Awards *(Professional development/Grant)* [2407]

TAC Foundation-Albert M. Stevens Scholarships *(Postgraduate/Scholarship)* [8931]

David Stockwood Memorial Prize *(Professional development/Prize)* [66]

Marlene Streit Golf Scholarships *(Undergraduate/Scholarship)* [4185]

Study Scholarships for Artists or Musicians *(Graduate/Scholarship)* [4123]

Summerside-Natick Hockey Scholarships *(Undergraduate/Scholarship)* [3185]

Sun Life Financial Peer Support Scholarships *(Professional development/Scholarship)* [2579]

Super Kutz Scholarships *(Undergraduate/Scholarship)* [8776]

TAC Foundation-3M Canada Company Scholarships *(Postgraduate, Undergraduate/Scholarship)* [8932]

TAC Foundation-Armtec Scholarships *(Undergraduate/Scholarship)* [8933]

TAC Foundation-Cement Association of Canada Scholarships *(Postgraduate, Undergraduate/Scholarship)* [8934]

TAC Foundation-Delcan Corporation Scholarships *(Postgraduate, Undergraduate/Scholarship)* [8935]

TAC Foundation-Dillon Consulting Scholarships *(Undergraduate/Scholarship)* [8936]

TAC Foundation-IBI Group Scholarships *(Postgraduate, Undergraduate/Scholarship)* [8938]

TAC Foundation-iTRANS Consulting Scholarships *(Postgraduate/Scholarship)* [8939]

TAC Foundation-McCormick Rankin Corporation Scholarships *(Undergraduate/Scholarship)* [8940]

TAC Foundation-MMM Group Limited Scholarships *(Postgraduate, Undergraduate/Scholarship)* [8941]

TAC Foundation-Municipalities Scholarships *(Postgraduate, Undergraduate/Scholarship)* [8942]

TAC Foundation-Provinces and Territories Scholarships *(Postgraduate, Undergraduate/Scholarship)* [8943]

TAC Foundation-Stantec Consulting Scholarships *(Postgraduate/Scholarship)* [8944]

TAC Foundation-UMA Engineering Ltd. Scholarships *(Undergraduate/Scholarship)* [8945]

TAC Foundation-Waterloo Alumni Scholarships *(Postgraduate/Scholarship)* [8946]

TD Meloche-Monnex Scholarships *(Doctorate/Scholarship)* [2555]

Barbara Thomas Bursary *(Undergraduate/Scholarship)* [5126]

Nadene M. Thomas Graduate Research Scholarships *(Graduate/Scholarship)* [275]

Rev. Chuck and Nancy Thomas Scholarships *(Graduate, Master's/Scholarship)* [9004]

Dr. Andrew Thomson Prize in Applied Meteorology *(Professional development/Prize)* [2529]

Thomson Reuters/MLA Doctoral Fellowships *(Doctorate/Fellowship)* [5748]

Ken Thomson Scholarships *(Undergraduate/Scholarship)* [2632]

TIAC / Parks Canada Sustainable Tourism Scholarships *(College, Undergraduate, Master's/Scholarship)* [8921]

Evald Torokvei Foundation Scholarships *(Graduate/Scholarship)* [9343]

Toronto Rehab Scholarships in Rehabilitation-Related Research *(Graduate/Scholarship)* [8918]

Toronto Rehabilitation Institute Graduate Student Scholarships - Ontario Student Opportunities Trust Fund (OSOTF) *(Graduate/Scholarship)* [8919]

Toyota Earth Day Scholarships *(Undergraduate/Scholarship)* [8925]

Transoft Solutions, Inc. Ahead of the Curve Scholarships (AOTC) *(Graduate, Undergraduate/Scholarship)* [4827]

Transportation Association of Canada Foundation Scholarships *(Postgraduate, Undergraduate/Scholarship)* [8947]

Marie Tremaine Fellowships *(Postgraduate, Professional development/Fellowship)* [2088]

Trudeau Foundation Doctoral Scholarships *(Doctorate/Scholarship)* [8968]

Sam Tughan Scholarships *(Undergraduate/Scholarship)* [2593]

Ukrainian Canadian Professional and Business Club Scholarships in Education *(Undergraduate/Scholarship)* [2505]

Underwriters' Laboratories of Canada Awards *(Postgraduate/Award)* [2472]

United Parcel Service Scholarships for Female Students *(Undergraduate/Scholarship)* [4810]

United Parcel Service Scholarships for Minority Students *(Undergraduate/Scholarship)* [4811]

University Summer Course Grants *(Undergraduate/Grant)* [4124]

University of Toronto Accenture Scholarships *(Undergraduate/Scholarship)* [9344]

University of Toronto SAC Undergraduate Grants *(Undergraduate/Grant)* [9345]

Claudette Upton Scholarships *(Undergraduate/Scholarship)* [3588]

Urban Financial Services Coalition Scholarships

CANADA (BY PROVINCE)

Alberta

British Columbia

Manitoba

New Brunswick

Newfoundland and Labrador

Nova Scotia

Leon Bradley Scholarships *(Undergraduate/Scholarship)* [548]
Scholarship Awards of The Aliant Pioneer Volunteers *(Postgraduate/Scholarship)* [2531]

Ontario

AEBC Toronto Chapter Scholarships *(Graduate, Undergraduate, Vocational/Occupational/Scholarship)* [335]
CAA National Capital Region Writing Contest *(All/Prize)* [2417]
George Joseph Cooper Awards *(Undergraduate/Scholarship)* [6995]
Lord Dundonald Chapter Imperial Order Daughters of the Empire Scholarships (IODE) *(Undergraduate/Scholarship)* [6996]
Guelph Caribbean Canadian Association Scholarships *(Undergraduate/Scholarship)* [4355]
Elizabeth Heath Technical, Trades Training and Development Awards *(Undergraduate/Scholarship)* [6997]
Dr. E. Bruce Hendrick Scholarships *(All/Scholarship)* [8647]
IHRDP Post-doctoral Fellowships *(Doctorate, Graduate, Master's, Postdoctorate/Fellowship, Scholarship)* [4756]
Kildonan Education Awards *(Undergraduate/Scholarship)* [6999]
Gloria Landis Bursary *(Undergraduate, Vocational/Occupational/Scholarship)* [5398]
Jack Meadows Memorial Awards *(Undergraduate/Scholarship)* [7000]
Nortel Institute Undergraduate Scholarships *(Undergraduate/Scholarship)* [9340]
Ontario Women's Institute Scholarships *(Undergraduate/Scholarship)* [3734]
Beatrice Drinnan Spence Scholarships *(Undergraduate, Vocational/Occupational/Scholarship)* [3573]
Tristin Memorial Scholarships *(Undergraduate, Vocational/Occupational/Scholarship)* [5395]

Prince Edward Island

Joan Auld Scholarships *(Undergraduate/Scholarship)* [3181]
Leon Bradley Scholarships *(Undergraduate/Scholarship)* [548]
Phillips Scholarships *(Undergraduate/Scholarship)* [3184]
Scholarship Awards of The Aliant Pioneer Volunteers *(Postgraduate/Scholarship)* [2531]

Quebec

Leon Bradley Scholarships *(Undergraduate/Scholarship)* [548]
IRSST Doctoral Scholarships Abroad *(Doctorate/Fellowship)* [4768]
IRSST Doctoral Scholarships Supplement *(Doctorate/Fellowship)* [4769]
IRSST Doctoral Scholarships *(Doctorate/Fellowship)* [4767]
IRSST Masters Scholarships Supplement *(Graduate/Fellowship)* [4771]
IRSST Masters Scholarships *(Graduate/Fellowship)* [4770]
IRSST Postdoctoral Scholarships Abroad *(Doctorate/Fellowship)* [4773]
IRSST Postdoctoral Scholarships *(Doctorate/Fellowship)* [4772]

Saskatchewan

Alliance Pipeline Scholarships *(Professional development/Scholarship)* [2005]
Cameco Northern Scholarships - Technical Institute *(Undergraduate/Scholarship)* [2346]
Cameco Northern Scholarships - University *(Undergraduate/Scholarship)* [2347]
Don Jaques Memorial Fellowships *(Graduate, Doctorate/Fellowship)* [8003]
Poundmaker Memorial Scholarships *(Undergraduate/Scholarship)* [6565]

Risk Management and Insurance Scholarships - University of Calgary *(Undergraduate/Scholarship)* [7995]
Saskatchewan Government Insurance Corporate Scholarships *(Undergraduate/Scholarship)* [7998]
Dr. Alfred E. Slinkard Scholarships *(Graduate, Doctorate/Scholarship)* [8005]
TAC Foundation-EBA Engineering Consultants Ltd. Scholarships *(Graduate, Postgraduate/Scholarship)* [8937]

INTERNATIONAL

American Association of University Women International Fellowships *(Graduate, Postgraduate/Fellowship)* [11]
American Welding Society International Scholarships *(Undergraduate/Scholarship)* [1425]
Jane Beattie Memorial Scholarships *(All/Scholarship)* [8362]
Myrna F. Bernath Fellowships *(Doctorate, Graduate/Fellowship)* [8337]
HHMI International Student Research Fellowships *(Doctorate/Fellowship)* [4622]
IOIA Organic Community Initiative Scholarships *(Professional development/Scholarship)* [4716]
Law and Society Association International Prize *(Professional development/Prize)* [5369]
Rice-Cullimore Scholarships *(Graduate/Scholarship)* [1662]
IOIA Andrew Rutherford Scholarships *(Professional development/Scholarship)* [4717]
Ryan and Jamie Smith Essay Contest *(Graduate, Postgraduate/Scholarship)* [8237]
University of Maryland International Student Scholarships *(Undergraduate/Scholarship)* [9076]
John D. Wirth Travel Grants for International Scholars *(Graduate, Professional development/Grant)* [1254]
Deborah Partridge Wolfe International Fellowships *(Graduate, Undergraduate/Fellowship)* [9807]

INTERNATIONAL (BY REGION)

Asia

University of Hawaii at Manoa East-West Center Graduate Fellowships *(Graduate, Postdoctorate/Fellowship)* [9206]

Caribbean

Caribbean Hotel and Tourism Association Academic Scholarships *(Graduate, Undergraduate/Scholarship)* [2653]

Eastern Europe

Prins Foundation Fellowship for Senior Scholars *(Doctorate/Fellowship)* [2696]
Prins Foundation Post-Doctoral and Early Career Fellowship for Emigrating Scholars *(Professional development, Postdoctorate/Fellowship)* [2697]

Eurasia region

Bill Maynes Fellowships *(Professional development/Fellowship)* [3691]

Europe

HAESF Graduate Scholarships *(Graduate/Scholarship)* [4640]
HAESF Professional Internship Program *(Doctorate/Internship)* [4641]
HAESF Senior Leaders and Scholars Fellowships *(Professional development/Fellowship)* [4642]
Monte R. Mitchell Global Scholarships *(Undergraduate/Scholarship)* [136]

Latin America

Fellowships to Promote Research on the Legal Framework for Civil Society in Latin America, Africa and Asia *(All/Fellowship)* [4892]
Pew Latin American Fellows Program in the Biomedical Sciences *(Professional development/Fellowship)* [7219]
Leo S. Rowe Pan American Fund *(Graduate, Undergraduate/Loan)* [6967]

North America

American Association of Professional Apiculturists Research Scholarships *(Graduate, Undergraduate/Scholarship)* [541]
American Wine Society Educational Foundation Scholarships *(Graduate/Scholarship)* [1450]
Robert E. Dougherty Scholarships *(Undergraduate/Scholarship)* [3209]
Independent Lubricant Manufacturers Association Scholarships *(Undergraduate/Scholarship)* [4712]
Irish-American Research Travel Fellowships *(Professional development/Fellowship)* [1230]
J. Merrill Knapp Research Fellowships *(Undergraduate/Fellowship)* [782]
Mary Fran Myers Scholarships *(All/Grant)* [6569]
North American Rolex Scholarships *(Professional development, Undergraduate/Scholarship)* [7002]
Galvanize the Future: Edgar K. Schutz Scholarships *(Graduate, Undergraduate/Prize, Scholarship)* [774]
Roger K. Summit Scholarships for North America *(Graduate/Scholarship)* [3436]
Wexner Graduate Fellowships/Davidson Scholars *(Graduate/Fellowship)* [9589]
Aubrey L. Williams Research Travel Fellowships *(Professional development/Fellowship)* [1236]

Scandinavia

ASF/Annika Teig/Skidmore, Owings and Merril Fellowships *(Undergraduate/Fellowship)* [1172]

Soviet Union

Prins Foundation Fellowship for Senior Scholars *(Doctorate/Fellowship)* [2696]
Prins Foundation Post-Doctoral and Early Career Fellowship for Emigrating Scholars *(Professional development, Postdoctorate/Fellowship)* [2697]

With citizenship in a developing country

Franklin Mosher Baldwin Memorial Fellowships *(Master's, Doctorate/Fellowship)* [5390]

INTERNATIONAL (BY COUNTRY)

Pamfil and Maria Bujea Family Orthodox Christian Seminarian Scholarships *(Undergraduate/Scholarship)* [1163]

American Samoa

Al Schuman Ecolab Undergraduate Entrepreneurial Scholarships *(Undergraduate/Scholarship)* [6463]

Australia

American Australian Association Neurological Fellowships *(Graduate/Fellowship)* [574]
Harkness Fellowships in Health Care Policy and Practice *(Doctorate, Graduate/Fellowship)* [3020]
ProWorld Study Abroad Scholarships *(Undergraduate/Scholarship)* [4178]
Morgan Stanley Pediatrics Fellowships *(Doctorate, Postdoctorate/Fellowship)* [575]

Barbados

Barbados Cancer Association Post-Graduate Scholarships (Graduate/Scholarship) [2021]

British Virgin Islands

Judith A. Towle Environmental Studies Fund (Undergraduate/Fellowship) [5082]

Bulgaria

Mellon Advanced Fellowships in Turkey for East European Scholars (Doctorate/Fellowship) [1152]

China

Lucy Hsu Ho Scholarships (Undergraduate/Scholarship) [2062]

Cuba

Cintas Foundation Fellowships in Architecture (Professional development/Fellowship) [2881]
Cintas Foundation Fellowships in Visual Arts (Professional development/Fellowship) [2882]
Brandon Fradd Fellowships in Music Competition (Professional development/Fellowship) [2883]

Czech Republic

Mellon Advanced Fellowships in Turkey for East European Scholars (Doctorate/Fellowship) [1152]

Denmark

American-Scandinavian Foundation Fellowships and Grants to Study in America (Graduate/Fellowship, Grant) [1168]
Edith and Arnold N. Bodtker Grants (All/Grant) [3339]
SSOC Scholarships (Undergraduate/Scholarship) [8014]

Estonia

Mellon Advanced Fellowships in Turkey for East European Scholars (Doctorate/Fellowship) [1152]

Finland

American-Scandinavian Foundation Fellowships and Grants to Study in America (Graduate/Fellowship, Grant) [1168]

Germany

American Society of Comparative Law TransCoop Programs (All/Fellowship) [1204]
APSA Congressional Fellowships (Professional development/Fellowship) [4131]
Harkness Fellowships in Health Care Policy and Practice (Doctorate, Graduate/Fellowship) [3020]

Ghana

African Humanities Fellowships (Postdoctorate/Fellowship) [673]
GCABS Youth Scholarship Awards (High School, Undergraduate/Scholarship) [4147]

Greenland

Fritz Schwartz Serials Education Scholarships (Graduate, Professional development/Scholarship) [6744]

Guam

Al Schuman Ecolab Undergraduate Entrepreneurial Scholarships (Undergraduate/Scholarship) [6463]

Hungary

Dr. Elemer and Eva Kiss Scholarship Fund (Undergraduate/Scholarship) [4638]
Mellon Advanced Fellowships in Turkey for East European Scholars (Doctorate/Fellowship) [1152]

Iceland

American-Scandinavian Foundation Fellowships and Grants to Study in America (Graduate/Fellowship, Grant) [1168]

India

Guthikonda BasavapunnaRao & Umadevi Scholarships (Graduate/Scholarship) [8829]
Chereddi NarayanaRao & Radhamanohari Scholarships (Graduate/Scholarship) [8830]
Guthikonda Ramabrahmam & Balamani (Graduate/Scholarship) [8831]
Gadde Sitaramamma & Tirupataiah Scholarships (Graduate/Scholarship) [8832]
Vallabhaneni Sukundamma & Lakshmaiah Scholarships (Graduate/Scholarship) [8833]
TANA Foundation Graduate Scholarships (Graduate/Scholarship) [8834]
Kodali Veeraiah & Sarojini Scholarships (Graduate/Scholarship) [8835]

Ireland

Irish-American Research Travel Fellowships (Professional development/Fellowship) [1230]

Israel

Israeli Fellowships (Doctorate, Postdoctorate/Fellowship) [2685]
Tikvah Fellowships (Graduate, Professional development/Fellowship) [8909]

Japan

Crown Prince Akihito Scholarship Foundation (Graduate/Scholarship) [5132]

Kazakhstan

Russian/Central Asian Student Scholarships (Undergraduate/Scholarship) [9172]

Kyrgyzstan

Russian/Central Asian Student Scholarships (Undergraduate/Scholarship) [9172]

Latvia

Mellon Advanced Fellowships in Turkey for East European Scholars (Doctorate/Fellowship) [1152]

Lebanon

American Lebanese Engineering Society Scholarship Program (Graduate, Undergraduate/Scholarship) [892]

Lithuania

Mellon Advanced Fellowships in Turkey for East European Scholars (Doctorate/Fellowship) [1152]

Marshall Islands

APIASF Scholarships (Undergraduate/Scholarship) [1655]

Mexico

Stan Beck Fellowships (Graduate, Undergraduate/Fellowship) [3652]
BioQuip Undergraduate Scholarships (Undergraduate/Scholarship) [3653]

Ginger and Fred Deines Mexico Scholarships (Undergraduate, Vocational/Occupational/Scholarship) [8950]
Fleming/Blaszcak Scholarships (Graduate, Undergraduate/Scholarship) [8447]
Geological Society of America Graduate Student Research Grants (Doctorate, Graduate/Grant) [4088]
IIE Council of Fellows Undergraduate Scholarships (Undergraduate/Scholarship) [4803]
Marvin Mundel Memorial Scholarships (Undergraduate/Scholarship) [4806]
Ronald L. Schmied Scholarships (Professional development, Undergraduate/Scholarship) [4362]
Fritz Schwartz Serials Education Scholarships (Graduate, Professional development/Scholarship) [6744]
Tribeca Film Institute Media Arts Fellowships in Mexico (Professional development/Fellowship) [8959]
UC MEXUS Grants for Dissertation Research (Graduate/Grant) [9199]
UC MEXUS Short-Term Projects (Master's, Doctorate, Postdoctorate/Grant) [9200]
United Parcel Service Scholarships for Female Students (Undergraduate/Scholarship) [4810]
United Parcel Service Scholarships for Minority Students (Undergraduate/Scholarship) [4811]
Abel Wolman Fellowships (Doctorate/Fellowship) [1419]

Micronesia

APIASF Scholarships (Undergraduate/Scholarship) [1655]

Nepal

Hugh and Helen Wood Nepales Scholarships (Undergraduate/Scholarship) [2066]

Netherlands

Harkness Fellowships in Health Care Policy and Practice (Doctorate, Graduate/Fellowship) [3020]
Netherlands-Florida Scholarship Foundation Scholarships (Doctorate, Graduate/Scholarship) [6615]

New Zealand

Harkness Fellowships in Health Care Policy and Practice (Doctorate, Graduate/Fellowship) [3020]

Nigeria

African Humanities Fellowships (Postdoctorate/Fellowship) [673]
NWAG Nigeria Scholarships (Undergraduate/Scholarship) [6719]

Northern Mariana Islands

APIASF Scholarships (Undergraduate/Scholarship) [1655]

Norway

American-Scandinavian Foundation Fellowships and Grants to Study in America (Graduate/Fellowship, Grant) [1168]
Harkness Fellowships in Health Care Policy and Practice (Doctorate, Graduate/Fellowship) [3020]
SSOC Scholarships (Undergraduate/Scholarship) [8014]

Palau

APIASF Scholarships (Undergraduate/Scholarship) [1655]

Panama

Fellowships and Internships Program in Latin America *(Graduate/Fellowship, Internship)* [8269]

Peru

William L. Brown Fellowships *(Graduate/Fellowship)* [6978]

David and Deborah Clark Fellowships *(Graduate/Fellowship)* [6979]

Rexford Daubenmire Fellowships *(Graduate/Fellowship)* [6980]

Dole Food Fellowships *(Graduate/Fellowship)* [6981]

Emily P. Foster Fellowships *(Graduate/Fellowship)* [6982]

Peace Frogs Fellowships *(Graduate/Fellowship)* [6984]

Lillian and Murray Slatkin Fellowships *(Graduate/Fellowship)* [6986]

F. Christian and Betty Thompson Fellowships *(Graduate/Fellowship)* [6988]

Poland

Mellon Advanced Fellowships in Turkey for East European Scholars *(Doctorate/Fellowship)* [1152]

Portugal

Al Schuman Ecolab Undergraduate Entrepreneurial Scholarships *(Undergraduate/Scholarship)* [6463]

Romania

Mellon Advanced Fellowships in Turkey for East European Scholars *(Doctorate/Fellowship)* [1152]

Russia

Russian/Central Asian Student Scholarships *(Undergraduate/Scholarship)* [9172]

Saint Kitts and Nevis

Judith A. Towle Environmental Studies Fund *(Undergraduate/Fellowship)* [5082]

Slovakia

Mellon Advanced Fellowships in Turkey for East European Scholars *(Doctorate/Fellowship)* [1152]

South Africa

African Humanities Fellowships *(Postdoctorate/Fellowship)* [673]

Sweden

American-Scandinavian Foundation Fellowships and Grants to Study in America *(Graduate/Fellowship, Grant)* [1168]

Harkness Fellowships in Health Care Policy and Practice *(Doctorate, Graduate/Fellowship)* [3020]

SSOC Scholarships *(Undergraduate/Scholarship)* [8014]

Switzerland

Harkness Fellowships in Health Care Policy and Practice *(Doctorate, Graduate/Fellowship)* [3020]

Taiwan

Joel R. Friend Scholarships *(Undergraduate/Scholarship)* [2060]

Tanzania

African Humanities Fellowships *(Postdoctorate/Fellowship)* [673]

Godparents for Tanzania Scholarships *(Undergraduate/Scholarship)* [4169]

Thailand

Joel R. Friend Scholarships *(Undergraduate/Scholarship)* [2060]

Turkey

Getty Research Exchange Fellowship Program for Cultural Heritage Preservation *(Doctorate/Fellowship)* [1149]

Turkmenistan

Russian/Central Asian Student Scholarships *(Undergraduate/Scholarship)* [9172]

Uganda

African Humanities Fellowships *(Postdoctorate/Fellowship)* [673]

Ukraine

Alberta Ukrainian Centennial Commemorative Scholarships *(Graduate/Scholarship)* [9496]

Canada-Ukraine Parliamentary Program Internship Scholarships (CUPP) *(Undergraduate/Scholarship)* [9497]

Chopivsky Fellowships *(Graduate/Scholarship)* [9498]

Eugene & Elinor Kotur Scholarship Trust Fund *(Undergraduate, Graduate/Scholarship)* [9499]

The Ivan Shandor Memorial Ukrainian American Bar Association Scholarships *(Master's/Scholarship)* [9500]

USA/USA-Ukramerazha Scholarships *(Undergraduate/Scholarship)* [9077]

Marusia Yaworska Entrance Scholarships *(Graduate/Scholarship)* [9501]

United Kingdom

Harkness Fellowships in Health Care Policy and Practice *(Doctorate, Graduate/Fellowship)* [3020]

United States Virgin Islands

Almeric Christian Memorial Scholarships *(Graduate/Scholarship)* [9438]

Al Schuman Ecolab Undergraduate Entrepreneurial Scholarships *(Undergraduate/Scholarship)* [6463]

Uzbekistan

Russian/Central Asian Student Scholarships *(Undergraduate/Scholarship)* [9172]

Vietnam

VEF Fellowship Program *(Doctorate, Master's/Fellowship)* [9424]

VEF Visiting Scholars Program *(Doctorate/Scholarship)* [9425]

Place of Study Index

This index lists awards that carry restrictions on where study may take place. Award citations are arranged alphabetically under the following geographic headings: United States, United States (by region), United States (by state), Canada, Canada (by province), International, International (by region), and International (by country). Each citation is followed by the study level and award type, which appear in parentheses. Numbers following the parenthetical information indicate book entry numbers for particular awards, not page numbers.

UNITED STATES

4th Infantry Division Association Scholarships *(All/Scholarship)* [5990]

92109 Community Fund-Mark and Karla Stuart Family Scholarships *(Undergraduate, Vocational/Occupational/Scholarship)* [7903]

AAA Leadership Mentoring/Shadow Award Program *(Graduate/Award)* [405]

AAA Minority Dissertation Fellowship Program *(Doctorate/Fellowship)* [406]

AAAA Scholarship Program *(Undergraduate/Scholarship)* [1611]

AAACN Scholarships *(Undergraduate/Scholarship)* [437]

AAAS Mass Media Science and Engineering Fellowships *(Graduate, Postgraduate, Undergraduate/Fellowship)* [430]

AAAS Science and Technology Policy Fellowships *(Postdoctorate/Fellowship)* [431]

AABP Amstutz Scholarships *(Undergraduate/Scholarship)* [443]

AABP Bovine Veterinary Student Recognition Awards *(Undergraduate/Scholarship)* [444]

AABP Education Grants *(Undergraduate/Grant)* [445]

AABP Research Assistantships *(Doctorate/Scholarship)* [446]

AABP Student Externship Program *(Undergraduate/Scholarship)* [447]

AACE International Competitive Scholarships *(Undergraduate/Scholarship)* [4]

AACN Continuing Professional Development Scholarships *(Graduate, Professional development/Scholarship)* [469]

AACN Minority Nurse Faculty Scholarships *(Graduate/Scholarship)* [457]

AACOM Scholar in Residence Program *(Graduate, Undergraduate/Scholarship)* [461]

AACT Undergraduate Scholarships *(Undergraduate/Scholarship)* [7153]

AACTE Outstanding Book Awards *(Professional development/Award)* [463]

AACTE Outstanding Dissertation Awards *(Doctorate/Award)* [464]

AAEP/ALSIC Scholarships *(Undergraduate/Scholarship)* [474]

AAEP Foundation Past Presidents' Research Fellowships *(Doctorate/Scholarship)* [475]

AAFPE LEX Scholarships *(Undergraduate/Scholarship)* [526]

AAGS Graduate Fellowship Awards *(Undergraduate/Fellowship)* [641]

AAHD Scholarships *(Graduate, Undergraduate/Scholarship)* [481]

AAIB Scholarships *(Undergraduate/Scholarship)* [485]

AAJ Trial Advocacy Scholarships *(Undergraduate/Scholarship)* [489]

AAJA/CNN Scholar Program *(Graduate, Undergraduate/Scholarship)* [1640]

AAJA/COX Foundation Scholarships *(Graduate, Undergraduate/Scholarship)* [1641]

AALL Leadership Academy Grants *(Professional development/Grant)* [507]

AALL Research Funds *(Professional development/Grant)* [495]

AALL Scholarships for Continuing Education Classes *(Postgraduate/Scholarship)* [496]

AALL Scholarships for Library School Graduates Seeking a Non-Law Degree *(Postgraduate/Scholarship)* [497]

AAMFT Minority Fellowships *(Doctorate, Graduate/Fellowship)* [511]

A&WMA-GWS Scholarships *(Graduate, Undergraduate/Scholarship)* [111]

A&WMA Louisiana Section Scholarships *(Graduate, Undergraduate/Scholarship)* [113]

A&WMA Scholarships *(Graduate/Scholarship)* [107]

AANS Medical Student Summer Research Fellowships (MSSRF) *(Undergraduate/Fellowship)* [515]

AAOHN Professional Development Scholarships - Academic Study *(Graduate, Undergraduate/Scholarship)* [522]

AAOHN Professional Development Scholarships - Continuing Education *(Professional development/Scholarship)* [523]

AAPM Fellowships for Graduate Study in Medical Physics *(Graduate/Fellowship)* [528]

AAPM Minority Undergraduate Summer Experience Fellowships (MUSE) *(Undergraduate/Fellowship)* [529]

AAPM Summer Undergraduate Fellowships *(Undergraduate/Fellowship)* [530]

Leroy F. Aaron Scholarships *(Graduate, Undergraduate/Scholarship)* [6391]

AAS-American Historical Print Collectors Society Fellowships *(Doctorate/Fellowship)* [410]

AAS-American Society for Eighteenth Century Studies Fellowships *(Postdoctorate/Fellowship)* [411]

AAS CIAC Small Grants *(Graduate/Grant)* [1709]

AAS Fellowships for Creative and Performing Artists and Writers *(All/Fellowship)* [412]

AAS Korean Studies Scholarship Program *(Doctorate, Graduate/Scholarship)* [1710]

AAS National Endowment for the Humanities Long-Term Fellowships *(Postdoctorate/Fellowship)* [413]

AAS-Northeast Modern Language Association Fellowships *(All/Fellowship)* [414]

AAST/ACS/NIGMS Scholarships *(Professional development/Scholarship)* [554]

AAST/KCI Research Grants *(All/Grant)* [555]

AAST Medical Student Scholarships *(All/Scholarship)* [556]

AAUW Legal Advocacy Fund American Fellowships *(Doctorate/Fellowship)* [15]

AAUW Legal Advocacy Fund Career Development Grants *(Professional development/Grant)* [16]

AAUW Legal Advocacy Fund International Fellowships *(Doctorate, Graduate/Fellowship)* [17]

AAUW Legal Advocacy Fund Selected Professions Fellowships *(Doctorate, Graduate/Fellowship)* [18]

ABA Diversity Scholarships *(Undergraduate/Scholarship)* [588]

ABA Legal Opportunity Scholarship Funds *(Undergraduate/Scholarship)* [4566]

ABA Members Scholarships for ABA Bus and Tour Operators Only *(Undergraduate/Scholarship)* [589]

ABA Members Scholarships for All ABA Member Companies *(Undergraduate/Scholarship)* [590]

ABA Scholarships *(Undergraduate/Scholarship)* [581]

Anthony Abbene Scholarships *(Undergraduate/Scholarship)* [4650]

Clifford V. Abbott Memorial Scholarships *(Undergraduate/Scholarship)* [8714]

ABC-Clio Research Grants *(Graduate/Grant)* [8412]

Alejandro "Alex" Abecia Reaching High Scholarships *(Undergraduate, Vocational/Occupational/Scholarship)* [2932]

Abercrombie and Fitch Global Diversity Scholar Awards *(High School/Scholarship)* [6501]

ABF Doctoral Fellowships *(Doctorate, Graduate/Fellowship)* [577]

ABFSE National Scholarship Program *(Undergraduate/Scholarship)* [584]

Kyutaro & Yasuo Abiko Memorial Scholarships *(Undergraduate/Scholarship)* [5140]

Above and Beyond Scholarships *(Graduate/Scholarship)* [2269]

Mandel & Lauretta Abrahamer Scholarships *(Undergraduate/Scholarship)* [8715]

Evelyn Abrams Memorial Scholarships *(Undergraduate/Scholarship)* [7462]

The Frederick B. Abramson Memorial Foundation Scholarships *(Undergraduate/Scholarship)* [22]

The Frederick B. Abramson Public Interest Fellowships Awards *(All/Fellowship)* [23]

Academic Scholarship Program A *(Undergraduate/Scholarship)* [6241]

Academic Scholarship Program B *(Undergraduate/Scholarship)* [6242]

L'Academie de Cuisine Culinary Arts Scholarships *(All, Professional development/Scholarship)* [3305]

Academy of Motion Picture Arts and Sciences Student Academy Awards *(Undergraduate/Award)* [33]

Accenture American Indian Scholarship Program *(Graduate, Undergraduate/Scholarship)* [825]

The Access Intelligence Scholarships *(Graduate, Undergraduate/Scholarship)* [8486]

The Achieve Physical Therapy & Fitness Scholarships *(Doctorate/Scholarship)* [8737]

ACI BASF Construction Chemicals Student Fellowships *(Graduate, Undergraduate/Fellowship)* [628]

ACI Cagley ACI Student Fellowships *(Graduate, Master's, Undergraduate/Fellowship)* [629]

ACI President's Fellowships *(Doctorate, Master's/Fellowship)* [630]

ACI Scholarships *(Graduate/Scholarship)* [631]

Ken and Pat Ackerman Family Scholarship Fund *(Undergraduate/Scholarship)* [3755]

Wayne D. Ackerman Family Scholarship Fund *(Undergraduate/Scholarship)* [8655]

ACLS Collaborative Research Fellowships *(Doctorate/Fellowship)* [671]

ACLS Digital Innovation Fellowships *(Doctorate/Fellowship)* [672]

ACMPE Scholarship Fund Program *(Graduate, Undergraduate/Scholarship)* [5739]

ACMS Intensive Mongolian Language Fellowship Program *(Undergraduate/Fellowship)* [601]

Horatio Alger Georgia Scholarships (Undergraduate/Scholarship) [302]

Horatio Alger Illinois Scholarships (Undergraduate/Scholarship) [304]

Horatio Alger Indiana Scholarships (Undergraduate/Scholarship) [305]

Horatio Alger Kentucky Scholarships (Undergraduate/Scholarship) [306]

Horatio Alger Minnesota Scholarships (Undergraduate/Scholarship) [309]

Horatio Alger Missouri Scholarships (Undergraduate/Scholarship) [310]

Horatio Alger National Scholarships (Undergraduate/Scholarship) [312]

Horatio Alger North Dakota Scholarships (Undergraduate/Scholarship) [313]

Horatio Alger Pennsylvania Scholarships (Undergraduate/Scholarship) [314]

Horatio Alger South Dakota Scholarships (Undergraduate/Scholarship) [315]

Horatio Alger Texas - Fort Worth Scholarships (Undergraduate/Scholarship) [316]

Horatio Alger Texas Scholarships (Undergraduate/Scholarship) [317]

Horatio Alger Utah Scholarships (Undergraduate/Scholarship) [318]

Horatio Alger Washington Scholarships (Undergraduate/Scholarship) [319]

Horatio Alger Wyoming Scholarships (Undergraduate/Scholarship) [320]

Emma and Meloid Algood Tuition Scholarships (Graduate, Undergraduate/Scholarship) [6039]

Margaret M. Alkek Scholarships (Undergraduate/Scholarship) [3362]

All-American Vector Marketing Scholarship Program (Undergraduate/Scholarship) [9416]

All-Ink Scholarships (Graduate, Undergraduate/Scholarship) [322]

ALL-SIS CONELL Grants (Professional development/Grant) [508]

Paul Shearman Allen and Associate Scholarships (Undergraduate/Scholarship) [9062]

Robinson G. Allen Athletic Memorial Scholarships (Undergraduate/Scholarship) [7618]

Peggy Allen Community Newspaper Internships (Undergraduate/Internship) [9255]

Frances C. Allen Fellowships (Graduate/Fellowship) [6692]

William A. Allen Memorial Metal Shop/Auto Body Scholarships (Undergraduate/Scholarship) [7619]

Allen - Marty Allen Scholarships (High School, Undergraduate, Vocational/Occupational/Scholarship) [2934]

Alliance of Black Culinarians Scholarships (Undergraduate/Scholarship) [7465]

Alliance Defense Fund - Blackstone Legal Fellowships (Undergraduate/Fellowship) [333]

ALOA Scholarship Foundation (Undergraduate/Scholarship) [1679]

Tillie B. Alperin Scholarships (Undergraduate/Scholarship) [9220]

ALPFA Scholarship Programs (Postgraduate, Undergraduate/Scholarship) [1824]

Alpha Chi Sigma Scholarship Awards (Graduate, Undergraduate/Scholarship) [348]

Alpha Delta Gamma Educational Foundation Scholarships (ADGEF) (All/Scholarship) [350]

Alpha Eta Scholarships (Undergraduate/Scholarship) [3363]

Alpha Kappa Alpha - Educational Advancement Foundation Financial Need-Based Scholarships (Graduate, Undergraduate/Scholarship) [352]

Alpha Kappa Alpha - Educational Advancement Foundation Merit Scholarships (Graduate, Undergraduate/Scholarship) [353]

Alpha Mu Tau Undergraduate Scholarships (Undergraduate/Scholarship) [1197]

Alpha Rho Leadership Scholarships (Undergraduate/Scholarship) [3364]

Alpha Tau Omega Graduate Scholarships (Graduate/Scholarship) [365]

Alpha Tau Omega Undergraduate Scholarships (Undergraduate/Scholarship) [366]

Justin Scot Alston Memorial Scholarships (Undergraduate/Scholarship) [4651]

Phillip Alston Scholarships (Undergraduate/Scholarship) [9256]

Martin K. Alsup Scholarships (Undergraduate/Scholarship) [7058]

Robert E. Altenhofen Memorial Scholarships (Graduate, Undergraduate/Scholarship) [1665]

Luis W. Alvarez Postdoctoral Fellowships in Computational Science (Doctorate/Fellowship) [5380]

AMA Foundation Minority Scholars Awards (Undergraduate/Scholarship) [922]

AMA Foundation Physicians of Tomorrow Scholarships (Undergraduate/Scholarship) [923]

AMACESP Student Scholarships (Undergraduate/Scholarship) [147]

Ambrose-Ramsey Trust Scholarships (Undergraduate/Scholarship) [7059]

AMBUCS Scholarships for Therapists Program (Graduate, Undergraduate/Scholarship) [371]

Lou Amen Legacy Scholarships (Undergraduate/Scholarship) [2240]

America Responds Memorial Scholarships (Undergraduate/Scholarship) [1330]

American Academy of Periodontology Educator Scholarships (Postdoctorate/Scholarship) [392]

American Academy of Periodontology Foundation Education Fellowships (Postdoctorate/Fellowship) [393]

American Academy of Periodontology Teaching Fellowships (Postdoctorate/Fellowship) [394]

American Advertising Federation-Cleveland College Scholarships (Undergraduate/Scholarship) [402]

American Advertising Federation-Cleveland High School Scholarships (Undergraduate/Scholarship) [403]

American Art Therapy Association Anniversary Scholarships (AATA) (Graduate/Scholarship) [426]

American Association of Blacks in Energy Scholarships (Undergraduate/Scholarship) [441]

American Association for Cancer Research - GlaxoSmithKline Clinical Cancer Research Scholar Awards (Graduate, Postdoctorate/Award) [449]

American Association for Cancer Research Minority Scholar Awards (Graduate/Award) [450]

American Association of Cereal Chemists Graduate Fellowships (Graduate/Fellowship) [455]

American Association of Family and Consumer Sciences Scholarships (Undergraduate/Scholarship) [477]

American Association for Hand Surgery Annual Research Awards (Professional development/Award) [479]

American Association of Law Libraries Library School Scholarships (Graduate, Postgraduate/Scholarship) [498]

American Association of Plastic Surgeons Academic Scholars Program (Graduate/Grant) [535]

American Association of State Troopers Scholarship Foundation First Scholarships (Undergraduate/Scholarship) [550]

American Association of State Troopers Scholarship Foundation Second Scholarships (Undergraduate/Scholarship) [551]

American Association of Stratigraphic Palynologists Student Scholarships (Graduate/Scholarship) [6]

American Association of University Women American Fellowships (Doctorate, Postdoctorate/Fellowship) [9]

American Association of University Women Career Development Grants (Postgraduate/Grant) [10]

American Association of University Women International Fellowships (Graduate, Postgraduate/Fellowship) [11]

American Association of University Women Master's and First Professional Awards (Professional development/Award) [12]

American Association of University Women Selected Professions Fellowships (Professional development/Fellowship) [13]

American Association for Women in Community Colleges Regional Scholarships (Undergraduate/Scholarship) [565]

American Association for Women in Community Colleges Scholarship Leaders Institute (Professional development/Scholarship) [566]

American Astronomical Society Small Research Grants (Doctorate/Grant) [568]

The American Automobile Association Five Diamond Hospitality Scholarships (AAA) (Undergraduate/Scholarship) [795]

American Bus Association Academic Merit Scholarships (Undergraduate/Scholarship) [591]

American Business Women's Association Sarasota Sunrise Chapter Scholarships (Undergraduate, Vocational/Occupational/Scholarship) [3187]

American Cancer Society - Postdoctoral Fellowships (Doctorate/Fellowship) [594]

American Cancer Society - Research Scholar Grants (Doctorate, Professional development/Grant) [595]

American College of Radiation Oncology Resident Scholarships (Graduate/Scholarship) [623]

American Composites Manufacturers Association Scholarships (Undergraduate/Scholarship) [625]

American Conifer Society Scholarships (Undergraduate/Scholarship) [652]

American Council of the Blind Scholarships (Graduate, Undergraduate/Scholarship) [658]

American Council of Independent Laboratories Scholarships (Undergraduate/Scholarship) [669]

American Council of Learned Societies Fellowships (Postdoctorate/Fellowship) [674]

American Counsel Association Scholarships (Undergraduate/Scholarship) [683]

American Criminal Justice Association Scholarships (Graduate, Undergraduate/Scholarship) [687]

American Culinary Federation Chair's Scholarship Grants (All/Scholarship) [689]

American Dental Association Dental Assisting Scholarship Program (Undergraduate/Scholarship) [701]

American Dental Association Dental Hygiene Scholarship Program (Undergraduate/Scholarship) [702]

American Dental Association Dental Laboratory Technology Scholarship Program (Undergraduate/Scholarship) [703]

American Dental Association Dental Student Scholarships (Undergraduate/Scholarship) [704]

American Dental Association Minority Dental Student Scholarships (Undergraduate/Scholarship) [705]

American Dental Hygienists' Association Institute for Oral Health Fellowships (Master's/Fellowship) [708]

American Division Veterans Association Scholarships (Undergraduate, Vocational/Occupational/Scholarship) [712]

American Dream Scholarship Program (Undergraduate/Scholarship) [7890]

American Express Professional Development Scholarships (Professional development/Scholarship) [796]

The American Express Scholarship Competition (Undergraduate/Scholarship) [797]

American Express Travel Scholarships (Undergraduate/Scholarship) [1363]

American Federation of Police and Concerned Citizen Scholarships (Undergraduate, Vocational/Occupational/Scholarship) [722]

American Fire Sprinkler Association Scholarships (Undergraduate/Scholarship) [4407]

American Foreign Service Association Scholarship Fund (Undergraduate/Scholarship) [744]

American Foundation for Pharmaceutical Education Gateway Research Scholarships (Professional development/Scholarship) [756]

American Foundation for Pharmaceutical Education Pre-Doctoral Fellowships in the Pharmaceutical Sciences (Doctorate/Fellowship) [757]

American Foundation for Suicide and Prevention Pilot Grants (Postgraduate/Grant) [770]

American GI Forum of San Jose Scholarships (Undergraduate/Scholarship) [780]

American Guild of Organists, Canton Chapter Charitable Fund (Undergraduate/Scholarship) [8656]

American History Scholarships (Undergraduate/Scholarship) [6496]

American Indian Endowed Scholarships (Graduate, Undergraduate/Scholarship) [9503]

American Indian Fellowship in Business Scholarships (Graduate, Master's, Undergraduate/Scholarship) [6180]

American Indian Program Fellowships (Graduate/Fellowship) [8260]

American Institute for Economic Research Student Summer Fellowships *(Doctorate, Graduate, Undergraduate/Fellowship)* [854]

American Institute of Physics Congressional Science Fellowships *(Doctorate/Fellowship)* [866]

American Institute of Physics State Department Science Fellowships *(Doctorate/Fellowship)* [867]

American Judges Association Law Student Essay Competition *(Undergraduate/Prize)* [890]

American Lebanese Engineering Society Scholarship Program *(Graduate, Undergraduate/Scholarship)* [892]

American Legion Eagle Scout of the Year Scholarships *(High School/Scholarship)* [6246]

The American Legion Legacy Scholarships *(Undergraduate/Scholarship)* [894]

The American Legion National High School Oratorical Scholarships Contest *(Undergraduate/Scholarship)* [895]

American Liver Foundation Liver Scholar Awards *(Doctorate/Award)* [903]

American Liver Foundation Special Research Initiatives *(Doctorate/Award)* [904]

American Lung Association/AAAAI Allergic Respiratory Diseases Awards *(Doctorate/Grant)* [908]

American Lung Association Biomedical Research Grants *(Doctorate/Grant)* [909]

American Lung Association Clinical Patient Care Research Grants *(Doctorate/Grant)* [910]

American Lung Association Dalsemer Research Grants *(Doctorate/Grant)* [911]

American Lung Association DeSousa Awards *(Doctorate/Grant)* [912]

American Lung Association Lung Cancer Discovery Awards *(Doctorate/Grant)* [913]

American Lung Association Senior Research Training Fellowships *(Doctorate/Fellowship)* [914]

American Lung Association Social-Behavioral Research Grants *(Doctorate/Grant)* [915]

American Marketing Association-Connecticut Chapter, Anna C. Klune Memorial Scholarships *(Graduate/Scholarship)* [4408]

American Nephrology Nurses' Association Evidence-Based Research Grants *(Professional development/Grant)* [943]

American Nephrology Nurses' Association Research Grants *(Doctorate, Graduate/Grant)* [944]

American Nuclear Society Incoming Freshman Scholarships *(Undergraduate/Scholarship)* [948]

American Nuclear Society Nevada Section Scholarships *(Undergraduate/Scholarship)* [7466]

American Nuclear Society Undergraduates Scholarships *(Undergraduate/Scholarship)* [949]

American Paint Horse Foundation Scholarships *(Undergraduate/Scholarship)* [976]

American Parkinson Disease Association Medical Students Summer Fellowships *(Doctorate/Fellowship)* [978]

American Pediatric Surgical Nurses Association Educational Grants *(Professional development/Grant)* [984]

American Philological Association Minority Student Summer Fellowships *(Undergraduate/Fellowship)* [986]

American Physical Society Minority Undergraduate Scholarships *(Undergraduate/Scholarship)* [996]

American Physiological Society Post-doctoral Fellowships in Physiological Genomics (APS) *(Postdoctorate/Fellowship)* [1003]

American Political Science Association Federal Executives Fellowships *(Professional development/Fellowship)* [1014]

American Political Science Association Journalists Fellowships *(Professional development/Fellowship)* [1015]

American Political Science Association/MCI Scholarships *(Postdoctorate/Scholarship)* [1016]

American Political Science Association Political Scientists Fellowships *(Postdoctorate/Fellowship)* [1017]

American Psychoanalytic Association Fellowships *(Doctorate, Postdoctorate, Professional development/Fellowship)* [1027]

American Psychology-Law Society Dissertation Awards *(Graduate/Award)* [1043]

American Psychology-Law Society Early Career Professional Grants-In-Aid *(Professional development/Grant)* [1044]

American Psychology-Law Society Student Grants-In-Aid *(Graduate/Grant)* [1045]

American Quarter Horse Foundation Scholarships *(Undergraduate/Scholarship)* [1063]

American Railway Engineering and Maintenance-of-Way Association Scholarships *(Undergraduate/Scholarship)* [1117]

American Rental Association Foundation Scholarships *(Graduate, Undergraduate, Vocational/Occupational/Scholarship)* [1137]

American Research in the Humanities in China Fellowships *(Doctorate/Fellowship)* [675]

American Roentgen Ray Society Scholarships *(Professional development/Scholarship)* [1159]

American-Scandinavian Foundation Fellowships and Grants to Study in America *(Graduate/Fellowship, Grant)* [1168]

American-Scandinavian Foundation Translation Prize *(Professional development/Prize)* [1171]

American Society of Colon and Rectal Surgeons International Fellowships *(Professional development/Fellowship)* [1201]

American Society of Colon and Rectal Surgeons Travel Scholarships *(Professional development/Scholarship)* [1202]

American Society of Comparative Law TransCoop Programs *(All/Fellowship)* [1204]

American Society of Crime Laboratory Directors Scholarships *(Graduate, Undergraduate/Scholarship)* [1217]

American Society of Electroneurodiagnostic Technologists Student Education Grants (ASET) *(Undergraduate/Grant)* [1238]

American Society for Enology and Viticulture Scholarships *(Graduate, Undergraduate/Scholarship)* [1243]

American Society for Environmental History Minority Travel Grants *(Graduate, Professional development/Grant)* [1245]

American Society of Heating, Refrigerating, and Air-Conditioning Memorial Scholarships *(Undergraduate/Scholarship)* [1263]

American Society of Heating, Refrigerating, and Air-Conditioning Undergraduate Scholarships *(Undergraduate/Scholarship)* [1264]

American Society for Horticultural Science Student Travel Grants *(Graduate, Undergraduate/Grant)* [1272]

American Society of Landscape Architects Council of Fellow Scholarships *(Undergraduate/Scholarship)* [1282]

American Society for Microbiology International Fellowships for Africa *(Postdoctorate/Fellowship)* [1295]

American Society for Microbiology International Fellowships for Asia *(Postdoctorate/Fellowship)* [1296]

American Society for Microbiology International Fellowships for Latin America and the Caribbean *(Postdoctorate/Fellowship)* [1297]

American Society for Microbiology Undergraduate Research Fellowships (URF) *(Undergraduate/Fellowship)* [1298]

American Society of Military Comptrollers National Scholarship Program *(Undergraduate/Scholarship)* [1305]

American Society of Mining and Reclamation Memorial Scholarships *(Undergraduate/Scholarship)* [1307]

American Society of Naval Engineers Scholarships (ASNE) *(Graduate, Undergraduate/Scholarship)* [1309]

American Society of Safety Engineers Construction Safety Scholarships *(Undergraduate/Scholarship)* [1331]

American Society of Travel Agents AVIS Scholarships *(Graduate, Professional development, Undergraduate/Scholarship)* [1364]

American Sokol Merit Awards *(Undergraduate/Scholarship)* [1379]

American Speech Language Hearing Foundation Clinical Research Grants *(Doctorate/Grant)* [1381]

American Speech Language Hearing Foundation Endowed Scholarships *(Postdoctorate/Scholarship)* [1382]

American Speech Language Hearing Foundation General Scholarships *(Postgraduate/Scholarship)* [1383]

American Speech Language Hearing Foundation Scholarships for International Students *(Graduate/Scholarship)* [1384]

American Speech Language Hearing Foundation Scholarships for Students with Disability *(Graduate/Scholarship)* [1385]

American Standard Scholarships *(Undergraduate/Scholarship)* [7344]

American Water Ski Educational Foundation Scholarships *(Undergraduate/Scholarship)* [1414]

American Watercolor Society Scholarship Program for Art Teachers *(Professional development/Scholarship)* [1421]

American Welding Society District Scholarships *(Undergraduate/Scholarship)* [1424]

American Welding Society National Scholarships *(Undergraduate/Scholarship)* [1426]

American Welding Society Past Presidents Scholarships *(Undergraduate/Scholarship)* [1427]

American Welding Society Research Fellowships *(Graduate/Scholarship)* [1428]

Americans for Informed Democracy Global Scholar Tuition *(Undergraduate/Scholarship)* [1454]

AmeriGlide Achiever Scholarships *(All/Scholarship)* [1456]

Amgen Scholars Fellowships *(Doctorate, Professional development/Fellowship)* [3637]

Arsham Amirikian Engineering Scholarships *(Undergraduate/Scholarship)* [1429]

AMS Centennial Fellowships *(Postdoctorate/Fellowship)* [2738]

AMS Freshman Undergraduate Scholarships *(Undergraduate/Scholarship)* [928]

AMS Graduate Fellowships in the History of Science *(Graduate/Fellowship)* [929]

AMS Industry/Government Graduate Fellowships *(Graduate/Fellowship)* [930]

AMS/Industry Minority Scholarships *(Undergraduate/Scholarship)* [931]

AMS Teacher Education Scholarships *(Undergraduate/Scholarship)* [938]

AMS Undergraduate Named Scholarships *(Undergraduate/Scholarship)* [932]

ISPE/M.E. Amstutz Memorial Awards *(Undergraduate/Scholarship)* [4690]

AMSUS Physician Awards *(Professional development/Award)* [1460]

AMVETS National Scholarships - Entering College Freshmen *(Undergraduate/Scholarship)* [1464]

AMVETS National Scholarships - For Veterans *(Undergraduate/Scholarship)* [1465]

AMVETS National Scholarships - JROTC *(Undergraduate/Scholarship)* [1466]

Anaheim Police Survivors and Scholarship Fund *(Undergraduate/Scholarship)* [1469]

ANCA Scholarships *(Graduate, Undergraduate/Scholarship)* [1613]

Anchor Environmental Scholarships *(Graduate/Scholarship)* [1471]

Anchor Plastics Scholarships *(Graduate, Undergraduate/Scholarship)* [7264]

Anchor Scholarship Foundation *(Undergraduate/Scholarship)* [8780]

William G. Anderson, DO, Minority Scholarships *(Undergraduate/Scholarship)* [969]

The Anderson Group Summer Institute Scholarships *(Professional development/Scholarship)* [1473]

Judge Isaac Anderson, Jr. Scholarships *(Undergraduate/Scholarship)* [8589]

A.T. Anderson Memorial Scholarships *(Graduate, Undergraduate/Scholarship)* [834]

Charles Lee Anderson Memorial Scholarships *(Undergraduate/Scholarship)* [3142]

Gladys C. Anderson Memorial Scholarships *(Graduate, Undergraduate/Scholarship)* [748]

Jane E. Anderson Scholarships *(Undergraduate/Scholarship)* [3365]

Kathy D. and Stephen J. Anderson Scholarships *(Graduate/Scholarship)* [3092]

Redlands Rotary Club - Donald C. Anderson Scholarships *(Undergraduate/Scholarship)* [7620]

ASPH/NHTSA Public Health Fellowships *(Postdoctorate/Fellowship)* [1866]
ASPH Public Health Policy Fellowships *(Doctorate, Postdoctorate/Fellowship)* [1867]
Myron Asplin Foundation Scholarships *(Undergraduate/Scholarship)* [4719]
ASPPB Larry J. Bass Jr., PhD. Memorial Scholarship Awards *(Graduate, Undergraduate/Grant)* [1031]
Len Assante Scholarship Fund *(Undergraduate/Scholarship)* [6311]
ASSE Diversity Committee Scholarships *(Graduate, Undergraduate/Scholarship)* [1332]
Darrell and Palchie Asselin Scholarships *(Undergraduate/Scholarship)* [3524]
Associate Fellowships *(Doctorate/Fellowship)* [4778]
Associated General Contractors of Connecticut Scholarships *(Undergraduate/Scholarship)* [3235]
Associates in Behavioral Health Scholarships *(Graduate/Scholarship)* [7398]
Association for the Advancement of Baltic Studies Dissertation Grants for Graduate Students *(Doctorate/Grant)* [1686]
Association of American Geographers IGIF Graduate Research Awards *(Graduate, Undergraduate/Scholarship)* [1691]
Association of American Geographers IGIF Student Travel Grants *(Graduate, Undergraduate/Grant)* [1692]
Association on American Indian Affairs Emergency Aid Scholarships *(Undergraduate/Scholarship)* [815]
Association of American Indian Physicians Scholarships *(Graduate, Undergraduate/Scholarship)* [1699]
Association of College and University Auditors Scholarships *(Graduate, Undergraduate/Scholarship)* [1742]
Association for Compensatory Educators of Texas Paraprofessionals Scholarships *(Professional development/Scholarship)* [1746]
Association for Compensatory Educators of Texas Scholarships *(Undergraduate/Scholarship)* [1747]
Association of Desk and Derrick Clubs Education Trust Scholarships *(Undergraduate/Scholarship)* [1749]
Association of Donor Recruitment Professionals Hughes Scholarships *(Professional development/Scholarship)* [1751]
Association of Donor Recruitment Professionals Presidential Scholarships *(Professional development/Scholarship)* [1752]
Association of Electronic Journalists Presidents Scholarships *(Undergraduate/Scholarship)* [7572]
Association of Energy Engineers Foundation Scholarship Program *(Graduate, Undergraduate/Scholarship)* [1766]
Association of Flight Attendants Scholarship Fund *(Undergraduate/Scholarship)* [1779]
Association of Government Accountants Undergraduate/Graduate Scholarships for Community Service Accomplishments *(Graduate, Undergraduate/Fellowship, Scholarship)* [1789]
Association of Government Accountants Undergraduate/Graduate Scholarships for Full-time study *(Graduate, Undergraduate/Fellowship, Scholarship)* [1790]
Association of Government Accountants Undergraduate/Graduate Scholarships for Part-time study *(Graduate, Undergraduate/Fellowship, Scholarship)* [1791]
Association of Health Care Journalists Media Fellowships on Health Performance *(Professional development/Fellowship)* [3017]
Association for Preservation Technology International Student Scholarships *(Graduate, Undergraduate/Scholarship)* [1843]
Association for Psychological Science Student Grants (APS) *(Graduate, Undergraduate/Grant)* [1845]
Association of Rehabilitation Nurses Scholarship Program *(Undergraduate/Scholarship)* [1855]
Association of State Dam Safety Officials Undergraduate Scholarships *(Undergraduate/Scholarship)* [1877]
Association of the United States Navy Scholarships

(Undergraduate/Scholarship) [1887]
Association for Women in Sports Media Internship Program *(Graduate, Undergraduate/Internship)* [1910]
Association for Women Veterinarians Foundation Student Scholarships *(Graduate/Scholarship)* [1912]
AST National Honor Society Student Scholarships *(Graduate/Scholarship)* [1879]
ASTR Research Fellowships *(Professional development/Fellowship)* [1359]
Astronaut Scholarship Foundation Scholarships *(Undergraduate/Scholarship)* [1916]
ASWA 2-Year College Scholarships *(Undergraduate/Scholarship)* [1374]
ASWA Undergraduate Scholarships *(Undergraduate/Scholarship)* [1375]
AT&T Business Internship Awards *(Postgraduate/Internship)* [9257]
Martha and Robert Atherton Ministerial Scholarships *(Graduate, Master's/Scholarship)* [8993]
Athletic Equipment Managers Association College Scholarships *(Undergraduate/Scholarship)* [1918]
ISA Aerospace Industries Division - William H. Atkinson Scholarships *(Graduate, Undergraduate/Scholarship)* [5052]
Atlanta Alumnae Achievement Scholarships *(Undergraduate/Scholarship)* [3366]
Atlantic Salmon Federation Olin Fellowships *(All/Fellowship)* [1929]
Atlas Shrugged Essay Contest *(Graduate, Undergraduate/Prize)* [7591]
Attorney-CPA Foundation Scholarships *(Undergraduate/Scholarship)* [439]
AUA Foundation/Astellas Rising Star in Urology Research Awards *(Postdoctorate, Professional development/Fellowship)* [1407]
AUA Foundation Bridge Awards *(Postgraduate/Fellowship)* [1408]
AUA Foundation - NIDDK/NCI Surgeon-Scientist Awards *(Postgraduate/Fellowship)* [1409]
AUA Foundation Ph.D. Post-Doctoral Fellowships *(Postdoctorate/Fellowship)* [1410]
Aubespin Scholarships *(Undergraduate/Scholarship)* [656]
Auburn Animal Science Department Graduate Student Scholarships *(Graduate/Scholarship)* [176]
Audio Engineering Society Educational Foundation Scholarships *(Graduate/Grant)* [1931]
Frank H. Ault Scholarships *(Undergraduate/Scholarship)* [7908]
H. Thomas Austern Memorial Writing Competition *(Undergraduate/Prize)* [3853]
Automotive Technician Scholarship Program *(Undergraduate/Scholarship)* [5686]
Automotive Women's Alliance Foundation Scholarships *(Undergraduate/Scholarship)* [1970]
Auxiliary Undergraduate Scholarships *(Graduate, High School, Undergraduate/Scholarship)* [1659]
Delores A. Auzenne Fellowships *(Postgraduate/Fellowship)* [3818]
Larry H. Averill Memorial Scholarships *(Undergraduate/Scholarship)* [1937]
AVI Scholarships *(Undergraduate/Scholarship)* [1963]
Aviation Distributors and Manufacturers Association Scholarship Fund *(All/Scholarship)* [1972]
AVS Applied Surface Science Division Awards *(Graduate/Award)* [1974]
AVS Biomaterial Interfaces Division Awards *(Graduate/Award)* [1975]
AVS Manufacturing Science and Technology Group Awards *(Graduate/Award)* [1976]
AVS MEMS and NEMS Technical Group Best Paper Awards *(Undergraduate, Graduate/Award)* [1977]
AVS Spectroscopic Ellipsometry Focus Topic Graduate Student Awards *(Graduate/Award)* [1978]
AVS Thin Film Division Harper Awards *(Graduate/Award)* [1979]
AWG Minority Scholarships *(Undergraduate/Scholarship)* [1900]
AWSCPA National Scholarships *(Graduate/Scholarship)* [1452]
AXA Achievement Scholarships *(Undergraduate/Scholarship)* [1989]

Susan Ayers Memorial Scholarships *(Undergraduate/Scholarship)* [7467]
John M. Azarian Memorial Armenian Youth Scholarship Fund *(Undergraduate/Scholarship)* [1586]
Tom Babcox Memorial Scholarships *(All/Scholarship)* [1964]
Bach Organ and Keyboard Music Scholarships *(Undergraduate/Scholarship)* [7786]
Bachelor of Science in Nursing Academic Scholarships *(Graduate/Scholarship)* [6099]
Paula Backscheider Archival Fellowships *(Professional development/Fellowship)* [1224]
BACUS Scholarships *(Graduate, Undergraduate/Scholarship)* [8637]
Leo Baeck Institute - DAAD Fellowships *(Doctorate/Fellowship)* [4115]
BAEO Children's Scholarship Fund *(High School/Scholarship)* [2106]
BAGNC Predoctoral Scholarships *(Doctorate, Graduate/Scholarship)* [382]
Baha'i Faith Scholarships for Racial Harmony *(Undergraduate/Scholarship)* [7625]
The Bailey Family Foundation College Scholarship Program *(Undergraduate/Scholarship)* [1994]
The Bailey Family Foundation High School Scholarships Program *(Undergraduate/Scholarship)* [1995]
Lincoln C. Bailey Memorial Scholarship Fund *(Undergraduate/Scholarship)* [4986]
Barbara Bailey Scholarships *(Undergraduate/Scholarship)* [7399]
Don Bailey Scholarships *(Undergraduate/Scholarship)* [6309]
Sandra Sebrell Bailey Scholarships *(Undergraduate/Scholarship)* [3406]
Marian Wood Baird Scholarships *(Undergraduate/Scholarship)* [9407]
Charly Baker and Heath Merriwether Memorial Scholarships *(Undergraduate/Scholarship)* [7400]
Baker and Hostetler Diversity Fellowships *(Undergraduate/Fellowship)* [1999]
Frances Warren Baker Memorial Scholarships *(Undergraduate/Scholarship)* [8157]
Richard L. Baker Memorial Scholarships *(Undergraduate/Scholarship)* [8717]
Robby Baker Memorial Scholarships *(Undergraduate/Scholarship)* [277]
Jerry Baker Scholarships *(Undergraduate/Scholarship)* [1430]
ACI Elmer Baker Student Fellowships *(Undergraduate/Fellowship)* [633]
ACI Baker Student Fellowships *(Undergraduate/Fellowship)* [632]
George C. Balch Scholarships *(Graduate, Undergraduate/Scholarship)* [9054]
Bernt Balchen, Jr. Hardingfele Scholarships *(All, Professional development/Scholarship)* [4393]
Birgit Baldwin Fellowships *(Graduate/Fellowship)* [5752]
Norman S. Baldwin Fishery Science Scholarships *(Doctorate, Graduate/Scholarship)* [4868]
Donald A. Baldwin Sr. Business Aviation Management Scholarships *(All/Scholarship)* [6161]
Balestreri/Cutino Scholarships *(Undergraduate/Scholarship)* [690]
Lloyd G. Balfour Fellowships *(Graduate/Fellowship)* [6739]
Ball Horticultural Company Scholarships *(Undergraduate/Scholarship)* [724]
Vic and Margaret Ball Student Intern Scholarships *(Undergraduate/Internship)* [725]
Ballantyne Resident Research Grants *(Professional development/Grant)* [787]
Ballard Family Foundation Scholarships *(Undergraduate, Vocational/Occupational/Scholarship)* [7909]
G. Thomas Balsbaugh Memorial Scholarship Fund *(Undergraduate/Scholarship)* [3935]
Bank of America Junior Achievement Scholarship Fund *(Undergraduate/Scholarship)* [3885]
Dr. Johnella Banks Memorial Scholarships *(Undergraduate/Scholarship)* [2137]
Harvey Washington Banks Scholarships in Astronomy *(Undergraduate/Scholarship)* [6486]
Sharon D. Banks Undergraduate Memorial Scholarships *(Undergraduate/Scholarship)* [9739]

Donald W. Banner Corporate Intern Scholarships *(Undergraduate/Scholarship)* [4844]

Donald W. Banner Diversity Scholarships for Law Students *(Undergraduate/Scholarship)* [2014]

Mark T. Banner Scholarships for Law Students *(Graduate, Undergraduate/Scholarship)* [7798]

CSF Michael Bany Memorial Scholarships *(Undergraduate/Scholarship)* [2793]

Bernice Barabash Sports Scholarships *(Undergraduate, Vocational/Occupational/Scholarship)* [5090]

Barakat Trust and Barakat Foundation Scholarships *(Graduate/Scholarship)* [1491]

Cynthia and Alan Baran Fine Arts and Music Scholarships *(Undergraduate/Scholarship)* [3093]

Leslie Baranowski Scholarships for Professional Excellence *(All/Scholarship)* [4764]

Joe Barbarow Memorial Scholarships *(Undergraduate/Scholarship)* [7060]

Lewis B. Barber Memorial Scholarships *(Undergraduate/Scholarship)* [8590]

Barbri Scholarships for Bar Preparation *(Undergraduate/Scholarship)* [4561]

Janice K. Barden Aviation Scholarships *(Undergraduate/Scholarship)* [6162]

Thomas J. Bardos Science Education Awards for Undergraduate Students *(Undergraduate/Award)* [451]

Edgar Barge Memorial Scholarships *(Undergraduate/Scholarship)* [4256]

Gina L. Barnhart Memorial Scholarship Fund *(Undergraduate/Scholarship)* [3759]

Robbie Baron Memorial Scholarships *(Undergraduate/Scholarship)* [3936]

Laura Beckley Barsotti Memorial Scholarships *(Undergraduate/Scholarship)* [4652]

Barta-Lehman Musical Scholarships *(Undergraduate/Scholarship)* [7910]

Avery Bayle Barth Scholarships *(Undergraduate/Scholarship)* [3367]

CSF Walter and Marilyn Bartlett Scholarships *(Undergraduate/Scholarship)* [2794]

Elsa Barton Educational Scholarship Fund *(Undergraduate, Vocational/Occupational/Scholarship)* [1023]

Guthikonda BasavapunnaRao & Umadevi Scholarships *(Graduate/Scholarship)* [8829]

Bascom Hill Society Scholarships *(Undergraduate/Scholarship)* [9349]

Basic Midwifery Student Scholarship Program *(Undergraduate/Scholarship)* [618]

Basic Research Fellowships *(Postdoctorate/Fellowship)* [586]

Diane Basilone-Engle Memorial Scholarships *(Undergraduate/Scholarship)* [2329]

Charles A. Bassett Endowed Memorial Scholarship Fund *(Undergraduate/Scholarship)* [4207]

Bat Conservation International Student Research Scholarships *(Graduate, Undergraduate/Scholarship)* [2028]

Jim Batten Community Newspaper Internships *(Undergraduate/Internship)* [9258]

Lewis and Gurry Batten/Sand Plains Educational Trust Scholarships *(Undergraduate/Scholarship)* [7061]

Jeannette Bautista Memorial Scholarships *(Undergraduate/Scholarship)* [7468]

Bob Baxter Scholarships *(Graduate, Undergraduate/Scholarship)* [6448]

Timothy Baylink Good Fellowship Awards *(Undergraduate/Fellowship)* [7626]

John Bayliss Broadcast Foundation Internship Programs *(Undergraduate/Internship)* [2030]

John Bayliss Broadcast Foundation Scholarships *(Undergraduate/Scholarship)* [2031]

BCA Ethnic Minority Postgraduate Scholarships for Careers in Athletics *(Postgraduate/Scholarship)* [2135]

BCCC Foundation Scholarships *(Undergraduate/Scholarship)* [2002]

BCCC Foundation Workforce Scholarships *(Undergraduate/Scholarship)* [2003]

BCEN Undergraduate Scholarships *(Undergraduate/Scholarship)* [3633]

BDC Visiting Fellowships *(Doctorate/Fellowship)* [2196]

Willa Beach-Porter Music Scholarships *(Undergraduate/Scholarship)* [2721]

Beacon of Hope Scholarships *(Undergraduate/Scholarship)* [2035]

James Beard Foundation/Art Institute of Colorado Scholarships *(Undergraduate/Scholarship)* [1626]

Beard Scholarships *(Master's/Scholarship)* [4104]

Beatitudes Fellowships *(Professional development/Fellowship)* [2037]

Catherine H. Beattie Fellowships *(Graduate/Fellowship)* [2705]

Jane Beattie Memorial Scholarships *(All/Scholarship)* [8362]

Beau Gunn Redlands Baseball For Youth Scholarships *(Undergraduate/Scholarship)* [7627]

Michael Beaudry Scholarships *(Undergraduate/Scholarship)* [4054]

Beaver Medical Clinic-H.E.A.R.T. Scholarship Awards *(Undergraduate/Scholarship)* [7628]

Beaver Medical Clinic-Premed Scholarship Awards *(Undergraduate/Scholarship)* [7629]

Don C. Beaver Memorial Scholarships *(Undergraduate/Scholarship)* [2241]

Bechtel Engineering and Science Scholarships *(High School/Scholarship)* [5645]

Stan Beck Fellowships *(Graduate, Undergraduate/Fellowship)* [3652]

Dennis J. Beck Memorial Scholarships *(Undergraduate, Vocational/Occupational/Scholarship)* [5091]

Beck-Pfann Memorial Scholarships *(Undergraduate/Scholarship)* [7168]

Garvin L. Beck Scholarships *(Undergraduate/Scholarship)* [7630]

Dr. Joyce Beckett Scholarships *(Graduate, Undergraduate/Scholarship)* [6040]

Beef Industry Scholarships *(Undergraduate/Scholarship)* [6174]

Raymond and Donald Beeler Memorial Scholarships *(Undergraduate/Scholarship)* [7631]

Notah Begay III Scholarship Program *(Undergraduate/Scholarship)* [278]

Behavioral Gerontology SIG Student Research Awards *(Undergraduate/Award)* [1712]

Behavioral Sciences Post-Doctoral Fellowships *(Postdoctorate/Fellowship)* [3660]

Behavioral Sciences Student Fellowships *(Graduate, Undergraduate/Fellowship)* [3661]

Norbert J. Beihoff Scholarships *(Undergraduate/Scholarship)* [2888]

N.S. Beinstock Fellowships *(Professional development/Fellowship)* [7573]

Hannah Beiter Graduate Student Research Grants *(Doctorate, Graduate/Grant)* [2762]

Bel Canto Vocal Scholarship Foundation Vocal Competition *(All/Award, Scholarship)* [2046]

Belfer-Aptman Dissertation Research Awards *(Doctorate/Grant)* [5761]

Marc and Ruti Bell Foundation Scholarships *(Undergraduate/Scholarship)* [2052]

John Bell and Lawrence Thornton Scholarship Fund *(Undergraduate/Scholarship)* [4412]

Ray and Mary Bell Memorial Scholarships *(Undergraduate/Scholarship)* [7911]

Alfred D. Bell Travel Grants *(All/Grant)* [3859]

Bellevue PFLAG Scholarships *(Undergraduate/Scholarship)* [7401]

David Beltran Memorial Scholarships *(Undergraduate/Scholarship)* [7632]

Samuel Flagg Bemis Dissertation Research Grants *(Doctorate, Graduate/Grant)* [8335]

CSF Johnny Bench Scholarships *(Undergraduate/Scholarship)* [2795]

Reckitt Benckiser Student Scholarships *(Graduate/Scholarship)* [6105]

Richard W. Bendicksen Memorial Scholarships *(Undergraduate/Scholarship)* [1071]

Bill Bendiner and Doug Morgenson Scholarships *(Undergraduate/Scholarship)* [7402]

H. Y. Benedict Fellowships *(Graduate/Fellowship)* [342]

Benign Essential Blepharospasm Research Foundation Research Grants *(Doctorate, Postdoctorate/Grant)* [2057]

Jean Bennett Memorial Student Travel Grants *(Graduate, Undergraduate/Grant)* [6909]

Casey Bennett Scholarships *(Undergraduate/Scholarship)* [3740]

Eleanor Bennett Scholarships *(All/Scholarship)* [8770]

William Bennett W7PHO Memorial Scholarships *(Undergraduate/Scholarship)* [1072]

Pete and Ellen Bensley Memorial Scholarship Fund *(Undergraduate/Scholarship)* [3886]

Elizabeth Benson Scholarship Awards *(Undergraduate/Scholarship)* [7727]

Benton-Meier Neuropsychology Scholarships *(Graduate/Scholarship)* [1038]

Linn Benton Scholarships *(Undergraduate/Scholarship)* [6952]

Lester G. Benz Memorial Scholarships for College Journalism Study *(Professional development/Scholarship)* [7562]

Fred Berg Awards *(All/Award)* [3594]

Charlotte V. Bergen Scholarships *(Undergraduate/Scholarship)* [1207]

Bergman Scholarships *(Undergraduate/Scholarship)* [6783]

The Joseph Berkman, and Michael and Sarah Chipkin Holocaust/Genocide Studies Awards *(Graduate/Scholarship)* [8738]

Berkowitz Fellowships *(Professional development/Fellowship)* [8902]

ARRS/Leonard Berlin Scholarships in Medical Professionalism *(Professional development/Scholarship)* [1160]

Stuart L. Bernath Dissertation Grants *(Doctorate, Graduate/Grant)* [8336]

Myrna F. Bernath Fellowships *(Doctorate, Graduate/Fellowship)* [8337]

Hon. Peggy Bernheim Memorial Scholarships *(Undergraduate/Scholarship)* [2190]

Donald H. Bernstein/John B. Talbert, Jr. Scholarships *(Undergraduate/Scholarship)* [3887]

The Berntsen International Scholarships in Surveying Technology *(Undergraduate/Scholarship)* [642]

Beta Sigma Scholarships *(Undergraduate/Scholarship)* [8159]

Bethune-Cookman University Excelsior Scholarships *(Undergraduate/Scholarship)* [2079]

Bethune-Cookman University Presidential Scholarships *(Undergraduate/Scholarship)* [2080]

Harold Bettinger Scholarships *(Undergraduate/Scholarship)* [726]

Leonard Bettinger Vocational Scholarships *(Undergraduate, Vocational/Occupational/Scholarship)* [727]

BIA Higher Education Grants *(Graduate, Postgraduate, Undergraduate/Grant)* [1509]

BIE-Loan for Service for Graduates *(Graduate/Loan)* [827]

James L. Biggane Fellowships in Finance *(Graduate/Fellowship)* [6677]

James Bilder Scholarships *(Undergraduate, Vocational/Occupational/Scholarship)* [8591]

Biocom Scholarships *(Undergraduate/Scholarship)* [7913]

BioQuip Undergraduate Scholarships *(Undergraduate/Scholarship)* [3653]

BioRx/Hemophilia of North Carolina Educational Scholarships *(Undergraduate/Scholarship)* [6317]

Birmingham District Alabama Dietetic Association Scholarships *(Graduate, Undergraduate/Scholarship)* [168]

Birmingham Student Scholarship Fund Association *(Undergraduate/Scholarship)* [2102]

BISA's Scholarship Assistance Program *(High School/Scholarship)* [2146]

Bisexual Foundation Scholarships *(Graduate/Scholarship)* [8471]

Lebbeus F. Bissell Scholarships *(Undergraduate/Scholarship)* [4413]

Mary E. Bivins Foundation Religious Scholarship Program *(Graduate, Undergraduate/Scholarship)* [2104]

Dr. Richard E. Bjork Memorial Graduate Study Awards *(Graduate/Scholarship)* [8739]

Norman Blachford Point Scholarships *(Graduate, Undergraduate/Scholarship)* [7355]

Thomas F. Black, Jr. Memorial Scholarships *(Undergraduate/Scholarship)* [7784]

Black Student Fund (High School/Scholarship) [2107]

Reid Blackburn Scholarships (Undergraduate/Scholarship) [6449]

Eileen Blackey Doctoral Fellowships (Doctorate/Fellowship) [6121]

William T. Blackwell Scholarship Fund (Undergraduate/Scholarship) [6358]

Beatrice K. Blair Scholarships (Undergraduate/Scholarship) [2149]

Thomas M. Blake Memorial Scholarships (Undergraduate/Scholarship) [3230]

Margaret Blanchard Dissertation Support Fund (Postgraduate/Grant) [9259]

Joan Blend Scholarship Fund (Undergraduate/Scholarship) [8657]

M. Hildred Blewett Fellowships (Postdoctorate/Scholarship) [997]

Bloch-Selinger Education Fund (Undergraduate/Scholarship) [3760]

F.A. and Charlotte Blount Scholarships (Undergraduate/Scholarship) [9625]

Blow Molding Division Memorial Scholarships (Graduate, Undergraduate/Scholarship) [8444]

Blues Ambassador Scholarships (Undergraduate/Scholarship) [7469]

Jordan ABDO/Michael Bluett Memorial Scholarships (Undergraduate/Scholarship) [8592]

Harry and Edith Blunt Scholarships (Undergraduate/Scholarship) [608]

BMES Graduate and Undergraduate Student Awards (Graduate, Undergraduate/Award) [2100]

Sandra Bobbitt Continuing Education Scholarships (Undergraduate/Scholarship) [1836]

Edith and Arnold N. Bodtker Grants (All/Grant) [3339]

Boeing Business Scholarships (Undergraduate/Scholarship) [4175]

Bohemian Lawyers Association of Chicago Scholarships (Graduate/Scholarship) [2162]

Frances P. Bolton Fellowships (Doctorate/Fellowship) [7051]

BOMA/NY Scholarships (Undergraduate/Scholarship) [2207]

Barbara Bonnema Memorial Scholarships (Undergraduate/Scholarship) [7633]

Ellis J. Bonner Scholarships (Doctorate, Graduate, Undergraduate/Scholarship) [6080]

Scott Bonners Memorial Scholarships (Undergraduate/Scholarship) [2330]

Admiral Mike Boorda Scholarship Program (Undergraduate, Vocational/Occupational/Scholarship) [6592]

Diane Booth Memorial Scholarships (Undergraduate/Scholarship) [3761]

National Security Education Program - David L. Boren Fellowships (Undergraduate/Fellowship) [9204]

David L. Boren Undergraduate Scholarships (Graduate, Undergraduate/Scholarship) [1784]

Dr. Anita Borg Memorial Scholarships - USA (Graduate, Undergraduate/Scholarship) [4193]

Maria Gonzales Borrero Scholarships (Undergraduate/Scholarship) [4414]

Tom Bost Scholarships (Undergraduate/Scholarship) [9260]

Boston City Federation "Return to School" Scholarships (Graduate, Undergraduate/Scholarship) [4074]

Stephen Botein Fellowships (Doctorate/Fellowship) [415]

Metropolitan Museum of Art Bothmer Fellowships (Doctorate/Fellowship) [5783]

Richard J. Bouchard Scholarships (Graduate, Undergraduate/Scholarship) [1050]

Bound to Stay Bound Books Scholarships (BTSB) (Graduate/Scholarship) [1826]

Rev. Andrew L. Bouwhuis Memorial Scholarship Program (Graduate/Scholarship) [2668]

MAC Louisa Bowen Memorial Scholarships for Graduate Students in Archival Administration (Graduate/Scholarship) [5854]

William R. Bowen Scholarships (Undergraduate/Scholarship) [3052]

Elizabeth W. Boyce Scholarships (Undergraduate/Scholarship) [2889]

W. Scott Boyd Group Grants (All/Grant) [4884]

Boyd N. Lyon Scholarships (Doctorate, Graduate/Scholarship) [5554]

Corris Boyd Scholarships (Master's/Scholarship) [1891]

Dody Boyd Scholarships (Undergraduate/Scholarship) [3096]

Verna Curry Boyer Scholarships (Undergraduate/Scholarship) [8718]

Mildred Cater Bradham Social Work Fellowships (Graduate/Fellowship) [9801]

Carol June Bradley Awards (All/Grant) [5955]

Charles Bradley Memorial Scholarships (Undergraduate/Scholarship) [4397]

Ed Bradley Scholarships (Undergraduate/Scholarship) [7574]

Edward J. Brady Memorial Scholarships (Undergraduate/Scholarship) [1432]

William E. "Buck" Bragunier Scholarships (Undergraduate/Scholarship) [1556]

The Helen and Edward Brancati Teacher Development Scholarships (Professional development/Scholarship) [2644]

Gladys Kamakakuokalani 'Ainoa Brandt Scholarships (Graduate, Undergraduate/Scholarship) [5209]

Barbara Brantley Nursing Education Scholarships (Graduate, Undergraduate/Scholarship) [1723]

Erika A. and George E. Brattain Sr. Scholarship Fund (Undergraduate/Scholarship) [9548]

Theodore E.D. Braun Research Travel Fellowships (Professional development/Fellowship) [1225]

Breakthrough to Nursing Scholarships (Undergraduate/Scholarship) [3976]

Ann Marie Bredefeld Scholarships (Undergraduate/Scholarship) [7170]

The Lela Breitbart Memorial Scholarship Fund (All/Scholarship) [8892]

Marion Breland-Bailey Awards (Graduate, Undergraduate/Award) [1713]

Brenda Renee Horn Memorial Scholarship (Undergraduate/Scholarship) [4029]

Breslauer Family Scholarships (Undergraduate/Scholarship) [7915]

Hilda E. Bretzlaff Foundation Scholarships (Undergraduate/Grant) [2173]

Rick Brewer Scholarships (Undergraduate/Scholarship) [9261]

James Bridenbaugh Memorial Scholarships (Undergraduate/Scholarship) [728]

Lloyd Bridges Scholarships (Graduate, Professional development/Scholarship) [2679]

Bridgestone Americas Fellowships (Graduate/Fellowship) [9414]

Bridging the GAP for Hispanic Success Awards (Undergraduate/Scholarship) [4545]

Parsons Brinckerhoff-Jim Lammie Scholarships (Graduate, Undergraduate/Scholarship) [1051]

Broadcast News Management Fellowships (Professional development/Scholarship) [7575]

Cathy L. Brock Memorial Scholarships (Graduate/Scholarship) [4787]

Kae and Kay Brockermeyer Endowed Scholarships (Undergraduate/Scholarship) [7172]

Louise A. Broderick San Diego County Scholarships (Undergraduate, Vocational/Occupational/Scholarship) [7916]

Julia Broderick Scholarships (Undergraduate/Scholarship) [8498]

Ross P. Broesamle Educational Scholarship Fund (Undergraduate/Scholarship) [5348]

John G. Brokaw Scholarships (Undergraduate/Scholarship) [6585]

Brookdale Leadership in Aging Fellowships (Professional development/Fellowship) [2194]

Shirley J. Brooke Endowed Scholarships (Undergraduate/Scholarship) [7173]

George M. Brooker Collegiate Scholarships for Minorities (Graduate, Postgraduate, Undergraduate/Scholarship) [4818]

Seth R. and Corrine H. Brooks Memorial Scholarships (All/Scholarship) [2075]

Carl E. Brooks Scholarships (Undergraduate/Scholarship) [8593]

Dorothy B. Brothers Executive Scholarship Program (High School/Scholarship) [9717]

William A. and Ann M. Brothers Scholarships (Undergraduate/Scholarship) [1433]

Henry Broughton, K2AE Memorial Scholarships (Undergraduate/Scholarship) [1073]

Selena Danette Brown Book Scholarships (Graduate, Undergraduate/Scholarship) [6041]

Marjorie M. Brown Fellowship Program (Postdoctorate/Fellowship) [5201]

Brown Foundation College Scholarships (Undergraduate/Scholarship) [816]

Mary L. Brown High School Student Scholarships (Undergraduate/Scholarship) [5037]

The John Carter Brown Library Long-Term Fellowships (All/Fellowship) [2198]

The John Carter Brown Library Short-Term Fellowships (Doctorate, Postdoctorate/Fellowship) [2199]

Olympia Brown and Max Kapp Awards (Graduate/Scholarship) [8994]

Quincy Brown Memorial Scholarships (Undergraduate/Scholarship) [7634]

Ruby A. Brown Memorial Scholarships (Undergraduate/Scholarship) [3566]

Jesse Brown Memorial Youth Scholarship Program (All/Scholarship) [3459]

Ron Brown Scholars Program (Undergraduate/Scholarship) [2201]

James W. Jr. and Jane T. Brown Scholarship Fund (Undergraduate/Scholarship) [4208]

CSF M. and E. Brown Scholarships (Undergraduate/Scholarship) [2796]

D.C. and Virginia Brown Scholarships (High School, Undergraduate/Scholarship) [2939]

Harry and Lucille Brown Scholarships (Undergraduate/Scholarship) [4273]

Jack H. Brown Scholarships (Undergraduate/Scholarship) [2242]

Mary Lou Brown Scholarships (Undergraduate/Scholarship) [1074]

Charles S. Brown Scholarships in Physics (Graduate, Undergraduate/Scholarship) [6487]

VPPPA Stephen Brown Scholarships (Graduate, Undergraduate/Scholarship) [9474]

Richard A. Brown Student Scholarships (Undergraduate/Scholarship) [8855]

Regina Brown Undergraduate Student Fellowships (Undergraduate/Fellowship) [6212]

Peggy Browning Fund - Chicago School-Year Fellowships (Graduate, Undergraduate/Fellowship) [2203]

Robert Browning Scholarships (Undergraduate/Scholarship) [7403]

Chester H. Bruce Memorial Scholarships (Undergraduate, Vocational/Occupational/Scholarship) [7063]

Sheriff W. Bruce Umpleby Law Enforcement Scholarship Fund (Undergraduate/Scholarship) [8658]

Bernard B. and Mary L. Brusin Scholarships (Undergraduate/Scholarship) [3526]

William and Clara Bryan Scholarships (Undergraduate/Scholarship) [3098]

Edward C. Bryant Scholarships Trust Fund (Graduate/Fellowship) [1394]

BSA Educational Scholarships (Undergraduate/Scholarship) [2224]

BSF Science and Medicine Research Grants (Professional development/Grant) [2026]

Lt. General Douglas D. Buchholz Memorial Scholarships (Undergraduate/Scholarship) [1557]

John and Elisabeth Buck Endowed Scholarships (Graduate, Postdoctorate/Scholarship) [5612]

Buder Scholarships for American Indian Law Students (Undergraduate/Scholarship) [9530]

Walter and Louise Buell Graduate Scholarships (Graduate/Scholarship) [3862]

Gary L. Buffington Memorial Scholarships (Undergraduate/Scholarship) [4760]

Tien Bui Memorial Scholarships (Undergraduate/Scholarship) [9627]

Builders Association of Northeast Indiana Scholarships (BANI) (Undergraduate/Scholarship) [8719]

Armen H. Bululian Scholarships (Undergraduate/Scholarship) [1588]

Mike Buoncristiano Memorial Scholarship Fund (Undergraduate/Scholarship) [3445]

William T. Burbage Family Memorial Scholarships (Undergraduate/Scholarship) [3053]

C. Lalor Burdick Scholarships *(Undergraduate/Scholarship)* [5613]

George M. Burditt Scholarships *(Undergraduate/Scholarship)* [1781]

Max M. Burger Endowed Scholarships in Embryology *(Undergraduate/Scholarship)* [5614]

Graduate Fellowship Program - Robert M Burger Fellowships (GFP) *(Doctorate, Graduate/Fellowship)* [8078]

Burger King Employee Scholars Program *(Undergraduate/Scholarship)* [4474]

Burger King Scholars Program *(Undergraduate/Scholarship)* [4475]

Dorothy and Dick Burgess Scholarships *(Undergraduate/Scholarship)* [5092]

Richard J. Burk, Jr. Fellowships *(Graduate/Fellowship)* [4488]

Eleanor McWilliams Burke Fund *(Undergraduate/Scholarship)* [3762]

ACLS Frederick Burkhardt Residential Fellowships *(Professional development/Fellowship)* [416]

Ralph Burkhardt Scholarship Fund *(Undergraduate/Scholarship)* [9549]

Cecil E. Burney Scholarships *(Undergraduate/Scholarship)* [2940]

Burroughs Wellcome Fund Career Awards at the Scientific Interface *(Doctorate, Postdoctorate/Fellowship)* [2211]

Burroughs Wellcome Fund Collaborative Research Travel Grants *(Doctorate/Grant)* [2212]

Ethel Beard Burstein Scholarship Program *(Postgraduate/Scholarship)* [951]

Wes Burton Memorial Scholarships *(Undergraduate/Scholarship)* [9628]

Bush Artist Fellowships *(All/Fellowship)* [2217]

Bush Leadership Fellows Program *(Professional development/Fellowship)* [2218]

Kathy Bush Memorial Scholarships *(Undergraduate/Scholarship)* [7635]

Lindsay Buster Memorial Scholarships *(Undergraduate/Scholarship)* [3144]

BWEL Law Student Scholarships *(Undergraduate/Scholarship)* [2142]

Walter Byers Postgraduate Scholarships *(Graduate, Postgraduate/Scholarship)* [6192]

Donald C. and Doris K. Byers Scholarships *(Undergraduate/Scholarship)* [3483]

Joe Bynum/Raymond James Investment Services Technical Excellence Scholarship Fund *(Undergraduate/Scholarship)* [3033]

Robert C. Byrd Honors Scholarships *(Undergraduate/Scholarship)* [4694]

Dr. F. Ross Byrd Scholarships *(Graduate, Vocational/Occupational/Scholarship)* [9523]

C200 Scholar Awards *(All/Scholarship)* [3015]

Johnston Cabaniss Scholarships *(Undergraduate/Scholarship)* [188]

Cabrillo Clubs of California Scholarships *(Undergraduate/Scholarship)* [7377]

Dr. Aurelio M. Caccomo Family Foundation Memorial Scholarships *(Undergraduate/Scholarship)* [1467]

Cal State San Macros Alumna Scholarships *(Undergraduate/Scholarship)* [2286]

Cesar A. Calas/FES Miami Chapter Scholarships *(Undergraduate/Scholarship)* [3824]

Tese Caldarelli Memorial Scholarships *(Graduate, Undergraduate/Scholarship)* [6045]

Joseph R. Calder, Jr., MD Scholarship Fund *(Undergraduate/Scholarship)* [3763]

J.E. Caldwell Centennial Scholarships *(Undergraduate/Scholarship)* [6498]

Calgary USAEE/IAEE North American Conference Registration Fee Scholarships *(Undergraduate/Scholarship)* [9034]

Calhoun County Auduburn University Scholarships *(Undergraduate/Scholarship)* [3034]

Hermione Grant Calhoun Scholarships *(Undergraduate/Scholarship)* [6273]

California Association of Family and Consumer Sciences -San Diego Chapter Scholarships (CAFCS) *(Graduate, Undergraduate, Vocational/Occupational/Scholarship)* [7917]

The California Endowment and AACN Minority Nurse Faculty Scholarships *(Graduate/Scholarship)* [459]

California Groundwater Association Scholarships *(Undergraduate/Scholarship)* [2258]

California Scottish Rite Foundation Scholarships *(Undergraduate/Scholarship)* [2275]

California Sea Grant State Fellowships *(Graduate/Fellowship)* [2277]

California Shopping Cart Retrieval Corporation Inc. Scholarships *(Undergraduate/Scholarship)* [2243]

Calista Scholarships *(Graduate, Undergraduate, Vocational/Occupational/Scholarship)* [2290]

Jodi Callahan Memorial Scholarships *(Undergraduate/Scholarship)* [91]

W.L. Calvert Memorial Scholarships *(Graduate/Scholarship)* [4610]

Calvin Alumni Association Arizona Central Chapter Scholarships *(Undergraduate/Scholarship)* [2292]

Calvin Alumni Association British Columbia Scholarships *(Undergraduate/Scholarship)* [2294]

Calvin Alumni Association California- Bay Area Scholarships *(Undergraduate/Scholarship)* [2295]

Calvin Alumni Association Colorado Chapter Scholarships *(Undergraduate/Scholarship)* [2296]

Calvin Alumni Association Southern California Chapter Scholarships *(Undergraduate/Scholarship)* [2309]

Camden County College Employee Memorial Scholarships *(Undergraduate/Scholarship)* [2331]

Camden County College Foundation Scholarships *(Undergraduate/Scholarship)* [2332]

Camden County Retired Educators Association Scholarships *(Undergraduate/Scholarship)* [2333]

Stuart Cameron and Margaret McLeod Memorial Scholarships (SCMS) *(Graduate, Undergraduate, Scholarship loan)* [4814]

Wesley C. Cameron Scholarships *(Undergraduate/Scholarship)* [6586]

Thomas R. Camp Scholarships *(Graduate/Scholarship)* [1416]

Lois Campbell Scholarship Awards *(Undergraduate/Scholarship)* [4930]

Lucille Campbell Scholarship Fund *(Undergraduate/Scholarship)* [9550]

Robert G. Campbell Scholarships *(Undergraduate/Scholarship)* [7636]

Campus Discovery Scholarships *(Graduate, Undergraduate/Scholarship)* [2352]

Cancer for College Scholarships *(Graduate, Undergraduate/Scholarship)* [2636]

Cancer Survivors' Fund Scholarships *(Undergraduate/Scholarship)* [2640]

Cancer Treatment Centers of America Post-Graduate Management Fellowships *(Postgraduate/Fellowship)* [2642]

CANFIT Scholarships *(Graduate, Undergraduate/Scholarship)* [2228]

Therese A. Cannon Educational Scholarships *(Professional development/Scholarship)* [4971]

John Cannon Memorial Scholarships *(Undergraduate/Scholarship)* [6009]

Agustin C. Cano Memorial Scholarships *(Undergraduate/Scholarship)* [7472]

Commander Ronald J. Cantin Scholarships *(Undergraduate/Scholarship)* [2921]

CAODC Occupational Health and Safety Scholarships *(Professional development/Scholarship)* [2399]

CAODC Scholarship Program *(Undergraduate/Scholarship)* [2400]

Cape Fear Community College Merit Scholarships *(Undergraduate, Vocational/Occupational/Scholarship)* [2647]

Rhea Sourifman Caplin Memorial Scholarships *(Undergraduate/Scholarship)* [4417]

Kasie Ford Capling Memorial Scholarship Endowment Fund *(Undergraduate/Scholarship)* [3890]

Lester J. Cappon Fellowships in Documentary Editing *(Postdoctorate/Fellowship)* [6694]

Daniel Cardillo Charitable Fund *(All/Scholarship)* [5573]

Career Colleges Scholarships *(Undergraduate/Scholarship)* [4706]

Career Development Scholarships *(Postdoctorate, Postgraduate/Scholarship)* [3855]

Career Fellowship Awards for Medical Scientists *(Postdoctorate, Professional development/Fellowship)* [2214]

Career Mobility Scholarship Awards *(Doctorate, Undergraduate/Scholarship)* [27]

Career Mobility Scholarships *(Graduate, Undergraduate, Vocational/Occupational/Scholarship)* [3977]

CareerFitter Scholarships *(Graduate, Undergraduate/Scholarship)* [2651]

Beth Carew Memorial Scholarships *(Undergraduate/Scholarship)* [6318]

John Carew Memorial Scholarships *(Undergraduate/Scholarship)* [729]

AABA Read Carlock Memorial Scholarship Fund *(Professional development/Scholarship)* [1507]

Walta Wilkinson Carmichael Scholarships *(Undergraduate/Scholarship)* [8160]

Carnegie Observatories Graduate Research Fellowships *(Doctorate, Graduate/Fellowship)* [2655]

Carolinas-Virginias Retail Hardware Scholarships *(Undergraduate/Scholarship)* [3893]

Carpenters' Company Scholarships *(Undergraduate/Scholarship)* [2657]

Commander James Carr Forensic Science Scholarships *(Undergraduate/Scholarship)* [356]

Willis H. Carrier Scholarships *(Undergraduate/Scholarship)* [1265]

CSF Eugene Carroll Scholarships *(Undergraduate/Scholarship)* [2797]

Karen D. Carsel Memorial Scholarships *(Graduate/Scholarship)* [749]

Rachel Carson Prize *(Professional development/Prize)* [1246]

Deloris Carter Hampton Scholarships *(Undergraduate/Scholarship)* [7404]

Leigh Carter Scholarships *(Undergraduate/Scholarship)* [3099]

Letitia B. Carter Scholarships *(All/Scholarship)* [7745]

CASBS Residential Fellowships *(Doctorate, Professional development/Fellowship)* [2681]

Casey Family Scholars Scholarships *(Undergraduate, Vocational/Occupational/Scholarship)* [3871]

Local 827 Peter J. Casey Scholarships *(Undergraduate/Scholarship)* [4888]

George H. and Anna Casper Fund *(Undergraduate/Scholarship)* [8660]

Carlos M. Castaneda Journalism Scholarships *(Graduate/Scholarship)* [4027]

Catching the Dream Scholarships *(Graduate, Undergraduate/Scholarship)* [817]

Caterpillar Scholars Award *(Undergraduate/Scholarship)* [8370]

Catholic Aid Association's Post-High School Tuition Scholarships *(Undergraduate/Scholarship)* [2670]

Catholic Biblical Association of America Scholarships *(Undergraduate/Scholarship)* [2666]

Robert A. Catlin/David W. Long Memorial Scholarships *(Graduate/Scholarship)* [1009]

Marshall Cavendish Scholarships *(Graduate/Scholarship)* [899]

Christine Kerr Cawthorne Scholarships *(Undergraduate/Scholarship)* [8161]

Llewellyn L. Cayvan String Instrument Scholarships *(Undergraduate/Scholarship)* [4275]

CBC Spouses Cheerios Brand Health Initiative Scholarships *(Undergraduate/Scholarship)* [3215]

CBC Spouses Education Scholarship Fund *(Doctorate, Graduate, Undergraduate/Scholarship)* [3216]

CBC Spouses Heineken USA Performing Arts Scholarships *(Undergraduate/Scholarship)* [3218]

CBC Spouses Visual Arts Scholarships *(Undergraduate/Scholarship)* [3219]

CBCF Congressional Fellows Program *(Professional development/Fellowship)* [3220]

CCFA Career Development Awards *(Doctorate, Graduate/Grant)* [3292]

CCFA Research Fellowship Awards *(Doctorate, Graduate/Fellowship)* [3293]

CCFA Student Research Fellowship Awards *(Graduate, Undergraduate/Grant)* [3294]

CCSD School Counselors' Scholarships *(Undergraduate/Scholarship)* [7474]

CCV Foundation Graduate and Undergraduate Fellowships *(Doctorate, Graduate, Undergraduate/Fellowship)* [2672]

CDC Presidential Management Fellows Program *(Graduate/Fellowship)* [2711]

CDC Preventive Medicine Residency and Fellowships *(Professional development/Fellowship)* [2712]

L.B. Cebik, W4RNL, and Jean Cebik, N4TZP, Memorial Scholarships *(Undergraduate/Scholarship)* [1075]

Betty J. Cecere Memorial Scholarship Endowment Fund *(Undergraduate/Scholarship)* [9551]

Cedarcrest Farms Scholarships *(Graduate, Undergraduate/Scholarship)* [884]

Delmar Cengage Learning-NAAE Upper Division Scholarships *(Undergraduate/Scholarship)* [6033]

Center for Congressional and Presidential Studies Endowment (CPPS) *(Graduate, Undergraduate/Scholarship)* [1404]

Center for Lesbian and Gay Studies Fellowships *(Graduate/Fellowship)* [2701]

Centerville-Abington Dollars for Scholars *(Undergraduate/Scholarship)* [9552]

Central Arizona DX Association Scholarships *(Undergraduate/Scholarship)* [1076]

Central Maine Power Scholarship Fund *(Undergraduate/Scholarship)* [5574]

CentraState Associated Auxiliaries Scholarships *(Undergraduate/Scholarship)* [2723]

CentraState Healthcare Foundation Health Professional Scholarships *(Undergraduate/Scholarship)* [2725]

CERT College Scholarships *(Graduate, Undergraduate/Scholarship)* [3272]

Certified Municipal Clerk Scholarships (CMC) *(Professional development/Scholarship)* [4957]

Certified Neuroscience Registered Nurse Recertification Grant Program (CNRN) *(Professional development/Grant)* [518]

Cerutti Group Scholarships *(Undergraduate, Graduate/Scholarship)* [4318]

Arthur and Gladys Cervenka Scholarships *(Undergraduate/Scholarship)* [8371]

CES Conference Travel Grants *(Graduate, Professional development/Grant)* [3274]

CES Dissertation Completion Fellowships *(Graduate/Fellowship)* [3275]

CfA Postdoctoral Fellowships *(Postdoctorate/Fellowship)* [4471]

CFERP Masters Fellowships *(Graduate/Fellowship)* [3030]

CFIDS Association of America NP Student Scholarships *(Graduate/Scholarship)* [376]

CFT/ACPSOP Scholarships *(Undergraduate/Scholarship)* [2798]

Rick Chace Foundation Scholarships *(Graduate/Scholarship)* [1829]

Chaine des Rotisseurs Scholarships *(Undergraduate/Scholarship)* [691]

Jeanne S. Chall Research Fellowships *(Doctorate, Graduate/Grant)* [4975]

Challenge Met Scholarships *(Undergraduate/Scholarship)* [1077]

Mariam K. Chamberlain Fellowships in Women and Public Policy *(Graduate/Fellowship)* [4835]

Logan S. Chambers Individual Scholarships *(Professional development/Scholarship)* [4885]

Chambersburg/Fannett-Metal School District Scholarship Fund *(Undergraduate/Scholarship)* [3937]

Chambliss Astronomy Achievement Student Awards *(Undergraduate, Graduate/Award)* [570]

Jason Chaney Memorial Scholarship Fund *(Undergraduate/Scholarship)* [9553]

Channabasappa Memorial Scholarships *(Graduate, Professional development/Scholarship)* [4918]

Harry H. and Floy B. Chapin Scholarships *(Undergraduate/Scholarship)* [3145]

Nancy J. Chapman Scholarships *(Professional development/Scholarship)* [1753]

S. Penny Chappell Scholarships *(Undergraduate/Scholarship)* [7279]

Chapter 17 - St. Louis Scholarships *(Undergraduate/Scholarship)* [8372]

Chapter 6 Fairfield County Scholarships *(Undergraduate/Scholarship)* [8379]

Charles "Chuck" McAdams Memorial Scholarships *(Graduate, Undergraduate/Scholarship)* [8809]

Charlotte Housing Authority Scholarship Fund (CHASF) *(Undergraduate, Vocational/Occupational/Scholarship)* [3894]

Charlotte-Mecklenburg Schools Scholarship Incentive Program *(Undergraduate/Scholarship)* [3895]

Abram and Sylvia Chasens Teaching and Research Fellowships *(Postdoctorate/Fellowship)* [395]

Emilie Du Chatelet Awards *(Doctorate/Award)* [1226]

Chautauqua Scholarships Program *(All/Scholarship)* [4969]

Cesar E. Chavez Scholarships *(Undergraduate/Scholarship)* [7637]

CHEA Undergraduate Scholarship Program for Students with Disabilities *(High School, Undergraduate/Scholarship)* [2260]

CHEA Vocational Grants *(High School/Grant)* [2261]

Cheatham County Scholarships *(Undergraduate/Scholarship)* [3100]

Cheerful Giver Scholarships *(Undergraduate/Scholarship)* [7918]

Chemical Heritage Foundation Travel Grants (CHF) *(All/Grant)* [2740]

Cherokee Nation Graduate Scholarships *(Graduate/Scholarship)* [2742]

Cherokee Nation Pell Scholarships *(Undergraduate/Scholarship)* [2743]

Cherokee Nation Scholarships *(Undergraduate/Scholarship)* [2744]

Cherry Lane Foundation/Music Alive! Scholarships *(Undergraduate/Scholarship)* [1208]

Sgt. Michael F. Cherven Memorial Scholarships *(Undergraduate/Scholarship)* [5666]

Chi Chapter Undergraduate Scholarships *(Undergraduate/Scholarship)* [3369]

Melba Dawn Chiarenza Scholarship Fund *(Undergraduate/Scholarship)* [9554]

Chicago Division Scholarships *(Undergraduate/Scholarship)* [5858]

Chicago FM Club Scholarships *(Undergraduate/Scholarship)* [1078]

Julia Child Memorial Scholarships *(Undergraduate/Scholarship)* [692]

Kevin Child Scholarships *(Undergraduate/Scholarship)* [6319]

Childbirth Educator Program Scholarships *(All/Scholarship)* [5326]

John and Ruth Childe Scholarships *(Undergraduate/Scholarship)* [8594]

Children of Evangeline Section Scholarships *(Graduate, Undergraduate/Scholarship)* [8435]

Children of Unitarian Universalist Ministers College Scholarships *(Undergraduate/Scholarship)* [8995]

Children's Memorial Hospital Postgraduate Administrative Fellowships *(Postgraduate/Fellowship)* [5539]

Jane Coffin Childs Memorial Fund - Medical Research Fellowships *(Doctorate/Fellowship)* [2764]

Charline Chilson Scholarships *(Undergraduate/Scholarship)* [3407]

Chinese American Medical Society Summer Research Fellowships Program *(Undergraduate/Fellowship)* [2766]

Helen Krich Chinoy Dissertation Research Fellowships *(Doctorate/Fellowship)* [1360]

Choose Your Future Scholarships *(Undergraduate/Scholarship)* [3101]

Chopin Foundation of the United States Scholarships *(Undergraduate/Scholarship)* [2777]

Chretien International Research Grants *(Doctorate, Professional development/Grant)* [571]

Frances N. Christian Memorial Endowment Nursing Scholarships *(Graduate, Undergraduate/Scholarship)* [8740]

Almeric Christian Memorial Scholarships *(Graduate/Scholarship)* [9438]

Christian Pharmacist Fellowship International *(All/Fellowship)* [2783]

Christmas Tree Chapter Scholarship Awards *(Undergraduate/Scholarship)* [6933]

Commander Daniel J. Christovich Scholarship Fund *(Undergraduate/Scholarship)* [2922]

Chrysalis Scholarships *(Graduate/Grant)* [1901]

Chrysler Foundation Scholarship Awards *(Undergraduate/Scholarship)* [4546]

Chrysler Technical Scholarship Fund *(Undergraduate/Scholarship)* [3358]

Churchill Family Scholarships *(Undergraduate/Scholarship)* [5575]

Edward D. Churchill Research Scholarships *(Professional development/Scholarship)* [562]

The Churchill Scholarships *(Postgraduate/Scholarship)* [2789]

CIA Undergraduate Scholarships *(Undergraduate/Scholarship)* [1785]

CIGNA Healthcare Graduate Scholarships *(Graduate/Scholarship)* [6290]

CIGNA Healthcare Undergraduate Scholarships *(Undergraduate/Scholarship)* [6291]

Cincinnati High School Scholarships *(High School/Scholarship)* [2799]

Cintas Foundation Fellowships in Architecture *(Professional development/Fellowship)* [2881]

Cintas Foundation Fellowships in Visual Arts *(Professional development/Fellowship)* [2882]

Antonio Cirino Memorial Art Education Fellowships *(Undergraduate/Fellowship)* [7787]

CISDL Associate Fellows *(Graduate/Fellowship)* [2730]

CISDL Legal Research Fellows *(Graduate/Fellowship)* [2731]

CISDL Senior Research Fellows *(Professional development/Fellowship)* [2732]

Citi Foundation Scholarship Program *(Undergraduate/Scholarship)* [805]

Citi/TELACU Scholarships *(Undergraduate/Scholarship)* [8820]

Citizens' Scholarship Foundation of Wakefield Scholarships *(All/Scholarship)* [2885]

City of Sanibel Employee Dependent Scholarships *(Undergraduate/Scholarship)* [8595]

Civil Air Patrol Scholarships for School and Flying *(Undergraduate/Scholarship)* [2893]

Civitan Shropshire Scholarships *(Undergraduate, Vocational/Occupational/Scholarship)* [2895]

Clackamas Chapter Scholarship Awards *(Undergraduate/Scholarship)* [6934]

Claes Nobel Academic Scholarships for Members *(High School/Scholarship)* [6502]

Clan Ross Foundation Scholarships *(Undergraduate/Scholarship)* [2897]

Michelle Clark Fellowships *(Undergraduate/Fellowship)* [7576]

Vickie Clark-Flaherty Scholarships *(Undergraduate, Vocational/Occupational/Scholarship)* [6772]

Willis W. and Ethel M. Clark Foundation Fellowships *(Graduate/Fellowship)* [2899]

Clark High School Academy of Finance Scholarships *(Undergraduate/Scholarship)* [7476]

Clark High School Alumni Leadership Circle Scholarships *(Undergraduate/Scholarship)* [7477]

Clark High School Teacher Education Academy Scholarships *(Undergraduate/Scholarship)* [7478]

Howard A. Clark Horticulture Scholarships *(Undergraduate/Scholarship)* [3102]

Robert A. Clark Memorial Educational Scholarships *(Postgraduate/Scholarship)* [6510]

Andrew Blake Clark Memorial Scholarships *(Undergraduate/Scholarship)* [9629]

Thomas Arkle Clark Scholar-Leader of the Year Endowed Scholarships *(Graduate, Undergraduate/Scholarship)* [7254]

Lucy and Charles W.E. Clarke Scholarships *(Undergraduate/Scholarship)* [1660]

CLASS Fund Irrigation Scholarship Program *(Graduate, Undergraduate/Scholarship)* [5331]

Classic Wines of California Scholarships *(Undergraduate/Scholarship)* [2244]

J. Clawson Mills Scholarships *(Doctorate/Scholarship)* [5784]

Clay Postdoctoral Fellowships *(Postdoctorate/Fellowship)* [4472]

Bruce Clement Post-Secondary Education Scholarships *(Undergraduate/Scholarship)* [6631]

Cleveland Executive Fellowships (CEF) *(Professional development/Fellowship)* [2903]

Geraldine Clewell Fellowships - Doctoral Student *(Graduate/Fellowship)* [7280]

Geraldine Clewell Fellowships - Masteral *(Graduate/Fellowship)* [7281]

Geraldine Clewell Scholarships - Undergraduate *(Undergraduate/Scholarship)* [7282]

Justice Robert L. Clifford Fellowships *(All/Fellowship)* [5930]

James L. Clifford Prize *(Professional development/Prize)* [1227]

David H. Clift Scholarships *(Graduate/Scholarship)* [900]

Bryan Cline Memorial Soccer Scholarship Program *(Undergraduate/Scholarship)* [279]

Clinical Laboratory Management Association High School Senior Scholarships *(High School/Scholarship)* [2907]

Clinical Laboratory Management Association Undergraduate Scholarships *(Undergraduate/Scholarship)* [2908]

Clinical Pharmacy Post-Pharm.D. Fellowships in the Biomedical Research Sciences *(Postdoctorate/Fellowship)* [758]

Clinical Research Fellowship for Medical Students *(Graduate/Fellowship)* [3522]

Clinical Research Training Fellowships *(Professional development/Fellowship)* [373]

Clinical Toxicology Fellowships *(Doctorate/Fellowship)* [537]

Clinician Scientist Development Awards *(Postgraduate/Fellowship)* [7127]

George H. Clinton Scholarship Fund *(Undergraduate/Scholarship)* [7065]

Closs/Parnitzke/Clarke Scholarships *(Undergraduate/Scholarship)* [7283]

Club Managers Association of America Research Grants (CMAA) *(All/Grant)* [2910]

The Club at Morningside Scholarships *(Undergraduate, Vocational/Occupational/Scholarship)* [7919]

CMAA Student Conference Travel Grants *(All/Grant)* [2911]

CNA Foundation Scholarships *(Graduate, Undergraduate/Scholarship)* [1335]

Coast Guard Foundation Enlisted Education Grants *(All/Grant)* [2923]

Coast Guard Foundation Scholarships *(Undergraduate/Scholarship)* [2924]

The Helena B. Cobb Annual Scholarships *(Undergraduate, Vocational/Occupational/Scholarship)* [9728]

The Helena B. Cobb Four-Year Higher Education Grants *(Undergraduate, Vocational/Occupational/Scholarship)* [9729]

J.C. and Rheba Cobb Memorial Scholarships *(Undergraduate/Scholarship)* [6198]

Gordon W. and Agnes P. Cobb Scholarships *(Undergraduate/Scholarship)* [3567]

John Coburn and Harold Winters Student Award in Plasma Science and Technology *(Graduate/Award)* [1980]

Coca-Cola First Generation Scholarships *(Undergraduate/Scholarship)* [806]

Coca-Cola Scholars Foundation Four-Year Awards for Seniors *(Undergraduate/Scholarship)* [2966]

Geri Coccodrilli Culinary Scholarship Fund *(Undergraduate/Scholarship)* [4209]

Johnnie L. Cochran, Jr./MWH Scholarships *(Graduate, Undergraduate/Scholarship)* [6292]

Frank M. Coda Scholarships *(Undergraduate/Scholarship)* [1266]

CODY Foundation Fund *(Undergraduate/Scholarship)* [3938]

Frank M. Coffin Family Law Fellowships *(Graduate/Fellowship)* [5569]

Donald O. Coffman Scholarships *(Undergraduate/Scholarship)* [7405]

COHEAO Scholarships *(Undergraduate/Scholarship)* [2919]

Maurice and Marilyn Cohen Fund for Doctoral Dissertation Fellowships in Jewish Studies *(Doctorate/Fellowship)* [3974]

Ardis Cohoon Scholarships *(Undergraduate/Scholarship)* [9263]

Cole Family Scholarships *(Undergraduate/Scholarship)* [7406]

Cole Foundation Undergraduate Scholarship Program *(Undergraduate/Scholarship)* [3898]

Arthur H. Cole Grants in Aid *(Doctorate/Grant)* [3582]

Paul Cole Scholarships *(Undergraduate/Scholarship)* [8420]

Sally Cole Visual Arts Scholarship Fund *(Undergraduate/Scholarship)* [3899]

Dennis Coleman Choral Conducting Scholarships *(Undergraduate/Scholarship)* [7407]

Colgate-Palmolive/HDA Foundation Scholarships

(Master's, Postgraduate/Scholarship) [4555]

College Art Association Professional Development Fellowships *(Graduate/Fellowship)* [2968]

College Art Association Wyeth Publication Grants *(Professional development/Grant)* [2969]

Captain Winifred Quick Collins Scholarships *(Undergraduate/Scholarship)* [6587]

Elmer and Rosa Lee Collins Scholarships *(Undergraduate/Scholarship)* [9630]

Lloyd E. and Rachel S. Collins Scholarships *(Undergraduate/Scholarship)* [9631]

Zoe E. Collymore Page Scholarships *(Undergraduate/Scholarship)* [6145]

Colorado Broadcasters Association Continuing Education Scholarships *(Professional development/Scholarship)* [2984]

Colorado PROSTART/Art Institute of Colorado Art Scholarships for High School Seniors *(Undergraduate/Scholarship)* [1627]

ColorMasters Scholarships *(Undergraduate/Scholarship)* [4055]

Columbian Lawyers Association of Westchester County Scholarships *(Undergraduate/Scholarship)* [3009]

Columbus Citizens Foundation College Scholarships *(Undergraduate/Scholarship)* [3012]

Columbus Citizens Foundation High School Scholarships *(High School/Scholarship)* [3013]

Robert N. Colwell Memorial Fellowships *(Doctorate, Graduate/Fellowship)* [1666]

Committee 12 - Rail Transit Scholarships *(Undergraduate/Scholarship)* [1122]

Committee 27 - Maintenance-of-Way Work Equipment Scholarships *(Undergraduate/Scholarship)* [1123]

Commonwealth Fund/Harvard University Fellowships in Minority Health Policy *(Professional development/Fellowship)* [3019]

Communal Studies Association Research Fellowships *(Graduate/Grant)* [3022]

Communication Disorder/Speech Therapy Scholarships *(Graduate/Scholarship)* [4075]

Communications Workers of America Scholarships *(Undergraduate/Scholarship)* [3024]

Community-based Natural Resource Management Assistantships *(All/Internship)* [3031]

The Community Foundation DBI Scholarships *(Undergraduate, Vocational/Occupational/Scholarship)* [3103]

Community Foundation of the Fox River Valley Scholarships *(Undergraduate/Scholarship)* [3073]

Community Foundation of Sarasota County Adult Learner Scholarships *(Undergraduate, Vocational/Occupational/Scholarship)* [3189]

Community Foundation Scholarships *(Undergraduate/Scholarship)* [3146]

The Community Foundation Student Education Loans *(Undergraduate/Loan)* [3104]

Community Foundation of Western Massachusetts Community Scholarship Program *(Undergraduate/Scholarship)* [3207]

Comparative Perspectives on Chinese Culture and Society Grants *(Doctorate/Grant)* [676]

Compassionate Care Scholarships *(Undergraduate/Scholarship)* [7408]

Alan Compton and Bob Stanley Professional Scholarships *(Undergraduate/Scholarship)* [2016]

Tom and Judith Comstock Scholarships *(Undergraduate/Scholarship)* [1079]

Richard G. Condon Prize *(Doctorate, Graduate, Undergraduate/Prize)* [8469]

Maridell Braham Condon Scholarships *(Undergraduate/Scholarship)* [8162]

Conference of State Bank Supervisors Graduate School Scholarships *(Graduate/Award)* [3213]

Congressional Hispanic Caucus Institute Graduate and Young Professional Fellowships *(Doctorate, Graduate/Fellowship)* [3224]

Congressional Hispanic Caucus Institute Public Policy Fellowships *(Graduate/Fellowship)* [3225]

Congressional Hispanic Caucus Institute Scholarships *(Community College, Graduate, Undergraduate/Scholarship)* [3226]

Congressional Science Fellowships *(Postdoctorate/Fellowship)* [1302]

Alan H. Conklin Business Aviation Management

Scholarships *(Undergraduate/Scholarship)* [6163]

CSF T.L. Conlan Memorial Scholarships *(Undergraduate/Scholarship)* [2800]

Connecticut Association of Land Surveyors Memorial Scholarships *(Undergraduate/Scholarship)* [3228]

Connecticut Association of Latinos in Higher Education Scholarships *(Undergraduate/Scholarship)* [4419]

Connecticut Building Congress Scholarships *(Undergraduate/Scholarship)* [4420]

Connecticut Nurserymen's Foundation Scholarships *(Undergraduate/Scholarship)* [4423]

Cecilia Connelly Memorial Scholarships in Underwater Archaeology *(Graduate, Undergraduate/Scholarship)* [9698]

Dwight O. Conner and Ellen Conner Lepp/Danhart Scholarships *(Undergraduate/Scholarship)* [7066]

Karen Connick Memorial Scholarships *(Undergraduate/Scholarship)* [4257]

Louis M. Connor Jr. Scholarships *(Undergraduate/Scholarship)* [9264]

Patricia Pownder Conolly Memorial Scholarships *(Undergraduate/Scholarship)* [5777]

Conservation Department Program Fellowships *(Graduate/Fellowship)* [8258]

Constant Memorial Scholarship for Aquidneck Island Resident *(Undergraduate/Scholarship)* [7788]

Construction Trades Scholarships *(Undergraduate/Scholarship)* [6131]

Consumer Law Public Service Fellowships *(All/Fellowship)* [7603]

Contemporary Club Scholarships *(Undergraduate/Scholarship)* [7638]

The Continental Group Scholarship Fund *(High School, Undergraduate/Scholarship)* [3316]

Continuing Education Awards *(All/Scholarship)* [6109]

Continuing Education Awards *(Graduate/Grant)* [5741]

Jorge Espejal Contreras Memorial Scholarships *(Graduate, Undergraduate/Scholarship)* [4873]

Convergence Assistantship Grants *(Undergraduate/Grant)* [4386]

James & Maryetta Cook Scholarships *(Undergraduate/Scholarship)* [2334]

Irvine W. Cook WA0CGS Scholarships *(Undergraduate/Scholarship)* [1080]

John Kent Cooke Foundation Graduate Scholarships *(Graduate/Scholarship)* [3245]

John Kent Cooke Foundation Undergraduate Transfer Scholarships *(Undergraduate/Scholarship)* [3246]

John Kent Cooke Foundation Young Scholars *(High School/Scholarship)* [3247]

Cooley's Anemia Foundation Research Fellowships *(Postdoctorate/Fellowship)* [3251]

Madison and Edith Cooper Scholarships *(Undergraduate, Vocational/Occupational/Scholarship)* [7920]

Milton E. Cooper/Young AFCEAN Graduate Scholarships *(Graduate/Scholarship)* [1558]

Cope Middle School PTSA Scholarships *(Undergraduate/Scholarship)* [7639]

Copper and Brass Servicenter Association Inc. Scholarship Program *(Undergraduate/Scholarship)* [3253]

Corbett-Porter Building Bridges Scholarships *(Undergraduate/Scholarship)* [7479]

Hazel Corbin/Childbirth Connection Grants for Evidence-based Midwifery Care *(Professional development/Grant)* [619]

Cornaro Scholarships for Graduate Studies *(Graduate/Scholarship)* [5191]

D.C. Cornelius Memorial Scholarships *(Undergraduate/Scholarship)* [9632]

Holly A. Cornell Scholarships *(Graduate/Scholarship)* [1417]

Corning Outstanding Student Paper Competition *(Graduate, Undergraduate/Award)* [6910]

The Corp - Students of Georgetown Inc.-Word Scholarships *(Undergraduate/Scholarship)* [3259]

Corporate Aviation Management Scholarships *(Professional development/Scholarship)* [6164]

Correctional Education Association Scholarships *(Graduate, Undergraduate/Scholarship)* [3266]

NSS Sara Corrie Memorial Grants *(All/Grant)* [6525]

Tom Cory Memorial Scholarships *(Undergraduate/Scholarship)* [1498]

Richard Cossette/Gale Memorial Scholarships *(All/Scholarship)* [1965]

James Costello Memorial Scholarships *(Undergraduate/Scholarship)* [5023]

Cotner Family Scholarships *(Undergraduate/Scholarship)* [3765]

George C. Cotzias, MD Memorial Fellowships *(Professional development/Fellowship)* [981]

Dave Couch Memorial Scholarships *(Undergraduate/Scholarship)* [7067]

SRC NRI Hans J. Coufal Fellowships *(Graduate/Fellowship)* [8086]

Jennifer Coulter Memorial Scholarships *(Undergraduate/Scholarship)* [7068]

Council on Social Work Education Minority Fellowship Programs *(Postdoctorate/Fellowship)* [3282]

Council on Social Work Education Scholars Program *(Postdoctorate/Scholarship)* [3283]

Courage to Grow Scholarships *(Undergraduate/Scholarship)* [3286]

Court Scholarships *(Undergraduate/Scholarship)* [3243]

Soozie Courter Sharing a Brighter Tomorrow Hemophilia Scholarship Program *(Graduate, Undergraduate, Vocational/Occupational/Scholarship)* [6320]

Paul Courtland Scholarships *(Undergraduate/Scholarship)* [5332]

COUSE-Gram Scholarships *(Undergraduate/Scholarship)* [8596]

Richard P. Covert, Ph.D./FHIMSS Scholarships for Management Systems *(Graduate, Postgraduate, Undergraduate/Scholarship)* [4504]

The Joe E. Covington Awards for Research on Bar Admissions Testing *(Doctorate, Graduate/Award)* [6204]

Reuben R. Cowles Youth Awards *(Undergraduate/Award)* [885]

Justin Forrest Cox "Beat the Odds" Memorial Scholarships *(Undergraduate/Scholarship)* [2942]

Gertrude M. Cox Scholarships *(Doctorate, Graduate/Fellowship)* [1395]

CPCU Loman Education Foundation Scholarships *(Professional development/Scholarship)* [4838]

Tommy Crabb Scholarship Fund *(Undergraduate/Scholarship)* [4480]

Craft Research Fund *(Professional development/Grant)* [2683]

Crafton Elementary School PTA Scholarships *(Undergraduate/Scholarship)* [7640]

Margaret T. Craig Community Service Scholarships *(Undergraduate/Scholarship)* [3147]

Robert E. Cramer Scholarships *(Graduate, Undergraduate/Scholarship)* [8445]

Meredith P. Crawford Fellowships in I/O Psychology *(Doctorate/Fellowship)* [4632]

AWG Maria Luisa Crawford Field Camp Scholarships *(Undergraduate/Scholarship)* [1902]

Crawford Scholarships *(Undergraduate/Scholarship)* [7921]

Creative Glass Center of America Fellowships *(All/Fellowship)* [3288]

Critical Language Scholarships for Intensive Summer Institutes *(Graduate, Undergraduate/Scholarship)* [1145]

CRMA Scholarships *(Graduate, Undergraduate/Scholarship)* [2748]

Crohn's and Colitis Foundation of America Senior Research Awards *(Doctorate, Graduate/Grant)* [3295]

Cromwell Fellowships *(Undergraduate/Fellowship)* [1291]

Redlands Rotary Club - Ernest L. Cronemeyer Memorial Scholarships *(Undergraduate/Scholarship)* [7642]

Kathryn M. Cronin Scholarships *(Graduate, Undergraduate/Scholarship)* [9265]

Albuquerque ARC/Toby Cross Scholarships *(Undergraduate/Scholarship)* [1082]

CrossLites Scholarships *(Graduate, High School, Undergraduate/Scholarship)* [3297]

R.G. and Ruth Crossno Memorial Scholarships *(Undergraduate/Scholarship)* [3569]

CROW Fellowships *(All/Fellowship)* [2905]

Crowder Scholarships *(Undergraduate/Scholarship)* [3901]

CRS Scholarships *(Undergraduate/Scholarship)* [2785]

Lydia Cruz and Sandra Maria Ramos Scholarships *(Undergraduate/Scholarship)* [3404]

The Crystal Green Blood Assurance Memorial Scholarships *(Undergraduate/Scholarship)* [2153]

CSA Fraternal Life Scholarships *(Undergraduate/Scholarship)* [3299]

CSF Ach Family Scholarships *(Undergraduate/Scholarship)* [2801]

CSF Barr Foundation Scholarships *(Undergraduate/Scholarship)* [2802]

CSF Barrett Family Scholarships *(Undergraduate/Scholarship)* [2803]

CSF Bigg's/Curtis Breeden Scholarships *(Undergraduate/Scholarship)* [2804]

CSF Borden Inc. Scholarships *(Undergraduate/Scholarship)* [2805]

CSF Castellini Foundation Scholarships *(Undergraduate/Scholarship)* [2806]

CSF Cincinnati Bell Scholarships *(Undergraduate/Scholarship)* [2807]

CSF Cincinnati Financial Corporation Scholarships *(Undergraduate/Scholarship)* [2808]

CSF Cincinnati Milacron Scholarships *(Undergraduate/Scholarship)* [2809]

CSF Crosset Family Scholarships *(Undergraduate/Scholarship)* [2810]

CSF Dater Foundation Scholarships *(Undergraduate/Scholarship)* [2811]

CSF Duke Energy Scholarships *(Undergraduate/Scholarship)* [2812]

CSF Farmer Family Foundation Scholarships *(Undergraduate/Scholarship)* [2813]

CSF Fifth Third Bank Combined Scholarships *(Undergraduate/Scholarship)* [2814]

CSF Fletemeyer Family Scholarships *(Undergraduate/Scholarship)* [2815]

CSF Gardner Foundation Scholarships *(Undergraduate/Scholarship)* [2816]

CSF G.E. Aircraft Engines Scholarships *(Undergraduate/Scholarship)* [2817]

CSF Goldman, Sachs and Company Scholarships *(Undergraduate/Scholarship)* [2818]

CSF Graduate Fellowships *(Graduate/Fellowship)* [2787]

CSF Greater Cincinnati Scholarships Association *(Undergraduate/Scholarship)* [2819]

CSF Heidelberg Distributing Co. Scholarships *(Undergraduate/Scholarship)* [2820]

CSF Heinz Pet Products Scholarships *(Undergraduate/Scholarship)* [2821]

CSF Juilfs Foundation Scholarships *(Undergraduate/Scholarship)* [2822]

CSF Kroger Cincinnati/Dayton Scholarships *(Undergraduate/Scholarship)* [2823]

CSF Lazarus/Federated Scholarships *(Undergraduate/Scholarship)* [2824]

CSF McCall Educational Scholarships *(Undergraduate/Scholarship)* [2825]

CSF Midland Company Scholarships *(Undergraduate/Scholarship)* [2826]

CSF Nethercott Family Scholarships *(Undergraduate/Scholarship)* [2827]

CSF Ohio National Foundation Scholarships *(Undergraduate/Scholarship)* [2828]

CSF Pepper Family Scholarships *(Undergraduate/Scholarship)* [2829]

CSF Pichler Family Scholarships *(Undergraduate/Scholarship)* [2830]

CSF PNC Bank Scholarships *(Undergraduate/Scholarship)* [2831]

CSF Procter and Gamble Scholarships *(Undergraduate/Scholarship)* [2832]

CSF SC Johnson, A Family Company Scholarships *(Undergraduate/Scholarship)* [2833]

CSF Scripps Headliners Scholarships *(Undergraduate/Scholarship)* [2834]

CSF Semple Foundation Scholarships *(Undergraduate/Scholarship)* [2835]

CSF Union Central 135th Anniversary Scholarships *(Undergraduate/Scholarship)* [2836]

CSF U.S. Bank N.A. Scholarships *(Undergraduate/Scholarship)* [2837]

CSF Western-Southern Foundation Scholarships *(Undergraduate/Scholarship)* [2838]

CSF Woodward Trustees Scholarships *(Undergraduate/Scholarship)* [2839]

CSF Wynne Family Memorial Scholarships *(Undergraduate/Scholarship)* [2840]

CSX Scholarships *(Undergraduate/Scholarship)* [1124]

CTFS Research Grants Program *(Graduate, Postdoctorate, Professional development/Grant)* [8268]

CTP Scholarship Program *(Professional development/Scholarship)* [6455]

CTRF Scholarships for Graduate Study in Transportation *(Graduate/Scholarship)* [2626]

John P. Culhane Memorial Scholarships *(Undergraduate/Scholarship)* [191]

Culinary and Hospitality Foundation of San Benito County Scholarships *(Undergraduate/Scholarship)* [3303]

Linda Cullen Memorial Scholarships *(High School/Scholarship)* [693]

Murtha Cullina Scholarships *(Undergraduate/Scholarship)* [3080]

Brian Cummins Memorial Scholarships *(Undergraduate/Scholarship)* [4424]

John S. and Marjoria R. Cunningham Camp Scholarships *(All/Scholarship)* [5576]

Claire V. Cunningham Masonic Fund for Supporting Leadership in Nursing Scholarships *(Professional development/Scholarship)* [1724]

John J. Cunningham Memorial Scholarships *(Undergraduate/Scholarship)* [1125]

Tsutako Curo Scholarships *(Undergraduate/Scholarship)* [7480]

Curry Awards for Girls and Young Women *(Undergraduate/Scholarship)* [8199]

Nancy Curry Scholarships *(Postgraduate, Vocational/Occupational/Scholarship)* [8028]

Michael D. Curtin Renaissance Student Memorial Scholarships *(Undergraduate/Scholarship)* [3570]

The Jennifer Curtis Byler Scholarships *(Undergraduate/Scholarship)* [6533]

Dewey Lee Curtis Scholarships *(All/Scholarship)* [3356]

Cushing Academy Fellowships on Environmental History *(Graduate, Doctorate/Fellowship)* [5669]

CVS/All Kids Can Scholars Program *(Undergraduate, Vocational/Occupational/Scholarship)* [1935]

Cystic Fibrosis Cholestatic Liver Disease Liver Scholarships *(Doctorate/Award)* [905]

Cystic Fibrosis Scholarship Foundation *(Undergraduate, Vocational/Occupational/Scholarship)* [3312]

Daddy Longlegs Scholarships *(Undergraduate, Vocational/Occupational/Scholarship)* [7922]

Daggy Youth/Student Scholarships *(Professional development/Scholarship)* [5016]

Jason Dahnert Memorial Scholarships *(Graduate, Undergraduate/Scholarship)* [3863]

Robert G. Daily Scholarships *(Graduate, Undergraduate/Scholarship)* [8446]

Dairy Farmers of America Scholarships *(Undergraduate/Scholarship)* [3331]

Dake Community Manufacturing Scholarships *(Undergraduate/Scholarship)* [4210]

Daland Fellowships in Clinical Investigation *(Doctorate/Fellowship)* [989]

Dalcroze Society of America Memorial Scholarships *(Graduate/Scholarship)* [3335]

Chester Dale Fellowships *(Doctorate/Fellowship)* [5785]

Angela D. Dales Merit Scholarship Program *(Undergraduate/Scholarship)* [1486]

The John L. Dales Scholarship Fund *(Undergraduate, Vocational/Occupational/Scholarship)* [8069]

Serena D. Dalton Scholarships *(Undergraduate/Scholarship)* [9633]

June Danby and Pat Pearse Education Scholarships *(Undergraduate/Scholarship)* [5093]

Dance Education Scholarship Program *(High School/Scholarship)* [7985]

Arthur H. Daniels Scholarships *(Undergraduate/Scholarship)* [7643]

Dante Prizes *(Undergraduate/Prize)* [3341]

Danville High School Class of 1963 Scholarship Fund *(Undergraduate/Scholarship)* [3767]

Danville Rotary Scholarships *(Undergraduate/Scholarship)* [3768]

Mary Mouzon Darby Undergraduate Scholarships *(Undergraduate/Scholarship)* [4627]

Daughters of the American Revolution American Indian Scholarships *(Undergraduate/Scholarship)* [818]

Frank L. Dautriel Memorial Scholarships for Graduates *(Graduate/Scholarship)* [5519]

Frank L. Dautriel Memorial Scholarships for Undergraduates *(Undergraduate/Scholarship)* [5520]

The Dave Family "Humor Studies" Scholarships *(Undergraduate/Scholarship)* [1703]

David G. Imig Awards for Distinguished Achievement in Teacher Education *(Professional development/Award)* [465]

David Library Fellowships *(Doctorate, Postdoctorate/Fellowship)* [3344]

Davis Educational Scholarship Fund *(Undergraduate, Vocational/Occupational/Scholarship)* [3190]

Davis Family Scholarships *(Undergraduate/Scholarship)* [7923]

Davis Foundation Postdoctoral Fellowships *(Postdoctorate/Fellowship)* [4494]

Davis Memorial Foundation Scholarship Awards Program *(Graduate, Undergraduate/Scholarship)* [3346]

CSF Estelle Davis Memorial Scholarships *(Undergraduate/Scholarship)* [2841]

Dwight F. Davis Memorial Scholarships *(Undergraduate/Scholarship)* [9408]

Johnny Davis Memorial Scholarships *(Undergraduate/Scholarship)* [125]

Larry Dean Davis Scholarship Program *(Undergraduate, Vocational/Occupational/Scholarship)* [2171]

Arlene Davis Scholarships *(Undergraduate/Scholarship)* [3408]

IS&T Raymond Davis Scholarships *(Graduate, Undergraduate/Scholarship)* [8352]

James Davis Scholarships *(Undergraduate/Scholarship)* [9267]

Kenneth D. and Katherine D. Davis Scholarships *(Undergraduate/Scholarship)* [7070]

Colonel Richard M. Dawson Scholarships *(Undergraduate/Scholarship)* [3105]

Brian M. Day Scholarships *(Undergraduate/Scholarship)* [7409]

Dayton Amateur Radio Association Scholarships *(Undergraduate/Scholarship)* [1083]

DBA Law School Scholarship Program *(Undergraduate/Scholarship)* [3471]

Edilia and Francois Auguste de Montequin Fellowships *(Doctorate/Fellowship)* [8295]

Elsie De Wolfe Point Scholarships *(Graduate, Undergraduate/Scholarship)* [7357]

Earl Deadman Memorial Scholarships *(Undergraduate/Scholarship)* [730]

Deafness Research Foundation Research Grants *(Doctorate/Grant)* [3350]

Alphonso Deal Scholarship Awards *(Undergraduate/Scholarship)* [6157]

Dean Prim Scholarships *(Undergraduate/Scholarship)* [9634]

Derek Lee Dean Soccer Scholarships *(High School/Scholarship)* [2943]

Steve Dearduff Scholarships *(Graduate, Undergraduate/Scholarship)* [3075]

Don Debolt Franchising Scholarship Program *(Undergraduate/Scholarship)* [4939]

Walter M. Decker Point Scholarships *(Graduate, Undergraduate/Scholarship)* [7358]

DEED Student Research Grant/Internships *(Graduate, Undergraduate/Grant)* [1048]

Ginger and Fred Deines Canada Scholarships *(Undergraduate, Vocational/Occupational/Scholarship)* [8949]

Ginger and Fred Deines Mexico Scholarships *(Undergraduate, Vocational/Occupational/Scholarship)* [8950]

Jane Delano Student Nurse Scholarships *(Undergraduate/Scholarship)* [1135]

Jan DiMartino Delany Memorial Scholarships *(Undergraduate/Scholarship)* [3939]

Alexander A. Delle Cese Memorial Scholarships *(Undergraduate/Scholarship)* [2191]

Delmar Cengage Surgical Technology Scholarships *(Graduate/Scholarship)* [1880]

Vine Deloria Jr. Memorial Scholarships *(Graduate/Scholarship)* [807]

Eric Delson Memorial Scholarships *(High School, Undergraduate, Vocational/Occupational/Scholarship)* [6321]

Delta Chi Alumnae Memorial Scholarships *(Undergraduate/Scholarship)* [8165]

Delta Epsilon Sigma Graduate Fellowships *(Graduate/Scholarship)* [3395]

Delta Epsilon Sigma Undergraduate Scholarships *(Undergraduate/Scholarship)* [3396]

Delta Faucet Scholarships *(Undergraduate/Scholarship)* [7345]

Delta Gamma Scholarships *(Undergraduate/Scholarship)* [3398]

Delta Iota Alumni Scholarships *(Undergraduate/Scholarship)* [8218]

Delta Nu Alpha Foundation Scholarships *(Undergraduate/Scholarship)* [3400]

Delta Phi Epsilon Educational Foundation Scholarships *(Undergraduate/Scholarship)* [3402]

Delta/VPPPA Safety, Health and Environmental Scholarships *(Undergraduate, Vocational/Occupational, Graduate/Scholarship)* [9475]

Delta Zeta Undergraduate Scholarships *(Undergraduate/Scholarship)* [3409]

Law Offices of Michael A. DeMayo Scholarships *(Undergraduate/Scholarship)* [5364]

DEMCO New Leaders Travel Grants *(All/Grant)* [7536]

Christopher Demetris Scholarships *(Undergraduate/Scholarship)* [4513]

Inez Demonet Scholarships *(Graduate/Scholarship)* [9421]

Cindy P. Dennis Scholarship Fund *(Undergraduate/Scholarship)* [3241]

Denver Scholarship Foundation Scholarships *(Undergraduate/Scholarship)* [3428]

Tommy Depaola Scholarship Awards *(Undergraduate/Scholarship)* [4931]

Dick Depaolis Memorial Scholarships *(Undergraduate/Scholarship)* [3196]

Depression and ADHD Fellowships *(Postdoctorate/Fellowship)* [5268]

DEPS Graduate Scholarship Program *(Graduate/Scholarship)* [3455]

Derivative Duo Scholarships *(Undergraduate/Scholarship)* [7410]

Pat Dermargosian Memorial Scholarships *(Undergraduate/Scholarship)* [7644]

Descendant Scholarships *(Undergraduate/Scholarship)* [3326]

Libby Deschenes Prize for Applied Research *(Undergraduate/Prize)* [9581]

Achille & Irene Despres, William & Andre Scholarships *(Undergraduate/Scholarship)* [4278]

Development Fund for Black Students in Science and Technology Scholarships *(Undergraduate/Scholarship)* [3432]

Albert and Jane Dewey Scholarships *(Undergraduate/Scholarship)* [4426]

DHCC Board Scholarships *(Graduate, Professional development, Undergraduate/Scholarship)* [3442]

William Diaz Fellowships *(Professional development/Fellowship)* [6729]

Julio C. Diaz Memorial Scholarship Fund *(High School/Scholarship)* [8662]

Jean Dearth Dickerscheid Fellowships *(Graduate/Fellowship)* [7284]

Dickey Rural Networks College Scholarship Program *(Undergraduate, Vocational/Occupational/Scholarship)* [3438]

Bill Dickey Scholarship Association Scholarships *(Undergraduate/Scholarship)* [3440]

Harold Dieckmann Draper, Sr. Scholarships *(Undergraduate/Scholarship)* [1938]

Rob Digiacomo Scholarship Fund *(Undergraduate/Scholarship)* [8663]

Rudolph Dillman Memorial Scholarships *(Graduate, Undergraduate/Scholarship)* [750]

Carol DiMaiti Scholarship Awards *(Undergraduate/Scholarship)* [5662]

The E.R. and Lilian B. Dimmette Scholarship Fund *(Undergraduate/Scholarship)* [3902]

Disabled War Veterans Scholarships *(Undergraduate/Scholarship)* [1559]

Walt Disney Company Foundation Scholarships *(Undergraduate/Scholarship)* [5173]

Dissertation Fellowships in East European Studies *(Doctorate/Fellowship)* [677]

Dissertation Proposal Development Fellowships *(Doctorate/Fellowship)* [8282]

Distinguished Flying Cross Society Scholarships *(Undergraduate/Scholarship)* [3461]

Distinguished Young Women Scholarships *(Undergraduate/Scholarship)* [3463]

LaRue A. Ditmore Music Scholarships *(Undergraduate/Scholarship)* [9706]

Diversified Investment Advisors Leaders in Healthcare Scholarships *(Graduate/Scholarship)* [4788]

Diversity Dissertation Scholarships *(Doctorate/Fellowship)* [1032]

Diversity Executive Leadership Program Scholarships *(Professional development/Scholarship)* [1184]

Diversity Fellowship Program (DFP) *(Undergraduate/Fellowship)* [5928]

Robert A. and Barbara Divine Graduate Student Travel Grants *(Graduate/Grant)* [8338]

Peggy Dixon Two-Year Scholarships *(Undergraduate/Scholarship)* [8438]

Grace O. Doane Scholarships *(Undergraduate/Scholarship)* [3485]

Charles Dobbins FTA Scholarships *(Undergraduate, Vocational/Occupational/Scholarship)* [4033]

Doctoral Degree Scholarships in Cancer Nursing *(Doctorate/Scholarship)* [596]

Doctoral Fellowships - Dissertation *(Doctorate/Fellowship)* [4779]

Doctoral Fellowships - Graduate *(Doctorate/Fellowship)* [4780]

Document Management and Graphic Communications Industry Scholarships *(Undergraduate/Scholarship)* [3627]

Doddridge County Promise Scholarships *(Undergraduate/Scholarship)* [7072]

F. Atlee Dodge Maintenance Scholarships *(Undergraduate/Scholarship)* [192]

Robert Winchester Dodson Scholarships *(Undergraduate/Scholarship)* [9268]

DOE Computational Science Graduate Fellowships (DOE CSGF) *(Doctorate, Graduate/Fellowship)* [5306]

Hans H. and Margaret B. Doe Scholarships *(Graduate, Undergraduate, Vocational/Occupational/Scholarship)* [7926]

Emmett J. Doerr Memorial Distinguished Scout Scholarships *(High School/Scholarship)* [6249]

Dofflemyer Scholarships *(Undergraduate/Scholarship)* [6250]

Dollar-A-Day Academic Scholarships *(Graduate, Undergraduate/Scholarship)* [3467]

Dolphin Scholarships *(Undergraduate/Scholarship)* [3469]

Scott Dominguez - Craters of the Moon Chapter Scholarships *(Graduate, Undergraduate/Scholarship)* [1336]

Don Aron Scholarships *(Undergraduate/Scholarship)* [6208]

Marian Jones Donaldson Scholarship Fund *(Undergraduate/Scholarship)* [3769]

Harvey N. Dondero Communication and Journalism Excellence Scholarships *(Undergraduate/Scholarship)* [7482]

Doniphan Community Foundation Scholarships *(Undergraduate/Scholarship)* [4258]

Jim Doogan Memorial Scholarships *(Undergraduate/Scholarship)* [9185]

Doraine Pursuit of Educational Excellence Scholarships *(Undergraduate/Scholarship)* [2944]

Dorchester Woman's Club Scholarships *(Undergraduate/Scholarship)* [4076]

Joseph M. Dorgan Scholarships *(Undergraduate/Scholarship)* [3486]

Dr. Michael Dorizas Memorial Scholarships *(Undergraduate/Scholarship)* [4514]

Pauly D'Orlando Memorial Art Scholarships *(Graduate, Undergraduate/Scholarship)* [8996]

Dosatron International Inc. Scholarships (Undergraduate/Scholarship) [731]

Eric Dostie Memorial College Scholarships (Undergraduate/Scholarship) [6322]

Father Connie Dougherty Scholarships (Undergraduate, Vocational/Occupational/Scholarship) [3191]

Robert E. Dougherty Scholarships (Undergraduate/Scholarship) [3209]

Sergeant Douglas and Charlotte DeHorse Scholarships (Graduate, Undergraduate/Scholarship) [2661]

Douglass Foundation Fellowships in American Art (Graduate/Fellowship) [5786]

Dow Chemical Company Fellowships (Graduate/Fellowship) [6427]

Margaret Dowell-Gravatt, M.D. Scholarships (Undergraduate/Scholarship) [2059]

Downeast Energy Scholarships (Undergraduate/Scholarship) [3477]

Downeast Feline Scholarships (Graduate/Scholarship) [5577]

Jay Downes Memorial Scholarships (Undergraduate/Scholarship) [2945]

Rodger Doxsey Travel Prizes (Graduate, Postdoctorate/Prize) [572]

Nettie Dracup Memorial Scholarships (Undergraduate/Scholarship) [643]

AAGS Joseph F. Dracup Scholarship Awards (Undergraduate/Scholarship) [644]

Drake University Law School Law Opportunity Scholarships - Disadvantage (Undergraduate/Scholarship) [3487]

Drake University Law School Law Opportunity Scholarships - Diversity (Undergraduate/Scholarship) [3488]

Drake University Law School Public Service Scholarships (Undergraduate/Scholarship) [3489]

The Drama Therapy Fund Graduate Research Grants (Graduate/Grant) [3518]

The Drama Therapy Fund Graduate Student Research Awards (Graduate/Grant) [3519]

Lou Drane Music Scholarships (Undergraduate/Scholarship) [3940]

The "Drawn to Art" Fellowships (Doctorate/Fellowship) [417]

Vivian Drenckhahn Student Scholarships (Graduate, Undergraduate/Scholarship) [8477]

Margaret Drew Alpha Fellowships (Graduate/Fellowship) [7285]

Charles Drew Scholarships (Professional development/Scholarship) [1754]

DRI Law Student Diversity Scholarships (Undergraduate/Scholarship) [2144]

Thomas J. Drinan Memorial Fellowships (All/Fellowship) [7604]

Drinkwater Family Scholarships (Undergraduate/Scholarship) [7928]

Lillian Cooper Droke Memorial Scholarships (Undergraduate/Scholarship) [5778]

Richard Drukker Memorial Scholarships (Undergraduate/Scholarship) [6651]

Drum Major Institute Scholars (Undergraduate/Scholarship) [8144]

Sergeant Major Douglas R. Drum Memorial Scholarship Fund (Undergraduate/Scholarship) [936]

W.E.B. Du Bois Fellowships (Doctorate/Fellowship) [6355]

Martin Duberman Fellowships (Professional development/Fellowship) [2702]

Lee Dubin Scholarship Fund (Undergraduate/Scholarship) [7848]

Charles Dubose Scholarships (Undergraduate/Scholarship) [4428]

John W. Duckett Jr., AFUD Pediatric Research Scholarships (Undergraduate/Scholarship) [8432]

Mark Duda Scholarship Fund (Graduate, Undergraduate/Scholarship) [3446]

Deborah Gandee Dudding Memorial Scholarships (Undergraduate/Scholarship) [7073]

Edward Leon Duhamel Freemasons Scholarships (Undergraduate/Scholarship) [7789]

Doris Duke Conservation Fellows Program (Graduate/Scholarship) [9615]

Edward J. Dulis Scholarships (Undergraduate/Scholarship) [5690]

Duluth Building and Construction Trades Council Scholarships (Undergraduate, Vocational/Occupational/Scholarship) [3527]

Dunbar Heritage Scholarships (Undergraduate/Scholarship) [8599]

Duncan Aviation Scholarships (Undergraduate/Scholarship) [126]

Wade and Marcelene Duncan Scholarships (Undergraduate/Scholarship) [9635]

Ed Dunkelblau Scholarships (All/Scholarship) [1704]

Travis Dunning Memorial Scholarships (Undergraduate/Scholarship) [7484]

William R. Durham/Theater Scholarships (Undergraduate/Scholarship) [3148]

Durning Sisters Scholarships (Graduate/Scholarship) [3370]

Joe Durso Memorial Scholarships (Undergraduate/Scholarship) [5921]

Roger C. Duvoisin, MD Research Grants (Professional development/Grant) [982]

Dystonia Medical Research Foundation Fellowships (Postdoctorate/Fellowship) [3557]

EAA Tuition Scholarships (College, Vocational/Occupational/Scholarship) [3647]

EAA Workshop Scholarships (College, Vocational/Occupational/Scholarship) [3648]

Josephine P. White Eagle Graduate Fellowships (Graduate, Master's, Doctorate/Fellowship) [4591]

Eagles Fly for Leukemia Scholarships (Undergraduate/Scholarship) [2755]

EAIA Research Grants (Professional development/Grant) [3561]

Howard G. and Gladys A. Eakes Memorial Scholarships (Undergraduate/Scholarship) [4259]

Amelia Earhart Fellowship Program (Postdoctorate/Fellowship) [9811]

Amelia Earhart Memorial Academic Scholarships (Undergraduate/Scholarship) [6724]

Early Career Postdoctoral Fellowships in East European Studies (Postdoctorate/Fellowship) [678]

Early Childhood Educators Scholarship Program (Undergraduate/Scholarship) [5684]

Robert E. Early Memorial Scholarships (Undergraduate/Scholarship) [3490]

Bob East Scholarships (Graduate, Undergraduate/Scholarship) [6450]

East Tennessee Foundation Scholarships (Undergraduate/Scholarship) [9223]

Eastern Orthodox Scouting Scholarships (High School/Scholarship) [6251]

Eastern Shore Building Industry Association Scholarships (Undergraduate/Scholarship) [3055]

David Eaton Scholarships (Graduate, Master's/Scholarship) [8997]

Ellen Eberhardt Memorial Scholarships (Undergraduate/Scholarship) [8720]

ECA Applied Urban Communication Research Grants (Professional development/Grant) [3575]

ECA Centennial Scholarships (Master's, Doctorate/Scholarship) [3576]

John E. Echlin Memorial Scholarships (Undergraduate/Scholarship) [1939]

ECMS Scholarships (Undergraduate/Scholarship) [3578]

Economic Development Division Graduate Scholarships (Graduate/Scholarship) [1010]

ECT Foundation Master Scholarships (Graduate, Master's/Scholarship) [1763]

Edgecliff Alumni Awards (Undergraduate/Scholarship) [9768]

Edgecliff McAuley Art Scholarships (Undergraduate/Scholarship) [9769]

Edgecliff McAuley Music Scholarships (Undergraduate/Scholarship) [9770]

Vivian Edmonds Scholarships (Undergraduate/Scholarship) [9269]

S. Randolph Edmonds Young Scholars Competition (Graduate, Undergraduate/Scholarship) [2140]

Melanie and Todd Edmonson Memorial Scholarships (Undergraduate/Scholarship) [3035]

Edon Farmers Cooperative Scholarships (Undergraduate/Scholarship) [3592]

Education Factor Scholarships (Graduate, Undergraduate/Scholarship) [5735]

Education is Power Scholarships (Undergraduate, Vocational/Occupational/Scholarship) [6323]

Education Resource Center Scholarships (ERC) (Undergraduate, Vocational/Occupational/Scholarship) [8211]

Educational Administration Scholarship Awards (Postgraduate/Scholarship) [545]

Educational Audiology Association Doctoral Scholarships (Doctorate/Scholarship) [3595]

Educational and Cultural Affairs Alumni Small Grants Program (ECA) (Professional development/Grant) [4980]

Educational Enrichment Awards (Undergraduate/Scholarship) [1510]

Educational Leadership Foundation Grants (Undergraduate/Grant) [2973]

Educational Portal of the Americas Graduate Scholarships (Postgraduate/Scholarship) [3604]

Educational Portal of the Americas Undergraduate Scholarships (Undergraduate/Scholarship) [3605]

Edward C. Pomeroy Awards for Outstanding Contributions to Teacher Education (Professional development/Award) [466]

Jimmy Edwards Scholarships (Undergraduate/Scholarship) [3107]

EERI/FEMA Graduate Fellowships (Graduate/Scholarship) [3563]

EFWA Moss Adams Foundation Scholarships (Graduate, Undergraduate/Scholarship) [3598]

John and Alice Egan Multi-Year Mentioning Scholarships (Undergraduate/Scholarship) [3327]

Bill Egan Scholarship Program (Undergraduate/Scholarship) [6935]

EHA Exploratory Travel and Data Grants (Doctorate/Grant) [3583]

EHA Graduate Dissertation Fellowships (Doctorate/Fellowship) [3584]

E.I. DuPont Fellowships (Graduate/Fellowship) [6428]

Christine H. Eide Memorial Scholarships (Graduate, Undergraduate/Scholarship) [5496]

Mike Eidson Scholarships (Graduate, Undergraduate/Scholarship) [490]

Eight and Forty Lung and Respiratory Disease Nursing Scholarships (Professional development/Scholarship) [896]

Hillel Einhorn New Investigator Awards (Doctorate/Award) [8363]

Albert Einstein Distinguished Educator Fellowships (Graduate, Professional development/Fellowship) [8956]

Harold E. Eisenberg Foundation Scholarships (Professional development/Scholarship) [4906]

Farouk El-Baz Student Research Grants (Doctorate, Graduate, Undergraduate/Grant) [4087]

El Dorado County Mineral and Gem Society Scholarships (Graduate, Undergraduate/Scholarship) [3620]

W. Eldridge and Emily Lowe Scholarships (Undergraduate/Scholarship) [8219]

Electric Cooperative Pioneer Trust Fund Scholarships (Undergraduate/Scholarship) [3491]

Electronic Materials and Processing Division - Postdoctoral Award (Postdoctorate/Award) [1981]

Elks National Foundation Scholarships (Undergraduate/Scholarship) [3629]

Mark Jonathan Elliot Scholarship Fund (Graduate, Undergraduate/Scholarship) [4722]

Robert A. Ellis Scholarships in Physics (Undergraduate/Scholarship) [6488]

William P. Elrod Memorial Scholarships (Undergraduate, Vocational/Occupational/Scholarship) [8815]

Emergency Medicine Physician Scholarships for Health Information Management Program (Undergraduate/Scholarship) [8664]

Emergency Nurses Association Undergraduate Scholarships (Undergraduate/Scholarship) [3634]

Emerging Teacher-Leaders in Elementary School Mathematics Grants for Grades K-5 Teachers (Professional development/Grant) [6221]

CSF Thomas J. Emery Memorial Scholarships (Undergraduate/Scholarship) [2842]

EMLF Law Student Scholarships (Undergraduate/Scholarship) [3643]

Emmanuel Bible College Scholarships (Undergraduate/Scholarship) [1592]

FTE Undergraduate Fellowships *(Undergraduate/Fellowship)* [4024]

FTE Volunteers Exploring Vocation Fellowships *(Graduate/Fellowship)* [4025]

Fuchs-Harden Educational Scholarships Fund *(Undergraduate/Scholarship)* [4337]

Gerard Swartz Fudge Memorial Scholarships *(Undergraduate/Scholarship)* [4653]

Keiko Fukuda Scholarships *(Undergraduate/Scholarship)* [9056]

Kathryn Fuller Science for Nature Post-Doctoral Fellowships *(Graduate, Postdoctorate/Fellowship)* [9759]

Don and Eileen Fulton Nursing Scholarships *(Undergraduate/Scholarship)* [8722]

Donald M. Furbush Professional Development Grants *(Professional development/Grant)* [4819]

Furman-Tikvah Scholarships *(Graduate/Scholarship)* [8903]

The Future Colleagues Scholarships *(Undergraduate/Scholarship)* [6293]

Future Leaders of Manufacturing Scholarships *(Graduate, Undergraduate/Scholarship)* [8385]

Mearl K. Gable II Memorial Grants *(Professional development/Grant)* [4387]

Gaddy Student Scholarships *(Undergraduate/Scholarship)* [9638]

Gaebe Eagle Scout Awards *(Undergraduate/Scholarship)* [6253]

Farley Moody Galbraith Scholarship Fund *(Undergraduate/Scholarship)* [3037]

Thomas W. Gallagher Scholarships Fund *(Undergraduate/Scholarship)* [8667]

Louise Bales Gallagher Scholarships *(Undergraduate/Scholarship)* [3372]

Whitney Laine Gallahar Memorial Scholarship Fund *(Undergraduate/Scholarship)* [3038]

The Gallery Collection's Greeting Card Scholarships *(Undergraduate/Scholarship)* [4035]

Carolyn Gallmeyer Scholarships *(Undergraduate/Scholarship)* [4281]

Gallo Blue Chip Scholarships *(Undergraduate/Scholarship)* [4398]

CSF Priscilla Gamble Scholarships *(Undergraduate/Scholarship)* [2846]

Gamewarden Scholarship program *(High School, Undergraduate, Vocational/Occupational/Scholarship)* [4037]

Gamma Sigma Alpha Graduate Scholarships *(Graduate/Scholarship)* [4039]

Guy P. Gannett Scholarships *(Undergraduate/Scholarship)* [5578]

Joel Garcia Memorial Scholarships *(Undergraduate/Scholarship)* [2237]

Michael and Gina Garcia Rail Engineering Scholarships *(Undergraduate/Scholarship)* [1129]

William R. Gard Memorial Scholarships *(Undergraduate/Scholarship)* [6091]

Garden Club of America Awards in Tropical Botany (GCA) *(Doctorate/Award)* [4041]

Garden Club Council of Winston-Salem and Forsyth County Council *(Undergraduate/Scholarship)* [9639]

Garden State Rotary Club of Cherry Hill Scholarships *(Undergraduate/Scholarship)* [2335]

Jewels Gardiner Scholarships *(Undergraduate/Scholarship)* [2270]

Gardner Foundation Infusion Nurses Society Education Scholarships *(All/Scholarship)* [4765]

Robert Gardner Memorial Fellowships *(Graduate/Fellowship)* [4489]

Dwight D. Gardner Scholarships *(Undergraduate/Scholarship)* [4801]

Victoria M. Gardner Scholarships *(Undergraduate/Scholarship)* [9272]

Eugene Garfield Doctoral Dissertation Fellowships *(Doctorate, Graduate/Fellowship)* [2070]

Peter M. Gargano Scholarship Fund *(Undergraduate/Scholarship)* [3529]

Garmin Scholarships *(Undergraduate/Scholarship)* [128]

Gail Garner R.I.S.E. Memorial Scholarships *(Undergraduate/Scholarship)* [7648]

Eileen J. Garrett Scholarships *(Undergraduate/Scholarship)* [7052]

Kays Gary Scholarships *(Undergraduate/Scholarship)* [9273]

Edwin W. Gaston Scholarships *(Undergraduate/Scholarship)* [343]

Gates Cambridge Scholarships *(Doctorate, Postgraduate/Scholarship)* [6072]

The Gates Millennium Scholars *(Undergraduate/Scholarship)* [4569]

Stephen Gates Scholarships *(Undergraduate/Scholarship)* [9274]

A.R.F.O.R.A. Martha Gavrila Scholarships for Women *(Postgraduate/Scholarship)* [1164]

GAWP Graduate Scholarships *(Graduate/Fellowship)* [4099]

Gay, Lesbian, Bisexual, Transgender Alumni Council Scholarships *(Undergraduate/Scholarship)* [9356]

Lowell Gaylor Memorial Scholarships *(Undergraduate/Scholarship)* [129]

Florence S. Gaynor Scholarships *(Doctorate, Graduate, Undergraduate/Scholarship)* [6081]

GCSAA Scholars Competition *(Undergraduate/Scholarship)* [4187]

GCSAA Student Essay Contest *(Graduate, Undergraduate/Prize)* [4188]

GE Healthcare Management Scholarship Program *(Graduate/Scholarship)* [1323]

GED Jump Start Scholarships *(Undergraduate/Scholarship)* [8029]

GEF Scholarship Program *(Undergraduate, Graduate/Scholarship)* [4319]

Gehring Memorial Foundation Scholarships *(Graduate, Undergraduate/Scholarship)* [4723]

Victoria S. and Bradley L. Geist Scholarships *(Undergraduate/Scholarship)* [4477]

Lawrence Gelfand - Armin Rappaport Fellowships *(Doctorate, Graduate/Fellowship, Grant)* [8339]

Irma Gelhausen Scholarship Fund *(Undergraduate/Scholarship)* [5349]

Joseph H. Gellert/Dutchess County Bar Association Scholarships *(Undergraduate/Scholarship)* [3555]

Elaine Gelman Scholarship Awards *(Undergraduate/Scholarship)* [6106]

The Gene and John Athletic Scholarships *(Undergraduate/Scholarship)* [8746]

General Falcon Scholarships *(Undergraduate/Scholarship)* [7372]

Generation III Scholarships *(Undergraduate/Scholarship)* [3586]

Geological Society of America Graduate Student Research Grants *(Doctorate, Graduate/Grant)* [4088]

Georgetown Working League Scholarships *(Undergraduate/Scholarship)* [4090]

Gerber Fellowships in Pediatric Nutrition *(Undergraduate/Fellowship)* [6401]

Gerber Foundation Merit Scholarships *(Undergraduate/Scholarship)* [4112]

Doris Y. and John J. Gerber Scholarships *(Undergraduate/Scholarship)* [9524]

Daniel Gerber, Sr. Medallion Scholarships *(Undergraduate/Scholarship)* [4113]

Walter Gerboth Awards *(Professional development/Grant)* [5958]

German Historical Institute Doctoral and Postdoctoral Fellowships *(Doctorate, Postgraduate/Fellowship)* [4126]

German Historical Institute Fellowships at the Horner Library *(Doctorate/Fellowship)* [4127]

German Society Scholarships *(Undergraduate/Scholarship)* [4137]

German Studies Research Grants *(Undergraduate/Grant)* [4119]

Eloise Gerry Fellowships *(Graduate, Postdoctorate/Fellowship)* [8151]

Getty GRI-NEH Postdoctoral Fellowships *(Postdoctorate/Fellowship)* [4140]

Getty Research Exchange Fellowship Program for Cultural Heritage Preservation *(Doctorate/Fellowship)* [1149]

GFWC Women's Club of South County Scholarships *(Undergraduate/Scholarship)* [7790]

GIA Endowment Scholarships - Distance Education *(Graduate/Scholarship)* [4056]

GIA Endowment Scholarships - On Campus *(Graduate/Scholarship)* [4057]

IDSA Gianninoto Graduate Scholarships *(Graduate/Scholarship)* [4758]

John J. Gibbons Fellowships in Public Interest and Constitutional Law *(All/Fellowship)* [4149]

Laverne L. Gibson Memorial Scholarships *(Undergraduate/Scholarship)* [7077]

Joy Gibson Scholarships *(Undergraduate/Scholarship)* [9275]

Shane Gilbert Memorial Scholarships *(Undergraduate/Scholarship)* [7078]

Gilbreth Memorial Fellowships *(Graduate/Scholarship)* [4802]

Gilder Lehrman Short-Term Fellowships *(Graduate, Postdoctorate/Fellowship)* [4151]

Terry M. Giles Honor Scholarships *(Undergraduate/Scholarship)* [7184]

Harold Giles Scholarships *(Graduate, Undergraduate/Scholarship)* [8448]

Midwest Chapter Scholarships - Jack Gill *(Undergraduate/Scholarship)* [1804]

R.L. Gillette Scholarships *(Undergraduate/Scholarship)* [751]

Gilliam Fellowships for Advanced Study *(Doctorate/Fellowship)* [4621]

Benjamin A. Gilman International Scholarships *(Undergraduate/Scholarship)* [9096]

Ethel Z. Gilman Scholarships *(Professional development/Scholarship)* [8804]

Leo Gilmartin Scholarships *(High School/Scholarship)* [7352]

Susan Kay Munson Gilmore Memorial Scholarships *(Undergraduate, Vocational/Occupational/Scholarship)* [3151]

Jack R. Gilstrap Scholarships *(Graduate, Undergraduate/Scholarship)* [1053]

Lawrence Ginocchio Aviation Scholarships *(Undergraduate/Scholarship)* [6168]

Nick Giorgione Hope for Hearts Scholarships *(Undergraduate/Scholarship)* [7493]

John Glaser Scholarships *(Undergraduate/Scholarship)* [2971]

Elizabeth Glaser Scientist Awards *(Professional development/Award)* [4157]

Ann and Brad Glassco Scholarships *(Undergraduate/Scholarship)* [7649]

GLATA Living Memorial Doctorate Scholarships *(Doctorate, Graduate/Fellowship)* [4325]

GLATA Living Memorial Undergraduate/Graduate Scholarships *(Graduate, Undergraduate/Fellowship, Scholarship)* [4326]

Glazing Industry Scholarships *(Undergraduate/Scholarship)* [7494]

Gleaner Life Insurance Scholarship Foundation *(Undergraduate/Scholarship)* [4159]

Glendale Latino Association Scholarships *(High School, Undergraduate/Scholarship)* [4161]

Global Volcanism Program for Visiting Scientist/Postdoctoral Fellowships *(Postdoctorate/Fellowship)* [8261]

Globe-Trotters Chapter Scholarships *(Undergraduate/Scholarship)* [1805]

Northeastern Ohio Chapter Scholarships - Alfred B. Glossbrenner and John Klusch Scholarships *(Undergraduate/Scholarship)* [1806]

Bud Glover Memorial Scholarships *(Undergraduate/Scholarship)* [130]

GLP Program Scholarships *(Professional development/Scholarship)* [4166]

Dr. Robert H. Goddard Memorial Scholarships *(Graduate, Undergraduate/Scholarship)* [6523]

Glenn Godfrey Memorial Scholarships *(Graduate, Undergraduate, Vocational/Occupational/Scholarship)* [5283]

John Goerlich Memorial Scholarships *(Undergraduate/Scholarship)* [1941]

Gogos Scholarships *(Undergraduate/Scholarship)* [2980]

Gold Award/Eagle Scout Scholarships *(Undergraduate/Scholarship)* [6254]

Gold Country Section & Region II Scholarships *(Graduate, Undergraduate/Scholarship)* [1337]

Gold Key Scholarships *(Undergraduate/Scholarship)* [5232]

William Goldberg Diamond Corp. Scholarships *(Undergraduate/Scholarship)* [4058]

Daniel B. Goldberg Scholarships *(Graduate/Scholarship)* [4197]

Golden Key Graduate Scholar Awards *(Postgraduate, Professional development/Fellowship)* [6073]

Golden Key International Honour Society Study Abroad Scholarships *(Undergraduate/Scholarship)* [4176]

Golden Key Math Scholarships *(Undergraduate/Scholarship)* [4177]

William R. Goldfarb Memorial Scholarships *(Undergraduate/Scholarship)* [1085]

Rhode Island Commission on Women/Freda H. Goldman Education Awards *(Undergraduate/Award)* [7791]

Dr. Guido Goldman Fellowships *(Doctorate, Postdoctorate/Fellowship)* [666]

Goldman Sachs/Matsuo Takabuki Commemorative Scholarships *(Graduate/Scholarship)* [5211]

American Radio Relay League Scholarships Honoring Barry Goldwater, K7UGA *(Undergraduate/Scholarship)* [1086]

Barry M. Goldwater Scholarships *(Undergraduate/Scholarship)* [9357]

Joshua Gomes Memorial Scholarship Fund *(Graduate, Undergraduate/Scholarship)* [6324]

Millie Gonzalez Memorial Scholarships *(Undergraduate, Vocational/Occupational/Scholarship)* [6325]

Victor and Ruth N. Goodman Memorial Scholarships *(Graduate/Scholarship)* [4373]

David B. Goodstein Point Scholarships *(Graduate, Undergraduate/Scholarship)* [7360]

James L. and Genevieve H. Goodwin Scholarships *(Undergraduate/Scholarship)* [4433]

Google-American Indian Science and Engineering Society Scholarships *(Graduate, Undergraduate/Scholarship)* [4194]

Google Hispanic College Fund Scholarships *(Graduate, Undergraduate/Scholarship)* [4195]

Richard Goolsby Scholarship Fund *(Graduate, Undergraduate/Scholarship)* [3905]

Barnett D. Gordon Scholarships *(Graduate, Undergraduate/Scholarship)* [4724]

Richard C. Gorecki Scholarships *(Undergraduate/Scholarship)* [7373]

Nettie and Jesse Gorov Scholarships *(Undergraduate/Scholarship)* [3152]

Consuelo W. Gosnell Memorial Scholarships *(Graduate/Fellowship)* [6122]

American Association of University Women-Mary Sue Gottcent Memorial Scholarships *(Undergraduate/Scholarship)* [8604]

Louis Gottschalk Prize *(Professional development/Prize)* [1228]

Carl W. Gottschalk Research Scholar Grants *(Doctorate/Grant)* [1312]

Government Documents Special Interest Section - Veronica Maclay Student Grants *(Master's/Grant)* [509]

Wilford Hayes Gowen Scholarships *(Undergraduate/Scholarship)* [9226]

ACI W.R. Grace Scholarships *(Graduate/Scholarship)* [634]

William L. Graddy Law School Scholarships *(Undergraduate/Scholarship)* [8605]

Graduate Fellowship Program - Mahboob Khan/Advanced Micro Devices Fellowships (GFP) *(Doctorate, Graduate/Fellowship)* [8079]

Graduate Fellowship Program - Research Fellowships (GFP) *(Doctorate, Graduate/Fellowship)* [8080]

Graduate Fellowships in Alternatives in Scientific Research *(Doctorate, Graduate/Fellowship)* [4937]

Graduate Realtor Institute Scholarships *(Graduate/Scholarship)* [5244]

Graduate Research Fellowships *(Doctorate/Fellowship)* [2694]

Graduate Scholarships in Cancer Nursing Practice *(Master's, Doctorate/Scholarship)* [597]

Graduate Student Travel Grants *(Graduate, Professional development/Grant)* [8314]

Graham & Dunn 1L Diversity Fellowships *(Graduate/Scholarship)* [4203]

Rachel Graham Memorial Scholarships *(Undergraduate/Scholarship)* [7650]

Jim Graham Scholarships *(Undergraduate/Scholarship)* [6781]

Grand Canyon Historical Society Scholarships *(Graduate/Scholarship)* [4205]

Grand Haven Offshore Challenge Scholarship Fund *(Undergraduate/Scholarship)* [4219]

Charles Hall Grandgent Awards *(Graduate/Award)* [3342]

Granger Business Association College Scholarships *(Undergraduate/Scholarship)* [4313]

Russ Grant Memorial Scholarship for Tennis *(Undergraduate/Scholarship)* [7079]

AMA/Charles H. Grant Scholarships *(Undergraduate/Scholarship)* [29]

Nicholas J. Grant Scholarships *(Undergraduate/Scholarship)* [5691]

Grass Fellowships *(Doctorate, Postdoctorate/Fellowship)* [4315]

Thomas B. Grave and Elizabeth F. Grave Scholarships *(Undergraduate/Scholarship)* [5615]

Caswell Grave Scholarships *(Undergraduate/Scholarship)* [5616]

Gravure Publishing Council Scholarships *(Undergraduate, Graduate/Scholarship)* [4320]

Alexander G. Gray, Jr. Scholarships *(Graduate/Scholarship)* [5682]

Grays Harbor Community Foundation Scholarships *(Graduate, Undergraduate/Scholarship)* [4323]

Great Lakes Commission Sea Grant Fellowships *(Graduate/Scholarship)* [4328]

GREAT MINDS Collegiate Scholarship Program *(Undergraduate/Scholarship)* [340]

Great Minds in STEM Scholarships *(Graduate, Undergraduate/Scholarship)* [4331]

Greater Research Opportunities Undergraduate Fellowships (GRO) *(Undergraduate/Fellowship)* [9041]

Greater Seattle Business Association Scholarships *(Undergraduate/Scholarship)* [4333]

Frank L. Greathouse Government Accounting Scholarships *(Graduate, Undergraduate/Scholarship)* [4198]

Bishop Charles P. Greco Graduate Fellowships *(Graduate/Fellowship)* [5277]

Greek Orthodox Archdiocese of America Paleologos Graduate Scholarships *(Graduate/Scholarship)* [4345]

Green Hill Yacht and Country Club Scholarships *(Undergraduate, Vocational/Occupational/Scholarship)* [3058]

Green Knight Economic Development Corporation Scholarships (GKEDC) *(Undergraduate/Scholarship)* [4347]

James H. and Shirley L. Green Scholarship Fund *(Undergraduate/Scholarship)* [8670]

William G. and Mayme J. Green Scholarships *(Undergraduate/Scholarship)* [4434]

K2TEO Martin J. Green, Sr. Memorial Scholarships *(Undergraduate/Scholarship)* [1088]

Helen R. Greenamyer Memorial Scholarships *(Undergraduate/Scholarship)* [8723]

Robert D. Greenberg Scholarships *(Graduate, Professional development/Scholarship)* [8304]

Michael Greenberg Student Writing Competition *(Graduate/Prize, Scholarship)* [6394]

Curt Greene Memorial Scholarships *(Undergraduate/Scholarship)* [4399]

Elizabeth Greenhalgh Memorial Scholarships in Journalism, Graphic Arts, or Photography *(Graduate, Undergraduate/Scholarship)* [9699]

Greenlining Institute Fellowships *(Graduate/Fellowship)* [4349]

Frances Harris Gresham Scholarships *(Undergraduate/Scholarship)* [8606]

Lily H. Gridley Memorial Scholarships *(Undergraduate/Scholarship)* [9707]

Velma Shotwell Griffin Memorial Scholarship Fund *(Undergraduate/Scholarship)* [8671]

Enid Hall Griswold Memorial Scholarships *(Undergraduate/Scholarship)* [6499]

Andrew Gronholdt Arts Scholarship Awards *(Undergraduate, Vocational/Occupational, Graduate, Master's/Scholarship)* [288]

Katherine M. Grosscup Scholarships *(Graduate, Undergraduate/Scholarship)* [4042]

Charles Grossman Graduate Scholarships *(Graduate/Scholarship)* [4908]

Grow Your Own Your Library Institutional Scholarships *(Graduate, Professional development/Scholarship)* [7537]

Katherin F. Gruber Scholarship Program *(All/Scholarship)* [2151]

Elizabeth M. Gruber Scholarships *(Graduate/Scholarship)* [3410]

Gruwell Scholarships *(Undergraduate/Scholarship)* [3059]

Ronald P. Guerrette Future Farmers of America Scholarship Fund *(Undergraduate/Scholarship)* [5579]

Harry Frank Guggenheim Fellowships *(Doctorate/Fellowship)* [4357]

Harry Frank Guggenheim Foundation Research Grants *(All/Grant)* [4358]

Community Bank - Lee Guggisberg Foundation Memorial Scholarships *(Undergraduate/Scholarship)* [7651]

Guide Dogs for the Blind Dorothea and Roland Bohde Leadership Scholarships *(Postgraduate/Scholarship)* [6275]

GuildScholar Awards *(Undergraduate/Scholarship)* [5159]

Guin-Stanford Scholarships *(Professional development/Scholarship)* [3039]

Calouste Gulbenkian Foundation Scholarships *(Graduate, Undergraduate/Scholarship)* [1595]

Gulf Coast Past President's Scholarships *(Undergraduate/Scholarship)* [1338]

Harold Gulliksen Psychometric Research Fellowships *(Doctorate, Graduate/Fellowship)* [3610]

Connie and Robert T. Gunter Scholarships *(Undergraduate/Scholarship)* [8386]

Guynn Family Foundation Scholarships *(Undergraduate/Scholarship)* [6042]

Guzkowski Family Scholarships *(Undergraduate/Scholarship)* [7652]

Sara Gwisdalla Memorial Scholarships *(Undergraduate/Scholarship)* [7080]

GWSCPA Scholarships *(Undergraduate/Scholarship)* [4343]

Ed Haas Memorial Scholarships *(Undergraduate/Scholarship)* [8724]

Wesley R. Habley NACADA Summer Institute Scholarships *(Professional development/Scholarship)* [5996]

Louise Wallace Hackney Fellowships for the Study of Chinese Art *(Doctorate, Postdoctorate/Fellowship)* [964]

HACU/Wal-Mart Achievers Scholarships *(Undergraduate/Scholarship)* [4547]

HAESF Graduate Scholarships *(Graduate/Scholarship)* [4640]

HAESF Senior Leaders and Scholars Fellowships *(Professional development/Fellowship)* [4642]

Nathaniel Hafer Memorial Scholarships *(Undergraduate/Scholarship)* [7081]

Joseph E. Hagan Memorial Scholarships *(Undergraduate/Scholarship)* [4030]

Charles V. Hagler Scholarships *(Undergraduate/Scholarship)* [1942]

Leslie Jane Hahn Memorial Scholarships *(Undergraduate/Scholarship)* [7931]

The Richard D. Hailey AAJ Law Student Scholarships *(Undergraduate/Scholarship)* [491]

Jerome Hake Engineering Scholarships *(Graduate, Undergraduate/Scholarship)* [3864]

Lee Hakel Graduate Student Scholarships *(Doctorate/Scholarship)* [8354]

Marion H. Halfacre Scholarships *(Graduate/Scholarship)* [4059]

Gene Halker Memorial Scholarships *(Graduate, Undergraduate/Scholarship)* [3865]

Hall of Achievement Scholarships *(Undergraduate/Scholarship)* [2246]

Stephen K. Hall ACWA Water Law and Policy Scholarships *(Graduate/Scholarship)* [1728]

Joyce C. Hall College Scholarships *(Undergraduate/Scholarship)* [7165]

Hall County Medical Society Scholarships *(Graduate/Scholarship)* [4260]

Anna E. Hall Memorial Scholarships *(Undergraduate/Scholarship)* [7251]

Chappie Hall Scholarship Program *(Graduate, Post-graduate, Undergraduate/Scholarship)* [2]

David J. Hallissey Memorial Scholarships *(Graduate, Undergraduate/Scholarship)* [1366]

Alice Hamilton Prize *(Professional development/Prize)* [1247]

TIAA-CREF Ruth Simms Hamilton Research Fellowships *(Graduate/Fellowship)* [8811]

Harold F. Hammond Scholarships *(Graduate/Scholarship)* [4822]

Tommie J. Hamner Scholarships *(Undergraduate/Scholarship)* [7288]

Adam Hampton Memorial Scholarship Fund *(Undergraduate/Scholarship)* [3773]

Hampton Roads Association of Social Workers Scholarships *(Graduate/Scholarship)* [4374]

Morris Hanauer Scholarships *(Undergraduate/Scholarship)* [4060]

Hancock Family Snow Hill High School Scholarships *(Undergraduate/Scholarship)* [3060]

Robert Hancock Memorial Scholarship Awards *(Undergraduate/Scholarship)* [5836]

H. Pauline Hand Memorial Scholarships *(Undergraduate/Scholarship)* [8725]

Handweavers Guild of America and Dendel Scholarships *(Graduate, Undergraduate/Scholarship)* [4388]

Vincent S. Haneman-Joseph B. Perskie Memorial Foundation Scholarships *(Graduate, Undergraduate/Scholarship)* [1924]

Ilse and George Hanfmann Fellowships *(Doctorate/Fellowship)* [1150]

John M. Haniak Scholarships *(Undergraduate/Scholarship)* [5692]

Byron Hanke Fellowships *(Doctorate, Graduate, Undergraduate/Fellowship)* [3933]

Clayburn and Garnet R. Hanna Scholarships *(Undergraduate/Scholarship)* [7082]

Zenon C.R. Hansen Leadership Scholarships *(Undergraduate/Scholarship)* [6255]

Zenon C.R. Hansen Memorial Scholarships *(Undergraduate/Scholarship)* [1943]

Penelope Hanshaw Scholarships *(Graduate, Undergraduate/Scholarship)* [1903]

Clem T. Hanson Scholarship Fund *(Undergraduate/Scholarship)* [5916]

Duane Hanson Scholarships *(Undergraduate/Scholarship)* [1267]

Isaac and Mary Harbottle Scholarships *(Graduate, Undergraduate/Scholarship)* [5212]

H.G. Hardbarger Science and Mathematics Awards *(Undergraduate/Award)* [7083]

Harkness Fellowships in Health Care Policy and Practice *(Doctorate, Graduate/Fellowship)* [3020]

Bryce Harlow Fellowship Program *(Graduate/Fellowship)* [4395]

Matt Harmon Memorial Scholarships *(Undergraduate/Scholarship)* [8607]

Harness Tracks of America Scholarship Fund *(Undergraduate/Scholarship)* [4401]

Walter and Lucille Harper Scholarships *(Undergraduate/Scholarship)* [5233]

Harris Corporation Merit Scholarships *(Undergraduate/Scholarship)* [4403]

Dorothy Harris Endowed Scholarships *(Graduate/Scholarship)* [9737]

H.H. Harris Foundation Scholarships *(Undergraduate/Scholarship)* [772]

Marcia S. Harris Legacy Fund Scholarships *(Undergraduate/Scholarship)* [7746]

Ruth Harris Memorial Scholarships *(Undergraduate/Scholarship)* [7084]

William H. Harris Memorial Scholarships *(Graduate, Undergraduate/Scholarship)* [7267]

Frank and Charlene Harris Scholarships *(Undergraduate/Scholarship)* [3109]

Eileen Harrison Education Scholarships *(Graduate, Undergraduate/Scholarship)* [3866]

Peg Hart Harrison Memorial Scholarships *(Undergraduate/Scholarship)* [3373]

Evelyn W. Harrison Point Scholarships *(Graduate, Undergraduate/Scholarship)* [7361]

Morton Harrison Scholarship Fund *(Undergraduate/Scholarship)* [3774]

Lullelia W. Harrison Scholarships in Counseling *(Graduate, Undergraduate/Scholarship)* [9802]

Harrisville Lions Club Scholarships *(Undergraduate, Vocational/Occupational/Scholarship)* [7085]

Claude B. Hart Memorial Scholarships *(Undergraduate/Scholarship)* [9641]

Mollie Harter Memorial Fund *(Undergraduate/Scholarship)* [3775]

Hartford Geriatrics Health Outcomes Research Scholars Award Program *(Professional development/Grant)* [80]

Hartford Grammar School Scholarships *(Undergraduate/Scholarship)* [4438]

Hartford Jazz Society Scholarships *(Undergraduate/Scholarship)* [4439]

Hartford Whalers Booster Club Scholarships *(Undergraduate/Scholarship)* [4440]

Gabe A. Hartl Scholarships *(Undergraduate/Scholarship)* [105]

Harry C. Hartleben III. Scholarships *(Undergraduate/Scholarship)* [7086]

Gail Hartshorn Scholarships *(Undergraduate/Scholarship)* [7087]

William T. Hartzell Memorial Scholarships *(Undergraduate/Scholarship)* [7653]

Delta Gamma Foundation Florence Margaret Harvey Memorial Scholarships *(Graduate, Undergraduate/Scholarship)* [752]

Donald F. Hastings Scholarships *(Undergraduate/Scholarship)* [1434]

Donald and Shirley Hastings Scholarships *(Undergraduate/Scholarship)* [1435]

Gretchen Hauff Memorial Scholarships *(Undergraduate/Scholarship)* [7496]

Gregory Lynn Haught Citizenship Awards *(Undergraduate/Award)* [7088]

Charles Hauser Scholarships *(Undergraduate/Scholarship)* [9277]

Hawaii Community Foundation Scholarships *(Undergraduate, Graduate/Scholarship)* [4478]

Lex and Scott Hawkins Endowed Scholarships *(Undergraduate/Scholarship)* [3495]

Don C. Hawkins Memorial Scholarships *(Undergraduate/Scholarship)* [132]

Thomas T. Hayashi Memorial Scholarships *(Graduate, Undergraduate/Scholarship)* [5142]

R. Garn Haycock Memorial Scholarships *(Undergraduate/Scholarship)* [7654]

Samuel P. Hays Research Fellowships *(Professional development/Fellowship)* [1248]

Dick and Pat Hazel Minority Scholarships *(Professional development/Scholarship)* [3061]

HBO Point Scholarships *(Graduate, Undergraduate/Scholarship)* [7362]

HDSA Research Grants *(Professional development/Grant)* [4644]

Edith Head Scholarships *(Undergraduate/Scholarship)* [3411]

Dr. M.G. "Doc" Headley Scholarships *(Undergraduate/Scholarship)* [8726]

Health and Aging Policy Fellows *(Professional development/Fellowship)* [1018]

Health Outcomes Post Doctoral Fellowships *(Postdoctorate/Fellowship)* [7223]

Health Outcomes Pre Doctoral Fellowships *(Doctorate/Fellowship)* [7224]

Health Outcomes Research Starter Grants *(Doctorate/Grant)* [7225]

Health Outcomes Sabbatical Fellowships *(Postdoctorate/Fellowship)* [7226]

Health Sciences Student Fellowships *(Doctorate, Graduate/Fellowship)* [3666]

Health, Sport, and Fitness SIG Student Research Awards *(Undergraduate/Award)* [1714]

Healthcare Information Management Systems Scholarships *(Graduate, Postgraduate, Undergraduate/Scholarship)* [4505]

Healy Graduate Scholarships *(Graduate/Scholarship)* [1367]

Annamae Heaps Law Scholarships *(Undergraduate/Scholarship)* [3497]

Erin Kumelos Heard Memorial Scholarships *(Undergraduate/Scholarship)* [3374]

William Randolph Hearst Educational Endowments *(Undergraduate/Scholarship)* [5617]

Dr. James H. Heckaman Memorial Scholarship Fund *(Undergraduate/Scholarship)* [8672]

Professor Ulla Hedner Scholarships *(Undergraduate, Vocational/Occupational/Scholarship)* [6326]

CSF Richard Heekin Scholarships *(Undergraduate/Scholarship)* [2847]

Lavonne Heghinian Scholarships *(Undergraduate/Scholarship)* [3412]

Helicopter Foundation International Commercial Helicopter Rating Scholarships *(Professional development/Scholarship)* [4508]

Helicopter Foundation International Maintenance Technician Certificate Scholarships *(Professional development/Scholarship)* [4509]

Hellenic University Club of Philadelphia Founders Scholarships *(Undergraduate/Scholarship)* [4515]

Joan Heller-Diane Bernard Fellowships *(Graduate, Undergraduate/Fellowship)* [2703]

Joseph T. Helling Scholarship Fund *(Undergraduate/Scholarship)* [4730]

PPQ William F. Helms Student Scholarships *(Undergraduate/Scholarship)* [9402]

ASIL Arthur C. Helton Fellowship Program *(All/Fellowship)* [1280]

Hemlow Prize in Burney Studies *(Graduate/Prize)* [1229]

Hemophilia Federation of America Educational Scholarships *(Undergraduate/Scholarship)* [4528]

Hemophilia Health Services Memorial Scholarship Program *(Graduate, Undergraduate/Scholarship)* [6327]

Hench Post-Dissertation Fellowships *(Postdoctorate/Fellowship)* [419]

Melvin Henderson-Rubio Scholarships *(Undergraduate/Scholarship)* [9605]

Edith H. Henderson Scholarships *(Undergraduate/Scholarship)* [1283]

Herb Kohl Educational Foundation Excellence Scholarships *(Undergraduate/Scholarship)* [4530]

Herb Kohl Educational Foundation Fellowships *(Professional development/Fellowship)* [4531]

Herb Kohl Educational Foundation Initiative Scholarships *(High School/Scholarship)* [4532]

Hereditary Disease Foundation Research Grants *(Postdoctorate/Grant)* [4540]

Michael Herman Memorial Scholarship Fund *(Undergraduate, Vocational/Occupational/Scholarship)* [4222]

Manuel Hernandez, Jr. Foundation Scholarships *(Undergraduate, Vocational/Occupational/Scholarship)* [2949]

Catarino and Evangelina Hernandez Research Fellowships in Latino History *(Professional development/Fellowship)* [8874]

Ella Beren Hersch Scholarships *(Undergraduate/Scholarship)* [7090]

Isabel M. Herson Scholarships in Education *(Graduate, Undergraduate/Scholarship)* [9803]

Hertz Foundation's Graduate Fellowships *(Doctorate, Graduate/Fellowship)* [6074]

Darrel Hess Community College Geography Scholarships *(Undergraduate/Scholarship)* [1693]

Beth B. Hess Memorial Scholarships *(Doctorate, Graduate/Fellowship)* [8518]

Peter Hess Scholarships *(Undergraduate/Scholarship)* [4061]

Nicholas S. Hetos, DDS, Memorial Graduate Scholarships *(Graduate/Scholarship)* [4516]

Caroline M. Hewins Scholarships *(Graduate/Scholarship)* [4465]

HFMA Connecticut Chapter Scholarships *(Graduate, Undergraduate/Scholarship)* [4501]

HGS Foundation Scholarships *(Undergraduate/Scholarship)* [4611]

HHMI International Student Research Fellowships *(Doctorate/Fellowship)* [4622]

HHMI Medical Research Fellowships *(Undergraduate/Fellowship)* [4623]

HHS Memorial Scholarships *(Graduate, Undergraduate/Scholarship)* [37]

HIAA Graduate Student Travel Grants *(Graduate/Grant)* [4588]

CSF Dwight Hibbard Scholarships *(Undergraduate/Scholarship)* [2848]

Mark and Michelle Hiepler Endowed Scholarships *(Undergraduate/Scholarship)* [7187]

Hierholzer-Fojtik Scholarship Fund *(Undergraduate/Scholarship)* [4223]

Jim Hierlihy Memorial Scholarships *(Undergraduate/ Scholarship)* [3672]

High School Councilors Scholarships *(Undergraduate/Scholarship)* [4707]

Robert S. Hilbert Memorial Student Travel Grants *(Graduate, Undergraduate/Grant)* [6911]

Wayne Hildebrant Police Scholarship Fund *(Undergraduate/Scholarship)* [5350]

Gus and Henrietta Hill Scholarships *(Undergraduate/Scholarship)* [3532]

D. Glenn Hilts Scholarships *(Graduate, Undergraduate/Scholarship)* [1872]

Lucy Hilty Research Grants *(All/Grant)* [1065]

Brooke Hindle Postdoctoral Fellowships *(Postdoctorate/Fellowship)* [8344]

Jim & Nancy Hinkle Travel Grants *(Postdoctorate/Grant)* [4525]

HIPLA Judicial Fellowships *(Undergraduate/Fellowship)* [4613]

HIPLA Scholarships for University of Houston Law Center Students *(Graduate, Undergraduate/Scholarship)* [4614]

Hispanic Association on Corporate Responsibility Scholarship Program *(Undergraduate/Scholarship)* [4553]

Hispanic Metropolitan Chamber Scholarships *(Graduate, Undergraduate/Scholarship)* [4564]

Hispanic Serving Institution Scholarships (HSIS) *(Undergraduate/Scholarship)* [9024]

Historically Black College or University Scholarships (HBCUS) *(Undergraduate/Scholarship)* [9025]

HLS/MLA Professional Development Grants *(Professional development/Grant)* [5742]

Lucy Hsu Ho Scholarships *(Undergraduate/Scholarship)* [2062]

James E. Hoff, S.J. Scholars *(Undergraduate/Scholarship)* [9771]

CSF Florette B. Hoffheimer Scholarships *(Undergraduate/Scholarship)* [2849]

Dorothy M. and Earl S. Hoffman Awards *(Graduate/Award)* [1982]

Hoffman Family Scholarship Fund *(Undergraduate/Scholarship)* [4224]

Henry Hoffman Memorial Scholarship Fund *(Undergraduate/Scholarship)* [6064]

Electronics Division Lewis C. Hoffman Scholarships *(Undergraduate/Scholarship)* [606]

Michael J. Hogan Fellowships *(Graduate/Fellowship)* [8340]

The Thelma S. Hoge Memorial Scholarship Fund *(Undergraduate/Scholarship)* [3087]

Raymond T. Hoge Scholarship Fund *(Undergraduate/Scholarship)* [8674]

Michael J. Hoggard Memorial Scholarships *(Undergraduate/Scholarship)* [7497]

R.W. "Bob" Holden Memorial Scholarships *(Undergraduate/Scholarship)* [4482]

Holland America Line-Westours Research Grants *(Undergraduate/Grant)* [1368]

Ann L. Holland Memorial Scholarships *(Graduate, Undergraduate/Scholarship)* [4077]

Houston/Nancy Holliman Scholarships *(Undergraduate/Scholarship)* [3413]

Ernest F. Hollings Undergraduate Scholarships *(Undergraduate/Scholarship)* [6417]

Cleve Holloway Memorial Scholarship Fund *(Undergraduate/Scholarship)* [3040]

Joseph A. Holmes Safety Association Scholarships *(Graduate, Undergraduate/Scholarship)* [4593]

Alan Holoch Memorial Grants *(Professional development/Grant)* [500]

W. Stull Holt Dissertation Fellowships *(Doctorate, Graduate/Fellowship, Grant)* [8341]

Caroline Holt Nursing Scholarships *(Undergraduate/Scholarship)* [4441]

The Homeland Security Undergraduate Scholarships *(Undergraduate/Scholarship)* [9039]

Honeywell Avionics Scholarships *(Undergraduate, Vocational/Occupational/Scholarship)* [133]

Jane Hood Memorial Fund *(Undergraduate/Scholarship)* [3776]

Hooper Memorial Scholarships *(Undergraduate, Vocational/Occupational/Scholarship)* [8951]

Lillie Hope-McGarvey Health Scholarship Awards *(Undergraduate, Vocational/Occupational, Graduate, Master's/Scholarship)* [289]

Hope for the Warriors Spouses Scholarships *(Graduate, Master's, Undergraduate, Vocational/Occupational/Scholarship)* [4599]

Hopi Education Awards *(Doctorate, Undergraduate/Award)* [1511]

Minnie Hopkins Memorial Scholarship Fund of Lathrop/Compton School *(Undergraduate/Scholarship)* [8675]

Sam J. Hord Memorial Scholarships *(Undergraduate/Scholarship)* [8563]

Seth Horen, K1LOM Memorial Scholarships *(Undergraduate/Scholarship)* [1091]

Hormel Foods Charitable Trust Scholarships *(Undergraduate/Scholarship)* [4601]

Edward L. Horne, Jr. Scholarships *(All/Scholarship)* [6969]

Judge and Mrs. Robert D. Horowitz Legal Scholarship Fund *(Graduate/Scholarship)* [8676]

Detroit Tigers Willie Horton Scholarships *(Undergraduate/Scholarship)* [3199]

Hospitality Food Service Scholarships *(Undergraduate/Scholarship)* [6621]

John C. "Jack" Hough Memorial Law Scholarships *(Undergraduate/Scholarship)* [9230]

Max and Julia Houghton Duluth Central Scholarships *(Undergraduate/Scholarship)* [3533]

Roberta L. Houpt Scholarship Fund *(Undergraduate/Scholarship)* [3946]

Houston Alumnae Chapter Graduate Fellowships *(Graduate/Fellowship)* [3375]

Paul Green Houston Scholarships *(Undergraduate/Scholarship)* [9278]

Sarah Jane Houston Scholarships *(Undergraduate/Scholarship)* [3414]

Houtan Scholarships *(Graduate/Scholarship)* [4616]

Kaspar Hovannisian Memorial Scholarships *(Graduate/Scholarship)* [1597]

NORDAM Dee Howard/Etienne Fage Scholarships *(Undergraduate/Scholarship)* [6169]

C.D. Howard Scholarships *(Undergraduate/Scholarship)* [4898]

CSF Roger and Joyce Howe Family Scholarships *(Undergraduate/Scholarship)* [2850]

William B. Howell Scholarships *(Undergraduate/Scholarship)* [1436]

Christopher Hoy/ERT Scholarships *(Graduate, Master's/Scholarship)* [901]

Carol Hoy Scholarship Fund *(Undergraduate/Scholarship)* [3947]

HRET Health Career Scholarships *(Graduate, Undergraduate/Scholarship)* [6644]

HRH Prince Alwaleed Bin Talal ISNA Fellowships *(Graduate/Fellowship)* [5080]

HSF/Citi Fellows Program *(Undergraduate/Scholarship)* [4573]

HSF/IDT Hope High School Scholarship Program *(Undergraduate/Scholarship)* [4575]

HSF/Nissan Community College Transfer Scholarship Program *(Undergraduate/Scholarship)* [4576]

HSF/Wal-Mart Stores Inc. Scholarship Program *(Graduate, Undergraduate/Scholarship)* [4577]

Albert W. and Mildred Hubbard Scholarships *(Undergraduate/Scholarship)* [7934]

Hubbard Scholarships *(Master's/Scholarship)* [4105]

Amber Huber Memorial Scholarships *(Undergraduate/Scholarship)* [3154]

Huenefeld/Denton Scholarships *(Undergraduate/Scholarship)* [3415]

Puedo Scholarships - Joseph Huerta *(Undergraduate/Scholarship)* [2950]

Dale Hughes, Jr. Memorial Scholarships *(Undergraduate/Scholarship)* [8727]

Roger K. Hughes Legacy Scholarships *(Undergraduate/Scholarship)* [2247]

Howard Hughes Medical Institute Predoctoral Fellowships *(Graduate/Fellowship)* [6075]

Hughes Memorial Foundation Scholarships *(Graduate/Scholarship)* [4625]

Paul A. Hughes Memorial Scholarships *(Undergraduate/Scholarship)* [2248]

Mary M. Hughes Research Fellowships in Texas History *(Professional development/Fellowship)* [8875]

Charles David Hughes Scholarships *(Graduate/Scholarship)* [3028]

Huguenot Society of South Carolina Graduate

Scholarships *(Graduate/Scholarship)* [4628]

Humane Studies Fellowships *(Graduate/Fellowship)* [4798]

Humanism in Medicine Scholarships *(Undergraduate/Scholarship)* [8766]

Kevin Hummer Point Scholarships *(Graduate, Undergraduate/Scholarship)* [7363]

Dr. Richard M. Hunt Fellowships *(Doctorate, Postdoctorate/Fellowship)* [667]

Hunt Postdoctoral Fellowships *(Doctorate/Fellowship)* [9561]

Frederick V. Hunt Postdoctoral Research Fellowships in Acoustics *(Postdoctorate/Fellowship)* [40]

Michael A. Hunter Memorial Scholarships *(Undergraduate/Scholarship)* [2757]

Clay Huntington Sports Communications Scholarships *(Undergraduate/Scholarship)* [4338]

Huntington's Disease Society of America Research Fellowships *(Postdoctorate/Fellowship)* [4645]

James F. Hurley III Bicentennial Merit Scholarships *(Undergraduate/Scholarship)* [9279]

Zora Neale Hurston Scholarships *(Graduate/Scholarship)* [9804]

Norman E. Huston Scholarships *(Graduate, Undergraduate/Scholarship)* [5053]

Dr. James L. Hutchinson and Evelyn Ribbs Hutchinson Medical School Scholarship Fund *(Undergraduate/Scholarship)* [8203]

Fred Hutchison Travel Scholarships *(Undergraduate/Scholarship)* [9280]

The Hyatt Hotels Fund For Minority Lodging Management Students *(Undergraduate/Scholarship)* [798]

Hydro Research Foundation Fellowships *(Master's/Fellowship)* [4648]

Mike Hylton and Ron Niederman Memorial Scholarships *(Undergraduate/Scholarship)* [6328]

Libbie H. Hyman Memorial Scholarships *(Graduate/Scholarship)* [8358]

The Steve Hymans Extended Stay Scholarship Program *(Undergraduate/Scholarship)* [799]

Hypertherm International HyTech Leadership Scholarships *(Graduate/Scholarship)* [1437]

IAAP Wings Chapter Scholarships *(Undergraduate, Vocational/Occupational/Scholarship)* [4854]

IADR David B. Ste. Scott Fellowships *(Undergraduate/Fellowship)* [4860]

IADR John Ste. Clarkson Fellowships *(Postdoctorate/Fellowship)* [4861]

IADR John Ste. Gray Fellowships *(Professional development/Fellowship)* [4862]

IADR Norton Ste. Ross Fellowships *(Postgraduate/Fellowship)* [4863]

IADR Toshio Ste. Nakao Fellowships *(Professional development/Fellowship)* [4864]

IAESTE United States Scholarships *(Undergraduate/Scholarship)* [3309]

IAHCSMM - Purdue University Scholarship Awards *(Professional development/Scholarship)* [4870]

IALD Education Trust Scholarship Program *(Graduate, Undergraduate/Scholarship)* [4878]

IAWP International Recognition and Scholarship Awards *(Professional development/Scholarship)* [4882]

ICDA Graduate Scholarships *(Graduate/Scholarship)* [5034]

ICDA Research Grants *(Graduate/Grant)* [5035]

Ice Skating Institute of America Education Foundation Scholarships *(Undergraduate/Scholarship)* [4657]

IDA Fellowship Awards *(Professional development/Fellowship)* [4919]

David Iden Memorial Safety Scholarships *(Undergraduate/Scholarship)* [1340]

Ella R. Ifill Fund *(Undergraduate/Scholarship)* [5580]

IFMA Foundation Certificate Program Scholarships *(Graduate/Scholarship)* [4926]

IFMA Foundation Graduate/Undergraduate Scholarships *(Graduate, Undergraduate/Scholarship)* [4927]

IFSEA Worthy Goal Scholarships *(Four Year College, Two Year College, Undergraduate, Vocational/Occupational/Scholarship)* [4933]

IIE Council of Fellows Undergraduate Scholarships *(Undergraduate/Scholarship)* [4803]

Illinois Association of Chamber of Commerce Ex-

ecutives Scholarships *(Postdoctorate/Scholarship)*
[4680]

Illuminator Educational Foundation Scholarships
(Undergraduate/Scholarship) [2249]

IMA Memorial Education Fund Scholarships (MEF)
(Graduate, Undergraduate/Scholarship loan)
[4815]

Imagine America Scholarships *(Undergraduate/
Scholarship)* [4708]

IMCEA Memorial Scholarships *(Graduate, Under-
graduate/Scholarship)* [4960]

Elmer S. Imes Scholarships in Physics *(Under-
graduate/Scholarship)* [6489]

John L. Imhoff Scholarships *(Graduate, Undergradu-
ate/Scholarship)* [4804]

Independent Professional Seed Association Student
Recognition Awards *(Undergraduate/Scholarship)*
[4720]

Independent University Alumni Association Scholarships *(Graduate, Undergraduate/Scholarship)*
[4725]

Indian Health Service Scholarship Program *(Under-
graduate/Scholarship)* [819]

Indiana Alumni Scholarships *(Undergraduate/Schol-
arship)* [9772]

Indiana Continuing Legal Education Forum Scholarship Fund *(Undergraduate/Scholarship)* [4731]

Indiana Library Federation AIME Scholarships *(Un-
dergraduate/Scholarship)* [4736]

Indiana State Alumni Association Rural Health
Scholarships *(Undergraduate/Scholarship)* [4748]

Informatics Post Doctoral Fellowships *(Doctorate/
Fellowship)* [7227]

Informatics Pre Doctoral Fellowships *(Doctorate/
Fellowship)* [7228]

Informatics Research Starter Grants *(Doctorate/
Grant)* [7229]

Informatics Sabbatical Fellowships *(Doctorate, Post-
doctorate/Fellowship)* [7230]

Information Age Publishing Graduate Student Book
Scholarships *(Doctorate, Graduate/Scholarship)*
[4762]

Terrance Ingraham Pediatric Optometry Residency
Awards *(Graduate/Award)* [386]

Jennifer Ingrum Scholarships *(Undergraduate/Schol-
arship)* [3111]

INIA Scholarships Program *(Undergraduate/Scholar-
ship)* [4965]

Injection Molding Division Scholarships *(Graduate,
Undergraduate/Scholarship)* [8450]

Inland Northwest Business Alliance Scholarships
(INBA) *(Undergraduate/Scholarship)* [7411]

Institute for Anarchist Studies Grants for Radical
Writers and Translators *(Professional develop-
ment/Grant)* [4785]

Institute of Food Technologists Graduate Scholarships *(Graduate/Scholarship)* [4791]

Institute of Food Technologists Junior/Senior Scholarships *(Undergraduate/Scholarship)* [4792]

Institute of Food Technologists Sophomore Scholarships *(Undergraduate/Scholarship)* [4793]

Institute for Health Metrics and Evaluation Post
Bachelor Fellowships *(Graduate/Fellowship)*
[4795]

Institute for Health Metrics and Evaluation Post
Graduate Fellowships *(Doctorate, Postdoctorate/
Fellowship)* [4796]

Institute for the International Education of Students
Faculty Fellowships *(Professional development/
Fellowship)* [6695]

Institute of Management Accountants FAR Doctoral
Student Grants Program *(Doctorate/Grant)* [4816]

Institute-NEH Postdoctoral Fellowships *(Doctorate,
Professional development/Fellowship)* [6882]

Institute of Turkish Studies Dissertation Writing
Grants *(Doctorate/Grant)* [4829]

Institutional Grants: Educational and Research
Projects *(All/Grant)* [9472]

Insurance Scholarship Foundation of America College Scholarships *(Undergraduate/Scholarship)*
[4840]

Insurance Scholarship Foundation of America Professional Scholarships *(Professional development/
Scholarship)* [4841]

Integra Foundation NNF Research Grant Awards
(Professional development/Grant) [519]

Inter American Press Association Scholarships *(Un-
dergraduate/Scholarship)* [4846]

Intermediaries and Reinsurance Underwriters Association Internships *(Undergraduate/Internship)*
[4852]

International Association of Black Actuaries Scholarships *(Undergraduate/Scholarship)* [4858]

International Association of Emergency Managers
Scholarships *(Graduate, Undergraduate/Scholar-
ship)* [4866]

International Association of Foundation Drilling
Scholarships for Civil Engineering Students *(Post-
graduate/Scholarship)* [1756]

International Association of Foundation Drilling
Scholarships for Part-time Civil Engineering
Graduate School Students *(Postgraduate/Scholar-
ship)* [1757]

International Association of Wildland Fire Graduate-
Level Scholarships *(Doctorate, Graduate/Scholar-
ship)* [4880]

International Code Council Foundation General
Scholarship Fund *(Undergraduate/Scholarship)*
[4899]

International Dairy-Deli-Bakery Association Undergraduate Scholarships *(Graduate, Undergraduate/
Scholarship)* [4916]

International Doctoral Scholarships for Studies Specializing in Jewish Fields *(Doctorate/Scholarship)*
[5763]

International Door Association Scholarship Foundation Program *(Undergraduate, Vocational/Occupa-
tional/Scholarship)* [4921]

International Executive Housekeepers Association
Education Foundation Scholarship Awards *(Un-
dergraduate/Scholarship)* [4923]

International Executive Housekeepers Association
Spartan Scholarship Awards *(Undergraduate/
Scholarship)* [4924]

International Fellowships in Jewish Studies *(Professional development/Fellowship)* [5764]

International Foodservice Editorial Council Scholarships *(Graduate, Undergraduate/Scholarship)*
[4935]

International Furnishings and Design Association
Educational Foundation Student Scholarships
(Undergraduate/Scholarship) [4942]

International Furnishings and Design Association
Part-time Student Scholarships *(Undergraduate/
Scholarship)* [4943]

International Harvester Collectors Scholarships *(Un-
dergraduate/Scholarship)* [4950]

International Management Council Scholarships
(IMC) *(Undergraduate/Scholarship)* [3155]

International Order of the King's Daughters and
Sons North American Indian Scholarship Program
(Undergraduate/Scholarship) [820]

International Peace Scholarships *(Undergraduate/
Scholarship)* [7305]

International Radio and Television Society Foundation Summer Fellowships Program *(Graduate, Un-
dergraduate/Fellowship)* [4973]

International Scholarship Programs for Community
Service *(All/Scholarship)* [5765]

International Society for Humor Studies Graduate
Student Awards (GSA) *(Graduate/Award)* [4996]

International Society for Humor Studies Scholarly
Contribution Awards (SCA) *(Professional develop-
ment/Award)* [4997]

International Trademark Association-Ladas Memorial
Awards *(Professional development, Undergradu-
ate/Award)* [5019]

International Women's Fishing Association Scholarships *(Graduate/Scholarship)* [5028]

Internet Society Fellowships to the IETF *(Doctorate/
Fellowship)* [5032]

Internships in International Civil Society Law *(Under-
graduate/Internship)* [4893]

InternXchange Internships *(Undergraduate/Intern-
ship)* [4121]

Investigators in the Pathogenesis of Infectious Disease Awards *(Doctorate, Postdoctorate/Grant)*
[2215]

IOIA Organic Community Initiative Scholarships
(Professional development/Scholarship) [4716]

Iowa Division Scholarships *(Undergraduate/Scholar-
ship)* [5859]

Iranian American Bar Association Scholarships *(Un-
dergraduate/Scholarship)* [5046]

The Iranian-American Scholarship Fund *(Graduate,
Undergraduate/Scholarship)* [6361]

Iranian Federated Women's Club Scholarships *(Un-
dergraduate/Scholarship)* [6363]

Greg Irons Student Scholarships *(Undergraduate/
Scholarship)* [3534]

Harriet Irsay Scholarships *(Graduate, Undergradu-
ate/Scholarship)* [869]

Irvington Institute Fellowships of the Cancer Research Institute *(Postdoctorate/Fellowship)* [2638]

ISA Educational Foundation Scholarships *(Graduate, Undergraduate/Scholarship)* [5054]

ISA Executive Board Scholarships *(Graduate, Un-
dergraduate/Scholarship)* [5055]

ISA Section and District Scholarships - Birmingham
(Graduate, Undergraduate/Scholarship) [5056]

ISA Section and District Scholarships - Houston
(Graduate, Undergraduate/Scholarship) [5057]

ISA Section and District Scholarships - Lehigh Valley *(Graduate, Undergraduate/Scholarship)* [5058]

ISA Section and District Scholarships - New Jersey
(Graduate, Undergraduate/Scholarship) [5059]

ISA Section and District Scholarships - Niagara
Frontier *(Graduate, Undergraduate/Scholarship)*
[5060]

ISA Section and District Scholarships - Northern
California *(Graduate, Undergraduate/Scholarship)*
[5061]

ISA Section and District Scholarships - Richmond
Hopewell *(Graduate, Undergraduate/Scholarship)*
[5062]

ISA Section and District Scholarships - Savannah
River *(Graduate, Undergraduate/Scholarship)*
[5063]

ISA Section and District Scholarships - Southwestern Wyoming *(Graduate, Undergraduate/Scholar-
ship)* [5064]

ISA Section and District Scholarships - Texas, Louisiana and Mississippi *(Graduate, Undergraduate/
Scholarship)* [5065]

ISA Section and District Scholarships - Wilmington
(Graduate, Undergraduate/Scholarship) [5066]

ISA Technical Division Scholarships - Analysis Division *(Graduate, Undergraduate/Scholarship)*
[5067]

ISA Technical Division Scholarships - Chemical and
Petroleum Industries Division *(Graduate, Under-
graduate/Scholarship)* [5068]

ISA Technical Division Scholarships - Computer
Technology Division *(Graduate, Undergraduate/
Scholarship)* [5069]

ISA Technical Division Scholarships - Food and
Pharmaceutical Industries Division *(Graduate, Un-
dergraduate/Scholarship)* [5070]

ISA Technical Division Scholarships - Power Industry Division *(Graduate, Undergraduate/Scholar-
ship)* [5071]

ISA Technical Division Scholarships - Process Measurement and Control Division *(Graduate, Under-
graduate/Scholarship)* [5072]

ISA Technical Division Scholarships - Pulp and Paper Industry Division *(Graduate, Undergraduate/
Scholarship)* [5073]

ISA Technical Division Scholarships - Test Measurement Division *(Graduate, Undergraduate/Scholar-
ship)* [5074]

ISA Technical Division Scholarships - Water and
Wastewater Industries Division *(Graduate, Under-
graduate/Scholarship)* [5075]

ISBA General Scholarships *(Undergraduate/Scholar-
ship)* [4678]

Hazel D. Isbell Fellowships *(Graduate/Fellowship)*
[3376]

(ISC)2 Information Security Scholarships *(Post-
graduate/Scholarship)* [4955]

ISCALC International Scholarship Fund *(Under-
graduate/Scholarship)* [3777]

ISDS Graduate Student Scholarships *(Doctorate,
Graduate/Scholarship)* [4990]

ISF Excellence in Community Service Scholarships
(Undergraduate/Scholarship) [5048]

ISF Undergraduate Scholarships *(Undergraduate/
Scholarship)* [5049]

Islamic Scholarship Fund Scholarships (ISF) *(Post-

graduate, Undergraduate/Scholarship) [5078]

Island Institute Scholarship Fund *(Undergraduate/ Scholarship)* [5581]

ISOPE Offshore Mechanics Scholarships for Outstanding Students *(Graduate/Scholarship)* [4999]

Israeli Fellowships *(Doctorate, Postdoctorate/Fellowship)* [2685]

ISRS Graduate Fellowships *(Doctorate, Graduate/ Fellowship)* [5001]

ISTU Student Prize *(All/Prize)* [5004]

Italian American Lawyers Association Annual Scholarships *(Undergraduate/Scholarship)* [5084]

Italian Language Scholarships *(Undergraduate/ Scholarship)* [6922]

ITE Transit Council Scholarships *(Graduate/Scholarship)* [4825]

ITEEA FTE Scholarships *(Undergraduate/Scholarship)* [5010]

ITEEA Greer/FTE Grants *(Professional development/Grant)* [5011]

ITEEA Litherland/FTE Scholarships *(Undergraduate/ Scholarship)* [5012]

ITNS Research Grants *(Professional development/ Grant)* [5021]

ITW Welding Companies Scholarships *(Undergraduate/Scholarship)* [1438]

Ivanhoe Foundation Fellowships *(Master's/Fellowship)* [5086]

Bob and Mary Ives Scholarships *(Graduate, Undergraduate/Scholarship)* [5076]

Virginia C. Jack and Ralph L. Jack Scholarships *(Undergraduate, Vocational/Occupational/Scholarship)* [8677]

Jackman Scholarships *(Undergraduate/Scholarship)* [7289]

The Jackson Club Scholarships *(Undergraduate/ Scholarship)* [3535]

Jackson High School Alumni Scholarship Fund *(Undergraduate/Scholarship)* [8678]

Edward Jackson International Scholarships *(Undergraduate/Scholarship)* [9281]

Gene Jackson Scholarships *(Undergraduate/Scholarship)* [9282]

Sylvia E. Jackson Scholarships *(Undergraduate/ Scholarship)* [8728]

Ruth K. Jacobs Memorial Scholarships *(Graduate, Undergraduate/Scholarship)* [2779]

Freddy L. Jacobs Scholarships *(Undergraduate/ Scholarship)* [4886]

Eric L. Jacobson Memorial Scholarships *(Undergraduate/Scholarship)* [7655]

Karl A. Jacobson Scholarships *(Undergraduate/ Scholarship)* [1341]

Peter Lars Jacobson Scholarships *(Undergraduate/ Scholarship)* [9283]

Dwight P. Jacobus Scholarships *(Undergraduate/ Scholarship)* [1860]

Jacque Placette Chapman Master's Fellowships *(Graduate/Fellowship)* [6918]

Louis I. Jaffe Memorial Scholarships-NSU Alumni *(Graduate/Scholarship)* [4376]

Gregori Jakovina Endowment Scholarships *(Undergraduate/Scholarship)* [3677]

Cory Jam Awards *(Undergraduate/Scholarship)* [3536]

Frederick George James Memorial Scholarships *(Undergraduate/Scholarship)* [7935]

The J. Franklin Jameson Fellowships in American History *(Doctorate/Fellowship)* [793]

Jan Jancin Competition Awards *(Undergraduate/ Award)* [881]

The Dawn Janisse Scholarships *(Undergraduate/ Scholarship)* [7140]

Japanese American Bar Association Scholarships *(Graduate, Undergraduate/Scholarship)* [5138]

Dr. Ali Jarrahi Merit Scholarships *(Undergraduate/ Scholarship)* [5050]

Carl and Lucille Jarrett Scholarship Fund *(Graduate, Undergraduate/Scholarship)* [3778]

Terry Jarvis Memorial Scholarships *(Undergraduate/ Scholarship)* [1439]

Dannie Jasmine Scholarships *(Undergraduate/ Scholarship)* [5944]

Jacob K. Javits Fellowships *(Doctorate, Master's/ Fellowship)* [6076]

JCC Association Graduate Education Scholarships

(Graduate/Scholarship) [5151]

J.D. Graduate Tikvah Scholarships *(Graduate/Scholarship)* [8904]

J.D. or LL.M. Tikvah Scholarships *(Graduate/Scholarship)* [8905]

Sister Rita Jeanne Scholarships *(Undergraduate/ Scholarship)* [5169]

Erin L. Jenkins Memorial Scholarship Fund *(Undergraduate/Scholarship)* [3948]

Elise Reed Jenkins Memorial Scholarships - Gamma Lambda *(Undergraduate/Scholarship)* [8175]

Elise Reed Jenkins Memorial Scholarships - Gamma Psi *(Undergraduate/Scholarship)* [8176]

John H. Jenkins Research Fellowships in Texas History *(Professional development/Fellowship)* [8876]

Martha Combs Jenkins Scholarships *(Undergraduate/Scholarship)* [7290]

Ruth E. Jenkins Scholarships *(Undergraduate/ Scholarship)* [7936]

Gaynold Jensen Education Stipends *(Postdoctorate, Professional development/Scholarship)* [3443]

Walter J. Jensen Fellowships *(Professional development/Fellowship)* [7248]

Nancy Lorraine Jensen Memorial Scholarships *(Undergraduate/Scholarship)* [8531]

Mike Jensen R.I.S.E. Memorial Scholarships *(Undergraduate/Scholarship)* [7656]

Stanley "Doc" Jensen Scholarships *(High School/ Scholarship)* [694]

Jerman-Cahoon Student Scholarship Program *(Undergraduate/Scholarship)* [1324]

Kenneth Jernigan Scholarships *(Undergraduate/ Scholarship)* [6276]

Jerome Fellowships *(Professional development/Fellowship)* [7337]

James Jesinski Scholarships *(Undergraduate/Scholarship)* [9359]

Jewish Caucus Scholarships *(Undergraduate/Scholarship)* [6559]

Brian Jimenez Memorial Scholarships *(Undergraduate/Scholarship)* [7657]

Rev. and Mrs. A.K. Jizmejian Educational Fund *(Undergraduate/Scholarship)* [1600]

JMA Architecture Studios Scholarships *(Undergraduate/Scholarship)* [7498]

John W. Webb Lecture Awards *(Professional development/Award)* [1260]

Alvin H. Johnson AMS Dissertation Fellowships *(Graduate/Fellowship)* [940]

Robert Wood Johnson Clinical Scholarships *(Graduate/Scholarship)* [5165]

The Robert Wood Johnson Health Policy Fellowship Program *(All/Fellowship)* [1019]

MCCA Lloyd M. Johnson, Jr. Scholarships *(Undergraduate/Scholarship)* [5904]

Joseph C. Johnson Memorial Grants *(Undergraduate/Scholarship)* [1191]

Fred Johnson Memorial Scholarships *(Doctorate, Graduate, Master's/Scholarship)* [6176]

Gregory D. Johnson Memorial Scholarships *(Doctorate, Graduate, Master's/Scholarship)* [6378]

V.J. Johnson Memorial Scholarships *(Undergraduate/Scholarship)* [552]

Sylvia Taylor Johnson Minority Fellowships in Educational Measurement *(Doctorate/Fellowship)* [3611]

CSF Ella Wilson Johnson Scholarships *(Undergraduate/Scholarship)* [2851]

Stella B. Johnson Scholarships *(Undergraduate/ Scholarship)* [9643]

Johnson and Wales University Scholarships *(Undergraduate/Scholarship)* [5175]

OOIDA Mary Johnston Scholarships *(Undergraduate/Scholarship)* [7025]

George E. Jonas Scholarships *(Graduate, Undergraduate/Scholarship)* [5167]

Napoleon A. Jones, III Memorial Scholarships *(Undergraduate/Scholarship)* [7937]

Edward H. Jones Scholarships *(Undergraduate/ Scholarship)* [3500]

Barbara Jordan Memorial Scholarships *(Graduate, Undergraduate/Scholarship)* [1884]

CSF David J. Joseph Company Scholarships *(Undergraduate/Scholarship)* [2852]

Joseph H. Fichter Research Grants *(Professional

development/Grant)* [1874]

E.J. Josey Scholarships *(Graduate/Scholarship)* [2133]

Journyx Scholarships *(Graduate, Undergraduate/ Scholarship)* [5171]

Leslie W. Joyce and Paul W. Thayer Graduate Fellowships in I-O Psychology *(Doctorate/Fellowship)* [8355]

JQSOW Scholarships *(Undergraduate/Scholarship)* [5149]

JSA/Jefferson Lab Graduate Fellowships *(Doctorate, Graduate/Fellowship)* [5155]

Clem Judd Jr. Memorial Scholarships *(Undergraduate/Scholarship)* [4483]

George E. Judd Scholarships *(Undergraduate/ Scholarship)* [8609]

Junior Achievement of East Central Ohio, Inc. Scholarship Fund *(Undergraduate/Scholarship)* [8679]

Junior Firefighter Scholarships *(Undergraduate/ Scholarship)* [6555]

Junior Women of the Contemporary Club Scholarships *(Undergraduate/Scholarship)* [7658]

George W. Juno Memorial Scholarships *(Graduate/ Scholarship)* [4062]

Just Out Scholarship Fund *(Undergraduate/Scholarship)* [3678]

Juvenile Arthritis Scholarships *(Undergraduate/ Scholarship)* [4444]

K-12 Edu-Grants *(Other/Grant)* [6329]

Mike Kabo Global Scholarships *(Professional development/Scholarship)* [4167]

Annette Kade Fellowships *(Graduate/Fellowship)* [5787]

Kade-Heideking Fellowships *(Doctorate/Fellowship)* [4128]

Edward G. Kaelber Scholarships *(Undergraduate/ Scholarship)* [5582]

Daniel Kahikina and Millie Akaka Scholarships *(Graduate, Undergraduate/Scholarship)* [5213]

Kaiser Media Fellowships in Health *(Advanced Professional/Fellowship)* [5180]

Stacy Kaiser Memorial Funds *(Undergraduate/ Scholarship)* [8984]

David A. Kaiser Memorial Scholarship Fund *(Undergraduate/Scholarship)* [8680]

Kaiser Permanente Northwest Pride Scholarships *(Undergraduate/Scholarship)* [3679]

Kamehameha Schools Class of 1968 "Ka Poli O Kaiona" Scholarships *(Graduate, Undergraduate/ Scholarship)* [5214]

Kamehameha Schools Class of 1972 Scholarships *(Graduate, Undergraduate/Scholarship)* [5215]

Benjamin Kaminer Endowed Scholarships in Physiology *(Undergraduate/Scholarship)* [5618]

Martin S. Kane Memorial Community Service Award Scholarships *(Undergraduate/Scholarship)* [3062]

Kansas Association of Broadcasters Scholarships *(Undergraduate/Scholarship)* [5182]

Kansas City Division Scholarships *(All/Scholarship)* [5860]

Kansas Osteopathic Medical Service Scholarships *(Graduate, Professional development/Scholarship)* [5185]

CSF M. Kantor and Brothers Scholarships *(Undergraduate/Scholarship)* [2853]

Walter Kapala Scholarships *(Undergraduate/Scholarship)* [4445]

Joseph Kaplan Fund *(Graduate, Undergraduate/ Scholarship)* [4726]

Don Kaplan Legacy Scholarships *(Undergraduate/ Scholarship)* [2250]

Kaplan Scholarships *(Undergraduate/Scholarship)* [4562]

Kaplan Test Prep and Admission Scholarships for NSHSS Members *(High School/Scholarship)* [6503]

Kappa Chapter Centennial Scholarships *(Undergraduate/Scholarship)* [3377]

Kappa Delta Phi Scholarship Program *(Postgraduate/Scholarship)* [952]

Kappa Kappa Gamma Graduate Scholarships *(Graduate/Scholarship)* [5193]

Kappa Kappa Gamma Undergraduate Scholarships *(Undergraduate/Scholarship)* [5194]

Kappa Omicron Nu National Alumni Fellowships

(Graduate/Fellowship) [5196]

Kappa Omicron Nu Undergraduate Scholarships (Undergraduate/Scholarship) [5197]

The ISASI Rudolf Kapustin Memorial Scholarships (Undergraduate/Scholarship) [4988]

J.S. Karling Graduate Student Research Awards (Graduate/Grant) [2164]

Josephine de Karman Fellowships (Graduate, Undergraduate/Fellowship) [5205]

Philip R. Karr, III Scholarship Fund (Graduate/Fellowship) [4100]

KASF Chair Scholarships (Graduate, Undergraduate/Scholarship) [5292]

KASF Designated Scholarships (Graduate, Undergraduate/Scholarship) [5293]

KASF General Scholarships (Graduate, Undergraduate/Scholarship) [5294]

Ken Kashiwahara Scholarships (Undergraduate/Scholarship) [7569]

Ken Kashiwara Scholarships (Undergraduate/Scholarship) [7578]

Katherine Singer Kovacs Book and Essay Awards (Professional development/Award) [8310]

Magoichi & Shizuko Kato Memorial Scholarships (Graduate/Scholarship) [5143]

KATS Graduate Scholarships (Graduate/Scholarship) [5246]

KATS Undergraduate Scholarships (Undergraduate/Scholarship) [5247]

Ka'u Chamber of Commerce College Scholarships (Undergraduate/Scholarship) [5207]

Ken and Romaine Kauffman Scholarship Fund (Undergraduate/Scholarship) [3949]

Lucile B. Kaufman Women's Scholarships (Undergraduate/Scholarship) [8388]

N.G. Kaul Memorial Scholarships (Doctorate, Graduate/Scholarship) [6687]

William and Beatrice Kavanaugh Scholarships (Undergraduate/Scholarship) [5100]

Kawano Family Scholarships (Undergraduate/Scholarship) [7938]

E. Wayne Kay Co-op Scholarships (Undergraduate/Scholarship) [8389]

E. Wayne Kay Community College Scholarships (Undergraduate/Scholarship) [8390]

E. Wayne Kay High School Scholarships (Undergraduate/Scholarship) [8391]

Doc Keen Memorial Scholarships (Undergraduate, Vocational/Occupational/Scholarship) [8610]

Keepers Preservation Education Fund (Undergraduate/Award) [5583]

Glenn Keever Scholarships (Undergraduate/Scholarship) [9284]

KEF Academic Scholarships (Graduate, Undergraduate, Vocational/Occupational/Scholarship) [5284]

KEF College/University Basic Scholarships (Graduate, Undergraduate, Vocational/Occupational/Scholarship) [5285]

KEF Vocational Education Scholarship (Vocational/Occupational/Scholarship) [5286]

Kegler Brown Minority Merit Scholarships (Undergraduate/Scholarship) [5229]

Keiser College Coast Guard Scholarships (Undergraduate/Scholarship) [2927]

Maude Keisling/Cumberland County Extension Homemakers Scholarships (Undergraduate/Scholarship) [3112]

John W. Kelley Memorial Scholarships (Undergraduate/Scholarship) [8729]

W.K. Kellogg Foundation Doctoral Fellowships in Health Policy (Professional development/Fellowship) [6402]

Willmoore H. Kendall Scholarships (Postgraduate/Scholarship) [2912]

Alexander Kendrick Memorial Scholarships (Graduate, Undergraduate/Scholarship) [7013]

Oscar Kenshur Book Prize (Professional development/Prize) [1231]

Raymond A. Kent-Navy V-12/ROTC Scholarships (Undergraduate/Scholarship) [9212]

Kentucky Alumni Club Scholarships - Capital Region Alumni Club (Undergraduate/Scholarship) [9213]

Kerr Foundation Scholarships (Undergraduate/Scholarship) [6867]

Kerrigan Scholarships (Undergraduate/Scholarship) [7191]

Judge Oliver Kessel Memorial Scholarships - Ripley Rotary (Undergraduate/Scholarship) [7094]

Ashley E. Ketcher Memorial Scholarships (Undergraduate/Scholarship) [3156]

Luella Akins Key Scholarships (Undergraduate/Scholarship) [3378]

KFC Colonel's Scholars Program (Undergraduate/Scholarship) [5249]

Debbie Khalil Memorial Scholarships (Graduate, Undergraduate/Scholarship) [7268]

Louise Nader Khourey/Kappa Delta Pi Scholarships (Undergraduate/Scholarship) [8681]

Julia Kiene Fellowships in Electrical Energy (Graduate/Fellowship) [9723]

Mary and Millard Kiker Scholarships (Undergraduate/Scholarship) [3910]

Bernard Kilgore Memorial Scholarships (Undergraduate/Scholarship) [6652]

Killam Fellowships Program (Undergraduate/Fellowship) [9100]

Killingworth Foundation Scholarships (Undergraduate/Scholarship) [5260]

Kimberly Elementary School PTA Scholarships (Undergraduate/Scholarship) [7660]

Douglas Gray Kimel Scholarships (Undergraduate/Scholarship) [9644]

Kimmel Scholarships (Doctorate, Graduate/Fellowship) [5264]

James N. Kincanon Scholarships (Undergraduate/Scholarship) [7806]

Dr. Martin Luther King & Coretta Scott King Student Leadership Scholarships (Undergraduate/Scholarship) [2336]

Arthur M. and Berdena King Eagle Scout Scholarships (High School/Scholarship) [6256]

Kit C. King Graduate Scholarships (Graduate/Scholarship) [6451]

Martin Luther King Law Scholarships (Undergraduate/Scholarship) [3501]

Steven G. King Play Environments Scholarships (Undergraduate/Scholarship) [5333]

Jessica King Scholarships (Professional development/Scholarship) [3310]

Don King Student Fellowships (Undergraduate/Fellowship) [4646]

Mackenzie King Travelling Scholarships (Graduate/Scholarship) [5724]

Kingsbury Elementary School PTA Scholarships (Undergraduate/Scholarship) [7661]

Treva C. Kintner Scholarships (Undergraduate/Scholarship) [7291]

Edyie G. Kirby Nursing Scholarship Awards (Undergraduate/Scholarship) [3041]

Isabel Mayer Kirkpatrick Scholarships (Undergraduate/Scholarship) [8611]

Dr. Elemer and Eva Kiss Scholarship Fund (Undergraduate/Scholarship) [4638]

Tamo Kitaura Scholarships (Professional development/Scholarship) [9057]

Kiwanis Club of Escondido Scholarships I (Undergraduate/Scholarship) [7939]

Kiwanis Club of Escondido Scholarships II (Undergraduate, Vocational/Occupational/Scholarship) [7940]

Louis T. Klauder Scholarships (Graduate, Undergraduate/Scholarship) [1054]

Jane M. Klausman Women in Business Scholarships (Graduate, Undergraduate/Scholarship) [9813]

Robert A. Kleckner Scholarships (Undergraduate/Scholarship) [8612]

Margie Klein "Paper Plate" Scholarships (All/Scholarship) [1705]

Gerda and Kurt Klein Scholarships (High School/Scholarship) [4606]

Klingenstein Fellowships in the Neurosciences (Doctorate, Professional development/Fellowship) [5266]

CSF Raymond and Augusta Klink Scholarships (Undergraduate/Scholarship) [2854]

Arthur Klorfein Scholarship and Fellowship Fund (Undergraduate/Scholarship) [5619]

Joseph H. Klupenger Scholarship Awards (Undergraduate/Scholarship) [6937]

AALL/Wolters Kluwer Law & Business Grants (Professional development/Grant) [501]

Robert C. and Judith L. Knapp Scholarships (Graduate, Undergraduate/Scholarship) [3867]

John A. Knauss Marine Policy Fellowships (Graduate/Fellowship) [2278]

John S. Knight Fellowships (Professional development/Fellowship) [8653]

Robert E. Knight Professional Scholarships (Doctorate, Graduate/Scholarship) [8856]

Elva Knight Research Grants (All/Grant) [4976]

Knights of Pythias Scholarships (Undergraduate/Scholarship) [7499]

Rhonda Knopp Memorial Scholarships (Undergraduate/Scholarship) [7095]

Harold Knopp Scholarships (Undergraduate/Scholarship) [7096]

Jane Shaw Knox Graduate Scholarships (Graduate/Scholarship) [3868]

Knox-Hume Scholarships (Undergraduate/Scholarship) [3113]

Glenn Knudsvig Memorial Scholarships (Graduate, Undergraduate/Scholarship) [611]

Ann Koby Legacy Scholarships (Undergraduate/Scholarship) [9740]

Kodak Fellowships in Film Preservation (Graduate/Fellowship) [1830]

Seth Koehler Central High School Scholarship Fund (Undergraduate, Vocational/Occupational/Scholarship) [4225]

Senator Carl O. Koella, Jr. Memorial Scholarships (Undergraduate/Scholarship) [3114]

CSF Bob and Linda Kohlhepp Scholarships (Undergraduate/Scholarship) [2855]

Christopher J. Kohlmeier Scholarships (Undergraduate/Scholarship) [7662]

James P. Kohn Memorial Scholarships (Graduate/Scholarship) [1344]

Michael Koizumi APWA Scholarships (Undergraduate/Scholarship) [1061]

Gwin J. and Ruth Kolb Travel Fellowships (Doctorate, Professional development/Fellowship) [1232]

Susan G. Komen for the Cure College Scholarship Awards (Undergraduate/Award, Scholarship) [5281]

John W. Koons, Sr. Memorial Scholarships (Undergraduate/Scholarship) [1944]

Elizabeth Munsterberg Koppitz Child Psychology Graduate Fellowships (Graduate/Fellowship) [1040]

Kor Memorial Scholarships (Graduate, Undergraduate/Scholarship) [5270]

Korean Language Study Awards (Graduate/Scholarship) [5290]

Korean Studies Dissertation Workshop Funds (Graduate/Fellowship, Grant) [8283]

AIST Willy Korf Memorial Fund (Undergraduate/Scholarship) [1807]

Kosciuszko Foundation Graduate Study and Research in Poland Scholarships (Graduate/Scholarship) [5296]

Kosciuszko Foundation Tuition Scholarships (Graduate/Scholarship) [5297]

Kosciuszko Foundation Year Abroad Scholarships (Graduate, Undergraduate/Scholarship) [5298]

Marcia J. Koslov Scholarships (Professional development/Scholarship) [502]

Eugene & Elinor Kotur Scholarship Trust Fund (Undergraduate, Graduate/Scholarship) [9499]

Marjorie Kovler Research Fellowships (All/Fellowship) [5239]

KPMG Foundation Minority Accounting Doctoral Scholarships (Postdoctorate/Scholarship) [5304]

Eve Kraft Education and College Scholarships (Undergraduate/Scholarship) [9409]

William D. Krahling Excellence in Journalism Scholarships (Undergraduate/Scholarship) [367]

Norman Kramer Scholarship Awards (Undergraduate/Scholarship) [5837]

Melvin Kranzberg Dissertation Fellowships (Doctorate/Fellowship) [8345]

Samuel C. Kraus, Jr. Memorial Scholarships (Undergraduate/Scholarship) [6534]

Kress Conservation Fellowships (Graduate/Fellowship) [5308]

Kress Curatorial Fellowships *(Doctorate/Fellowship)* [5309]

Kress Fellowships in Art History at Foreign Institutions *(Doctorate/Fellowship)* [5310]

Samuel H. Kress Foundation Dissertation Fellowships *(Doctorate/Fellowship)* [8296]

Kress Pre-Doctoral Fellowships in the History of Art and Archeology in Turkey *(Postdoctorate/Fellowship)* [1151]

Kress Travel Fellowships in the History of Art *(Doctorate/Fellowship)* [5311]

Krist-Reavley Minority Scholarships *(Undergraduate/Scholarship)* [7192]

David A. Kronick Travelling Fellowships *(Doctorate/Fellowship)* [5743]

Cooley Godward Kronish Diversity Fellowships *(Graduate, Undergraduate/Fellowship)* [3249]

Eugene S. Kropf Scholarships *(Undergraduate/Scholarship)* [9192]

Melvin Kruger Endowed Scholarship Program *(Undergraduate, Vocational/Occupational/Scholarship)* [6465]

Melvin Kruger Endowed Scholarships *(Graduate, Undergraduate, Vocational/Occupational/Scholarship)* [7817]

Samuel Krugliak Legal Scholarship Fund *(Undergraduate/Scholarship)* [8682]

Ken Krum/Bud Kouts Memorial Scholarships *(Undergraduate/Scholarship)* [1945]

KSA Scholarships *(Undergraduate/Scholarship)* [5262]

Kuchler-Killian Memorial Scholarships *(Undergraduate/Scholarship)* [6277]

Don Kuhn Memorial Scholarship Fund *(Graduate/Scholarship)* [3449]

Heloise Werthan Kuhn Scholarships *(Undergraduate/Scholarship)* [3116]

Irene Corbally Kuhn Scholarships *(Graduate, Undergraduate/Scholarship)* [7014]

Kumin Scholars Program *(Undergraduate/Scholarship)* [8204]

Kris M. Kunze Memorial Scholarships *(Undergraduate/Scholarship)* [645]

Charles Kuralt Fellowships in International Broadcasting *(Postgraduate/Scholarship)* [9285]

Chris Kurzweil Scholarships *(Undergraduate/Scholarship)* [3200]

Sam S. Kuwahara Memorial Scholarships *(Undergraduate/Scholarship)* [5144]

L-3 Avionics Systems Scholarships *(Undergraduate, Vocational/Occupational/Scholarship)* [134]

La Voz Latina Scholarships *(Undergraduate/Scholarship)* [3157]

Gretchen Laatsch Scholarships *(Graduate/Scholarship)* [1740]

LAF/Class Fund AILA/YAMAGAMI/Hope Fellowships *(Postgraduate/Fellowship)* [1284]

The Lagrant Foundation - Graduate Students Scholarships *(Graduate/Scholarship)* [5315]

The Lagrant Foundation - Undergraduate Students Scholarships *(Undergraduate/Scholarship)* [5316]

Casey Laine Armed Forces Scholarships *(Undergraduate/Scholarship)* [2951]

Lake Dollars for Scholars Endowment Fund *(Undergraduate, Vocational/Occupational/Scholarship)* [8683]

Lake George Dollars for Scholars Awards *(Undergraduate/Scholarship)* [5318]

Lalor Foundation Post-Doctoral Fellowships *(Postdoctorate/Fellowship)* [5322]

Lam Research Corporation Core Values Scholarships *(Undergraduate/Scholarship)* [5324]

Lamaku Post-Secondary Scholarships *(Undergraduate/Scholarship)* [83]

Lamar University College of Engineering Scholarships *(Undergraduate/Scholarship)* [6257]

Frank S. Land Scholarships *(Undergraduate/Scholarship)* [3425]

Robert S. Landauer, Sr. Memorial Fellowships *(Graduate/Fellowship)* [4490]

Landscape Forms Design for People Scholarships *(Undergraduate/Scholarship)* [5334]

The Lanford Family Highway Worker Memorial Scholarship Program *(Undergraduate/Scholarship)* [1157]

Langfitt-Ambrose Trust Funds *(Undergraduate/Scholarship)* [7097]

Paul J. Laninga Memorial Scholarship Fund *(Undergraduate/Scholarship)* [4226]

Lapeer County Medical Scholarship Fund *(Undergraduate/Scholarship)* [5351]

The Otis and Florence Lapham Memorial Scholarships *(Undergraduate/Scholarship)* [5101]

Christian Larew Memorial Scholarships *(Graduate/Scholarship)* [5484]

Peter and Jody Larkin Legacy Scholarships *(Undergraduate/Scholarship)* [2251]

Arnold Les Larsen, FAIA, Memorial Scholarships *(Graduate, Master's/Scholarship)* [841]

Larson Aquatic Research Support Scholarships (LARS) *(Doctorate, Graduate/Scholarship)* [1418]

Joseph C. Larson Entrepreneurial Scholarships *(Undergraduate/Scholarship)* [7942]

Las Limas Community Scholarships *(Undergraduate/Scholarship)* [8730]

Las Vegas Elks Scholarships for the Physically Challenged *(Undergraduate, Vocational/Occupational/Scholarship)* [7502]

Las Vegas Elks Scholarships *(Undergraduate, Vocational/Occupational/Scholarship)* [7501]

Laser Technology, Engineering and Applications Scholarships *(Graduate, Undergraduate/Scholarship)* [8639]

Jay and Deborah Last Fellowships *(Doctorate/Fellowship)* [420]

Latham Diversity Scholars *(Undergraduate/Scholarship)* [5354]

Latin American Educational Foundation Scholarships *(Undergraduate, Vocational/Occupational/Scholarship)* [5356]

Rick and Beverly Lattin Education Scholarship Fund *(Undergraduate/Scholarship)* [4227]

Robert J. Lavidge Nonprofit Marketing Research Scholarships *(Professional development/Scholarship)* [919]

Law Foundation of Ontario Community Leadership in Justice Fellowships *(Professional development/Fellowship)* [5362]

Law and Social Science Dissertation Fellowship and Mentoring Program *(Doctorate, Graduate/Fellowship)* [578]

Law and Society Association Article Prize *(Professional development/Prize)* [5367]

Law and Society Association Dissertation Prize *(Professional development/Prize)* [5368]

Law and Society Association International Prize *(Professional development/Prize)* [5369]

Law and Society Association Student Paper Prize *(Graduate, Undergraduate/Prize)* [5370]

Willie D. Lawson, Jr. Memorial Scholarships *(Doctorate, Graduate, Professional development/Scholarship)* [6150]

Dr. James L. Lawson Memorial Scholarships *(Undergraduate/Scholarship)* [1092]

Lawton Minority Retention Grants *(Undergraduate/Scholarship)* [9362]

Lazarian Graduate Scholarships *(Graduate/Scholarship)* [1578]

Richard J. Lazzara Fellowships in Advanced Implant Surgery *(Postdoctorate/Fellowship)* [396]

Betsy B. and Garold A. Leach Scholarships for Museum Studies *(Undergraduate/Scholarship)* [3416]

LeaderShape Institute Scholarships *(Undergraduate/Grant)* [5202]

Leadership Development Scholarships *(Professional development/Scholarship)* [524]

League of Attorneys' Wives Scholarships *(Undergraduate/Scholarship)* [3504]

LEAGUE Foundation Scholarships *(Undergraduate/Scholarship)* [7855]

League of Latin American Citizens General Electric Scholarships *(Undergraduate, Vocational/Occupational/Scholarship)* [5386]

Leakey Foundation Research Grants *(Doctorate/Grant)* [5391]

William C. Leary Memorial Emergency Services Scholarships *(Undergraduate/Scholarship)* [8985]

Jack W. Leatherman Family Scholarship Fund *(Graduate/Scholarship)* [4228]

Ken Lee Memorial Scholarships *(Undergraduate/Scholarship)* [7944]

Bruce Lee Scholarships *(Undergraduate/Scholarship)* [9064]

Harold Leeming Memorial Scholarships *(Undergraduate/Scholarship)* [7663]

The Leesfield/AAJ Law Student Scholarships *(Undergraduate/Scholarship)* [493]

The Legacy Fellowships *(Doctorate/Fellowship)* [421]

Legacy Scholarship Program *(Undergraduate/Scholarship)* [8870]

Legacy Scholarships for Graduate Students *(Graduate/Scholarship)* [1278]

Legal Research Service Scholarships *(Undergraduate/Scholarship)* [3505]

Doreen Legg Memorial Scholarships *(Undergraduate/Scholarship)* [7664]

Jay C. and B. Nadine Leggett Charitable Scholarship Fund *(Undergraduate/Scholarship)* [8684]

Herbert Lehman Education Scholarships *(Undergraduate/Scholarship)* [5971]

Lehman Family Scholarships *(Undergraduate/Scholarship)* [7945]

PCH Architects/Steven J. Lehnhof Memorial Architectural Scholarships *(Undergraduate/Scholarship)* [7665]

Imelda and Ralph LeMar Scholarship Program *(Undergraduate/Scholarship)* [3201]

Lemelson Center Fellowships *(Doctorate, Postdoctorate, Professional development/Fellowship)* [8255]

Lemelson Center Travel to Collections Awards *(Graduate, Professional development/Award)* [8256]

The Lemon Grove Education Foundation Scholarships *(Undergraduate, Vocational/Occupational/Scholarship)* [7946]

John Lennon Scholarships *(All/Prize, Scholarship)* [2159]

Craig Lensch Memorial Scholarships *(Undergraduate/Scholarship)* [2192]

V.A. Leonard Scholarships *(Graduate, Undergraduate/Scholarship)* [357]

Leopold Education Project Scholarships *(Undergraduate/Scholarship)* [3158]

Sherman L. & Mabel C. Lepard Scholarships *(Undergraduate/Scholarship)* [4291]

Lerner-Scott Dissertation Prizes *(Doctorate/Prize)* [6959]

Irwin S. Lerner Student Scholarships *(Undergraduate/Scholarship)* [6513]

Les Dames D'Escoffier New York Scholarships *(Undergraduate/Scholarship)* [5405]

The Irving Leuchter Memorial Scholarships *(All/Scholarship)* [6714]

Gerald J. Levandoski Memorial Scholarship Fund *(Undergraduate/Scholarship)* [3779]

Myra Levick Scholarships *(Graduate/Scholarship)* [427]

Jack A. and Louise S. Levine Memorial Scholarships *(Undergraduate/Scholarship)* [7666]

Herbert Levy Memorial Endowment Fund Scholarships *(Undergraduate/Scholarship)* [8439]

Erwin Lew Memorial Scholarships *(Graduate, Undergraduate/Scholarship)* [8451]

Lewis and Clark Fund for Exploration and Field Research *(Doctorate/Grant)* [992]

Lloyd Lewis Fellowships in American History *(Postdoctorate/Fellowship)* [6696]

George T. Lewis, Jr. Academic Scholarship Fund *(Undergraduate/Scholarship)* [3912]

Flora Lewis Memorial Scholarships *(Graduate, Undergraduate/Scholarship)* [7015]

S. Evelyn Lewis Memorial Scholarships in Medical Health Sciences *(Graduate, Undergraduate/Scholarship)* [9805]

Jonathan D. Lewis Point Scholarships *(Graduate, Undergraduate/Scholarship)* [7365]

Marvin Lewis Scholarships *(Undergraduate/Scholarship)* [5471]

Lexington Alumni Scholarships *(Undergraduate/Scholarship)* [5473]

Lexington Community Foundation Annual Scholarships *(Undergraduate/Scholarship)* [5474]

Lexington Community Foundation/CCC Scholarships *(Undergraduate/Scholarship)* [5475]

LGBT HEART Scholarships *(Graduate/Scholarship)* [5407]

Ta Liang Memorial Awards *(Graduate/Grant)* [1669]

Liberace Scholarship Fund *(Undergraduate/Scholarship)* [5482]

Liberty Mutual Scholarships *(Undergraduate/Scholarship)* [1346]

Library Media Teacher Scholarships *(Graduate/Scholarship)* [2271]

Library Resident Research Fellowships *(Doctorate/Fellowship)* [993]

Richard T. Liddicoat Scholarships *(Graduate/Scholarship)* [4063]

Dolores Zohrab Liebmann Fund - Graduate School Fellowships *(Graduate/Fellowship)* [5488]

Dolores Zohrab Liebmann Fund - Independent Research/Study Grants *(Graduate/Grant)* [5489]

Dolores Zohrab Liebmann Fund - Publication Grants *(Graduate/Grant)* [5490]

LIFE Lessons Scholarship Program *(Undergraduate/Scholarship)* [5492]

Life Sciences Research Foundation Postdoctoral Fellowship Program *(Graduate, Doctorate/Fellowship)* [5494]

Lighthouse International Scholarships - College-bound Awards *(High School, Undergraduate/Scholarship)* [5497]

Lighthouse International Scholarships - Graduate Awards *(Graduate/Scholarship)* [5498]

Lighthouse International Scholarships - Undergraduate Awards *(Undergraduate/Scholarship)* [5499]

Frank R. Lillie Fellowships and Scholarships *(Undergraduate/Scholarship)* [5620]

Eli Lilly and Company/Black Data Processing Associates Scholarships *(High School/Scholarship)* [2033]

Lilly Endocrine Scholars Fellowship Awards *(Doctorate, Professional development/Fellowship)* [3638]

Lilly Reintegration Scholarships *(All, Vocational/Occupational/Scholarship)* [2707]

Lily Scholarships in Religion for Journalists *(Professional development/Scholarship)* [7732]

Esther Lim Memorial Scholarships *(Undergraduate/Scholarship)* [2767]

Lim, Ruger and Kim Scholarships *(Undergraduate/Scholarship)* [6027]

LIN Media Minority Scholarships and Training Program *(Undergraduate/Scholarship)* [5501]

AIST Ronald E. Lincoln Memorial Scholarships *(Undergraduate/Scholarship)* [1808]

John C. Lincoln Memorial Scholarships *(Undergraduate/Scholarship)* [1440]

Linda's Scholarships *(All/Scholarship)* [5882]

Donald A.B. Lindberg Research Fellowships *(Doctorate, Graduate/Fellowship)* [5744]

Lindenwood University Scouting Scholarships *(Undergraduate/Scholarship)* [6258]

CSF Carl H. Lindner Family Scholarships *(Undergraduate/Scholarship)* [2856]

George N. Lindsay Civil Rights Legal Fellowships *(Graduate/Fellowship)* [5384]

Johnny Lineberry Memorial Scholarships *(Undergraduate, Vocational/Occupational/Scholarship)* [9645]

Link Foundation/Smithsonian Graduate Fellowships in Marine Science *(Graduate/Fellowship)* [8262]

F. Maynard Lipe Scholarship Awards *(Postdoctorate, Postgraduate/Scholarship)* [615]

Lawrence Lipking Fellowships at the Newberry Library *(Graduate/Fellowship)* [6697]

Ruth Lister Scholarships *(Undergraduate, Vocational/Occupational/Scholarship)* [8986]

LIT Scholarships *(Graduate, Undergraduate/Scholarship)* [5328]

LITA and LSSI Minority Scholarships *(Graduate/Scholarship)* [5485]

LITA/OCLC Minority Scholarships *(Graduate/Scholarship)* [5486]

Litherland/FTE Scholarships *(Undergraduate/Scholarship)* [5007]

Ruth Liu Memorial Scholarships *(Undergraduate/Scholarship)* [2768]

Live Out Loud Annual Scholarships *(Undergraduate/Scholarship)* [7856]

Lawrence Livermore National Laboratory Fellowships *(Doctorate/Fellowship)* [5382]

David C. Lizarraga Graduate Fellowships *(Graduate, Master's/Fellowship)* [8821]

LLN Scholarships *(Community College/Scholarship)* [5358]

E.C. Lloyd and J.C.U. Johnson Scholarship Fund *(Undergraduate/Scholarship)* [3042]

Loan Forgiveness Scholarships *(Graduate, Undergraduate/Loan, Scholarship)* [8634]

Virgil K. Lobring Scholarships *(Undergraduate/Scholarship)* [3202]

Local Wound Haemostatics and Hemorrhage Control Scholarships *(All/Scholarship)* [557]

William J. Locklin Scholarships *(Undergraduate/Scholarship)* [1285]

Lodging Management Program Scholarships (LMP) *(Undergraduate/Scholarship)* [800]

Audrey Loftus Memorial Scholarships *(Undergraduate/Scholarship)* [9188]

Lone Star GIA Associate and Alumni Scholarships *(Undergraduate/Scholarship)* [4064]

Lawrence A. Long Memorial Law Scholarships *(Undergraduate/Scholarship)* [368]

James E. Long Memorial Post Doctoral Fellowships *(Postdoctorate/Fellowship)* [4913]

Long-Term Research Fellowship Programs *(Professional development/Fellowship)* [5672]

Kay Longscope Scholarships *(Graduate, Undergraduate/Scholarship)* [6392]

Megan Nicole Longwell Scholarships *(Undergraduate/Scholarship)* [7098]

Audre Lord Scholarships *(Graduate, Undergraduate/Scholarship)* [7857]

Suzanne and Caleb Loring Research Fellowships *(Graduate, Doctorate/Fellowship)* [5673]

Barbara Lotze Scholarships for Future Teachers *(Undergraduate/Scholarship)* [533]

Willie T. Loud - CH2M Hill Scholarships *(Undergraduate/Scholarship)* [6295]

Louisiana Agricultural Consultants Association Scholarships *(Graduate, Undergraduate/Scholarship)* [5517]

Louisiana Library Association Scholarships *(Graduate, Master's/Scholarship)* [5522]

Louisville Institute Dissertation Fellowships *(Doctorate/Fellowship)* [5527]

Louisville Institute First Book Grants for Minority Scholars *(Doctorate/Grant)* [5528]

Louisville Institute Project Grants for Researchers *(Doctorate/Grant)* [5529]

Louisville Institute Sabbatical Grants for Researchers *(Doctorate/Grant)* [5530]

Love of Bonita Empowerment Scholarships *(Undergraduate/Scholarship)* [8613]

First Lieutenant Scott McClean Love Memorial Scholarship - Children of Soldiers *(Undergraduate, Vocational/Occupational/Scholarship)* [1615]

First Lieutenant Scott McClean Love Memorial Scholarship - Spouses of Soldiers *(Undergraduate, Vocational/Occupational/Scholarship)* [1616]

D.J. Lovell Scholarships *(Graduate, Undergraduate/Scholarship)* [8640]

The Lowell H. and Dorothy Loving Undergraduate Scholarships *(Undergraduate/Scholarship)* [646]

Diane G. Lowe and John Gomez, IV Scholarships *(Undergraduate/Scholarship)* [3117]

H.B. Paul Lowenberg Lions Scholarships *(Undergraduate/Scholarship)* [4447]

LPHA Scholarships *(Graduate, Undergraduate/Scholarship)* [5525]

LRF Post-Doctoral Fellowships *(Doctorate, Graduate/Fellowship)* [5552]

Henry Luce Foundation Dissertation Fellowships in American Art *(Doctorate/Fellowship)* [679]

Elsa Ludeke Graduate Scholarships *(Graduate/Scholarship)* [3417]

Lugonia Alumni/Harrison Lightfoot Scholarships *(Undergraduate/Scholarship)* [7667]

Mollie Lukken Memorial Scholarships *(Graduate, Professional development/Scholarship)* [5178]

LULAC GM Scholarships *(Graduate, High School, Undergraduate, Vocational/Occupational/Award)* [5387]

LULAC National Scholarship Fund *(Graduate, High School, Undergraduate, Vocational/Occupational/Scholarship)* [5388]

Audrey Lumsden-Kouvel Fellowships *(Postdoctorate/Fellowship)* [6698]

Lung Health Dissertation Grants *(Graduate/Grant)* [916]

Luso-American Education Foundation C-1 General Scholarships *(Undergraduate/Scholarship)* [5541]

Luso-American Education Foundation G-1 Grants *(Professional development/Grant)* [5542]

Luso-American Education Foundation G-2 Grants *(Professional development/Grant)* [5543]

Luso-American Education Foundation G-3 Grants *(Postgraduate/Grant)* [5544]

Luso-American Fraternal Federation B-2 Scholarships *(Postgraduate/Scholarship)* [5545]

Luso-American Fraternal Federation B-3 Scholarships *(All, Vocational/Occupational/Scholarship)* [5546]

Luso-American Fraternal Federation B-4 Scholarships *(All/Scholarship)* [5547]

Lycoming County Medical Society Scholarships (LCMS) *(Undergraduate/Scholarship)* [3986]

Denny Lydic Scholarships *(Undergraduate, Vocational/Occupational/Scholarship)* [8952]

Melissa A. Lyles Memorial Scholarships *(Undergraduate/Scholarship)* [7503]

The C. Lyons Fellowship Program *(All/Fellowship)* [6389]

Linda Lyons Memorial Scholarship Fund *(Undergraduate/Scholarship)* [5779]

Verne LaMarr Lyons Memorial Scholarships *(Graduate/Fellowship)* [6123]

Carie and George Lyter Scholarship Fund *(Undergraduate/Scholarship)* [3951]

John Mabry Forestry Scholarships *(Undergraduate/Scholarship)* [7587]

MAC Emeritus Scholarships for First-Time Meeting Attendees *(All/Scholarship)* [5855]

Bill MacAloney Legacy Scholarships *(Undergraduate/Scholarship)* [2252]

Catharine Macaulay Prize *(Graduate/Prize)* [1233]

MACC Scholarships *(Professional development/Scholarship)* [5796]

Katie MacDonald Memorial Scholarships *(Graduate, Undergraduate/Scholarship)* [9018]

Irene and Daisy MacGregor Memorial Scholarships *(Graduate/Scholarship)* [4448]

Nate Mack/Cindi Turner Scholarships *(Undergraduate/Scholarship)* [7504]

Robert Mack Scholarships *(Graduate, Undergraduate/Scholarship)* [5556]

James Mackenzie Fallows Scholarships Honoring William Cunningham *(Undergraduate/Scholarship)* [7668]

Thermoset Division/James I. Mackenzie and James H. Cunningham Scholarships *(Graduate, Undergraduate/Scholarship)* [8452]

Mackey-Byars Scholarships for Communication Excellence *(Undergraduate/Scholarship)* [9287]

MACPA Scholarships *(Graduate, Undergraduate/Scholarship)* [5652]

Andrew Macrina Scholarships *(High School/Scholarship)* [695]

Pat and John MacTavish Scholarship Fund *(Undergraduate/Scholarship)* [4229]

Eileen C. Maddex Fellowships *(Graduate/Fellowship)* [5198]

Lawrence Madeiros Scholarships *(Undergraduate/Scholarship)* [6330]

James Madison Foundation - Junior Fellowships *(Graduate/Fellowship)* [5564]

James Madison Foundation - Senior Fellowships *(Graduate/Fellowship)* [5565]

MAES Founders Scholarships *(Graduate, Undergraduate/Scholarship)* [5798]

MAES General Scholarships *(Graduate, Undergraduate/Scholarship)* [5799]

MAES Graduate Scholarships *(Graduate/Scholarship)* [5800]

MAES Padrino/Madrina Scholarships *(Graduate, Undergraduate/Scholarship)* [5801]

MAES Pipeline Scholarships *(Graduate, Undergraduate/Scholarship)* [5802]

MAES Presidential Scholarships *(Graduate, Undergraduate/Scholarship)* [5803]

The Brandon Magalassi Memorial Scholarship

Foundation Scholarships (Undergraduate/Scholarship) [5567]

Jay Magazine Memorial Fund College Scholarships (JMMF) (Graduate, Undergraduate/Scholarship) [5759]

Magnetic Interfaces and Nanostructures Division - The Leo M. Falicov Student Award (Graduate/Award) [1983]

Dr. Edward May Magruder Medical Scholarships (Undergraduate/Scholarship) [609]

Sonia S. Maguire Outstanding Scholastic Achievement Awards (Graduate, Undergraduate/Scholarship) [8782]

Lillian Grace Mahan Scholarship Fund (Graduate/Scholarship) [8685]

Dan and Rachel Mahi Educational Scholarships (Graduate, Undergraduate/Scholarship) [5216]

Maiman Student Paper Competition (Graduate, Undergraduate/Award) [6912]

Maine Community Foundation - CWG Scholarship Fund (Graduate/Scholarship) [5584]

Maine Community Foundation - Rice Scholarships (Undergraduate/Scholarship) [5585]

Maine Graphic Arts Association Scholarships (Undergraduate/Scholarship) [5597]

Maine Nutrition Council Scholarships (Undergraduate/Scholarship) [5599]

Maine Vietnam Veterans Scholarships (All/Scholarship) [5586]

Maintenance Technical Reward and Career Scholarships (Undergraduate/Scholarship) [6170]

MALDEF Dream Act Student Activist Scholarships (Undergraduate, Graduate/Scholarship) [5805]

Maley/FTE Scholarships (Graduate/Scholarship) [5013]

Maley/FTEE Teacher Scholarships (Graduate/Scholarship) [5008]

Joseph J. Malone Fellowships in Arab and Islamic Studies (Professional development/Fellowship) [6227]

Reba Malone Scholarships (Graduate, Undergraduate/Scholarship) [1055]

David C. Maloney Scholarships (Undergraduate/Scholarship) [6423]

MALSCE Scholarships (Undergraduate/Scholarship) [5660]

Dr. Julianne Malveaux Scholarships (Undergraduate/Scholarship) [6093]

Malyon-Smith Scholarships (Graduate/Scholarship) [8472]

Lyle Mamer Fellowships (Graduate/Fellowship) [9724]

MANAA Media Scholarships (Graduate, Undergraduate/Scholarship) [5737]

Manchester Scholarship Foundation Scholarships (Undergraduate/Scholarship) [4450]

Norm Manly - YMTA Maritime Educational Scholarships (Undergraduate/Scholarship) [9795]

Horace Mann Insurance Scholarships (High School/Scholarship) [6878]

Raleigh Mann Scholarships (Undergraduate/Scholarship) [9288]

Mansfield Soccer Association Scholarships (Undergraduate/Scholarship) [5603]

Honorable Carol Los Mansmann Memorial Scholarships (Graduate, Undergraduate/Scholarship) [329]

Paul Mansur Scholarships (Undergraduate/Scholarship) [4952]

Many Voices Fellowships (Professional development/Fellowship) [7338]

Manzer-Keener-Wefler Scholarships (Undergraduate/Scholarship) [8686]

Marathon Oil Corporation College Scholarship Program (Graduate, Undergraduate/Scholarship) [4578]

March of Dimes Graduate Nursing Scholarships (Graduate/Scholarship) [5607]

Stephen T. Marchello Scholarships (Undergraduate/Scholarship) [5609]

Harold and Inge Marcus Scholarships (Undergraduate/Scholarship) [4805]

The Eric Marder Scholarships (Undergraduate/Scholarship) [4710]

American Turkish Society Arif Mardin Music Fellow-

ships (Professional development/Fellowship) [8976]

Margaret B. Lindsey Awards for Distinguished Research in Teacher Education (Professional development/Award) [467]

Aurella Varallo Mariani Scholarship Program (Undergraduate/Scholarship) [5985]

Marine Biological Laboratory Pioneers Fund (Undergraduate/Scholarship) [5621]

Marine Corps Engineer Association Assistance Fund (Graduate, High School, Undergraduate/Scholarship) [5635]

Marine Corps League National Scholarships (Undergraduate/Scholarship) [5637]

Marine Technology Society ROV Scholarships (Graduate, Undergraduate/Scholarship) [5639]

Marine Technology Society Scholarships for Graduate and Undergraduate Students (Graduate, Undergraduate/Scholarship) [5640]

Marine Technology Society Student Scholarships for Graduating High School Seniors (Undergraduate/Scholarship) [5641]

Marine Technology Society Student Scholarships for Two-year Technical, Engineering and Community College Students (Community College, Two Year College, Undergraduate/Scholarship) [5642]

Mariposa Elementary School PTA Scholarships (Undergraduate, Vocational/Occupational/Scholarship) [7669]

Howard T. Markey Memorial Scholarships (Undergraduate/Scholarship) [3717]

Ed Markham International Scholarships (Undergraduate/Scholarship) [733]

Markley Scholarships (Graduate, Undergraduate/Scholarship) [6046]

Richard Marks Educational Fund (Graduate/Scholarship) [5217]

Marliave Scholarship Fund (Undergraduate/Scholarship) [1768]

Marmot Leadership Scholarships (Postgraduate, Professional development, Undergraduate/Scholarship) [7008]

Marsh College Scholarships (Undergraduate/Scholarship) [4842]

Burton W. Marsh Fellowships (Graduate/Fellowship) [4826]

George Perkins Marsh Prize (Professional development/Prize) [1249]

Marsh Risk Consulting Scholarships (Undergraduate/Scholarship) [1347]

Marshall-Baruch Fellowships (Doctorate/Fellowship) [5649]

Marshall Memorial Fellowships (Professional development/Fellowship) [4132]

Ray and Gertrude Marshall Scholarships (Undergraduate/Scholarship) [696]

Ron Marshall Scholarships (Undergraduate/Scholarship) [1138]

Sarah Shinn Marshall Scholarships (Undergraduate/Scholarship) [3379]

Marshall Undergraduate Scholars Program (Undergraduate/Award) [5650]

E.H. Marth Food and Environmental Scholarships (Undergraduate/Scholarship) [9674]

Lockheed Martin Graduate Scholarships (Graduate/Scholarship) [1560]

Lockheed Martin IT Scholarships (Undergraduate/Scholarship) [1561]

Bryce-Lietzke Martin Scholarships (Undergraduate/Scholarship) [7099]

Edna Martin Scholarships (Undergraduate/Scholarship) [3119]

Martin Sisters Scholarships (Undergraduate/Scholarship) [3380]

Dottie Martin Teacher Scholarships (Graduate, Undergraduate/Scholarship) [6765]

John S. Martinez and Family Scholarship Fund (Undergraduate/Scholarship) [3081]

Eric Martinez Memorial Scholarships (Graduate, Undergraduate/Scholarship) [9019]

Corporal Joseph Martinez U.S. Army Memorial Scholarships (Undergraduate/Scholarship) [7505]

Michael Marucci Memorial Scholarships (Undergraduate/Scholarship) [6278]

Maryland Poison Center Clinical Toxicology Fellowships (Doctorate, Graduate/Fellowship) [5654]

Maryland Speech Language Hearing Association Scholarships (Graduate/Scholarship) [5656]

Mas Family Scholarships (Graduate, Undergraduate/Scholarship) [5658]

The Maschhoffs Pork Production Scholarships (Undergraduate/Scholarship) [6379]

Masonic-Range Science Scholarships (Undergraduate/Scholarship) [8484]

Massachusetts Bar Foundation Legal Intern Fellowship Program (LIFP) (All/Fellowship) [5664]

Massachusetts Federation of Polish Women's Clubs Scholarships (Undergraduate/Scholarship) [5299]

Massachusetts Society of the Cincinnati Fellowships (Graduate, Doctorate/Fellowship) [5674]

S.O. Mast Founder's Scholarships (Undergraduate/Scholarship) [5622]

The Master Gardeners of Pierce County Scholarships (Undergraduate/Scholarship) [4339]

Master Municipal Clerks Academy Scholarships (Professional development/Scholarship) [4958]

Master's Degree with a Major in Nursing Academic Scholarships (Graduate/Scholarship) [6100]

Master's Scholarships Program (MSP) (Graduate, Master's/Scholarship) [8081]

Mat-Su Health Foundation Scholarships (Undergraduate/Scholarship) [9159]

Matching Scholarships Program (Undergraduate/Scholarship) [3328]

Material Handling Education Foundation Scholarships (Doctorate, Graduate, Undergraduate/Scholarship) [5688]

Materials Information Society National Merit Scholarships (Undergraduate/Scholarship) [5693]

Larry Matfay Scholarships (Graduate, Undergraduate/Scholarship) [5287]

Katharine & Bryant Mather Scholarships (Graduate/Scholarship) [635]

Noel D. Matkin Awards (Undergraduate/Award) [3596]

Rene Matos Memorial Scholarships (Undergraduate, Vocational/Occupational/Scholarship) [6338]

The Renardo A. Matteucci Scholarship Fund (Undergraduate/Scholarship) [3088]

Antonio Mattos Memorial Scholarships (Undergraduate/Scholarship) [5548]

Mature Student Scholarships (Undergraduate/Scholarship) [3673]

Donald Mauer Scholarships (Undergraduate/Scholarship) [9289]

Maxwell Graduate Scholarships in Medical Journalism (Postgraduate/Scholarship) [9290]

Edmund F. Maxwell Scholarships (Undergraduate/Scholarship) [5698]

Juliann and Joseph Maxwell Scholarships (Undergraduate/Scholarship) [3120]

Juliann King Maxwell Scholarships for Riverview High School Students (Undergraduate, Vocational/Occupational/Scholarship) [3121]

May-Cassioppi Scholarships (Undergraduate/Scholarship) [3159]

Howard Mayer Brown Fellowships (Graduate/Fellowship) [941]

John E. Mayfield ABLE Scholarships (Undergraduate/Scholarship) [3122]

John E. Mayfield Scholarships for Cheatham County Central High School (Undergraduate/Scholarship) [3123]

John E. Mayfield Scholarships for Harpeth High School (Undergraduate/Scholarship) [3124]

John E. Mayfield Scholarships Pleasant View Christian School (Undergraduate/Scholarship) [3125]

John E. Mayfield Scholarships for Sycamore High School (Undergraduate/Scholarship) [3126]

Bill Maynes Fellowships (Professional development/Fellowship) [3691]

Joseph W. Mayo ALS Scholarships (Undergraduate/Scholarship) [5587]

Clara Mayo Grants (Graduate/Grant) [8474]

Charles D. Mayo Student Scholarships (Undergraduate/Scholarship) [4944]

Giuliano Mazzetti Scholarships (Undergraduate/Scholarship) [8392]

Bill McAdam Scholarships (Undergraduate/Scholarship) [6331]

Walter Samuel McAfee Scholarships in Space Physics (Undergraduate/Scholarship) [6490]

NACA Foundation Graduate Scholarships *(Graduate, Master's, Postdoctorate/Scholarship)* [6050]

NACA Regional Council Student Leadership Scholarships *(Undergraduate/Scholarship)* [6051]

NACADA Scholarships *(Doctorate, Graduate/Scholarship)* [5997]

Albert and Alice Nacinovich Music Scholarships *(Undergraduate/Scholarship)* [3787]

NAED/Spencer Dissertation Fellowship Program *(Doctorate/Fellowship)* [6005]

NAFA International Dissertation Research Fellowships *(Graduate/Fellowship)* [6078]

NAFEO Internship Program *(Undergraduate/Internship)* [6068]

Jack Nagasaka Memorial Scholarships *(Undergraduate/Scholarship)* [7677]

NAJA Scholarships *(Graduate/Scholarship)* [6086]

Gongoro Nakamura Memorial Scholarships *(Undergraduate/Scholarship)* [5145]

NALS of Detroit Scholarships *(Undergraduate/Scholarship)* [5977]

NAMTA - International Art Materials Trade Association Visual Arts Major Scholarships *(Graduate, Undergraduate/Scholarship)* [5981]

NANBPWC National Scholarships *(Undergraduate/Scholarship)* [6095]

Robyn Nance Memorial Scholarships *(Undergraduate/Scholarship)* [7678]

Nanometer-Scale Science and Technology Division Graduate Award *(Graduate/Award)* [1984]

NAPABA Law Foundation Scholarships *(Undergraduate/Scholarship)* [6028]

Chereddi NarayanaRao & Radhamanohari Scholarships *(Graduate/Scholarship)* [8830]

NARFE-FEEA Scholarship Awards Program *(Undergraduate/Scholarship)* [6011]

NARRP Student Conference Scholarships *(Graduate, Undergraduate/Scholarship)* [6111]

NASA Aeronautics Scholarships - Undergraduate Program *(Undergraduate/Scholarship)* [1241]

NASCOE Scholarships *(Undergraduate/Scholarship)* [6070]

NASE Future Entrepreneur Scholarships *(Undergraduate/Scholarship)* [6117]

Kermit B. Nash Academic Scholarships *(Undergraduate/Scholarship)* [8137]

Elizabeth Nash Foundation Scholarships *(Graduate, Undergraduate/Scholarship)* [5983]

Mike Nash Memorial Scholarships *(Undergraduate/Scholarship)* [9427]

Nashville Unit Scholarships *(Undergraduate/Scholarship)* [4534]

NASIG Conference Student Grants *(Graduate, Postdoctorate/Grant)* [6743]

NASP-ERT Minority Scholarships for Graduate Training in School Psychology *(Graduate/Scholarship)* [6113]

National AAHAM Scholarships *(Undergraduate/Scholarship)* [483]

National Academy of Education Scholarships *(Postdoctorate/Scholarship)* [6006]

National Air Filtration Association Scholarship Fund *(Undergraduate/Scholarship)* [6015]

National Alliance of Preservation Commission Student Scholarships *(Undergraduate/Scholarship)* [6017]

National American Arab Nurses Association Scholarships *(Master's, Undergraduate/Scholarship)* [6022]

National Association of Abandoned Mine Land Programs Scholarships *(Undergraduate/Scholarship)* [6031]

National Association for Armenian Studies and Research Scholarships *(Graduate, Postgraduate/Scholarship)* [1603]

National Association of Biology Teachers BioClub Student Awards *(Undergraduate/Award)* [6035]

National Association of Campus Activities Multicultural Scholarship Programs *(Undergraduate/Scholarship)* [6053]

National Association of Campus Activities Scholarships for Student Leaders *(Undergraduate/Scholarship)* [6054]

National Association of Multicultural Engineering Program Advocates Beginning Freshmen Awards (NAMEPA) *(Undergraduate/Scholarship)* [6088]

National Association of Multicultural Engineering Program Advocates Transfer Engineering Student Awards (NAMEPA) *(Undergraduate/Scholarship)* [6089]

National Association of Pastoral Musicians Academic Scholarships *(Graduate, Undergraduate/Scholarship)* [6102]

National Association of School Safety and Law Enforcement Officers Scholarships (NASSLEO) *(Undergraduate/Scholarship)* [6115]

National Association for the Self-Employed Scholarships *(Undergraduate/Scholarship)* [6118]

National Association of Women in Construction Founders Undergraduate Scholarships *(Undergraduate/Scholarship)* [6132]

National Ataxia Foundation Research Fellowships *(Professional development/Fellowship)* [6136]

National Ataxia Foundation Research Grants *(Professional development/Fellowship)* [6137]

National Beta Club Scholarships *(Undergraduate/Scholarship)* [6139]

National Biosafety and Biocontainment Training Program Fellowships *(Graduate/Fellowship)* [6141]

National Black Coalition of Federal Aviation Employees Scholarships *(Other, Vocational/Occupational/Scholarship)* [6143]

National Black Deaf Advocate Scholarships *(Graduate, Undergraduate/Scholarship)* [6147]

National Black Nurses Association Scholarships *(Undergraduate/Scholarship)* [6155]

The National Board Technical Scholarships *(Undergraduate/Scholarship)* [6159]

National Center for Health Statistics Postdoctoral Research Awards *(Postdoctorate/Fellowship)* [2714]

National Co-op Scholarship Program *(Undergraduate/Scholarship)* [9750]

National Coal Transportation Association At Large Scholarships *(Undergraduate/Scholarship)* [6190]

National College Scholarship Awards *(Undergraduate/Scholarship)* [5088]

National Collegiate Athletic Association Postgraduate Scholarships *(Postgraduate/Scholarship)* [6194]

National Collegiate Cancer Foundation Scholarships *(Undergraduate/Scholarship)* [6196]

National Community Pharmacists Association Presidential Scholarships *(Undergraduate/Scholarship)* [6199]

National Community Pharmacists Association Summer Internship Programs *(Undergraduate/Internship)* [6200]

National Costumers Association Scholarships *(Undergraduate/Scholarship)* [6210]

National Council on Public History Graduate Student Travel Awards *(Doctorate, Graduate/Grant)* [6215]

National Council on Public History Student Project Awards *(Undergraduate/Award)* [6216]

National Dairy Herd Information Association Scholarship Program *(Undergraduate/Scholarship)* [6231]

National Dental Hygienists' Association Scholarships *(Undergraduate/Scholarship)* [6244]

National Endowment for the Humanities Fellowships *(Doctorate/Fellowship)* [6700]

The National Endowment for the Humanities Fellowships *(Doctorate, Graduate/Fellowship)* [1142]

National Environmental Health Association Scholarship Fund *(Graduate, Undergraduate/Scholarship)* [6269]

National Federation of the Blind Educator of Tomorrow Awards *(Undergraduate/Scholarship)* [6279]

National GEM Consortium - MS Engineering Fellowships *(Graduate/Fellowship)* [6305]

National GEM Consortium - PhD Engineering Fellowships *(Doctorate, Graduate/Fellowship)* [6306]

National GEM Consortium - PhD Science Fellowships *(Doctorate, Graduate/Fellowship)* [6307]

National Greenhouse Manufacturers Association Scholarships *(Undergraduate/Scholarship)* [734]

National Heartburn Alliance NP Student Scholarships *(Graduate/Scholarship)* [377]

National Honor Roll Scholarships *(Undergraduate/Scholarship)* [2222]

National Huguenot Society Scholarships *(Undergraduate/Scholarship)* [6347]

National Humanities Center Fellowships *(Doctorate, Postdoctorate/Fellowship)* [6349]

National Institute of Health Undergraduate Scholarship Program *(Undergraduate/Scholarship)* [6353]

National Iranian American Council Fellowships *(Graduate, Undergraduate/Fellowship)* [6365]

National Italian American Bar Association Scholarships *(Postgraduate/Scholarship)* [6367]

National Judges Association Scholarships *(Professional development/Scholarship)* [6372]

National Junior Horticultural Association Alumni Scholarships *(Undergraduate/Scholarship)* [6376]

National Junior Swine Association Outstanding Member Scholarships *(Graduate/Scholarship)* [6380]

National Kindergarten Alliance Graduate Scholarships *(Graduate/Scholarship)* [6385]

National Medical Fellowships Need-Based Scholarships *(Undergraduate/Scholarship)* [6403]

National Merit Scholarship Program *(Undergraduate/Scholarship)* [6405]

National Organization of Black Law Enforcement Executives Fellowship Programs *(All/Fellowship)* [6421]

National Organization of Italian-American Women Scholarships *(All/Scholarship)* [6425]

National Pathfinder Scholarships *(Graduate, Master's, Undergraduate/Scholarship)* [6287]

National Poultry and Food Distributors Association Scholarships *(Undergraduate/Scholarship)* [6444]

National Preservation Institute Scholarships *(All/Scholarship)* [6446]

National Recreation and Park Association Diversity Scholarships *(Undergraduate/Scholarship)* [6459]

National Sculpture Society Scholarships *(Undergraduate/Scholarship)* [6470]

National Security Technology Engineering and Science Scholarships *(Undergraduate/Scholarship)* [7510]

National Sheriffs' Association Scholarship Program *(Graduate, Undergraduate/Scholarship)* [6474]

National Slovak Society of the USA Scholarships *(Undergraduate, Vocational/Occupational/Scholarship)* [6478]

National Slovak Society of the USA Senior Scholarships *(Undergraduate, Vocational/Occupational/Scholarship)* [6479]

National Society of Accountants Scholarship Program *(Undergraduate/Scholarship)* [6481]

National Space Biomedical Research Institute Postdoctoral Fellowships *(Postdoctorate/Fellowship)* [6521]

National Swimming Pool Foundation Board of Directors' Scholarship Awards *(Professional development/Scholarship)* [6539]

National Swimming Pool Foundation Scholarship Awards *(Professional development/Scholarship)* [6540]

National Technical Honor Society Scholarships *(Undergraduate/Scholarship)* [3710]

National Women's Studies Association Lesbian Caucus Scholarships *(Doctorate, Graduate/Scholarship)* [6560]

Native American Community Scholars Awards *(Graduate/Award)* [8243]

Native American Education Grants *(Graduate, Undergraduate/Grant)* [821]

Native American Leadership Education Scholarships (NALE) *(Postdoctorate, Undergraduate/Scholarship)* [2663]

Native American Visiting Student Awards *(Graduate/Award)* [8244]

Native Hawaiian Chamber of Commerce Scholarships *(Graduate, Undergraduate/Scholarship)* [5219]

Native Hawaiian Visual Arts Scholarships *(Graduate, Undergraduate/Scholarship)* [5220]

Naval Helicopter Association Scholarships *(Graduate, Undergraduate/Scholarship)* [6575]

Naval Weather Service Association Scholarships *(High School, Undergraduate/Scholarship)* [6583]

Navy, Army or Air Force ROTC Scholarship Program *(Undergraduate/Scholarship)* [3329]

NBMBAA Graduate Scholarships Program *(Graduate/Scholarship)* [6152]

NBMBAA PhD Fellowship Program *(Doctorate/Fellowship)* [6153]

N.C. Psychoanalytic Foundation Journalism Scholarships *(Graduate, Postgraduate/Scholarship)* [9297]

NCAEA Scholarships *(Graduate/Scholarship)* [6746]

NCCPAP and AICPA Scholarships for Graduating High School Seniors *(Undergraduate/Scholarship)* [6206]

NCECA Graduate Student Fellowships *(Graduate/Fellowship)* [6213]

NCF Fort Dodge Animal Health Legacy Scholarships for Undergraduate Students *(Undergraduate/Scholarship)* [6177]

NCF Fort Dodge Animal Health Legacy Scholarships for Veterinary Students *(Undergraduate/Scholarship)* [6178]

NCTE Research Foundation Grants *(Professional development/Grant)* [6218]

NDIA Picatinny Chapter Scholarships *(Undergraduate/Scholarship)* [6237]

NDSEG Fellowships *(Graduate/Fellowship)* [6239]

H.N. Neal Memorial Scholarships *(Undergraduate/Scholarship)* [2338]

Nebraska Farm Bureau Young Farmers and Ranchers Greater Horizon Scholarships *(Undergraduate/Scholarship)* [6599]

Nebraska Hospital Association Tuition Aid and Scholarships *(Undergraduate/Scholarship)* [6606]

Nebraska Paralegal Association Student Scholarships *(Undergraduate/Scholarship)* [6610]

J.W. "Bill" Neese Scholarships *(Undergraduate/Scholarship)* [4900]

NEH Fellowships for Senior Scholars *(Doctorate/Fellowship)* [2695]

Paul and Ruth Neidhold Business Scholarships *(Undergraduate/Scholarship)* [3161]

Edward J. Nell Memorial Scholarships in Journalism *(Undergraduate/Scholarship)* [7563]

Dave Nelsen Scholarships *(Undergraduate/Scholarship)* [6097]

Midwest Chapter Scholarships - Don Nelson *(Undergraduate/Scholarship)* [1813]

Bill Nelson Scholarship Endowment *(Graduate, Undergraduate/Scholarship)* [7004]

NEMLA Book Prize *(Professional development/Prize)* [6798]

NEMLA Summer Fellowships *(Graduate, Professional development/Fellowship)* [6799]

NEMRA Educational Scholarship Foundation *(Undergraduate, Vocational/Occupational/Scholarship)* [6267]

Nephrology Nurse Researcher Awards *(Doctorate, Graduate/Award)* [945]

NERRS Graduate Research Fellowships (GRF) *(Graduate, Master's/Fellowship)* [6271]

Amelia and Emanuel Nessell Scholarships *(Undergraduate/Scholarship)* [3540]

Netherlands-Florida Scholarship Foundation Scholarships *(Doctorate, Graduate/Scholarship)* [6615]

Reverend John S. Nettled Scholarships *(Undergraduate/Scholarship)* [3045]

Elizabeth Neuffer Fellowships *(Professional development/Fellowship)* [5030]

Nevada Black Police Association Scholarships *(Undergraduate/Scholarship)* [7511]

Nevada Parent Teacher Association Scholarships *(Undergraduate/Scholarship)* [7512]

New Century Scholars Doctoral Scholarships *(Postdoctorate/Scholarship)* [1387]

New Century Scholars Research Grants *(Doctorate/Grant)* [1388]

New England FEMARA Scholarships *(Undergraduate/Scholarship)* [1096]

New Hampshire Snowmobile Association Scholarships *(Undergraduate, Vocational/Occupational/Scholarship)* [6633]

New Jersey Association of Osteopathic Physicians and Surgeons Scholarships *(Undergraduate/Scholarship)* [6637]

New Mexico Manufactured Housing Association Scholarship Program *(Undergraduate/Scholarship)* [281]

New York State Senate - Legislative Fellowships *(Graduate, Postgraduate/Fellowship)* [6678]

New York Water Environment Association Scholarships *(Undergraduate/Scholarship)* [6688]

New York Women in Communications, Inc. Foundation Scholarships *(Graduate, Undergraduate/Scholarship)* [6690]

Ted and Ruth Neward Scholarships *(Graduate, Undergraduate/Scholarship)* [8453]

Newberry Consortium on American Indian Studies Faculty Fellowships *(Professional development/Fellowship)* [6701]

Newberry Consortium on American Indian Studies Graduate Student Fellowships *(Doctorate/Fellowship)* [6702]

Newberry Library ACM/GLCA Faculty Fellowships *(Professional development/Fellowship)* [6703]

Newberry Library Short-Term Fellowships in the History of Cartography *(Doctorate/Fellowship)* [6706]

Newberry Library Short-Term Resident Fellowships for Individual Research *(Postdoctorate/Fellowship)* [6707]

The Shanon Newberry Physical Therapy Scholarship Endowment *(Doctorate/Scholarship)* [8741]

Charlotte W. Newcombe Doctoral Dissertation Fellowships *(Doctorate/Fellowship)* [9618]

Newcomer Supply Student Scholarships *(Undergraduate/Scholarship)* [6514]

AAJA/S.I. Newhouse Foundation Scholarships *(Graduate, Undergraduate/Scholarship)* [1642]

Frank Newman Leadership Awards *(Undergraduate/Scholarship)* [2350]

Edsel Newman Scholarships *(Undergraduate/Scholarship)* [5476]

Newman University Scouting Scholarships *(Undergraduate/Scholarship)* [6260]

Jerry Newson Scholarships *(Undergraduate/Scholarship)* [3128]

Alwin B. Newton Scholarships *(Undergraduate/Scholarship)* [1268]

Newtonville Woman's Club Scholarships *(Undergraduate/Scholarship)* [4079]

NFBPA/CDM Scholarships *(Graduate, Undergraduate/Scholarship)* [6296]

NFDA Professional Women's Conference Scholarships *(Undergraduate/Scholarship)* [4031]

NFPA/PACE Scholarships *(Professional development/Scholarship)* [6284]

NFPA and Thomson West Scholarships *(Undergraduate/Scholarship)* [6285]

NFPA Youth Scholarships *(Undergraduate, Vocational/Occupational/Scholarship)* [6299]

NGAT Educational Scholarships *(Graduate, Undergraduate/Scholarship)* [6313]

NGC College Scholarships *(Graduate, Undergraduate/Scholarship)* [6303]

NHAEOP Member Scholarships *(Undergraduate/Scholarship)* [6626]

NHFA Scholarships *(Graduate/Scholarship)* [6340]

NHLBI Individual Pre-Doctoral Fellowships *(Doctorate, Graduate/Fellowship)* [6315]

NHS National Scholarships *(Undergraduate/Scholarship)* [6342]

NHSCPA Scholarships *(Graduate, Undergraduate/Scholarship)* [6635]

NIAF Scholarships - General Category I *(Undergraduate/Scholarship)* [6369]

NIAF Scholarships - General Category II *(Undergraduate/Scholarship)* [6370]

NIBA Presidential Scholarships *(Undergraduate/Scholarship)* [6351]

Donald E. Nichols Scholarships *(Undergraduate/Scholarship)* [1269]

Midwest Chapter Scholarships - Mel Nickel *(Undergraduate/Scholarship)* [1814]

"Nickels for Notes" Scholarships *(Undergraduate/Scholarship)* [4080]

Herbert W. Nickens Medical Student Scholarships *(Undergraduate/Scholarship)* [1701]

Virginia Nicklas Scholarships *(Undergraduate/Scholarship)* [3382]

George A. Nielsen Public Investor Scholarships *(Graduate, Undergraduate/Scholarship)* [4200]

Mike Niemeyer Memorial Football Scholarships *(Undergraduate/Scholarship)* [7679]

Helen W. Nies Memorial Scholarships *(Undergraduate/Scholarship)* [3718]

NIJ Visiting Fellowships *(Professional development/Fellowship)* [6356]

Evelyn S. Nish Scholarships *(Undergraduate/Scholarship)* [8180]

Nissan North America, Inc. Scholarships *(Undergraduate/Scholarship)* [809]

Nixon Family Scholarship Fund *(Undergraduate/Scholarship)* [9556]

CSF Corwin Nixon Scholarships *(Undergraduate/Scholarship)* [2857]

Louise A. Nixon Scholarships *(Graduate/Scholarship)* [6608]

NJLA Scholarships *(Graduate, Postgraduate/Scholarship)* [6646]

NJSA Visionary Leader Scholarships *(Graduate/Scholarship)* [6381]

NJSCPA High School Scholarships *(Undergraduate/Scholarship)* [6658]

NLBRA/Wrangler Academic Scholarships *(Undergraduate/Scholarship)* [6398]

NLM Associate Fellowships *(Graduate, Postgraduate/Fellowship)* [6396]

NMCRS Gold Star Scholarship Program *(Undergraduate, Vocational/Occupational/Scholarship)* [6593]

NMIA Scholarship Program *(Undergraduate/Scholarship)* [6415]

NMSC College and University Sponsorship of Merit Scholarship Awards *(Undergraduate/Scholarship)* [6406]

NMSC Corporate-Sponsored Achievement Scholarship Awards *(Undergraduate/Scholarship)* [6407]

NMSC National Achievement Scholarship Program *(Undergraduate/Scholarship)* [6408]

NMSC Special Scholarships *(Undergraduate/Scholarship)* [6409]

NNF Scholarship Program *(Graduate, Undergraduate/Scholarship)* [520]

NOAA Graduate Sciences Scholarships *(Graduate/Scholarship)* [6418]

NOAA Undergraduate Scholarships *(Undergraduate/Scholarship)* [6419]

NOBCChE Procter and Gamble Fellowships *(Graduate/Fellowship)* [6430]

Leonard Noble Educational Scholarships *(Postgraduate/Scholarship)* [6515]

Charles S. Noble Scholarships for Study at Harvard *(Undergraduate/Scholarship)* [258]

Stuart L. Noderer Memorial Scholarships *(Undergraduate/Scholarship)* [7949]

George H. Nofer Scholarships for Law and Public Policy *(Doctorate, Graduate/Scholarship)* [2049]

Alfred H. Nolle Scholarships *(Undergraduate/Scholarship)* [344]

Helen Woodruff Nolop Scholarships in Audiology and Allied Fields *(Graduate/Scholarship)* [3419]

Non Commissioned Officers Association Scholarships *(Undergraduate/Scholarship)* [6726]

Nonproliferation Graduate Fellowships Program (NGFP) *(Graduate/Fellowship)* [7033]

Nor' Easters Scholarships - Four-year Program *(Undergraduate/Scholarship)* [6732]

Nor' Easters Scholarships - Two-year Program *(Undergraduate/Scholarship)* [6733]

Norall Scholarship Trust *(Undergraduate/Scholarship)* [5477]

Arthur L. Norberg Travel Grants *(All/Grant)* [1991]

Marian Norby Scholarships *(Professional development/Scholarship)* [8495]

Nordic Ski Association of Anchorage Scholarships *(Undergraduate/Scholarship)* [197]

Norfolk Southern Foundation Scholarships *(Undergraduate/Scholarship)* [1131]

North Alabama Dietetic Association Scholarships *(Graduate, Undergraduate/Scholarship)* [169]

North American Conference on British Studies Dissertation Year Fellowships *(Doctorate, Postdoctorate/Fellowship)* [6735]

North American Conference on British Studies-Huntington Library Fellowships *(Doctorate, Postdoctorate/Fellowship)* [6736]

North American Rolex Scholarships *(Professional development, Undergraduate/Scholarship)* [7002]

North Carolina Commercial Flower Growers Association Floriculture Scholarships *(Graduate, Undergraduate/Scholarship)* [6757]

North Carolina Council of Epsilon Sigma Alpha Scholarships *(Graduate, Professional develop-

Scholarship Awards (Undergraduate/Scholarship) [849]

Ellis R. Ott Scholarships (Graduate, Master's/Scholarship) [1321]

Ottawa Police 150th Anniversary Scholarships (Undergraduate/Scholarship) [2168]

Outlaw Student's Medical Professions Scholarships (Undergraduate/Scholarship) [8752]

Outlaw Student's Minority Scholarships (Undergraduate/Scholarship) [8753]

Outlaw Student's Nursing School Scholarships (Undergraduate/Scholarship) [8754]

Outlaw Student's Teacher Scholarships (Undergraduate/Scholarship) [8755]

Outstanding Undergraduate Scholarships, Student Organization for Alumni Relations (SOAR) (Undergraduate/Scholarship) [9217]

Outward Bound Leadership Scholarships for Educators (Professional development/Scholarship) [7009]

Outward Bound Wilderness Leadership Awards for Youth (High School, Professional development/Award) [7010]

Helene M. Overly Memorial Scholarships (Undergraduate/Scholarship) [9741]

Overseas Press Club Foundation Harper's Magazine Scholarships (Graduate, Undergraduate/Scholarship) [7016]

Overseas Press Club Foundation Reuters Scholarships (Graduate, Undergraduate/Scholarship) [7017]

Charles and Melva T. Owen Memorial Scholarships (Undergraduate/Scholarship) [6280]

Ozarks Division Scholarships (Undergraduate/Scholarship) [5863]

PABA Foundation Community Service Scholarships (Graduate, Undergraduate/Scholarship) [7308]

The Pac-10 Postgraduate Scholarships (Graduate/Scholarship) [7027]

PACE/Columbian Lawyers Association of Westchester County Endowed Scholarships (Undergraduate/Scholarship) [3010]

Pacific Legal Foundation Faculty Grants (All/Grant) [7031]

The Arthur J. Packard Memorial Scholarship Competition (Undergraduate/Scholarship) [801]

Dr. Nicholas Padis Memorial Graduate Scholarships (Graduate/Scholarship) [4517]

Casilda Pagan Educational/Vocational Scholarships (Graduate, Undergraduate/Scholarship) [4608]

Laurie Page-Peck Scholarship Fund (Undergraduate/Scholarship) [1914]

Raymond E. Page Scholarships (Undergraduate/Scholarship) [1286]

AFCEA General Emmett Paige Scholarships (Undergraduate/Scholarship) [1562]

Ben Palacio Scholarships (Undergraduate/Scholarship) [9058]

Paleontological Society Student Research Grants (Graduate, Undergraduate/Grant) [7]

Robert R. Palmer Research Travel Fellowships (Professional development/Fellowship) [1234]

PAMA Foundation Scholarship Program (Graduate, Undergraduate/Scholarship) [7437]

Pan-Macedonian National Scholarships (Undergraduate/Scholarship) [7039]

The PanHellenic Scholarships (Undergraduate/Scholarship) [7041]

ACI Charles Pankow Foundation ACI Student Fellowships (Graduate, Undergraduate/Fellowship) [637]

Katharine Pantzer Fellowships in the British Book Trades (Professional development/Fellowship) [2085]

Paper Stock Industries Chapter of ISRI Scholarship Program (Undergraduate/Scholarship) [7047]

Paper Stock Industries/RRF Scholarships (Undergraduate/Scholarship) [7045]

Parapsychological Association Research Endowments (All/Grant) [7049]

Joseph M. Parish Memorial Grants (Undergraduate/Scholarship) [1192]

William Park Woodside Founder's Scholarships (Undergraduate/Scholarship) [5694]

Cissy McDaniel Parker Scholarships (Undergraduate/Scholarship) [3384]

E.U. Parker Scholarships (Undergraduate/Scholarship) [6281]

Parking Industry Institute Scholarship Program (Undergraduate/Scholarship) [6436]

Parkinson's Disease Foundation International Research Grants Program (Postdoctorate/Grant) [7128]

PARMA Scholarships (Undergraduate/Scholarship) [7460]

The Paros-Digiquartz Scholarships (Graduate, Undergraduate/Scholarship) [5643]

William E. Parrish Scholarships (Graduate, Master's/Scholarship) [7242]

Carl Parsell Scholarship Fund (Undergraduate/Scholarship) [5810]

Elizabeth M. and Winchell M. Parson Scholarships (Doctorate/Scholarship) [1661]

Partnership for Pediatric Epilepsy Research (Doctorate/Grant) [3667]

Pathways to Success Scholarships (Undergraduate/Scholarship) [3954]

James H. Patrenos Memorial Scholarships (Undergraduate/Scholarship) [8220]

Gail Patrick Charitable Trust Scholarships (Undergraduate/Scholarship) [3420]

Marvin R. and Pearl E. Patterson Family Scholarships Fund (Undergraduate/Scholarship) [4232]

Walter S. Patterson Scholarships (All/Scholarship) [2183]

Joanne Holbrook Patton Military Spouse Scholarships (Graduate, Undergraduate/Scholarship) [6411]

Joanne Holbrook Patton Military Spouse Scholarships for Spouses of the Fallen (Graduate, Undergraduate/Scholarship) [6412]

Joanne Holbrook Patton Military Spouse Scholarships for Spouses of the Wounded (Graduate, Undergraduate/Scholarship) [6413]

Paul and Inger Friend 4-H Scholarships (Undergraduate/Scholarship) [8731]

Ray, NORP and Katie, WOKTE Pautz Scholarships (Undergraduate/Scholarship) [1098]

Kenyon T. Payne Outstanding Student Awards (Undergraduate/Award) [5838]

PB Rail Engineering Scholarships (Undergraduate/Scholarship) [1132]

PDC Scholarships (Undergraduate/Scholarship) [1351]

Chuck Peacock Memorial Scholarships (Undergraduate/Scholarship) [137]

Charles S. Pearce Scholarships (Undergraduate/Prize, Scholarship) [9365]

Scott Pearlman Field Awards for Science and Exploration (Professional development/Award) [3698]

Pearman Family Scholarships (Undergraduate/Scholarship) [7950]

Robert L. Peaslee-Detroit Brazing and Soldiering Division Scholarships (Undergraduate/Scholarship) [1442]

Pediatric Endocrinology Nursing Society Academic Education Scholarships (Undergraduate/Scholarship) [7136]

Pediatric Endocrinology Nursing Society Convention Reimbursement Awards (Undergraduate/Award) [7137]

Mario Pedrozzi Scholarships (Graduate, Undergraduate, Vocational/Occupational/Scholarship) [7145]

Peermusic Latin Scholarships (All/Prize, Scholarship) [2160]

Peierls Rising Star Scholarship Program (Undergraduate/Scholarship) [4580]

Pellegrini Scholarships (Graduate, Undergraduate, Vocational/Occupational/Scholarship) [8784]

Adolph Van Pelt Special Fund for Indians Scholarships (Undergraduate/Scholarship) [1696]

Louis Pelzer Memorial Awards (Graduate/Award) [6961]

Margaret Pemberton Scholarships (Undergraduate/Scholarship) [2138]

Robert B. and Dorothy Pence Scholarships (Undergraduate/Scholarship) [8616]

Penn-Bird Family Memorial Scholarships (Undergraduate/Scholarship) [7516]

Penndelphia Scholarship Foundation (Undergraduate, Vocational/Occupational/Scholarship) [7147]

Pennies for Art Scholarships (Undergraduate/Scholarship) [4081]

Pennsboro Alumni Scholarship Fund (Undergraduate/Scholarship) [7101]

Pennsylvania Heartland Unit Scholarships (Undergraduate/Scholarship) [4535]

Pennsylvania Land Surveyors Foundation Scholarships (Undergraduate/Scholarship) [7149]

Pennsylvania Library Association Scholarships for MLS Students (Graduate/Scholarship) [7151]

Pension Real Estate Association Scholarships (Undergraduate/Scholarship) [7163]

P.E.O. Chapter Scholarship Fund (Undergraduate, Vocational/Occupational/Scholarship) [4233]

PEO Educational Loan Funds (Graduate, Undergraduate, Vocational/Occupational/Loan) [7306]

Peoria Area Amateur Radio Club Scholarships (Undergraduate/Scholarship) [1099]

Pepsi Scholarships (Undergraduate/Scholarship) [802]

Pepsi Wood County Technical/Caperton Center Scholarship Fund (Undergraduate/Scholarship) [7102]

Pepsico Scholarships (Undergraduate/Scholarship) [9066]

Joe Perdue Scholarships (Undergraduate/Scholarship) [2913]

Joaquin Pereira Memorial Scholarships (Undergraduate/Scholarship) [5549]

Rudy Perez Songwriting Scholarships (Undergraduate/Scholarship) [1214]

The A.W. Perigard Fund (Graduate, Undergraduate/Scholarship) [8487]

Sanky Perlowin Memorial Scholarships (Undergraduate/Scholarship) [3453]

Zoe Gore Perrin Scholarships (Undergraduate/Scholarship) [3385]

Chet and Jannett Perry Scholarships (Undergraduate/Scholarship) [8617]

Perry Township School Memorial Scholarship Fund (Undergraduate/Scholarship) [8695]

Jim Perry Vocational Scholarships (Undergraduate, Vocational/Occupational/Scholarship) [737]

Leonard M. Perryman Communications Scholarships for Ethnic Minority Students (Undergraduate/Scholarship) [9013]

Persian Language Study in Tehran Scholarships (Doctorate, Graduate/Fellowship) [856]

Dr. Connell Persico Scholarships (Undergraduate/Scholarship) [7865]

Gilberto and Lennetta Pesquera Medical School Scholarships (Graduate/Scholarship) [4163]

Peter Buck Fellowships Program - Graduate (Graduate/Fellowship) [8263]

Peter Buck Fellowships Program - Postdoctoral (Postdoctorate/Fellowship) [8264]

Peter R. Weitz Prize (Professional development/Prize) [4133]

Jerome Peters Family Scholarships (Undergraduate/Scholarship) [5592]

Kate B. and Hall J. Peterson Fellowships (Doctorate/Fellowship) [422]

Lizette Peterson Homer Injury Prevention Grant Awards (Professional development, Undergraduate/Grant) [8426]

Steve Petix Journalism Scholarships (Undergraduate/Scholarship) [7951]

William H. and Lena M. Petree Scholarships (Undergraduate/Scholarship) [9650]

Silvio and Eugenio Petrini Grants (Professional development/Grant) [4389]

Petroleum Packaging Council Scholarships (Undergraduate/Scholarship) [7217]

Pew Latin American Fellows Program in the Biomedical Sciences (Professional development/Fellowship) [7219]

Chuck Pezzano Scholarships (Undergraduate, Vocational/Occupational/Scholarship) [2166]

Pfafftown Jaycees/Lynn Canada Memorial Scholarships (Undergraduate/Scholarship) [9651]

William R. Pfalzgraf Scholarships (Undergraduate/Scholarship) [7103]

Dr. Harry V. Pfautz Memorial Scholarship Fund (Undergraduate/Scholarship) [3955]

Ruth Cook Pfautz Memorial Scholarship Fund (Undergraduate/Scholarship) [3956]

Pfizer Epilepsy Scholarships *(Graduate, Undergraduate/Scholarship)* [7221]

Pfizer Inc. Endowed Scholarships *(Undergraduate/Scholarship)* [5625]

Pfizer Inc. NP Student Scholarships *(Graduate/Scholarship)* [378]

Pfizer Minority Medical Journalism Scholarships *(Postgraduate/Scholarship)* [9298]

Carl H. Pforzheimer, Jr. Research Grants *(Graduate, Professional development/Grant)* [5225]

PGSF-GATF Scholarships *(Graduate, Undergraduate/Scholarship)* [61]

Pharmaceutics Post Doctoral Fellowships *(Postdoctorate/Fellowship)* [7231]

Pharmaceutics Pre Doctoral Fellowships *(Doctorate/Fellowship)* [7232]

Pharmaceutics Research Starter Grants *(Doctorate/Grant)* [7233]

Pharmaceutics Sabbatical Fellowships *(Postdoctorate/Fellowship)* [7234]

Pharmacology/Toxicology Post Doctoral Fellowships *(Postdoctorate/Fellowship)* [7235]

Pharmacology/Toxicology Pre Doctoral Fellowships *(Doctorate/Fellowship)* [7236]

Pharmacology/Toxicology Research Starter Grants *(Doctorate/Grant)* [7237]

Pharmacology/Toxicology Sabbatical Fellowships *(Postdoctorate/Fellowship)* [7238]

Pharmacy Faculty Fellowships in Community Pharmacy Practice *(Postdoctorate/Fellowship)* [762]

Pharmacy Faculty Fellowships in Geriatric Pharmacy/Geriatric Pharmaceutical Science *(Postdoctorate/Fellowship)* [763]

Pharmacy Faculty New Investigator Grants Program *(Doctorate/Grant)* [764]

Pharmacy Student Scholarship Program *(Postdoctorate/Scholarship)* [6060]

Pharmavite LLC NP Doctoral Education Scholarships *(Doctorate/Scholarship)* [379]

PHD ARA Scholarships *(Doctorate, Undergraduate/Scholarship)* [1100]

Marshall Phelps Athletic Memorial Scholarships *(Undergraduate/Scholarship)* [7682]

Phi Alpha Theta Doctoral Scholarships *(Doctorate/Scholarship)* [7243]

Phi Eta Sigma Distinguished Member Scholarships (Graduate or Professional) *(Graduate, Professional development/Scholarship)* [7255]

Phi Eta Sigma Distinguished Member Scholarships (Undergraduate) *(Undergraduate/Scholarship)* [7256]

Phi Eta Sigma Undergraduate Scholarship Awards *(Undergraduate/Scholarship)* [7257]

Phi Kappa Phi Fellowships *(Graduate, Undergraduate/Fellowship)* [7259]

Phi Kappa Sigma Need-Based Scholarships *(Undergraduate/Scholarship)* [7261]

Phi Kappa Sigma Participation-Based Scholarships *(Undergraduate/Scholarship)* [7262]

Phi Sigma Epsilon Past National President Scholarships *(Graduate, Undergraduate/Scholarship)* [7271]

Phi Upsilon Omicron Candle Fellowships *(Graduate/Fellowship)* [7292]

Phi Upsilon Omicron Challenge Scholarships *(Undergraduate/Scholarship)* [7293]

Phi Upsilon Omicron Diamond Anniversary Fellowships *(Graduate/Fellowship)* [7294]

Phi Upsilon Omicron Founders Fellowships *(Graduate/Fellowship)* [7295]

Phi Upsilon Omicron Golden Anniversary Scholarships *(Undergraduate/Scholarship)* [7296]

Phi Upsilon Omicron Past Presidents Scholarships *(Undergraduate/Scholarship)* [7297]

Phi Upsilon Omicron Presidents Research Fellowships *(Graduate/Fellowship)* [7298]

Catherine E. Philbin Scholarships *(Graduate, Undergraduate/Scholarship)* [4082]

Philip Morris USA Scholarships *(Undergraduate/Scholarship)* [9067]

Phillips Fund Grants for Native American Research *(Graduate/Grant)* [994]

CSF Charles and Claire Phillips Scholarships *(Undergraduate/Scholarship)* [2858]

William Philpott Scholarships *(All/Scholarship)* [2098]

Ed Phinney Commemorative Scholarships *(Graduate, Undergraduate/Scholarship)* [613]

Howard and Mildred Phoenix Scholarships *(Undergraduate/Scholarship)* [7683]

The Physical Therapy Faculty Scholarship Endowment *(Graduate/Scholarship)* [8742]

Pi Gamma Mu Scholarships *(Graduate/Scholarship)* [7330]

Thomas R. Pickering Graduate Foreign Affairs Fellowships *(Graduate/Fellowship)* [9619]

Mary Pickford Scholarships *(Graduate/Scholarship)* [1831]

Peter L. Picknelly Honorary Scholarships *(Undergraduate/Scholarship)* [592]

Ronald C. and Joyce Pierce Scholarships *(Undergraduate/Scholarship)* [1443]

Herschel Pifer Memorial Scholarships *(Undergraduate/Scholarship)* [7104]

William Pigott Memorial Scholarships *(Undergraduate/Scholarship)* [3164]

David Pilon Scholarships for Training in Professional Psychology *(Doctorate, Graduate/Scholarship)* [1035]

John Pine Memorial Scholarships *(Doctorate/Scholarship)* [7244]

Julia T. Pingree Student Scholarships *(Undergraduate/Scholarship)* [6627]

Pioneer Hi-Bred International Graduate Student Fellowships *(Graduate/Fellowship)* [3654]

Stephen D. Pisinski Memorial Scholarships *(Undergraduate/Scholarship)* [7539]

Christopher Pitkin Memorial Scholarships *(Undergraduate, Vocational/Occupational/Scholarship)* [6332]

Day Pitney LLP Scholarships *(Undergraduate/Scholarship)* [4456]

Peter George Pitsakis Memorial Scholarships *(Undergraduate/Scholarship)* [4518]

Pitsco/Hearlihy/FTE Grants *(Professional development/Grant)* [5014]

Pitsenbarger Awards *(Undergraduate/Scholarship)* [93]

Robert Pittman Scholarships *(Undergraduate/Scholarship)* [9299]

PKD Foundation Fellowships *(Doctorate, Graduate/Fellowship)* [7335]

Al Plamann Legacy Scholarships *(Undergraduate/Scholarship)* [2253]

TFC Edward A. Plank, Jr. Memorial Scholarships *(Undergraduate/Scholarship)* [3063]

Betsy Plank/PRSSA Scholarships *(Undergraduate/Scholarship)* [7540]

Plastics Pioneers Association Scholarships *(Graduate, Undergraduate/Scholarship)* [8454]

Katherine Barton Platt Excavation Fellowships *(Professional development, Undergraduate/Fellowship)* [1178]

Platt Family Scholarship Prize Essay Contest *(Graduate, Undergraduate/Prize, Scholarship)* [5503]

Pleasant Hawaiian Holidays Scholarships *(Undergraduate/Scholarship)* [1369]

Pleasantview Public Schools Fund *(Undergraduate/Scholarship)* [4261]

PLSCA Scholarships *(Undergraduate/Scholarship)* [5505]

Harold and Harriet Plum Memorial Scholarships *(Undergraduate/Scholarship)* [2320]

Plumbing-Heating-Cooling Contractors Association Educational Foundation Massachusetts Auxiliary Scholarships *(Undergraduate/Scholarship)* [7346]

Plumbing-Heating-Cooling Contractors Association Educational Foundation Need-Based Scholarships *(Undergraduate/Scholarship)* [7347]

Plumbing-Heating-Cooling Contractors Association Educational Foundation Scholarships *(Undergraduate/Scholarship)* [7348]

David Pohl Scholarships *(Graduate, Master's/Scholarship)* [8998]

Point Foundation Scholarships *(Graduate, Postgraduate, Undergraduate/Scholarship)* [7866]

Daniel H. Pokorny Memorial Scholarship Awards *(Undergraduate/Scholarship)* [7728]

Pokross/Curhan Family Fund Prize *(Graduate, Undergraduate/Prize)* [888]

Police Explorer Scholarships Program *(Undergraduate/Scholarship)* [3844]

Polish American Club of North Jersey Scholarships *(Graduate, Undergraduate/Scholarship)* [5300]

Polish National Alliance of Brooklyn, USA Scholarships *(Undergraduate/Scholarship)* [5301]

Political Leadership Scholarships *(Undergraduate/Scholarship)* [7415]

Political Studies Scholarships *(Undergraduate, Graduate/Scholarship)* [9447]

Roy H. Pollack Scholarships *(Graduate, Master's/Scholarship)* [8999]

Stan and Leone Pollard Scholarships *(Undergraduate/Scholarship)* [1370]

CSF George and Amy Polley Scholarships *(Undergraduate/Scholarship)* [2859]

Harvey M. Pollicove Memorial Scholarships *(Undergraduate/Scholarship)* [6913]

Justice Stewart G. Pollock Fellowships *(All/Fellowship)* [5931]

The Sidney M. Pols Scholarships *(Undergraduate/Scholarship)* [7142]

Harold F. Polston Scholarships *(Graduate, Undergraduate/Scholarship)* [1352]

Polymer Modifiers and Additives Division Scholarships *(Graduate, Undergraduate/Scholarship)* [8455]

Henry Belin du Pont Dissertation Fellowships *(Doctorate, Graduate/Fellowship)* [4364]

Henry Belin du Pont Fellowships *(Graduate/Fellowship)* [4365]

Buster Pool Memorial Scholarships *(Undergraduate/Scholarship)* [3130]

Jim Poore Memorial Scholarships *(Undergraduate/Scholarship)* [4672]

Port with No Borders Scholarships *(Undergraduate/Scholarship)* [7953]

Portable Sanitation Association International Scholarship Fund *(Undergraduate/Scholarship)* [7375]

Porter Physiology Development Fellowship Awards *(Doctorate/Fellowship)* [1005]

Thomas W. Porter, W8KYZ Scholarships Honoring Michael Daugherty, W8LSE *(Undergraduate/Scholarship)* [1101]

Gail Porterfield Memorial Scholarships *(Undergraduate/Scholarship)* [7684]

Portland Area Business Association Scholarships *(Undergraduate/Scholarship)* [3681]

Portuguese American Police Association Scholarships *(Undergraduate/Scholarship)* [7380]

Portuguese-American Scholarship Foundation *(Undergraduate/Scholarship)* [7378]

Post-doctoral Residential Research and Teaching Fellowships *(Postdoctorate/Fellowship)* [9743]

Post-Doctoral or Sabbatical Fellowships *(Doctorate/Fellowship)* [9248]

Post-Doctoral Tikvah Scholarships *(Postdoctorate/Scholarship)* [8906]

Postdoctoral Fellowships *(Postdoctorate/Fellowship)* [4781]

Postdoctoral Research Fellowships *(Postdoctorate/Award)* [906]

Poteet Strawberry Festival Association Scholarships *(Graduate, Undergraduate/Scholarship)* [7382]

Terry Linda Potter Scholarship Fund *(Undergraduate/Scholarship)* [4234]

Erwin Potts Scholarships *(Undergraduate/Scholarship)* [9300]

George V. Powell Diversity Scholarships *(Undergraduate/Scholarship)* [5339]

Gerald Powell Scholarships *(Undergraduate/Scholarship)* [3046]

The Power to Continue Learning Scholarships *(Undergraduate, Vocational/Occupational/Scholarship)* [7685]

Susan Kelly Power and Helen Hornbeck Tanner Fellowships *(Doctorate, Postdoctorate/Fellowship)* [6708]

Master Sergeant Neal E. Powers Memorial Scholarships *(Undergraduate/Scholarship)* [100]

Practising Law Institute Law Student Scholarships *(Undergraduate/Scholarship)* [7384]

Lou and Carole Prato Sports Reporting Scholarships *(Undergraduate/Scholarship)* [7580]

Praxair International Scholarships *(Undergraduate/Scholarship)* [1444]

Pre-doctoral Residential Research Fellowships *(Doctorate/Fellowship)* [9744]

Presbyterian Association of Musicians Scholarships *(All/Scholarship)* [7386]

Prescott Fine Arts Association Scholarship Program *(Undergraduate/Scholarship)* [7390]

Presidents Scholarships *(Undergraduate/Scholarship)* [4807]

Prevent Cancer Foundation Fellowships *(Doctorate, Graduate/Fellowship)* [7394]

Jim and Dee Price Scholarships *(Undergraduate/Scholarship)* [4262]

Judith McManus Price Scholarships *(Graduate, Undergraduate/Scholarship)* [1012]

Rae L. Price Scholarships *(Undergraduate/Scholarship)* [1287]

Pride Foundation Regional Scholarships *(Undergraduate/Scholarship)* [7416]

Pride Foundation Scholarships *(Undergraduate/Scholarship)* [7867]

Pride of the Rose Scholarship Fund *(Undergraduate/Scholarship)* [3682]

Lendon N. Pridgen, GlaxoSmithKline - NOBCChE Fellowships *(Graduate/Fellowship)* [6431]

Josef Princ Memorial Scholarships *(Undergraduate/Scholarship)* [7517]

R.M. Princ Scholarships *(Undergraduate/Scholarship)* [7518]

Graduate Fellowship Program - GRC/John L. Prince Fellowships (GFP) *(Graduate/Fellowship)* [8082]

Prince Henry Society Scholarships *(Undergraduate/Scholarship)* [7433]

Prins Foundation Fellowship for Senior Scholars *(Doctorate/Fellowship)* [2696]

Prins Foundation Post-Doctoral and Early Career Fellowship for Emigrating Scholars *(Professional development, Postdoctorate/Fellowship)* [2697]

Print Graphics Scholarship Foundation (PGSF) *(Graduate, Undergraduate/Fellowship, Scholarship)* [7435]

Private High School Awards *(Undergraduate/Award)* [1512]

Miguel Pro Scholarships *(Undergraduate/Scholarship)* [9774]

Procter and Gamble Complex PE Scholars Grant *(Undergraduate/Award)* [971]

Procter & Gamble Professional Oral Health/HDA Foundation Scholarships *(Undergraduate/Scholarship)* [4556]

Producers Academy Scholarships *(All/Scholarship)* [3264]

Professional Association Leadership Alumni Scholarships (PAL) *(Graduate/Scholarship)* [8805]

Professional Women in Pest Management Scholarships (PWIPM) *(Graduate, Professional development/Scholarship)* [6438]

Progress Lane Scholarships *(Undergraduate/Scholarship)* [3064]

Progressive Dairy Producer Awards *(All/Grant)* [6233]

Project Red Flag Academic Scholarships for Women with Bleeding Disorders *(Undergraduate/Scholarship)* [6333]

Project10 - Models of Excellence Scholarships *(Undergraduate/Scholarship)* [7448]

Property and Environment Research Center Graduate Fellowships *(Graduate/Fellowship)* [7452]

Property and Environment Research Center Lone Mountain Fellowships *(Professional development/Fellowship)* [7453]

Property and Environment Research Center Media Fellowships *(Professional development/Fellowship)* [7454]

Prospective Secondary Teacher Course Work Scholarships *(Postgraduate/Scholarship)* [6222]

Barbara F. Prowant Nursing Research Grants *(Graduate/Grant)* [946]

ProWorld Study Abroad Scholarships *(Undergraduate/Scholarship)* [4178]

PRSSA Multicultural Affairs Scholarships *(Undergraduate/Scholarship)* [7541]

Neil Pruitt, Sr. Memorial Scholarships *(Undergraduate/Scholarship)* [6201]

Pryor Graduate Fellowships *(Graduate/Fellowship)* [345]

Cheryl White Pryor Memorial Scholarships *(Undergraduate/Scholarship)* [3386]

The PSSC Legacy Fund *(Graduate, Undergraduate/Scholarship)* [8488]

Public Agency Training Council Criminal Justice Scholarships *(Undergraduate/Scholarship)* [358]

Public Employee Retirement Research and Administration Scholarships *(Graduate/Scholarship)* [4201]

Public Interest Environmental Law Fellowships *(Postgraduate/Fellowship)* [3656]

Public Service International Law Fellowships *(All/Fellowship)* [7607]

Duane V. Puerde Memorial Scholarships *(Undergraduate, Vocational/Occupational/Scholarship)* [3065]

Puget Sound LGBT Leadership Scholarships Fund *(Undergraduate/Scholarship)* [7868]

Eugene C. Pulliam Fellowships for Editorial Writing *(Professional development/Fellowship)* [8149]

Pulliam/Kilgore Freedom of Information Internships *(Undergraduate/Internship)* [8466]

Elizabeth Pusey Scholarships *(Undergraduate/Scholarship)* [3066]

A.O. Putnam Memorial Scholarships *(Undergraduate/Scholarship)* [4808]

The Henley Putnam University Scholarships *(Professional development/Scholarship)* [4874]

Davis Putter Scholarships Fund *(Undergraduate/Scholarship)* [7869]

Harry V. Quadracci Memorial Scholarships *(Undergraduate, Graduate/Scholarship)* [4321]

Quarter Century Wireless Association Scholarships *(Undergraduate/Scholarship)* [7554]

Queer Foundation Effective Writing and Scholarships *(Undergraduate/Prize, Scholarship)* [7560]

Rosa Quezada Memorial Education Scholarships *(Undergraduate/Scholarship)* [3231]

Michael J. Quill Scholarships *(Undergraduate/Scholarship)* [8929]

Salvatore E. Quinci Foundation Scholarships *(Undergraduate, Vocational/Occupational/Scholarship)* [6334]

Bob Quincy Scholarships *(Undergraduate/Scholarship)* [9302]

Chips Quinn Scholarships *(Graduate, Undergraduate/Scholarship)* [7565]

Dr. J. Glenn Radcliffe Memorial Scholarships *(Undergraduate/Scholarship)* [8732]

Marjorie Usher Ragan Scholarships *(Undergraduate/Scholarship)* [9303]

Rain Bird Intelligent Use of Water Scholarships *(Undergraduate/Scholarship)* [5336]

J.J. Rains Memorial Scholarships *(High School/Scholarship)* [2954]

Rainwater Family Scholarships *(Undergraduate/Scholarship)* [6399]

Frederick Rakestraw Law Scholarships *(Graduate/Scholarship)* [6803]

Tom D. Ralls Memorial Scholarships *(Professional development/Scholarship)* [3849]

The NASSCO Jeffrey D. Ralston Memorial Scholarships *(Undergraduate/Scholarship)* [5988]

Rama Scholarships for the American Dream *(Graduate, Undergraduate/Scholarship)* [803]

Guthikonda Ramabrahmam & Balamani *(Graduate/Scholarship)* [8831]

RAMEF Co-Branded Scholarships for High School Seniors *(Undergraduate/Scholarship)* [7747]

Raul Ramirez Memorial Scholarships *(Undergraduate/Scholarship)* [7686]

CSF Marvin Rammelsberg Memorial Scholarships *(Undergraduate/Scholarship)* [2860]

Herbert W. Rand Fellowships and Scholarships *(Undergraduate/Scholarship)* [5626]

Ayn Rand Institute Anthem Essay Contest *(High School, Undergraduate/Prize)* [7592]

Ayn Rand Institute Former Participants' Essay Contest *(High School, Undergraduate/Prize)* [7593]

Ayn Rand Institute Fountainhead Essay Contest *(High School, Undergraduate/Prize)* [7594]

Ayn Rand Institute We the Living Essay Contest *(High School, Undergraduate/Prize)* [7595]

Newell S. Rand Jr. Memorial Scholarships *(Undergraduate/Scholarship)* [7055]

James Randi Educational Foundation Scholarships *(Graduate, Undergraduate/Scholarship)* [7597]

The Jennings Randolph Peace Scholar Dissertation Program *(Doctorate/Scholarship)* [9081]

United States Institute of Peace Jennings Randolph Senior Fellowship Program *(All/Fellowship)* [9082]

Rangel Graduate Fellowships *(Graduate/Fellowship)* [7599]

Jeannette Rankin Scholarships *(Undergraduate, Vocational/Occupational/Scholarship)* [7601]

Rappaport Fellows Program in Law and Public Policy *(All/Fellowship)* [7608]

General John Paul Ratay Educational Grants *(Undergraduate/Grant)* [5876]

Dr. Mark Rathke Family Scholarships *(Undergraduate/Scholarship)* [3542]

Carol A. Ratza Memorial Scholarships *(Undergraduate/Scholarship)* [4329]

Dennis Raveling Scholarships *(Undergraduate/Scholarship)* [2288]

Lenny Ravich "Shalom" Scholarships *(All/Scholarship)* [1706]

Rawley Silver Awards for Excellence *(Graduate/Scholarship)* [428]

Mary C. Rawlins Scholarships *(Undergraduate/Scholarship)* [4458]

William C. Ray, CIH, CSP Arizona Scholarships *(Graduate, Undergraduate/Scholarship)* [1353]

W.B. Ray HS Class of '56 Averill Johnson Scholarships *(Undergraduate/Scholarship)* [2955]

Raytheon Scholarship Program *(Undergraduate/Scholarship)* [7611]

RBPA Scholarships *(All/Scholarship)* [7589]

RCSA Cottrell Scholarships *(Graduate/Scholarship)* [7734]

Ronald Reagan College Leaders Scholarship Program *(Undergraduate/Scholarship)* [7313]

CSF Robert H. Reakirt Foundation Scholarships *(Undergraduate/Scholarship)* [2861]

William Reaser Scholarships *(Undergraduate, Vocational/Occupational/Scholarship)* [7105]

Carl C. and Abbie Rebman Trust Scholarships *(Undergraduate/Scholarship)* [4263]

Rechsteiner Family Scholarship Fund *(Undergraduate/Scholarship)* [3788]

Redlands Area Interfaith Council Scholarships *(Undergraduate/Scholarship)* [7687]

Redlands Community Scholarship Foundation Scholarships *(Undergraduate/Scholarship)* [7688]

Redlands Council PTA - Dorathy Jolley Memorial Scholarships *(Undergraduate/Scholarship)* [7689]

Redlands High School Academic Decathalon Scholarships *(Undergraduate/Scholarship)* [7690]

Redlands High School Boy's Varsity Volleyball Scholarships *(Undergraduate/Scholarship)* [7691]

Redlands High School Drama Boosters Awards *(Undergraduate/Scholarship)* [7692]

Redlands High School Girls' Volleyball Boosters Scholarship Awards *(Undergraduate/Scholarship)* [7693]

Redlands High School Mock Trial Scholarships *(Undergraduate/Scholarship)* [7694]

Redlands High School-PTSA Scholarships *(Undergraduate, Vocational/Occupational/Scholarship)* [7695]

Redlands High School Soccer Boosters Scholarship Awards *(Undergraduate/Scholarship)* [7696]

Redlands High School Softball Booster Scholarship Awards *(Undergraduate/Scholarship)* [7697]

Redlands High School Speech Boosters Scholarship Awards *(Undergraduate/Scholarship)* [7698]

Redlands High School Spiritleaders Scholarships *(Undergraduate/Scholarship)* [7699]

Redlands High School Terrier Band Boosters Club Scholarships *(Undergraduate/Scholarship)* [7700]

Redlands High School Vocal Music Boosters Scholarship Awards *(Undergraduate/Scholarship)* [7701]

Redlands Morning Kiwanis Club Foundation Scholarships *(Undergraduate, Vocational/Occupational/Scholarship)* [7702]

Redlands Noon Kiwanis Club Foundation Scholarships *(Undergraduate/Scholarship)* [7703]

Redlands Noon Kiwanis Club - Martin and Dorothy Munz Scholarships *(Undergraduate/Scholarship)* [7704]

Redlands Rotary Club Foundation Discretionary Scholarships *(Undergraduate/Scholarship)* [7705]

Redlands Teachers Association Scholarships *(Undergraduate/Scholarship)* [7706]

Sarah Rebecca Reed Scholarships *(Graduate/ Scholarship)* [2071]

The Reese Fellowships *(Doctorate/Fellowship)* [423]

Bob Reeve Aviation Management Scholarships *(Undergraduate/Scholarship)* [193]

REFORMA Scholarship Program *(Doctorate, Graduate, Professional development/Scholarship)* [7721]

Dan M. Reichard, Jr. Scholarships *(Graduate, Undergraduate/Scholarship)* [1056]

Reid Hospital Graduate Student Scholarships *(Graduate/Scholarship)* [9557]

Mark A. Reid Memorial Scholarship Grants *(Undergraduate/Scholarship)* [3165]

Henry J. Reilly Memorial Scholarships - For Freshmen in College *(Undergraduate/Scholarship)* [7738]

Henry J. Reilly Memorial Scholarships - For Graduating High School Seniors *(Undergraduate/Scholarship)* [7739]

Henry J. Reilly Memorial Scholarships - For Sophomores and Juniors in College *(Undergraduate/ Scholarship)* [7740]

Henry J. Reilly Memorial Scholarships - Graduate Program *(Graduate, Professional development/ Scholarship)* [7741]

Jacob L. Reinecke Memorial Scholarship Fund *(Undergraduate/Scholarship)* [4235]

George Reinke Scholarships *(Professional development/Scholarship)* [1371]

REMSA Scholarships *(Undergraduate/Scholarship)* [1133]

Betty Rendel Scholarships *(Undergraduate/Scholarship)* [6288]

Don Renschler Scholarships *(Graduate/Scholarship)* [7417]

Bertha and Byron L. Reppert Scholarship Fund *(Undergraduate/Scholarship)* [3957]

Republic Services Environmental Studies Scholarships *(Undergraduate/Scholarship)* [7521]

Research Grants in Speech Science *(Doctorate/ Grant)* [1389]

Reserve Officers Training Corps Scholarships (ROTC) *(Undergraduate/Scholarship)* [9368]

Resistance Welder Manufacturers' Association Scholarships *(Undergraduate/Scholarship)* [1445]

Retail Chapter Scholarship Awards *(Undergraduate/ Scholarship)* [6942]

Retail Packaging Association Scholarships (RPA) *(Undergraduate/Scholarship)* [7751]

Retired League Postmasters Scholarship Program *(Undergraduate/Scholarship)* [7755]

Mike Reynolds Journalism Scholarships *(Undergraduate/Scholarship)* [7581]

RFDF MBA Preparation Fellowships *(Graduate, Undergraduate/Fellowship)* [7800]

RFDF Pre-MBA Fellowships *(Graduate/Fellowship)* [7801]

Rho Chi, AFPE First Year Graduate Fellowships *(Doctorate, Graduate/Fellowship)* [7781]

Rho Chi Society Clinical Research Scholarships *(Postdoctorate/Scholarship)* [7782]

Rhode Island Association of Former Legislators Scholarships *(Undergraduate/Scholarship)* [7793]

Rice-Cullimore Scholarships *(Graduate/Scholarship)* [1662]

Haynes Rice Scholarships *(Doctorate, Graduate, Undergraduate/Scholarship)* [6082]

James Edward "Bill" Richards Scholarships *(Undergraduate/Scholarship)* [3132]

Ellen Swallow Richards Travel Grants *(Graduate, Professional development/Grant)* [1251]

Phillip Guy Richardson Memorial Scholarships *(Undergraduate/Scholarship)* [5103]

J. Milton Richardson Theological Fellowships *(Graduate/Fellowship)* [369]

Frank J. Richter Scholarships *(Graduate, Undergraduate/Scholarship)* [543]

Howard Brown Rickard Scholarships *(Undergraduate/Scholarship)* [6282]

Honorable Joseph H. Ridge Memorial Scholarships *(Undergraduate/Scholarship)* [330]

Jasper Ridge Restoration Fellowships Jasper Ridge Biological Preserve *(Graduate, Postdoctorate/Fellowship)* [3580]

Donald Riebhoff Memorial Scholarships *(Undergraduate/Scholarship)* [1102]

CSF William J. Rielly/MCURC Scholarships *(Undergraduate/Scholarship)* [2862]

Rieser Fellowships *(Undergraduate/Fellowship)* [2209]

Jerrothia Allenfonzo Riggs & Anna & Dorothy Mae Barnes Scholarships *(Undergraduate/Scholarship)* [2339]

Riggs Cove Foundation Scholarships *(Undergraduate/Scholarship)* [4091]

Benjamin Riggs Scholarships *(Undergraduate/ Scholarship)* [4092]

Ameen Rihani Scholarship Program *(Undergraduate/Scholarship)* [1492]

RA Consulting Service/Maria Riley Scholarships *(Graduate, Undergraduate/Scholarship)* [6297]

Susan E. Riley Scholarships *(Undergraduate/Scholarship)* [3387]

John T. Riordan Professional Education Scholarships *(Professional development/Scholarship)* [4909]

Ritchie-Jennings Memorial Scholarships *(Graduate, Undergraduate/Scholarship)* [1738]

Paul H. Rittle Sr. Professional Development Grants *(Professional development/Grant)* [4820]

Thomas and Ruth River International Scholarships *(Undergraduate, Graduate/Scholarship)* [9756]

Riverside Sheriffs Association Member Scholarship Program *(Graduate, Undergraduate/Scholarship)* [7803]

Jean Wiggin Roach Scholarships *(Undergraduate/ Scholarship)* [3388]

Lawrence and Louise Robbins Scholarships *(Undergraduate/Scholarship)* [5593]

Robert J. McNamara Student Paper Awards *(Graduate/Award)* [1875]

Faye Lynn Roberts Educational Scholarships *(Undergraduate/Scholarship)* [8618]

Clifford Roberts Graduate Fellowships *(Doctorate/ Fellowship)* [3614]

Eugene L. Roberts Jr. Prize *(Undergraduate/Prize)* [9304]

Liz Roberts Memorial Scholarships *(Undergraduate/ Scholarship)* [7707]

Smiley Elementary School PTA - Beverly Roberts Memorial Scholarships *(Undergraduate/Scholarship)* [7708]

CSF Mary Roberts Scholarships *(Undergraduate/ Scholarship)* [2863]

Elliott C. Roberts Scholarships *(Graduate/Scholarship)* [4789]

George A. Roberts Scholarships *(Undergraduate/ Scholarship)* [5695]

Thomas Warren Roberts Scholarships *(Undergraduate/Scholarship)* [7107]

Lola Ellis Robertson Scholarships *(Undergraduate/ Scholarship)* [5627]

Robinhood Marine Center Scholarships *(Undergraduate/Scholarship)* [4093]

David G. Robinson Arts Scholarships *(Undergraduate/Scholarship)* [8619]

Samuel Robinson Awards *(Undergraduate/Award)* [7388]

Jackie Robinson Foundation Minority Scholarships *(Undergraduate/Scholarship)* [822]

Helen M. Robinson Grants *(Doctorate/Grant)* [4977]

Jerry Robinson Inweld Corporation Scholarships *(Undergraduate/Scholarship)* [1446]

Claude Robinson Scholarships *(Undergraduate/ Scholarship)* [6382]

Jackie Robinson Scholarships *(Undergraduate/ Scholarship)* [7808]

Nell Bryant Robinson Scholarships *(Undergraduate/ Scholarship)* [7299]

Paul S. Robinson Scholarships *(Undergraduate/ Scholarship)* [8318]

James and Marilyn Rockfeller Scholarships *(Undergraduate/Scholarship)* [5594]

Rockford Area Habitat for Humanity College Scholarships *(Undergraduate/Scholarship)* [3166]

Rockford Chapter Daughters of the American Revolution Memorial Scholarships *(Undergraduate/ Scholarship)* [3167]

Rockin' Christmas Fund Scholarships *(Undergraduate/Scholarship)* [8620]

Rockwell Collins Scholarships *(Undergraduate/ Scholarship)* [138]

Rocky Mountain Coal Mining Institute Engineering/ Geology Scholarships *(Undergraduate/Scholarship)* [7810]

Rocky Mountain Coal Mining Institute Technical Scholarships *(Undergraduate, Vocational/Occupational/Scholarship)* [7811]

Rocky Mountain Research Fellowships *(Graduate/ Fellowship)* [7815]

R.O.E.A. Dumitru Golea Goldy-Gemu Scholarships *(Undergraduate/Scholarship)* [1165]

ROFY Scholarships *(Undergraduate/Scholarship)* [7613]

Kimberly Marie Rogers Memorial Scholarship Fund *(Undergraduate, Vocational/Occupational/Scholarship)* [3789]

Fred Rogers Memorial Scholarships *(Graduate, Undergraduate/Scholarship)* [35]

Joseph Wood Rogers Memorial Scholarships *(Undergraduate/Scholarship)* [8122]

Mary Stuart Rogers Scholarships *(Undergraduate/ Scholarship)* [9606]

Mary Louise Roller Pan-Hellenic Scholarships *(Undergraduate/Scholarship)* [6741]

Rome Prize *(Doctorate, Graduate/Prize)* [400]

Charles and Ruth Ronin Memorial Scholarships *(Undergraduate/Scholarship)* [7709]

Dorothy Worden Ronken Scholarships *(Graduate/ Scholarship)* [3421]

Alice W. Rooke Scholarships *(Undergraduate/Scholarship)* [4459]

Roothbert Fund Scholarships *(Undergraduate/Scholarship)* [7819]

ROP - Rob Bruce Memorial Scholarships *(Undergraduate/Scholarship)* [7710]

Barnes W. Rose, Jr. and Eva Rose Nichol Scholarship Fund *(Undergraduate/Scholarship)* [282]

Carl M. Rose Memorial Scholarship Fund *(Undergraduate/Scholarship)* [7109]

Florence C. Rose and S. Meryl Rose Scholarships *(Undergraduate/Scholarship)* [5628]

Dr. Wayne F. Rose Scholarship Fund *(Undergraduate/Scholarship)* [3790]

David Rose Scholarships *(Undergraduate/Scholarship)* [1215]

Esther Katz Rosen Fellowships *(Graduate/Fellowship)* [1041]

Mandell and Lester Rosenblatt and Robert N. Herbert Undergraduate Scholarships *(Undergraduate/ Scholarship)* [8417]

Barbara Rosenblum Cancer Dissertation Scholarships *(Doctorate, Graduate/Fellowship)* [8520]

ASPH/CDC Allan Rosenfield Global Health Fellowships *(Postdoctorate, Postgraduate/Fellowship)* [1868]

Jean and Tom Rosenthal Scholarship Program *(Undergraduate/Scholarship)* [3204]

Bettsy Ross Educational Fund *(All, Professional development/Scholarship)* [6727]

S. Byrl Ross Memorial Scholarship Fund *(Undergraduate/Scholarship)* [7110]

Dorothy M. Ross Memorial Scholarships *(Undergraduate/Scholarship)* [1948]

The Bea and Harry Ross Scholarship Endowment *(Graduate/Scholarship)* [8743]

Ross Trust Graduate Student Scholarships *(Graduate, Postdoctorate/Scholarship)* [685]

The Rotary Club of Cape Coral Goldcoast Scholarship Fund *(Undergraduate/Scholarship)* [2645]

The Rotary Club of Rancho Bernardo Sunrise Abraxas Student Scholarships *(Undergraduate, Vocational/Occupational/Scholarship)* [7956]

The Rotary Foundation Ambassadorial Scholarships *(Undergraduate/Scholarship)* [7821]

Rotary Public Safety Scholarships *(Undergraduate/ Scholarship)* [3920]

Bernard Rotberg Memorial Scholarships *(Undergraduate/Scholarship)* [5163]

Richard J. Roth Journalism Fellowships *(Graduate/ Fellowship)* [6679]

Isaac Roth Newspaper Carrier Scholarship Program *(Undergraduate/Scholarship)* [6653]

Marjorie Roy Rothermel Scholarships *(Graduate/ Scholarship)* [1663]

Hal Rothman Dissertation Fellowships *(Doctorate/ Fellowship)* [1252]

Theodore Rousseau Fellowships *(Graduate/Fellowship)* [5790]

Marion and Donald Routh Student Research Grants *(Undergraduate/Grant)* [8427]

Roy Rowan Scholarships *(Graduate, Undergraduate/Scholarship)* [7018]

Leo S. Rowe Pan American Fund *(Graduate, Undergraduate/Loan)* [6967]

Ellis W. Rowe Scholarships *(Undergraduate/Scholarship)* [4380]

Royal Palm Audubon Society Environmental Fellowships *(Postgraduate/Fellowship)* [3820]

Lucille and Edward R. Roybal Foundation Public Health Scholarships *(Graduate, Undergraduate/Scholarship)* [7827]

Royce-Osborn Minority Scholarship Program *(Undergraduate/Scholarship)* [8293]

RSDSA Research Grants *(Postdoctorate, Professional development/Grant)* [7719]

RSNA/AAPM Fellowships for Graduate Study in Medical Physics *(Graduate/Fellowship)* [531]

Rubber Division American Chemical Society Undergraduate Scholarships *(Undergraduate/Scholarship)* [7829]

Mike Ruben Scholarships *(Undergraduate/Scholarship)* [7111]

IRARC Memorial Joseph P. Rubino WA4MMD Scholarships *(Undergraduate/Scholarship)* [1103]

William Rucker Greenwood Scholarships *(Graduate, Undergraduate/Scholarship)* [1326]

Paul and Ellen Ruckes Scholarships *(Graduate, Undergraduate/Scholarship)* [753]

Lawrence E. & Mabel Jackson Rudberg Scholarships *(Undergraduate/Scholarship)* [3543]

Joe Rudd Scholarships *(Undergraduate/Scholarship)* [7813]

Anna M. Rundquist Memorial Scholarships *(Undergraduate/Scholarship)* [4340]

Damon Runyon Cancer Research Foundation Fellowships *(Doctorate, Graduate, Postdoctorate/Fellowship)* [7831]

Damon Runyon Clinical Investigator Awards *(Doctorate, Graduate, Postdoctorate/Fellowship)* [7832]

Damon Runyon-Rachleff Innovation Awards *(Postdoctorate/Fellowship)* [7833]

Rural Telephone Company Scholarships *(Undergraduate/Scholarship)* [7835]

Hermann G. Rusch Scholarships *(Professional development/Scholarship)* [697]

Norman K. Russell Scholarships *(Doctorate, Graduate/Scholarship)* [6434]

Michael A. Russo Memorial Scholarships *(Undergraduate/Scholarship)* [7711]

The Anthony C. Russo Scholarships *(Graduate/Scholarship)* [6457]

Lucile Rust Scholarships *(Undergraduate/Scholarship)* [7300]

IOIA Andrew Rutherford Scholarships *(Professional development/Scholarship)* [4717]

Ralph and Clara Rutledge Memorial Scholarships *(Graduate/Scholarship)* [3869]

Deborah Jean Rydberg Memorial Scholarships *(Undergraduate/Scholarship)* [3168]

Jeanne Graves Ryland Scholarships *(Undergraduate/Scholarship)* [3389]

Charles A. Ryskamp Research Fellowships *(Doctorate/Fellowship)* [681]

SAA Native American Scholarships *(Graduate, Professional development, Undergraduate/Scholarship)* [8293]

SABA Foundation Fellowships *(Undergraduate/Fellowship)* [8538]

SACHS Foundation Graduate Scholarships *(Graduate/Scholarship)* [7840]

SACHS Foundation Undergraduate Scholarships for Colorado Black Students *(High School/Scholarship)* [7841]

Sacks For CF Scholarships *(All/Scholarship)* [3687]

Julie Anne Sadlier Memorial Scholarships *(Undergraduate/Scholarship)* [3390]

Safer Athletic Field Environments Scholarships (SAFE) *(Graduate, Undergraduate/Scholarship)* [8649]

Russell Sage Foundation Visiting Scholars *(Postdoctorate/Fellowship)* [7880]

Ruth Sager Scholarships *(Undergraduate/Scholarship)* [5629]

SAH Study Tour Fellowships *(Doctorate/Fellowship)* [8297]

Virginia Hartford Saharov Memorial Scholarships *(Undergraduate/Scholarship)* [3391]

Don Sahli-Kathy Woodall Graduate Scholarships *(Graduate/Scholarship)* [8841]

Sons and Daughters Don Sahli-Kathy Woodall Scholarships *(Graduate, Undergraduate/Scholarship)* [8842]

St. Francis Xavier Scholarships *(Undergraduate/Scholarship)* [9775]

St. James Armenian Church Memorial Scholarships *(All/Scholarship)* [1604]

St. Joseph's Hospital School of Nursing Alumnae Scholarships *(Undergraduate/Scholarship)* [7112]

St. Louis Division Scholarships *(Undergraduate/Scholarship)* [5864]

St. Louis Paralegal Association Student Scholarships *(Undergraduate/Scholarship)* [7884]

Saint Vincent College Eagle Scout Scholarships *(Undergraduate/Scholarship)* [6261]

Saints Cyril and Methodius Scholarships *(Undergraduate/Scholarship)* [7838]

SAJA Journalism Scholarships *(Graduate, Undergraduate/Scholarship)* [8540]

Casey Sakir Point Scholarships *(Graduate, Undergraduate/Scholarship)* [7366]

Joseph and Amelia Saks Scholarship Fund *(Undergraduate/Scholarship)* [3047]

Bill Salerno, W2ONV, Memorial Scholarships *(Undergraduate/Scholarship)* [1104]

Eugene Gene Sallee, W4YFR Memorial Scholarships *(Undergraduate/Scholarship)* [1105]

The Sallie Mae 911 Education Fund *(Undergraduate/Scholarship)* [7891]

Sally Beauty Scholarships for High School Graduates *(Undergraduate/Scholarship)* [7439]

Ann S. Salsberg Scholarship Awards *(Undergraduate/Award, Scholarship)* [2323]

Henry Salvatori Scholarships *(Undergraduate/Scholarship)* [6924]

Samalot - Sebastian Scholarship Fund *(High School/Scholarship)* [3320]

The Walter Samek III Memorial Scholarship Fund *(Undergraduate/Scholarship)* [3089]

SAMFund Scholarships *(Graduate, Undergraduate/Scholarship)* [7897]

Margaret Jerome Sampson Scholarships *(Undergraduate/Scholarship)* [7301]

Samsung American Legion Scholarships *(Undergraduate/Scholarship)* [897]

San Angelo Area Foundation Scholarships *(All/Scholarship)* [7901]

San Diego City College Study Abroad Scholarships *(Undergraduate/Scholarship)* [7957]

The San Diego Foundation Community Scholarships I *(Undergraduate, Vocational/Occupational/Scholarship)* [7958]

San Pasqual Academy Scholarships *(Undergraduate, Vocational/Occupational/Scholarship)* [7962]

Barbara Sanchez Scholarships *(Undergraduate/Scholarship)* [8348]

Major General Jerry Sanders Scholarship Program *(High School, Undergraduate/Scholarship)* [1461]

Bill Sanderson Aviation Maintenance Technician Scholarships *(Postgraduate/Scholarship)* [4511]

Santa Clara La Raza Lawyers Scholarships *(Graduate/Scholarship)* [5313]

Bert Saperstein Communication Scholarships *(Undergraduate/Scholarship)* [7987]

Saratoga County Bar Association Law Student Scholarships *(All/Scholarship)* [7989]

Saskatchewan Trucking Association Scholarships *(Undergraduate/Scholarship)* [8010]

Malini E. Sathyadev Memorial Scholarships *(Undergraduate/Scholarship)* [7963]

Curtis M. Saulsbury Scholarship Fund *(Undergraduate/Scholarship)* [3082]

Savatori Fellowships *(Graduate/Fellowship)* [4848]

Save Mart Legacy Scholarships *(Undergraduate/Scholarship)* [2254]

John A. Savoy Scholarship Fund *(Undergraduate/Scholarship)* [3792]

SBA Four-Year Scholarships Program *(Undergraduate/Scholarship)* [8644]

SBA One-Year Scholarship Program *(Undergraduate, Vocational/Occupational/Scholarship)* [8645]

SC and R Foundation Grant Program *(Undergraduate, Vocational/Occupational/Grant)* [8631]

SC and R Foundation Scholarships *(Undergraduate/Scholarship)* [8632]

SCACPA Educational Foundation Scholarships *(Graduate, Undergraduate/Scholarship)* [8542]

Leslie and Mary Ella Scales Memorial Scholarships *(Undergraduate/Scholarship)* [3048]

Edith Scandlyn/Sammie Lynn Scandlyn Puett Memorial Scholarships *(Undergraduate/Scholarship)* [3392]

SCCLA Fellowships *(All/Fellowship)* [8578]

SCCLA Scholarships *(All/Scholarship)* [8579]

SCDAA Post-Doctoral Research Fellowships *(Doctorate/Fellowship)* [8138]

David W. Schacht Native American Student Scholarships *(Undergraduate/Scholarship)* [2064]

Millicent M. Schaffner Endowed Memorial Scholarships *(Undergraduate/Scholarship)* [4239]

Schallek Awards *(Graduate/Award)* [5754]

Schallek Fellowships *(Graduate/Fellowship)* [5755]

Abe Schechter Graduate Scholarships *(Graduate/Scholarship)* [7570]

Abe Schecter Graduate Scholarships *(Postgraduate/Scholarship)* [7582]

Scheduler and Dispatchers Scholarships *(Professional development/Scholarship)* [6171]

Leopold Schepp Foundation Scholarships *(Doctorate, Graduate, Undergraduate/Scholarship)* [8018]

Robert C. and Margaret A. Schikora Scholarships *(Undergraduate/Scholarship)* [8621]

Victor E. Schimmel Memorial Nursing Scholarships *(Doctorate, Graduate, Master's/Scholarship)* [1725]

Arthur M. Schlesinger, Jr. Fellowships *(All/Fellowship)* [5240]

Julie Schmid Research Scholarships *(All/Scholarship)* [1837]

CSF Charlotte R. Schmidlapp Scholarships *(Undergraduate/Scholarship)* [2864]

Ronald L. Schmied Scholarships *(Professional development, Undergraduate/Scholarship)* [4362]

David M. Schneider Awards *(Doctorate/Award)* [408]

Richard J. Schnell Memorial Scholarships *(Postdoctorate/Scholarship)* [3169]

Lillian P. Schoephoerster Scholarships *(Undergraduate/Scholarship)* [7302]

The Scholarship Foundation of St. Louis Scholarships *(Graduate, Undergraduate/Scholarship)* [8022]

Scholarship Foundation of Santa Barbara Art Scholarship Program *(Undergraduate/Scholarship)* [8024]

Scholarship for Junior PHS Commissioned Officers *(Undergraduate, Vocational/Occupational/Scholarship)* [7315]

Scholarships of the Arts *(Graduate, Undergraduate/Scholarship)* [3688]

Scholarships for Disadvantaged Students *(Undergraduate/Scholarship)* [4499]

Scholarships for Leadership Training and Coaching *(Professional development/Scholarship)* [3457]

Scholarships for Lutheran College Students *(Undergraduate/Scholarship)* [2077]

Scholarships of the Morris Radio Club of New Jersey *(Undergraduate/Scholarship)* [1106]

The Schonstedt Scholarships in Surveying *(Undergraduate/Scholarship)* [650]

School Age Financial Aid Program *(Undergraduate/Scholarship)* [2050]

School In-Service Training Grants for Grades 6-8 Teachers *(High School/Grant)* [6223]

School In-Service Training Grants for Grades 9-12 Teachers *(High School/Grant)* [6224]

School In-Service Training Grants for Grades K-5 Teachers *(High School/Grant)* [6225]

School Library Paraprofessional Scholarships *(Graduate/Scholarship)* [2273]

Schoolsfirst Federal Credit Union Scholarships *(Undergraduate/Scholarship)* [7712]

CSF H.C. Schott Foundation Scholarships *(Undergraduate/Scholarship)* [2865]

Kurt H. and Donna M. Schuler Cash Grants *(Undergraduate, Graduate/Scholarship)* [1193]

Richard E. Schultes Research Awards *(Graduate/Grant)* [8316]

David and Ginny Schultz Family Scholarship Fund *(Undergraduate/Scholarship)* [4240]

Galvanize the Future: Edgar K. Schutz Scholarships *(Graduate, Undergraduate/Prize, Scholarship)* [774]

CSF Nelson Schwab Jr. Family Scholarships *(Undergraduate/Scholarship)* [2866]

AIST William E. Schwabe Memorial Scholarships *(Undergraduate/Scholarship)* [1817]

Schwan's Food Service Scholarships *(Undergraduate, Vocational/Occupational/Scholarship)* [8030]

Marla Schwartz Grants *(Professional development, Graduate/Grant)* [504]

Abba P. Schwartz Research Fellowships *(All/Fellowship)* [5241]

CSF Judge Benjamin Schwartz Scholarships *(Undergraduate/Scholarship)* [2867]

Fritz Schwartz Serials Education Scholarships *(Graduate, Professional development/Scholarship)* [6744]

Evalee C. Schwarz Educational Loans *(Graduate, Undergraduate/Loan)* [8052]

David R. Schweisberg Memorial Scholarships *(Graduate, Undergraduate/Scholarship)* [7019]

Science to Achieve Results Fellowships (STAR) *(Graduate/Fellowship)* [9042]

SCLEOA Scholarships *(Undergraduate/Scholarship)* [8547]

Scleroderma Foundation Established Investigator Grants *(Doctorate/Grant)* [8058]

Scleroderma Foundation New Investigator Grants *(Doctorate/Grant)* [8059]

SCLMA Scholarships *(Graduate, Undergraduate/Scholarship)* [8581]

SCMS Dissertation Awards *(Postdoctorate/Award)* [8311]

SCMS Student Writing Awards *(Graduate/Award)* [8312]

NASCAR/Wendell Scott Awards *(Graduate, Undergraduate/Scholarship)* [4550]

Carl A. Scott Book Scholarships *(Undergraduate/Scholarship)* [3284]

Herbert Scoville Jr. Peace Fellowships *(Graduate/Fellowship)* [8067]

CSF E.W. Scripps Scholarships *(Undergraduate/Scholarship)* [2868]

Bonnie Sorenson Scudder Scholarships *(Undergraduate/Scholarship)* [3170]

SDF Community College Transfer Scholarships for Math and Science *(Undergraduate/Scholarship)* [7964]

Lewis L. Seaman Junior Enlisted Awards for Outstanding Operational Support *(Professional development/Award)* [1462]

Seaspace Scholarships *(Graduate, Undergraduate/Scholarship)* [8073]

David and Sharon Seaver Family Scholarship Fund *(Undergraduate/Scholarship)* [4241]

SEE Education Foundation Scholarships *(Doctorate, Graduate, Undergraduate/Scholarship)* [4992]

Seed Companies Scholarships *(Undergraduate/Scholarship)* [739]

Margery J. Seeger Scholarships *(Undergraduate/Scholarship)* [4298]

Aaron Seesan Memorial Scholarship Fund *(Undergraduate/Scholarship)* [8697]

Detective Cheryl Seiden Memorial Scholarships *(Undergraduate/Scholarship)* [359]

Seldovia Native Association Achievement Scholarships *(Undergraduate, Graduate/Scholarship)* [8075]

Seldovia Native Association General Scholarships *(Undergraduate, Graduate/Scholarship)* [8076]

David W. Self Scholarships *(Undergraduate/Scholarship)* [9015]

June M. Seneca Scholarships *(Graduate/Scholarship)* [8088]

Senior Memorial Scholarships *(Undergraduate/Scholarship)* [3172]

Sentinels of Freedom "Life Scholarships" *(All/Scholarship)* [8090]

William "Buddy" Sentner Scholarship Awards *(Undergraduate/Scholarship)* [539]

Felix R. Sepulveda Memorial Scholarships - Northside Booster Club *(Undergraduate/Scholarship)* [7713]

Serbian Bar Association of America Scholarships *(Undergraduate/Scholarship)* [8092]

Sertoma Communicative Disorders Scholarships *(Graduate/Scholarship)* [8094]

Sertoma Hard of Hearing and Deaf Scholarships *(Undergraduate/Scholarship)* [8095]

Service League Volunteer Scholarships *(Undergraduate/Scholarship)* [9510]

Captain Anthony D. Sesow Scholarships *(Undergraduate/Scholarship)* [6578]

Frank B. Sessa Scholarships for Continuing Professional Education *(Professional development/Scholarship)* [2072]

Margaret B. Sevcenko Prize in Islamic Art and Culture *(Doctorate/Prize)* [4589]

Hubert K. Seymour Scholarships *(Undergraduate/Scholarship)* [6788]

SFFS Education Colleges & Universities Scholarship Program *(Undergraduate, Graduate/Scholarship)* [7980]

SFP Junior Investigator's Career Development Awards *(Professional development/Grant)* [8322]

SFP Mid-Career/Mentor Awards for Family Planning *(Professional development/Grant)* [8323]

SFP Student and Resident Research Grants *(Graduate/Grant)* [8324]

Al Shackleford and Dan Martin Professional Scholarships *(Undergraduate/Scholarship)* [2017]

Charles Shafae' Scholarships *(Undergraduate/Prize, Scholarship)* [7043]

Elizabeth Shafer Memorial Scholarships *(Undergraduate/Scholarship)* [7522]

SHAFR Dissertation Completion Fellowships *(Doctorate/Fellowship)* [8342]

Saleem Shah Early Career Development Awards *(Doctorate/Award)* [1046]

Josephine Hooker Shain Scholarships *(Undergraduate/Scholarship)* [4094]

John M. and Mary A. Shanley Memorial Scholarships *(Undergraduate/Scholarship)* [8622]

William H. Shannon Fellowships *(Graduate, Undergraduate/Fellowship)* [5017]

Commander Dan F. Shanower Scholarships *(Undergraduate/Scholarship)* [8067]

Ken and Sandy Sharkey Family Scholarship Fund *(Undergraduate/Scholarship)* [4242]

W.L. Shattuck Scholarships *(Undergraduate/Scholarship)* [4674]

Benjamin G. Shatz Scholarships *(Undergraduate/Scholarship)* [7207]

Anne Shaw Fellowships *(Graduate/Fellowship)* [8890]

Luci Shaw Fellowships *(Undergraduate/Fellowship)* [4704]

Regina B. Shearn Scholarships *(Graduate, Undergraduate/Scholarship)* [360]

Dezna C. Sheehan Memorial Educational Scholarships *(Postgraduate/Scholarship)* [6516]

Sheet Metal And Air Conditioning Contractors' National Association College of Fellows Scholarships *(Undergraduate/Scholarship)* [8101]

Shell Incentive Scholarship Fund *(Undergraduate/Scholarship)* [8103]

Shell Process Technology Scholarships *(Undergraduate/Scholarship)* [8104]

Shell Technical Scholarships *(Undergraduate/Scholarship)* [8105]

Bill and Ann Sheperd Legal Scholarship Fund *(Undergraduate/Scholarship)* [3683]

Robert P. Sheppard Leadership Awards *(High School/Scholarship)* [6506]

Marion A. and Ruth Sherwood Family Fund Education Scholarships *(Undergraduate/Scholarship)* [4243]

Marion A. and Ruth K. Sherwood Family Fund Engineering Scholarships *(Undergraduate/Scholarship)* [4244]

Miller G. Sherwood Family Scholarship Fund *(Undergraduate/Scholarship)* [4245]

Morgan and Jeanie Sherwood Travel Grants *(Graduate, Professional development/Grant)* [1253]

Shields-Gillespie Scholarships *(All, Professional development/Scholarship)* [962]

Drs. Poh Shien and Judy Young Scholarships *(Undergraduate/Scholarship)* [9068]

Milton L. Shifman Endowed Scholarships *(Undergraduate/Scholarship)* [5630]

Everett Oscar Shimp Memorial Scholarships *(Undergraduate/Scholarship)* [7113]

Pat Shimp Memorial Scholarships *(Undergraduate/Scholarship)* [7114]

The Shincho Graduate Fellowships for Study in Japan *(Graduate/Fellowship)* [5227]

Joseph Shinoda Memorial Scholarships *(Undergraduate/Scholarship)* [8109]

Jason Shipley Memorial Scholarships *(Undergraduate/Scholarship)* [6383]

Shohet Scholars Program *(Postdoctorate/Fellowship)* [4890]

CSF S. David Shor Scholarships *(Undergraduate/Scholarship)* [2869]

Short-Term Fellowships *(Undergraduate, Graduate, Postdoctorate/Fellowship)* [8271]

Short-term Senior Fellowships in Iranian Studies *(Doctorate, Graduate/Fellowship)* [858]

SHOT-NASA Fellowships *(Doctorate, Postdoctorate/Fellowship)* [8346]

SHPE Foundation Dissertation Scholarships *(Doctorate/Scholarship)* [8131]

SHPE Foundation General Scholarships *(High School, Undergraduate, Graduate/Scholarship)* [8132]

SHPE Foundation Professional Scholarships *(Master's, Doctorate/Scholarship)* [8134]

SHPE Foundation Verizon Scholarships *(Undergraduate/Scholarship)* [8135]

Ralph W. Shrader Diversity Scholarships *(Graduate/Scholarship)* [1563]

Jack Shrader Memorial Awards *(Professional development/Scholarship)* [1744]

SHRM Certification Scholarships - Individual *(Graduate/Scholarship)* [8349]

SHRM Foundation Regional Academic Scholarships *(Graduate, Undergraduate/Scholarship)* [8350]

Phil Shykes Memorial Scholarships *(Undergraduate, Vocational/Occupational/Scholarship)* [3544]

Mary Isabel Sibley Fellowships *(Doctorate/Fellowship)* [7249]

SICB Fellowships of Graduate Student Travel (FGST) *(Graduate/Fellowship)* [8359]

SICB Grants-in-Aid of Research Program (GIAR) *(Graduate/Grant)* [8360]

Don and Madalyn Sickafoose Educational Trust *(Undergraduate/Scholarship)* [8698]

Sidley Prelaw Scholars Initiative *(Undergraduate/Scholarship)* [8140]

Norman Siegel Research Scholar Grants *(Doctorate/Grant)* [1313]

Jeff Siegel Scholarships *(Undergraduate/Scholarship)* [6669]

Myrtle Siegfried, MD and Michael Vigilante, MD Scholarships *(Undergraduate/Scholarship)* [3988]

Siemens Clinical Advancement Scholarship Program *(Postgraduate/Scholarship)* [1327]

Siemens Teacher Scholarships *(Graduate, Undergraduate/Scholarship)* [8142]

E.J. Sierleja Memorial Fellowships *(Graduate/Fellowship)* [4809]

Sig Memorial Scholarships *(Undergraduate/Scholarship)* [30]

Sigma Delta Epsilon Fellowships *(Graduate, Postdoctorate/Fellowship)* [8154]

Sigma Diagnostics Student Scholarships *(Undergraduate/Scholarship)* [6517]

Sigma Kappa Foundation Alumnae Continuing Education Scholarships *(Undergraduate/Scholarship)* [8182]

Sigma Kappa Foundation Alzheimer's/Gerontology Scholarships *(Undergraduate/Scholarship)* [8183]

Sigma Kappa Foundation Founders' Scholarships *(Undergraduate/Scholarship)* [8184]

Sigma Kappa Foundation Gerontology Scholarships *(Undergraduate/Scholarship)* [8185]

Sigma Pi Sigma Undergraduate Research Awards

(Undergraduate/Grant) [8440]

Silver Nugget Family Scholarships (Undergraduate/Scholarship) [7523]

APSAIL's Ralph Silverman Memorial Scholarships (Undergraduate/Scholarship) [1967]

Meyer and Dorothy Silverman Scholarships (Undergraduate/Scholarship) [3133]

Harvey L. Simmons Memorial Scholarships (Undergraduate/Scholarship) [7965]

Linda Simmons Memorial Scholarships (Undergraduate/Scholarship) [195]

Willard B. Simmons Sr. Memorial Scholarships (Undergraduate/Scholarship) [6202]

Julian Simon Fellowships (Professional development/Fellowship) [7455]

Simon Youth Foundation Community Scholarships (Undergraduate, Vocational/Occupational/Scholarship) [8212]

Simonton Windows Scholarships (Undergraduate, Vocational/Occupational/Scholarship) [7115]

DW Simpson Actuarial Science Scholarship Program (Undergraduate/Scholarship) [8214]

Carole Simpson Scholarships (Undergraduate/Scholarship) [7583]

CSF Lowe Simpson Scholarships (Undergraduate/Scholarship) [2870]

Single Parent Scholarships (Graduate, Undergraduate/Scholarship) [1549]

Sino-American Pharmaceutical Professionals Association Scholarships (Undergraduate/Scholarship) [8222]

Helen J. Sioussat/Fay Wells Scholarships (All/Scholarship) [2184]

Gadde Sitaramamma & Tirupataiah Scholarships (Graduate/Scholarship) [8832]

Bill Six Memorial Scholarship Fund (Undergraduate/Scholarship) [7116]

Six Meter Club of Chicago Scholarships (Undergraduate/Scholarship) [1107]

Leif and Inger Sjoberg Awards (Professional development/Award) [1173]

Skadden Fellowships (Graduate/Fellowship) [8229]

R. Skeeles Memorial Scholarship Fund (Undergraduate/Scholarship) [8699]

CSF Frank Foster Skillman Scholarships (Undergraduate/Scholarship) [2871]

Francelene Skinner Memorial Scholarships (Undergraduate/Scholarship) [5478]

Allogan Slagle Memorial Scholarships (All/Scholarship) [1697]

SLEAMC Scholarships (Graduate, Undergraduate/Scholarship) [8107]

Robert W. Sledge Fellowships (Graduate/Fellowship) [346]

J. Ward Sleichter and Frances F. Sleichter Memorial Scholarship Fund (Undergraduate/Scholarship) [3960]

Slifka Foundation Interdisciplinary Fellowships (Doctorate/Fellowship) [5791]

Sloan Northwood University Heavy-Duty Scholarships (Undergraduate/Scholarship) [1968]

Sloan Research Fellowships (Doctorate/Fellowship) [8235]

The Aaron and Rita Slom Scholarships (Undergraduate/Scholarship) [8923]

SMART Scholarships (Graduate, Undergraduate/Scholarship) [8056]

SME Coal and Energy Division Scholarships (Undergraduate/Scholarship) [8414]

SME Directors Scholarships (Undergraduate/Scholarship) [8398]

SME Education Foundation Family Scholarships (Undergraduate/Scholarship) [8399]

SME Environmental Division Scholarships (Undergraduate/Scholarship) [8415]

Dr. George M. Smerk Scholarships (Graduate, Undergraduate/Scholarship) [1057]

SMFM/AAOGF Scholarship Awards (Graduate/Scholarship) [8410]

Ryan and Jamie Smith Essay Contest (Graduate, Postgraduate/Scholarship) [8237]

Gladys Ann Smith Greater Los Angeles Women's Council Scholarships (Undergraduate/Scholarship) [6588]

Stanley Smith Horticultural Fellowships (Graduate, Undergraduate/Fellowship) [6987]

James I. Smith, III Notre Dame Law School Scholarship Fund (Graduate, Undergraduate/Scholarship) [331]

Boy Scouts of America Troop 3 Scholarships - Art Till/Nathan E. Smith Memorial Scholarships (Undergraduate, Vocational/Occupational/Scholarship) [7714]

Colonel Nate Smith Memorial Scholarships (Graduate, Undergraduate/Scholarship) [5731]

Drew Smith Memorial Scholarships (Undergraduate/Scholarship) [3068]

Smith-Reynolds Founder Fellowships (Graduate/Fellowship) [4526]

The Eileen J. Smith, R.N. Memorial Scholarships (Undergraduate/Scholarship) [5105]

Ralph and Josephine Smith Scholarship Fund (Undergraduate/Scholarship) [3793]

A.O. Smith Scholarships (Undergraduate/Scholarship) [7349]

Chapter 63 - Portland Uncle Bud Smith Scholarships (Graduate, Undergraduate/Scholarship) [8400]

Esther M. Smith Scholarships (Undergraduate/Scholarship) [3069]

Helen J. and Harold Gilman Smith Scholarships (Graduate, Undergraduate/Scholarship) [2065]

Richard S. Smith Scholarships (Undergraduate/Scholarship) [9016]

William E. Smith Scholarships (Graduate/Scholarship) [171]

Drue Smith/Society of Professional Journalists Scholarships (Undergraduate/Scholarship) [3134]

Nadine Barrie Smith Student Awards (All/Award) [5005]

Smith's Personal Best Scholarships (Undergraduate/Scholarship) [7525]

Smithsonian Fellowships in Museum Practice (Professional development/Fellowship) [8266]

Smithsonian Institution Graduate Student Fellowships (Graduate/Fellowship) [8245]

Smithsonian Institution Postdoctoral Fellowships (Doctorate/Fellowship) [8246]

Smithsonian Institution Senior Fellowships (Doctorate/Fellowship) [8248]

Smithsonian Postgraduate Fellowships in Conservation of Museum Collection Program (Postgraduate/Fellowship) [8249]

Gladys Snauble Scholarships (Undergraduate/Scholarship) [4299]

SNF Professional Growth Scholarships (Graduate, Undergraduate/Scholarship) [8031]

SNMTS Bachelor's Degree Completion Scholarships (Undergraduate/Scholarship) [8421]

SNMTS Clinical Advancement Scholarships (Professional development/Scholarship) [8422]

Helen D. Snow Memorial Scholarships (Undergraduate/Scholarship) [7252]

A.C. Snow Scholarships (Undergraduate/Scholarship) [9305]

Snowmobile Association of Massachusetts Scholarships (Undergraduate, Vocational/Occupational/Scholarship) [8274]

Stuart H. Snyder Memorial Scholarships (Undergraduate/Scholarship) [1949]

Arnold Sobel Scholarships (Undergraduate/Scholarship) [2929]

Social Work Scholarships (Undergraduate/Scholarship) [7420]

Society of Allied Weight Engineers Scholarships (Undergraduate/Scholarship) [8291]

Society for the Arts in Healthcare Environmental Research Grants (Professional development/Grant) [8300]

Society for the Arts in Healthcare Student Scholarships (Doctorate, Graduate, Undergraduate/Scholarship) [8301]

Society of Exploration Geophysicists Foundation Scholarships (Graduate, Undergraduate/Scholarship) [8320]

Society for Linguistic Anthropology Student Essay Prize (Graduate, Undergraduate/Prize) [8365]

Society of Manufacturing Engineers Ford PAS Scholarships (SME) (Undergraduate/Scholarship) [8401]

Society of Marine Port Engineers Scholarship Loans (Undergraduate/Scholarship loan, Loan) [8408]

Society of Naval Architects and Marine Engineers Undergraduate Scholarships (Undergraduate/Scholarship) [8418]

Society of Pediatric Nurses Educational Scholarships (Graduate, Professional development/Scholarship) [8424]

Society for Pediatric Radiology Research Fellows (Graduate, Professional development/Fellowship) [8429]

Society for Pediatric Radiology Seed Grants (Graduate, Professional development/Grant) [8430]

Society for Pediatric Urology Research Grant Program (Undergraduate/Grant) [8433]

Society of Plastics Engineers General Scholarships (Graduate, Undergraduate/Scholarship) [8456]

Society of Plastics Engineers Pittsburgh Section Scholarships (Graduate, Undergraduate/Scholarship) [8457]

Society for the Scientific Study of Sexuality Student Research Grants (Undergraduate/Grant) [8493]

Society of Vacuum Coaters Foundation Scholarships (Vocational/Occupational, Two Year College, Undergraduate, Graduate/Scholarship) [8514]

Society of Women Engineers Scholarships (Undergraduate/Scholarship) [8516]

Louis B. Sohn Fellowships in Human Rights and Environment (Graduate/Fellowship) [2692]

Dale and Betty George Sola Scholarships (Undergraduate/Scholarship) [3545]

CFI Sid Solow Scholarships (Graduate/Scholarship) [1832]

SON Scholarships (Undergraduate/Scholarship) [7899]

Dr. Kiyoshi Sonoda Memorial Scholarships (Graduate/Scholarship) [5146]

Sons of Union Veterans of the Civil War Scholarships (Undergraduate/Scholarship) [8534]

Sony Pictures Scholarships (Graduate/Scholarship) [1833]

SOPHE/ATSDR Student Fellowships in Environmental Health or Emergency Preparedness (Doctorate, Graduate, Master's/Fellowship) [8478]

SOPHE/CDC Student Fellowships in Child, Adolescent and School Health (Doctorate, Graduate, Master's/Fellowship) [8479]

SOPHE/CDC Student Fellowships in Injury Prevention (Graduate/Fellowship) [8480]

Theodore C. Sorensen Fellowships (All/Fellowship) [5242]

Soroptimist International of Chambersburg Scholarship Fund (Undergraduate/Scholarship) [3961]

Soroptimist International of Redlands Scholarships (Undergraduate/Scholarship) [7715]

Paul and Daisy Soros Fellowships (Graduate/Fellowship) [8536]

Eastman Kodak Dr. Theophilus Sorrell Fellowships (Graduate/Fellowship) [6432]

John Soto Scholarships (Undergraduate/Scholarship) [3232]

South Carolina Association for Financial Professionals Certified Treasury Professional Scholarships (Professional development/Scholarship) [8544]

South Carolina Tourism and Hospitality Educational Foundation Scholarships (Undergraduate/Scholarship) [4603]

South Central Modern Language Association Fellowships (Doctorate/Fellowship) [6709]

South Central Power Scholarships (Undergraduate, Vocational/Occupational/Scholarship) [8556]

South Coast Area High School Senior Honors Scholarship Program (Undergraduate/Scholarship) [8025]

South Jersey Golf Association Scholarships (Undergraduate/Scholarship) [8561]

South Kentucky RECC High School Senior Scholarships (Undergraduate/Scholarship) [8564]

Southeast Aerospace Inc. Scholarships (Undergraduate/Scholarship) [140]

Southeast Alabama Dietetic Association Scholarships (Graduate, Undergraduate/Scholarship) [172]

Southeast Member Chapter Scholarships (Undergraduate/Scholarship) [1818]

Southern Maine Women's Golf Association Scholarships (All/Scholarship) [8583]

Southern Nevada Sports Hall of Fame Athletic Scholarships *(Undergraduate/Scholarship)* [7526]

Southwest Florida Community Foundation College Assistance Scholarships *(Undergraduate/Scholarship)* [8623]

Southwest Movers Association Scholarships *(Undergraduate/Scholarship)* [8629]

Sovereign Nations Scholarships *(Undergraduate/Scholarship)* [810]

Iwalani Carpenter Sowa Scholarships *(Graduate/Scholarship)* [5222]

Master Sergeant William Sowers Memorial Scholarships *(Undergraduate/Scholarship)* [101]

SPA Certified Legal Assistant Scholarships *(Professional development/Scholarship)* [7885]

Willard and Spackman Scholarship Program *(Postgraduate/Scholarship)* [956]

Kathy Spadoni Memorial Scholarships *(Undergraduate/Scholarship)* [7421]

Nathan Sparks Memorial Scholarships *(Undergraduate/Scholarship)* [3049]

Spartan Staff Scholarships *(Undergraduate/Scholarship)* [7527]

Special Education Scholarships *(Graduate, Undergraduate/Scholarship)* [362]

Specialty Equipment Market Association Scholarships *(Graduate, Undergraduate, Vocational/Occupational/Scholarship)* [8635]

Specialty Nursing Scholarships *(Undergraduate/Scholarship)* [3979]

Faith Speckhard Scholarships *(Undergraduate, Vocational/Occupational/Scholarship)* [5106]

Spencer Foundation Research Grants *(All/Grant)* [6007]

Spice Box Grants *(Professional development/Grant)* [698]

Lawrence Alan Spiegel Remembrance Scholarships *(Undergraduate/Scholarship)* [4595]

Patrick Spielman Memorial Scholarship Program *(Undergraduate, Vocational/Occupational/Scholarship)* [8071]

Enid W. and Bernard B. Spigel Architectural Scholarships *(Graduate, Undergraduate/Scholarship)* [4384]

The Spirit Square Center for Arts and Education Scholarship Fund *(Undergraduate/Scholarship)* [3922]

SPOOM Research Grants *(Graduate/Grant)* [8463]

Sporty's Pilot Shop/Cincinnati Avionics Scholarships *(Undergraduate, Vocational/Occupational/Scholarship)* [141]

Spouse Tuition Aids Program (STAP) *(Graduate, Undergraduate/Loan)* [6594]

SPPSI Grants-In-Aid Program *(Graduate, Postdoctorate/Grant)* [8475]

Spring Internships in International Civil Society Law *(Undergraduate/Internship)* [4894]

Jim Springer Memorial Scholarships *(Undergraduate/Scholarship)* [2959]

SPS Future Teacher Scholarships *(Undergraduate/Scholarship)* [8441]

SPS Leadership Scholarships *(Undergraduate/Scholarship)* [8442]

SPSmedical CS Scholarships *(Professional development/Scholarship)* [4871]

SREB-State Doctoral Scholarships *(Doctorate, Graduate/Scholarship)* [8585]

SRF Post-doctoral Fellowships *(Postdoctorate/Fellowship)* [8061]

SSAWMA Scholarships *(Graduate/Scholarship)* [120]

SSC-Building Environmental Campus Community Fellowships (BECC) *(Undergraduate/Scholarship)* [8146]

SSF Research Grants *(Professional development/Grant)* [8226]

SSF Student Fellowships *(Graduate, Undergraduate/Fellowship)* [8227]

The SSPI Mid-Atlantic Chapter Scholarships *(Graduate, Undergraduate/Scholarship)* [8489]

The SSPI Northeast Chapter Scholarships *(Graduate, Undergraduate/Scholarship)* [8490]

The SSPI Southern California Scholarships *(Graduate, Undergraduate/Scholarship)* [8491]

John F. and Anna Lee Stacey Scholarships *(All/Scholarship)* [6229]

Ernest and Charlene Stachowiak Memorial Scholarships *(Undergraduate/Scholarship)* [3173]

Matt Stager Memorial Scholarship Fund *(Undergraduate/Scholarship)* [9538]

Steven A. Stahl Research Grants *(Graduate/Grant)* [4978]

Standard and Poor's Award for Economic and Business Reporting - S&P Scholarships *(Graduate, Undergraduate/Scholarship)* [7020]

Marion Barr Stanfield Art Scholarships *(Graduate, Undergraduate/Scholarship)* [9002]

Otto M. Stanfield Law Scholarships *(Graduate/Scholarship)* [9003]

A.R.O.Y. Stanitz Scholarships *(Undergraduate/Scholarship)* [1166]

Morgan Stanley Pediatrics Fellowships *(Doctorate, Postdoctorate/Fellowship)* [575]

Morgan Stanley Tribal Scholars Program *(Undergraduate/Scholarship)* [811]

J. Newell Stannard Fellowships *(Graduate/Fellowship)* [4492]

Stark County Bar Association Fund *(Undergraduate/Scholarship)* [8700]

Stark County Dairy Promoters Scholarships *(Undergraduate/Scholarship)* [8701]

Starker Fellowships for White Matter Disease Clinical Research *(Doctorate, Professional development/Fellowship)* [5113]

Starr Foundation Graduate Fellowships in Asian Studies *(Graduate/Grant)* [9205]

State Farm Insurance Doctoral Dissertation Awards *(Doctorate/Award)* [8712]

Robert W. and Bernice Ingalls Staton Scholarships *(Undergraduate/Scholarship)* [9314]

Matt Stauffer Memorial Scholarships *(Undergraduate, Vocational/Occupational/Scholarship)* [2758]

STC Scholarships *(Graduate, Undergraduate/Scholarship)* [8496]

The Stanley H. Stearman Awards *(Undergraduate/Scholarship)* [6482]

Robert P. Stearns/SCS Engineers Scholarships *(Graduate/Scholarship)* [8526]

Tom Steel Post-Graduate Fellowships *(Postgraduate, Professional development/Fellowship)* [7431]

Joseph L. and Vivian E. Steele Music Scholarship Fund *(Undergraduate/Scholarship)* [3962]

CSF Helen Steiner Rice Scholarships *(Undergraduate/Scholarship)* [2872]

Elin J. Stene/Xi Scholarships *(Undergraduate/Scholarship)* [8187]

Step Up Scholarships *(Undergraduate/Scholarship)* [7966]

Gabe Stepetin Business Scholarship Awards *(Undergraduate, Vocational/Occupational, Graduate, Master's/Scholarship)* [290]

Elizabeth Coulter Stephenson Scholarships *(Undergraduate/Scholarship)* [3422]

CSF Joseph S. Stern, Jr. Scholarships *(Undergraduate/Scholarship)* [2873]

Raymond H. Stetson Scholarships in Phonetics and Speech Science *(Graduate/Scholarship)* [41]

Stevens Doctoral Awards *(Doctorate/Award)* [4914]

Benjamin F. Stevens Fellowships *(Graduate, Doctorate/Fellowship)* [5678]

Zachary Taylor Stevens Memorial Scholarships *(Undergraduate/Scholarship)* [1108]

David Stevenson Fellowships *(Doctorate, Graduate, Professional development/Fellowship)* [6730]

H.L. Stevenson Scholarships *(Graduate, Undergraduate/Scholarship)* [7021]

Richie Stevenson Scholarships *(Undergraduate, Vocational/Occupational/Scholarship)* [3135]

Nancy Stewart Scholarships *(Undergraduate/Scholarship)* [1372]

Stewart Title Firefighters Scholarships *(High School, Undergraduate/Scholarship)* [2960]

Mary Stewart and William T. Covington, Jr. Scholarship Fund *(Undergraduate/Scholarship)* [3923]

Dr. Gunnar B. Stickler Scholarships *(Undergraduate, Vocational/Occupational/Scholarship)* [8735]

Walter W. Stillman Scholarships *(Undergraduate/Scholarship)* [1950]

Hartman E. Stime Scholarships *(Undergraduate/Scholarship)* [3553]

The Richard Stockton College of New Jersey Foundation Alumni Association Graduate Awards *(Graduate/Scholarship)* [8744]

Louis Stokes Health Scholars Program *(Undergraduate, Vocational/Occupational/Scholarship)* [3221]

Louis Stokes Urban Health Policy Fellows Program *(Graduate, Professional development/Fellowship)* [3222]

Ralph W. Stone Graduate Fellowships *(Graduate/Fellowship, Grant)* [6528]

James E. Stoner Memorial Scholarships *(Undergraduate/Scholarship)* [1777]

Stop Hunger Scholarships *(Undergraduate/Scholarship)* [546]

Martin L. Stout Scholarships *(Undergraduate/Scholarship)* [1769]

StraightForward Media's Art School Scholarships *(Undergraduate/Scholarship)* [8756]

StraightForward Media's Business School Scholarships *(Undergraduate/Scholarship)* [8757]

StraightForward Media's Engineering Scholarships *(Undergraduate/Scholarship)* [8758]

StraightForward Media's Law Enforcement Scholarships *(Professional development, Undergraduate/Scholarship)* [8759]

StraightForward Media's Law School Scholarships *(Undergraduate/Scholarship)* [8760]

StraightForward Media's Liberal Arts Scholarships *(Undergraduate/Scholarship)* [8761]

StraightForward Media's Media and Communications Scholarships *(Undergraduate/Scholarship)* [8762]

StraightForward Media's Science Scholarships *(Undergraduate/Scholarship)* [8763]

StraightForward Media's Vocational-Technical School Scholarships *(Undergraduate, Vocational/Occupational/Scholarship)* [8764]

AALL & Thomson West - George A. Strait Minority Scholarship Endowments *(Postgraduate/Scholarship)* [505]

Bonnie Strangio Education Scholarships *(Graduate, Undergraduate/Scholarship)* [3689]

Donald A. Strauss Scholarships *(Undergraduate/Scholarship)* [9196]

Carole J. Streeter, KB9JBR Scholarships *(Undergraduate/Scholarship)* [1109]

Stanley W. Strew Educational Fund Scholarships *(Undergraduate/Scholarship)* [2230]

Norman E. Strohmeier, W2VRS Memorial Scholarships *(Undergraduate/Scholarship)* [1110]

Structural Engineering Travel Fellowships *(Doctorate, Graduate, Undergraduate/Fellowship)* [8232]

E.L. Stubbs Research Grants *(Graduate/Grant)* [5847]

Student Osteopathic Medical Student Fellowships and Research *(Undergraduate/Fellowship)* [8767]

Student Research Grants in Audiology *(Doctorate/Grant)* [1390]

Student Research Grants in Early Childhood Language Development *(Doctorate/Grant)* [1391]

Student Travel Grants *(Graduate, Undergraduate/Grant)* [8642]

Marco Polo Stufano Garden Conservancy Fellowships *(Professional development/Fellowship)* [4044]

Stultz Scholarships *(Undergraduate/Scholarship)* [9656]

Horace W. Stunkard Scholarships *(Undergraduate/Scholarship)* [5631]

Anne Sturrock Nursing Scholarships *(Undergraduate/Scholarship)* [8624]

Subic Bay-Cubi Point 1 Scholarships *(Undergraduate/Scholarship)* [6589]

Edward P. Suchecki Family Scholarship Fund *(Undergraduate/Scholarship)* [4246]

Caroline tum Suden Professional Opportunity Awards *(Postdoctorate, Professional development/Award)* [1006]

Suffolk Public Interest Law Group Summer Fellowships (SPILG) *(All/Fellowship)* [7609]

Vallabhaneni Sukundamma & Lakshmaiah Scholarships *(Graduate/Scholarship)* [8833]

Phil Sullivan Scholarships *(Undergraduate/Scholarship)* [7422]

VPPPA William Sullivan Scholarships *(Graduate, Undergraduate/Scholarship)* [9476]

William A. Sullivan Scholarships (Undergraduate/ Scholarship) [6590]

Summer Fellowships of The Electrochemical Society (Graduate/Fellowship) [3625]

Summer Intern Scholarships in Cardiothoracic Surgery (Undergraduate/Scholarship) [563]

Summer Research Diversity Fellowships in Law and Social Science (Undergraduate/Fellowship) [579]

Summer Research Fellowships (Graduate, Undergraduate/Fellowship) [3639]

Surety Industry Scholarship Program for Minority Students (Undergraduate/Scholarship) [8778]

Surgeon Scientist Career Development Awards (Professional development/Grant) [788]

SUS Foundation Junior Faculty Grants (Professional development/Grant) [8511]

Sussman-Miller Educational Assistance Award Program (Undergraduate/Scholarship) [283]

SUT Houston Graduate Scholarships (Graduate/ Scholarship) [8508]

SUT Houston Undergraduate Scholarships (Undergraduate/Scholarship) [8509]

Sutherland/Purdy Scholarships (Undergraduate/ Scholarship) [7303]

Michael Bendix Sutton Foundation (Undergraduate/ Scholarship) [6335]

Daniel Swarovski and Company Scholarships (Graduate/Scholarship) [4068]

Henry D. and Ruth G. Swartz Family Scholarship Fund (Undergraduate/Scholarship) [4247]

Hanns Swarzenski and Brigitte Horney Swarzenski Fellowships (Graduate/Fellowship) [5792]

Hugh B. Sweeny Scholarships (Undergraduate/ Scholarship) [5176]

Jeffery Tyler Sweitzer Wrestling Memorial Scholarship Fund (Undergraduate/Scholarship) [8702]

Swensrud Teacher Fellowships at MHS (Massachusetts Historical Society) (Professional development/Fellowship) [5679]

Timothy S. Sweterlitsch Memorial Scholarship Fund (Undergraduate/Scholarship) [8703]

SWFL Deputy Sheriffs Association Fund Scholarships (Undergraduate/Scholarship) [8625]

SWFL Professional Golfers Association Scholarships (Undergraduate/Scholarship) [8626]

Stan Swinton Scholarships (Graduate, Undergraduate/Scholarship) [7022]

Symantec Research Labs Graduate Fellowships (Doctorate, Graduate/Fellowship) [8789]

Harry Taback 9/11 Memorial Scholarships (Undergraduate/Scholarship) [1354]

Hazaros Tabakoglu Scholarship Fund (Undergraduate/Scholarship) [1605]

The Tabat Scholarship Fund (Graduate/Scholarship) [3738]

TAC Foundation-EBA Engineering Consultants Ltd. Scholarships (Graduate, Postgraduate/Scholarship) [8937]

TAC Foundation-Stantec Consulting Scholarships (Postgraduate/Scholarship) [8944]

The Tacoma Athletic Commission Scholarships (Undergraduate, Vocational/Occupational/Scholarship) [4341]

John I. and Madeleine R. Taeni Scholarships (Undergraduate/Scholarship) [8627]

Tag and Label Manufacturers Institute Scholarships - Four-Year Colleges (Undergraduate/Scholarship) [8793]

Tag and Label Manufacturers Institute Scholarships - Two-Year Colleges (Undergraduate/Scholarship) [8794]

Tagged for Greatness Scholarships (Undergraduate/ Scholarship) [180]

Tailhook Educational Foundation Scholarship Program (Undergraduate/Scholarship) [8796]

Taiwanese American Community Scholarships (Undergraduate/Scholarship) [8798]

Kei Takemoto Memorial Scholarships (Undergraduate/Scholarship) [142]

Tall Awareness Scholarships (Undergraduate/Scholarship) [7529]

Tall Clubs International Student Scholarships (Undergraduate/Scholarship) [8802]

TANA Foundation Graduate Scholarships (Graduate/ Scholarship) [8834]

Alexander M. Tanger Scholarships (All/Scholarship) [2185]

William J. Tangye Scholarships (Undergraduate/ Scholarship) [4902]

Hal Tanner Jr. Scholarships (Undergraduate/Scholarship) [9306]

CSF Martha W. Tanner Memorial Scholarships (Undergraduate/Scholarship) [2874]

Alex Tanous Scholarship Awards (Undergraduate/ Scholarship) [8807]

Lee Tarbox Memorial Scholarships (Undergraduate/ Scholarship) [143]

Targeted Research Initiative for Health Outcomes (Doctorate/Grant) [3668]

Targeted Research Initiative for Mood Disorders (Doctorate/Grant) [3669]

Targeted Research Initiative for Seniors (Doctorate/ Grant) [3670]

Tarkanian Teacher Education Academy at Clark High School Scholarships (TEACH) (Undergraduate/Scholarship) [7530]

Bud and Linda Tarrson Fellowships (Postdoctorate/ Fellowship) [397]

Tarrson Regeneration Scholarships (Postdoctorate/ Scholarship) [398]

Charles T. and Judith A. Tart Student Incentive Awards (Graduate, Postdoctorate, Undergraduate/ Grant) [7053]

Graduate Fellowship Program - GRC/AI Tasch Fellowships (GFP) (Graduate/Fellowship) [8083]

Jordan B. Tatter Scholarships (Undergraduate/ Scholarship) [5832]

Taylor/Blakeslee University Fellowships (Professional development, Undergraduate/Fellowship) [3268]

Charles "Buck" and Dora Taylor Endowed Law Scholarships (Undergraduate/Scholarship) [3514]

Ryan "Munchie" Taylor Memorial Scholarships (Undergraduate/Scholarship) [5550]

TCA-BAACBH Scholarships (Undergraduate/Scholarship) [8977]

TCA Outstanding Graduate Student Awards (Graduate/Award) [8859]

TCA Turkish American Scholarships (Undergraduate/Scholarship) [8978]

TCA-UMD Scholarships (Undergraduate/Scholarship) [8979]

TCATA College Scholarship Program (Undergraduate/Scholarship) [8886]

TDKF Scholarships (Undergraduate/Scholarship) [5237]

Teammates Mentoring Scholarship Program (Undergraduate/Scholarship) [4264]

Technical Services Special Interest Section Grants (Professional development/Grant) [506]

Technical Women's Organization Scholarship Program (TWO) (Undergraduate/Scholarship) [8813]

Dwight Teed Scholarships (Undergraduate/Scholarship) [8772]

Marvin H. and Kathleen G. Teget Leadership Scholarships (Undergraduate/Scholarship) [8768]

Paul Tejada Memorial Scholarships (Undergraduate/ Scholarship) [5107]

Telecommunications Association of Michigan Scholarship Fund (Undergraduate/Scholarship) [8825]

Television News Scholarships (Undergraduate/ Scholarship) [6453]

Telford Scholarships (Undergraduate/Scholarship) [31]

Telluride Association Summer Program Scholarships (High School/Scholarship) [8827]

Templeton-Cambridge Journalism Fellowships (All/ Fellowship) [8839]

Mary L. Tenopyr Graduate Student Scholarships (Doctorate/Scholarship) [8356]

Charles L. Terrell/New Haven Savings Bank Scholarship Fund (Undergraduate/Scholarship) [3083]

Steven M. Teutsch Prevention Effectiveness Fellowships (Doctorate/Fellowship) [2715]

Texas Computer Education Association Professional Educator Grants (Professional development/ Grant) [8857]

Texas Mutual Scholarship Program (Undergraduate, Vocational/Occupational/Scholarship) [8868]

Texas Society of Professional Engineers Scholarships (Undergraduate/Scholarship) [8872]

Texas State Technical College Scholarships (Undergraduate/Scholarship) [145]

Texas Transportation Scholarships (Undergraduate, Vocational/Occupational/Scholarship) [8953]

Jim and Pat Thacker Sports Communication Internships (Undergraduate/Internship) [9307]

ThanksUSA Scholarships (Undergraduate, Vocational/Occupational/Scholarship) [8888]

The Rodney Thaxton Justice Fund (Undergraduate/ Scholarship) [3322]

Dr. Peter A. Theodos Memorial Graduate Scholarships (Graduate/Scholarship) [4519]

Thermo Scientific Educational Scholarships (Postgraduate/Scholarship) [6518]

Thermoforming Division Memorial Scholarships (Graduate, Undergraduate/Scholarship) [8458]

Thermoplastic Materials and Foams Division Scholarships (Graduate, Undergraduate/Scholarship) [8459]

Thermoplastics Elastomers Special Interest Group Scholarships (Graduate, Undergraduate/Scholarship) [8460]

Thesaurus Linguae Latinae Fellowships (TTL) (Doctorate/Fellowship) [987]

E.D. Thomas Post Doctoral Fellowships (Postdoctorate/Fellowship) [4014]

C.R. Thomas Scholarships (Undergraduate/Scholarship) [7118]

Rev. Chuck and Nancy Thomas Scholarships (Graduate, Master's/Scholarship) [9004]

Madlyn D. Thompson Memorial Scholarships (Undergraduate/Scholarship) [2340]

Barbara and Howard Thompson Scholarships (Undergraduate/Scholarship) [5108]

Marjorie Anderson Thompson Scholarships (Graduate, Undergraduate/Scholarship) [363]

Thompson Scholarships for Women in Safety (Graduate/Scholarship) [1355]

Thomson Reuters/MLA Doctoral Fellowships (Doctorate/Fellowship) [5748]

Thornberg/Havens Scholarships (Undergraduate/ Scholarship) [3423]

Thyssen-Heideking Fellowships (Postdoctorate/Fellowship) [4129]

Tidewater Builders Association Scholarships (Undergraduate/Scholarship) [8900]

Tikvah Fellowships (Graduate, Professional development/Fellowship) [8909]

Patricia Tillinghast Memorial Scholarships (Graduate, Undergraduate/Scholarship) [879]

Time Warner Point Scholarships (Graduate, Undergraduate/Scholarship) [7367]

Time Warner Tribal Scholars Program (Undergraduate/Scholarship) [812]

Eben Tisdale Fellowships (Graduate, Undergraduate/Fellowship) [4017]

TMA Research Fellowships (Graduate, Postdoctorate/Grant) [5967]

TMCF Scholarships (Undergraduate/Scholarship) [5647]

Mario J. Tocco Hydrocephalus Foundation Scholarships (Undergraduate/Scholarship) [4654]

Richard Cecil Todd and Clauda Pennock Todd Tripod Scholarships (Graduate, Undergraduate/ Scholarship) [7276]

CSF Christopher Todd Grant Memorial Scholarships (Undergraduate/Scholarship) [2875]

Robert Toigo Foundation Fellowships (Master's/Fellowship) [8911]

The Adelle and Erwin Tomash Fellowships (Doctorate/Fellowship) [1992]

John Tomasovic, Sr. Scholarships (Undergraduate/ Scholarship) [740]

Tomato Fest Scholarship Grants (Undergraduate/ Scholarship) [699]

George Torkildsen Literary Awards (Professional development/Award) [9757]

Ferdinand Torres Scholarships (Graduate, Undergraduate/Scholarship) [754]

Touchstone Special Achievement Scholarships (Undergraduate, Vocational/Occupational/Scholarship) [8557]

Judith A. Towle Environmental Studies Fund (Undergraduate/Fellowship) [5082]

Joseph Towner Fund for Gay and Lesbian Families (Undergraduate/Scholarship) [7872]

Toyota Community Scholars *(Undergraduate/Scholarship)* [8927]

Toyota High School Scholarship Program *(Undergraduate/Scholarship)* [4581]

Toyota/TELACU Scholarships *(Undergraduate/Scholarship)* [8822]

The Joyce Tracy Fellowships *(Doctorate/Fellowship)* [424]

Traditional Student Scholarships *(Undergraduate/Scholarship)* [3194]

TRALA Scholarship Program *(Undergraduate/Scholarship)* [8964]

Reuben Trane Scholarships *(Undergraduate/Scholarship)* [1270]

Transatlantic Fellows Program *(Professional development/Fellowship)* [4134]

Transoft Solutions, Inc. Ahead of the Curve Scholarships (AOTC) *(Graduate, Undergraduate/Scholarship)* [4827]

Traub-Dicker Rainbow Scholarships *(Undergraduate/Scholarship)* [8747]

Morton M. Traum Surface Science Student Awards *(Graduate, Doctorate/Award)* [1986]

Travel Fellowships in Architecture, Design and Urban Design *(Graduate, Undergraduate/Fellowship)* [8233]

Travel Grants for Women Researchers *(Postdoctorate/Fellowship)* [1908]

Trelut Family Legacy Scholarships *(Undergraduate/Scholarship)* [2255]

Davis Wright Tremaine 1L Diversity Scholarships *(Undergraduate/Scholarship)* [3348]

Tribal Business Management Program Scholarships (TBM) *(Undergraduate/Scholarship)* [2664]

Tribeca Film Institute Film and Video Fellowships *(Professional development/Fellowship)* [8958]

Tribeca Film Institute New Media Fellowships *(Professional development/Fellowship)* [8960]

Tim Triner Letter Carriers Scholarship Fund *(Undergraduate/Scholarship)* [8704]

J.P. and Madeline Trinkaus Endowed Scholarships in Embryology *(Undergraduate/Scholarship)* [5632]

Johnny Trombly Scholarships *(Undergraduate/Scholarship)* [5919]

Vincent Trotter Health Care Scholarships *(Undergraduate, Vocational/Occupational/Scholarship)* [7969]

Charlie Trotters's Culinary Education Foundation Culinary Study Scholarships *(Professional development, Undergraduate/Scholarship)* [8962]

Jo Anne J. Trow Scholarships *(Undergraduate/Scholarship)* [6020]

Troy University Rodeo Team Scholarships *(Graduate/Scholarship)* [181]

Truckload Carriers Association Scholarships *(Undergraduate/Scholarship)* [8966]

Harry S. Truman Scholarships *(Postgraduate/Scholarship)* [8970]

Trustee, Schawe, and Presidential Scholarships *(Undergraduate/Scholarship)* [9776]

Trustee Scholarships *(Undergraduate/Scholarship)* [5235]

TSA Teach Technology Scholarships *(Undergraduate/Scholarship)* [8816]

Norman J. Tschantz/Walter C. Deuble Scholarships *(Undergraduate/Scholarship)* [8705]

TSHP R&E Foundation Scholarship Program *(Undergraduate, Graduate/Scholarship)* [8972]

Tucker Family Scholarships *(Undergraduate/Scholarship)* [9308]

Barry Tuckwell Scholarships *(All/Scholarship)* [4953]

Richard R. Tufenkian Memorial Scholarships *(Undergraduate/Scholarship)* [1571]

Graydon A. Tunstall Undergraduate Student Scholarships *(Undergraduate/Scholarship)* [7245]

Turf and Ornamental Communicators Association Scholarship Program *(Undergraduate/Scholarship)* [8974]

Hans Turley Prize in Queer Eighteenth-Century Studies *(Graduate, Professional development/Prize)* [1235]

Jeff Turner-Forsyth Audubon Society Scholarships *(Undergraduate/Scholarship)* [9658]

James A. Turner, Jr. Memorial Scholarships *(Undergraduate/Scholarship)* [1447]

Lydia Donaldson Tutt-Jones Memorial Research Grant *(Graduate, Professional development/Grant)* [72]

Vice Adm. Jerry O. Tuttle, USN (Ret.) and Mrs. Barbara A. Tuttle Science and Technology Scholarships *(Undergraduate/Scholarship)* [1564]

Two Year/Community Broadcast Education Association Scholarship Awards *(All/Scholarship)* [2186]

UAA Alaska Kidney Foundation Scholarships *(Graduate, Undergraduate/Scholarship)* [9115]

UAL/UABT Scholarship Program *(Undergraduate/Scholarship)* [9007]

UCB, Inc. NP Student Scholarships *(Graduate/Scholarship)* [380]

Morris K. Udall Scholarships *(Undergraduate/Scholarship)* [8991]

Udall Scholarships *(Undergraduate/Scholarship)* [9197]

UFCW Scholarships *(Undergraduate/Scholarship)* [9011]

Sandy Ulm Scholarships *(Undergraduate/Scholarship)* [3816]

Ric Ulrich and Chuck Pischke Scholarships *(Undergraduate/Scholarship)* [7423]

Undergraduate and Medical/Graduate General Scholarships and Loans Program *(Undergraduate, Vocational/Occupational/Scholarship)* [8026]

Union of Marash Armenian Scholarships *(Graduate, Undergraduate/Scholarship)* [1607]

Union Plus Scholarship Program *(Undergraduate/Scholarship)* [5025]

United Engineering Foundation Grants *(All/Grant)* [9009]

United Health Foundation National Association of Hispanic Nurses Scholarships *(Graduate, Undergraduate/Scholarship)* [6084]

United Parcel Service Scholarships for Female Students *(Undergraduate/Scholarship)* [4810]

United Parcel Service Scholarships for Minority Students *(Undergraduate/Scholarship)* [4811]

United South and Eastern Tribes Scholarship Fund *(Undergraduate/Scholarship)* [9021]

U.S. Air Force ROTC Express Scholarships *(Undergraduate/Scholarship)* [9027]

U.S. Air Force ROTC High School Scholarships *(Undergraduate/Scholarship)* [9028]

U.S. Air Force ROTC In-College Scholarships *(Undergraduate/Scholarship)* [9029]

U.S. Aircraft Insurance Group Professional Development Program (USAIG PDP) Scholarships *(Undergraduate/Scholarship)* [6172]

U.S. Bates Scholarship Program *(Undergraduate/Scholarship)* [5026]

U.S. BIA Indian Higher Education Grants *(Undergraduate/Grant)* [823]

United States Capitol Historical Society Fellowships *(Graduate/Fellowship)* [9037]

The United States Department of State, Bureau of Educational & Cultural Affairs Fellowships *(Doctorate, Graduate/Fellowship)* [1143]

United States Geospatial Intelligence Foundation Graduate Scholarships *(Postgraduate/Scholarship)* [9044]

United States Geospatial Intelligence Foundation High School Scholarships *(Undergraduate/Scholarship)* [9045]

United States Geospatial Intelligence Foundation Undergraduate Scholarships *(Undergraduate/Scholarship)* [9046]

United States Golf Association Fellowship Program *(All/Fellowship)* [9048]

United States Golf Association Scholarship Program *(Undergraduate/Scholarship)* [9049]

U.S. Pan Asian American Chamber of Commerce McDonald's Scholarships *(Undergraduate/Scholarship)* [9069]

U.S. Pan Asian American Chamber of Commerce UPS Scholarships *(Undergraduate/Scholarship)* [9070]

United States Society on Dams Scholarships *(Graduate/Scholarship)* [9072]

Universal Studios Preservation Scholarships *(Graduate/Scholarship)* [1834]

University Alliance HSF/UGA College Scholarship Program *(Undergraduate/Scholarship)* [4583]

University of California LGBT Alumni Scholarships (UCGALA) *(Undergraduate/Scholarship)* [7874]

University of Hawaii at Manoa Graduate Assistantship Awards *(Graduate/Award)* [9207]

University of Hawaii at Manoa Graduate Student Organization Travel Funds *(Graduate/Grant)* [9208]

University of Hawaii at Manoa Japan Travel Bureau Scholarships *(Graduate, Undergraduate/Scholarship)* [9209]

University of Louisville Eagle Scout Scholarships *(Undergraduate/Scholarship)* [6262]

University of Lowell Bookstore Associates Scholarships *(Graduate, Undergraduate/Scholarship)* [4727]

University of New Hampshire Parent's Association Endowment Scholarship Fund *(Undergraduate/Scholarship)* [9252]

University of Oregon Dean's Scholarships *(Undergraduate/Scholarship)* [9315]

University of Oregon General University Scholarships *(Undergraduate/Scholarship)* [9317]

University of Oregon Presidential Scholarships *(Undergraduate/Scholarship)* [9318]

University of West Alabama Rodeo Team Scholarships *(Graduate/Scholarship)* [182]

University of Wisconsin-Madison Chancellor's Scholarships *(Undergraduate/Scholarship)* [9376]

University of Wisconsin-Madison Hispanic/Latino Alumni Scholarships *(Undergraduate/Scholarship)* [9377]

University of Wisconsin-Madison Single Parent and Adult Scholarships *(Undergraduate/Scholarship)* [9382]

Upakar Indian-American Scholarships *(Undergraduate/Scholarship)* [9389]

Samuel Upchurch Memorial Scholarships *(Undergraduate/Scholarship)* [183]

UPE/ACM Scholarship Awards *(Graduate, Undergraduate/Award)* [9391]

UPE Scholarship Awards *(Graduate, Undergraduate/Award)* [9392]

Upper Midwest Human Rights Fellowship Program *(Professional development/Fellowship)* [9246]

UPS Diversity Scholarships *(Undergraduate/Scholarship)* [1356]

Urban and Regional Policy (Comparative Domestic Policy) Fellowships *(Professional development/Fellowship)* [4135]

The Urban Scholarship Fund *(Undergraduate/Scholarship)* [8844]

USA Funds Access to Education Scholarships *(Graduate, Undergraduate, Vocational/Occupational/Scholarship)* [9079]

USA/USA-Ukramerazha Scholarships *(Undergraduate/Scholarship)* [9077]

USAWOASF/Grantham University On-Line Scholarships *(Graduate, Undergraduate, Vocational/Occupational/Scholarship)* [9031]

USAWOASF Regular Scholarships *(Undergraduate, Vocational/Occupational/Scholarship)* [9032]

USHJA General Scholarships *(Undergraduate/Scholarship)* [9051]

USHJA Postgraduate Scholarships *(Postgraduate/Scholarship)* [9052]

USS Coral Sea Remembrance Scholarships *(Undergraduate/Scholarship)* [9405]

USS Tennessee Scholarship Fund *(Undergraduate, Vocational/Occupational/Scholarship)* [6595]

USTA Serves College Education Scholarships *(Undergraduate/Scholarship)* [9411]

USTA Tennis and Education Foundation College Textbook Scholarships *(Undergraduate/Scholarship)* [9412]

Utility Workers Union of America Scholarship Program *(Undergraduate/Scholarship)* [70]

John D. Utterback Scholarship Program *(Undergraduate/Scholarship)* [324]

Uva Faculty Fellowships *(Professional development/Fellowship)* [4782]

VABANC Scholarships *(Graduate, Undergraduate/Scholarship)* [9429]

Valley Alliance of Mentors for Opportunities and Scholarship Program (VAMOS) *(Undergraduate/Scholarship)* [4584]

Marta Vallin Memorial Scholarships *(Undergraduate/Scholarship)* [3233]

Valpak Scholarships *(Graduate, Undergraduate/Scholarship)* [7272]

Valuing Diversity PhD Scholarships *(Doctorate/Scholarship)* [920]

H. Wayne Van Agtmael Cosmetology Scholarship Fund *(Undergraduate/Scholarship)* [4248]

Hurad Van Der Bedrosian Memorial Scholarships *(Graduate/Scholarship)* [1608]

Patricia Van Kirk Scholarships *(Undergraduate/Scholarship)* [7424]

William P. Van Wagenen Fellowships *(Undergraduate/Fellowship)* [516]

The Vander Putten Family Scholarships *(All/Scholarship)* [2930]

Jacob VanNamen-Vans Marketing Scholarships *(Undergraduate/Scholarship)* [742]

Varian Radiation Therapy Scholarship Program *(Postdoctorate/Scholarship)* [1328]

Vector Marketing Canadian Scholarship Awards *(Undergraduate/Scholarship)* [9417]

Vector Marketing Scholarships *(Graduate, Undergraduate/Scholarship)* [7273]

Kodali Veeraiah & Sarojini Scholarships *(Graduate/Scholarship)* [8835]

VEF Fellowship Program *(Doctorate, Master's/Fellowship)* [9424]

VEF Visiting Scholars Program *(Doctorate/Scholarship)* [9425]

Ventana Medical Systems In Situ Hybridization Awards *(Professional development/Award)* [6519]

Veolia ES Waste-to-Energy/Terrence L. Guest Memorial Awards *(Graduate/Scholarship)* [8527]

Helen Veress-Mitchell Scholarship Fund *(Graduate, Undergraduate/Scholarship)* [2649]

Graduate Fellowship Program - Peter Verhofstadt Fellowships (GFP) *(Graduate/Fellowship)* [8084]

Vermont Paralegal Organization Scholarships *(Undergraduate/Scholarship)* [9419]

Chester M. Vernon Memorial Eagle Scout Scholarships *(High School/Scholarship)* [6263]

Dimitri J. Ververelli Memorial Scholarships *(Undergraduate/Scholarship)* [4520]

Vesalius Trust Student Scholarships *(Graduate, Undergraduate/Scholarship)* [9422]

Veterans of Enduring Freedom (Afghanistan) and Iraqi Freedom Scholarships *(Undergraduate/Scholarship)* [1565]

Veterans of Foreign Wars Scout of the Year *(High School/Scholarship)* [6264]

Zelda Walling Vicha Memorial Scholarships *(Undergraduate, Vocational/Occupational/Scholarship)* [1319]

Villers Fellowships for Health Care Justice *(Graduate/Fellowship)* [3706]

Vinyl Plastics Division Scholarships *(Graduate, Undergraduate/Scholarship)* [8461]

Violin Society of America Scholarships *(Undergraduate/Scholarship)* [9436]

Virginia Museum of Fine Arts Visual Arts Fellowships *(Graduate, Professional development, Undergraduate/Fellowship)* [9457]

Visiting Doctoral Tikvah Scholarships *(Doctorate/Scholarship)* [8907]

Visiting Fellowships *(Professional development/Fellowship)* [4783]

Visiting Scholars Program *(Doctorate/Fellowship)* [2699]

VISTAKON Research Grants *(All/Grant)* [389]

John D. Voelker Foundation Native American Scholarships *(Undergraduate/Scholarship)* [9470]

Von Ogden Vogt Scholarships *(Graduate, Master's/Scholarship)* [9005]

Miki Vohryzek-Bolden Student Paper Awards *(Undergraduate/Award)* [9583]

Vorgin-Bell Scholarships *(Graduate, Master's, Undergraduate/Scholarship)* [6848]

The Sibyl Jennings Vorheis Memorial Undergraduate Scholarships *(Undergraduate/Scholarship)* [3926]

Abe Voron Scholarships *(All/Scholarship)* [2187]

VPPPA June Brothers Scholarships *(Graduate, Undergraduate/Scholarship)* [9477]

VSP Research Grants *(All/Grant)* [390]

Wachovia Scholars Program *(Undergraduate/Scholarship)* [4551]

Wachovia/TELACU Excellence in Teaching Scholar-

ships *(Undergraduate/Scholarship)* [8823]

Chapter 4 - Lawrence A. Wacker Memorial Awards *(Undergraduate/Scholarship)* [8402]

CSF Dee Wacksman Memorial Scholarships *(Undergraduate/Scholarship)* [2876]

Bruce Wade Memorial Scholarships for Lesbian, Gay and Bisexual *(Undergraduate/Scholarship)* [7875]

Mercedes Laurie Wade Scholarships *(Undergraduate/Scholarship)* [2341]

Wadsworth International Fellowships *(Graduate/Fellowship)* [9562]

Ed Wadsworth Memorial Scholarships *(Undergraduate/Scholarship)* [184]

WAEPA Scholarship Program *(Undergraduate, Vocational/Occupational/Scholarship)* [9763]

Nell and Spencer Waggoner Scholarships *(Undergraduate/Scholarship)* [9659]

Selman A. Waksman Endowed Scholarships in Microbial Diversity *(Undergraduate/Scholarship)* [5633]

Jane C. Waldbaum Archaeological Field School Scholarships *(Undergraduate/Scholarship)* [1496]

Laramie Walden Memorial Fund *(Undergraduate/Scholarship)* [3927]

Margaret E. Waldron Scholarship Fund *(Undergraduate/Scholarship)* [3794]

Gary Walker Memorial Scholarships *(Professional development/Scholarship)* [3972]

Arthur BC Walker Scholarships *(Undergraduate/Scholarship)* [6494]

Myrtle and Earl Walker Scholarships *(Undergraduate/Scholarship)* [8403]

Walmart Associate Scholarships *(Undergraduate/Scholarship)* [9479]

Sam Walton Community Scholarships *(Undergraduate/Scholarship)* [9480]

Walton Family Foundation Scholarships *(Undergraduate/Scholarship)* [9481]

Francis Walton Memorial Scholarships *(Undergraduate/Scholarship)* [1112]

Alice Glaisyer Warfield Scholarships *(Undergraduate, Vocational/Occupational/Scholarship)* [8954]

Rachel Warner Memorial Scholarships *(Graduate, Undergraduate/Scholarship)* [6336]

Earl Warren Civil Rights Training Scholarships *(Graduate/Scholarship)* [5972]

Earl Warren Shearman and Sterling Scholarships *(Graduate/Scholarship)* [5973]

Washington College Bound Scholarships *(Undergraduate/Scholarship)* [9504]

Washington County Farm Bureau Scholarships *(Undergraduate/Scholarship)* [6948]

Washington CPA Foundation Scholarships *(Graduate, Undergraduate/Scholarship)* [9514]

Washington Group International Safety Scholarships *(Undergraduate/Scholarship)* [1357]

Washington Higher Education Coordinating Board Educational Opportunity Grants *(Undergraduate/Grant)* [9505]

Washington Higher Education Coordinating Board Health Professional Scholarships *(Graduate/Scholarship)* [9506]

Washington Higher Education Coordinating Board - State Need Grants (SNG) *(Undergraduate/Grant)* [9507]

Washington University Law School Chancellor's Graduate Fellowships *(Graduate/Fellowship)* [9532]

Vincent T. Wasilewski Scholarships *(All/Scholarship)* [2188]

John J. Wasmuth Postdoctoral Fellowships *(Postdoctorate/Fellowship)* [4541]

George Waterman Memorial Scholarships *(Graduate, Undergraduate/Scholarship)* [9515]

Stand Watie Scholarships *(Undergraduate/Scholarship)* [8529]

Robert D. Watkins Graduate Research Fellowships *(Postdoctorate/Fellowship)* [1303]

Watson-Brown Scholarships *(Undergraduate/Scholarship)* [9540]

Dr. James Watson Fellowship Program *(Doctorate, Graduate/Fellowship)* [4189]

Jeannette K. Watson Fellowships *(Undergraduate/Fellowship)* [9542]

Watsontown Volunteer Fire Company Scholarships

(Undergraduate/Scholarship) [2342]

Wayne-Meador-Elliott Scholarships *(Undergraduate/Scholarship)* [7120]

Kurt Wayne Scholarships *(Graduate/Scholarship)* [4069]

W.B.H. Dowse Fellowships *(Graduate, Doctorate/Fellowship)* [5680]

WBSN Foundation Scholarships *(Graduate, Professional development/Scholarship)* [9719]

WDA Full-Time Graduate Scholarships *(Graduate/Scholarship)* [9684]

WDA Part-Time Graduate Scholarships *(Graduate/Scholarship)* [9685]

WDHOF Scholarships in Marine Conservation *(Graduate, Undergraduate/Scholarship)* [9700]

Richard M. Weaver Fellowships *(Graduate/Fellowship)* [4849]

Monica M. Weaver Memorial Fund *(Undergraduate/Scholarship)* [3795]

Art and Dannie Weber Scholarships *(Undergraduate/Scholarship)* [9660]

Jerome P. Webster Fellowships *(Professional development/Fellowship)* [7749]

Webster Society Scholarships *(Undergraduate/Scholarship)* [9534]

WEF Canham Graduate Studies Scholarships *(Graduate/Scholarship)* [9536]

Frank L. Weil Memorial Eagle Scout Scholarships *(Undergraduate/Scholarship)* [6265]

Arthur Weinberg Fellowships for Independent Scholars *(Professional development/Fellowship)* [6710]

ACI Bertold E. Weinberg Scholarships *(Graduate/Scholarship)* [638]

Edith Weingarten Scholarship Program *(Postgraduate/Scholarship)* [957]

The Bee Winkler Weinstein Scholarship Fund *(All, Vocational/Occupational/Scholarship)* [8748]

William E. Weisel Scholarships *(Undergraduate/Scholarship)* [8405]

Polaire Weissman Funds *(Graduate/Fellowship)* [5793]

Welch Scholars Grants *(Undergraduate/Grant)* [972]

Welder Wildlife Foundation Fellowships *(Doctorate, Graduate/Fellowship)* [9559]

Sue Marsh Weller Memorial Scholarships *(Graduate, Postgraduate, Undergraduate/Scholarship)* [4738]

Wells Fargo American Indian Scholarships - Graduate *(Graduate/Scholarship)* [828]

Wells Fargo Scholarship Program *(Graduate, Undergraduate/Scholarship)* [4585]

Wells Fargo Scholarships *(Undergraduate/Scholarship)* [7425]

Wellstone Fellowships for Social Justice *(Graduate/Fellowship)* [3707]

Francis X. Weninger Scholarships *(Undergraduate/Scholarship)* [9777]

Wenner-Gren Foundation Dissertation Fieldwork Grants *(Doctorate/Grant)* [9563]

Wenner-Gren Foundation Post-PhD Research Grants *(Doctorate/Grant)* [9564]

Lucille and Charles A. Wert Scholarships *(Undergraduate/Scholarship)* [5696]

West Michigan Nursery and Landscape Association Scholarship Fund *(Undergraduate/Scholarship)* [4249]

West Virginia Educational Foundation Hospitality Business Alliance Scholarships *(Undergraduate/Scholarship)* [9570]

West Virginia Hospitality and Travel Association General Scholarships *(Undergraduate/Scholarship)* [9571]

West Virginia Nurses Association District No. 3 Scholarships *(Undergraduate/Scholarship)* [7121]

Redlands Evening Lions Club - Barbara Westen Scholarships *(Undergraduate/Scholarship)* [7716]

Western Civilization Fellowships *(Graduate/Fellowship)* [4850]

Western Governors University Scholarship Program *(Undergraduate/Scholarship)* [4586]

Western Michigan Society of Health-System Pharmacists Scholarships *(Undergraduate/Scholarship)* [9577]

Western Reserve Herb Society Scholarships *(Undergraduate/Scholarship)* [4537]

Western Society of Weed Science Outstanding Student Scholarship Program (Doctorate, Graduate, Undergraduate/Scholarship) [9585]

Robert B. Westover Scholarships (Undergraduate/Scholarship) [4070]

Dr. William "Tim" Whalen Memorial Scholarships (Undergraduate/Scholarship) [6792]

Whan Memorial Scholarships (Graduate, Undergraduate/Scholarship) [7274]

Edwyna Wheadon Postgraduate Training Scholarship Fund (Professional development/Scholarship) [6219]

Stan Wheeler Mentorship Awards (Professional development/Award) [5371]

Seitlin Franklin E. Wheeler Scholarship Fund (Undergraduate/Scholarship) [3324]

Paul A. Whelan Aviation Scholarships (Undergraduate, Graduate/Scholarship) [9193]

Whidbey Island Giving Circle Scholarships (Undergraduate/Scholarship) [7426]

Whitaker-Minard Memorial Scholarships (Undergraduate/Scholarship) [7122]

Brian J. White Endowed Law Scholarships (Undergraduate/Scholarship) [7212]

Richard S. White Fellowships (Undergraduate/Fellowship) [4522]

White House Fellows (Professional development/Fellowship) [7392]

Mary Kean White Memorial Scholarship Fund (Undergraduate/Scholarship) [8709]

White Rose Scholarships (Undergraduate/Scholarship) [7876]

Bradford White Scholarships (Undergraduate/Scholarship) [7350]

Paul D. White Scholarships (Undergraduate/Award) [2000]

ACI Richard N. White Student Fellowships (Master's/Fellowship) [639]

Robert B. and Sophia Whiteside Scholarships (Undergraduate/Scholarship) [3547]

Ann Cook Whitman Scholarships for Perry High School (Undergraduate/Scholarship) [3615]

Ann Cook Whitman Washington, DC Scholarships (Undergraduate/Scholarship) [3616]

Jane and Morgan Whitney Fellowships (Graduate/Fellowship) [5794]

Helen Hay Whitney Foundation Fellowships (Doctorate, Graduate/Fellowship) [9595]

Donna Axum Whitworth Scholarships (Undergraduate/Scholarship) [3393]

David Julian Wichard Scholarships (Undergraduate/Scholarship) [9309]

Louise Wachter Wichman Scholarship Fund (Undergraduate/Scholarship) [4250]

Alice Hersey Wick Scholarships (Undergraduate/Scholarship) [8192]

Tom Wicker Scholarships (Undergraduate/Scholarship) [9310]

AFCEA General John A. Wickham Scholarships (Undergraduate/Scholarship) [1566]

Wicomico High School Class of '55 Scholarships (Undergraduate/Scholarship) [3070]

Lois Widley Student Scholarships (Graduate, Undergraduate/Scholarship) [4967]

WIEA Scholarships (Doctorate, Graduate, Undergraduate, Vocational/Occupational/Scholarship) [9687]

Richard A. Wiebe Public Service Fellowships (Graduate/Fellowship) [6681]

Ethyl and Armin Wiebke Memorial Scholarships (Undergraduate/Scholarship) [9708]

Barbara Wiedner and Dorothy Vandercook Memorial Peace Scholarships (Undergraduate/Scholarship) [4311]

Elmo Wierenga Alumni Scholarships (Undergraduate/Scholarship) [4308]

Elie Wiesel Prize in Ethics (Undergraduate/Prize) [9597]

Fred Wiesner Educational Excellence Scholarships (Graduate, Undergraduate/Scholarship) [1885]

The WIFLE Scholarship Fund (Graduate, Postdoctorate, Undergraduate/Scholarship) [9702]

Fred C. Wikoff, Jr. Scholarships (Undergraduate, Vocational/Occupational/Scholarship) [3928]

Wild Felid Legacy Scholarships (Graduate/Scholarship) [9599]

Wilder Dimension Scholarships for Advanced Study

in Theatre Arts (Graduate/Scholarship) [3520]

Wiley Publishing Inc. Scholarships (Undergraduate/Scholarship) [3711]

Samuel S. Wilks Memorial Awards (Undergraduate/Award) [1396]

Willamette Chapter Scholarship Awards (Undergraduate/Scholarship) [6943]

M. William and Frances J. Tilghman Scholarships (Undergraduate/Scholarship) [3071]

William J. Brennan Graduate Assistant Fellowships (Graduate/Fellowship) [6920]

S. William & Martha R. Goff Educational Scholarships (Undergraduate/Scholarship) [7123]

Williams Chorale Bacardi Fallon Performing Arts Scholarships (Undergraduate/Award, Scholarship) [9608]

Williams Foundation Scholarships (Undergraduate/Scholarship) [7534]

Sidney B. Williams, Jr. Scholarships (Undergraduate/Scholarship) [882]

BM1 James Elliott Williams and LCDR Jack Graf Memorial Scholarship Fund (Undergraduate/Scholarship) [7134]

Rodney Williams Legacy Scholarships (Undergraduate/Grant) [9218]

Alice Hinchcliffe Williams, RDH, MS Graduate Scholarships (Graduate/Scholarship) [9445]

T. Franklin Williams Research Scholars Award Program (Professional development/Grant) [81]

Aubrey L. Williams Research Travel Fellowships (Professional development/Fellowship) [1236]

John G. Williams Scholarship Fund (Undergraduate/Scholarship) [9610]

CSM Virgil R. Williams Scholarships (Undergraduate/Scholarship) [3645]

Dr. Dana Williams Scholarships (Undergraduate/Scholarship) [2964]

Leon Williams Scholarships (Undergraduate/Scholarship) [7974]

Maxine Williams Scholarships (Postdoctorate/Scholarship) [513]

Randy Williams Scholarships (Undergraduate, Vocational/Occupational/Scholarship) [7975]

Redlands Footlighters, Inc. - Merle and Peggy Williams Scholarships (Undergraduate/Scholarship) [7717]

Cenie Jomo Williams Tuition Scholarships (Graduate, Undergraduate/Scholarship) [6043]

Mary Katherine "Kathy" Williamson Scholarship Fund (Undergraduate/Scholarship) [3050]

Beverly Willis Architecture Foundation Dissertation Fellowships (Doctorate/Fellowship) [8298]

Gary S. Wilmer RAMI Music Scholarships (Undergraduate/Scholarship) [3174]

The Wilmore Scholarship Fund (Undergraduate, Vocational/Occupational/Scholarship) [3929]

Glenn Wilson Broadcast Journalism Scholarships (Undergraduate/Scholarship) [7124]

Woodrow Wilson Dissertation Fellowships in Women's Studies (Graduate/Fellowship) [9620]

Pete Wilson Graduate Scholarships (Graduate, Undergraduate/Scholarship) [7584]

Woodrow Wilson International Center for Scholars Fellowships (Doctorate/Fellowship) [9612]

Pete Wilson Journalism Scholarships (Graduate, Undergraduate/Scholarship) [7585]

Saul T. Wilson, Jr. Scholarships (Graduate, Undergraduate/Scholarship) [9403]

Bob Wilson Legacy Scholarships (Undergraduate/Scholarship) [2256]

The Arthur N. Wilson, MD, Scholarships (Undergraduate/Scholarship) [924]

Woodrow Wilson-Rockefeller Brothers Fund Fellowships for Aspiring Teachers of Color (Graduate/Fellowship) [9621]

John Charles Wilson Scholarships (Undergraduate/Scholarship) [4856]

Theo Wilson Scholarships (Graduate, Undergraduate/Scholarship) [7023]

Harriet Barnhart Wimmer Scholarships (Undergraduate/Scholarship) [1288]

David A. Winston Health Policy Scholarships (Graduate/Scholarship) [1892]

Winston-Salem Foundation Scholarships (Undergraduate/Scholarship) [9664]

Winston Scholarships (Graduate, Undergraduate,

Vocational/Occupational/Scholarship) [8032]

Marine Corps Sgt. Jeannette L. Winters Memorial Scholarships (Undergraduate/Scholarship) [1567]

Winterthur Research Fellowships (All/Fellowship) [9668]

John D. Wirth Travel Grants for International Scholars (Graduate, Professional development/Grant) [1254]

Wisconsin Laboratory Association Graduate Student Scholarships (Graduate/Scholarship) [9689]

Wisconsin Laboratory Association Technical Student Scholarships (Undergraduate/Scholarship) [9690]

Wisconsin Laboratory Association Undergraduate University Student Scholarships (Undergraduate/Scholarship) [9691]

CSF HCRTA/Glen O. and Wyllabeth Wise Scholarships (Undergraduate/Scholarship) [2877]

WKIX Alumni Association Scholarships (Undergraduate/Scholarship) [9311]

WMA Memorial Scholarships (Undergraduate/Scholarship) [9709]

WNBA Eastman Grants (Professional development/Grant) [9731]

WOCN Accredited Nursing Education Scholarships (Graduate, Undergraduate/Scholarship) [9765]

WOCN Advanced Education Scholarships (Doctorate, Graduate, Undergraduate/Scholarship) [9766]

Woksape Oyate: "Wisdom of the People" Distinguished Scholars Awards (Undergraduate/Scholarship) [813]

Paul R. Wolf Memorial Scholarships (Graduate/Scholarship) [1672]

Emil Wolf Outstanding Student Paper Competition (Graduate, Undergraduate/Award) [6914]

Wolf Trap Foundation Scholarship Program for Performing Arts Teachers (Professional development/Scholarship) [9693]

The Wolf Trap Internship Program (Graduate, Professional development, Undergraduate/Internship) [9694]

Deborah Partridge Wolfe International Fellowships (Graduate, Undergraduate/Fellowship) [9807]

Abel Wolman Fellowships (Doctorate/Fellowship) [1419]

Lee Womack Scholarship Fund (Undergraduate/Scholarship) [5917]

Woman In Rural Electrification Scholarships (WIRE) (Undergraduate/Scholarship) [8565]

Woman's Club of Grand Haven Scholarships Fund (Undergraduate/Scholarship) [4251]

The Woman's Club of Nashville Scholarships (Undergraduate/Scholarship) [3139]

Women in Cancer Research Scholar Awards (Graduate, Postdoctorate/Award) [453]

Women In Defense HORIZONS Scholarships (Graduate, Undergraduate/Scholarship) [9696]

Women In Need Scholarships (Undergraduate/Scholarship) [3601]

Women In Transition Scholarships (Undergraduate/Scholarship) [3602]

Women of Today's Manufacturing Scholarships (Undergraduate/Scholarship) [3175]

Women of WSAJ Bar Preparation Scholarships (Undergraduate/Scholarship) [9518]

Women's Army Corps Veterans Association Scholarships (Undergraduate/Scholarship) [9711]

Women's Independence Scholarship Programs (Undergraduate/Scholarship) [8774]

Women's Italian Club of Boston Scholarships (Undergraduate/Scholarship) [4083]

Women's Jewelry Association Member Grants (All/Grant) [9726]

Women's Leadership in Agriculture Scholarship Program (Undergraduate/Scholarship) [6855]

Women's Overseas and Service League Scholarships for Women (Undergraduate/Scholarship) [9733]

Carolyn Wones Recruitment Scholarship Grants (Undergraduate/Scholarship) [3176]

Dennis Wong and Associates Scholarships (Graduate, Undergraduate/Scholarship) [5223]

Dr. Harold S. Wood Awards for Excellence (Undergraduate/Award) [4072]

Wood County Bar Association Memorial Scholarships (Undergraduate/Scholarship) [7125]

Mary and Elliot Wood Foundation Undergraduate

Scholarship Fund *(Undergraduate/Scholarship)* [3931]

Wood Fruitticher Grocery Company, Inc. Scholarships *(Graduate, Undergraduate/Scholarship)* [173]

Rolla F. Wood Graduate Scholarships *(Graduate/Scholarship)* [7277]

Hugh and Helen Wood Nepales Scholarships *(Undergraduate/Scholarship)* [2066]

Irene Woodall Graduate Scholarships *(Master's/Scholarship)* [710]

Woodcock Family Education Scholarship Program *(Undergraduate/Scholarship)* [284]

Woodex Bearing Company Scholarships *(Undergraduate/Scholarship)* [4095]

Betsy B. Woodward Scholarships *(Undergraduate/Scholarship)* [1782]

Woodyard Family Scholarships *(Undergraduate/Scholarship)* [4265]

Marilyn Graboys Wool Scholarships *(Undergraduate/Scholarship)* [7796]

CSF L and T Woolfolk Memorial Scholarships *(Undergraduate/Scholarship)* [2878]

Blance E. Woolls Scholarships *(Graduate/Scholarship)* [2073]

David T. Woolsey Scholarships *(Undergraduate/Scholarship)* [1289]

Hawaii Chapter/David T. Woolsey Scholarships *(Graduate, Undergraduate/Scholarship)* [5337]

Patty Wooten Scholarships *(Undergraduate/Scholarship)* [1707]

Worcester District Medical Society Scholarship Fund *(Undergraduate/Scholarship)* [9746]

John W. Work III Memorial Foundation Scholarships *(Undergraduate/Scholarship)* [3140]

Working for Farmers' Success Scholarships *(Undergraduate/Scholarship)* [9748]

The Working Press Internships *(Undergraduate/Internship)* [8467]

Workshop, Inc. and Stark MRDD Fostering Diversity Through Special Needs Scholarship Fund *(Undergraduate/Scholarship)* [8710]

Worldstudio AIGA Scholarships *(Graduate, Undergraduate/Scholarship)* [9761]

Donald Worster Travel Grants *(Graduate, Professional development/Grant)* [1255]

James and Colin Lee Wozumi Scholarships *(Undergraduate/Scholarship)* [7427]

WREI Congressional Fellows on Women and Public Policy *(Doctorate, Graduate, Master's/Fellowship)* [9735]

WRI Education Foundation Scholarships - Graduate *(Graduate/Scholarship)* [9670]

WRI Education Foundation Scholarships - High School Seniors *(Undergraduate/Scholarship)* [9671]

WRI Education Foundation Scholarships - Undergraduate *(Undergraduate/Scholarship)* [9672]

Jean Wright-Elson Scholarships *(Doctorate, Graduate, Undergraduate/Scholarship)* [7976]

WSAJ American Justice Essay Scholarships *(Undergraduate/Scholarship)* [9519]

WSAJ Diversity Bar Preparation Scholarships *(Undergraduate/Scholarship)* [9520]

WSAJ Presidents' Scholarships *(Undergraduate/Scholarship)* [9521]

WSCPA Chapter Scholarships *(Graduate, Undergraduate/Scholarship)* [9516]

WSSA Students Paper Competition *(Undergraduate/Award)* [9579]

WTVD Endowment Scholarships *(Undergraduate/Scholarship)* [9312]

Wyatt, Tarrant and Combs, LLP Scholarships *(Undergraduate/Scholarship)* [9242]

WYCUP Scholarships *(Professional development/Scholarship)* [9752]

Margaret Wyeth Scholarships *(Undergraduate/Scholarship)* [3177]

Wyeth-SUS Clinical Scholar Awards *(Professional development/Award)* [8512]

Xavier Community-Engaged Fellowships *(Undergraduate/Fellowship)* [9778]

Xavier University Chancellor Scholarships *(Undergraduate/Scholarship)* [9779]

Xavier University Departmental Scholarships *(Undergraduate/Scholarship)* [9780]

Xavier University Honors Bachelor of Arts Scholarships *(Undergraduate/Scholarship)* [9781]

Xavier University Legacy Scholarships *(Undergraduate/Scholarship)* [9782]

Xavier University ROTC Scholarships - Air Force ROTC *(Undergraduate/Scholarship)* [9783]

Xavier University Williams Scholarships *(Undergraduate/Scholarship)* [9785]

Xerox Technical Minority Scholarships *(Graduate, Undergraduate/Scholarship)* [9787]

M.H. Yager Memorial Scholarships *(Undergraduate/Scholarship)* [1953]

Yankee Clipper Contest Club, Inc. Youth Scholarships *(Undergraduate/Scholarship)* [1114]

William J. Yankee Memorial Scholarships *(Undergraduate/Scholarship)* [1021]

Gwen Yarnell Theatre Scholarships *(Undergraduate/Scholarship)* [3751]

Yasme Foundation Scholarships *(Undergraduate/Scholarship)* [1115]

Minoru Yasui Memorial Scholarships *(Graduate/Scholarship)* [5147]

Marusia Yaworska Entrance Scholarships *(Graduate/Scholarship)* [9501]

Willa Yeck Memorial Scholarship Fund *(Undergraduate/Scholarship)* [3450]

Marilyn Yetso Memorial Scholarships *(Undergraduate, Vocational/Occupational/Scholarship)* [2759]

Vera Yip Memorial Scholarships *(Undergraduate, Vocational/Occupational/Scholarship)* [2760]

YMF Scholarships *(All/Scholarship)* [9791]

York Rite Grand Chapter Royal Arch Masons Scholarships *(Undergraduate/Scholarship)* [3426]

Gary Yoshimura Scholarships *(Undergraduate/Scholarship)* [7542]

Jack and Edna May Yost Scholarships *(Undergraduate/Scholarship)* [3964]

You Go Girl! Scholarships *(Undergraduate/Scholarship)* [7428]

Alma H. Young Emerging Scholar Awards *(Doctorate/Scholarship)* [9394]

Young Investigator Grants *(Undergraduate/Grant)* [6529]

Searle Young Legal Scholars Research Fellowships *(Professional development/Fellowship)* [3732]

Young People For Fellowships (YP4) *(Undergraduate/Fellowship)* [8147]

Donnell B. Young Scholarships *(Undergraduate/Scholarship)* [286]

Elmer Cooke Young - Taylor Young Scholarships *(Undergraduate/Scholarship)* [4463]

Youth Empowerment Summit Scholarships *(Undergraduate/Scholarship)* [6148]

Youth Leadership Scholarships *(Undergraduate/Scholarship)* [2265]

Youth Partners Accessing Capital (PAC) *(Graduate, Undergraduate/Scholarship)* [354]

The Youth Scholarship Program *(Undergraduate/Scholarship)* [2719]

Youth Scholarships *(Undergraduate/Scholarship)* [8305]

Youth for Understanding Scholarships *(Undergraduate/Scholarship)* [9797]

Diane Yu Loan Repayment Assistance Program *(Undergraduate/Loan)* [6029]

Z/I Imaging Scholarships *(Graduate/Scholarship)* [1673]

Lisa Zaken Awards For Excellence *(Graduate, Undergraduate/Award)* [4812]

Dr. Marie E. Zakrzewski Medical Scholarships *(Doctorate/Scholarship)* [5302]

James and Joy Zana Memorial Scholarships *(Undergraduate/Scholarship)* [4266]

CSF L.B. Zapoleon Scholarships *(Undergraduate/Scholarship)* [2879]

Zarley, McKee, Thomte, Voorhees, Sease Law Scholarships *(Undergraduate/Scholarship)* [3516]

Urashi Zen Scholarships *(Undergraduate/Scholarship)* [7429]

Zenko Family Scholarship Fund *(Undergraduate/Scholarship)* [4252]

Zeta Chapter Memorial Scholarship Awards *(Undergraduate/Scholarship)* [3178]

Zeta Phi Beta Sorority General Graduate Scholarships *(Graduate, Postdoctorate/Scholarship)* [9808]

Zeta Phi Beta Sorority General Undergraduate Scholarships *(Undergraduate/Scholarship)* [9809]

A.F. Zimmerman Scholarships *(Graduate, Master's/Scholarship)* [7246]

Blanche Raper Zimmerman Scholarships *(Professional development/Scholarship)* [9665]

Zimmermann Scholarships *(Graduate/Scholarship)* [8785]

A.R. Zipf Fellowships *(Graduate/Fellowship)* [3280]

Jacob Ziskind Memorial Fund for Upperclassmen *(Graduate, Undergraduate/Scholarship)* [4728]

Morris L. and Rebecca Ziskind Memorial Scholarships *(Undergraduate/Scholarship)* [4655]

Lorraine Zitone Memorial Scholarship Fund *(Undergraduate/Scholarship)* [3451]

Ruth and Sherman Zudekoff Scholarships *(Undergraduate/Scholarship)* [3084]

Francis Sylvia Zverina Scholarships *(Undergraduate/Scholarship)* [4538]

UNITED STATES (BY REGION)

Eastern states

NACA East Coast Graduate Student Scholarships *(Graduate, Postdoctorate/Scholarship)* [6047]

New England states

Armenian American Medical Association Scholarships *(Undergraduate/Scholarship)* [1581]

Dvora Brodie Scholarships *(Graduate, Postgraduate, Undergraduate/Scholarship)* [4503]

NELA Scholarships *(Graduate, Master's/Scholarship)* [6624]

Shaw-Worth Memorial Scholarships *(Undergraduate/Scholarship)* [4636]

Switzer Environmental Fellowships *(Graduate/Fellowship)* [8787]

Northeastern states

Connecticut Capitol Scholarship Program *(Undergraduate/Scholarship)* [4421]

Juvenile Arthritis Scholarships *(Undergraduate/Scholarship)* [4444]

Northwestern states

Lori Rhett Memorial Scholarships *(Graduate, Undergraduate/Scholarship)* [6055]

WFI International Fellowships *(Undergraduate/Fellowship)* [9754]

Southeastern states

Leighton M. Ballew Directing Scholarships *(Undergraduate/Scholarship)* [8569]

Polly Holliday Scholarships *(Undergraduate/Scholarship)* [8570]

Robert Porterfield Graduate Scholarships *(Graduate/Scholarship)* [8571]

Marian A. Smith Scholarships *(Graduate/Scholarship)* [8572]

Southeastern Theatre Conference Secondary School Scholarships *(Undergraduate/Scholarship)* [8573]

William E. Wilson Scholarships *(Graduate/Scholarship)* [8574]

Western states

American Composites Manufacturers Association Western Chapter Scholarships *(Undergraduate/Scholarship)* [626]

Institute of Transportation Engineers - Western District Fellowships *(Graduate/Fellowship)* [4824]

UNITED STATES (BY STATE)

Alabama

ACHE/American Legion Auxiliary Scholarships *(Undergraduate/Scholarship)* [155]

ACHE/American Legion Scholarships (Undergraduate/Scholarship) [156]
ACHE Junior and Community College Athletic Scholarships (Undergraduate/Scholarship) [157]
ACHE Junior and Community College Performing Arts Scholarships (Undergraduate/Scholarship) [158]
ACHE Police Officers and Firefighters Survivors' Educational Assistance Programs (Undergraduate/Scholarship) [159]
ACHE Senior Adult Scholarships (Undergraduate/Scholarship) [160]
ACHE Two-Year College Academic Scholarships (Undergraduate/Scholarship) [161]
Air Force ROTC Enhanced HBCU Scholarships (Undergraduate/Scholarship) [9023]
AISC/Southern Association of Steel Fabricators Fellowships (Graduate/Fellowship) [873]
AISC/Southern Association of Steel Fabricators Scholarships (Undergraduate/Scholarship) [874]
Alabama Gi Dependents Educational Benefit Program (Undergraduate/Scholarship) [162]
Alabama National Guard Educational Assistance Program (Undergraduate/Scholarship) [163]
Alabama Power Scholarships (Undergraduate/Scholarship) [6809]
Alabama Scholarships for Dependents of Blind Parents (Undergraduate/Scholarship) [164]
Alabama Student Assistance Programs (Undergraduate/Scholarship) [165]
Alabama Student Grant Programs (Undergraduate, Vocational/Occupational/Grant) [166]
Auburn University College of Veterinary Medicine Scholarships (Undergraduate/Scholarship) [177]
Birmingham-Southern College Eagle Scout Scholarships (Undergraduate/Scholarship) [6248]
William Verbon Black Scholarships (Undergraduate/Scholarship) [187]
Miranda Bouldin General Scholarships (Undergraduate/Scholarship) [5513]
Billy Bowling Memorial Scholarships (Undergraduate/Scholarship) [6810]
Calhoun Scholarships (Undergraduate/Scholarship) [2226]
Cecil Earl Clapp, Sr. Memorial Scholarships (Undergraduate/Scholarship) [6811]
Charles Clarke Cordle Memorial Scholarships (Undergraduate/Scholarship) [1081]
J. Craig and Page T. Smith Scholarships (Undergraduate/Scholarship) [8239]
Marvin E. Daly Memorial Scholarships (Undergraduate/Scholarship) [6812]
Michael Denton Scholarships (Undergraduate/Scholarship) [6813]
Harriet Erich Graduate Fellowships (Graduate/Fellowship) [3371]
Gadsden State/McClellan Campus Nursing Scholarship Awards (Undergraduate/Scholarship) [3036]
Homajean Grisham Memorial Scholarships (Undergraduate/Scholarship) [6814]
Gulf Coast Hurricane Scholarships (Graduate, Undergraduate/Scholarship) [8449]
Howell Heflin Memorial Scholarships (Undergraduate/Scholarship) [6815]
Broughton Isom Memorial Scholarships (Undergraduate/Scholarship) [6816]
Cecil Lane Family Scholarships (Undergraduate/Scholarship) [178]
Legacy Inc. College Undergraduate and Graduate Scholarships (Graduate, Undergraduate/Scholarship) [5400]
Franklin A. Lentesty Scholarships (Undergraduate/Scholarship) [6817]
Gertie S. Lowe Nursing Scholarship Awards (Undergraduate/Scholarship) [3043]
The Medalist Club Post Graduate Scholarships (Postgraduate/Scholarship) [5733]
Jerry Medforth Nursing Scholarship Awards (Undergraduate/Scholarship) [3044]
Muscle Shoals Kiwanis/Wal-Mart Scholarships (Undergraduate/Scholarship) [6818]
NACA Southeast Student Leadership Scholarships (Undergraduate/Scholarship) [6052]
Northwest-Shoals Community College Bank Independent Scholarships (Undergraduate/Scholarship) [6822]
Northwest-Shoals Community College Independent Computer Scholarships (Undergraduate/Scholarship) [6827]
Ina E. Powell Memorial Scholarships (Undergraduate/Scholarship) [179]
Lori Rhett Memorial Scholarships (Graduate, Undergraduate/Scholarship) [6055]
D. Mitchell Self Memorial Scholarships (Undergraduate/Scholarship) [6829]
Justice Janie L. Shores Scholarships (Undergraduate/Scholarship) [189]
Aaron B. Singleton Memorial Scholarships (Undergraduate/Scholarship) [6830]
Tuscumbia Kiwanis Scholarships (Undergraduate/Scholarship) [6831]
The Wax Company Scholarships (Undergraduate/Scholarship) [185]
Wayne County Bank Scholarships (Undergraduate/Scholarship) [6832]

Alaska

AISC/US Steel Fellowships (Graduate/Fellowship) [876]
Alaska Aerospace Development Corporation Scholarships (Undergraduate/Scholarship) [9130]
Alaska Native Medical Center Auxiliary Scholarships (Undergraduate/Scholarship) [9131]
Alaska Press Club Scholarships (Undergraduate/Scholarship) [9132]
Alaska Support Industry Alliance Scholarships (Undergraduate/Scholarship) [9133]
Alaska Visitors Association/Gomar Scholarships (Undergraduate/Scholarship) [9134]
Alaska Yukon Pioneer Memorial Scholarships (Undergraduate/Scholarship) [9135]
Amos Joe Alter ASCE Section Alaska Section Scholarships (Undergraduate/Scholarship) [9136]
APTRA Scholarships (Undergraduate/Scholarship) [1684]
Mike Ardaw Scholarships (Undergraduate/Scholarship) [9137]
UAA Elaine Atwood Scholarships (Undergraduate/Scholarship) [9084]
UAA Dr. Jon Baker Memorial Scholarships (Graduate, Undergraduate, Vocational/Occupational/Scholarship) [9085]
UAA Michael Baring-Gould Memorial Scholarships (Graduate, Undergraduate/Scholarship) [9086]
Lawrence Bayer Business Administration Scholarships (Undergraduate/Scholarship) [9138]
Charles E. Behlke Engineering Memorial Scholarships (Undergraduate/Scholarship) [9139]
UAA Mark A. Beltz Scholarships (Graduate, Undergraduate, Vocational/Occupational/Scholarship) [9087]
Bill & Nell Biggs Scholarships (Undergraduate/Scholarship) [9140]
Bolick Foreign Student Scholarships (Undergraduate/Scholarship) [9141]
Dr. Betty J. Boyd-Beu & Edwin G. Beu, Jr. Scholarships (Undergraduate/Scholarship) [9142]
UAA Pat Brakke Political Science Scholarships (Undergraduate/Scholarship) [9088]
Charles E. Bunnell Scholarships (Undergraduate/Scholarship) [9143]
Loyal D. Burkett Memorial Scholarships (Undergraduate/Scholarship) [9144]
Lyle Carlson Wildlife Management Scholarships (Undergraduate/Scholarship) [9145]
Chugach Gem & Mineral Society Scholarships (Undergraduate/Scholarship) [9089]
UAA Edward Rollin Clinton Memorial for Music (Undergraduate/Scholarship) [9090]
Mable B. Crawford Memorial Scholarships (Undergraduate/Scholarship) [9146]
Patricia Ann Hughes Eastaugh Memorial Teaching Scholarships (Undergraduate/Scholarship) [9147]
UAA Governor William A. Egan Scholarships (Undergraduate/Scholarship) [9091]
Alaska Community Foundation Sven E. & Lorraine Eriksson Scholarships (Undergraduate/Scholarship) [9092]
Excellence in Geographic Information Systems Scholarships (Undergraduate/Scholarship) [9148]
Fairbanks Chapter Legacy Scholarships (Undergraduate/Scholarship) [9186]
Lydia Fohn-Hansen/Lola Hill Memorial Scholarships (Undergraduate/Scholarship) [9149]
UAA Michael D. Ford Memorial Scholarships (Graduate, Undergraduate/Scholarship) [9093]
Johnny and Sarah Frank Scholarships (Undergraduate/Scholarship) [9150]
UAA Jan & Glenn Fredericks Scholarships (Graduate, Undergraduate/Scholarship) [9094]
UAA Ardell French Memorial Scholarships (Undergraduate/Scholarship) [9095]
Mary Ghezzi Nursing Scholarships (Undergraduate/Scholarship) [8983]
Charles F. Gould Endowment Scholarships (Undergraduate/Scholarship) [9151]
UAA Ken Gray Endowment Scholarships (Undergraduate/Scholarship) [9097]
Patty Hamilton Early Childhood Development Scholarships (Undergraduate/Scholarship) [9152]
Jay Hammond Memorial Scholarships (Undergraduate/Scholarship) [9187]
UAA Muriel Hannah Scholarships in Art (Undergraduate, Vocational/Occupational/Scholarship) [9098]
Lenore & George Hedla Accounting Scholarships (Undergraduate/Scholarship) [9099]
John B. Henderson Scholarships (Undergraduate/Scholarship) [9153]
Donald Wills Jacobs Scholarships (Undergraduate/Scholarship) [9154]
UAA Chris L. Kleinke Scholarships (Graduate, Undergraduate/Scholarship) [9101]
Iver & Cora Knapstad Scholarships (Undergraduate/Scholarship) [9155]
UAA Kris Knudson Memorial Scholarships (Graduate, Undergraduate/Scholarship) [9102]
Robert Wade Korn Endowed Scholarships (Undergraduate/Scholarship) [9156]
Arlene Kuhner Memorial Scholarships (Undergraduate/Scholarship) [9103]
UAA Paul G. Landis Scholarships (Undergraduate/Scholarship) [9104]
Austin E. Lathrop Scholarships (Undergraduate/Scholarship) [9157]
Franklin M. Leach Scholarships (Undergraduate/Scholarship) [9158]
Matanuska-Susitna College Regent's Scholarships (Undergraduate/Scholarship) [9160]
Dave McCloud Aviation Memorial Scholarships (Undergraduate/Scholarship) [9161]
Richard Mellon Endowment Scholarships (Undergraduate/Scholarship) [9162]
Molly Ann Mishler Memorial Scholarships (Undergraduate/Scholarship) [9163]
Andrew Nerland Endowment Scholarships (Undergraduate/Scholarship) [9164]
Maureen E. Nolan-Cahill Memorial Scholarships (Undergraduate/Scholarship) [9165]
Don & Jan O'Dowd/SWAA Scholarships (Undergraduate/Scholarship) [9166]
UAA Diane Olsen Memorial Scholarships (Undergraduate/Scholarship) [9105]
Alvin G. Ott Fish and Wildlife Scholarships (Undergraduate/Scholarship) [9167]
Rachael Patterson Memorial Scholarships (Undergraduate/Scholarship) [8987]
Point Lay Memorial Scholarships (Undergraduate/Scholarship) [9168]
Providence Alaska Medical Center Auxiliary Scholarships (Undergraduate/Scholarship) [9106]
UAA April Relyea Scholarships (Graduate, Undergraduate, Vocational/Occupational/Scholarship) [9107]
A.D. 'Al' Robertson Memorial Scholarships (Undergraduate/Scholarship) [9169]
UAA Jack & Martha Roderick Scholarships (Graduate, Undergraduate/Scholarship) [9108]
Pat and Cliff Rogers Nursing Scholarships (Undergraduate/Scholarship) [9170]

Dr. Orrin J. Rongstad Wildlife Management Scholarships (*Undergraduate/Scholarship*) [9171]

Russian/Central Asian Student Scholarships (*Undergraduate/Scholarship*) [9172]

Schaible Health Care Services Scholarships (*Undergraduate/Scholarship*) [8988]

UAA Brown Schoenheit Memorial Scholarships (*Undergraduate/Scholarship*) [9109]

UAA Eveline Schuster Memorial Award/Scholarships (*Graduate, Undergraduate/Scholarship*) [9110]

Clair Shirey Scholarships (*Undergraduate/Scholarship*) [9173]

Ward Sims Memorial Scholarships (*Undergraduate/Scholarship*) [9174]

Lillian Smith Scholarship for Teaching Students (*Graduate, Undergraduate/Scholarship*) [9111]

Snodgrass Scholarships (*Undergraduate/Scholarship*) [9175]

Sourdough Reunion Memorial Scholarships (*Undergraduate/Scholarship*) [9176]

Sheri Stears Education Scholarships (*Undergraduate/Scholarship*) [9112]

Sturgulewski Family Scholarships (*Graduate, Undergraduate, Vocational/Occupational/Scholarship*) [9113]

Tanana Valley Campus Culinary Arts Scholarships (*Undergraduate/Scholarship*) [8989]

UAA Accounting Club Scholarships (*Undergraduate/Scholarship*) [9114]

UAA Alumni Association Scholarships (*Undergraduate/Scholarship*) [9116]

UAA Anchorage Daily News Journalism Scholarships (*Undergraduate/Scholarship*) [9117]

UAA College of Business & Public Policy Scholarships (*Graduate, Undergraduate, Vocational/Occupational/Scholarship*) [9118]

UAA Emi Chance Memorial Scholarships (*Undergraduate/Scholarship*) [9119]

UAA Friends of the Performing Arts Scholarships (*Undergraduate/Scholarship*) [9120]

UAA GCI, Inc. Scholarships (*Undergraduate/Scholarship*) [9121]

UAA Kimura Scholarship Fund Illustration Scholarships (*Undergraduate/Scholarship*) [9122]

UAA Kimura Scholarship Fund Photography Scholarships (*Undergraduate/Scholarship*) [9123]

UAA Pignalberi Public Policy Scholarships (*Graduate/Scholarship*) [9124]

UAA Quanterra Scholarships (*Undergraduate/Scholarship*) [9125]

UAA RRANN Program Scholarships (*Undergraduate/Scholarship*) [9126]

UAA Wells Fargo Career Scholarships (*Graduate/Scholarship*) [9127]

UAF Alumni Association Scholarships (*Undergraduate/Scholarship*) [9189]

Umialik Scholarships (*Undergraduate/Scholarship*) [9177]

University of Alaska Scholars Program (*Undergraduate/Scholarship*) [9178]

William S. Wilson Memorial Scholarships (*Undergraduate/Scholarship*) [9179]

UAA Melissa J. Wolf Scholarships (*Undergraduate/Scholarship*) [9128]

Guy A. Woodings Scholarships (*Undergraduate/Scholarship*) [9180]

Ralph Yetka Memorial Scholarships (*Undergraduate/Scholarship*) [9181]

Joan C. Yoder Memorial Nursing Scholarships (*Undergraduate/Scholarship*) [9182]

Yukon Delta Fisheries Development Association Scholarships (*Undergraduate/Scholarship*) [9183]

Arizona

Marvin A. Andrews Scholarships/Internships (*Graduate/Internship, Scholarship*) [1517]

APTRA Scholarships (*Undergraduate/Scholarship*) [1684]

Arizona Hydrological Society Scholarships (*Graduate, Undergraduate/Scholarship*) [1522]

ASCPA High School Scholarships (*Undergraduate/Scholarship*) [1528]

Walt Bartram Memorial Education Award, Region 12 and Chapter 119 (*Undergraduate/Scholarship*) [8369]

CBC Spouses Flexible Education Scholarships (*Graduate, Master's, Undergraduate/Scholarship*) [3217]

Chapter 67 - Phoenix Scholarships (*Undergraduate/Scholarship*) [8380]

Charles A. Esser Memorial Scholarships (*Graduate/Scholarship*) [1518]

Gail Goodell Folsom Memorial Scholarships (*Undergraduate/Award*) [5975]

Future CPA Scholarships (*Community College, Graduate, Undergraduate/Scholarship*) [1529]

Sam Gallant Memorial Scholarships (*Graduate, Undergraduate/Scholarship*) [1530]

Marty Rosness Student Scholarships (*Undergraduate/Scholarship*) [1505]

Science Foundation Arizona Graduate Research Fellowships (GRF) (*Graduate/Fellowship*) [8054]

Tribal Priority Scholarships (*Graduate, Professional development, Undergraduate/Scholarship*) [1513]

University Junior Standing Scholarships (*Undergraduate/Scholarship*) [1531]

University Senior and Master's Program Scholarships (*Graduate/Scholarship*) [1532]

Arkansas

AISC/Southern Association of Steel Fabricators Fellowships (*Graduate/Fellowship*) [873]

AISC/Southern Association of Steel Fabricators Scholarships (*Undergraduate/Scholarship*) [874]

ARAFCS Doctoral Scholarships (*Doctorate/Scholarship*) [1534]

ARAFCS Masters Scholarships (*Graduate/Scholarship*) [1535]

Arkansas State University Mountain Home Scholarships (*Undergraduate/Scholarship*) [1551]

Arkansas Nursing Foundation - Dorothea Fund Scholarships (*Professional development/Scholarship*) [1543]

Arkansas Nursing Foundation - Mary Gray Scholarships (*Professional development/Scholarship*) [1544]

Randall Matthis for Environmental Studies Scholarships (*Graduate, Undergraduate/Scholarship*) [1537]

Hatton W. Sumners Scholarships (*Undergraduate/Scholarship*) [6869]

Larry Wilson for Environmental Studies Scholarships (*Graduate, Undergraduate/Scholarship*) [1538]

Larry Wilson Scholarships for Undergraduate Civil Engineering Students (*Undergraduate/Scholarship*) [1539]

California

AAAA Operation Jumpstart III Scholarships (*Graduate/Scholarship*) [433]

AAJUW Scholarships (*Graduate, Undergraduate/Scholarship*) [487]

Ruth Adams Memorial Scholarships (*Undergraduate/Scholarship*) [7615]

Carl Joseph Adelhardt Memorial Scholarships (*Undergraduate/Scholarship*) [4050]

AeA Scholarships (*Undergraduate/Scholarship*) [7904]

AIDS Awareness Scholarships (*Undergraduate/Scholarship*) [7843]

AISC/Structural Steel Education Council Fellowships (*Graduate/Fellowship*) [875]

Horatio Alger Louisiana Scholarships (*Undergraduate/Scholarship*) [308]

Dan Allen Memorial Scholarships (*Undergraduate/Scholarship*) [7844]

Anna Ames Clinical Excellence Student Grants (*Undergraduate/Grant*) [2281]

APTRA Scholarships (*Undergraduate/Scholarship*) [1684]

APWA Engineering Scholarships (*Undergraduate/Scholarship*) [1059]

Marvin Arnold and Irene Jaquetta Heye Scholarships (*Undergraduate/Scholarship*) [7906]

Asian/Pacific Bar Association of Sacramento Law Foundation Scholarships (*Graduate, Postgraduate/Scholarship*) [1650]

Associated Women for Pepperdine Scholarships (AWP) (*Undergraduate/Scholarship*) [7167]

Association of California Water Agencies Scholarships (*Undergraduate/Scholarship*) [1727]

Association for Women in Architecture Scholarships (*Undergraduate/Scholarship*) [1894]

Walt Bartram Memorial Education Award, Region 12 and Chapter 119 (*Undergraduate/Scholarship*) [8369]

Hazel Reed Baumeister Scholarship Program (*Undergraduate/Scholarship*) [8197]

Bay Area Minority Law Student Scholarships (*Graduate, Undergraduate/Scholarship*) [2019]

BECA Foundation-CUSM Scholarships (*Undergraduate/Scholarship*) [2039]

BECA Foundation General Scholarships Fund (*Undergraduate/Scholarship*) [2040]

James R. and Geraldine F. Bertelsen Scholarships (*Undergraduate/Scholarship*) [7912]

BIGALA Scholarships (Bisexual Gay and Lesbian Alliance) (*Undergraduate/Scholarship*) [7845]

Bill Bernbach Diversity Scholarships (*Undergraduate/Scholarship*) [434]

David and Camille Boatwright Endowed Scholarships (*Undergraduate/Scholarship*) [7169]

Dorothy M. Bolyard Memorial Scholarships (*Undergraduate/Scholarship*) [7914]

Margaret Martin Brock Scholarships in Law (*Undergraduate/Scholarship*) [7171]

Edwin Anthony and Adelaine Bordeaux Cadogan Fellowships (*Graduate/Fellowship*) [7982]

California Association of Private Postsecondary Schools Scholarships (*Undergraduate/Scholarship*) [2232]

CANFIT Nutrition, Physical Education and Culinary Arts Scholarships (*Graduate, Undergraduate/Scholarship*) [3026]

Pete Carpenter Fellowships (*All/Fellowship*) [2157]

CDA Foundation Allied Dental Student Scholarships (*All/Scholarship*) [2674]

CDA Foundation Dental Student Scholarships (*All/Scholarship*) [2675]

Chicana Latina Scholarship Fund (*Graduate, Undergraduate/Scholarship*) [2750]

Athalie Clarke Endowed Scholarships (*Undergraduate/Scholarship*) [7174]

CLASS Fund Irrigation Scholarship Program (*Graduate, Undergraduate/Scholarship*) [5331]

CLCA Landscape Educational Advancement Foundation Scholarships (*Undergraduate/Scholarship*) [2263]

Brian Dane Cleary Memorial Scholarships (*Undergraduate/Scholarship*) [7175]

College of Marin Gay and Lesbian Student Scholarships (*Undergraduate/Scholarship*) [7847]

Conservation Guest Scholar Grants (*Professional development/Grant*) [4139]

Coro Fellows Program in Public Affairs (*Graduate/Fellowship*) [3255]

CPA-F Minority Scholarships (*Graduate/Scholarship*) [2267]

Crafton Hills College Foundation Scholarships (*Undergraduate/Scholarship*) [7641]

Crain Educational Grant Program (*Undergraduate/Scholarship*) [8198]

Hugh and Hazel Darling Dean Scholarships (*Undergraduate/Scholarship*) [7176]

Darling Foundation Endowed School of Law Scholarships (*Undergraduate/Scholarship*) [7177]

Death Valley '49ers Scholarships (*Undergraduate/Scholarship*) [3352]

Martha Delman and Milton Arthur Krug Endowed Scholarships (*Undergraduate/Scholarship*) [7178]

Ruth DeMoss Scholarships (*Undergraduate/Scholarship*) [7924]

Karekin DerAvedision Memorial Endowment Fund (*Undergraduate/Scholarship*) [1590]

Herman H. Derksen Scholarships (*Undergraduate, Vocational/Occupational/Scholarship*) [7925]

Edward D. Di Loreto-Odell S. McConnell Scholarships (*Undergraduate/Scholarship*) [7179]

Dokmo Family Scholarships (Undergraduate/Scholarship) [7927]

R. Wayne Estes Endowed Scholarships (Undergraduate/Scholarship) [7180]

Farella Braun Martel LLP Diversity Scholarships (Undergraduate/Scholarship) [3715]

Judge McIntyre Faries Scholarships (Undergraduate/Scholarship) [7181]

Dr. Mary Finegold Scholarships (Undergraduate/Scholarship) [8201]

Reuben H. Fleet Memorial Scholarships (Undergraduate/Scholarship) [7929]

Jonathan Hastings Foster Scholarships (Undergraduate/Scholarship) [7930]

GAPA Scholarships (Undergraduate/Scholarship) [4048]

John Gardner Fellowships (Undergraduate/Fellowship) [9195]

Garikian Scholarship Fund (Undergraduate/Scholarship) [1593]

Gerald Garner Memorial Scholarships (Undergraduate/Scholarship) [7183]

Raffin Gathercole Scholarships (Undergraduate/Scholarship) [4051]

Getty Postdoctoral Fellowships (Postdoctorate/Fellowship) [4141]

Getty Predoctoral Fellowships (Doctorate/Fellowship) [4142]

Getty Scholar Grants (Professional development/Grant) [4143]

Father Rutilio Grande Scholarships (Graduate, Undergraduate/Scholarship) [7893]

Lucile Cheever Graubart/Lambda Scholarships (Undergraduate/Scholarship) [8174]

Guy P. Greenwald Jr. Endowed Scholarships (Undergraduate/Scholarship) [7185]

Bobette Bibo Gugliotta Memorial Scholarships for Creative Writing (Undergraduate/Scholarship) [8202]

Warren and Rosalie Gummow Endowed Scholarships (Undergraduate/Scholarship) [7186]

Jaye Haddad Memorial Fund (Undergraduate/Scholarship) [7851]

Sophia Hagopian Memorial Fund (Undergraduate/Scholarship) [1596]

James J. Harvey Dissertation Fellowships (Doctorate/Fellowship) [7852]

Helm Family Scholarships (Undergraduate/Scholarship) [7932]

Doris Hendren Memorial Scholarships (Undergraduate/Scholarship) [7933]

Clair A. Hill Scholarships (Undergraduate/Scholarship) [1729]

JD/MBA Scholarships (Undergraduate/Scholarship) [7188]

Nancy Johnston Memorial Scholarships (Graduate, Undergraduate/Scholarship) [8837]

Alice Newell Joslyn Medical Fund (Undergraduate/Scholarship) [2041]

JSR Foundation Endowed School of Law Scholarships (Undergraduate/Scholarship) [7189]

Woodrow Judkins Endowed Scholarships (Undergraduate/Scholarship) [7190]

Steve Kaplan TV and Film Studies Scholarships (Professional development/Scholarship) [1212]

Annette and Ernest Keith Scholarships (Undergraduate/Scholarship) [7659]

Knights of Vartan, Fresno Lodge No. 9 Scholarships (Undergraduate/Scholarship) [1601]

Judith Keller Marx Krumholz Scholarships (Undergraduate/Scholarship) [7941]

Julia Kwan Endowed Scholarships (Graduate/Scholarship) [7193]

Lambda Alumni, UCLA Lesbian & Gay Alumni Association Scholarships Program (Undergraduate/Scholarship) [7854]

Frank H. Lang Merit Scholarships (Undergraduate/Scholarship) [5341]

Latinos for Dental Careers Scholarships (All/Scholarship) [2676]

Patrick Ledden Honorary Scholarships (Undergraduate/Scholarship) [7943]

Rebecca Lee, M.D. Scholarships (Undergraduate/Scholarship) [1720]

Albert J. and Mae Lee Memorial Scholarships (Undergraduate/Scholarship) [7194]

Library Research Grants (All/Grant) [4144]

Stephen Logan Memorial Scholarships (Undergraduate/Scholarship) [4052]

Mangasar M. Mangasarian Scholarship Fund (Graduate/Scholarship) [1602]

Markowski-Leach Scholarship Fund (Graduate, Undergraduate/Scholarship) [7858]

Michael L. Marx and Donald K. Marshall Scholarships (Undergraduate/Scholarship) [7860]

Greg Matthews Memorial Scholarships (Undergraduate/Scholarship) [7195]

J. McDonald and Judy Williams School of Law Scholarships (Undergraduate/Scholarship) [7196]

Charles McMahon Memorial Construction Management/Engineering Scholarship Awards (Undergraduate/Scholarship) [1632]

Ruth McMillan Student Grants (Undergraduate/Grant) [2282]

Medical Staff Scholarships (Undergraduate/Scholarship) [9509]

John Merrick Law Scholarships (Undergraduate/Scholarship) [7197]

Mexican American Alumni Association Scholarships (Graduate, Undergraduate/Scholarship) [9400]

Wilma Motley Memorial California Merit Scholarships (Undergraduate, Master's, Doctorate, Professional development/Scholarship) [709]

Jack and Gertrude Murphy Fellowships (Graduate/Fellowship) [7983]

Charles I. Nelson Endowed Scholarships (Undergraduate/Scholarship) [7198]

Newkirk Center for Science and Society Graduate Student Fellowships (Doctorate, Graduate/Fellowship) [6712]

Gunnar Nicholson Endowed Scholarships (Undergraduate/Scholarship) [7199]

Northern California Chapter of HIMSS Scholarships (Graduate, Postgraduate, Undergraduate/Scholarship) [4506]

PABA Foundation Fellowships (Postdoctorate/Fellowship) [7309]

PABA Foundation Incentive Scholarships (Graduate, Undergraduate/Scholarship) [7310]

PABA Foundation Merit Scholarships (Graduate, Undergraduate/Scholarship) [7311]

Pan Pacific Law Enforcement Scholarships (Undergraduate/Scholarship) [7978]

Pepperdine University Armenian Student Scholarships (Undergraduate/Scholarship) [7200]

Pepperdine University Dean's Scholarships (Doctorate, Graduate/Scholarship) [7201]

Pepperdine University Diversity Scholarships (Doctorate, Graduate/Scholarship) [7202]

Pepperdine University Faculty Scholarships (Doctorate, Graduate/Scholarship) [7203]

Peridian International, Inc./Rae L. Price, FASLA Scholarships (Undergraduate/Scholarship) [5335]

Jamie Phillips Endowed Scholarships (Undergraduate/Scholarship) [7204]

Pollard-Bailey Scholarships (Undergraduate/Scholarship) [7952]

Postdoctoral Fellowships in Conservation Science (Doctorate/Fellowship) [4145]

Public Interest Scholarships (Undergraduate/Scholarship) [2234]

John Purfield Endowed Scholarships (Undergraduate/Scholarship) [7205]

Qualcomm San Diego Science, Technology, Engineering and Mathematics Scholarships (Undergraduate/Scholarship) [7954]

Rambus Scholarship Fund (Undergraduate/Scholarship) [8205]

Rancho Bernardo/Smith Scholarships (Undergraduate/Scholarship) [7955]

Fauneil J. Rinn Scholarships (Undergraduate/Scholarship) [8206]

Rosenthal Bar Exam Scholarships (Undergraduate/Scholarship) [2235]

Edward S. Roth Manufacturing Engineering Scholarships (Graduate, Undergraduate/Scholarship) [8396]

Ruppert Educational Grant Program (Undergraduate/Grant) [8207]

SALEF Health Career Scholarships (Graduate, Undergraduate/Scholarship) [7894]

The San Diego Foundation Community Scholarships II (Undergraduate/Scholarship) [7959]

San Diego National Bank Scholarships (Undergraduate, Vocational/Occupational/Scholarship) [7960]

San Diego Regional Aviation Association Scholarships (Undergraduate/Scholarship) [7961]

Leo and Trinidad Sanchez Scholarships (Undergraduate/Scholarship) [8208]

Sand Hill Scholars Program (Undergraduate/Scholarship) [8209]

Mary Turnbull Schacht Memorial Scholarships (Undergraduate/Scholarship) [8181]

Schatz Energy Fellowships for Graduate Studies (Graduate/Fellowship) [8016]

Al Schuman Ecolab Undergraduate Entrepreneurial Scholarships (Undergraduate/Scholarship) [6463]

Barbara A. Shacochis Scholarships (Undergraduate/Scholarship) [7206]

SHPE Foundation Northrop Grumman Scholarships (Undergraduate/Scholarship) [8133]

Stuart Silverman Scholarships (Undergraduate/Scholarship) [7208]

Wiggsy Sivertsen Scholarships (Undergraduate/Scholarship) [7871]

Charles Smith Memorial Scholarship Awards (Undergraduate/Scholarship) [1633]

Special Law School Scholarships (Undergraduate/Scholarship) [7209]

Superior District Legislative Mentoring Student Grants RT to DC (Undergraduate/Grant) [2284]

Superior District Legislative Mentoring Student Grants (Undergraduate/Grant) [2283]

Switzer Environmental Fellowships (Graduate/Fellowship) [8787]

Robert M. Takasugi Public Interest Fellowships (Postgraduate/Fellowship) [8800]

Honorable Raymond Thompson Endowed Scholarships (Undergraduate/Scholarship) [7210]

Raymond A. Tice Scholarships I (Undergraduate/Scholarship) [7967]

Raymond A. Tice Scholarships II (Undergraduate/Scholarship) [7968]

Aram Torossian Memorial Scholarships (Undergraduate/Scholarship) [1606]

Thomas and Glenna Trimble Endowed Scholarships (Undergraduate/Scholarship) [7211]

Two Nineteen Scholarships (Community College, Graduate, Undergraduate/Scholarship) [7895]

UC MEXUS Grants for Dissertation Research (Graduate/Grant) [9199]

UC MEXUS Short-Term Projects (Master's, Doctorate, Postdoctorate/Grant) [9200]

The UCSD Black Alumni Scholarship for Arts and Humanities (Undergraduate/Scholarship) [7970]

The UCSD Black Alumni Scholarships for Engineering, Mathematics and Science (Undergraduate/Scholarship) [7971]

Bettie Underwood Dental Assisting Scholarships (All/Scholarship) [2677]

U.S. Air Force ROTC Enhanced HSI Scholarships (Undergraduate/Scholarship) [9026]

United Teachers Los Angeles Stonewall Scholarship Fund (Undergraduate/Scholarship) [7873]

USA Freestyle Martial Arts Scholarships (Undergraduate, Vocational/Occupational/Scholarship) [7972]

Weissbuch Family Scholarships (Undergraduate/Scholarship) [7973]

West Coast Sea Grant Fellowships (Graduate/Fellowship) [2279]

Howard A. White Endowed Scholarships (Undergraduate/Scholarship) [7213]

Tim Wolfred Scholarships (Undergraduate/Scholarship) [7877]

Michael A. Zamperini/W. Clay Burchell Scholarships (Undergraduate/Scholarship) [7878]

Colorado

AISC/Rocky Mountain Steel Construction Association Fellowships (Graduate/Fellowship) [872]

Roy Anderson Memorial Scholarships (Graduate,

Undergraduate/Scholarship) [2990]

APTRA Scholarships *(Undergraduate/Scholarship)* [1684]

Banner Health System - McKee Medical Center, Loveland: Nightingale Scholarships *(Graduate, Undergraduate/Scholarship)* [2991]

Banner Health System - North Colorado Medical Center, Greeley: Nightingale Scholarships *(Graduate, Undergraduate/Scholarship)* [2992]

CCU Alumni Endowed Scholarships *(Undergraduate/Scholarship)* [2986]

Colorado Nurses Association: Nightingale Scholarships *(Graduate, Undergraduate/Scholarship)* [2993]

Colorado Nurses Foundation Nightingale Scholarships *(Graduate, Undergraduate/Scholarship)* [2994]

Colorado Organization of Nursing Leaders Scholarships *(Graduate, Undergraduate/Scholarship)* [2995]

CSCPA College Scholarships *(Graduate, Undergraduate/Scholarship)* [3005]

CSCPA High School Scholarships *(Undergraduate/Scholarship)* [3006]

CSCPA Sophomore Scholarships *(Undergraduate/Scholarship)* [3007]

John Denver Music Scholarships *(Undergraduate/Scholarship)* [1210]

El Pomar Fellowships *(Graduate/Fellowship)* [3622]

Red and Lola Fehr: Nightingale Scholarships *(Graduate, Undergraduate/Scholarship)* [2996]

Griffin Foundation Scholarships *(Undergraduate/Scholarship)* [4353]

Dwight A. Hamilton Scottish Rite Foundation of Colorado Graduate Scholarships *(Graduate/Scholarship)* [8063]

Clinton J. Helton Manufacturing Scholarships *(Undergraduate/Scholarship)* [8387]

Richard A. Herbert Memorial Scholarships *(Undergraduate/Scholarship)* [1412]

Johnson and Johnson: Nightingale Scholarships *(Graduate, Undergraduate/Scholarship)* [2997]

Kaiser Permanente: Nightingale Scholarships *(Graduate, Undergraduate/Scholarship)* [2998]

Dorothy Mountain Memorial Scholarships *(Graduate/Scholarship)* [5532]

H.M. Muffly Memorial Scholarships *(Graduate, Undergraduate/Scholarship)* [2999]

Colorado Nurses Association: Virginia Paulson Memorial Scholarships *(Graduate, Undergraduate/Scholarship)* [3000]

Poudre Valley Health System, Fort Collins: Nightingale Scholarships *(Graduate, Undergraduate/Scholarship)* [3001]

St. Anthony's Hospitals, Denver: Nightingale Scholarships *(Graduate, Undergraduate/Scholarship)* [3002]

Thomas J. Slocum Memorial Scholarships to Westwood College of Aviation Technology *(Undergraduate/Scholarship)* [139]

Lorraine E. Swain Scholarships *(Undergraduate/Scholarship)* [8188]

CASFM-Ben Urbonas Scholarships *(Graduate/Scholarship)* [2982]

Patty Walter Memorial Scholarships *(Graduate, Undergraduate/Scholarship)* [3003]

Connecticut

Frederick G. Adams Scholarships *(Undergraduate/Scholarship)* [4405]

Alliance Francaise of Hartford Harpin/Rohinsky Scholarships *(Undergraduate/Scholarship)* [4406]

AMLN Scholarships *(Graduate, Undergraduate/Scholarship)* [934]

Armenian American Pharmacists' Association Scholarships *(Doctorate, Graduate/Scholarship)* [1582]

ARTC Glenn Moon Scholarships *(Undergraduate/Scholarship)* [4409]

ASI Fellowships *(Doctorate/Fellowship)* [1481]

Malcolm Baldridge Scholarships *(Undergraduate/Scholarship)* [4411]

Leon Bradley Scholarships *(Undergraduate/Scholarship)* [548]

W. Philip Braender and Nancy Coleman Braender Scholarships *(Undergraduate/Scholarship)* [4415]

Gail Burns-Smith "Dare to Dream" Fund *(Undergraduate/Scholarship)* [4416]

George J. Bysiewicz Scholarship Fund *(Undergraduate/Scholarship)* [3079]

Chopivsky Fellowships *(Graduate/Scholarship)* [9498]

CLN Scholarships *(Graduate, Undergraduate/Scholarship)* [3237]

The College Club of Hartford Scholarships *(Undergraduate/Scholarship)* [4418]

Connecticut Mortgage Bankers Scholarships-Social Affairs Committee *(Undergraduate/Scholarship)* [4422]

B.J. Dean Scholarships *(Undergraduate/Scholarship)* [3106]

C. Rodney Demarest Memorial Scholarships *(Undergraduate/Scholarship)* [4425]

Harry A. Donn Scholarships *(Undergraduate/Scholarship)* [4427]

Symee Ruth Feinburg Memorial Scholarships *(Undergraduate/Scholarship)* [4431]

Kennedy T. Friend Scholarships *(Graduate, Undergraduate/Scholarship)* [327]

Greenwich Scholarship Association Scholarships (GSA) *(Undergraduate/Scholarship)* [4351]

Ida L. Hartenberg Charitable Scholarships *(Undergraduate/Scholarship)* [4435]

Hartford County Retired Teachers Association Scholarships *(Undergraduate/Scholarship)* [4436]

Hartford Foundation College Scholarship Program *(Undergraduate/Scholarship)* [4437]

Doc Hurley Scholarships *(Undergraduate/Scholarship)* [4442]

Interracial Scholarship Fund of Greater Hartford *(Undergraduate/Scholarship)* [4443]

Iranian Association of Boston's IAB Scholarships *(Undergraduate/Scholarship)* [6362]

Herman P. Kopplemann Scholarships *(Undergraduate/Scholarship)* [4446]

Mary Main Memorial Scholarships *(Undergraduate/Scholarship)* [4449]

Dr. Frank and Florence Marino Scholarships *(Undergraduate/Scholarship)* [4451]

Sylvia Parkinson Scholarships *(Undergraduate/Scholarship)* [4453]

Patterson Trust Postdoctoral Fellowships in Brain Circuitry *(Postdoctorate/Fellowship)* [4496]

Dorothy E. Hofmann Pembroke Scholarships *(Undergraduate/Scholarship)* [4454]

Nicholas J. Piergrossi Scholarships *(Undergraduate/Scholarship)* [4455]

Dr. Sidney Rafal Memorial Scholarships *(Undergraduate/Scholarship)* [4457]

Ross-Fahey Scholarships *(Graduate, Postgraduate/Scholarship)* [6056]

Peter T. Steinwedell Scholarships *(Undergraduate/Scholarship)* [4461]

Town and County Club Scholarships *(Undergraduate/Scholarship)* [4462]

Visiting Scholars Fellowships *(Postdoctorate/Fellowship)* [2043]

Eleanor M. Wolfson Memorial Scholarship Fund *(Undergraduate/Scholarship)* [3797]

Wendy Y. Wolfson Memorial Scholarship Fund *(Undergraduate/Scholarship)* [3798]

Delaware

AISC/US Steel Fellowships *(Graduate/Fellowship)* [876]

Leon Bradley Scholarships *(Undergraduate/Scholarship)* [548]

District of Columbia

American Enterprise Institute National Research Initiative Fellowships (NRI) *(Graduate/Fellowship)* [718]

Carlos Enrique Cisneros Point Scholarships *(Graduate, Undergraduate/Scholarship)* [7356]

Conference on Asian Pacific American Leadership Scholarships *(Graduate, Undergraduate/Scholarship)* [3211]

Congressional Scholarship Awards *(Undergraduate/Scholarship)* [4016]

The Corp - Students of Georgetown Inc. Coke Scholarships *(Undergraduate/Scholarship)* [3257]

The Corp - Students of Georgetown Inc. Textbook Scholarships *(Undergraduate/Scholarship)* [3258]

Dumbarton Oaks Fellowships *(Doctorate, Graduate/Fellowship)* [3549]

Dumbarton Oaks Junior Fellowships *(Graduate/Fellowship)* [3550]

Federal Communication Bar Association Foundation Scholarships *(Undergraduate/Scholarship)* [3720]

Andrew Foster Scholarships *(Undergraduate/Scholarship)* [6146]

Guggenheim Fellowships *(Doctorate/Fellowship)* [8251]

IWPR/GW Fellowships in Women's Public Policy Research *(Graduate/Fellowship)* [4836]

Kislak Fellowships in American Studies *(Graduate, Postdoctorate/Fellowship)* [5272]

Kislak Short Term Fellowships Opportunities in American Studies *(All/Fellowship)* [5273]

Kluge Fellowships *(Doctorate, Graduate/Fellowship)* [5274]

David B. Larson Fellowships in Health and Spirituality *(Doctorate/Fellowship)* [5275]

Charles A. Lindbergh Fellowships *(Graduate/Fellowship)* [8252]

More Uncommon Grounds Scholarships (MUG) *(Undergraduate/Scholarship)* [3260]

MPAC-DC Graduate Policy Fellowships *(Graduate/Fellowship)* [5960]

Norfolk Southern Foundation Scholarships *(Undergraduate/Scholarship)* [1131]

Post-Doctoral Teaching Fellowships *(Postdoctorate/Fellowship)* [3551]

The Ivan Shandor Memorial Ukrainian American Bar Association Scholarships *(Master's/Scholarship)* [9500]

A. Verville Fellowships *(All/Fellowship)* [8253]

Florida

AAAA Operation Jumpstart III Scholarships *(Graduate/Scholarship)* [433]

AISC/Southern Association of Steel Fabricators Fellowships *(Graduate/Fellowship)* [873]

AISC/Southern Association of Steel Fabricators Scholarships *(Undergraduate/Scholarship)* [874]

Horatio Alger Florida Scholarships *(Undergraduate/Scholarship)* [300]

Earl I. Anderson Scholarships *(Undergraduate/Scholarship)* [1068]

Judge Sidney M. Aronovitz Memorial Scholarships *(High School, Undergraduate/Scholarship)* [3314]

Jaimes F. Bailey, Jr. Scholarships *(Undergraduate/Scholarship)* [5111]

Beta Gamma Memorial Scholarships *(Undergraduate/Scholarship)* [3368]

Bill Bernbach Diversity Scholarships *(Undergraduate/Scholarship)* [434]

byourself Scholarship Fund *(Undergraduate, Vocational/Occupational/Scholarship)* [3188]

Calvin Alumni Association Florida-Gulf Coast Scholarships *(Undergraduate/Scholarship)* [2297]

Central Florida Jazz Society Scholarships *(Undergraduate/Award, Scholarship)* [2717]

Jennet Colliflower Nursing Scholarships *(Undergraduate/Scholarship)* [3315]

Cuban American Bar Association Scholarships *(All/Scholarship)* [3301]

D&A Florida Scholarships *(Undergraduate/Scholarship)* [8597]

James H. Davis Scholarships *(Undergraduate/Scholarship)* [3838]

DBPR Division of CPA - BOA Minority Scholarships *(Undergraduate/Scholarship)* [3430]

Doctors IRA & UDAYA Nursing Scholarships *(Un-

dergraduate/Scholarship) [8598]

Anne M. Fassett Scholarships (Undergraduate/ Scholarship) [8600]

Fecon Scholarships (Undergraduate/Scholarship) [3825]

FICPA Educational Foundation 1040K Race Scholarships (Undergraduate/Scholarship) [3836]

Florida Education Fund McKnight Doctoral Fellowships (Graduate/Fellowship) [3822]

Florida Engineering Society Junior College Scholarships (Undergraduate/Scholarship) [3827]

Florida Engineering Society University Scholarships (Undergraduate/Scholarship) [3828]

Florida Fertilizer and Agrichemical Association Scholarships (Graduate, Undergraduate/Scholarship) [3834]

Florida Outdoor Writers Association Scholarships (Undergraduate/Scholarship) [3842]

Charles and Margaret Foster Scholarships (Undergraduate/Scholarship) [8602]

Randy Green Memorial Scholarship Fund (High School/Scholarship) [3318]

Gulf Coast Hurricane Scholarships (Graduate, Undergraduate/Scholarship) [8449]

Chip Johnson Scholarships (Undergraduate/ Scholarship) [8608]

Michael Kidger Memorial Scholarships in Optical Design (Graduate/Scholarship) [8638]

David F. Ludovici Scholarships (Undergraduate/ Scholarship) [3829]

Robert V. McKenna Scholarships (Undergraduate/ Scholarship) [8818]

Raymond W. Miller, PE and Alice E. Miller Scholarships (Undergraduate/Scholarship) [3830]

Raymond W. Miller, PE Scholarships (Undergraduate/Scholarship) [3831]

NACA Southeast Student Leadership Scholarships (Undergraduate/Scholarship) [6052]

Judge William J. Nelson Scholarships (Undergraduate/Scholarship) [8615]

North Florida Chapter Safety Education Scholarships (Graduate, Undergraduate/Scholarship) [1349]

Melissa Pellegrin Memorial Scholarships (Graduate, Undergraduate/Scholarship) [8504]

Eric Primavera Memorial Scholarships (Undergraduate/Scholarship) [3832]

Helen F. "Jerri" Rand Memorial Scholarships (Undergraduate, Vocational/Occupational/Scholarship) [3193]

Dr. Felix H. Reyler Memorial Scholarships (Undergraduate/Scholarship) [3319]

Edward S. Roth Manufacturing Engineering Scholarships (Graduate, Undergraduate/Scholarship) [8396]

Al Schuman Ecolab Undergraduate Entrepreneurial Scholarships (Undergraduate/Scholarship) [6463]

Southern Scholarship Foundation Scholarships (Undergraduate/Scholarship) [8587]

Leo Suarez Journalism Scholarships (Undergraduate/Scholarship) [3321]

Jacki Tuckfield Memorial Graduate Business Scholarship Fund (Doctorate, Graduate, Master's/Scholarship) [3323]

Imogene Ward Nursing Scholarships (Undergraduate/Scholarship) [3814]

Ted C. Wilson Memorial Scholarships (Undergraduate/Scholarship) [7441]

Georgia

AAAA Operation Jumpstart III Scholarships (Graduate/Scholarship) [433]

AISC/Southern Association of Steel Fabricators Fellowships (Graduate/Fellowship) [873]

AISC/Southern Association of Steel Fabricators Scholarships (Undergraduate/Scholarship) [874]

Brenda S. Bank Educational Workshop Scholarships (Undergraduate/Scholarship) [8326]

Bill Bernbach Diversity Scholarships (Undergraduate/Scholarship) [434]

Kenneth H. Breeden Scholarships (Undergraduate/Scholarship) [5343]

CDC Public Health Informatics Fellowships

(Graduate, Postdoctorate/Fellowship) [2713]

Charles Clarke Cordle Memorial Scholarships (Undergraduate/Scholarship) [1081]

Anthony R. Dees Educational Workshop Scholarships (Undergraduate/Scholarship) [8327]

Forsyth County United Way Scholarships (Undergraduate/Scholarship) [5344]

Georgia Engineering Foundation Scholarships (Graduate/Scholarship) [4102]

Larry Gulley Scholarships (Undergraduate/Scholarship) [8328]

Richard A. Hammill Scholarship Fund (Undergraduate/Scholarship) [918]

Carroll Hart Scholarships (Graduate/Scholarship) [8329]

Gene Henson Scholarships (High School, Undergraduate/Scholarship) [1922]

Durwood McAlister Scholarships (Undergraduate/ Scholarship) [4107]

NACA Southeast Student Leadership Scholarships (Undergraduate/Scholarship) [6052]

Edna A. Noblin Dawsonville Lions Club Scholarships (Undergraduate/Scholarship) [5345]

NWAG Georgia, USA Scholarships (High School/ Scholarship) [6718]

William C. Rogers Scholarships (Undergraduate/ Scholarship) [4109]

SHPE Foundation Northrop Grumman Scholarships (Undergraduate/Scholarship) [8133]

George and Pearl Strickland Scholarships (Graduate, Undergraduate/Scholarship) [3076]

Kirk Sutlive Scholarships (Undergraduate/Scholarship) [4110]

Ted C. Wilson Memorial Scholarships (Undergraduate/Scholarship) [7441]

Hawaii

AISC/US Steel Fellowships (Graduate/Fellowship) [876]

APTRA Scholarships (Undergraduate/Scholarship) [1684]

HPGS/ALOH Graduate Scholarships (Graduate/ Scholarship) [4485]

HPGS Undergraduate Scholarships (Undergraduate/Scholarship) [4486]

PATCH Early Childhood Education Scholarships (Professional development/Scholarship) [7132]

PSHF Good Idea Grants (Professional development/Grant) [7544]

William S. Richardson Commemorative Scholarships (Graduate/Scholarship) [5221]

University of Hawaii at Manoa East-West Center Graduate Fellowships (Graduate, Postdoctorate/ Fellowship) [9206]

Idaho

The "21" Endowed Scholarships (Undergraduate/ Scholarship) [5409]

Mamie Adams Memorial Awards (Undergraduate/ Scholarship) [5410]

Horatio Alger Idaho University Scholarships (Undergraduate/Scholarship) [303]

Horatio Alger Lola and Duane Hagadone Idaho Scholarships (Undergraduate/Scholarship) [307]

American Legion Boys/Girls State Scholarships (Undergraduate/Scholarship) [5411]

APTRA Scholarships (Undergraduate/Scholarship) [1684]

Avista Corporation Minds in Motion Scholarships (Undergraduate/Scholarship) [5412]

Banner Bank Business Scholarships (Undergraduate/Scholarship) [5413]

Ted Bjornn University of Idaho Graduate Student Scholarships (Graduate/Scholarship) [4661]

Ted Bjornn University of Idaho Undergraduate Student Scholarships (Undergraduate/Scholarship) [4662]

Diana Brown Endowed Scholarships (Undergraduate/Scholarship) [5414]

Glen and Babs Carlson Endowed Scholarships (Undergraduate/Scholarship) [5415]

Walter & Elsie Carr Endowed Scholarships (Undergraduate/Scholarship) [5416]

Caterpillar Scholarships in Diesel Mechanics (Un-

dergraduate/Scholarship) [5417]

Church Family Scholarships (Undergraduate/ Scholarship) [5418]

Fisher Clark Memorial Endowed Scholarships (Undergraduate/Scholarship) [5419]

Coeur d'Alene Alumni Scholarships (Undergraduate/Scholarship) [5420]

Rob Copeland Memorial Scholarships (Undergraduate/Scholarship) [5421]

The Rick Crane Group Real Estate Scholarship Fund (Undergraduate/Scholarship) [5422]

Mike Crapo Math and Science Scholarship Fund (Undergraduate/Scholarship) [4668]

Laura Moore Cunningham Foundation General Scholarships (Undergraduate/Scholarship) [5423]

Kenneth and Kathleen Davis Endowed Scholarships (Undergraduate/Scholarship) [5424]

Gretchen Dimico Memorial Scholarships (Undergraduate/Scholarship) [5425]

Bus and Mary Ellen Durant Timberline High School Endowed Scholarships (Undergraduate/ Scholarship) [5426]

First Security Foundation Business Scholarships (Undergraduate/Scholarship) [5427]

Dean A. Froehlich Endowed Scholarships (Undergraduate/Scholarship) [5428]

Irene Carlson Gnaedinger Memorial Scholarships (Undergraduate/Scholarship) [5429]

Alois and Marie Goldmann Scholarship Fund (Undergraduate/Scholarship) [4669]

Jack & Mary Lou Gruber Scholarships (Undergraduate/Scholarship) [5430]

Jimmy Guild Memorial Scholarships (Undergraduate/Scholarship) [5431]

Henderson Memorial Endowed Scholarships (Undergraduate/Scholarship) [5432]

Hinman-Jensen Endowed Scholarships (Undergraduate/Scholarship) [5433]

Frank and Gladys Hopkins Endowed Scholarships (Undergraduate/Scholarship) [5434]

ICAFS Idaho Graduate Student Scholarships (Graduate/Scholarship) [4663]

ICAFS Idaho High School Student Scholarships (Undergraduate/Scholarship) [4664]

ICAFS Idaho Undergraduate Student Scholarships (Undergraduate/Scholarship) [4665]

Idaho Attorney General Scholarships (Undergraduate/Scholarship) [5435]

Idaho Nursery and Landscape Association Scholarships (Undergraduate/Scholarship) [4676]

Idaho Nursing Scholarships (Undergraduate/ Scholarship) [4670]

Idaho Promise Category B Scholarships (Undergraduate/Scholarship) [5436]

Idaho Society of CPA's Scholarships (Undergraduate/Scholarship) [4671]

Margaret G. Johnson and Marge J. Stout Scholarships (Undergraduate, Vocational/Occupational/ Scholarship) [5437]

LCSC Welding Club Scholarships (Undergraduate/Scholarship) [5438]

Lewis-Clark Coin Club Endowed Scholarships (Undergraduate/Scholarship) [5439]

Lewis-Clark State College/American Chemical Society Scholars Program (Undergraduate/Scholarship) [5440]

Lewis-Clark State College Foundation Scholars Scholarships (Undergraduate/Scholarship) [5441]

Lewis-Clark State College Freshman Scholarships (Undergraduate/Scholarship) [5442]

Lewis-Clark State College Governor's Cup Scholarships (Undergraduate/Scholarship) [5443]

Lewis-Clark State College/Idaho Society of CPAs Scholarships Fund (Undergraduate/Scholarship) [5444]

Lewis-Clark State College Non-Traditional Student Scholarships (Undergraduate/Scholarship) [5445]

Lewis-Clark State College Presidential Out-of-State Scholarships (Undergraduate/Scholarship) [5446]

Lewis-Clark State College Presidential Technical Out-of-State Scholarships (Undergraduate/ Scholarship) [5447]

Lewis-Clark State College Provost Scholarships *(Undergraduate/Scholarship)* [5448]

Lewis-Clark State College Transfer Scholarships *(Undergraduate/Scholarship)* [5449]

Lewis-Clark State College Valley Scholarships *(Undergraduate/Scholarship)* [5450]

Lewiston Clarkston Kiwanis Club Scholarships *(Undergraduate/Scholarship)* [5451]

Lewiston Service League Memorial Scholarships *(Undergraduate/Scholarship)* [5452]

Kaia Lynn Markwalter Endowed Scholarships *(Undergraduate/Scholarship)* [5453]

Susan B. Martin Memorial Scholarships *(Graduate/Scholarship)* [4666]

Monna Mawson Scholarships *(Undergraduate/Scholarship)* [4659]

Elizabeth McKissick Memorial Scholarships *(Undergraduate/Scholarship)* [5454]

Military Order of the Purple Heart Foundation Scholarships *(Undergraduate/Scholarship)* [5455]

Robbie Miller Memorial Scholarships *(Undergraduate/Scholarship)* [5456]

Eugene Northrup Scholarships *(Undergraduate/Scholarship)* [5457]

Odd Fellows Lodge No. 8 Endowed Scholarships *(Undergraduate/Scholarship)* [5458]

Laura Ann Peck Memorial Endowed Scholarships *(Undergraduate/Scholarship)* [5460]

Eleanor Perry Memorial Endowed Scholarships *(Undergraduate/Scholarship)* [5461]

Lori Rhett Memorial Scholarships *(Graduate, Undergraduate/Scholarship)* [6055]

Kenneth Rogers Memorial Scholarships *(Undergraduate/Scholarship)* [5462]

Rosenberg-Ibarra Scholarships *(Undergraduate/Scholarship)* [7419]

Roger C. Sathre Memorial Scholarship Fund *(Undergraduate/Scholarship)* [4673]

Bill Sawyer Memorial Scholarships *(Undergraduate/Scholarship)* [5463]

Susan P. Schroeder Memorial Scholarships *(Undergraduate/Scholarship)* [5464]

Ethel Shinn Alumni-Vocational Scholarships *(Undergraduate/Scholarship)* [5465]

State of Idaho Scholarships Category A *(Undergraduate, Vocational/Occupational/Scholarship)* [5466]

John Streiff Memorial Scholarships *(Undergraduate/Scholarship)* [5467]

Tschudy Family Scholarships *(Undergraduate/Scholarship)* [5468]

WALPA Lake Scholarships *(Graduate, Undergraduate/Scholarship)* [9526]

Washington City/County Management Association Scholarships *(Graduate/Scholarship)* [9494]

Washington Reciprocity Out-of-State Scholarships *(Undergraduate/Scholarship)* [5469]

Illinois

Horatio Alger Louisiana Scholarships *(Undergraduate/Scholarship)* [308]

Allied Health Care Professional Scholarships *(Undergraduate/Scholarship)* [4693]

American Council of Engineering Companies of Illinois Scholarships *(Doctorate, Graduate, Undergraduate/Scholarship)* [660]

Earl I. Anderson Scholarships *(Undergraduate/Scholarship)* [1068]

Richard L. Bernardi Memorial Scholarships *(Undergraduate/Scholarship)* [3143]

Calvin Alumni Association-Illinois Scholarships *(Undergraduate/Scholarship)* [2298]

Chapter 23 - Quad Cities Iowa/Illinois Scholarships *(Undergraduate/Scholarship)* [8374]

Chapter 31 - Peoria Endowed Scholarships *(Undergraduate/Scholarship)* [8375]

CMSF Scholarships *(Graduate, Undergraduate/Scholarship)* [2781]

Beta Nu/Caryl Cordis D'hondt Scholarships *(Undergraduate/Scholarship)* [8163]

Felicia De Bow Memorial Scholarships *(All/Scholarship)* [7037]

Engineers for Tomorrow Scholarship Program *(Undergraduate/Scholarship)* [5915]

Robert Esser Student Achievement Scholarships *(Graduate, Undergraduate/Fellowship, Scholarship)* [4685]

Larry L. Etherton Scholarships *(Graduate, Undergraduate/Scholarship)* [1126]

Michael W. and Jean D. Franke Family Foundation Scholarships *(Graduate, Undergraduate/Scholarship)* [1127]

Karen Harter Recruitment Scholarship Grants *(Undergraduate/Scholarship)* [3153]

IBEA Graduate Scholarships *(Graduate/Scholarship)* [4682]

IBEA Undergraduate Scholarships *(Undergraduate/Scholarship)* [4683]

Illinois Future Teacher Corps Scholarships *(Undergraduate/Scholarship)* [4695]

Illinois Lake Management Association Undergraduate/Graduate Scholarships *(Graduate, Undergraduate/Fellowship, Scholarship)* [4686]

Illinois Landscape Contractors Association Scholarships *(Undergraduate/Scholarship)* [4688]

Illinois Special Education Teacher Tuition Waiver Scholarships (SETTW) *(Undergraduate/Scholarship)* [4696]

Illinois Student Assistance Commission Medical Student Scholarships *(Undergraduate/Scholarship)* [4697]

Illinois Student Assistance Commission Merit Recognition Scholarships (MRS) *(Undergraduate/Scholarship)* [4698]

Illinois Student Assistance Commission Nurse Educator Scholarships (NESP) *(Undergraduate/Scholarship)* [4699]

Illinois Student Assistance Commission Nursing Education Scholarships *(Undergraduate/Scholarship)* [4700]

Iowa Journalism Institute Scholarships *(Undergraduate/Scholarship)* [5043]

ISPE Advantage Award/Foundation Scholarships *(Undergraduate/Scholarship)* [4691]

Jewish Federation Academic Scholarships *(Graduate, Undergraduate/Scholarship)* [5161]

Abraham Lincoln Marovitz Public Interest Law Scholarships *(Undergraduate/Scholarship)* [2746]

Edmond A. Metzger Scholarships *(Undergraduate/Scholarship)* [1094]

Minority Teachers of Illinois Scholarships (MTI) *(Undergraduate/Scholarship)* [4701]

Muddy Waters Scholarships *(Undergraduate/Scholarship)* [2155]

Northeastern Illinois Chapter Scholarships *(Graduate, Undergraduate/Scholarship)* [1350]

Edward S. Roth Manufacturing Engineering Scholarships *(Graduate, Undergraduate/Scholarship)* [8396]

The Dr. William M. Scholl College of Podiatric Medicine Scholarships *(Undergraduate/Scholarship)* [7143]

Al Schuman Ecolab Undergraduate Entrepreneurial Scholarships *(Undergraduate/Scholarship)* [6463]

Elisabeth Seegmiller Recruitment Scholarship Grants *(Undergraduate/Scholarship)* [3171]

SHPE Foundation Northrop Grumman Scholarships *(Undergraduate/Scholarship)* [8133]

Donald M. Wells Scholarships *(Undergraduate/Scholarship)* [4307]

Andrea Will Memorial Scholarships *(Undergraduate/Scholarship)* [8193]

Indiana

Academic Promise Scholarships *(Undergraduate/Scholarship)* [4740]

Earl I. Anderson Scholarships *(Undergraduate/Scholarship)* [1068]

Warren M. Anderson Scholarships *(Undergraduate/Scholarship)* [4741]

Warren K. Brown Scholarships *(Undergraduate/Scholarship)* [1334]

Chapter 56 - Fort Wayne Scholarships *(Graduate, Undergraduate/Scholarship)* [8378]

Child of Alumni Book Voucher Awards *(Undergraduate/Scholarship)* [4742]

Gongaware Scholarships *(Undergraduate/Scholarship)* [4743]

Illinois Lake Management Association Undergraduate/Graduate Scholarships *(Graduate, Undergraduate/Fellowship, Scholarship)* [4686]

Indiana Broadcasters Association College Scholarship Program *(Undergraduate/Scholarship)* [4733]

Indiana Broadcasters Association High School Scholarship Program *(Undergraduate/Scholarship)* [4734]

Indiana State Alumni Association Academic Excellence Scholarships *(Undergraduate/Scholarship)* [4744]

Indiana State Alumni Association Creative and Performing Arts Awards *(Undergraduate/Scholarship)* [4745]

Indiana State Alumni Association Incentive Scholarships *(Undergraduate/Scholarship)* [4746]

Indiana State Alumni Association President's Scholarships *(Undergraduate/Scholarship)* [4747]

Indiana State Alumni Association Transfer Student Scholarships *(Undergraduate/Scholarship)* [4749]

Central Indiana ASSE Jim Kriner Memorial Scholarships *(Graduate, Undergraduate/Scholarship)* [1345]

Edmond A. Metzger Scholarships *(Undergraduate/Scholarship)* [1094]

Clarence and Josephine Myers Scholarships *(Graduate, Undergraduate/Scholarship)* [8394]

Networks Scholarships College of Business *(Undergraduate/Scholarship)* [4750]

Notre Dame Club of Canton Scholarships *(Undergraduate/Scholarship)* [8693]

Noyce Scholarships for Secondary Math and Science Education *(Undergraduate/Scholarship)* [4751]

Phi Theta Kappa Scholarships *(Undergraduate/Scholarship)* [4752]

Purdue Krannert School of Management SHPE Scholarships *(Undergraduate, Master's/Scholarship)* [8130]

August M. Rocco Scholarship Fund *(Undergraduate/Scholarship)* [8696]

Esther Schlundt Memorial Scholarships *(Graduate/Scholarship)* [4737]

Nettie and Edward Shelah Scholarships *(Undergraduate/Scholarship)* [8733]

SHPE Foundation Northrop Grumman Scholarships *(Undergraduate/Scholarship)* [8133]

Spotlight on Nursing Graduate Nursing Scholarships *(Graduate/Scholarship)* [8651]

Barber Owen Thomas Scholarships *(Undergraduate/Scholarship)* [8190]

Iowa

AISC/US Steel Fellowships *(Graduate/Fellowship)* [876]

William Stone Ayres Scholarships *(Undergraduate/Scholarship)* [3479]

Beverly Estate Scholarships *(Undergraduate/Scholarship)* [3480]

George and Mary Brammer Scholarships *(Undergraduate/Scholarship)* [3481]

Gregory Brunk Scholarships *(Undergraduate/Scholarship)* [3482]

Chapter 23 - Quad Cities Iowa/Illinois Scholarships *(Undergraduate/Scholarship)* [8374]

CMSF Scholarships *(Graduate, Undergraduate/Scholarship)* [2781]

Raymond DiPaglia Endowment Scholarships *(Undergraduate/Scholarship)* [3484]

Herman E. Elgar Memorial Scholarships *(Undergraduate/Scholarship)* [3492]

D.J. Fairgrave Education Trust *(Undergraduate/Scholarship)* [3493]

Leland Stanford Forrest Scholarships *(Undergraduate/Scholarship)* [3494]

Paul and Helen L. Grauer Scholarships *(Undergraduate/Scholarship)* [1087]

Edward and Cora Hayes Scholarships *(Undergraduate/Scholarship)* [3496]

John M. Helmick Law Scholarships (Undergraduate/Scholarship) [3498]

Herbert Hoover Uncommon Student Awards (Undergraduate/Scholarship) [4597]

INF Scholarships (Undergraduate/Scholarship) [5042]

Iowa Journalism Institute Scholarships (Undergraduate/Scholarship) [5043]

Iowa Library Association Foundation Scholarships (Graduate/Scholarship) [5039]

James P. Irish Scholarships (Undergraduate/Scholarship) [3499]

Forest A. King Scholarships (Undergraduate/Scholarship) [3502]

Verne Lawyer Scholarships (Undergraduate/Scholarship) [3503]

Frederick D. Lewis Jr. Scholarships (Undergraduate/Scholarship) [3506]

Gordon and Delores Madson Scholarships (Undergraduate/Scholarship) [3507]

Jake S. More Scholarships (Undergraduate/Scholarship) [3508]

North Central, Region 9 Scholarships (Undergraduate/Scholarship) [8395]

Dwight D. Opperman Scholarships (Undergraduate/Scholarship) [3509]

Jerome S. Petz, S.J., Scholarships (Undergraduate/Scholarship) [3510]

Carter Pitts Scholarships (Undergraduate/Scholarship) [5044]

Janet Reynoldson Memorial Scholarships (Undergraduate/Scholarship) [3511]

Isador M. Robinson Endowment Scholarships (Undergraduate/Scholarship) [3512]

Walter and Rita Selvy Scholarships (Undergraduate/Scholarship) [3513]

Matthew Shepard Scholarships (Undergraduate/Scholarship) [7870]

Jack E. Tillson Scholarships (Graduate/Scholarship) [5040]

Haemer Wheatcraft Scholarships (Undergraduate/Scholarship) [3515]

Kansas

Business and Transactional Law Center Scholarships (Undergraduate/Scholarship) [9485]

Chapter 52 - Wichita Scholarships (Graduate, Undergraduate/Scholarship) [8377]

Child and Family Advocacy Fellowships (Undergraduate/Scholarship) [9486]

Theta/Caryl Cordis D'hondt Scholarships (Undergraduate/Scholarship) [8164]

Paul and Helen L. Grauer Scholarships (Undergraduate/Scholarship) [1087]

AISC/Fred R. Havens Fellowships (Graduate, Undergraduate/Fellowship) [877]

Judge Delmas C. Hill Scholarships (Undergraduate/Scholarship) [9487]

KHIMA Graduate Scholarships (Graduate/Scholarship) [5187]

Koch Scholarships (Undergraduate/Scholarship) [9488]

Sue A. Malone Scholarships (Doctorate, Graduate/Scholarship) [5188]

John J. Mingenback Memorial Scholarships (Graduate, Undergraduate/Scholarship) [4173]

Pittsburg State University Distinguished Graduate Scholarships (Undergraduate/Scholarship) [9489]

Polsinelli Diversity Scholarships (Undergraduate/Scholarship) [9490]

Karen Schuvie Scholarships (Undergraduate/Scholarship) [5189]

Shamberg Scholarships (Undergraduate/Scholarship) [9491]

Hatton W. Sumners Scholarships (Undergraduate/Scholarship) [6869]

Theta Tau Scholarships (Undergraduate/Scholarship) [8189]

J.L. Weigand, Jr. Legal Education Trust Scholarships (Undergraduate/Scholarship) [9492]

Kentucky

AISC/Southern Association of Steel Fabricators Fellowships (Graduate/Fellowship) [873]

AISC/Southern Association of Steel Fabricators Scholarships (Undergraduate/Scholarship) [874]

Bechtel Group Foundation Scholarships for Safety & Health (Undergraduate/Scholarship) [1333]

Warren K. Brown Scholarships (Undergraduate/Scholarship) [1334]

Kentucky Alumni Club Scholarships - Central Kentucky Alumni Club (Undergraduate/Scholarship) [9214]

Kentucky Alumni Club Scholarships - Lake Cumberland Alumni Club (Undergraduate/Scholarship) [9215]

Kentucky Alumni Club Scholarships - Northern Kentucky Alumni Club (Undergraduate/Scholarship) [9216]

Kentucky Educational Excellence Scholarships (Graduate, Undergraduate/Scholarship) [2090]

Kentucky Paralegal Association Student Scholarships (Undergraduate/Scholarship) [5251]

KHEAA Teacher Scholarships (Undergraduate/Scholarship) [2091]

KYCPA Scholarships (Undergraduate/Scholarship) [5253]

Joan Reagin McNeill Scholarships - Alpha Theta (Undergraduate/Scholarship) [8178]

Joan Reagin McNeill Scholarships - Theta Phi (Undergraduate/Scholarship) [8179]

Allen and Loureena Weber Scholarships (Undergraduate/Scholarship) [8404]

Zagunis Student Leader Scholarships (Graduate, Undergraduate/Scholarship) [6058]

Louisiana

AISC/Southern Association of Steel Fabricators Fellowships (Graduate/Fellowship) [873]

AISC/Southern Association of Steel Fabricators Scholarships (Undergraduate/Scholarship) [874]

Horatio Alger Louisiana Scholarships (Undergraduate/Scholarship) [308]

American Radio Relay League Louisiana Memorial Scholarships (Undergraduate/Scholarship) [1067]

Coro Fellows Program in Public Affairs (Graduate/Fellowship) [3255]

Gulf Coast Hurricane Scholarships (Graduate, Undergraduate/Scholarship) [8449]

Greater Baton Rouge Chapter - Don Jones Excellence in Safety Scholarships (Undergraduate/Scholarship) [1342]

Petroleum Engineering Scholarships (Graduate, Undergraduate/Scholarship) [8436]

Society of Louisiana Certified Public Accountants Scholarships (Undergraduate/Scholarship) [8367]

Hatton W. Sumners Scholarships (Undergraduate/Scholarship) [6869]

Maine

Leon Bradley Scholarships (Undergraduate/Scholarship) [548]

Iranian Association of Boston's IAB Scholarships (Undergraduate/Scholarship) [6362]

Ruth Milan-Altrusa Scholarships (Undergraduate/Scholarship) [5589]

Patriot Education Scholarships (Undergraduate/Scholarship) [5591]

Ross-Fahey Scholarships (Graduate, Postgraduate/Scholarship) [6056]

Henry L.P. Schmelzer College Transitions Scholarships (Undergraduate/Scholarship) [5595]

Maryland

AISC/US Steel Fellowships (Graduate/Fellowship) [876]

Irene Culver Collins and Louis Franklin Collins Scholarships (Undergraduate/Scholarship) [3054]

Land-Use Planning Scholarships (Graduate/Scholarship) [6294]

Dolphus E. Milligan Graduate Fellowships (Graduate/Fellowship) [6429]

Lana K. Rinehart Scholarships (Undergraduate/Scholarship) [3067]

SHPE Foundation Northrop Grumman Scholarships (Undergraduate/Scholarship) [8133]

Spirit of Allison Graduation Awards (Undergraduate/Award) [3806]

Charles A. Townsend Scholarships (Undergraduate/Scholarship) [7119]

University of Maryland International Student Scholarships (Undergraduate/Scholarship) [9076]

Gary Wagner, K3OMI Scholarships (Undergraduate/Scholarship) [1111]

Massachusetts

Charles Abrams Scholarships (Graduate/Scholarship) [1008]

Armenian American Pharmacists' Association Scholarships (Doctorate, Graduate/Scholarship) [1582]

Asian American Lawyers Associations of Massachusetts Scholarships (Undergraduate/Scholarship) [1644]

Bambi Bailey Scholarships (Undergraduate/Scholarship) [3078]

Hagop Bogigian Scholarship Fund (Undergraduate/Scholarship) [1587]

Leon Bradley Scholarships (Undergraduate/Scholarship) [548]

Tom Gifford Scholarships (Undergraduate/Scholarship) [4218]

Hai Guin Scholarships Association (Undergraduate/Scholarship) [1594]

AISC/Fred R. Havens Fellowships (Graduate, Undergraduate/Fellowship) [877]

Henigson Human Rights Fellowships (Graduate/Fellowship) [4467]

HRP Global Human Rights Fellowships (Graduate/Fellowship) [4468]

Iranian Association of Boston's IAB Scholarships (Undergraduate/Scholarship) [6362]

Charles A. King Trust Postdoctoral Fellowships (Postdoctorate/Fellowship) [4495]

Leiber and Stoller Music Scholarships (Undergraduate/Scholarship) [1213]

Harry B. Pulver Scholarships (Undergraduate/Scholarship) [4164]

Edward S. Roth Manufacturing Engineering Scholarships (Graduate, Undergraduate/Scholarship) [8396]

Satter Human Rights Fellowships (Graduate/Fellowship) [4469]

Al Schuman Ecolab Undergraduate Entrepreneurial Scholarships (Undergraduate/Scholarship) [6463]

SHPE Foundation Northrop Grumman Scholarships (Undergraduate/Scholarship) [8133]

Harry and Angel Zerigian Scholarships (Undergraduate/Scholarship) [1609]

Michigan

Air Force ROTC Enhanced HBCU Scholarships (Undergraduate/Scholarship) [9023]

AISC/Great Lakes Fabricators and Erectors Association Fellowships (Graduate/Fellowship) [871]

Harvey and Laura Alpert Scholarship Awards (Undergraduate/Scholarship) [4929]

Altrusa International of Grand Rapids Scholarships (Undergraduate/Scholarship) [4270]

Earl I. Anderson Scholarships (Undergraduate/Scholarship) [1068]

Ann Arbor AWC Scholarships for Women in Computing (Professional development, Undergraduate/Scholarship) [1896]

Michael M. Assarian Scholarships (Undergraduate/Scholarship) [1585]

Dr. Noyes L. Avery, Jr. & Ann E. Avery Scholarships (Undergraduate/Scholarship) [4271]

Geraldine Geistert Boss Scholarships (Undergraduate/Scholarship) [4272]

Calvin Alumni Association-Black Alumni Chapter

Scholarships *(Undergraduate/Scholarship)* [2293]

Calvin Alumni Association-Iowa/Pella Scholarships *(Undergraduate/Scholarship)* [2299]

Calvin Alumni Association-Maryland/Baltimore Scholarships *(Undergraduate/Scholarship)* [2300]

Calvin Alumni Association-Michigan Lakeshore Scholarships *(Undergraduate/Scholarship)* [2301]

Calvin Alumni Association-Michigan, Lansing Scholarships *(Undergraduate/Scholarship)* [2302]

Calvin Alumni Association-New Jersey Scholarships *(Undergraduate/Scholarship)* [2303]

Calvin Alumni Association-New York, Rochester Scholarships *(Undergraduate/Scholarship)* [2304]

Calvin Alumni Association-South Florida Scholarships *(Undergraduate/Scholarship)* [2305]

Calvin Alumni Association-South Florida Sophomore Scholarships *(Undergraduate/Scholarship)* [2306]

Calvin Alumni Association-Southeast Michigan Scholarships *(Undergraduate/Scholarship)* [2307]

Calvin Alumni Association-Southeastern Wisconsin Scholarships *(Undergraduate/Scholarship)* [2308]

Calvin Alumni Association-Southwest Michigan, Kalamazoo Scholarships *(Undergraduate/Scholarship)* [2310]

Calvin Alumni Association-Washington, D.C. Scholarships *(Undergraduate/Scholarship)* [2311]

Calvin Alumni Association-Washington, Lynden Scholarships *(Undergraduate/Scholarship)* [2312]

Calvin Alumni Association-Washington-Seattle/Tacoma Scholarships *(Undergraduate/Scholarship)* [2313]

Orrie & Dorothy Cassada Scholarships *(Undergraduate/Scholarship)* [4274]

Center for the Education of Women Scholarships *(Graduate, Undergraduate/Scholarship)* [2687]

Center for the Education of Women Student Research Grants *(Graduate, Undergraduate/Grant)* [2688]

Chapter 198 - Downriver Detroit Scholarships *(Graduate, Undergraduate/Scholarship)* [8373]

Chapter 311 - Tri City Scholarships *(Undergraduate/Scholarship)* [8376]

Chapter One - Detroit Founding Chapter Scholarships *(Graduate, Undergraduate/Scholarship)* [8382]

CMSF Scholarships *(Graduate, Undergraduate/Scholarship)* [2781]

Thomas D. Coffield Scholarships *(Undergraduate/Scholarship)* [4276]

Paul Collins Scholarships *(Undergraduate/Scholarship)* [4277]

Antenore C. "Butch" Davanzo Scholarships *(Graduate, Undergraduate/Scholarship)* [5840]

Antonia Dellas Memorial Scholarships *(Undergraduate/Scholarship)* [5094]

Detroit Economic Club Scholarships *(Undergraduate/Scholarship)* [3197]

Chapter 116 - Kalamazoo - Roscoe Douglas Scholarships *(Undergraduate/Scholarship)* [8383]

Wilma Sackett Dressel Scholarships *(Undergraduate/Scholarship)* [8166]

George & Isabelle Elanjian Scholarships *(Undergraduate/Scholarship)* [1591]

Virginia Valk Fehsenfeld Scholarships *(Undergraduate/Scholarship)* [4279]

Henry Ford Academy Scholarships *(Undergraduate/Scholarship)* [8384]

Carlyle Fraser/Wilton Looney Scholarships *(Undergraduate/Scholarship)* [1940]

Melbourne & Alice E. Frontjes Scholarships *(Undergraduate/Scholarship)* [4280]

Mathilda & Carolyn Gallmeyer Scholarships *(Undergraduate/Scholarship)* [4282]

Gauthier Family Scholarship Fund *(Undergraduate/Scholarship)* [4217]

Grand Rapids Scholarship Association *(Undergraduate/Scholarship)* [4283]

Philip F. Greco Memorial Scholarships *(Undergraduate/Scholarship)* [5560]

Guy D. & Mary Edith Halladay Graduate Scholarships *(Undergraduate/Scholarship)* [4284]

Guy D. & Mary Edith Halladay Music Scholarships *(Graduate, Undergraduate/Scholarship)* [4285]

Martha and Oliver Hansen Memorial Scholarships *(Undergraduate/Scholarship)* [5098]

Bob and Dawn Hardy Automotive Scholarships *(Undergraduate/Scholarship)* [5099]

Marjorie M. Hendricks Environmental Education Scholarship Fund *(Undergraduate/Scholarship)* [4221]

John P. Hennessey Scholarships *(Graduate, Undergraduate/Scholarship)* [5841]

Robert Holmes Scholarships *(Undergraduate/Scholarship)* [3198]

Donald & Florence Hunting Scholarships *(Undergraduate/Scholarship)* [4286]

Illinois Lake Management Association Undergraduate/Graduate Scholarships *(Graduate, Undergraduate/Fellowship, Scholarship)* [4686]

Jack Family Scholarships *(Undergraduate/Scholarship)* [4287]

Camilla C. Johnson Scholarships *(Undergraduate/Scholarship)* [4288]

Kellogg Company Career Scholarships *(Undergraduate/Scholarship)* [5234]

Lavina Laible Scholarships *(Undergraduate/Scholarship)* [4289]

Stephen Lankester Scholarships *(Undergraduate/Scholarship)* [4290]

Law Student Diversity Scholarships *(Undergraduate/Scholarship)* [5814]

John T. & Frances Maghielse Scholarships *(Undergraduate/Scholarship)* [4292]

Michigan Accountancy Foundation Fifth/Graduate Year Scholarships (MAF) *(Graduate/Scholarship)* [5808]

Michigan Education Association Scholarships *(Undergraduate/Scholarship)* [5819]

Michigan Nurses Foundation Scholarships *(Doctorate, Undergraduate/Scholarship)* [5825]

Michigan Society of Professional Engineers Scholarships *(Undergraduate/Scholarship)* [5829]

Michigan Tech Alumni Scholarships *(Graduate, Undergraduate/Scholarship)* [1130]

NALS of Michigan Scholarships *(Undergraduate/Award)* [5979]

The Nazareth Scholarships *(Undergraduate/Scholarship)* [6597]

North Central, Region 9 Scholarships *(Undergraduate/Scholarship)* [8395]

Peggy Kommer Novosad Scholarships *(Graduate, Postgraduate/Scholarship)* [4295]

Patricia & Armen Oumedian Scholarships *(Undergraduate/Scholarship)* [4296]

Daniel L. Reiss Memorial Scholarship Fund *(Undergraduate/Scholarship)* [4236]

Harold and Eleanor Ringelberg Scholarship Fund *(Undergraduate/Scholarship)* [4237]

Josephine Ringold Scholarships *(Undergraduate/Scholarship)* [4297]

Charles and Eleonor Rycenga Education Scholarship Fund *(Undergraduate/Scholarship)* [4238]

Dr. William A. and Marcelein J. Sautter Hanover-Horton High School Youth of Promise Scholarships *(Undergraduate/Scholarship)* [5104]

Prof. George Schneider, Jr. Manufacturing Technology Education Scholarships *(Undergraduate/Scholarship)* [8397]

Jeptha Wade Schureman Scholarship Program *(Undergraduate/Scholarship)* [3205]

SHPE Foundation Northrop Grumman Scholarships *(Undergraduate/Scholarship)* [8133]

Sigma Kappa Foundation Michigan Scholarships *(Undergraduate/Scholarship)* [8186]

Hazel Simms Nursing Scholarships *(Professional development/Scholarship)* [5352]

Christine Soper Scholarships *(Undergraduate/Scholarship)* [4300]

Dorothy B. & Charles E. Thomas Scholarships *(Undergraduate/Scholarship)* [4302]

Dorothy J. Thurston Graduate Scholarships *(Undergraduate/Scholarship)* [4303]

Mildred E. Troske Music Scholarships *(Undergraduate/Scholarship)* [4304]

Trustees College Scholarships *(Undergraduate/Scholarship)* [5561]

Trustees Law School Scholarships *(Undergraduate/Scholarship)* [5562]

TRW Foundation Scholarships *(Undergraduate/Scholarship)* [1951]

Edward Tuinier Memorial Scholarships *(Undergraduate/Scholarship)* [741]

Keith C. Vanderhyde Scholarships *(Undergraduate/Scholarship)* [4305]

Jacob R. & Mary M. VanLoo & Lenore K. VanLoo Scholarships *(Undergraduate/Scholarship)* [4306]

Jack H. Wagner Scholarships *(Graduate, Undergraduate/Scholarship)* [5842]

Sue Walicki Nursing Scholarships *(Undergraduate/Scholarship)* [5109]

Warner Norcross & Judd LLP Minorty Scholarships *(Undergraduate/Scholarship)* [9483]

Donald M. Wells Scholarships *(Undergraduate/Scholarship)* [4307]

J. Irving Whalley Memorial Scholarships *(Undergraduate/Scholarship)* [1952]

Amos and Marilyn Winsand-Detroit Section Named Scholarships *(Undergraduate/Scholarship)* [1448]

Wisconsin Region Student Leadership Scholarships *(Graduate, Undergraduate/Scholarship)* [6057]

Audrey L. Wright Scholarships *(Undergraduate/Scholarship)* [4309]

Zagunis Student Leader Scholarships *(Graduate, Undergraduate/Scholarship)* [6058]

Leo Zupin Memorial Scholarship Fund *(Undergraduate, Vocational/Occupational/Scholarship)* [4253]

Minnesota

AISC/US Steel Fellowships *(Graduate/Fellowship)* [876]

William E. Barto Scholarships *(Undergraduate/Scholarship)* [3525]

Duluth Central High School Alumni Scholarships *(Undergraduate/Scholarship)* [3528]

General Mills Foundation Scholarships *(Undergraduate/Scholarship)* [808]

Patricia S. Gustafson '56 Memorial Scholarships *(Undergraduate/Scholarship)* [3530]

Jeanne H. Hemmingway Scholarships *(Undergraduate/Scholarship)* [3531]

Illinois Lake Management Association Undergraduate/Graduate Scholarships *(Graduate, Undergraduate/Fellowship, Scholarship)* [4686]

Gunnar Isberg Student Scholarships *(Undergraduate/Scholarship)* [5896]

Lakselaget Foundation Scholarships *(Graduate, Undergraduate/Scholarship)* [5320]

Carol E. Macpherson Memorial Scholarship and Alumnae Society Scholarships *(Graduate, Undergraduate/Scholarship)* [9244]

Minnesota Division Scholarships *(Undergraduate/Scholarship)* [5861]

Minnesota GLBT Educational Fund *(Undergraduate/Scholarship)* [7862]

Minnesota Health Information Management Association Scholarships *(Undergraduate/Scholarship)* [5898]

Hubert A. Nelson Scholarships *(Undergraduate/Scholarship)* [3539]

Anderson Niskanen Scholarships *(Undergraduate/Scholarship)* [3541]

North Central, Region 9 Scholarships *(Undergraduate/Scholarship)* [8395]

Edward S. Roth Manufacturing Engineering Scholarships *(Graduate, Undergraduate/Scholarship)* [8396]

University of Minnesota Women Student Travel Grants *(Graduate, Undergraduate/Grant)* [9245]

Mississippi

AISC/Southern Association of Steel Fabricators Fellowships *(Graduate/Fellowship)* [873]
AISC/Southern Association of Steel Fabricators Scholarships *(Undergraduate/Scholarship)* [874]
Gulf Coast Hurricane Scholarships *(Graduate, Undergraduate/Scholarship)* [8449]
MSCPA Undergraduate Scholarships *(Undergraduate/Scholarship)* [5910]
NACA Southeast Student Leadership Scholarships *(Undergraduate/Scholarship)* [6052]
Ross-Fahey Scholarships *(Graduate, Postgraduate/Scholarship)* [6056]
Ross/Nickey Scholarships and Gary E. Thornton Memorial Scholarships *(Graduate/Scholarship)* [5911]

Missouri

Chapter 52 - Wichita Scholarships *(Graduate, Undergraduate/Scholarship)* [8377]
Coro Fellows Program in Public Affairs *(Graduate/Fellowship)* [3255]
Paul and Helen L. Grauer Scholarships *(Undergraduate/Scholarship)* [1087]
AISC/Fred R. Havens Fellowships *(Graduate, Undergraduate/Fellowship)* [877]
Kansas Optometry Service Scholarships *(Graduate, Undergraduate/Scholarship)* [5184]
MPTA Doctoral Scholarships *(Doctorate/Scholarship)* [5913]
Hatton W. Sumners Scholarships *(Undergraduate/Scholarship)* [6869]
Washington University Law School Olin Fellowships for Women *(Graduate/Fellowship)* [9533]

Montana

Horatio Alger Montana Scholarships *(Undergraduate/Scholarship)* [311]
APTRA Scholarships *(Undergraduate/Scholarship)* [1684]
Bechtel Group Foundation Scholarships for Safety & Health *(Undergraduate/Scholarship)* [1333]
Great Falls Broadcasters Association Scholarships *(Undergraduate/Scholarship)* [5922]
Donald E. Pizzini Memorial Nurse Scholarships *(Professional development/Scholarship)* [5926]
Lori Rhett Memorial Scholarships *(Graduate, Undergraduate/Scholarship)* [6055]

Nebraska

AISC/US Steel Fellowships *(Graduate/Fellowship)* [876]
Artistic Scholarship Awards *(Undergraduate, Vocational/Occupational/Scholarship)* [2023]
Beta Omega Scholarships *(Undergraduate/Scholarship)* [8158]
Tom Boots Memorial Scholarships *(Undergraduate/Scholarship)* [6601]
BSF General Scholarship Awards *(Undergraduate, Vocational/Occupational/Scholarship)* [2024]
Susan Thompson Buffett Foundation Scholarships *(Undergraduate/Scholarship)* [2205]
Paul and Helen L. Grauer Scholarships *(Undergraduate/Scholarship)* [1087]
Sharon Kreikemeier Memorial Scholarships *(Undergraduate/Scholarship)* [6602]
Brittany Mueller Memorial Scholarships *(High School/Scholarship)* [6603]
NESCPA Fifth-Year Scholarships *(Graduate/Scholarship)* [6612]
NESCPA General Scholarships *(Graduate, Undergraduate/Scholarship)* [6613]
North Central, Region 9 Scholarships *(Undergraduate/Scholarship)* [8395]
Hatton W. Sumners Scholarships *(Undergraduate/Scholarship)* [6869]
Swede Swanson Memorial Scholarships *(Undergraduate/Scholarship)* [6604]
Mark and Vera Turner Memorial Scholarships *(Undergraduate/Scholarship)* [5479]
Robert & Barbara Wade Scholarships *(Undergraduate/Scholarship)* [5480]

Nevada

AISC/Structural Steel Education Council Fellowships *(Graduate/Fellowship)* [875]
APTRA Scholarships *(Undergraduate/Scholarship)* [1684]
Aaron Edward Arnoldsen Memorial Scholarships *(Undergraduate/Scholarship)* [1620]
Donald Franklin Bradley Memorial Scholarships *(Undergraduate/Scholarship)* [7470]
Susan Brager Occupational Education Scholarships *(Undergraduate/Scholarship)* [7471]
John Caoile Memorial Scholarships *(Undergraduate/Scholarship)* [7473]
Cheyenne High School Faculty Memorial Scholarships *(Undergraduate/Scholarship)* [7475]
Robin M. Daniels Memorial Scholarships *(Undergraduate/Scholarship)* [7481]
Mickey Donnelly Memorial Scholarships *(Undergraduate/Scholarship)* [7483]
Palo Verde High School - Barbara Edwards Memorial Scholarships *(Undergraduate/Scholarship)* [7485]
Gordy Fink Memorial Scholarships *(Undergraduate/Scholarship)* [7488]
Veronica Gantt Memorial Scholarships *(Undergraduate/Scholarship)* [7491]
Dr. Virginia Gilbert Memorial Scholarships *(Undergraduate/Scholarship)* [7492]
North Las Vegas Firefighters - William J. Harnedy Memorial Scholarships *(Undergraduate/Scholarship)* [7495]
Las Vegas Chinatown Scholarships *(Undergraduate/Scholarship)* [7500]
Aaron Matusek Memorial Scholarships *(Undergraduate/Scholarship)* [7506]
Ronald McDonald House Charities of Las Vegas Scholarships *(Undergraduate/Scholarship)* [7507]
Mesquite Club Evening Chapter Scholarships *(Undergraduate/Scholarship)* [7508]
Palo Verde High School Faculty Follies Scholarships *(Undergraduate/Scholarship)* [7513]
Panther Cafe Scholarships *(Undergraduate/Scholarship)* [7514]
Pardee Community Building Scholarships *(Undergraduate/Scholarship)* [7515]
Procida Tile Importers Scholarships *(Undergraduate/Scholarship)* [7519]
Public Education Foundation Opportunity Scholarships *(Undergraduate/Scholarship)* [7520]
Silver Nugget Gaming Ambassadors Scholarships *(Undergraduate/Scholarship)* [7524]
Striving for Success Scholarships *(Undergraduate/Scholarship)* [7528]
Sheila Tarr-Smith Memorial Scholarships *(Undergraduate/Scholarship)* [7531]
Judith Warner Memorial Scholarships *(Undergraduate/Scholarship)* [7532]
Edwin F. Wiegand Science and Technology Scholarships *(Undergraduate/Scholarship)* [7533]

New Hampshire

Dr. George T. Bottomley Scholarships *(Undergraduate/Scholarship)* [5707]
Leon Bradley Scholarships *(Undergraduate/Scholarship)* [548]
CEPS-Tyco Scholarships *(Undergraduate/Scholarship)* [9250]
Dr. Robert Elliott Memorial Scholarships *(Undergraduate/Scholarship)* [5708]
Pauline Elliott Scholarships *(Undergraduate/Scholarship)* [5709]
Robert C. Erb Sr. Scholarships *(Undergraduate/Scholarship)* [5710]
Phil Friel Scholarships *(Undergraduate/Scholarship)* [5711]
Alex Gissler Memorial Scholarships *(Undergraduate/Scholarship)* [5712]
Iranian Association of Boston's IAB Scholarships *(Undergraduate/Scholarship)* [6362]
Bill Kidder Fund Awards *(Undergraduate/Scholarship)* [7853]
Stan Lencki Scholarships *(Undergraduate/Scholarship)* [5713]

Rick Mahoney Scholarships *(Undergraduate/Scholarship)* [5714]
NHPGA Apprentice Scholarships *(Undergraduate/Scholarship)* [5715]
Walter T. Philippy Scholarships *(Undergraduate/Scholarship)* [5716]
David J. Pollini Scholarships *(Undergraduate/Scholarship)* [5717]
Pope Scholarship Awards *(Undergraduate/Scholarship)* [5718]
Harry B. Pulver Scholarships *(Undergraduate/Scholarship)* [4164]
Ross-Fahey Scholarships *(Graduate, Postgraduate/Scholarship)* [6056]
Jim Sheerin Scholarships *(Undergraduate/Scholarship)* [5719]
University of New Hampshire Alumni Association Legacy Scholarships *(Undergraduate/Scholarship)* [9251]

New Jersey

A&WMA NCNJ Chapter Scholarships *(Graduate, Undergraduate/Scholarship)* [118]
AMLN Scholarships *(Graduate, Undergraduate/Scholarship)* [934]
Benjamin Asbell Memorial Scholarships *(Undergraduate/Scholarship)* [2315]
Leon Bradley Scholarships *(Undergraduate/Scholarship)* [548]
Jeffrey Carollo Music Scholarships *(Undergraduate/Scholarship)* [6648]
CentraState Band Aid Open Committee Scholarships *(Undergraduate/Scholarship)* [2724]
Constantinople Armenian Relief Society Scholarships (CARS) *(Undergraduate/Scholarship)* [1589]
Hon. Joseph W. Cowgill Memorial Scholarships *(Undergraduate/Scholarship)* [2316]
DCH Freehold Toyota Scholarships *(Undergraduate/Scholarship)* [2726]
Hon. Ralph W.E. Donges Memorial Scholarships *(Undergraduate/Award)* [2317]
DuBois Brothers Scholarships *(Undergraduate/Scholarship)* [2318]
Hirair and Anna Hovnanian Foundation Scholarships *(Undergraduate/Scholarship)* [1599]
Bernadine Johnson-Marshall and Martha Bell Williams Scholarships *(Undergraduate/Award)* [1718]
George F. Kugler, Jr. Scholarships *(Undergraduate/Scholarship)* [2319]
The Labor Law Scholarships *(Undergraduate/Scholarship)* [6660]
Abram D. and Maxine H. Londa Scholarships *(Undergraduate/Scholarship)* [6661]
Sonia Morgan Scholarships *(Undergraduate/Scholarship)* [6662]
New Jersey Psychological Association Scholarships for Minority Graduate Students *(Postgraduate/Scholarship)* [6655]
NJCBIR Individual Research Grants *(Professional development/Grant)* [6639]
NJCBIR Pilot Research Grants *(Professional development/Grant)* [6640]
NJCBIR Postdoctoral and Graduate Student Fellowships *(Graduate, Postdoctorate/Fellowship)* [6641]
NJCBIR Programmatic Multi-Investigator Project Grants *(Professional development/Grant)* [6642]
NJSCPA College Scholarships *(Graduate, Undergraduate/Scholarship)* [6657]
Norkus Charitable Foundation Scholarships *(Undergraduate/Scholarship)* [2727]
Patterson Trust Postdoctoral Fellowships in Brain Circuitry *(Postdoctorate/Fellowship)* [4496]
Louis C. Portella Memorial Scholarships *(Graduate/Scholarship)* [2321]
Hon. Rudolph J. Rossetti Memorial Scholarships *(Undergraduate/Award)* [2322]
Seton Hall Law School's Merit Scholarship Program *(Undergraduate/Scholarship)* [8097]
Star-Ledger Scholarships for the Performing Arts *(Undergraduate/Scholarship)* [6649]
Jay A. Strassberg Memorial Scholarships *(Undergraduate/Scholarship)* [2324]

Star and Barry Tobias Scholarships (Undergraduate/Scholarship) [2728]

Daniel B. Toll Memorial Scholarships (Undergraduate/Scholarship) [2325]

William Tomar Memorial Scholarships (Undergraduate/Scholarship) [2326]

Wallace Vail Scholarships (Undergraduate/Scholarship) [6663]

Bruce A. Wallace Memorial Scholarships (Undergraduate/Scholarship) [2327]

New Mexico

APTRA Scholarships (Undergraduate/Scholarship) [1684]

Walt Bartram Memorial Education Award, Region 12 and Chapter 119 (Undergraduate/Scholarship) [8369]

Chapter 93 - Albuquerque Scholarships (Undergraduate/Scholarship) [8381]

General Mills Foundation Scholarships (Undergraduate/Scholarship) [808]

New Mexico Association for Bilingual Education Scholarships (Undergraduate/Scholarship) [6665]

Hatton W. Sumners Scholarships (Undergraduate/Scholarship) [6869]

Charles A. Townsend Scholarships (Undergraduate/Scholarship) [7119]

U.S. Air Force ROTC Enhanced HSI Scholarships (Undergraduate/Scholarship) [9026]

New York

AAAA Operation Jumpstart III Scholarships (Graduate/Scholarship) [433]

Charles Abrams Scholarships (Graduate/Scholarship) [1008]

Advertising Production Club Scholarship Awards (Graduate, Undergraduate/Scholarship) [59]

AMLN Scholarships (Graduate, Undergraduate/Scholarship) [934]

Louis Armstrong Scholarships (High School/Scholarship) [1206]

AWMA Niagara Frontier Section College Scholarships (Graduate, Undergraduate/Scholarship) [115]

Leon Bradley Scholarships (Undergraduate/Scholarship) [548]

Center for Women in Government and Civil Society Fellowships (Graduate/Fellowship) [2709]

Constantinople Armenian Relief Society Scholarships (CARS) (Undergraduate/Scholarship) [1589]

Coro Fellows Program in Public Affairs (Graduate/Fellowship) [3255]

Fran Morgenstern Davis Scholarships (Undergraduate/Scholarship) [1209]

Louis Dreyfus Warner-Chappell City College Scholarships (Undergraduate/Scholarship) [1211]

The Eneslow Pedorthic Institute Scholarships (Undergraduate/Scholarship) [7139]

GFLC-A&WMA Scholarships (Graduate, Undergraduate/Scholarship) [109]

Woody Guthrie Fellowships (All/Fellowship) [2158]

Perry F. Hadlock Memorial Scholarships (Undergraduate/Scholarship) [1089]

Hudson River Graduate Fellowships (Doctorate, Master's/Fellowship) [4618]

Bryan L. Knapp Point Scholarships (Graduate, Undergraduate/Scholarship) [7364]

Anne O'Hare McCormick Scholarship Fund (Graduate/Scholarship) [6716]

Senator Patricia K. McGee Nursing Faculty Scholarships (Doctorate, Graduate/Scholarship) [6675]

McKelvey Scholarships (Undergraduate/Scholarship) [5729]

William J. Merriman American Council on Exercise Educational Scholarships (Undergraduate/Scholarship) [663]

NELA Scholarships (Graduate, Master's/Scholarship) [6624]

New York Financial Writers' Associations Scholar-

ships (Graduate, Undergraduate/Scholarship) [6667]

New York State Association of Agricultural Fairs Scholarships (Undergraduate/Scholarship) [6671]

The New York Times College Scholarships (Undergraduate/Scholarship) [6685]

Faith E. O'Neal Scholarships (Undergraduate/Scholarship) [7558]

Victoria Ovis Memorial Scholarships (Undergraduate/Scholarship) [6387]

Patterson Trust Postdoctoral Fellowships in Brain Circuitry (Postdoctorate/Fellowship) [4496]

Tibor T. Polgar Fellowships (Graduate, Undergraduate/Fellowship) [4619]

Paul Resnick and Bruce Donnelly Scholarships (Undergraduate/Scholarship) [2928]

Saint Andrews Scholarships (Undergraduate/Scholarship) [7882]

Dave Sauer Memorial College Scholarships (Undergraduate/Scholarship) [116]

Stanley M. Schoenfeld Memorial Scholarships (Postgraduate/Fellowship) [6673]

Scholarships for Emigres in the Health Sciences (Undergraduate/Scholarship) [5157]

Al Schuman Ecolab Undergraduate Entrepreneurial Scholarships (Undergraduate/Scholarship) [6463]

Undergraduate Session Assistants Program (Undergraduate/Other) [6680]

Albert E. Wischmeyer Memorial Scholarships (Undergraduate/Scholarship) [8406]

North Carolina

Herb Adrian Memorial Scholarship Fund (Undergraduate/Scholarship) [3881]

African American Network - Carolinas Scholarship Fund (Undergraduate/Scholarship) [3882]

Air Force ROTC Enhanced HBCU Scholarships (Undergraduate/Scholarship) [9023]

Andersen Nontraditional Scholarships for Women's Education and Retraining (Undergraduate/Scholarship) [3884]

Carol Bond Community College Scholarships (Undergraduate/Scholarship) [6748]

Carol Bond Environmental Educator Scholarships (Professional development/Scholarship) [6749]

Carol Bond University Scholarships (Undergraduate/Scholarship) [6750]

Sam L. Booke, Sr. Scholarships (Undergraduate/Scholarship) [9626]

T. Frank Booth Memorial Scholarship Fund (Undergraduate/Scholarship) [3888]

Cadmus Communications Corporation Graphics Scholarship Endowment Fund (Undergraduate/Scholarship) [3889]

Career Awards for Science and Mathematics Teachers (Professional development/Award) [2213]

William F. Carl Scholarships (Undergraduate, Vocational/Occupational/Scholarship) [6771]

Julian E. Carnes Scholarship Fund (Undergraduate/Scholarship) [3891]

Carolina Panthers Scholarship Fund (Graduate/Scholarship) [3892]

Carolina's Gay & Lesbian Scholarships (Undergraduate/Scholarship) [7846]

Elton Casey Scholarships (Undergraduate/Scholarship) [9262]

Children's Scholarship Fund of Charlotte (Undergraduate/Scholarship) [3896]

Lula Faye Clegg Memorial Scholarship Fund (Undergraduate/Scholarship) [3897]

Don and Barbara Curtis Excellence Fund for Extracurricular Student Activities (Undergraduate/Grant) [9266]

C.V. Starr Scholarships (Undergraduate, Graduate/Scholarship) [2690]

Jack Ervin EDI Scholarships (Professional development/Scholarship) [6761]

Judge Samuel J. Ervin, III Fellowships (Graduate/Fellowship) [5402]

Clifton W. Everett, Sr. Community Lawyer Fellowships (Graduate/Fellowship) [5403]

L.C. Gifford Distinguished Journalism Scholar-

ships (Undergraduate/Scholarship) [9276]

Golden Corral Scholarships (Undergraduate/Scholarship) [6773]

L. Gordon, Jr. and June D. Pfefferkorn Scholarships (Undergraduate/Scholarship) [9640]

Governor James E. Holshouser Professional Development Scholarships (Professional development/Scholarship) [6762]

IFH Foodservice Distribution Scholarships (Undergraduate/Scholarship) [6774]

Oliver Joel and Ellen Pell Denny Healthcare Scholarship Fund (Undergraduate/Scholarship) [9642]

James V. Johnson Scholarship Fund (Undergraduate/Scholarship) [3908]

Annabel Lambeth Jones Scholarships (Undergraduate/Scholarship) [3909]

K & W Cafeterias Scholarships (Undergraduate/Scholarship) [6775]

Kappa Zeta Scholarships (Undergraduate/Scholarship) [8177]

Law Enforcement Memorial Scholarship Fund (Undergraduate/Scholarship) [3911]

L.D. and Elsie Long Memorial Scholarships (Graduate/Scholarship) [9646]

Norval Neil Luxon Prize for Scholarships to Juniors (Undergraduate/Scholarship) [9286]

Carolina Panthers Players Sam Mills Memorial Scholarship Fund (Undergraduate/Scholarship) [3914]

Minority Presence Grant Program for Doctoral Study (Doctorate, Graduate/Grant) [9295]

N.W. Mitchell-Piedmont Federal Savings and Loans Endowed Scholarships (Undergraduate/Scholarship) [9647]

NACA Southeast Student Leadership Scholarships (Undergraduate/Scholarship) [6052]

NC Hospitality Education Foundation Scholarships - Four Year College or University (Undergraduate/Scholarship) [6776]

NC Hospitality Education Foundation Scholarships - Graduate (Graduate/Scholarship) [6777]

NC Hospitality Education Foundation Scholarships - High School (Undergraduate, Vocational/Occupational/Scholarship) [6778]

NC Hospitality Education Foundation Scholarships - Two Year Community or Junior College (Undergraduate/Scholarship) [6779]

North Carolina Association of Health Care Recruiters Scholarships (Undergraduate/Scholarship) [6755]

North Carolina CPA Foundation Scholarships (Undergraduate/Scholarship) [6752]

North Carolina Nursery and Landscape Association Horticulture Scholarships (Undergraduate/Scholarship) [6769]

Orthopaedic Specialists Nursing Scholarships (Undergraduate/Scholarship) [9648]

Ted H. Ousley Scholarship Fund (Undergraduate/Scholarship) [3917]

Outstanding Minority Accounting Student Scholarships (All/Scholarship) [6753]

Alice Conger Patterson Scholarships (Undergraduate/Scholarship) [9649]

Peter DeWitt Pruden and Phyliss Harrill Pruden Scholarships (Undergraduate/Scholarship) [9301]

John S. and Jacqueline P. Rider Scholarships (Undergraduate/Scholarship) [9652]

Ben Robinette Scholarship Endowment Fund (Undergraduate/Scholarship) [3919]

Ray and Pearl Sams Scholarships (Undergraduate/Scholarship) [9653]

William Shannon American Council on Exercise Certification Scholarships (Professional development, Undergraduate/Scholarship) [664]

Bruce Shelton Scholarships (Undergraduate/Scholarship) [9654]

Tom Shown Scholarships (Undergraduate/Scholarship) [9655]

SHPE Foundation Northrop Grumman Scholarships (Undergraduate/Scholarship) [8133]

Tacy Ana Smith Memorial Scholarships (Undergraduate/Scholarship) [3921]

The Dan Stewart Scholarships (Professional development/Scholarship) [6763]

Charles H. Stone Scholarships (Undergraduate/ Scholarship) [559]

Jack Tate/ThinkCOLLEGE Scholarship Fund (Undergraduate/Scholarship) [3924]

Virginia Elizabeth and Alma Vane Taylor Student Nurse Scholarships (Undergraduate/Scholarship) [9657]

Turner Family Scholarships (Undergraduate, Vocational/Occupational/Scholarship) [3925]

Gary Wagner, K3OMI Scholarships (Undergraduate/Scholarship) [1111]

Edward Kent Welch Memorial Scholarships (Undergraduate/Scholarship) [8661]

Frederick K. Weyerhaeuser Forest History Fellowships (Graduate/Fellowship) [3860]

L. Phil Wicker Scholarships (Undergraduate/ Scholarship) [1113]

Elizabeth T. Williams Scholarships (Undergraduate/Scholarship) [9662]

Edwin H. and Louise N. Williamson Endowed Scholarships (Undergraduate/Scholarship) [9663]

Ted C. Wilson Memorial Scholarships (Undergraduate/Scholarship) [7441]

Mary and Elliot Wood Foundation Graduate Scholarship Fund (Graduate/Scholarship) [3930]

North Dakota

North Central, Region 9 Scholarships (Undergraduate/Scholarship) [8395]

North Dakota Farmers Union Co-op House Scholarships (Undergraduate/Scholarship) [6786]

North Dakota Veterinary Medical Association Scholarships (Undergraduate/Scholarship) [6791]

Ohio

AISC/US Steel Fellowships (Graduate/Fellowship) [876]

Akron Bar Association Foundation Scholarships (Undergraduate/Scholarship) [151]

American Advertising Federation-Cleveland College Scholarships (Undergraduate/Scholarship) [402]

American Advertising Federation-Cleveland High School Scholarships (Undergraduate/Scholarship) [403]

Ora E. Anderson Scholarships (Undergraduate/ Scholarship) [3875]

Jack R. Barckhoff Welding Management Scholarships (Undergraduate/Scholarship) [1431]

William (Billbo) Boston Scholarships (Undergraduate/Scholarship) [7062]

Harry D. Callahan Educational Trust (Undergraduate/Scholarship) [8659]

Ruth M. Cogan Scholarship Fund (Undergraduate/ Scholarship) [8661]

Lawrence E. Davis Scholarships (Undergraduate/ Scholarship) [7071]

Harold K. Douthit Regional Scholarships (Undergraduate/Scholarship) [6857]

Epsilon Tau Pi's Soaring Eagle Scholarships (Undergraduate/Scholarship) [6252]

David A. and Pamela A. Gault Charitable Fund (Undergraduate/Scholarship) [8668]

Zelma Gray Medical School Scholarships (Doctorate/Fellowship) [3876]

Dorcas Edmonson Haught Scholarships (Undergraduate/Scholarship) [7089]

Dale O. Heimberger CRNA Memorial Scholarship Fund (Graduate/Scholarship) [8673]

Illinois Lake Management Association Undergraduate/Graduate Scholarships (Graduate, Undergraduate/Fellowship, Scholarship) [4686]

Susan K. Ipacs Nursing Legacy Scholarships (Undergraduate/Scholarship) [3877]

Markley Family Scholarship Fund (Undergraduate/ Scholarship) [8687]

Harry Mestel Memorial Accounting Scholarship Fund (Undergraduate/Scholarship) [8690]

John G. and Betty J. Mick Scholarship Fund (Undergraduate/Scholarship) [8691]

Lt. Colonel Robert G. Moreland Vocational/Technical Fund (Undergraduate, Vocational/Occupa-

tional/Scholarship) [8692]

NOHIMSS Student Scholarship Program (Undergraduate, Master's, Doctorate/Scholarship) [6805]

Ohio Newspaper Association Minority Scholarships (Undergraduate/Scholarship) [6858]

Ohio Newspaper Association University Journalism Scholarships (Undergraduate/Scholarship) [6859]

Ohio Newspaper Association Women's Scholarships (Undergraduate/Scholarship) [6860]

OSCA Graduate Student Scholarship Program (Graduate/Scholarship) [6861]

OSU Gay, Lesbian, Bisexual and Transgender Alumni Society PFLAG Scholarships (Undergraduate/Scholarship) [7864]

Edward S. Roth Manufacturing Engineering Scholarships (Graduate, Undergraduate/Scholarship) [8396]

Stephen Schwartz Musical Theatre Scholarships (Undergraduate/Scholarship) [4630]

SHPE Foundation Northrop Grumman Scholarships (Undergraduate/Scholarship) [8133]

Dr. William E. & Norma Sprague Scholarships (Undergraduate/Scholarship) [4301]

SSOC Scholarships (Undergraduate/Scholarship) [8014]

Ira G. Turpin Scholars Fund (Undergraduate/ Scholarship) [8706]

Irma E. Voigt Memorial Scholarships (Undergraduate/Scholarship) [8191]

Lester and Eleanor Webster Charitable Trust Fund (Undergraduate/Scholarship) [8707]

Wayne F. White and Bob Evans Legacy Scholarships (Undergraduate/Scholarship) [3878]

Xavier University ROTC Scholarships - Army ROTC (Undergraduate/Scholarship) [9784]

Zagunis Student Leader Scholarships (Graduate, Undergraduate/Scholarship) [6058]

Oklahoma

Chapter 52 - Wichita Scholarships (Graduate, Undergraduate/Scholarship) [8377]

Leon Harris/Les Nichols Memorial Scholarships to Spartan College of Aeronautics & Technology (Undergraduate/Scholarship) [131]

Kansas Optometry Service Scholarships (Graduate, Undergraduate/Scholarship) [5184]

Southwest Chapter Roy Kinslow Scholarships (Undergraduate/Scholarship) [1343]

OSHA Graduate Scholarships (Graduate/Scholarship) [6873]

Hatton W. Sumners Scholarships (Undergraduate/ Scholarship) [6869]

Tom Taylor Memorial Scholarships to Spartan College of Aeronautics and Technology (Undergraduate/Scholarship) [144]

Oregon

APTRA Scholarships (Undergraduate/Scholarship) [1684]

Clackamas County Farm Bureau Scholarships (Undergraduate/Scholarship) [6946]

Emerald Empire Chapter Scholarship Awards (Undergraduate/Scholarship) [6936]

William Harrison Gill Education Fund (Undergraduate/Scholarship) [2061]

Kilbuck Family Native American Scholarships (Undergraduate/Scholarship) [2063]

Christopher Mesi Memorial Music Scholarships (Undergraduate/Scholarship) [2659]

Chapter 63 - Portland James E. Morrow Scholarships (Graduate, Undergraduate/Scholarship) [8393]

Oregon Association of Broadcasters Scholarships (Undergraduate/Scholarship) [6929]

OSCPA Educational Foundation College Scholarships (Community College, Graduate, Undergraduate/Scholarship) [6954]

OSCPA Educational Foundation High School Scholarships (Community College, Undergraduate/Scholarship) [6955]

Lori Rhett Memorial Scholarships (Graduate, Undergraduate/Scholarship) [6055]

University of Oregon Diversity Excellence Scholarships (Graduate, Undergraduate/Scholarship) [9316]

Washington City/County Management Association Scholarships (Graduate/Scholarship) [9494]

West Coast Sea Grant Fellowships (Graduate/ Fellowship) [2279]

Willamette Valley AG Association Scholarships (Undergraduate/Scholarship) [6949]

Ed Wood Memorial Scholarship Awards (Undergraduate/Scholarship) [6944]

Yamhill County Farm Bureau Scholarships (Undergraduate/Scholarship) [6950]

Pennsylvania

Charles Abrams Scholarships (Graduate/Scholarship) [1008]

Air Products and Chemicals, Inc. Scholarships (Undergraduate/Scholarship) [1793]

Allegheny County Medical Society Medical Student Scholarships (ACMS) (Undergraduate/ Scholarship) [3983]

Alliance Medical Education Scholarship Fund (AMES) (Undergraduate/Scholarship) [3984]

B-Brave McMahon/Stratton Scholarship Fund (Undergraduate/Scholarship) [3758]

Michael Baker Inc. Scholarships for Diversity in Engineering (Undergraduate/Scholarship) [1794]

Leon Bradley Scholarships (Undergraduate/Scholarship) [548]

Joe Q. Bryant American Council on Exercise Educational Scholarships (Undergraduate/Scholarship) [662]

Warren E. "Whitey" Cole American Society of Highway Engineers Scholarships (Undergraduate/Scholarship) [3764]

Commonwealth "Good Citizen" Scholarships (Undergraduate/Scholarship) [1795]

Coro Fellows Program in Public Affairs (Graduate/ Fellowship) [3255]

Malcolm U. Dantzler Scholarships (Professional development/Scholarship) [8549]

Danville Education Association Scholarship Fund (Undergraduate/Scholarship) [3766]

The William H. Davis, Jr. Scholarship Fund (Undergraduate/Scholarship) [3086]

Daniel B. Dixon Scholarships (Undergraduate/ Scholarship) [326]

Sue and Ken Dyer Foundation Travel Scholarships (Undergraduate/Scholarship) [3941]

Wayne G. Failor Scholarships (High School/Scholarship) [7158]

Nolan W. Feeser Scholarship Fund (Undergraduate/Scholarship) [3771]

Belknap Freeman Carnegie Mellon Scholarships (Undergraduate/Scholarship) [1128]

Daniel G. and Helen I. Fultz Scholarship Fund (Undergraduate/Scholarship) [3772]

Norma Gotwalt Scholarship Fund (Undergraduate/ Scholarship) [3945]

F.C. Grote Fund Scholarships (Graduate, Undergraduate/Scholarship) [328]

Scott A. Gunder, MD, DCMS Presidential Scholarships (Undergraduate/Scholarship) [3985]

HDR Engineering, Inc. Scholarships for Diversity in Engineering (Undergraduate/Scholarship) [1796]

Alia Herrera Memorial Scholarships (Undergraduate/Scholarship) [492]

Conrad N. Hilton Scholarships (Undergraduate/ Scholarship) [3613]

Hirair and Anna Hovnanian Foundation Presidential Scholarships (Undergraduate/Scholarship) [1598]

James Hughes Memorial Scholarship Fund (Undergraduate/Scholarship) [7159]

Leon I. Lock and Barbara R. Lock Scholarship Fund (Undergraduate/Scholarship) [3950]

Carl J. Marrara Memorial Scholarship Fund (Undergraduate/Scholarship) [3780]

Barry H. Marshal Scholarships (Undergraduate/ Scholarship) [7859]

Walter A. and Nan C. McCloskey Memorial Scholarships (Undergraduate/Scholarship) [3781]

McKelvey Scholarships (Undergraduate/Scholarship) [5729]

Joseph and Catherine Missigman Memorial Nursing Scholarships (Undergraduate/Scholarship) [3782]

Missigman Scholarship Fund (Undergraduate/Scholarship) [3783]

Robert E. and Judy More Scholarship Fund (Undergraduate/Scholarship) [3784]

Pennsylvania Society of Professional Engineers Scholarships (Undergraduate/Scholarship) [7156]

PMCA Graduate Fellowships for Confectionery Research at Pennsylvania State University (Graduate/Fellowship) [7154]

Ollie Rosenberg Educational Trust (Undergraduate/Scholarship) [3958]

Jane Salanky-Onzik Scholarship Fund (Undergraduate/Scholarship) [3791]

SHPE Foundation Northrop Grumman Scholarships (Undergraduate/Scholarship) [8133]

South Carolina Public Health Association Scholarships (Undergraduate/Scholarship) [8550]

Minnie Patton Stayman Scholarships (Undergraduate/Scholarship) [7161]

Anil and Neema Thakrar Family Fund (Undergraduate/Scholarship) [3963]

John R. and Joan F. Werren Scholarships Fund (Undergraduate/Scholarship) [8708]

Williamsport-Lycoming Community Foundation - Benjamin Franklin Scholarships (Undergraduate, Vocational/Occupational/Scholarship) [3796]

Zagunis Student Leader Scholarships (Graduate, Undergraduate/Scholarship) [6058]

Rhode Island

Armenian American Pharmacists' Association Scholarships (Doctorate, Graduate/Scholarship) [1582]

Leon Bradley Scholarships (Undergraduate/Scholarship) [548]

Iranian Association of Boston's IAB Scholarships (Undergraduate/Scholarship) [6362]

Ross-Fahey Scholarships (Graduate, Postgraduate/Scholarship) [6056]

Al Schuman Ecolab Undergraduate Entrepreneurial Scholarships (Undergraduate/Scholarship) [6463]

Lily and Catello Sorrentino Memorial Scholarships (Undergraduate/Scholarship) [7794]

Bruce and Marjorie Sundlun Scholarships (Undergraduate/Scholarship) [7795]

South Carolina

African American Network - Carolinas Scholarship Fund (Undergraduate/Scholarship) [3882]

Andersen Nontraditional Scholarships for Women's Education and Retraining (Undergraduate/Scholarship) [3884]

Julian E. Carnes Scholarship Fund (Undergraduate/Scholarship) [3891]

Carolina Panthers Scholarship Fund (Graduate/Scholarship) [3892]

Judy Crocker Memorial Scholarship Fund (Undergraduate/Scholarship) [3900]

Howard B. Higgins South Carolina Dental Scholarships (Undergraduate/Scholarship) [3906]

Wilbert L. and Zora F. Holmes Scholarship Endowment Fund (Undergraduate, Vocational/Occupational/Scholarship) [3907]

Albert and Eloise Midyette Memorial Scholarship Fund (Undergraduate/Scholarship) [3913]

Carolina Panthers Players Sam Mills Memorial Scholarship Fund (Undergraduate/Scholarship) [3914]

NACA Southeast Student Leadership Scholarships (Undergraduate/Scholarship) [6052]

Henry DeWitt Plyler Scholarship Fund (Undergraduate/Scholarship) [3918]

South Carolina Association for Financial Professionals College Education Scholarships (Undergraduate/Scholarship) [8545]

South Carolina Scholastic Press Association

Scholarships (Undergraduate/Scholarship) [8553]

South Carolina Scholastic Press Association Yearbook Scholarships (Undergraduate/Scholarship) [8554]

South Carolina Undergraduate Scholarships (Undergraduate/Scholarship) [4604]

L. Phil Wicker Scholarships (Undergraduate/Scholarship) [1113]

Ted C. Wilson Memorial Scholarships (Undergraduate/Scholarship) [7441]

South Dakota

North Central, Region 9 Scholarships (Undergraduate/Scholarship) [8395]

South Dakota Division Scholarships (Undergraduate/Scholarship) [5865]

Jerry Wheeler Scholarships (Undergraduate/Scholarship) [8559]

Tennessee

Air Force ROTC Enhanced HBCU Scholarships (Undergraduate/Scholarship) [9023]

AISC/Southern Association of Steel Fabricators Fellowships (Graduate/Fellowship) [873]

AISC/Southern Association of Steel Fabricators Scholarships (Undergraduate/Scholarship) [874]

B&W Y-12 Scholarship Fund (Undergraduate/Scholarship) [3565]

Belmont University Commercial Music Scholarships (Undergraduate/Scholarship) [3094]

George Oliver Benton Memorial Scholarships (Undergraduate/Scholarship) [3095]

JoAhn Brown-Nash Memorial Scholarships (Undergraduate/Scholarship) [3097]

Steven L. Coffey Memorial Scholarships (Undergraduate/Scholarship) [3568]

Claude T. Coffman Memorial Scholarships (Undergraduate/Scholarship) [9221]

Cleveland Drennon, Jr. Memorial Scholarships (Undergraduate/Scholarship) [9222]

Federal Court Bench and Bar Scholarships (Undergraduate/Scholarship) [9225]

Pauline LaFon Gore Scholarships (Undergraduate/Scholarship) [3106]

Herbert Herff Presidential Law Scholarships (Undergraduate/Scholarship) [9227]

Regina Higdon Scholarships (Undergraduate/Scholarship) [3110]

Robert and Elaine Hoffman Memorial Scholarships (Undergraduate/Scholarship) [9228]

Kathryn Hookanson Law Fellowships (Undergraduate/Scholarship) [9229]

Cecil C. Humphreys Law Fellowships (Undergraduate/Fellowship) [9231]

Kansas Optometry Service Scholarships (Graduate, Undergraduate/Scholarship) [5184]

Michael B. Kruse Scholarships (Graduate, Undergraduate/Scholarship) [3115]

Judge William B. Leffler Scholarships (Undergraduate/Scholarship) [9232]

Liberty Bell Award Law Scholarships (Graduate/Scholarship) [2736]

Dr. Mac Scholarships (Undergraduate/Scholarship) [3118]

Joan Reagin McNeill Scholarships - Alpha Theta (Undergraduate/Scholarship) [8178]

Joan Reagin McNeill Scholarships - Theta Phi (Undergraduate/Scholarship) [8179]

Mid-South STC Chapter Scholarships (Graduate, Undergraduate/Scholarship) [8502]

Sam A. Myar Jr. Law Scholarships (Undergraduate/Scholarship) [9235]

NACA Southeast Student Leadership Scholarships (Undergraduate/Scholarship) [6052]

Archie Hartwell Nash Memorial Scholarships (Graduate, Undergraduate/Scholarship) [3127]

NCBWL Scholarships (High School/Scholarship) [5986]

Eloise Pitts O'More Scholarships (Undergraduate/Scholarship) [3129]

Donald and Susie Polden Dean's Scholarships (Undergraduate/Scholarship) [9236]

Peter DeWitt Pruden and Phyliss Harrill Pruden

Scholarships (Undergraduate/Scholarship) [9301]

Ratner and Sugarmon Scholarships (Undergraduate/Scholarship) [9237]

Barbara Hagan Richards Scholarships (Undergraduate/Scholarship) [3131]

Joseph Henry Shepherd Scholarships (Undergraduate/Scholarship) [9238]

Amy E. Spain Memorial Scholarships (Undergraduate/Scholarship) [9239]

James F. and Donna Springfield Scholarships (Undergraduate/Scholarship) [9240]

Tennessee Bar Foundation IOLTA Law School Scholarships (Undergraduate/Scholarship) [9241]

Tennessee Trucking Association Scholarships (Undergraduate/Scholarship) [3136]

Emmett H. Turner Scholarships (Undergraduate/Scholarship) [3137]

Gary Wagner, K3OMI Scholarships (Undergraduate/Scholarship) [1111]

Teddy Wilburn Scholarships (Undergraduate/Scholarship) [3138]

Texas

AAAA Operation Jumpstart III Scholarships (Graduate/Scholarship) [433]

AAMA Houston Chapter - Medical Student Scholarships (Professional development/Scholarship) [1494]

Adelante Fund Hope Scholarships, CPS Energy Dependents (Undergraduate/Scholarship) [43]

Adelante Fund Hope Scholarships, San Antonio, TX Students (Undergraduate/Scholarship) [44]

Adelante Fund UPS Scholarships (Undergraduate/Scholarship) [45]

AISC/US Steel Fellowships (Graduate/Fellowship) [876]

BAFTX Early Starters Awards (Undergraduate/Scholarship) [2175]

BAFTX Graduate Awards (Undergraduate/Scholarship) [2176]

BAFTX Junior Achievers Awards (Undergraduate/Scholarship) [2177]

BAFTX Undergraduate Awards (Undergraduate/Scholarship) [2178]

TCDA Carroll Barnes Student Scholarships (Graduate, Undergraduate/Scholarship) [8846]

Zachary Barriger Memorial Scholarships (Undergraduate/Scholarship) [2935]

O.J. Beck, Jr. Memorial Scholarships (Undergraduate/Scholarship) [2936]

Reverend E.F. Bennett Scholarships (Undergraduate/Scholarship) [2937]

Bill Bernbach Diversity Scholarships (Undergraduate/Scholarship) [434]

Kathi Bowles Scholarships for Women in Technology (Graduate, Undergraduate/Scholarship) [1898]

Marion Luna Brem/Pat McNeil Health and Education Scholarships (Undergraduate/Scholarship) [2938]

TCDA Jim and Glenda Casey Professional Scholarships (Graduate, Professional development/Scholarship) [8847]

C.C.H.R.M.A. Scholarships (High School, Undergraduate/Scholarship) [2941]

Bill Cormack Scholarships (Undergraduate/Scholarship) [8865]

Dallas Hispanic Bar Association Scholarships (Undergraduate/Scholarship) [3337]

DeBakey International Society Fellowship Awards (Professional development/Award) [3354]

Educational and Professional Achievement Scholarships (Undergraduate, Vocational/Occupational/Scholarship) [1933]

John R. Eidson Jr., Scholarships (Undergraduate/Scholarship) [2946]

George Foreman Tribute to Lyndon B. Johnson Scholarships (Undergraduate/Scholarship) [7577]

Gamma Iota Scholarships - Gamma Tau (Undergraduate/Scholarship) [8170]

Gamma Iota Scholarships - Kappa Eta (Undergraduate/Scholarship) [8171]

Gamma Iota Scholarships - Zeta Kappa (Undergraduate/Scholarship) [8172]

Gamma Iota Scholarships - Zeta Nu (Undergraduate/Scholarship) [8173]

Max Godwin Endowed Scholarships (Undergraduate/Scholarship) [8880]

TCDA Bill Gorham Student Scholarships (Graduate, Undergraduate/Scholarship) [8848]

Melissa Guerra Scholarships (Undergraduate/Scholarship) [2948]

Gulf Coast Hurricane Scholarships (Graduate, Undergraduate/Scholarship) [8449]

George Gustafson HSE Memorial Scholarships (Graduate, Undergraduate/Scholarship) [1339]

George and Mary Josephine Hamman Foundation Scholarships (Undergraduate/Scholarship) [4369]

Haraldson Foundation Scholarships (Graduate, Undergraduate/Scholarship) [4391]

Hill Country Master Gardeners Horticulture Scholarships (Graduate, Undergraduate/Scholarship) [4543]

Hispanic Association of Colleges and Universities Scholarships (Undergraduate/Scholarship) [4548]

Institute of Transportation Engineers - Texas District Fellowships (Graduate/Fellowship) [4823]

Jamail/Long Challenge Grant Scholarships (Graduate, Undergraduate/Scholarship) [4559]

JLTLA Scholarships (Undergraduate/Scholarship) [8981]

Craig Johnson Family Scholarships (Undergraduate/Scholarship) [8884]

Mary Jon and J. P. Bryan Leadership in Education Awards (Professional development/Award) [8877]

Sue Kay Lay Memorial Scholarships (Undergraduate/Scholarship) [2952]

Danny T. Le Memorial Scholarships (High School, Undergraduate/Scholarship) [9431]

MillerCoors Chicago Scholarships (Community College, Undergraduate/Scholarship) [46]

Le Hoang Nguyen College Scholarships (LHN) (High School/Scholarship) [9432]

The Thuy Nguyen Scholarships (High School/Scholarship) [9433]

Rotary Club of Corpus Christi Scholarships (Undergraduate/Scholarship) [2956]

Edward S. Roth Manufacturing Engineering Scholarships (Graduate, Undergraduate/Scholarship) [8396]

Seaman Family Scholarships (Undergraduate/Scholarship) [2957]

Judge Terry Shamsie Scholarships (High School/Scholarship) [2958]

Herman J. Smith Scholarships (Undergraduate/Scholarship) [6345]

South Texas Unit Scholarships (Undergraduate/Scholarship) [4536]

Cecilia Steinfeldt Fellowships for Research in the Arts and Material Culture (Professional development/Fellowship) [8878]

Hatton W. Sumners Scholarships (Undergraduate/Scholarship) [6869]

Talbert Family Memorial Accounting and Financial Management Scholarships (Undergraduate/Scholarship) [2961]

TCDA Abbott IPCO Professional Scholarships (Graduate, Professional development/Scholarship) [8849]

TCDA Gandy Ink Student Scholarships (Graduate, Undergraduate/Scholarship) [8850]

TCDA General Fund Scholarships (Graduate, Undergraduate/Scholarship) [8851]

TCDA Past Presidents Student Scholarships (Graduate, Undergraduate/Scholarship) [8852]

Texas Elks State Association Eagle Scout Scholarships (High School/Scholarship) [8861]

Texas Elks State Association Girl Scout Gold Award Scholarships (High School, Undergraduate/Scholarship) [8862]

Texas Elks State Association Scholarships (Undergraduate/Scholarship) [8863]

Texas Music Educators Association Past-Presidents Memorial Scholarships (Undergraduate/Scholarship) [8866]

Texas Muslims Scholarship Fund (TMSF) (Graduate, Undergraduate/Scholarship) [4006]

Texas Telephone Association Foundation Scholarships (Undergraduate/Scholarship) [8882]

Traditional Education Scholarships (Graduate, Undergraduate/Scholarship) [8500]

Vera Tran Memorial Scholarships (Undergraduate/Scholarship) [9434]

TUUT HSF College Scholarship Program (Undergraduate/Scholarship) [4582]

U.S. Air Force ROTC Enhanced HSI Scholarships (Undergraduate/Scholarship) [9026]

Dr. Juan D. Villarreal/HDA Foundation Scholarships (Graduate/Scholarship) [4557]

Faye and Rendell Webb Scholarships (Undergraduate/Scholarship) [2962]

TCDA Cloys Webb Student Scholarships (Graduate, Undergraduate/Scholarship) [8853]

Wheelchair Success Foundation Scholarships (Undergraduate/Scholarship) [2963]

YWA Foundation Scholarships (Graduate, Undergraduate/Scholarship) [9793]

Utah

APTRA Scholarships (Undergraduate/Scholarship) [1684]

Edward S. Roth Manufacturing Engineering Scholarships (Graduate, Undergraduate/Scholarship) [8396]

Vermont

Leon Bradley Scholarships (Undergraduate/Scholarship) [548]

Iranian Association of Boston's IAB Scholarships (Undergraduate/Scholarship) [6362]

Ross-Fahey Scholarships (Graduate, Postgraduate/Scholarship) [6056]

Virginia

AAAA Operation Jumpstart III Scholarships (Graduate/Scholarship) [433]

H. Burton Bates Jr. Scholarships (Graduate, Undergraduate/Scholarship) [9459]

Thomas M. Berry Jr. Scholarships (Graduate, Undergraduate/Scholarship) [9460]

Bill Bernbach Diversity Scholarships (Undergraduate/Scholarship) [434]

Leo Bourassa Scholarships (Undergraduate, Graduate/Scholarship) [9455]

Buena M. Chesshir Memorial Women's Educational Scholarships (Graduate, Master's, Undergraduate/Scholarship) [9440]

Austin M. Cloyd, Matthew G. Gwaltney and Maxine S. Turner Doctoral Scholarships (Doctorate/Scholarship) [9461]

Cocke, Szpanka and Taylor Scholarships (Undergraduate/Scholarship) [9462]

Richard D. and Sheppard R. Cooke Memorial Scholarships (Graduate/Scholarship) [4371]

Dixon Hughes Goodman LLP Annual Scholarship (Undergraduate/Scholarship) [3465]

Palmer Farley Memorial Scholarships (Undergraduate/Scholarship) [4372]

Jane S. Glenn Memorial Endowed Scholarships (Undergraduate/Scholarship) [7805]

Goodman & Company Scholarships (Undergraduate/Scholarship) [9463]

Hampton Roads Sanitation District Environmental Scholarships (Graduate/Scholarship) [4375]

Hilb, Rogal and Hobbs Scholarships (Undergraduate/Scholarship) [9449]

Louis I. Jaffe Memorial Scholarships-ODU (Graduate/Scholarship) [4377]

Jefferson Graduate Fellowships (Doctorate, Graduate/Fellowship) [5153]

Karen B. Lewis Career Education Scholarships (Undergraduate/Scholarship) [9441]

Lewis K. Martin II, M.D. and Cheryl Rose Martin Scholarship Fund (Graduate/Scholarship) [4378]

NACA Southeast Student Leadership Scholarships (Undergraduate/Scholarship) [6052]

Norfolk Southern Scholarships (Undergraduate/Scholarship) [9450]

Peter DeWitt Pruden and Phyliss Harrill Pruden

Scholarships (Undergraduate/Scholarship) [9301]

Drs. Kirkland Ruffin & Willcox Ruffin Scholarships (Graduate/Scholarship) [4381]

SHPE Foundation Northrop Grumman Scholarships (Undergraduate/Scholarship) [8133]

Hy Smith Endowment Fund (Undergraduate/Scholarship) [4382]

Florence L. Smith Medical Scholarships (Graduate/Scholarship) [4383]

Virginia Historical Society Research Fellowships (Doctorate/Fellowship) [9453]

VSCPA Educational Foundation Graduate Scholarships (Graduate/Scholarship) [9464]

VSCPA Educational Foundation Minority Scholarships (Graduate, Undergraduate/Scholarship) [9465]

VSCPA Educational Foundation Undergraduate Scholarships (Undergraduate/Scholarship) [9466]

VSCPA PhD Accounting Scholarships (Doctorate, Graduate/Scholarship) [9467]

Gary Wagner, K3OMI Scholarships (Undergraduate/Scholarship) [1111]

West Virginia PTA Scholarships (Undergraduate/Scholarship) [9568]

L. Phil Wicker Scholarships (Undergraduate/Scholarship) [1113]

Ted C. Wilson Memorial Scholarships (Undergraduate/Scholarship) [7441]

Witt Mares Scholarships (Undergraduate/Scholarship) [9451]

Women in Science and Technology Scholarships (Doctorate, Graduate, Master's, Undergraduate/Scholarship) [9442]

Yount, Hyde & Barbour Scholarships (Undergraduate/Scholarship) [9468]

Nettie Tucker Yowell Scholarships (Undergraduate/Scholarship) [9443]

Washington

Air Force ROTC Enhanced HBCU Scholarships (Undergraduate/Scholarship) [9023]

APTRA Scholarships (Undergraduate/Scholarship) [1684]

Bechtel Group Foundation Scholarships for Safety & Health (Undergraduate/Scholarship) [1333]

Beta Sigma Phi - Fine Arts Scholarships (Undergraduate/Scholarship) [8111]

Boeing Company Scholarships (Undergraduate/Scholarship) [8112]

Chateau Ste. Michelle Scholarship Fund (Undergraduate/Scholarship) [2975]

Dr. Princeton L. Co Emergency Fund for Dental Hygiene Scholarships (Undergraduate/Scholarship) [8113]

Carli Edwards Memorial Scholarships (Undergraduate/Scholarship) [8114]

Ruth Murphy Evans Scholarships (Undergraduate/Scholarship) [4335]

Dayton E. Finnigan Scholarships (Undergraduate/Scholarship) [4336]

Friends of Mary Automotive Scholarships (Undergraduate/Scholarship) [8115]

William H. Gates Public Service Law Scholarships (Undergraduate/Scholarship) [4046]

Margaret S. Gilbert Scholarship Fund (Undergraduate/Scholarship) [8669]

Dr. Bill Johnson Scholarships (Undergraduate/Scholarship) [8116]

Ina Knutsen Scholarships (Undergraduate/Scholarship) [8117]

Ken LaFountaine First Nations Scholarships (Undergraduate/Scholarship) [8118]

Ron LaFreniere Business Scholarships (Undergraduate/Scholarship) [8119]

Leadership 1000 Scholarships (Undergraduate/Scholarship) [2976]

Mallet Nursing Scholarships (Undergraduate/Scholarship) [8120]

Christopher Mesi Memorial Music Scholarships (Undergraduate/Scholarship) [2659]

Mill Creek Business Association Scholarships (Undergraduate/Scholarship) [5878]

Chapter 63 - Portland James E. Morrow Scholarships *(Graduate, Undergraduate/Scholarship)* [8393]

Eric Niemitalo Scholarships in Earth and Environmental Science *(Undergraduate/Scholarship)* [8121]

Olympia Tumwater Foundation Traditional Scholarships *(Undergraduate/Scholarship)* [6875]

Olympia Tumwater Foundation Transitional (nontraditional) Scholarships *(Undergraduate/Scholarship)* [6876]

Realize the Dream Scholarships *(Undergraduate/Scholarship)* [2977]

Lori Rhett Memorial Scholarships *(Graduate, Undergraduate/Scholarship)* [6055]

Richard C. Rolfs Scholarships *(Undergraduate/Scholarship)* [7418]

Seattle Chapter ASWA Scholarships *(Undergraduate/Scholarship)* [3600]

Shoreline Community College Academic Excellence Scholarships for Graduating High School Seniors *(Undergraduate/Scholarship)* [8123]

Shoreline Community College Academic Improvement Scholarships for Graduating High School Seniors *(Undergraduate/Scholarship)* [8124]

Shoreline Community College Continuing Students Scholarships *(Undergraduate/Scholarship)* [8125]

Shoreline Community College Part-Time Students Scholarships *(Undergraduate/Scholarship)* [8126]

STC-PSC Scholarships *(Graduate, Undergraduate/Scholarship)* [8506]

Margaret Svec Scholarships *(Undergraduate/Scholarship)* [8127]

Janet Cullen Tanaka Scholarships *(Undergraduate/Scholarship)* [1905]

Elizabeth R. Thomas Scholarships *(Undergraduate/Scholarship)* [8128]

WALPA Lake Scholarships *(Graduate, Undergraduate/Scholarship)* [9526]

Washington City/County Management Association Scholarships *(Graduate/Scholarship)* [9494]

Washington State Governors' Scholarship for Foster Youth *(Undergraduate/Scholarship)* [2978]

Washington State Nurses Association Foundation Scholarships (WSNF) *(Graduate, Undergraduate/Scholarship)* [9528]

West Coast Sea Grant Fellowships *(Graduate/Fellowship)* [2279]

Why Get Your Blue On? Video Scholarships *(Graduate, Undergraduate/Award, Scholarship)* [9587]

WIGA Scholarships *(Postgraduate, Professional development, Undergraduate/Scholarship)* [9512]

West Virginia

Bob Adkins Memorial Scholarships *(Undergraduate/Scholarship)* [7057]

William (Billbo) Boston Scholarships *(Undergraduate/Scholarship)* [7062]

Leon Bradley Scholarships *(Undergraduate/Scholarship)* [548]

Freda Burge Scholarships *(Undergraduate/Scholarship)* [7064]

Cindy Curry Memorial Scholarships *(Undergraduate/Scholarship)* [7069]

Lawrence E. Davis Scholarships *(Undergraduate/Scholarship)* [7071]

David Edward Farson Scholarships *(Undergraduate/Scholarship)* [7074]

William E. "Bill" Gallagher Scholarships *(Undergraduate/Scholarship)* [7076]

Albert H. Hix, W8AH Memorial Scholarships *(Undergraduate/Scholarship)* [1090]

Holly Jackson-Wuller Memorial Scholarships *(Undergraduate/Scholarship)* [7091]

K.A.S.A Memorial Scholarships *(Undergraduate/Scholarship)* [7092]

Dr. Charles Kelly Memorial Scholarships *(Undergraduate/Scholarship)* [7093]

McKelvey Scholarships *(Undergraduate/Scholarship)* [5729]

James H. Roberts Athletic Scholarships *(Undergraduate/Scholarship)* [7106]

James Robinson Memorial Scholarships *(Undergraduate/Scholarship)* [7108]

Mary K. Smith Rector Scholarships *(Undergraduate, Vocational/Occupational/Scholarship)* [7117]

Gary Wagner, K3OMI Scholarships *(Undergraduate/Scholarship)* [1111]

L. Phil Wicker Scholarships *(Undergraduate/Scholarship)* [1113]

Zagunis Student Leader Scholarships *(Graduate, Undergraduate/Scholarship)* [6058]

Wisconsin

AISC/US Steel Fellowships *(Graduate/Fellowship)* [876]

Victor Albright Scholarships-Dane County *(Undergraduate/Scholarship)* [9347]

Victor Albright Scholarships *(Undergraduate/Scholarship)* [9348]

John D. Anello Sr. and Albert A. Silverman Memorial Scholarships *(Undergraduate/Scholarship)* [2887]

William E. Barto Scholarships *(Undergraduate/Scholarship)* [3525]

Mary Ann Brichta Scholarships *(Undergraduate/Scholarship)* [9350]

Patricia Buchanan Memorial Scholarships *(Undergraduate/Scholarship)* [9351]

Duluth Central High School Alumni Scholarships *(Undergraduate/Scholarship)* [3528]

Engineering Departmental Scholarships *(Undergraduate/Scholarship)* [9352]

Engineering Diversity Affairs Scholarships *(All/Scholarship)* [9353]

Founding Fathers Leadership Scholarships *(Undergraduate/Scholarship)* [9676]

Carleton A. Friday Memorial Scholarships *(Undergraduate/Scholarship)* [5867]

Human Ecology Continuing Undergraduate Student Scholarships *(Undergraduate/Scholarship)* [9358]

Illinois Lake Management Association Undergraduate/Graduate Scholarships *(Graduate, Undergraduate/Fellowship, Scholarship)* [4686]

Iowa Journalism Institute Scholarships *(Undergraduate/Scholarship)* [5043]

Kemper K. Knapp Scholarships *(Undergraduate/Scholarship)* [9360]

George Koeppel and Roland W. Zinns Scholarships *(Undergraduate/Scholarship)* [9361]

Harold A. Levin Scholarships *(Undergraduate/Scholarship)* [2890]

McBurney Disability Scholarships *(Undergraduate/Scholarship)* [9363]

Edmond A. Metzger Scholarships *(Undergraduate/Scholarship)* [1094]

John P. and Tashia F. Morgridge Scholarships *(Undergraduate/Scholarship)* [9364]

Hubert A. Nelson Scholarships *(Undergraduate/Scholarship)* [3539]

North Central, Region 9 Scholarships *(Undergraduate/Scholarship)* [8395]

Pi Lambda Theta Scholarships *(Undergraduate/Scholarship)* [9366]

Powers-Knapp Scholarships *(Undergraduate/Scholarship)* [9367]

School of Education Scholarships for Students from Underrepresented Groups *(Undergraduate/Scholarship)* [9369]

School of Pharmacy Continuing Student Scholarships *(Undergraduate/Scholarship)* [9370]

John A. Sullivan Scholarships *(Undergraduate/Scholarship)* [3546]

Dean James Thomas Memorial Scholarships *(Undergraduate/Scholarship)* [9680]

University of Wisconsin-Madison Academic Excellence Scholarships *(Undergraduate/Scholarship)* [9371]

University of Wisconsin-Madison African American Alumni Scholarships *(Undergraduate/Scholarship)* [9372]

University of Wisconsin-Madison American Indian Alumni Scholarships *(Undergraduate/Scholarship)* [9373]

University of Wisconsin-Madison/CALS Continuing

Student Scholarships *(Undergraduate/Scholarship)* [9374]

University of Wisconsin-Madison/CALS Minority Scholarships *(Undergraduate/Scholarship)* [9375]

University of Wisconsin-Madison Minority Teacher Loans *(Professional development, Undergraduate/Loan, Scholarship)* [9378]

University of Wisconsin-Madison Music Scholarships *(Undergraduate/Scholarship)* [9379]

University of Wisconsin-Madison National Merit Scholarships *(Undergraduate/Scholarship)* [9380]

University of Wisconsin-Madison Pharmacy New Student Scholarships *(Undergraduate/Scholarship)* [9381]

Vilas Equity Scholarships *(Undergraduate/Scholarship)* [9383]

William F. Vilas Scholarships *(Undergraduate/Scholarship)* [9384]

Kenneth G. Weckel Scholarships *(Undergraduate/Scholarship)* [5868]

Wisconsin Broadcasters Association Scholarships *(Undergraduate/Scholarship)* [9682]

Wisconsin High School Scholarships *(Undergraduate/Scholarship)* [9385]

Wisconsin-Madison Journalism Scholarships *(Undergraduate/Scholarship)* [9386]

Wisconsin-Madison Music Clinic Scholarships *(Undergraduate/Scholarship)* [9387]

Wisconsin Region Student Leadership Scholarships *(Graduate, Undergraduate/Scholarship)* [6057]

Wyoming

AISC/Rocky Mountain Steel Construction Association Fellowships *(Graduate/Fellowship)* [872]

APTRA Scholarships *(Undergraduate/Scholarship)* [1684]

Dorothy Mountain Memorial Scholarships *(Graduate/Scholarship)* [5532]

Harry Walts Memorial Graduate Scholarships *(Graduate/Scholarship)* [5533]

CANADA

AABP Amstutz Scholarships *(Undergraduate/Scholarship)* [443]

AABP Student Externship Program *(Undergraduate/Scholarship)* [447]

AANS Medical Student Summer Research Fellowships (MSSRF) *(Undergraduate/Fellowship)* [515]

AAS Korean Studies Scholarship Program *(Doctorate, Graduate/Scholarship)* [1710]

Aboriginal Traditional Arts Project Grants *(Professional development/Grant)* [215]

Jack Ackroyd Scholarships *(Professional development/Scholarship)* [2372]

ADAC Foundation Scholarships *(Undergraduate/Scholarship)* [1622]

AECT Foundation Mentor Endowment Scholarships *(Doctorate, Graduate/Scholarship)* [1761]

AIA and the Global Automotive Aftermarket Symposium Scholarships *(Undergraduate/Scholarship)* [1955]

Airports Council International-North America Scholarships *(Graduate, Undergraduate/Scholarship)* [149]

Alberta Agricultural Economics Association Masters Scholarships *(Graduate/Scholarship)* [203]

Alberta Agricultural Economics Association Undergraduate Scholarships *(Undergraduate/Scholarship)* [204]

Alberta Association of Gerontology Student Awards - Edmonton Chapter *(Graduate, Undergraduate/Award)* [207]

Alberta Centennial Premier's Scholarships - Alberta *(Undergraduate/Scholarship)* [237]

Alexander Graham Bell Canada Graduate Scholarship Program *(Doctorate, Master's/Scholarship)* [6571]

Hon. Lincoln Alexander Scholarships *(Undergraduate/Scholarship)* [2109]

Janet and Horace Allen Scholarships *(Undergraduate/Scholarship)* [238]

Alliance Pipeline Scholarships *(Professional development/Scholarship)* [2005]

Lorraine Allison Scholarships *(Graduate/Scholarship)* [1500]

AMEC Aboriginal Undergraduate Scholarships *(Undergraduate/Scholarship)* [2453]

AMEC Masters Scholarships *(Graduate, Master's/Scholarship)* [2454]

American College of Radiation Oncology Resident Scholarships *(Graduate/Scholarship)* [623]

American Judges Association Law Student Essay Competition *(Undergraduate/Prize)* [890]

Bernard Amtmann Fellowships *(Postgraduate, Professional development/Fellowship)* [2087]

Dr. Andy Anderson Young Professional Awards *(Professional development/Award)* [7317]

Aplastic Anemia and Myelosdysplasia Scholarships *(Graduate/Scholarship)* [2533]

Applied Hospitality Degree Scholarships *(Undergraduate/Scholarship)* [2487]

Architects Association of PEI Scholarships *(Undergraduate/Scholarship)* [3180]

Robin P. Armstrong Memorial Prize for Excellence in Native Studies Awards *(Doctorate, Graduate/Award)* [2377]

Art Graduate Scholarships *(Graduate/Scholarship)* [239]

ASA Graduate Scholarships *(Graduate/Scholarship)* [1182]

ASAC-CJAS PhD Research Grant Awards *(Doctorate/Grant)* [52]

Association of Desk and Derrick Clubs Education Trust Scholarships *(Undergraduate/Scholarship)* [1749]

Association of Universities and Colleges of Canada Public Scholarships *(Undergraduate/Scholarship)* [1889]

Association for Women Veterinarians Foundation Student Scholarships *(Graduate/Scholarship)* [1912]

AstraZeneca RURAL Scholarships *(Doctorate/Scholarship)* [2534]

Atkinson Fellowships in Public Policy *(Professional development/Fellowship)* [1920]

Atlantic Provinces Library Association Memorial Awards *(Professional development/Scholarship)* [1926]

Atlantic Salmon Federation Olin Fellowships *(All/Fellowship)* [1929]

Joan Auld Scholarships *(Undergraduate/Scholarship)* [3181]

Jerry Baker Scholarships *(Undergraduate/Scholarship)* [1430]

Lynn Ann Baldwin Scholarships *(Master's/Scholarship)* [2395]

Bank of Canada Fellowships *(Doctorate, Professional development/Fellowship)* [2011]

Bank of Canada Governor's Awards *(Doctorate, Professional development/Award)* [2012]

Helen Bassett Commemorative Scholarships *(Undergraduate/Scholarship)* [6567]

Baxter Corporation Canadian Research Awards in Anesthesia *(Professional development/Award)* [2356]

BBM Canada Scholarships *(Undergraduate/Scholarship)* [2365]

BCPA Bursaries *(Undergraduate/Scholarship)* [2180]

Suzanne Beauregard Scholarships *(Undergraduate/Scholarship)* [4180]

Stan Beck Fellowships *(Graduate, Undergraduate/Fellowship)* [3652]

Anne Beckingham Scholarships *(Graduate, Professional development/Scholarship)* [2474]

Dr. Ann C. Beckingham Scholarships *(Doctorate/Scholarship)* [2535]

Harvey Bell Memorial Prize *(Graduate/Prize)* [6564]

Beverlee Bell Scholarships in Human Rights and Democracy *(Graduate/Scholarship)* [3473]

Louise Bennett-Coverley Scholarships *(Undergraduate/Scholarship)* [2110]

The Viscount Bennett Fellowships *(Graduate/Fellowship)* [2419]

Dr. Noorali & Sabiya Bharwani Endowment *(Undergraduate/Scholarship)* [2082]

Hussein Jina Bharwani Memorial Endowment *(Undergraduate/Scholarship)* [2083]

Dr. Biljan Memorial Awards *(Graduate/Award)* [2466]

BioQuip Undergraduate Scholarships *(Undergraduate/Scholarship)* [3653]

Birks Family Foundation Scholarships *(Undergraduate/Scholarship)* [2536]

Bison Transport Scholarships *(Undergraduate/Scholarship)* [6897]

Lucie and Thornton Blackburn Scholarships *(Undergraduate/Scholarship)* [2363]

Alex Blaski Memorial Scholarships *(Undergraduate/Scholarship)* [7757]

M. Hildred Blewett Fellowships *(Postdoctorate/Scholarship)* [997]

Lawrence Bloomberg Entrance Awards *(Postgraduate/Award)* [8034]

BMO Financial Group Scholarships *(Undergraduate/Scholarship)* [2111]

Edith and Arnold N. Bodtker Grants *(All/Grant)* [3339]

Steve Bonk Scholarships *(Postgraduate/Scholarship)* [2634]

Lorne and Ruby Bonnell Scholarships *(Undergraduate/Scholarship)* [3182]

Maria and Czeslaw Borek Scholarships *(Undergraduate/Scholarship)* [7758]

Jim Bourque Scholarships *(Postgraduate, Undergraduate/Scholarship)* [1501]

CAG Margery Boyce Bursary Awards *(Postgraduate/Award)* [2381]

Charles F. Brandenburg Memorial Scholarships *(Undergraduate/Scholarship)* [2622]

Louis J. Brody Q.C. Entrance Scholarships *(Postgraduate/Scholarship)* [8035]

Peter F. Bronfman Entrance Awards *(Postgraduate/Award)* [8036]

Peter F. Bronfman Scholarships of Merit *(Postgraduate/Scholarship)* [8037]

William A. and Ann M. Brothers Scholarships *(Undergraduate/Scholarship)* [1433]

Randall Brown and Associates Awards *(Postgraduate/Award)* [2468]

Tropicana Community Services - Robert K. Brown Scholarships *(Undergraduate/Scholarship)* [2112]

Pamfil and Maria Bujea Family Orthodox Christian Seminarian Scholarships *(Undergraduate/Scholarship)* [1163]

Sam Bull Memorial Scholarships *(Undergraduate/Scholarship)* [227]

Burger King Scholars Program *(Undergraduate/Scholarship)* [4475]

Burroughs Wellcome Fund Career Awards at the Scientific Interface *(Doctorate, Postdoctorate/Fellowship)* [2211]

Business, Education and Technology Scholarships *(Graduate, Undergraduate, Vocational/Occupational/Scholarship)* [336]

Peter Butler III - Rose Fortune Scholarship Program *(Undergraduate/Scholarship)* [1716]

CAA National Capital Region Writing Contest *(All/Prize)* [2417]

CADE Bursary *(Undergraduate/Scholarship)* [2374]

CADE Scholarships *(Undergraduate/Scholarship)* [2375]

CAG Health and Health Care Study Group Awards *(Graduate/Award)* [2378]

CAHR Master's Level Scholarships *(Master's/Scholarship)* [2384]

CALL/ACBD Education Reserve Fund Grants *(Graduate/Grant)* [2388]

Cameco Corporation Scholarships in the Geological Sciences - Continuing Students *(Undergraduate/Scholarship)* [2344]

Cameco Corporation Scholarships in the Geological Sciences - Entering Students *(Undergraduate/Scholarship)* [2345]

Cameco Northern Scholarships - University *(Undergraduate/Scholarship)* [2347]

Dalton Camp Awards *(All/Prize)* [4012]

Thomas R. Camp Scholarships *(Graduate/Scholarship)* [1416]

Theodore R. Campbell Scholarships *(Undergraduate/Scholarship)* [240]

Canada Graduate Scholarship Program *(Graduate/Scholarship)* [8285]

Canada-Ukraine Parliamentary Program Internship Scholarships (CUPP) *(Undergraduate/Scholarship)* [9497]

Canadian Anesthesiologists' Society Research Awards *(Professional development/Award)* [2357]

Canadian Association of Cardiac Rehabilitation Graduate Scholarship Awards *(Graduate/Scholarship)* [2370]

Canadian Association of Geographers Historical Geography Study Group Awards *(Doctorate, Graduate, Undergraduate/Award)* [2379]

Canadian Association of Law Libraries CALL Research Grants *(Graduate/Grant)* [2389]

Canadian Association of Law Teachers Award for Academic Excellence *(Professional development/Award)* [2393]

Canadian Association for the Practical Study of Law in Education Fellowships *(Graduate/Fellowship)* [2402]

Canadian Association for Studies in Co-operation Scholarships Lemaire Co-operative Studies Awards (CASC) *(Graduate, Undergraduate/Scholarship)* [2431]

Canadian Blood Services Graduate Fellowships *(Graduate/Fellowship)* [2421]

Canadian Blood Services Postdoctoral Fellowships *(Postdoctorate/Fellowship)* [2422]

Canadian Council of Technicians and Technologists Scholarships for Technology Students *(Postgraduate/Scholarship)* [2445]

Canadian Evaluation Society Educational Fund Scholarships *(Graduate/Scholarship)* [2459]

Canadian Evaluation Society Memorial Scholarships *(Graduate, Professional development/Scholarship)* [2475]

Canadian Federation of Independent Grocers National Scholarships *(Undergraduate/Scholarship)* [2461]

Canadian Federation of University Women Etobicoke Bursary *(Undergraduate/Scholarship)* [9324]

Canadian Hard of Hearing Association Scholarships *(Undergraduate/Scholarship)* [2481]

Canadian Hospitality Foundation College Entrance Scholarships *(Undergraduate/Scholarship)* [2488]

Canadian Hospitality Foundation University Entrance Scholarships *(Undergraduate/Scholarship)* [2489]

Canadian Hydrographic Association Student Awards *(Undergraduate/Award)* [2492]

Canadian Identification Society Essay Scholarship Awards *(Professional development/Prize)* [2494]

Canadian Iranian Foundation Scholarships *(Undergraduate/Scholarship)* [2509]

Canadian IT Law Association Student Writing Contest *(Doctorate/Prize)* [2511]

Canadian Japanese-Mennonite Scholarships *(Graduate/Scholarship)* [5767]

Canadian Nurses Foundation - Baxter Corporation Scholarships *(Graduate/Scholarship)* [2537]

Canadian Nurses Foundation Northern Scholarships *(Undergraduate/Scholarship)* [2538]

Canadian Nurses Foundation Scholarships *(Undergraduate/Scholarship)* [2539]

Canadian Occupational Therapy Foundation Graduate Scholarships *(Graduate/Scholarship)* [2558]

Canadian Occupational Therapy Foundation Invacare Master's Scholarships *(Graduate/Scholarship)* [2559]

Canadian Pain Society Post-Doctoral Fellowship Awards *(Doctorate/Fellowship)* [2567]

Canadian Parking Association Scholarships *(Undergraduate/Scholarship)* [2581]

Canadian Picture Pioneers Scholarships *(Undergraduate/Scholarship)* [2583]

Canadian Polar Commission Scholarships *(Doctorate, Graduate/Scholarship)* [1734]

Canadian Poultry Research Council Postgraduate Scholarships *(Postgraduate/Scholarship)* [2588]

Canadian Purchasing Research Foundation Prize *(Doctorate, Graduate/Scholarship)* [2590]

Canadian Sanitation Supply Association Scholarships *(Undergraduate/Scholarship)* [2592]

Canadian Seniors' Golf Association Scholarships *(Undergraduate/Scholarship)* [4181]

Canadian Society for the Study of Education Mentorship Awards *(Professional development/Award)* [2615]

Canadian Society for the Study of Education New Scholar Fellowships (CSSE) *(Professional development/Fellowship)* [2616]

Canadian Technical Asphalt Association Scholarships *(Undergraduate/Scholarship)* [2624]

Canadian Urological Association Community-based Research Awards *(Doctorate/Award)* [2628]

Canadian Urological Association Fellowships *(Graduate/Fellowship)* [2629]

Canadian Water Resources Association Scholarships *(All/Scholarship)* [2631]

Dr. John Big Canoe Memorial Scholarships *(Undergraduate/Scholarship)* [2523]

Thelma Cardwell Scholarships *(Graduate/Scholarship)* [2560]

Carmangay Home and School Association Scholarships *(Undergraduate/Scholarship)* [241]

Herb Carnegie Scholarships *(Undergraduate/Scholarship)* [2113]

CARO-ELEKTA Research Fellowship Program *(Professional development/Fellowship)* [2404]

CAS/GE Healthcare Canada Inc. Research Awards *(Professional development/Award)* [2358]

CAS/Vitaid-LMA Residents' Research Grant Competition *(Professional development/Award)* [2359]

CASAA Scholarships *(Undergraduate/Scholarship)* [2410]

Fraser Milner Casgrain LLP Scholarships *(Undergraduate/Scholarship)* [2114]

Caterpillar Scholars Award *(Undergraduate/Scholarship)* [8370]

Catzman Awards for Professionalism and Civility *(Professional development/Award)* [65]

Marshall Cavendish Scholarships *(Graduate/Scholarship)* [899]

CAWEE International Student Fellowships *(Postgraduate/Fellowship)* [8038]

CC Times Scholarships *(Undergraduate/Scholarship)* [2770]

CCFF Clinical Fellowships *(Doctorate, Graduate/Fellowship)* [2447]

CCFF Fellowships *(Doctorate, Graduate/Fellowship)* [2448]

CCFF Scholarships *(Doctorate, Graduate/Scholarship)* [2449]

CCLA Summer Legal Internships *(Undergraduate, Graduate/Internship)* [2428]

CEMF Undergraduate Engineering Scholarships *(Undergraduate/Scholarship)* [2455]

CGPF Endowments Conference Scholarships *(Professional development/Scholarship)* [2478]

Chapter 6 Fairfield County Scholarships *(Undergraduate/Scholarship)* [8379]

Chernos Essay Competition *(High School/Prize)* [2429]

Childhood Cancer Foundation Scholarships *(Undergraduate/Scholarship)* [2752]

Childhood Cancer Survivor Scholarships *(All/Scholarship)* [2753]

Chinese Professionals Association of Canada BMO Diversity Scholarships *(Undergraduate/Scholarship)* [2771]

Chinese Professionals Association of Canada Education Foundation Awards *(High School/Award)* [2772]

Chinese Professionals Association of Canada Journalism Scholarships *(Undergraduate/Scholarship)* [2773]

Chinese Professionals Association of Canada Professional Achievement Awards *(Professional development/Award)* [2774]

Patricia Smith Christensen Scholarships *(Postdoctorate/Scholarship)* [8195]

CHS - Bursary Program Scholarships *(Undergraduate/Scholarship)* [2483]

CHS - Mature Student Bursary Program Scholarships *(Professional development/Scholarship)* [2484]

CHS Scholarships *(Undergraduate, Vocational/Occupational/Scholarship)* [2485]

CIBC Scholarships *(Undergraduate/Scholarship)* [2115]

CIHR Health Law and Policy Fellowships *(Graduate/Fellowship)* [2791]

CIP Fellow's Travel Scholarships *(Postgraduate/Scholarship)* [2502]

CISDL Legal Research Fellows *(Graduate/Fellowship)* [2731]

CISDL Senior Research Fellows *(Professional development/Fellowship)* [2732]

City of Toronto Graduate Scholarships for Women in Mathematics *(Graduate/Scholarship)* [9325]

City of Toronto Queen Elizabeth II Sesquicentennial Scholarships in Community Health Nursing for Graduates *(Graduate/Scholarship)* [9326]

City of Toronto Queen Elizabeth II Sesquicentennial Scholarships in Community Health Nursing for Undergraduates *(Undergraduate/Scholarship)* [9327]

City of Toronto Scholarships for Aboriginal Students *(Graduate, Undergraduate/Scholarship)* [9328]

City of Toronto Women's Studies Scholarships *(Graduate, Undergraduate/Scholarship)* [9329]

Greg Clerk Awards *(Professional development/Award)* [2514]

David H. Clift Scholarships *(Graduate/Scholarship)* [900]

Clinical Pain Management Fellowship Awards *(Postgraduate/Fellowship)* [2568]

CN Scholarships for Women *(Postgraduate/Scholarship)* [8307]

CNST Scholarships *(Doctorate, Graduate/Scholarship)* [1735]

Marshall A. Cohen Entrance Awards *(Postgraduate/Award)* [8039]

Erma Collins Scholarships *(Undergraduate/Scholarship)* [2116]

Robert N. Colwell Memorial Fellowships *(Doctorate, Graduate/Fellowship)* [1666]

Desmond Conacher Scholarships *(Graduate/Scholarship)* [2901]

Connor/Spafford Scholarships *(Undergraduate/Scholarship)* [4182]

Continuing Education Awards *(Graduate/Grant)* [5741]

George Joseph Cooper Awards *(Undergraduate/Scholarship)* [6995]

Roy Cooper Scholarships *(Undergraduate/Scholarship)* [5397]

COPA Scholarship Fund *(Undergraduate/Scholarship)* [2563]

Copnick/Hilliard Scholarships *(Professional development/Scholarship)* [2578]

Steve Cowan Memorial Scholarships *(Undergraduate/Scholarship)* [3290]

CPS Excellence in Interprofessional Pain Education Awards *(Professional development/Award)* [2569]

CPS Interprofessional Nursing Project Awards *(Professional development/Award)* [2570]

CPS Knowledge Translation Research Awards *(Professional development/Grant)* [2571]

CPS Nursing Excellence in Pain Management Awards *(Professional development/Award)* [2572]

CPS Nursing Research and Education Awards *(Professional development/Award)* [2573]

CPS Outstanding Pain Mentorship Awards *(Professional development/Award)* [2574]

CPS Toronto Poly Clinic - ROD Inter-Disciplinary Pain Education Grants *(Professional development/Grant)* [2575]

CPS Trainee Research Awards *(Doctorate/Grant)* [2576]

CRM-ISM Postdoctoral Fellowships *(Postdoctorate/Fellowship)* [2734]

CSBS Student Prize Competition *(Graduate/Prize)* [2598]

CSCI Distinguished Scientist Lectures and Awards *(Doctorate/Award)* [2600]

CSEG Scholarship Trust Fund *(Graduate, Undergraduate/Scholarship)* [2607]

CSMLS Student Scholarship Awards *(Postgraduate/Scholarship)* [2609]

CSOHNS Fellowships *(Graduate/Fellowship)* [2611]

CSSHE Masters Thesis/Project Awards *(Master's/Award)* [2619]

CSSHE Research Awards *(Professional development/Award)* [2620]

CTRF Scholarships for Graduate Study in Transportation *(Graduate/Scholarship)* [2626]

Culinary (1-Year Program) Scholarships *(Undergraduate/Scholarship)* [2490]

Cultural Relations Project Grants *(Professional development/Grant)* [217]

CWEDA Scholarship Program *(Undergraduate/Scholarship)* [2354]

CLA/ACB Dafoe Scholarships *(Graduate/Scholarship)* [2519]

Roger Daley Postdoctoral Publication Awards *(Postdoctorate/Award)* [2525]

Dance Project Grants *(Professional development/Grant)* [218]

Dante Prizes *(Undergraduate/Prize)* [3341]

Canadian Association for Studies in Co-operation Scholarships - Amy and Tim Dauphinee Scholarships (CASC) *(Graduate/Scholarship)* [2432]

Ginger and Fred Deines Canada Scholarships *(Undergraduate, Vocational/Occupational/Scholarship)* [8949]

Helen L. Dewar Scholarships *(Undergraduate/Scholarship)* [8894]

Diabetes Hope Foundation Scholarships *(Undergraduate/Scholarship)* [3434]

Dr. Allan A. Dixon Memorial Scholarships *(Postgraduate/Scholarship)* [2596]

William Donald Dixon Research Grants *(Graduate/Grant)* [2495]

Julian Dobranowski Memorial Scholarships *(Undergraduate/Scholarship)* [7759]

Dominio of Canada Insurance Scholarships *(Graduate/Scholarship)* [7324]

Douglas-Coldwell Foundation Scholarships in Social Affairs *(Graduate/Scholarship)* [3474]

Tommy Douglas Scholarships *(Undergraduate/Scholarship)* [6548]

Mary Ellen Driscoll Scholarships *(Undergraduate/Scholarship)* [4183]

Janusz & Roma Drzymala Scholarships *(Undergraduate/Scholarship)* [7760]

Aleksander & Stefania Dulemba Scholarships *(Undergraduate/Scholarship)* [7761]

Lord Dundonald Chapter Imperial Order Daughters of the Empire Scholarships (IODE) *(Undergraduate/Scholarship)* [6996]

Joshua Dyke Family Scholarships *(Undergraduate/Scholarship)* [8895]

Fernandez Earle Undergraduate Entrance Scholarships *(Undergraduate/Scholarship)* [3559]

Edmonton Epilepsy Continuing Education Scholarships *(Undergraduate/Scholarship)* [3590]

EJLB Foundation's Scholar Research Programme *(Graduate, Postgraduate/Scholarship)* [3618]

Clay Elliott Scholarship Foundation Scholarships *(Undergraduate/Scholarship)* [3631]

Environmental History of Quebec Scholarships *(Postdoctorate, Postgraduate/Scholarship)* [6617]

Erb Group Companies Service to Community Scholarships *(Undergraduate/Scholarship)* [6898]

Extendicare Scholarships in Gerontology *(Graduate/Scholarship)* [2540]

Fellowships for Full-time Studies in French *(Undergraduate/Fellowship)* [245]

Fellowships in the Humanities and Social Sciences in Turkey *(Postdoctorate/Fellowship)* [1147]

FFB-C Postdoctoral Fellowships *(Postdoctorate/Fellowship)* [3968]

Field Aviation Co., Inc. Scholarships *(Undergraduate/Scholarship)* [127]

Fields Research Immersion Fellowships *(Postdoctorate/Fellowship)* [3744]

Film and Video Arts Project Grants *(Professional development/Grant)* [219]

Fire Safety Awards *(Postgraduate/Award)* [2469]

Martin Fischer Awards *(All/Award)* [2479]

Flamenco Student Scholarships *(Undergraduate/Scholarship)* [3808]

Walter & Anna Flis Memorial Scholarships *(Undergraduate/Scholarship)* [7762]

Foresters Scholarships *(Undergraduate/Scholarship)* [4714]

Edward Foster Awards *(All/Award)* [2496]

Foundation for the Advancement of Aboriginal Youth Bursary Program *(Undergraduate/Scholarship)* [2440]

Foundation for the Advancement of Aboriginal Youth Scholarships *(Undergraduate/Scholarship)* [2441]

Terry Fox Memorial Scholarships *(Undergraduate/Scholarship)* [6549]

Fraser Milner Casgrain Scholarships (Professional development/Scholarship) [2006]

Henry Friesen Awards and Lectures (Doctorate/Award) [2601]

Future Leader in Radiocommunications Scholarships (Undergraduate/Scholarship) [7567]

FXRFC Medical Research Postdoctoral Fellowships (Postdoctorate/Fellowship) [3994]

Franciszek Gadzala Memorial Scholarships (Undergraduate/Scholarship) [7763]

Harry Gairey Scholarships (Undergraduate/Scholarship) [2117]

Dwight D. Gardner Scholarships (Undergraduate/Scholarship) [4801]

Geological Association of Canada Student Prizes (Undergraduate/Award) [4085]

Geological Society of America Graduate Student Research Grants (Doctorate, Graduate/Grant) [4088]

Gilbreth Memorial Fellowships (Graduate/Scholarship) [4802]

Keith Gilmore Foundation - Diploma Scholarships (Professional development/Scholarship) [4153]

Keith Gilmore Foundation - Postgraduate Scholarships (Postgraduate/Scholarship) [4154]

Keith Gilmore Foundation - Undergraduate Scholarships (Undergraduate/Scholarship) [4155]

Senator James Gladstone Memorial Scholarships (Graduate, Undergraduate/Scholarship) [228]

Dr. Helen Preston Glass Fellowships (Doctorate/Fellowship) [2541]

Franciszek Glogowski Memorial Scholarships (Undergraduate/Scholarship) [7764]

Charles D. Gonthier Research Fellowships (Graduate, Professional development/Fellowship) [2498]

Goodfellow Nursing Scholarships (Master's, Undergraduate/Scholarship) [5507]

Goodfellow Professional Development Fund (Professional development/Scholarship) [5508]

Baxter Corporation - Jean Goodwill Scholarships (Postgraduate/Scholarship) [20]

Lucille May Gopie Scholarships (Undergraduate/Scholarship) [2118]

Charles Hall Grandgent Awards (Graduate/Award) [3342]

Reginald K. Groome Memorial Scholarships (Undergraduate/Scholarship) [8065]

Guelph Caribbean Canadian Association Scholarships (Undergraduate/Scholarship) [4355]

Guntley-Lorimer Science and Arts Scholarships (Undergraduate/Scholarship) [2119]

Hamilton Industrial Environmental Association Bursaries-Mohawk College (Undergraduate/Scholarship) [4367]

Al Hamilton Scholarships (Undergraduate/Scholarship) [2120]

Ruth Hancock Scholarships (Undergraduate/Scholarship) [2366]

Handweavers Guild of America and Dendel Scholarships (Graduate, Undergraduate/Scholarship) [4388]

Byron Hanke Fellowships (Doctorate, Graduate, Undergraduate/Fellowship) [3933]

Hannah Junior General Scholarships (Graduate/Scholarship) [1681]

Hannah Senior General Scholarships (Graduate/Scholarship) [1682]

Tom Hanson Photojournalism Awards (Professional development/Internship) [2515]

B. Harper Bull Conservation Fellowships (Graduate/Fellowship) [8913]

Phyllis P. Harris Scholarships (Postgraduate/Award) [2463]

Heart and Stroke Foundation of Canada/Physiotherapy Foundation of Canada Scholarships in Physiotherapy Research (Doctorate, Master's/Scholarship) [7325]

Dr. E. Bruce Hendrick Scholarships (All/Scholarship) [8647]

Mary Jane Hendrie Memorial Scholarships (Graduate, Undergraduate/Scholarship) [9330]

Jim Hierlihy Memorial Scholarships (Undergraduate/Scholarship) [3672]

Judy Hill Scholarships (Undergraduate/Scholarship) [2542]

Geordie Hilton Academic Scholarships (Undergraduate/Scholarship) [4184]

Hispanic Serving Institution Scholarships (HSIS) (Undergraduate/Scholarship) [9024]

C.H.(Chuck) Hodgson Scholarships (Undergraduate/Scholarship) [9591]

Irving J. Hoffman Memorial Scholarships (Undergraduate/Scholarship) [9331]

Lois Hole Humanities and Social Sciences Scholarships (Undergraduate/Scholarship) [247]

Hosinec Family Scholarships (Graduate, Undergraduate/Scholarship) [9332]

Lloyd Houlden Research Fellowships (Professional development/Fellowship) [2386]

William B. Howell Scholarships (Undergraduate/Scholarship) [1436]

Goldwin Howland Scholarships (Graduate/Scholarship) [2561]

Christopher Hoy/ERT Scholarships (Graduate, Master's/Scholarship) [901]

William Peyton Hubbard Scholarships (Undergraduate/Scholarship) [2121]

Steven Huesing Scholarships (Graduate, Undergraduate/Scholarship) [2915]

Tertia M.C. Hughes Memorial Graduate Student Prizes (Graduate/Prize) [2526]

John Peter Humphrey Student Fellowships (Graduate/Fellowship) [2443]

IBA Law Student Scholarship Foundation Scholarships (Undergraduate/Scholarship) [4754]

IHRDP Post-doctoral Fellowships (Doctorate, Graduate, Master's, Postdoctorate/Fellowship, Scholarship) [4756]

IIE Council of Fellows Undergraduate Scholarships (Undergraduate/Scholarship) [4803]

In-course Scholarships - Chinese Dance Workshop Scholarships (Undergraduate/Scholarship) [9333]

Institute Community Support Publication Prizes (Doctorate, Graduate, Undergraduate/Prize) [2507]

Intensive Language Course Grants (Doctorate/Grant) [4120]

Inter American Press Association Scholarships (Undergraduate/Scholarship) [4846]

International Association of Foundation Drilling Scholarships for Civil Engineering Students (Postgraduate/Scholarship) [1756]

International Association of Foundation Drilling Scholarships for Part-time Civil Engineering Graduate School Students (Postgraduate/Scholarship) [1757]

International Association of Law Libraries Scholarship Program (Professional development/Scholarship) [4876]

International Council for Canadian Studies Graduate Student Scholarships (Postgraduate/Scholarship) [4904]

International Education Awards - Ukraine (Undergraduate/Scholarship) [249]

International Grenfell Association Bursary (Undergraduate/Scholarship) [4946]

International Grenfell Association Secondary/High School Scholarships (Undergraduate/Scholarship) [4947]

International Grenfell Association University/College Scholarships (Undergraduate/Scholarship) [4948]

International Municipal Lawyers Association Canadian Scholarships (Professional development/Scholarship) [4963]

Investigators in the Pathogenesis of Infectious Disease Awards (Doctorate, Postdoctorate/Grant) [2215]

Investors Group Scholarships for Not-For-Profit Leaders (Professional development/Scholarship) [2007]

IRSST Doctoral Scholarships Abroad (Doctorate/Fellowship) [4768]

IRSST Doctoral Scholarships Supplement (Doctorate/Fellowship) [4769]

IRSST Doctoral Scholarships (Doctorate/Fellowship) [4767]

IRSST Masters Scholarships Supplement (Graduate/Fellowship) [4771]

IRSST Masters Scholarships (Graduate/Fellowship) [4770]

IRSST Postdoctoral Scholarships Abroad (Doctorate/Fellowship) [4773]

IRSST Postdoctoral Scholarships (Doctorate/Fellowship) [4772]

ISM Doctoral Fellowships (Doctorate/Fellowship) [4775]

ISM Scholarships for Graduate Studies (Graduate/Scholarship) [4776]

Dr. Karl C. Ivarson Scholarships (Postgraduate/Scholarship) [74]

Jamaican Canadian Association Alberta Scholarship Program (Undergraduate/Scholarship) [5130]

Terry Jarvis Memorial Scholarships (Undergraduate/Scholarship) [1439]

Right Hon. Michaelle Jean Legacy Scholarships (Undergraduate/Scholarship) [2122]

Harry Jerome Scholarships (Undergraduate/Scholarship) [2123]

Johnson & Johnson Scholarships (Undergraduate/Scholarship) [2543]

Robert V.A. Jones Canadians Corporate Counsel Awards (Professional development/Award) [2438]

Kazimiera Juchniewicz Memorial Scholarships (Undergraduate/Scholarship) [7765]

Stefan & Weronika Kacperski Memorial Scholarships (Undergraduate/Scholarship) [7766]

Kalmen Kaplansky Scholarships in Economic and Social Rights (Graduate/Scholarship) [3475]

Lucile B. Kaufman Women's Scholarships (Undergraduate/Scholarship) [8388]

E. Wayne Kay Co-op Scholarships (Undergraduate/Scholarship) [8389]

E. Wayne Kay Community College Scholarships (Undergraduate/Scholarship) [8390]

Gunild Keetman Scholarships (Professional development, Undergraduate/Scholarship) [6957]

Dr. Dorothy J. Kergin Scholarships (Doctorate/Scholarship) [2544]

Edgar Kerstan Memorial Scholarships (Undergraduate/Scholarship) [5771]

KFOC Allied Health Fellowships (Doctorate/Fellowship) [5255]

KFOC Allied Health Scholarships (Graduate/Scholarship) [5256]

KFOC Biomedical Fellowships (Postdoctorate/Fellowship) [5257]

KFOC Biomedical Scholarships (Doctorate/Scholarship) [5258]

Khaki University and Y.M.C.A. Memorial Scholarships (Undergraduate/Scholarship) [9334]

Kildonan Education Awards (Undergraduate/Scholarship) [6999]

Helen and George Kilik Scholarships (Undergraduate/Scholarship) [250]

Killam Fellowships Program (Undergraduate/Fellowship) [9100]

Mackenzie King Open Scholarships (Graduate/Scholarship) [5723]

Annie Kirshenblatt Memorial Scholarships (Graduate, Undergraduate/Scholarship) [8915]

Stefan & Janina Klimt Scholarships (Undergraduate/Scholarship) [7767]

George Kokocinski Memorial Scholarships (Undergraduate/Scholarship) [7768]

Anna and John Kolesay Memorial Scholarships (Undergraduate/Scholarship) [251]

Bernie Kom Memorial Awards (Postgraduate/Award) [8040]

Korean Studies Dissertation Workshop Funds (Graduate/Fellowship, Grant) [8283]

Krawczyk-Krane Family Scholarships (Undergraduate/Scholarship) [7769]

Robert Krembil Scholarships of Merit (Postgraduate/Scholarship) [8041]

Kress Pre-Doctoral Fellowships in the History of Art and Archeology in Turkey (Postdoctorate/Fellowship) [1151]

Leo J. Krysa Family Undergraduate Scholarships (Undergraduate/Scholarship) [2504]

Jan Kuropas Memorial Scholarships (Undergraduate/Scholarship) [7770]

Lafarge Community Leaders Scholarships (Professional development/Scholarship) [2008]

Canadian Association for Studies in Co-operation Scholarships Alexander Fraser Laidlaw Fellowships (CASC) (Graduate/Fellowship) [2433]

Allen T. Lambert Scholarships *(Postgraduate/Scholarship)* [8042]

John and Lois Lamont Graduate Scholarships *(Postgraduate/Award)* [2464]

Gloria Landis Bursary *(Undergraduate, Vocational/Occupational/Scholarship)* [5398]

James D. Lang Memorial Scholarships *(Graduate/Scholarship)* [2390]

Language Teacher Bursary Program Awards *(Professional development/Award)* [253]

Languages In Teacher Education Scholarships *(Undergraduate/Scholarship)* [254]

Larson Aquatic Research Support Scholarships (LARS) *(Doctorate, Graduate/Scholarship)* [1418]

Stanislaw & Aniela Lasek Scholarships *(Undergraduate/Scholarship)* [7771]

Kenneth Laundy Entrance Scholarships *(Postgraduate/Scholarship)* [8043]

Law Foundation of British Columbia Graduate Fellowships *(Graduate/Fellowship)* [5360]

Robert G. Lawrence Prize *(Doctorate, Graduate, Professional development/Prize)* [2412]

The Leaders of Tomorrow Scholarships *(Undergraduate, Vocational/Occupational/Scholarship)* [3572]

Leber Rubes Inc. Awards *(Postgraduate/Award)* [2470]

Carol Anne Letheren Entrance Awards *(Postgraduate/Award)* [8044]

Eli Lilly Graduate Scholarships *(Graduate/Scholarship)* [2451]

Tecla Lin & Nelia Laroza Memorial Scholarships *(Undergraduate/Scholarship)* [2545]

Linda's Scholarships *(All/Scholarship)* [5882]

Literary Arts Project Grants *(Professional development/Grant)* [220]

Ian Lithgow Memorial Awards *(Postgraduate/Award)* [8045]

Nancy Llewellyn, RN Pediatric Nursing Bursaries *(Graduate, Professional development/Scholarship)* [1849]

Lo Family Scholarships *(Undergraduate/Scholarship)* [9335]

Sir James Lougheed Awards of Distinction *(Doctorate, Graduate/Award)* [255]

John Macara, Barrister of Goderich, Scholarships *(Undergraduate/Scholarship)* [9336]

CEMF Claudette MacKay-Lassonde Graduate Scholarships *(Doctorate, Postdoctorate/Scholarship)* [2456]

R. Tait Mackenzie Awards *(Professional development/Award)* [7318]

MAF Canada Scholarship Fund *(Undergraduate/Scholarship)* [5908]

Major Collaborative Research Initiatives Grants *(Graduate/Grant)* [8286]

Dick Martin Scholarships *(Postgraduate/Scholarship)* [2426]

Eleanor Jean Martin Scholarships *(Graduate/Scholarship)* [2546]

Beverly Mascoll Scholarships *(Undergraduate/Scholarship)* [2124]

Val Mason Scholarships *(Postgraduate/Scholarship)* [2603]

Mature Student Scholarships *(Undergraduate/Scholarship)* [3673]

Tadeusz Maziarz Scholarships *(Undergraduate/Scholarship)* [7772]

John Mazurek Memorial-Morgex Insurance Scholarships *(Professional development/Scholarship)* [274]

Giuliano Mazzetti Scholarships *(Undergraduate/Scholarship)* [8392]

Heather McCallum Scholarships *(Doctorate, Graduate, Professional development/Scholarship)* [2413]

Hans McCorriston Motive Power Machinist Grant Programs *(Undergraduate, Vocational/Occupational/Scholarship)* [1956]

Joseph McCulley Educational Scholarships *(Graduate, Undergraduate/Scholarship)* [9337]

William H. McGannon Foundation Scholarships *(Graduate, Undergraduate/Scholarship)* [5721]

McGill University Scholarships for Research Trips to Europe *(Graduate/Scholarship)* [5725]

John J. McKetta Undergraduate Scholarships *(Undergraduate/Scholarship)* [846]

Louise McKinney Post-secondary Scholarships *(Undergraduate/Scholarship)* [256]

James H. McLaughlin Scholarships *(Undergraduate/Scholarship)* [6740]

Douglas McRorie Memorial Scholarships *(Postgraduate/Scholarship)* [75]

Jack Meadows Memorial Awards *(Undergraduate/Scholarship)* [7000]

Medical Student Summer Research Scholarships *(Undergraduate/Scholarship)* [374]

Dr. Ernest and Minnie Mehl Scholarships *(Undergraduate/Scholarship)* [257]

Mensa Canada General Scholarships *(Undergraduate/Scholarship)* [5772]

CAG Donald Menzies Bursary Awards *(Postgraduate/Award)* [2382]

Merck Frosst Canada Ltd. Postgraduate Pharmacy Fellowships *(Doctorate, Postgraduate/Fellowship)* [1771]

Al Mercury Scholarships *(Undergraduate/Scholarship)* [9338]

Bronislaw Michno Memorial Scholarships *(Undergraduate/Scholarship)* [7773]

Microsoft Research Graduate Women's Scholarships *(Graduate/Scholarship)* [5844]

Microsoft Research PhD Fellowships *(Doctorate/Fellowship)* [5845]

Military Nurses Association Scholarships *(Graduate, Master's/Scholarship)* [2547]

Miller Thomson Foundation Scholarships *(Undergraduate/Scholarship)* [5884]

Mineralogical Association of Canada Scholarships *(Doctorate, Postgraduate/Scholarship)* [5886]

Minerva Scholarships *(Undergraduate/Scholarship)* [2125]

Murray Montague Memorial Scholarships *(Undergraduate/Scholarship)* [4268]

Thomas More Scholarships *(Undergraduate/Scholarship)* [4191]

John H. Moss Scholarships *(Undergraduate/Scholarship)* [9339]

Marvin Mundel Memorial Scholarships *(Undergraduate/Scholarship)* [4806]

Margaret Munro Scholarships *(Undergraduate/Scholarship)* [2548]

Music Project Grants *(Professional development/Grant)* [221]

Dr. Helen K. Mussallem Fellowships *(Graduate/Scholarship)* [2549]

NAAF Aboriginal Health Careers Bursary and Scholarships *(Graduate, Undergraduate/Scholarship)* [5992]

NAAF Post-Secondary Education Scholarships *(Graduate, Undergraduate/Scholarship)* [5993]

NAAMA Scholarships *(Undergraduate/Scholarship)* [6024]

Irwin Allen Nadal Entrance Awards *(Postgraduate/Award)* [8046]

Miles Spencer Nadal Entrance Awards *(Postgraduate/Award)* [8047]

Nadine International Inc. Awards *(Postgraduate/Award)* [2471]

National Association of Women in Construction Founders Undergraduate Scholarships *(Undergraduate/Scholarship)* [6132]

The National Board Technical Scholarships *(Undergraduate/Scholarship)* [6159]

National Society of Accountants Scholarship Program *(Undergraduate/Scholarship)* [6481]

Natural Sciences and Engineering Research Council Postgraduate Scholarships *(Doctorate/Scholarship)* [6572]

Marek Nawrot Memorial Scholarships *(Undergraduate/Scholarship)* [7774]

NCLEJ Law School Graduate Fellows and Volunteers *(Graduate/Fellowship)* [6184]

Alan H. Neville Memorial Scholarships *(Graduate, Undergraduate, Vocational/Occupational/Scholarship)* [337]

New Brunswick Law Foundation Graduate Scholarships in Law *(Graduate/Scholarship)* [5375]

New Brunswick Nurses Association Scholarships *(Graduate/Scholarship)* [2550]

Norman Nicholson Scholarships *(Undergraduate/Scholarship)* [2424]

Sharon Nield Memorial Scholarships *(Undergraduate/Scholarship)* [2551]

Norfolk Southern Foundation Scholarships *(Undergraduate/Scholarship)* [1131]

Nortel Institute Undergraduate Scholarships *(Undergraduate/Scholarship)* [9340]

North American Conference on British Studies Dissertation Year Fellowships *(Doctorate, Postdoctorate/Fellowship)* [6735]

North American Conference on British Studies-Huntington Library Fellowships *(Doctorate, Postdoctorate/Fellowship)* [6736]

North American Society Fellowships *(Professional development/Fellowship)* [7319]

Northern Alberta Development Council Bursary Awards *(Undergraduate/Award)* [259]

Northern Alberta Development Council Bursary Partnership Program *(Undergraduate/Award)* [260]

Northern Resident Scholarships *(Doctorate, Graduate/Scholarship)* [1736]

Nova Scotia Salmon Association Scholarships *(All/Scholarship)* [6834]

NRC-HIA Plaskett Fellowships *(Doctorate/Fellowship)* [6461]

NSF Pickwick Postdoctoral Research Fellowships *(Postdoctorate/Fellowship)* [6476]

Nueroscience Certification Bursary Awards *(Professional development/Award)* [2396]

Nuffield Canada Farming Scholarships *(Undergraduate/Scholarship)* [6838]

AEBC Rick Oakes Scholarships for the Arts *(Graduate, Undergraduate, Vocational/Occupational/Scholarship)* [338]

OHTN Postdoctoral Fellowships *(Doctorate/Fellowship)* [6893]

Oil and Gas Trades and Technology Bursary and Scholarships (OGTT) *(All/Scholarship)* [5994]

OMHF Postdoctoral Fellowships *(Postdoctorate/Fellowship)* [6895]

Ontario Hockey Association War Memorial Scholarships *(Undergraduate/Scholarship)* [9341]

Ellis R. Ott Scholarships *(Graduate, Master's/Scholarship)* [1321]

Senator Norman Paterson Fellowships *(Doctorate/Fellowship)* [2552]

Q.O.(Quint) Patrick Scholarships *(Undergraduate/Scholarship)* [9592]

Arthur Paulin Automotive Aftermarket Scholarship Awards *(Postgraduate, Undergraduate/Scholarship)* [1957]

PEA Bursaries *(Undergraduate/Scholarship)* [7443]

PEA Scholarships *(Undergraduate/Scholarship)* [7444]

Florrie Penney, RN Rehabilitation Nursing Bursaries *(Graduate, Professional development/Scholarship)* [1850]

PEO Educational Loan Funds *(Graduate, Undergraduate, Vocational/Occupational/Loan)* [7306]

Mary Perlmutter Scholarships *(Postgraduate/Award)* [2565]

Petroleum History Society Graduate Scholarships *(Graduate/Scholarship)* [7215]

PHE Canada Health Educator Awards *(Professional development/Award)* [7320]

PHE Canada Student Awards *(Undergraduate/Award)* [7321]

Shoshana Philipp (Kirshenblatt) R.N. Memorial Scholarships *(Graduate, Undergraduate/Scholarship)* [8917]

Phillips Fund Grants for Native American Research *(Graduate/Grant)* [994]

George Phillips Scholarships *(Undergraduate/Scholarship)* [5509]

Phillips Scholarships *(Undergraduate/Scholarship)* [3184]

Physical Education Teaching Excellence (PETE) Awards *(Professional development/Award)* [7322]

Physiotherapy Foundation of Canada Research Grants *(Professional development/Grant)* [7326]

Eleonora Pidperyhora Scholarship *(Undergraduate/Scholarship)* [7775]

Ronald C. and Joyce Pierce Scholarships *(Undergraduate/Scholarship)* [1443]

PIMS Postdoctoral Fellowships *(Doctorate/Fellowship)* [7029]

Dr. Adolph Piotrowski Memorial Art Scholarships

(Undergraduate/Scholarship) [7776]

D.F. Plett Graduate Fellowships (Graduate/Fellowship) [7342]

Post Basic Course Bursaries (Graduate, Professional development/Scholarship) [1851]

Postdoctoral Fellowships at the Fields Institute (Postdoctorate/Fellowship) [3745]

J.R. (Joe) Power National Scholarships (Postgraduate/Scholarship) [7546]

Gerald Pratley Awards (Doctorate, Graduate/Award) [3747]

President's Prize (Professional development/Prize) [2527]

Diana M. Priestly Memorial Scholarships (Undergraduate/Scholarship) [2391]

Prince Edward Island Law Student Scholarships (Undergraduate/Scholarship) [5377]

Professional Institute of the Public Service of Canada Expanded Scholarships (Undergraduate/Scholarship) [7446]

Provincial and Regional 4-H Scholarships (Undergraduate/Scholarship) [200]

PSAC - Coughlin National Scholarships (Postgraduate/Scholarship) [7547]

PSAC - Groulx National Scholarships (Postgraduate/Scholarship) [7548]

PSAC National Scholarships (Postgraduate/Scholarship) [7549]

PSAC Regional Scholarships (Postgraduate/Scholarship) [7550]

Public Employee Retirement Research and Administration Scholarships (Graduate/Scholarship) [4201]

Doug Purvis Prize (Professional development/Prize) [2368]

A.O. Putnam Memorial Scholarships (Undergraduate/Scholarship) [4808]

RBC Financial Group Scholarships (Graduate/Scholarship) [2126]

RBC Royal Bank Scholarships for First Year Medical & Dental Students (Undergraduate/Scholarship) [7823]

RBC Royal Bank Scholarships for New Canadians (Undergraduate/Scholarship) [7824]

RBC Royal Bank Scholarships for Undergraduates (Undergraduate/Scholarship) [7825]

Pat Redden Memorial Scholarships (Undergraduate/Scholarship) [5510]

Registered Apprenticeship Program Scholarships (RAP) (Undergraduate/Scholarship) [264]

J.H. Stewart Reid Memorial Fellowship Trust (Doctorate/Fellowship) [2415]

J.H. Stewart Reid Memorial Fellowships (Doctorate, Graduate/Fellowship) [7730]

W. Reymonta Scholarships (Undergraduate/Scholarship) [7777]

Risk Management and Insurance Scholarships - University of Calgary (Undergraduate/Scholarship) [7995]

Marion Roberts Memorial Scholarships (Undergraduate/Scholarship) [1958]

Gertrude J. Robinson Book Prize (Professional development/Prize) [2436]

R.O.E.A. Dumitru Golea Goldy-Gemu Scholarships (Undergraduate/Scholarship) [1165]

Geraldine Ruth Rogers Scholarships (Undergraduate/Scholarship) [8897]

Mandell and Lester Rosenblatt and Robert N. Herbert Undergraduate Scholarships (Undergraduate/Scholarship) [8417]

Robert Roy Awards (Professional development/Award) [2406]

RPNAS Baccalaureate Level Program Scholarships (Graduate/Scholarship) [7723]

RPNAS Doctorate Level Program Scholarships (Doctorate/Scholarship) [7724]

RPNAS Master's Level Program Scholarships (Graduate, Master's/Scholarship) [7725]

Glen Ruby Memorial Scholarships (Undergraduate/Scholarship) [2613]

Violet D. Ruelokke Primary Health Care Awards (Graduate, Professional development/Scholarship) [1852]

Rutherford Scholars (Undergraduate/Scholarship) [265]

Alexander Rutherford Scholarships for High School Achievement (Undergraduate/Scholarship) [266]

Chester & Maria Sadowski Memorial Scholarships (Undergraduate/Scholarship) [7778]

St. Clare's Mercy Hospital School of Nursing Alumni Association Scholarships (Graduate/Scholarship) [1853]

Saint Paul University Excellence Scholarships (Undergraduate/Scholarship) [7887]

Saint Paul University Financial Aid Bursaries (Undergraduate/Scholarship) [7888]

AIST David H. Samson Scholarships (Undergraduate/Scholarship) [1816]

Sanofi Pasteur Scholarships (Graduate/Scholarship) [2553]

Saskatchewan Government Insurance Anniversary Scholarships (Undergraduate/Scholarship) [7997]

Saskatchewan Government Insurance Corporate Scholarships (Undergraduate/Scholarship) [7998]

Francois J. Saucier Prize in Applied Oceanography (Professional development/Prize) [2528]

Savoy Foundation Postdoctoral and Clinical Research Fellowships (Postdoctorate/Fellowship) [8012]

SCA Nursing Scholarships (Graduate, Professional development/Scholarship) [2476]

Richard J. Schmeelk Fellowships (Graduate/Fellowship) [8020]

B.E. Schnurr Memorial Fund Research Grants (Professional development/Grant) [7327]

Scholarship Awards of The Aliant Pioneer Volunteers (Postgraduate/Scholarship) [2531]

Scholarships for Aboriginal Canadians (Undergraduate/Scholarship) [6550]

Scholarships for Visible Minorities (Undergraduate/Scholarship) [6551]

School Age Financial Aid Program (Undergraduate/Scholarship) [2050]

Tanna H. Schulich MBA Entrance Scholarships (Postgraduate/Scholarship) [8048]

Scotiabank Scholarship for Business Studies (Graduate/Scholarship) [2127]

SEMA Memorial Scholarships (Graduate, Undergraduate, Vocational/Occupational/Scholarship) [1959]

Lal Bahadur Shastri Student Prize (Graduate, Undergraduate/Prize) [8099]

Dr. Robert and Anna Shaw Scholarships (Undergraduate/Scholarship) [267]

Dr. Robert Norman Shaw Scholarships (Undergraduate/Scholarship) [268]

David S. Sheridan Canadian Research Awards (Professional development/Award) [2360]

Sigma Theta Tau International Scholarships (Doctorate/Scholarship) [2554]

Julia Viola Simms Science Scholarships (Postgraduate/Scholarship) [2128]

Sloan Research Fellowships (Doctorate/Fellowship) [8235]

SME Directors Scholarships (Undergraduate/Scholarship) [8398]

SME Education Foundation Family Scholarships (Undergraduate/Scholarship) [8399]

Donald Smiley Prize (Professional development/Prize) [2585]

David W. Smith Fellowships (Postdoctorate/Fellowship) [2605]

Smiths Medical Canada Ltd. Research Awards (Professional development/Award) [2361]

Boleslaw & Irena Sobczak Scholarships (Undergraduate/Scholarship) [7779]

Frank H. Sobey Awards for Excellence in Business Studies (Undergraduate/Award) [8277]

Sobeys & Empire Work Experience & Scholarship Program - Future Leaders Awards (Professional development/Award) [8278]

Social Sciences and Humanities Research Council of Canada Standard Research Grants (Doctorate, Graduate/Grant) [8287]

Society of Graphic Designers of Canada Adobe Scholarships (Undergraduate/Scholarship) [8331]

Society of Graphic Designers of Canada Applied Arts Scholarships (Undergraduate/Scholarship) [8332]

Society of Graphic Designers of Canada Veer Scholarships (Undergraduate/Scholarship) [8333]

Society of Naval Architects and Marine Engineers

Undergraduate Scholarships (Undergraduate/Scholarship) [8418]

Carin Alma E. Somers Scholarship Trust (Undergraduate/Scholarship) [1927]

Specialty Equipment Market Association Scholarships (Graduate, Undergraduate, Vocational/Occupational/Scholarship) [8635]

Beatrice Drinnan Spence Scholarships (Undergraduate, Vocational/Occupational/Scholarship) [3573]

Patrick Spielman Memorial Scholarship Program (Undergraduate, Vocational/Occupational/Scholarship) [8071]

SSHRC Doctoral Fellowship Program (Doctorate/Fellowship, Scholarship) [8288]

Ken Stanley Memorial Scholarships (Undergraduate/Scholarship) [5511]

Taylor Statten Memorial Fellowships (Graduate/Scholarship) [9342]

The Stanley H. Stearman Awards (Undergraduate/Scholarship) [6482]

Harry Steele Entrance Awards (Postgraduate/Award) [8049]

H.H. Stern Grant Awards (Professional development/Grant) [2407]

TAC Foundation-Albert M. Stevens Scholarships (Postgraduate/Scholarship) [8931]

David Stockwood Memorial Prize (Professional development/Prize) [66]

Marlene Streit Golf Scholarships (Undergraduate/Scholarship) [4185]

Summerside-Natick Hockey Scholarships (Undergraduate/Scholarship) [3185]

Sun Life Financial Peer Support Scholarships (Professional development/Scholarship) [2579]

Super Kutz Scholarships (Undergraduate/Scholarship) [8776]

Syncrude/Athabasca University Aboriginal Scholarships (All/Scholarship) [8791]

TAC Foundation-3M Canada Company Scholarships (Postgraduate, Undergraduate/Scholarship) [8932]

TAC Foundation-Armtec Scholarships (Undergraduate/Scholarship) [8933]

TAC Foundation-Cement Association of Canada Scholarships (Postgraduate, Undergraduate/Scholarship) [8934]

TAC Foundation-Delcan Corporation Scholarships (Postgraduate, Undergraduate/Scholarship) [8935]

TAC Foundation-Dillon Consulting Scholarships (Undergraduate/Scholarship) [8936]

TAC Foundation-IBI Group Scholarships (Postgraduate, Undergraduate/Scholarship) [8938]

TAC Foundation-iTRANS Consulting Scholarships (Postgraduate/Scholarship) [8939]

TAC Foundation-McCormick Rankin Corporation Scholarships (Undergraduate/Scholarship) [8940]

TAC Foundation-MMM Group Limited Scholarships (Postgraduate, Undergraduate/Scholarship) [8941]

TAC Foundation-Municipalities Scholarships (Postgraduate, Undergraduate/Scholarship) [8942]

TAC Foundation-Provinces and Territories Scholarships (Postgraduate, Undergraduate/Scholarship) [8943]

TAC Foundation-Stantec Consulting Scholarships (Postgraduate/Scholarship) [8944]

TAC Foundation-UMA Engineering Ltd. Scholarships (Undergraduate/Scholarship) [8945]

TAC Foundation-Waterloo Alumni Scholarships (Postgraduate/Scholarship) [8946]

TD Meloche-Monnex Scholarships (Doctorate/Scholarship) [2555]

Theatre and Performance Art Project Grants (Professional development/Grant) [222]

Nadene M. Thomas Graduate Research Scholarships (Graduate/Scholarship) [275]

Dr. Andrew Thomson Prize in Applied Meteorology (Professional development/Prize) [2529]

Ken Thomson Scholarships (Undergraduate/Scholarship) [2632]

TIAC / Parks Canada Sustainable Tourism Scholarships (College, Undergraduate, Master's/Scholarship) [8921]

Evald Torokvei Foundation Scholarships (Graduate/Scholarship) [9343]

Toronto Rehab Scholarships in Rehabilitation-Related Research (Graduate/Scholarship) [8918]

Toyota Earth Day Scholarships *(Undergraduate/ Scholarship)* [8925]

Transoft Solutions, Inc. Ahead of the Curve Scholarships (AOTC) *(Graduate, Undergraduate/Scholarship)* [4827]

Transportation Association of Canada Foundation Scholarships *(Postgraduate, Undergraduate/ Scholarship)* [8947]

Marie Tremaine Fellowships *(Postgraduate, Professional development/Fellowship)* [2088]

Tristin Memorial Scholarships *(Undergraduate, Vocational/Occupational/Scholarship)* [5395]

Trudeau Foundation Doctoral Scholarships *(Doctorate/Doctorate)* [8968]

Sam Tughan Scholarships *(Undergraduate/Scholarship)* [2593]

Underwriters' Laboratories of Canada Awards *(Postgraduate/Award)* [2472]

United Parcel Service Scholarships for Female Students *(Undergraduate/Scholarship)* [4810]

United Parcel Service Scholarships for Minority Students *(Undergraduate/Scholarship)* [4811]

University of Toronto SAC Undergraduate Grants *(Undergraduate/Grant)* [9345]

Claudette Upton Scholarships *(Undergraduate/ Scholarship)* [3588]

Urban Financial Services Coalition Scholarships *(Undergraduate/Scholarship)* [2129]

USA/USA-Ukramerazha Scholarships *(Undergraduate/Scholarship)* [9077]

Vale Inco Limited Masters Scholarships *(Graduate/ Scholarship)* [2457]

John Vanderlee Scholarships *(Undergraduate/Scholarship)* [2556]

Vanier Canada Graduate Scholarships *(Graduate/ Scholarship)* [6573]

Jill Vickers Prize *(Professional development/Prize)* [2586]

Philip F. Vineberg Travelling Fellowships in the Humanities *(Undergraduate/Scholarship)* [5726]

Visual Arts and New Media Project Grants *(Professional development/Grant)* [223]

Chapter 4 - Lawrence A. Wacker Memorial Awards *(Undergraduate/Scholarship)* [8402]

Jane C. Waldbaum Archaeological Field School Scholarships *(Undergraduate/Scholarship)* [1496]

Myrtle and Earl Walker Scholarships *(Undergraduate/Scholarship)* [8403]

Martin Walmsley Fellowships for Technological Entrepreneurship *(Graduate/Fellowship)* [6891]

Robert E. Walter Memorial Scholarships *(Undergraduate/Scholarship)* [5558]

War Memorial Doctoral Scholarships *(Postgraduate/ Scholarship)* [6188]

Mary-Claire Ward Geoscience Awards *(Graduate/ Award)* [7458]

Glenn Watson Scholarships *(Undergraduate/Scholarship)* [8576]

Dorothy Wellnitz Canadian Scholarships *(Undergraduate/Scholarship)* [1139]

Portia White Scholarships *(Undergraduate/Scholarship)* [2130]

Ann Collins Whitmore Memorial Scholarships (ACWMS) *(Graduate/Scholarship)* [7328]

Dwight Whylie Scholarships *(Undergraduate/Scholarship)* [2131]

Wilkinson & Company LLP Secondary School Scholarships *(Undergraduate/Scholarship)* [9603]

RS Williamson and Eliford Mott Memorial Scholarships *(Undergraduate/Scholarship)* [9593]

H.W. Wilson Scholarships *(Graduate/Scholarship)* [2520]

Ross A. Wilson Science Scholarships *(Undergraduate/Scholarship)* [8898]

Abel Wolman Fellowships *(Doctorate/Fellowship)* [1419]

Women in Coaching National Coaching Institute Scholarships *(Undergraduate/Scholarship)* [2917]

Women's Association of the Mining Industry of Canada Foundation National Geophysics Scholarships *(Undergraduate/Scholarship)* [9713]

Women's Association of the Mining Industry of Canada Foundation National Scholarships *(Undergraduate/Scholarship)* [9714]

Women's Association of the Mining Industry of Canada Foundation Wood Bursary Awards *(Un-*

dergraduate/Award)* [9715]

Geoffrey H. Wood Scholarships *(Undergraduate/ Scholarship)* [2594]

Frank and Betty Woodhams Memorial Scholarships *(Undergraduate/Scholarship)* [5773]

World Book Graduate Scholarships in Library and Information Science *(Graduate/Scholarship)* [2521]

WRI Education Foundation Scholarships - Graduate *(Graduate/Scholarship)* [9670]

WRI Education Foundation Scholarships - High School Seniors *(Undergraduate/Scholarship)* [9671]

WRI Education Foundation Scholarships - Undergraduate *(Undergraduate/Scholarship)* [9672]

Pang Xiaoyan Scholarships *(Undergraduate/Scholarship)* [2775]

York Graduate Scholarships *(Graduate/Scholarship)* [8050]

Jessie Young Bursary Awards *(Professional development/Award)* [2397]

Youth or the Environment Scholarships *(Professional development/Scholarship)* [2009]

Yukon Law Foundation Scholarships *(Undergraduate/Scholarship)* [9799]

CANADA (BY PROVINCE)

Alberta

Alberta Association of Gerontology Student Awards *(Graduate/Award)* [206]

Alberta Award for the Study of Canadian Human Rights and Multiculturalism *(Doctorate, Graduate/Award)* [236]

Alberta Blue Cross Scholarships for Aboriginal Students *(Undergraduate/Scholarship)* [211]

Alberta Child Care Association Professional Development Grants *(Professional development/ Grant)* [213]

Alberta Ingenuity Graduate Student Scholarships in Nanotechnology *(Doctorate, Graduate/Scholarship)* [231]

Alberta Ingenuity Graduate Student Scholarships *(Doctorate, Graduate/Scholarship)* [230]

Alberta Innovates Graduate Student Scholarship *(Graduate/Scholarship)* [234]

Alberta Press Council Scholarships *(Undergraduate/Scholarship)* [270]

Alberta Teachers Association Doctoral Fellowships in Education *(Doctorate/Fellowship)* [272]

Alberta Teachers Association Educational Research Awards *(Professional development/ Grant)* [273]

Alberta Ukrainian Centennial Commemorative Scholarships *(Graduate/Scholarship)* [9496]

Eugene Boyko Scholarships *(Undergraduate/ Scholarship)* [209]

Robert C. Carson Memorial Bursary *(Undergraduate/Scholarship)* [242]

CLA Student Summer Internship Program *(Undergraduate/Internship)* [2517]

Laurence Decore Awards for Student Leadership *(Undergraduate/Scholarship)* [243]

Earl and Countess of Wessex - World Championships in Athletics Scholarships *(Undergraduate/ Scholarship)* [244]

Graduate Student Scholarships *(Graduate/Scholarship)* [246]

Grande Prairie 4-H District Scholarships *(Undergraduate/Scholarship)* [199]

iCORE ICT Graduate Student Scholarships *(Doctorate, Graduate, Master's/Scholarship)* [232]

Informatics Circle of Research Excellence Scholarships *(Doctorate, Graduate/Scholarship)* [248]

Jason Lang Scholarships *(Undergraduate/Scholarship)* [252]

Persons Case Scholarships *(Undergraduate, Graduate/Scholarship)* [261]

Prairie Baseball Academy Scholarships *(Undergraduate/Scholarship)* [262]

Queen Elizabeth II Graduate Scholarship Program *(Doctorate, Graduate/Scholarship)* [263]

Siobhan Isabella Reid Memorial Scholarships *(Graduate, Undergraduate/Scholarship)* [5393]

Servus Credit Union 4-H Scholarships *(Undergraduate/Scholarship)* [201]

Ukrainian Canadian Professional and Business Club Scholarships in Education *(Undergraduate/ Scholarship)* [2505]

British Columbia

CLA Student Summer Internship Program *(Undergraduate/Internship)* [2517]

GCABS Youth Scholarship Awards *(High School, Undergraduate/Scholarship)* [4147]

Law Society of British Columbia Scholarships *(Graduate, Undergraduate/Scholarship)* [5373]

SPEATBC Scholarships *(Undergraduate/Scholarship)* [8482]

Women's Health Research Foundation of Canada Scholarship Program *(Graduate/Scholarship)* [9721]

New Brunswick

Leon Bradley Scholarships *(Undergraduate/Scholarship)* [548]

CLA Student Summer Internship Program *(Undergraduate/Internship)* [2517]

Newfoundland and Labrador

Leon Bradley Scholarships *(Undergraduate/Scholarship)* [548]

Ocean Industries Student Research Awards *(Undergraduate, Graduate/Award)* [7736]

Dennis R. Prince Scholarships *(Undergraduate/ Scholarship)* [7457]

Nova Scotia

Leon Bradley Scholarships *(Undergraduate/Scholarship)* [548]

CLA Student Summer Internship Program *(Undergraduate/Internship)* [2517]

Ontario

Dr. Anderson Abbott Awards *(Undergraduate/ Scholarship)* [9320]

AEBC Toronto Chapter Scholarships *(Graduate, Undergraduate, Vocational/Occupational/Scholarship)* [335]

Stephanie Ali Memorial Scholarships *(Undergraduate/Scholarship)* [9321]

J.P. Bickell Mining Scholarships *(Undergraduate/ Scholarship)* [9322]

Black Canadian Scholarships *(Undergraduate/ Scholarship)* [6994]

Anne-Marie Bonner Scholarships *(Undergraduate/ Scholarship)* [5115]

Brown Dental Scholarships *(Undergraduate/Scholarship)* [5116]

Leon C. Bynoe Memorial Scholarships *(Undergraduate/Scholarship)* [9323]

Mary Anne Chambers Scholarships *(Undergraduate/Scholarship)* [5117]

CJF Canadian Journalism Fellowships *(Graduate, Professional development, Undergraduate/Fellowship)* [2513]

CLA Student Summer Internship Program *(Undergraduate/Internship)* [2517]

D&R Sobey Scholarships *(Undergraduate/Scholarship)* [8276]

Marcus Mosiah Garvey Scholarships *(Undergraduate/Scholarship)* [5118]

J.O. Goodman Scholarship Awards *(Undergraduate/Scholarship)* [6899]

Elizabeth Heath Technical, Trades Training and Development Awards *(Undergraduate/Scholarship)* [6997]

C.V. Hoar Scholarship Awards *(Undergraduate/ Scholarship)* [6900]

Norm Hollend Fellowships in Oncology *(Postdoctorate/Fellowship)* [5535]

Humber College Institute of Technology and Advanced Learning Scholarships *(Undergraduate/ Scholarship)* [5119]

I Have a Dream Scholarships *(Undergraduate/ Scholarship)* [5120]

John S.W. Fargher Scholarships *(Graduate/Scholarship)* [4800]

Gaebe Eagle Scout Awards *(Undergraduate/Scholarship)* [6253]

Gongaware Scholarships *(Undergraduate/Scholarship)* [4743]

John Simon Guggenheim Memorial Fellowships - U.S. and Canadian Competition *(Advanced Professional/Fellowship)* [4360]

Zenon C.R. Hansen Leadership Scholarships *(Undergraduate/Scholarship)* [6255]

Clinton J. Helton Manufacturing Scholarships *(Undergraduate/Scholarship)* [8387]

Klingenstein Fellowships in the Neurosciences *(Doctorate, Professional development/Fellowship)* [5266]

Lindenwood University Scouting Scholarships *(Undergraduate/Scholarship)* [6258]

Lodging Management Program Scholarships (LMP) *(Undergraduate/Scholarship)* [800]

Marmot Leadership Scholarships *(Postgraduate, Professional development, Undergraduate/Scholarship)* [7008]

Giuliano Mazzetti Scholarships *(Undergraduate/Scholarship)* [8392]

McNamara Family Creative Arts Project Grants *(Graduate, Undergraduate/Grant)* [4579]

MESBEC Scholarships *(Undergraduate/Scholarship)* [2662]

Outward Bound Leadership Scholarships for Educators *(Professional development/Scholarship)* [7009]

Pharmavite LLC NP Doctoral Education Scholarships *(Doctorate/Scholarship)* [379]

Phi Theta Kappa Scholarships *(Undergraduate/Scholarship)* [4752]

Saint Vincent College Eagle Scout Scholarships *(Undergraduate/Scholarship)* [6261]

Alice Southworth Schulman Simmons Scholarships for UU Women *(Undergraduate/Scholarship)* [9000]

AIST William E. Schwabe Memorial Scholarships *(Undergraduate/Scholarship)* [1817]

SME Directors Scholarships *(Undergraduate/Scholarship)* [8398]

Joseph Sumner Smith Scholarships *(All/Scholarship)* [9001]

Society of Manufacturing Engineers Ford PAS Scholarships (SME) *(Undergraduate/Scholarship)* [8401]

University of Louisville Eagle Scout Scholarships *(Undergraduate/Scholarship)* [6262]

INTERNATIONAL (BY COUNTRY)

AMSUS Dentist Awards *(Professional development/Award)* [1458]

AMSUS Nursing Awards *(Professional development/Award)* [1459]

Art Acquisition by Application Project Grants *(Professional development/Grant)* [216]

Baker Donelson Diversity Scholarships *(Undergraduate/Scholarship)* [1997]

Beaverbrook Media at McGill Student Paper Prize *(Graduate/Prize)* [2435]

Pamfil and Maria Bujea Family Orthodox Christian Seminarian Scholarships *(Undergraduate/Scholarship)* [1163]

Annie J. Cannon Awards in Astronomy *(Doctorate/Award)* [569]

CASAA Leaders of Distinction Scholarships *(Professional development/Scholarship)* [2409]

Fellowships in the PMAC-AGPC *(Professional development/Fellowship)* [7450]

Insurance and Risk Management Scholarships - Grant MacEwan *(Undergraduate/Scholarship)* [7994]

Molecular Evolution Fellowships *(Doctorate/Fellowship)* [8242]

Nellie Yeoh Whetten Award *(Graduate/Recognition, Award)* [1985]

Smithsonian Institution Predoctoral Fellowships *(Doctorate/Fellowship)* [8247]

Russell and Sigurd Varian Award *(Graduate/Award)* [1987]

Yale Graduate and Professional Students Research Fellowships *(Graduate, Professional development/Fellowship)* [2044]

Australia

American Australian Association Neurological Fellowships *(Graduate/Fellowship)* [574]

Australian-American Health Policy Fellowships *(Doctorate, Graduate/Fellowship)* [3018]

EAPSI Fellowships *(Doctorate, Graduate/Fellowship)* [6467]

Morgan Stanley Pediatrics Fellowships *(Doctorate, Postdoctorate/Fellowship)* [575]

Austria

Barbara Potter Scholarships *(All/Scholarship)* [961]

Bangladesh

AIBS Junior Fellowships *(Doctorate/Fellowship)* [843]

AIBS Senior Fellowships *(Doctorate, Postdoctorate/Fellowship)* [844]

Barbados

Barbados Cancer Association Post-Graduate Scholarships *(Graduate/Scholarship)* [2021]

British Virgin Islands

Judith A. Towle Environmental Studies Fund *(Undergraduate/Fellowship)* [5082]

China

EAPSI Fellowships *(Doctorate, Graduate/Fellowship)* [6467]

Costa Rica

Rowe Family Fellowships *(Graduate/Fellowship)* [6985]

Denmark

Edith and Arnold N. Bodtker Grants *(All/Grant)* [3339]

France

Kennedy T. Friend Scholarships *(Graduate, Undergraduate/Scholarship)* [327]

Newberry Library/Ecole Nationale des Chartes Exchange Fellowships *(Graduate/Fellowship)* [6705]

NFID Advanced Vaccinology Course Travel Grants *(Postdoctorate/Grant)* [6301]

Pasteur Foundation Postdoctoral Fellowships *(Graduate/Fellowship)* [7130]

Germany

Herzog August Bibliothek Wolfenbuttel Fellowships *(Doctorate/Fellowship)* [6693]

DAAD Study Scholarship Awards *(Graduate/Scholarship)* [4116]

DAAD Undergraduate Scholarship Program *(Undergraduate/Scholarship)* [4117]

The Christoph Daniel Ebeling Fellowships *(Doctorate/Fellowship)* [418]

European College of Liberal Arts Scholarships (ECLA) *(Undergraduate/Scholarship)* [9075]

Faculty Research Visit Grants *(Doctorate/Grant)* [4118]

Intensive Language Course Grants *(Doctorate/Grant)* [4120]

Learn German in Germany Grants *(Doctorate/Grant)* [4122]

Study Scholarships for Artists or Musicians *(Graduate/Scholarship)* [4123]

University Summer Course Grants *(Undergraduate/Grant)* [4124]

Ghana

African Humanities Fellowships *(Postdoctorate/Fellowship)* [673]

GCABS Youth Scholarship Awards *(High School, Undergraduate/Scholarship)* [4147]

Guam

APIASF Scholarships *(Undergraduate/Scholarship)* [1655]

Thomas R. Camp Scholarships *(Graduate/Scholarship)* [1416]

Hispanic Scholarship Fund College Scholarship Program (HSF) *(Graduate, Undergraduate/Scholarship)* [4570]

HSBC-North America Scholarship Program *(Undergraduate/Scholarship)* [4571]

HSF/Atrisco Heritage Foundation Scholarship Program *(Graduate, Undergraduate/Scholarship)* [4572]

HSF/General Motors Scholarship Program *(Undergraduate/Scholarship)* [4574]

Larson Aquatic Research Support Scholarships (LARS) *(Doctorate, Graduate/Scholarship)* [1418]

India

Malayalee Engineers Association Scholarships *(Graduate/Fellowship)* [5601]

Ireland

Irish-American Research Travel Fellowships *(Professional development/Fellowship)* [1230]

Israel

Jane R. Glaser Scholarships *(Undergraduate/Scholarship)* [1405]

Ollie Rosenberg Scholarship Travel Fund *(Undergraduate/Scholarship)* [3959]

Japan

Crown Prince Akihito Scholarship Foundation *(Graduate/Scholarship)* [5132]

EAPSI Fellowships *(Doctorate, Graduate/Fellowship)* [6467]

Japan Foundation, New York Doctoral Fellowship Program *(Doctorate/Fellowship)* [5134]

Japan Foundation, New York Research Fellowship Program *(Undergraduate/Fellowship)* [5135]

Japan Foundation, New York Short-Term Fellowship Program *(Doctorate/Fellowship)* [5136]

KCC-JEE Graduate Fellowships *(Graduate/Fellowship)* [5279]

Marshall Islands

APIASF Scholarships *(Undergraduate/Scholarship)* [1655]

Mexico

Stan Beck Fellowships *(Graduate, Undergraduate/Fellowship)* [3652]

BioQuip Undergraduate Scholarships *(Undergraduate/Scholarship)* [3653]

Thomas R. Camp Scholarships *(Graduate/Scholarship)* [1416]

Ginger and Fred Deines Mexico Scholarships *(Undergraduate, Vocational/Occupational/Scholarship)* [8950]

Dwight D. Gardner Scholarships *(Undergraduate/Scholarship)* [4801]

Geological Society of America Graduate Student Research Grants *(Doctorate, Graduate/Grant)* [4088]

Gilbreth Memorial Fellowships *(Graduate/Scholarship)* [4802]

IIE Council of Fellows Undergraduate Scholarships *(Undergraduate/Scholarship)* [4803]

Larson Aquatic Research Support Scholarships (LARS) *(Doctorate, Graduate/Scholarship)* [1418]

John J. McKetta Undergraduate Scholarships *(Undergraduate/Scholarship)* [846]

Marvin Mundel Memorial Scholarships *(Undergraduate/Scholarship)* [4806]

NWF's Women for Sustainable Development Scholarships (WSD) *(Undergraduate/Scholarship)* [8145]

A.O. Putnam Memorial Scholarships *(Undergraduate/Scholarship)* [4808]

Ronald L. Schmied Scholarships *(Professional development, Undergraduate/Scholarship)* [4362]

Tribeca Film Institute Media Arts Fellowships in Mexico *(Professional development/Fellowship)* [8959]

United Parcel Service Scholarships for Female Students *(Undergraduate/Scholarship)* [4810]

United Parcel Service Scholarships for Minority Students *(Undergraduate/Scholarship)* [4811]

Abel Wolman Fellowships *(Doctorate/Fellowship)* [1419]

Micronesia

APIASF Scholarships *(Undergraduate/Scholarship)* [1655]

Mongolia

ACMS Faculty Research Fellowships *(Professional development/Fellowship)* [600]

ACMS Library Fellowships *(Graduate, Professional development/Fellowship)* [602]

ACMS Research Fellowships *(Doctorate, Postdoctorate/Fellowship)* [603]

ACMS U.S.-Mongolia Field Research Fellowship Program *(Graduate, Undergraduate/Fellowship)* [604]

Netherlands

Netherlands-Florida Scholarship Foundation Scholarships *(Doctorate, Graduate/Scholarship)* [6615]

New Zealand

EAPSI Fellowships *(Doctorate, Graduate/Fellowship)* [6467]

Nigeria

African Humanities Fellowships *(Postdoctorate/Fellowship)* [673]

NWAG Nigeria Scholarships *(Undergraduate/Scholarship)* [6719]

Northern Mariana Islands

APIASF Scholarships *(Undergraduate/Scholarship)* [1655]

Norway

Sons of Norway Foundation Scholarships to Oslo International School *(Undergraduate/Scholarship)* [8532]

Pakistan

Dr. Feroz Ahmed Memorial Educational Post-Graduate Scholarships *(Doctorate, Postgraduate/Scholarship)* [8216]

Palau

APIASF Scholarships *(Undergraduate/Scholarship)* [1655]

Panama

Fellowships and Internships Program in Latin America *(Graduate/Fellowship, Internship)* [8269]

A. Stanley Rand Fellowships Program *(Undergraduate, Doctorate, Postdoctorate/Fellowship)* [8270]

Earl S. Tupper 3-year Postdoctoral Fellowships in Tropical Biology *(Postdoctorate/Fellowship)* [8272]

Peru

William L. Brown Fellowships *(Graduate/Fellowship)* [6978]

David and Deborah Clark Fellowships *(Graduate/Fellowship)* [6979]

Rexford Daubenmire Fellowships *(Graduate/Fellowship)* [6980]

Dole Food Fellowships *(Graduate/Fellowship)* [6981]

Emily P. Foster Fellowships *(Graduate/Fellowship)* [6982]

Peace Frogs Fellowships *(Graduate/Fellowship)* [6984]

Lillian and Murray Slatkin Fellowships *(Graduate/Fellowship)* [6986]

F. Christian and Betty Thompson Fellowships *(Graduate/Fellowship)* [6988]

Poland

Tadeusz Sendzimir Scholarships *(Undergraduate/Scholarship)* [4460]

Puerto Rico

Thomas R. Camp Scholarships *(Graduate/Scholarship)* [1416]

Hispanic Scholarship Fund College Scholarship Program (HSF) *(Graduate, Undergraduate/Scholarship)* [4570]

HSBC-North America Scholarship Program *(Undergraduate/Scholarship)* [4571]

HSF/Atrisco Heritage Foundation Scholarship Program *(Graduate, Undergraduate/Scholarship)* [4572]

HSF/General Motors Scholarship Program *(Undergraduate/Scholarship)* [4574]

Larson Aquatic Research Support Scholarships (LARS) *(Doctorate, Graduate/Scholarship)* [1418]

McNamara Family Creative Arts Project Grants *(Graduate, Undergraduate/Grant)* [4579]

SHPE Foundation Dissertation Scholarships *(Doctorate/Scholarship)* [8131]

SHPE Foundation General Scholarships *(High School, Undergraduate, Graduate/Scholarship)* [8132]

SHPE Foundation Northrop Grumman Scholarships *(Undergraduate/Scholarship)* [8133]

SHPE Foundation Professional Scholarships *(Master's, Doctorate/Scholarship)* [8134]

SHPE Foundation Verizon Scholarships *(Undergraduate/Scholarship)* [8135]

Rwanda

Social Equity Venture Fund Teaching Fellowships *(Professional development/Fellowship)* [8280]

Saint Kitts and Nevis

Judith A. Towle Environmental Studies Fund *(Undergraduate/Fellowship)* [5082]

Singapore

EAPSI Fellowships *(Doctorate, Graduate/Fellowship)* [6467]

South Africa

African Humanities Fellowships *(Postdoctorate/Fellowship)* [673]

South Korea

EAPSI Fellowships *(Doctorate, Graduate/Fellowship)* [6467]

Sweden

Lilly Lorenzen Scholarships *(Undergraduate/Scholarship)* [1400]

Malmberg Fellowships *(Undergraduate/Fellowship)* [1401]

Malmberg Scholarships *(Undergraduate/Scholarship)* [1402]

Taiwan

EAPSI Fellowships *(Doctorate, Graduate/Fellowship)* [6467]

Tanzania

African Humanities Fellowships *(Postdoctorate/Fellowship)* [673]

Godparents for Tanzania Scholarships *(Undergraduate/Scholarship)* [4169]

Turkey

Institute of Turkish Studies Sabbatical Research Grants *(Professional development/Grant)* [4830]

Institute of Turkish Studies Undergraduate Study Grants *(Undergraduate/Grant)* [4831]

Post-Doctoral Summer Travel-Research Grants *(Doctorate/Grant)* [4832]

Summer Language Study Grants in Turkey *(Graduate/Grant)* [4833]

Uganda

African Humanities Fellowships *(Postdoctorate/Fellowship)* [673]

Ukraine

Alberta Ukrainian Centennial Commemorative Scholarships *(Graduate/Scholarship)* [9496]

Mychajlo Dmytrenko Fine Arts Foundation Scholarships *(Undergraduate/Scholarship)* [9074]

United Kingdom

Mackenzie King Travelling Scholarships *(Graduate/Scholarship)* [5724]

London Goodenough Association of Canada Scholarships *(Graduate/Scholarship)* [5515]

Right Honourable Paul Martin Sr. Scholarships *(Graduate/Scholarship)* [2500]

Newberry Library/British Academy Fellowships for Study in Great Britain *(Doctorate/Fellowship)* [6704]

Joseph S. Steinberg Emerging Jewish Filmmaker Fellowships *(Undergraduate, Graduate/Fellowship)* [2698]

USA/USA-Ukramerazha Scholarships *(Undergraduate/Scholarship)* [9077]

United States Virgin Islands

Hispanic Scholarship Fund College Scholarship Program (HSF) *(Graduate, Undergraduate/Scholarship)* [4570]

HSBC-North America Scholarship Program *(Undergraduate/Scholarship)* [4571]

HSF/Atrisco Heritage Foundation Scholarship Program *(Graduate, Undergraduate/Scholarship)* [4572]

HSF/General Motors Scholarship Program *(Undergraduate/Scholarship)* [4574]

McNamara Family Creative Arts Project Grants *(Graduate, Undergraduate/Grant)* [4579]

This index arranges awards according to qualifying factors related to membership or affiliation. Awards are listed under all appropriate headings. Each citation is followed by the study level and award type, which appear in parentheses. Numbers following the parenthetical information indicate the book entry number for particular awards, not page numbers.

African American

AAA Minority Dissertation Fellowship Program *(Doctorate/Fellowship)* [406]

AAAA Operation Jumpstart III Scholarships *(Graduate/Scholarship)* [433]

AAMFT Minority Fellowships *(Doctorate, Graduate/Fellowship)* [511]

Acoustical Society of America Minority Fellowships *(Graduate/Fellowship)* [39]

Affirmative Action Mini Grants and Student Scholarships *(All/Grant)* [25]

African American Network - Carolinas Scholarship Fund *(Undergraduate/Scholarship)* [3882]

Air Products and Chemicals, Inc. Scholarships *(Undergraduate/Scholarship)* [1793]

Emma and Meloid Algood Tuition Scholarships *(Graduate, Undergraduate/Scholarship)* [6039]

AMA Foundation Minority Scholars Awards *(Undergraduate/Scholarship)* [922]

American Dream Scholarship Program *(Undergraduate/Scholarship)* [7890]

AMS/Industry Minority Scholarships *(Undergraduate/Scholarship)* [931]

APS Scholarships for Minority Undergraduate Physics Majors *(Undergraduate/Scholarship)* [6485]

APTA Minority Scholarships - Faculty Development Scholarships *(Postdoctorate/Scholarship)* [999]

APTA Minority Scholarships - Physical Therapist Assistant Students *(All/Scholarship)* [1000]

APTA Minority Scholarships - Physical Therapist Students *(All/Scholarship)* [1001]

ASC Graduate Fellowships for Ethnic Minorities *(Doctorate, Graduate/Fellowship)* [1219]

AWG Minority Scholarships *(Undergraduate/Scholarship)* [1900]

Michael Baker Inc. Scholarships for Diversity in Engineering *(Undergraduate/Scholarship)* [1794]

Ballard Family Foundation Scholarships *(Undergraduate, Vocational/Occupational/Scholarship)* [7909]

Beacon of Hope Scholarships *(Undergraduate/Scholarship)* [2035]

Dr. Joyce Beckett Scholarships *(Graduate, Undergraduate/Scholarship)* [6040]

Bill Bernbach Diversity Scholarships *(Undergraduate/Scholarship)* [434]

Black Student Fund *(High School/Scholarship)* [2107]

Leon Bradley Scholarships *(Undergraduate/Scholarship)* [548]

Selena Danette Brown Book Scholarships *(Graduate, Undergraduate/Scholarship)* [6041]

Ron Brown Scholars Program *(Undergraduate/Scholarship)* [2201]

CANFIT Scholarships *(Graduate, Undergraduate/Scholarship)* [2228]

Robert A. Catlin/David W. Long Memorial Scholarships *(Graduate/Scholarship)* [1009]

Cherry Lane Foundation/Music Alive! Scholarships *(Undergraduate/Scholarship)* [1208]

CIGNA Healthcare Graduate Scholarships *(Graduate/Scholarship)* [6290]

CIGNA Healthcare Undergraduate Scholarships *(Undergraduate/Scholarship)* [6291]

Johnnie L. Cochran, Jr./MWH Scholarships *(Graduate, Undergraduate/Scholarship)* [6292]

Zoe E. Collymore Page Scholarships *(Undergraduate/Scholarship)* [6145]

Ruth DeMoss Scholarships *(Undergraduate/Scholarship)* [7924]

Development Fund for Black Students in Science and Technology Scholarships *(Undergraduate/Scholarship)* [3432]

William Diaz Fellowships *(Professional development/Fellowship)* [6729]

Joseph M. Dorgan Scholarships *(Undergraduate/Scholarship)* [3486]

DRI Law Student Diversity Scholarships *(Undergraduate/Scholarship)* [2144]

Dunbar Heritage Scholarships *(Undergraduate/Scholarship)* [8599]

Evans and Petree Law Firm Scholarships *(Undergraduate/Scholarship)* [9224]

FICPA Educational Foundation 1040K Race Scholarships *(Undergraduate/Scholarship)* [3836]

Florida Education Fund McKnight Doctoral Fellowships *(Graduate/Fellowship)* [3822]

Andrew Foster Scholarships *(Undergraduate/Scholarship)* [6146]

Franchise Law Diversity Scholarship Awards *(Undergraduate/Scholarship)* [4940]

John Hope Franklin Dissertation Fellowships *(Doctorate/Fellowship)* [990]

Fraser Stryker Diversity Scholarships *(Undergraduate/Scholarship)* [3998]

Richard Gregory Freeland, II Educational Scholarships *(High School/Scholarship)* [2147]

FTE Dissertation Fellowships *(Graduate/Fellowship)* [4020]

FTE Doctoral Fellowships *(Doctorate, Graduate/Fellowship)* [4021]

Fuchs-Harden Educational Scholarships Fund *(Undergraduate/Scholarship)* [4337]

The Future Colleagues Scholarships *(Undergraduate/Scholarship)* [6293]

Sam Gallant Memorial Scholarships *(Graduate, Undergraduate/Scholarship)* [1530]

The Gates Millennium Scholars *(Undergraduate/Scholarship)* [4569]

Gerber Fellowships in Pediatric Nutrition *(Undergraduate/Fellowship)* [6401]

Guynn Family Foundation Scholarships *(Undergraduate/Scholarship)* [6042]

The Richard D. Hailey AAJ Law Student Scholarships *(Undergraduate/Scholarship)* [491]

HDR Engineering, Inc. Scholarships for Diversity in Engineering *(Undergraduate/Scholarship)* [1796]

The Hyatt Hotels Fund For Minority Lodging Management Students *(Undergraduate/Scholarship)* [798]

International Association of Black Actuaries Scholarships *(Undergraduate/Scholarship)* [4858]

Ruth E. Jenkins Scholarships *(Undergraduate/Scholarship)* [7936]

E.J. Josey Scholarships *(Graduate/Scholarship)* [2133]

W.K. Kellogg Foundation Doctoral Fellowships in Health Policy *(Professional development/Fellowship)* [6402]

Martin Luther King Law Scholarships *(Undergraduate/Scholarship)* [3501]

KPMG Foundation Minority Accounting Doctoral Scholarships *(Postdoctorate/Scholarship)* [5304]

The Lagrant Foundation - Graduate Students Scholarships *(Graduate/Scholarship)* [5315]

The Lagrant Foundation - Undergraduate Students Scholarships *(Undergraduate/Scholarship)* [5316]

Land-Use Planning Scholarships *(Graduate/Scholarship)* [6294]

Lewis-Clark State College/American Chemical Society Scholars Program *(Undergraduate/Scholarship)* [5440]

LITA and LSSI Minority Scholarships *(Graduate/Scholarship)* [5485]

LITA/OCLC Minority Scholarships *(Graduate/Scholarship)* [5486]

Audre Lord Scholarships *(Graduate, Undergraduate/Scholarship)* [7857]

Willie T. Loud - CH2M Hill Scholarships *(Undergraduate/Scholarship)* [6295]

Dr. Julianne Malveaux Scholarships *(Undergraduate/Scholarship)* [6093]

Many Voices Fellowships *(Professional development/Fellowship)* [7338]

Marathon Oil Corporation College Scholarship Program *(Graduate, Undergraduate/Scholarship)* [4578]

Howard Mayer Brown Fellowships *(Graduate/Fellowship)* [941]

Ronald McDonald House Charities African American Future Achievers Scholarships *(Undergraduate/Scholarship)* [5700]

Medical Library Association Scholarships for Minority Students *(Graduate/Scholarship)* [5745]

Minorities in Government Finance Scholarships *(Graduate, Undergraduate/Scholarship)* [4199]

Minority Pharmacy Faculty New Investigator Grants *(Professional development/Grant)* [759]

Minority Presence Grant Program for Doctoral Study *(Doctorate, Graduate/Grant)* [9295]

Minority Scholarship Awards for College Students *(Undergraduate/Scholarship)* [847]

Minority Student Gateway to Research Scholarships *(Professional development/Scholarship)* [760]

Minority Student Pre-Doctoral Fellowship Program *(Doctorate, Graduate/Fellowship)* [761]

Minority Teachers of Illinois Scholarships (MTI) *(Undergraduate/Scholarship)* [4701]

MLA/NLM Spectrum Scholarship Program *(Undergraduate/Scholarship)* [5746]

Dr. Blanca Moore-Velez Woman of Substance Scholarships *(Undergraduate/Scholarship)* [6094]

Archie Motley Memorial Scholarships for Minority

Students *(Graduate/Scholarship)* [5856]

Multicultural Advertising Intern Program *(Graduate, Undergraduate/Internship)* [435]

NANBPWC National Scholarships *(Undergraduate/Scholarship)* [6095]

National Association of Campus Activities Multicultural Scholarship Programs *(Undergraduate/Scholarship)* [6053]

National Association of Multicultural Engineering Program Advocates Beginning Freshmen Awards (NAMEPA) *(Undergraduate/Scholarship)* [6088]

National Association of Multicultural Engineering Program Advocates Transfer Engineering Student Awards (NAMEPA) *(Undergraduate/Scholarship)* [6089]

National Black Deaf Advocate Scholarships *(Graduate, Undergraduate/Scholarship)* [6147]

National College Scholarship Awards *(Undergraduate/Scholarship)* [5088]

National Dental Hygienists' Association Scholarships *(Undergraduate/Scholarship)* [6244]

National Medical Fellowships Need-Based Scholarships *(Undergraduate/Scholarship)* [6403]

Nevada Black Police Association Scholarships *(Undergraduate/Scholarship)* [7511]

NFBPA/CDM Scholarships *(Graduate, Undergraduate/Scholarship)* [6296]

OAH-IEHS Huggins-Quarles Dissertation Awards *(Doctorate/Grant)* [6960]

Ohio Newspaper Association Minority Scholarships *(Undergraduate/Scholarship)* [6858]

Pearman Family Scholarships *(Undergraduate/Scholarship)* [7950]

Judith McManus Price Scholarships *(Graduate, Undergraduate/Scholarship)* [1012]

PRSSA Multicultural Affairs Scholarships *(Undergraduate/Scholarship)* [7541]

Jerrothia Allenfonzo Riggs & Anna & Dorothy Mae Barnes Scholarships *(Undergraduate/Scholarship)* [2339]

RA Consulting Service/Maria Riley Scholarships *(Graduate, Undergraduate/Scholarship)* [6297]

SACHS Foundation Undergraduate Scholarships for Colorado Black Students *(High School/Scholarship)* [7841]

Carl A. Scott Book Scholarships *(Undergraduate/Scholarship)* [3284]

Faith Speckhard Scholarships *(Undergraduate, Vocational/Occupational/Scholarship)* [5106]

David Stevenson Fellowships *(Doctorate, Graduate, Professional development/Fellowship)* [6730]

Summer Research Diversity Fellowships in Law and Social Science *(Undergraduate/Fellowship)* [579]

Robert Toigo Foundation Fellowships *(Master's/Fellowship)* [8911]

Jacki Tuckfield Memorial Graduate Business Scholarship Fund *(Doctorate, Graduate, Master's/Scholarship)* [3323]

The UCSD Black Alumni Scholarship for Arts and Humanities *(Undergraduate/Scholarship)* [7970]

The UCSD Black Alumni Scholarships for Engineering, Mathematics and Science *(Undergraduate/Scholarship)* [7971]

University of Wisconsin-Madison African American Alumni Scholarships *(Undergraduate/Scholarship)* [9372]

Valuing Diversity PhD Scholarships *(Doctorate/Scholarship)* [920]

Earl Warren Shearman and Sterling Scholarships *(Graduate/Scholarship)* [5973]

Francis X. Weninger Scholarships *(Undergraduate/Scholarship)* [9777]

Ann Cook Whitman Washington, DC Scholarships *(Undergraduate/Scholarship)* [3616]

Leon Williams Scholarships *(Undergraduate/Scholarship)* [7974]

Cenie Jomo Williams Tuition Scholarships *(Graduate, Undergraduate/Scholarship)* [6043]

Woodrow Wilson-Rockefeller Brothers Fund Fellowships for Aspiring Teachers of Color *(Graduate/Fellowship)* [9621]

Hugh and Helen Wood Nepales Scholarships *(Undergraduate/Scholarship)* [2066]

Xerox Technical Minority Scholarships *(Graduate, Undergraduate/Scholarship)* [9787]

Youth Empowerment Summit Scholarships *(Undergraduate/Scholarship)* [6148]

Asian American

AAA Minority Dissertation Fellowship Program *(Doctorate/Fellowship)* [406]

AAAA Operation Jumpstart III Scholarships *(Graduate/Scholarship)* [433]

AAMFT Minority Fellowships *(Doctorate, Graduate/Fellowship)* [511]

Kyutaro & Yasuo Abiko Memorial Scholarships *(Undergraduate/Scholarship)* [5140]

Affirmative Action Mini Grants and Student Scholarships *(All/Grant)* [25]

Air Products and Chemicals, Inc. Scholarships *(Undergraduate/Scholarship)* [1793]

Paul Shearman Allen and Associate Scholarships *(Undergraduate/Scholarship)* [9062]

Anheuser-Busch NAPABA Law Foundation Presidential Scholarships *(Undergraduate/Scholarship)* [6026]

APA Minority Fellowships Program *(Postdoctorate/Fellowship)* [1646]

APALA Scholarships *(Doctorate, Graduate/Scholarship)* [1648]

APBASV Scholarships *(All/Scholarship)* [1652]

APIASF Scholarships *(Undergraduate/Scholarship)* [1655]

APTA Minority Scholarships - Faculty Development Scholarships *(Postdoctorate/Scholarship)* [999]

APTA Minority Scholarships - Physical Therapist Assistant Students *(All/Scholarship)* [1000]

APTA Minority Scholarships - Physical Therapist Students *(All/Scholarship)* [1001]

ASC Graduate Fellowships for Ethnic Minorities *(Doctorate, Graduate/Fellowship)* [1219]

Asian American Lawyers Associations of Massachusetts Scholarships *(Undergraduate/Scholarship)* [1644]

Asian American Scholarships *(Undergraduate/Scholarship)* [9063]

Michael Baker Inc. Scholarships for Diversity in Engineering *(Undergraduate/Scholarship)* [1794]

Leon Bradley Scholarships *(Undergraduate/Scholarship)* [548]

CANFIT Scholarships *(Graduate, Undergraduate/Scholarship)* [2228]

CBCF Congressional Fellows Program *(Professional development/Fellowship)* [3220]

William Diaz Fellowships *(Professional development/Fellowship)* [6729]

DRI Law Student Diversity Scholarships *(Undergraduate/Scholarship)* [2144]

Alice Yuriko Endo Memorial Scholarships *(Undergraduate/Scholarship)* [5141]

Franchise Law Diversity Scholarship Awards *(Undergraduate/Scholarship)* [4940]

Aracelis Francis Minority Scholarships in Gerontology *(Master's/Scholarship)* [1787]

Fraser Stryker Diversity Scholarships *(Undergraduate/Scholarship)* [3998]

The Gates Millennium Scholars *(Undergraduate/Scholarship)* [4569]

The Richard D. Hailey AAJ Law Student Scholarships *(Undergraduate/Scholarship)* [491]

HDR Engineering, Inc. Scholarships for Diversity in Engineering *(Undergraduate/Scholarship)* [1796]

The Hyatt Hotels Fund For Minority Lodging Management Students *(Undergraduate/Scholarship)* [798]

W.K. Kellogg Foundation Doctoral Fellowships in Health Policy *(Professional development/Fellowship)* [6402]

Sam S. Kuwahara Memorial Scholarships *(Undergraduate/Scholarship)* [5144]

The Lagrant Foundation - Graduate Students Scholarships *(Graduate/Scholarship)* [5315]

The Lagrant Foundation - Undergraduate Students Scholarships *(Undergraduate/Scholarship)* [5316]

Las Vegas Chinatown Scholarships *(Undergraduate/Scholarship)* [7500]

Bruce Lee Scholarships *(Undergraduate/Scholarship)* [9064]

Herbert Lehman Education Scholarships *(Undergraduate/Scholarship)* [5971]

LITA and LSSI Minority Scholarships *(Graduate/Scholarship)* [5485]

LITA/OCLC Minority Scholarships *(Graduate/Scholarship)* [5486]

Marathon Oil Corporation College Scholarship Program *(Graduate, Undergraduate/Scholarship)* [4578]

Howard Mayer Brown Fellowships *(Graduate/Fellowship)* [941]

Ronald McDonald House Charities Scholarships in Asia *(Undergraduate/Scholarship)* [5702]

Medical Library Association Scholarships for Minority Students *(Graduate/Scholarship)* [5745]

Minorities in Government Finance Scholarships *(Graduate, Undergraduate/Scholarship)* [4199]

Minority Teachers of Illinois Scholarships (MTI) *(Undergraduate/Scholarship)* [4701]

MLA/NLM Spectrum Scholarship Program *(Undergraduate/Scholarship)* [5746]

Archie Motley Memorial Scholarships for Minority Students *(Graduate/Scholarship)* [5856]

Ruth Mu-Lan and James S.C. Chao Scholarships *(Undergraduate/Scholarship)* [9065]

Multicultural Advertising Intern Program *(Graduate, Undergraduate/Internship)* [435]

Gongoro Nakamura Memorial Scholarships *(Undergraduate/Scholarship)* [5145]

National Association of Campus Activities Multicultural Scholarship Programs *(Undergraduate/Scholarship)* [6053]

Ohio Newspaper Association Minority Scholarships *(Undergraduate/Scholarship)* [6858]

PABA Foundation Community Service Scholarships *(Graduate, Undergraduate/Scholarship)* [7308]

PABA Foundation Fellowships *(Postdoctorate/Fellowship)* [7309]

PABA Foundation Incentive Scholarships *(Graduate, Undergraduate/Scholarship)* [7310]

PABA Foundation Merit Scholarships *(Graduate, Undergraduate/Scholarship)* [7311]

Pepsico Scholarships *(Undergraduate/Scholarship)* [9066]

Philip Morris USA Scholarships *(Undergraduate/Scholarship)* [9067]

PRSSA Multicultural Affairs Scholarships *(Undergraduate/Scholarship)* [7541]

Rosa Quezada Memorial Education Scholarships *(Undergraduate/Scholarship)* [3231]

SCCLA Fellowships *(All/Fellowship)* [8578]

SCCLA Scholarships *(All/Scholarship)* [8579]

Carl A. Scott Book Scholarships *(Undergraduate/Scholarship)* [3284]

Drs. Poh Shien and Judy Young Scholarships *(Undergraduate/Scholarship)* [9068]

David Stevenson Fellowships *(Doctorate, Graduate, Professional development/Fellowship)* [6730]

Taiwanese American Community Scholarships *(Undergraduate/Scholarship)* [8798]

Robert Toigo Foundation Fellowships *(Master's/Fellowship)* [8911]

U.S. Pan Asian American Chamber of Commerce McDonald's Scholarships *(Undergraduate/Scholarship)* [9069]

U.S. Pan Asian American Chamber of Commerce UPS Scholarships *(Undergraduate/Scholarship)* [9070]

Woodrow Wilson-Rockefeller Brothers Fund Fellowships for Aspiring Teachers of Color *(Graduate/Fellowship)* [9621]

Xerox Technical Minority Scholarships *(Graduate, Undergraduate/Scholarship)* [9787]

Association membership

4th Infantry Division Association Scholarships *(All/Scholarship)* [5990]

AAA Leadership Mentoring/Shadow Award Program *(Graduate/Award)* [405]

Awards *(Graduate/Award)* [1043]
American Psychology-Law Society Early Career Professional Grants-In-Aid *(Professional development/Grant)* [1044]
American Psychology-Law Society Student Grants-In-Aid *(Graduate/Grant)* [1045]
American Society for Microbiology International Fellowships for Africa *(Postdoctorate/Fellowship)* [1295]
American Society for Microbiology International Fellowships for Asia *(Postdoctorate/Fellowship)* [1296]
American Society for Microbiology International Fellowships for Latin America and the Caribbean *(Postdoctorate/Fellowship)* [1297]
American Society for Microbiology Undergraduate Research Fellowships (URF) *(Undergraduate/Fellowship)* [1298]
American Society of Military Comptrollers National Scholarship Program *(Undergraduate/Scholarship)* [1305]
American Society of Naval Engineers Scholarships (ASNE) *(Graduate, Undergraduate/Scholarship)* [1309]
American Sokol Merit Awards *(Undergraduate/Scholarship)* [1379]
American Water Ski Educational Foundation Scholarships *(Undergraduate/Scholarship)* [1414]
American Welding Society International Scholarships *(Undergraduate/Scholarship)* [1425]
Anna Ames Clinical Excellence Student Grants *(Undergraduate/Grant)* [2281]
AMS Teacher Education Scholarships *(Undergraduate/Scholarship)* [938]
Bernard Amtmann Fellowships *(Postgraduate, Professional development/Fellowship)* [2087]
Anaheim Police Survivors and Scholarship Fund *(Undergraduate/Scholarship)* [1469]
ANCA Scholarships *(Graduate, Undergraduate/Scholarship)* [1613]
The Anderson Group Summer Institute Scholarships *(Professional development/Scholarship)* [1473]
A.T. Anderson Memorial Scholarships *(Graduate, Undergraduate/Scholarship)* [834]
Earl I. Anderson Scholarships *(Undergraduate/Scholarship)* [1068]
Dr. Andy Anderson Young Professional Awards *(Professional development/Award)* [7317]
Richard E. Andrews Memorial Scholarships *(Undergraduate/Scholarship)* [582]
Angus Foundation General Undergraduate Student Scholarships *(High School, Undergraduate/Scholarship)* [1477]
Angus Foundation Graduate Student Degree Scholarship Program *(Graduate/Scholarship)* [1478]
Angus Foundation Scholarships *(Undergraduate/Scholarship)* [6374]
AOA Research Grants *(Graduate/Grant)* [63]
AOFAS Research Grants Program *(Graduate/Grant)* [966]
AOSA Research Grants *(All/Grant)* [959]
AOSA Research Partnership Grants *(All/Grant)* [960]
APACVS Scholarships *(Postgraduate, Professional development/Scholarship)* [1841]
APAGS-CLGBTC Grant Program *(Graduate/Grant)* [1029]
APAGS' Committee on Ethic Minority Affairs (CEMA) Grant Program *(Graduate/Grant)* [1030]
APC Tuition-Assist Scholarship Awards *(Graduate, Undergraduate/Scholarship)* [60]
APT US&C Scholarships *(All/Scholarship)* [1847]
ARA Scholarship Awards *(Undergraduate/Scholarship)* [1961]
ARAFCS Doctoral Scholarships *(Doctorate/Scholarship)* [1534]
ARAFCS Masters Scholarships *(Graduate/Scholarship)* [1535]
AREMA Committee 24 - Education and Training Scholarships *(Undergraduate/Scholarship)* [1119]
A.R.F.O.R.A. Undergraduate Scholarships for

Women *(Undergraduate/Scholarship)* [1162]
Jane B. Aron Doctoral Fellowships *(Doctorate/Fellowship)* [6120]
ASBA College Scholarship Program *(Undergraduate/Scholarship)* [1180]
ASBC Foundation Graduate Scholarships *(Doctorate, Graduate/Scholarship)* [1186]
ASBC Foundation Undergraduate Scholarships *(Undergraduate/Scholarship)* [1187]
ASCEND/ING Scholarships *(Undergraduate/Scholarship)* [1635]
ASECS Innovative Course Design Competition *(Undergraduate/Award)* [1222]
ASECS Women's Caucus Editing and Translation Fellowships *(Doctorate/Fellowship)* [1223]
ASET Educational Seminars, Courses and Program Scholarships *(All, Professional development/Scholarship)* [1239]
ASHA Student Research Grants *(Graduate, Undergraduate/Scholarship)* [1176]
ASIS Foundation Chapter Matching Scholarships *(Undergraduate/Scholarship)* [1657]
ASNT Fellow Awards *(Postdoctorate/Fellowship)* [1315]
Myron Asplin Foundation Scholarships *(Undergraduate/Scholarship)* [4719]
ASPPB Larry J. Bass Jr., PhD. Memorial Scholarship Awards *(Graduate, Undergraduate/Grant)* [1031]
Association of Desk and Derrick Clubs Education Trust Scholarships *(Undergraduate/Scholarship)* [1749]
Association of Donor Recruitment Professionals Hughes Scholarships *(Professional development/Scholarship)* [1751]
Association of Donor Recruitment Professionals Presidential Scholarships *(Professional development/Scholarship)* [1752]
Association of Flight Attendants Scholarship Fund *(Undergraduate/Scholarship)* [1779]
Association of Government Accountants Undergraduate/Graduate Scholarships for Community Service Accomplishments *(Graduate, Undergraduate/Fellowship, Scholarship)* [1789]
Association of Government Accountants Undergraduate/Graduate Scholarships for Full-time study *(Graduate, Undergraduate/Fellowship, Scholarship)* [1790]
Association of Government Accountants Undergraduate/Graduate Scholarships for Part-time study *(Graduate, Undergraduate/Fellowship, Scholarship)* [1791]
Association for Psychological Science Student Grants (APS) *(Graduate, Undergraduate/Grant)* [1845]
Association of Rehabilitation Nurses Scholarship Program *(Undergraduate/Scholarship)* [1855]
Association of the United States Navy Scholarships *(Undergraduate/Scholarship)* [1887]
AST National Honor Society Student Scholarships *(Graduate/Scholarship)* [1879]
ASTR Research Fellowships *(Professional development/Fellowship)* [1359]
AUA Foundation Bridge Awards *(Postgraduate/Fellowship)* [1408]
AUA Foundation - NIDDK/NCI Surgeon-Scientist Awards *(Postgraduate/Fellowship)* [1409]
AUA Foundation Ph.D. Post-Doctoral Fellowships *(Postdoctorate/Fellowship)* [1410]
AWMA Niagara Frontier Section College Scholarships *(Graduate, Undergraduate/Scholarship)* [115]
Bachelor of Science in Nursing Academic Scholarships *(Graduate/Scholarship)* [6099]
Paula Backscheider Archival Fellowships *(Professional development/Fellowship)* [1224]
BACUS Scholarships *(Graduate, Undergraduate/Scholarship)* [8637]
Lincoln C. Bailey Memorial Scholarship Fund *(Undergraduate/Scholarship)* [4986]
Sandra Sebrell Bailey Scholarships *(Undergraduate/Scholarship)* [3406]
Lynn Ann Baldwin Scholarships *(Master's/Scholarship)* [2395]
Balestreri/Cutino Scholarships *(Undergraduate/Scholarship)* [690]

Brenda S. Bank Educational Workshop Scholarships *(Undergraduate/Scholarship)* [8326]
Leslie Baranowski Scholarships for Professional Excellence *(All/Scholarship)* [4764]
Barbri Scholarships for Bar Preparation *(Undergraduate/Scholarship)* [4561]
Thomas J. Bardos Science Education Awards for Undergraduate Students *(Undergraduate/Award)* [451]
Walt Bartram Memorial Education Award, Region 12 and Chapter 119 *(Undergraduate/Scholarship)* [8369]
Basic Midwifery Student Scholarship Program *(Undergraduate/Scholarship)* [618]
Baxter Corporation Canadian Research Awards in Anesthesia *(Professional development/Award)* [2356]
BCEN Undergraduate Scholarships *(Undergraduate/Scholarship)* [3633]
Suzanne Beauregard Scholarships *(Undergraduate/Scholarship)* [4180]
Beaverbrook Media at McGill Student Paper Prize *(Graduate/Prize)* [2435]
Bechtel Engineering and Science Scholarships *(High School/Scholarship)* [5645]
Anne Beckingham Scholarships *(Graduate, Professional development/Scholarship)* [2474]
Hannah Beiter Graduate Student Research Grants *(Doctorate, Graduate/Grant)* [2762]
Samuel Flagg Bemis Dissertation Research Grants *(Doctorate, Graduate/Grant)* [8335]
Reckitt Benckiser Student Scholarships *(Graduate/Scholarship)* [6105]
The Viscount Bennett Fellowships *(Graduate/Fellowship)* [2419]
Eleanor Bennett Scholarships *(All/Scholarship)* [8770]
Elizabeth Benson Scholarship Awards *(Undergraduate/Scholarship)* [7727]
Fred Berg Awards *(All/Award)* [3594]
ARRS/Leonard Berlin Scholarships in Medical Professionalism *(Professional development/Scholarship)* [1160]
Stuart L. Bernath Dissertation Grants *(Doctorate, Graduate/Grant)* [8336]
The Berntsen International Scholarships in Surveying Technology *(Undergraduate/Scholarship)* [642]
Dr. Biljan Memorial Awards *(Graduate/Award)* [2466]
Eileen Blackey Doctoral Fellowships *(Doctorate/Fellowship)* [6121]
William T. Blackwell Scholarship Fund *(Undergraduate/Scholarship)* [6358]
Beatrice K. Blair Scholarships *(Undergraduate/Scholarship)* [2149]
Harry and Edith Blunt Scholarships *(Undergraduate/Scholarship)* [608]
BMES Graduate and Undergraduate Student Awards *(Graduate, Undergraduate/Award)* [2100]
Sandra Bobbitt Continuing Education Scholarships *(Undergraduate/Scholarship)* [1836]
Edith and Arnold N. Bodtker Grants *(All/Grant)* [3339]
Boeing Business Scholarships *(Undergraduate/Scholarship)* [4175]
Frances P. Bolton Fellowships *(Doctorate/Fellowship)* [7051]
BOMA/NY Scholarships *(Undergraduate/Scholarship)* [2207]
Ellis J. Bonner Scholarships *(Doctorate, Graduate, Undergraduate/Scholarship)* [6080]
Stephen Botein Fellowships *(Doctorate/Fellowship)* [415]
Bound to Stay Bound Books Scholarships (BTSB) *(Graduate/Scholarship)* [1826]
CAG Margery Boyce Bursary Awards *(Postgraduate/Award)* [2381]
W. Scott Boyd Group Grants *(All/Grant)* [4884]
Theodore E.D. Braun Research Travel Fellowships *(Professional development/Fellowship)* [1225]
Dvora Brodie Scholarships *(Graduate, Postgraduate, Undergraduate/Scholarship)* [4503]

ships *(Undergraduate/Scholarship)* [8327]

Delta Gamma Scholarships *(Undergraduate/Scholarship)* [3398]

Delta/VPPPA Safety, Health and Environmental Scholarships *(Undergraduate, Vocational/Occupational, Graduate/Scholarship)* [9475]

DEMCO New Leaders Travel Grants *(All/Grant)* [7536]

Descendant Scholarships *(Undergraduate/Scholarship)* [3326]

Diversity Dissertation Scholarships *(Doctorate/Fellowship)* [1032]

Diversity Executive Leadership Program Scholarships *(Professional development/Scholarship)* [1184]

Robert A. and Barbara Divine Graduate Student Travel Grants *(Graduate/Grant)* [8338]

Dr. Allan A. Dixon Memorial Scholarships *(Postgraduate/Scholarship)* [2596]

William Donald Dixon Research Grants *(Graduate/Grant)* [2495]

Peggy Dixon Two-Year Scholarships *(Undergraduate/Scholarship)* [8438]

Charles Dobbins FTA Scholarships *(Undergraduate, Vocational/Occupational/Scholarship)* [4033]

Chapter 116 - Kalamazoo - Roscoe Douglas Scholarships *(Undergraduate/Scholarship)* [8383]

Tommy Douglas Scholarships *(Undergraduate/Scholarship)* [6548]

Nettie Dracup Memorial Scholarships *(Undergraduate/Scholarship)* [643]

AAGS Joseph F. Dracup Scholarship Awards *(Undergraduate/Scholarship)* [644]

The "Drawn to Art" Fellowships *(Doctorate/Fellowship)* [417]

Vivian Drenckhahn Student Scholarships *(Graduate, Undergraduate/Scholarship)* [8477]

Charles Drew Scholarships *(Professional development/Scholarship)* [1754]

Richard Drukker Memorial Scholarships *(Undergraduate/Scholarship)* [6651]

Edward J. Dulis Scholarships *(Undergraduate/Scholarship)* [5690]

Josephine P. White Eagle Graduate Fellowships *(Graduate, Master's, Doctorate/Fellowship)* [4591]

Amelia Earhart Memorial Academic Scholarships *(Undergraduate/Scholarship)* [6724]

The Christoph Daniel Ebeling Fellowships *(Doctorate/Fellowship)* [418]

ECA Applied Urban Communication Research Grants *(Professional development/Grant)* [3575]

ECT Foundation Master Scholarships *(Graduate, Master's/Scholarship)* [1763]

Educational Audiology Association Doctoral Scholarships *(Doctorate/Scholarship)* [3595]

UAA Governor William A. Egan Scholarships *(Undergraduate/Scholarship)* [9091]

EHA Exploratory Travel and Data Grants *(Doctorate/Grant)* [3583]

EHA Graduate Dissertation Fellowships *(Doctorate/Fellowship)* [3584]

Harold E. Eisenberg Foundation Scholarships *(Professional development/Scholarship)* [4906]

Farouk El-Baz Student Research Grants *(Doctorate, Graduate, Undergraduate/Grant)* [4087]

Emergency Nurses Association Undergraduate Scholarships *(Undergraduate/Scholarship)* [3634]

Emerging Teacher-Leaders in Elementary School Mathematics Grants for Grades K-5 Teachers *(Professional development/Grant)* [6221]

Endourological Society Fellowships *(Professional development/Fellowship)* [3641]

Vice Admiral Donald D. Engen Scholarships *(Undergraduate/Scholarship)* [6577]

Harold E. Ennes Scholarships *(Graduate, Professional development/Scholarship)* [8303]

ERDAS Internships *(Graduate/Internship)* [1667]

Jack Ervin EDI Scholarships *(Professional development/Scholarship)* [6761]

NSPF Ray B. Essick Scholarship Awards *(Professional development/Scholarship)* [6538]

FACT Graduating Senior Scholarship Program *(Undergraduate/Scholarship)* [3736]

Faculty Doctoral Scholarships *(Doctorate/Scholarship)* [3635]

AIST Benjamin F. Fairless Scholarships, American Institute of Mining, Metallurgical and Petroleum Engineers (AIME) *(Undergraduate/Scholarship)* [1803]

Families of Freedom Scholarship Fund - America Scholarships *(Undergraduate, Vocational/Occupational/Scholarship)* [3704]

John S.W. Fargher Scholarships *(Graduate/Scholarship)* [4800]

Harold E. Fellows Scholarships *(All/Scholarship)* [2182]

Fellowships in the PMAC-AGPC *(Professional development/Fellowship)* [7450]

William A. Fischer Memorial Scholarships *(Graduate/Scholarship)* [1668]

Carol C. Fitzgerald Scholarship Program *(Professional development/Scholarship)* [3722]

Dr. Joseph J. Fitzsimmons Scholarships *(Doctorate/Scholarship)* [9055]

Flamenco Student Scholarships *(Undergraduate/Scholarship)* [3808]

Charlie Fleming Education Fund Scholarships *(Undergraduate/Scholarship)* [6542]

FLEOA Foundation Scholarship Program *(Undergraduate/Scholarship)* [3727]

Grant H. Flint International Scholarships - Category I *(Undergraduate/Scholarship)* [8524]

Grant H. Flint International Scholarships - Category II *(Undergraduate/Scholarship)* [8525]

Florida Public Health Association Public Health Graduate Scholarships *(Graduate/Scholarship)* [3846]

FMA-FEEA Scholarship Program *(Undergraduate/Scholarship)* [3729]

Frank Fong Scholarships *(Undergraduate/Scholarship)* [8290]

Nancy B. Forest and L. Michael Honaker Master's Scholarships for Research *(Doctorate, Graduate/Scholarship)* [1033]

Foresters Scholarships *(Undergraduate/Scholarship)* [4714]

Edward Foster Awards *(All/Award)* [2496]

Foundation for Surgical Technology Advanced Education/Medical Mission Scholarships *(Graduate/Scholarship)* [1881]

Founding Fathers Leadership Scholarships *(Undergraduate/Scholarship)* [9676]

Terry Fox Memorial Scholarships *(Undergraduate/Scholarship)* [6549]

Kevin Freeman Travel Grants *(Graduate, Professional development/Grant)* [5957]

Future Leaders of Manufacturing Scholarships *(Graduate, Undergraduate/Scholarship)* [8385]

Mearl K. Gable II Memorial Grants *(Professional development/Grant)* [4387]

Gamewarden Scholarship program *(High School, Undergraduate, Vocational/Occupational/Scholarship)* [4037]

Gamma Sigma Alpha Graduate Scholarships *(Graduate/Scholarship)* [4039]

William R. Gard Memorial Scholarships *(Undergraduate/Scholarship)* [6091]

Gardner Foundation Infusion Nurses Society Education Scholarships *(All/Scholarship)* [4765]

Dwight D. Gardner Scholarships *(Undergraduate/Scholarship)* [4801]

Peter M. Gargano Scholarship Fund *(Undergraduate/Scholarship)* [3529]

Eileen J. Garrett Scholarships *(Undergraduate/Scholarship)* [7052]

A.R.F.O.R.A. Martha Gavrila Scholarships for Women *(Postgraduate/Scholarship)* [1164]

GAWP Graduate Scholarships *(Graduate/Fellowship)* [4099]

Florence S. Gaynor Scholarships *(Doctorate, Graduate, Undergraduate/Scholarship)* [6081]

GCSAA Scholars Competition *(Undergraduate/Scholarship)* [4187]

GCSAA Student Essay Contest *(Graduate, Undergraduate/Prize)* [4188]

GED Jump Start Scholarships *(Undergraduate/Scholarship)* [8029]

Generation III Scholarships *(Undergraduate/Scholarship)* [3586]

Geological Society of America Graduate Student Research Grants *(Doctorate, Graduate/Grant)* [4088]

Walter Gerboth Awards *(Professional development/Grant)* [5958]

IDSA Gianninoto Graduate Scholarships *(Graduate/Scholarship)* [4758]

Gilbreth Memorial Fellowships *(Graduate/Scholarship)* [4802]

Midwest Chapter Scholarships - Jack Gill *(Undergraduate/Scholarship)* [1804]

Leo Gilmartin Scholarships *(High School/Scholarship)* [7352]

John Glaser Scholarships *(Undergraduate/Scholarship)* [2971]

GLATA Living Memorial Doctorate Scholarships *(Doctorate, Graduate/Fellowship)* [4325]

GLATA Living Memorial Undergraduate/Graduate Scholarships *(Graduate, Undergraduate/Fellowship, Scholarship)* [4326]

Globe-Trotters Chapter Scholarships *(Undergraduate/Scholarship)* [1805]

Northeastern Ohio Chapter Scholarships - Alfred B. Glossbrenner and John Klusch Scholarships *(Undergraduate/Scholarship)* [1806]

GLP Program Scholarships *(Professional development/Scholarship)* [4166]

Golden Key International Honour Society Study Abroad Scholarships *(Undergraduate/Scholarship)* [4176]

Golden Key Math Scholarships *(Undergraduate/Scholarship)* [4177]

Goodfellow Professional Development Fund *(Professional development/Scholarship)* [5508]

Consuelo W. Gosnell Memorial Scholarships *(Graduate/Fellowship)* [6122]

Louis Gottschalk Prize *(Professional development/Prize)* [1228]

Carl W. Gottschalk Research Scholar Grants *(Doctorate/Grant)* [1312]

Graduate Realtor Institute Scholarships *(Graduate/Scholarship)* [5244]

Graduate Student Travel Grants *(Graduate, Professional development/Grant)* [8314]

Grande Prairie 4-H District Scholarships *(Undergraduate/Scholarship)* [199]

AMA/Charles H. Grant Scholarships *(Undergraduate/Scholarship)* [29]

Bishop Charles P. Greco Graduate Fellowships *(Graduate/Fellowship)* [5277]

Robert D. Greenberg Scholarships *(Graduate, Professional development/Scholarship)* [8304]

Reginald K. Groome Memorial Scholarships *(Undergraduate/Scholarship)* [8065]

Charles Grossman Graduate Scholarships *(Graduate/Scholarship)* [4908]

Gulf Coast Past President's Scholarships *(Undergraduate/Scholarship)* [1338]

Larry Gulley Scholarships *(Undergraduate/Scholarship)* [8328]

Scott A. Gunder, MD, DCMS Presidential Scholarships *(Undergraduate/Scholarship)* [3985]

Wesley R. Habley NACADA Summer Institute Scholarships *(Professional development/Scholarship)* [5996]

The Richard D. Hailey AAJ Law Student Scholarships *(Undergraduate/Scholarship)* [491]

Lee Hakel Graduate Student Scholarships *(Doctorate/Scholarship)* [8354]

Joyce C. Hall College Scholarships *(Undergraduate/Scholarship)* [7165]

Chappie Hall Scholarship Program *(Graduate, Postgraduate, Undergraduate/Scholarship)* [2]

John M. Haniak Scholarships *(Undergraduate/Scholarship)* [5692]

Harris Corporation Merit Scholarships *(Undergraduate/Scholarship)* [4403]

Carroll Hart Scholarships *(Graduate/Scholarship)* [8329]

Gabe A. Hartl Scholarships *(Undergraduate/Scholarship)* [105]

Thomas T. Hayashi Memorial Scholarships *(Graduate, Undergraduate/Scholarship)* [5142]

Health, Sport, and Fitness SIG Student Research

Awards *(Undergraduate/Award)* [1714]

Healthcare Information Management Systems Scholarships *(Graduate, Postgraduate, Undergraduate/Scholarship)* [4505]

Joseph T. Helling Scholarship Fund *(Undergraduate/Scholarship)* [4730]

Hench Post-Dissertation Fellowships *(Postdoctorate/Fellowship)* [419]

John P. Hennessey Scholarships *(Graduate, Undergraduate/Scholarship)* [5841]

Alia Herrera Memorial Scholarships *(Undergraduate/Scholarship)* [492]

Peter Hess Scholarships *(Undergraduate/Scholarship)* [4061]

Jim Hierlihy Memorial Scholarships *(Undergraduate/Scholarship)* [3672]

Jim & Nancy Hinkle Travel Grants *(Postdoctorate/Grant)* [4525]

Hispanic Association of Colleges and Universities Scholarships *(Undergraduate/Scholarship)* [4548]

Hispanic Association on Corporate Responsibility Scholarship Program *(Undergraduate/Scholarship)* [4553]

HLS/MLA Professional Development Grants *(Professional development/Grant)* [5742]

C.H.(Chuck) Hodgson Scholarships *(Undergraduate/Scholarship)* [9591]

Henry Hoffman Memorial Scholarship Fund *(Undergraduate/Scholarship)* [6064]

Michael J. Hogan Fellowships *(Graduate/Fellowship)* [8340]

Alan Holoch Memorial Grants *(Professional development/Grant)* [500]

Governor James E. Holshouser Professional Development Scholarships *(Professional development/Scholarship)* [6762]

Sam J. Hord Memorial Scholarships *(Undergraduate/Scholarship)* [8563]

Edward L. Horne, Jr. Scholarships *(All/Scholarship)* [6969]

C.D. Howard Scholarships *(Undergraduate/Scholarship)* [4898]

Goldwin Howland Scholarships *(Graduate/Scholarship)* [2561]

Humanism in Medicine Scholarships *(Undergraduate/Scholarship)* [8766]

IADR David B. Ste. Scott Fellowships *(Undergraduate/Fellowship)* [4860]

IADR John Ste. Clarkson Fellowships *(Postdoctorate/Fellowship)* [4861]

IADR John Ste. Gray Fellowships *(Professional development/Fellowship)* [4862]

IADR Norton Ste. Ross Fellowships *(Postgraduate/Fellowship)* [4863]

IADR Toshio Ste. Nakao Fellowships *(Professional development/Fellowship)* [4864]

IAESTE United States Scholarships *(Undergraduate/Scholarship)* [3309]

IBEA Graduate Scholarships *(Graduate/Scholarship)* [4682]

ICDA Graduate Scholarships *(Graduate/Scholarship)* [5034]

ICDA Research Grants *(Graduate/Grant)* [5035]

Ice Skating Institute of America Education Foundation Scholarships *(Undergraduate/Scholarship)* [4657]

IDA Fellowship Awards *(Professional development/Fellowship)* [4919]

Ella R. Ifill Fund *(Undergraduate/Scholarship)* [5580]

Illinois Association of Chamber of Commerce Executives Scholarships *(Postdoctorate/Scholarship)* [4680]

IMA Memorial Education Fund Scholarships (MEF) *(Graduate, Undergraduate/Scholarship loan)* [4815]

IMCEA Memorial Scholarships *(Graduate, Undergraduate/Scholarship)* [4960]

Independent Professional Seed Association Student Recognition Awards *(Undergraduate/Scholarship)* [4720]

Indiana Continuing Legal Education Forum Scholarship Fund *(Undergraduate/Scholarship)* [4731]

INIA Scholarships Program *(Undergraduate/Scholarship)* [4965]

International Association of Wildland Fire Graduate-Level Scholarships *(Doctorate, Graduate/Scholarship)* [4880]

International Code Council Foundation General Scholarship Fund *(Undergraduate/Scholarship)* [4899]

International Door Association Scholarship Foundation Program *(Undergraduate, Vocational/Occupational/Scholarship)* [4921]

International Executive Housekeepers Association Education Foundation Scholarship Awards *(Undergraduate/Scholarship)* [4923]

International Executive Housekeepers Association Spartan Scholarship Awards *(Undergraduate/Scholarship)* [4924]

International Harvester Collectors Scholarships *(Undergraduate/Scholarship)* [4950]

IOIA Organic Community Initiative Scholarships *(Professional development/Scholarship)* [4716]

Iranian Association of Boston's IAB Scholarships *(Undergraduate/Scholarship)* [6362]

Irish-American Research Travel Fellowships *(Professional development/Fellowship)* [1230]

ISDS Graduate Student Scholarships *(Doctorate, Graduate/Scholarship)* [4990]

ISPE Advantage Award/Foundation Scholarships *(Undergraduate/Scholarship)* [4691]

ISRS Graduate Fellowships *(Doctorate, Graduate/Fellowship)* [5001]

ITEEA FTE Scholarships *(Undergraduate/Scholarship)* [5010]

ITEEA Greer/FTE Grants *(Professional development/Grant)* [5011]

ITEEA Litherland/FTE Scholarships *(Undergraduate/Scholarship)* [5012]

ITNS Research Grants *(Professional development/Grant)* [5021]

Dr. Karl C. Ivarson Scholarships *(Postgraduate/Scholarship)* [74]

Freddy L. Jacobs Scholarships *(Undergraduate/Scholarship)* [4886]

Jamaican Canadian Association Alberta Scholarship Program *(Undergraduate/Scholarship)* [5130]

Frederick George James Memorial Scholarships *(Undergraduate/Scholarship)* [7935]

Sister Rita Jeanne Scholarships *(Undergraduate/Scholarship)* [5169]

Elise Reed Jenkins Memorial Scholarships - Gamma Lambda *(Undergraduate/Scholarship)* [8175]

Gaynold Jensen Education Stipends *(Postdoctorate, Professional development/Scholarship)* [3443]

Nancy Lorraine Jensen Memorial Scholarships *(Undergraduate/Scholarship)* [8531]

Stanley "Doc" Jensen Scholarships *(High School/Scholarship)* [694]

Joseph C. Johnson Memorial Grants *(Undergraduate/Scholarship)* [1191]

Gregory D. Johnson Memorial Scholarships *(Doctorate, Graduate, Master's/Scholarship)* [6378]

V.J. Johnson Memorial Scholarships *(Undergraduate/Scholarship)* [552]

OOIDA Mary Johnston Scholarships *(Undergraduate/Scholarship)* [7025]

Greater Baton Rouge Chapter - Don Jones Excellence in Safety Scholarships *(Undergraduate/Scholarship)* [1342]

Joseph H. Fichter Research Grants *(Professional development/Grant)* [1874]

Mike Kabo Global Scholarships *(Professional development/Scholarship)* [4167]

Kaplan Scholarships *(Undergraduate/Scholarship)* [4562]

Kaplan Test Prep and Admission Scholarships for NSHSS Members *(High School/Scholarship)* [6503]

Kappa Delta Phi Scholarship Program *(Postgraduate/Scholarship)* [952]

The ISASI Rudolf Kapustin Memorial Scholarships *(Undergraduate/Scholarship)* [4988]

J.S. Karling Graduate Student Research Awards *(Graduate/Grant)* [2164]

Philip R. Karr, III Scholarship Fund *(Graduate/Fellowship)* [4100]

Magoichi & Shizuko Kato Memorial Scholarships *(Graduate/Scholarship)* [5143]

KATS Graduate Scholarships *(Graduate/Scholarship)* [5246]

KATS Undergraduate Scholarships *(Undergraduate/Scholarship)* [5247]

Gunild Keetman Scholarships *(Professional development, Undergraduate/Scholarship)* [6957]

Willmoore H. Kendall Scholarships *(Postgraduate/Scholarship)* [2912]

KHIMA Graduate Scholarships *(Graduate/Scholarship)* [5187]

Michael Kidger Memorial Scholarships in Optical Design *(Graduate/Scholarship)* [8638]

Julia Kiene Fellowships in Electrical Energy *(Graduate/Fellowship)* [9723]

Margie Klein "Paper Plate" Scholarships *(All/Scholarship)* [1705]

AALL/Wolters Kluwer Law & Business Grants *(Professional development/Grant)* [501]

Robert E. Knight Professional Scholarships *(Doctorate, Graduate/Scholarship)* [8856]

Elva Knight Research Grants *(All/Grant)* [4976]

Glenn Knudsvig Memorial Scholarships *(Graduate, Undergraduate/Scholarship)* [611]

Gwin J. and Ruth Kolb Travel Fellowships *(Doctorate, Professional development/Fellowship)* [1232]

AIST Willy Korf Memorial Fund *(Undergraduate/Scholarship)* [1807]

Marcia J. Koslov Scholarships *(Professional development/Scholarship)* [502]

Eugene & Elinor Kotur Scholarship Trust Fund *(Undergraduate, Graduate/Scholarship)* [9499]

David A. Kronick Travelling Fellowships *(Doctorate/Fellowship)* [5743]

Melvin Kruger Endowed Scholarships *(Graduate, Undergraduate, Vocational/Occupational/Scholarship)* [7817]

Kris M. Kunze Memorial Scholarships *(Undergraduate/Scholarship)* [645]

Frank S. Land Scholarships *(Undergraduate/Scholarship)* [3425]

Cecil Lane Family Scholarships *(Undergraduate/Scholarship)* [178]

James D. Lang Memorial Scholarships *(Graduate/Scholarship)* [2390]

Laser Technology, Engineering and Applications Scholarships *(Graduate, Undergraduate/Scholarship)* [8639]

Jay and Deborah Last Fellowships *(Doctorate/Fellowship)* [420]

Willie D. Lawson, Jr. Memorial Scholarships *(Doctorate, Graduate, Professional development/Scholarship)* [6150]

The Leesfield/AAJ Law Student Scholarships *(Undergraduate/Scholarship)* [493]

The Legacy Fellowships *(Doctorate/Fellowship)* [421]

Legal Research Service Scholarships *(Undergraduate/Scholarship)* [3505]

Myra Levick Scholarships *(Graduate/Scholarship)* [427]

Herbert Levy Memorial Endowment Fund Scholarships *(Undergraduate/Scholarship)* [8439]

Ta Liang Memorial Awards *(Graduate/Grant)* [1669]

Library Media Teacher Scholarships *(Graduate/Scholarship)* [2271]

Eli Lilly and Company/Black Data Processing Associates Scholarships *(High School/Scholarship)* [2033]

Eli Lilly Graduate Scholarships *(Graduate/Scholarship)* [2451]

AIST Ronald E. Lincoln Memorial Scholarships *(Undergraduate/Scholarship)* [1808]

Litherland/FTE Scholarships *(Undergraduate/Scholarship)* [5007]

Nancy Llewellyn, RN Pediatric Nursing Bursaries *(Graduate, Professional development/Scholarship)* [1849]

D.J. Lovell Scholarships *(Graduate, Undergraduate/Scholarship)* [8640]

The Lowell H. and Dorothy Loving Undergraduate

Scholarships *(Undergraduate/Scholarship)* [646]

LPHA Scholarships *(Graduate, Undergraduate/Scholarship)* [5525]

Luso-American Fraternal Federation B-2 Scholarships *(Postgraduate/Scholarship)* [5545]

Luso-American Fraternal Federation B-3 Scholarships *(All, Vocational/Occupational/Scholarship)* [5546]

Luso-American Fraternal Federation B-4 Scholarships *(All/Scholarship)* [5547]

The C. Lyons Fellowship Program *(All/Fellowship)* [6389]

Verne LaMarr Lyons Memorial Scholarships *(Graduate/Fellowship)* [6123]

Carol E. Macpherson Memorial Scholarship and Alumnae Society Scholarships *(Graduate, Undergraduate/Scholarship)* [9244]

Andrew Macrina Scholarships *(High School/Scholarship)* [695]

MAES Founders Scholarships *(Graduate, Undergraduate/Scholarship)* [5798]

MAES General Scholarships *(Graduate, Undergraduate/Scholarship)* [5799]

MAES Graduate Scholarships *(Graduate/Scholarship)* [5800]

MAES Padrino/Madrina Scholarships *(Graduate, Undergraduate/Scholarship)* [5801]

MAES Pipeline Scholarships *(Graduate, Undergraduate/Scholarship)* [5802]

MAES Presidential Scholarships *(Graduate, Undergraduate/Scholarship)* [5803]

Dr. Edward May Magruder Medical Scholarships *(Undergraduate/Scholarship)* [609]

Maley/FTE Scholarships *(Graduate/Scholarship)* [5013]

Maley/FTEE Teacher Scholarships *(Graduate/Scholarship)* [5008]

Sue A. Malone Scholarships *(Doctorate, Graduate/Scholarship)* [5188]

David C. Maloney Scholarships *(Undergraduate/Scholarship)* [6423]

Lyle Mamer Fellowships *(Graduate/Fellowship)* [9724]

March of Dimes Graduate Nursing Scholarships *(Graduate/Scholarship)* [5607]

Harold and Inge Marcus Scholarships *(Undergraduate/Scholarship)* [4805]

Marine Technology Society Scholarships for Graduate and Undergraduate Students *(Graduate, Undergraduate/Scholarship)* [5640]

Marine Technology Society Student Scholarships for Two-year Technical, Engineering and Community College Students *(Community College, Two Year College, Undergraduate/Scholarship)* [5642]

Ray and Gertrude Marshall Scholarships *(Undergraduate/Scholarship)* [696]

The Maschhoffs Pork Production Scholarships *(Undergraduate/Scholarship)* [6379]

Val Mason Scholarships *(Postgraduate/Scholarship)* [2603]

Master Municipal Clerks Academy Scholarships *(Professional development/Scholarship)* [4958]

Master's Degree with a Major in Nursing Academic Scholarships *(Graduate/Scholarship)* [6100]

Materials Information Society National Merit Scholarships *(Undergraduate/Scholarship)* [5693]

Noel D. Matkin Awards *(Undergraduate/Award)* [3596]

Rene Matos Memorial Scholarships *(Undergraduate, Vocational/Occupational/Scholarship)* [6338]

Antonio Mattos Memorial Scholarships *(Undergraduate/Scholarship)* [5548]

Mature Student Scholarships *(Undergraduate/Scholarship)* [3673]

Clara Mayo Grants *(Graduate/Grant)* [8474]

John Mazurek Memorial-Morgex Insurance Scholarships *(Professional development/Scholarship)* [274]

Hans McCorriston Motive Power Machinist Grant Programs *(Undergraduate, Vocational/Occupational/Scholarship)* [1956]

The Cady McDonnell Memorial Scholarships *(Undergraduate/Scholarship)* [647]

McJulien Minority Graduate Scholarships *(Graduate/Scholarship)* [1764]

Midwest Chapter Scholarships - Betty McKern *(Undergraduate/Scholarship)* [1809]

John J. McKetta Undergraduate Scholarships *(Undergraduate/Scholarship)* [846]

Arthur Patch McKinlay Scholarships *(Graduate, Undergraduate/Scholarship)* [612]

McKinney Sisters Undergraduate Scholarships *(Undergraduate/Scholarship)* [3381]

Charles McMahon Memorial Construction Management/Engineering Scholarship Awards *(Undergraduate/Scholarship)* [1632]

Ruth McMillan Student Grants *(Undergraduate/Grant)* [2282]

National Association of Pediatric Nurse Practitioners McNeil Rural and Underserved Scholarships *(Graduate/Scholarship)* [6107]

MDA Development Grants *(Doctorate/Grant)* [5952]

MDA Research Grants *(Doctorate/Grant)* [5953]

David Meador Student Scholarships *(Undergraduate/Scholarship)* [6622]

The Medalist Club Post Graduate Scholarships *(Postgraduate/Scholarship)* [5733]

Medical Student Summer Research Scholarships *(Undergraduate/Scholarship)* [374]

Frederic G. Melcher Scholarships *(Graduate/Scholarship)* [1827]

CAG Donald Menzies Bursary Awards *(Postgraduate/Award)* [2382]

MESA Student Travel Fund *(Undergraduate/Grant)* [5852]

Scott Mesh Honorary Scholarships for Research in Psychology *(Graduate/Fellowship)* [1034]

Edmond A. Metzger Scholarships *(Undergraduate/Scholarship)* [1094]

Michigan Education Association Scholarships *(Undergraduate/Scholarship)* [5819]

Beth Middleton Memorial Scholarships *(Undergraduate/Scholarship)* [3709]

Midwest Chapter Scholarships - Engineering *(Undergraduate/Scholarship)* [1810]

Midwest Chapter Scholarships - Non-Engineering *(Undergraduate/Scholarship)* [1811]

Midwest Chapter Scholarships - Western States Awards *(Undergraduate/Scholarship)* [1812]

Milan Getting Scholarships *(Undergraduate/Scholarship)* [8522]

Military Intelligence Corps Association Scholarships *(Undergraduate, Vocational/Occupational/Scholarship)* [5872]

Cheryl Allyn Miller Awards *(Doctorate, Graduate/Fellowship)* [8519]

Mary Minglen Scholarship Program *(Postgraduate/Scholarship)* [953]

Minnesota Health Information Management Association Scholarships *(Undergraduate/Scholarship)* [5898]

Minority Leadership Development Awards *(Graduate/Award)* [503]

Minority Scholarship Awards for College Students *(Undergraduate/Scholarship)* [847]

MLA Research, Development, and Demonstration Project Grants *(Graduate/Grant)* [5747]

MODNA Nursing Education Scholarships *(Doctorate, Graduate/Fellowship)* [5849]

Mook & Blanchard Honorary Scholarships *(Graduate/Scholarship)* [2272]

Chapter 63 - Portland James E. Morrow Scholarships *(Graduate, Undergraduate/Scholarship)* [8393]

Mortar Board National Foundation Fellowships *(Postdoctorate/Fellowship)* [5937]

Wilma Motley Memorial California Merit Scholarships *(Undergraduate, Master's, Doctorate, Professional development/Scholarship)* [709]

MPI CRV Scholarships *(Professional development/Scholarship)* [5757]

MPTA Doctoral Scholarships *(Doctorate/Scholarship)* [5913]

Mueller Undergraduate Scholarships *(Undergraduate/Scholarship)* [9677]

Marvin Mundel Memorial Scholarships *(Under-*

graduate/Scholarship)* [4806]

Clarence and Josephine Myers Scholarships *(Graduate, Undergraduate/Scholarship)* [8394]

NABA National Scholarship Program *(Graduate, Undergraduate/Scholarship)* [6037]

NACADA Scholarships *(Doctorate, Graduate/Scholarship)* [5997]

NARFE-FEEA Scholarship Awards Program *(Undergraduate/Scholarship)* [6011]

NASE Future Entrepreneur Scholarships *(Undergraduate/Scholarship)* [6117]

National AAHAM Scholarships *(Undergraduate/Scholarship)* [483]

National Air Filtration Association Scholarship Fund *(Undergraduate/Scholarship)* [6015]

National Association for the Self-Employed Scholarships *(Undergraduate/Scholarship)* [6118]

National Ataxia Foundation Research Grants *(Professional development/Fellowship)* [6137]

National Beta Club Scholarships *(Undergraduate/Scholarship)* [6139]

National Black Coalition of Federal Aviation Employees Scholarships *(Other, Vocational/Occupational/Scholarship)* [6143]

National Black Deaf Advocate Scholarships *(Graduate, Undergraduate/Scholarship)* [6147]

National Black Nurses Association Scholarships *(Undergraduate/Scholarship)* [6155]

National Coal Transportation Association At Large Scholarships *(Undergraduate/Scholarship)* [6190]

National Community Pharmacists Association Presidential Scholarships *(Undergraduate/Scholarship)* [6199]

National Council on Public History Student Project Awards *(Undergraduate/Award)* [6216]

National Dairy Herd Information Association Scholarship Program *(Undergraduate/Scholarship)* [6231]

National Dental Hygienists' Association Scholarships *(Undergraduate/Scholarship)* [6244]

National Heartburn Alliance NP Student Scholarships *(Graduate/Scholarship)* [377]

National Honor Roll Scholarships *(Undergraduate/Scholarship)* [2222]

National Huguenot Society Scholarships *(Undergraduate/Scholarship)* [6347]

National Italian American Bar Association Scholarships *(Postgraduate/Scholarship)* [6367]

National Judges Association Scholarships *(Professional development/Scholarship)* [6372]

National Junior Swine Association Outstanding Member Scholarships *(Graduate/Scholarship)* [6380]

National Kindergarten Alliance Graduate Scholarships *(Graduate/Scholarship)* [6385]

National Organization of Black Law Enforcement Executives Fellowship Programs *(All/Fellowship)* [6421]

National Recreation and Park Association Diversity Scholarships *(Undergraduate/Scholarship)* [6459]

National Slovak Society of the USA Scholarships *(Undergraduate, Vocational/Occupational/Scholarship)* [6478]

National Slovak Society of the USA Senior Scholarships *(Undergraduate, Vocational/Occupational/Scholarship)* [6479]

National Swimming Pool Foundation Board of Directors' Scholarship Awards *(Professional development/Scholarship)* [6539]

National Swimming Pool Foundation Scholarship Awards *(Professional development/Scholarship)* [6540]

National Technical Honor Society Scholarships *(Undergraduate/Scholarship)* [3710]

National Women's Studies Association Lesbian Caucus Scholarships *(Doctorate, Graduate/Scholarship)* [6560]

NBMBAA Graduate Scholarships Program *(Graduate/Scholarship)* [6152]

NCECA Graduate Student Fellowships *(Graduate/Fellowship)* [6213]

NCTE Research Foundation Grants *(Professional development/Grant)* [6218]

NDIA Picatinny Chapter Scholarships *(Under-*

Alice Hinchcliffe Williams, RDH, MS Graduate Scholarships *(Graduate/Scholarship)* [9445]

Aubrey L. Williams Research Travel Fellowships *(Professional development/Fellowship)* [1236]

CSM Virgil R. Williams Scholarships *(Undergraduate/Scholarship)* [3645]

Cenie Jomo Williams Tuition Scholarships *(Graduate, Undergraduate/Scholarship)* [6043]

RS Williamson and Eliford Mott Memorial Scholarships *(Undergraduate/Scholarship)* [9593]

John Charles Wilson Scholarships *(Undergraduate/Scholarship)* [4856]

Winston Scholarships *(Graduate, Undergraduate, Vocational/Occupational/Scholarship)* [8032]

WOCN Advanced Education Scholarships *(Doctorate, Graduate, Undergraduate/Scholarship)* [9766]

Paul R. Wolf Memorial Scholarships *(Graduate/Scholarship)* [1672]

Women in Cancer Research Scholar Awards *(Graduate, Postdoctorate/Award)* [453]

Women's Jewelry Association Member Grants *(All/Grant)* [9726]

Dr. Harold S. Wood Awards for Excellence *(Undergraduate/Award)* [4072]

Irene Woodall Graduate Scholarships *(Master's/Scholarship)* [710]

Patty Wooten Scholarships *(Undergraduate/Scholarship)* [1707]

Pang Xiaoyan Scholarships *(Undergraduate/Scholarship)* [2775]

Minoru Yasui Memorial Scholarships *(Graduate/Scholarship)* [5147]

York Rite Grand Chapter Royal Arch Masons Scholarships *(Undergraduate/Scholarship)* [3426]

Gary Yoshimura Scholarships *(Undergraduate/Scholarship)* [7542]

Young Investigator Grants *(Undergraduate/Grant)* [6529]

Z/I Imaging Scholarships *(Graduate/Scholarship)* [1673]

Lisa Zaken Awards For Excellence *(Graduate, Undergraduate/Award)* [4812]

Disabled

AAHD Scholarships *(Graduate, Undergraduate/Scholarship)* [481]

AEBC Toronto Chapter Scholarships *(Graduate, Undergraduate, Vocational/Occupational/Scholarship)* [335]

Alabama Scholarships for Dependents of Blind Parents *(Undergraduate/Scholarship)* [164]

American Council of the Blind Scholarships *(Graduate, Undergraduate/Scholarship)* [658]

American Speech Language Hearing Foundation Scholarships for Students with Disability *(Graduate/Scholarship)* [1385]

Gladys C. Anderson Memorial Scholarships *(Graduate, Undergraduate/Scholarship)* [748]

Elsa Barton Educational Scholarship Fund *(Undergraduate, Vocational/Occupational/Scholarship)* [1023]

BCPA Bursaries *(Undergraduate/Scholarship)* [2180]

Business, Education and Technology Scholarships *(Graduate, Undergraduate, Vocational/Occupational/Scholarship)* [336]

Hermione Grant Calhoun Scholarships *(Undergraduate/Scholarship)* [6273]

Canadian Hard of Hearing Association Scholarships *(Undergraduate/Scholarship)* [2481]

Karen D. Carsel Memorial Scholarships *(Graduate/Scholarship)* [749]

CHEA Undergraduate Scholarship Program for Students with Disabilities *(High School, Undergraduate/Scholarship)* [2260]

Kevin Child Scholarships *(Undergraduate/Scholarship)* [6319]

John and Ruth Childe Scholarships *(Undergraduate/Scholarship)* [8594]

Zoe E. Collymore Page Scholarships *(Undergraduate/Scholarship)* [6145]

Roy Cooper Scholarships *(Undergraduate/Scholarship)* [5397]

Copnick/Hilliard Scholarships *(Professional development/Scholarship)* [2578]

Soozie Courter Sharing a Brighter Tomorrow Hemophilia Scholarship Program *(Graduate, Undergraduate, Vocational/Occupational/Scholarship)* [6320]

CRS Scholarships *(Undergraduate/Scholarship)* [2785]

Cystic Fibrosis Scholarship Foundation *(Undergraduate, Vocational/Occupational/Scholarship)* [3312]

Eric Delson Memorial Scholarships *(High School, Undergraduate, Vocational/Occupational/Scholarship)* [6321]

C. Rodney Demarest Memorial Scholarships *(Undergraduate/Scholarship)* [4425]

Rudolph Dillman Memorial Scholarships *(Graduate, Undergraduate/Scholarship)* [750]

Disabled War Veterans Scholarships *(Undergraduate/Scholarship)* [1559]

Diversity Executive Leadership Program Scholarships *(Professional development/Scholarship)* [1184]

Eric Dostie Memorial College Scholarships *(Undergraduate/Scholarship)* [6322]

Edmonton Epilepsy Continuing Education Scholarships *(Undergraduate/Scholarship)* [3590]

Education is Power Scholarships *(Undergraduate, Vocational/Occupational/Scholarship)* [6323]

Christine H. Eide Memorial Scholarships *(Graduate, Undergraduate/Scholarship)* [5496]

Boomer Esiason Foundation Scholarship Program *(All/Scholarship)* [3685]

ExeptionalNurse.com College Scholarships *(Graduate, Undergraduate/Scholarship)* [3696]

Exercise For Life Athletic Scholarships Program *(Undergraduate/Scholarship)* [3686]

Families of Freedom Scholarship Fund - America Scholarships *(Undergraduate, Vocational/Occupational/Scholarship)* [3704]

Anne M. Fassett Scholarships *(Undergraduate/Scholarship)* [8600]

Jennica Ferguson Memorial Scholarships *(Undergraduate/Scholarship)* [6274]

William and Dorothy Ferrell Scholarship Program *(Undergraduate/Scholarship)* [1759]

Andrew Foster Scholarships *(Undergraduate/Scholarship)* [6146]

Terry Fox Memorial Scholarships *(Undergraduate/Scholarship)* [6549]

R.L. Gillette Scholarships *(Undergraduate/Scholarship)* [751]

Joshua Gomes Memorial Scholarship Fund *(Graduate, Undergraduate/Scholarship)* [6324]

Millie Gonzalez Memorial Scholarships *(Undergraduate, Vocational/Occupational/Scholarship)* [6325]

Guide Dogs for the Blind Dorothea and Roland Bohde Leadership Scholarships *(Postgraduate/Scholarship)* [6275]

GuildScholar Awards *(Undergraduate/Scholarship)* [5159]

Delta Gamma Foundation Florence Margaret Harvey Memorial Scholarships *(Graduate, Undergraduate/Scholarship)* [752]

Professor Ulla Hedner Scholarships *(Undergraduate, Vocational/Occupational/Scholarship)* [6326]

Hemophilia Health Services Memorial Scholarship Program *(Graduate, Undergraduate/Scholarship)* [6327]

Dr. E. Bruce Hendrick Scholarships *(All/Scholarship)* [8647]

HHS Memorial Scholarships *(Graduate, Undergraduate/Scholarship)* [37]

Jim Hierlihy Memorial Scholarships *(Undergraduate/Scholarship)* [3672]

Irving J. Hoffman Memorial Scholarships *(Undergraduate/Scholarship)* [9331]

Mike Hylton and Ron Niederman Memorial Scholarships *(Undergraduate/Scholarship)* [6328]

Kenneth Jernigan Scholarships *(Undergraduate/Scholarship)* [6276]

K-12 Edu-Grants *(Other/Grant)* [6329]

Kuchler-Killian Memorial Scholarships *(Undergraduate/Scholarship)* [6277]

Gloria Landis Bursary *(Undergraduate, Vocational/Occupational/Scholarship)* [5398]

The Lanford Family Highway Worker Memorial Scholarship Program *(Undergraduate/Scholarship)* [1157]

Las Vegas Elks Scholarships for the Physically Challenged *(Undergraduate, Vocational/Occupational/Scholarship)* [7502]

The Leaders of Tomorrow Scholarships *(Undergraduate, Vocational/Occupational/Scholarship)* [3572]

Lighthouse International Scholarships - College-bound Awards *(High School, Undergraduate/Scholarship)* [5497]

Lighthouse International Scholarships - Graduate Awards *(Graduate/Scholarship)* [5498]

Lighthouse International Scholarships - Undergraduate Awards *(Undergraduate/Scholarship)* [5499]

Katie MacDonald Memorial Scholarships *(Graduate, Undergraduate/Scholarship)* [9018]

Lawrence Madeiros Scholarships *(Undergraduate/Scholarship)* [6330]

Mary Main Memorial Scholarships *(Undergraduate/Scholarship)* [4449]

Eric Martinez Memorial Scholarships *(Graduate, Undergraduate/Scholarship)* [9019]

Michael Marucci Memorial Scholarships *(Undergraduate/Scholarship)* [6278]

Mature Student Scholarships *(Undergraduate/Scholarship)* [3673]

McBurney Disability Scholarships *(Undergraduate/Scholarship)* [9363]

National Black Deaf Advocate Scholarships *(Graduate, Undergraduate/Scholarship)* [6147]

National Federation of the Blind Educator of Tomorrow Awards *(Undergraduate/Scholarship)* [6279]

Alan H. Neville Memorial Scholarships *(Graduate, Undergraduate, Vocational/Occupational/Scholarship)* [337]

NHLBI Individual Pre-Doctoral Fellowships *(Doctorate, Graduate/Fellowship)* [6315]

AEBC Rick Oakes Scholarships for the Arts *(Graduate, Undergraduate, Vocational/Occupational/Scholarship)* [338]

Charles and Melva T. Owen Memorial Scholarships *(Undergraduate/Scholarship)* [6280]

E.U. Parker Scholarships *(Undergraduate/Scholarship)* [6281]

Pfizer Epilepsy Scholarships *(Graduate, Undergraduate/Scholarship)* [7221]

Phillips Scholarships *(Undergraduate/Scholarship)* [3184]

Christopher Pitkin Memorial Scholarships *(Undergraduate, Vocational/Occupational/Scholarship)* [6332]

Project Red Flag Academic Scholarships for Women with Bleeding Disorders *(Undergraduate/Scholarship)* [6333]

Salvatore E. Quinci Foundation Scholarships *(Undergraduate, Vocational/Occupational/Scholarship)* [6334]

Betty Rendel Scholarships *(Undergraduate/Scholarship)* [6288]

Howard Brown Rickard Scholarships *(Undergraduate/Scholarship)* [6282]

Paul and Ellen Ruckes Scholarships *(Graduate, Undergraduate/Scholarship)* [753]

Sacks For CF Scholarships *(All/Scholarship)* [3687]

SBA Four-Year Scholarships Program *(Undergraduate/Scholarship)* [8644]

SBA One-Year Scholarship Program *(Undergraduate, Vocational/Occupational/Scholarship)* [8645]

Scholarships of the Arts *(Graduate, Undergraduate/Scholarship)* [3688]

School Age Financial Aid Program *(Undergraduate/Scholarship)* [2050]

Sertoma Communicative Disorders Scholarships *(Graduate/Scholarship)* [8094]

Sertoma Hard of Hearing and Deaf Scholarships *(Undergraduate/Scholarship)* [8095]

Esther M. Smith Scholarships *(Undergraduate/Scholarship)* [3069]

Beatrice Drinnan Spence Scholarships *(Undergraduate, Vocational/Occupational/Scholarship)* [3573]

Dr. Gunnar B. Stickler Scholarships *(Undergraduate, Vocational/Occupational/Scholarship)* [8735]

Bonnie Strangio Education Scholarships *(Graduate, Undergraduate/Scholarship)* [3689]

Sun Life Financial Peer Support Scholarships *(Professional development/Scholarship)* [2579]

Michael Bendix Sutton Foundation *(Undergraduate/Scholarship)* [6335]

Marjorie Anderson Thompson Scholarships *(Graduate, Undergraduate/Scholarship)* [363]

Toronto Rehab Scholarships in Rehabilitation-Related Research *(Graduate/Scholarship)* [8918]

Ferdinand Torres Scholarships *(Graduate, Undergraduate/Scholarship)* [754]

Tristin Memorial Scholarships *(Undergraduate, Vocational/Occupational/Scholarship)* [5395]

Rachel Warner Memorial Scholarships *(Graduate, Undergraduate/Scholarship)* [6336]

Wheelchair Success Foundation Scholarships *(Undergraduate/Scholarship)* [2963]

Youth Empowerment Summit Scholarships *(Undergraduate/Scholarship)* [6148]

Employer affiilation

Adelson Family Scholarships *(Undergraduate/Scholarship)* [7463]

Tom Babcox Memorial Scholarships *(All/Scholarship)* [1964]

Donald H. Bernstein/John B. Talbert, Jr. Scholarships *(Undergraduate/Scholarship)* [3887]

Dr. George T. Bottomley Scholarships *(Undergraduate/Scholarship)* [5707]

BSA Educational Scholarships *(Undergraduate/Scholarship)* [2224]

Burger King Employee Scholars Program *(Undergraduate/Scholarship)* [4474]

Carolinas-Virginias Retail Hardware Scholarships *(Undergraduate/Scholarship)* [3893]

Christmas Tree Chapter Scholarship Awards *(Undergraduate/Scholarship)* [6933]

City of Sanibel Employee Dependent Scholarships *(Undergraduate/Scholarship)* [8595]

The Community Foundation DBI Scholarships *(Undergraduate, Vocational/Occupational/Scholarship)* [3103]

The Continental Group Scholarship Fund *(High School, Undergraduate/Scholarship)* [3316]

Copper and Brass Servicenter Association Inc. Scholarship Program *(Undergraduate/Scholarship)* [3253]

Richard Cossette/Gale Memorial Scholarships *(All/Scholarship)* [1965]

Crowder Scholarships *(Undergraduate/Scholarship)* [3901]

Colonel Richard M. Dawson Scholarships *(Undergraduate/Scholarship)* [3105]

Don Aron Scholarships *(Undergraduate/Scholarship)* [6208]

Downeast Energy Scholarships *(Undergraduate/Scholarship)* [3477]

Dr. Robert Elliott Memorial Scholarships *(Undergraduate/Scholarship)* [5708]

Pauline Elliott Scholarships *(Undergraduate/Scholarship)* [5709]

Robert C. Erb Sr. Scholarships *(Undergraduate/Scholarship)* [5710]

Jack B. Fisher Scholarship Fund *(Undergraduate/Scholarship)* [8665]

Laura M. Fleming Scholarships *(Undergraduate, Vocational/Occupational/Scholarship)* [3903]

Captain Ernest Fox Perpetual Scholarships *(Undergraduate/Scholarship)* [2926]

Phil Friel Scholarships *(Undergraduate/Scholarship)* [5711]

Peter M. Gargano Scholarship Fund *(Undergraduate/Scholarship)* [3529]

Leo Gilmartin Scholarships *(High School/Scholarship)* [7352]

Alex Gissler Memorial Scholarships *(Undergraduate/Scholarship)* [5712]

Henry Hoffman Memorial Scholarship Fund *(Undergraduate/Scholarship)* [6064]

Melvin Kruger Endowed Scholarship Program *(Undergraduate, Vocational/Occupational/Scholarship)* [6465]

Stan Lencki Scholarships *(Undergraduate/Scholarship)* [5713]

Loan Forgiveness Scholarships *(Graduate, Undergraduate/Loan, Scholarship)* [8634]

Rick Mahoney Scholarships *(Undergraduate/Scholarship)* [5714]

Horace Mann Insurance Scholarships *(High School/Scholarship)* [6878]

McKelvey Foundation Entrepreneurial Scholarships *(Undergraduate/Scholarship)* [5728]

National Sheriffs' Association Scholarship Program *(Graduate, Undergraduate/Scholarship)* [6474]

Nebraska Hospital Association Tuition Aid and Scholarships *(Undergraduate/Scholarship)* [6606]

NHPGA Apprentice Scholarships *(Undergraduate/Scholarship)* [5715]

Ohio Association of Broadcaster's Kids Scholarships *(Undergraduate/Scholarship)* [6852]

Paper Stock Industries/RRF Scholarships *(Undergraduate/Scholarship)* [7045]

PARMA Scholarships *(Undergraduate/Scholarship)* [7460]

Walter T. Philippy Scholarships *(Undergraduate/Scholarship)* [5716]

David J. Pollini Scholarships *(Undergraduate/Scholarship)* [5717]

Pope Scholarship Awards *(Undergraduate/Scholarship)* [5718]

Raytheon Scholarship Program *(Undergraduate/Scholarship)* [7611]

Retail Chapter Scholarship Awards *(Undergraduate/Scholarship)* [6942]

Rotary Public Safety Scholarships *(Undergraduate/Scholarship)* [3920]

SACHS Foundation Undergraduate Scholarships for Colorado Black Students *(High School/Scholarship)* [7841]

Saskatchewan Government Insurance Anniversary Scholarships *(Undergraduate/Scholarship)* [7997]

Saskatchewan Trucking Association Scholarships *(Undergraduate/Scholarship)* [8010]

Jim Sheerin Scholarships *(Undergraduate/Scholarship)* [5719]

Simonton Windows Scholarships *(Undergraduate, Vocational/Occupational/Scholarship)* [7115]

Sobeys & Empire Work Experience & Scholarship Program - Future Leaders Awards *(Professional development/Award)* [8278]

Matt Stager Memorial Scholarship Fund *(Undergraduate/Scholarship)* [9538]

Charles H. Stone Scholarships *(Undergraduate/Scholarship)* [559]

Texas Mutual Scholarship Program *(Undergraduate, Vocational/Occupational/Scholarship)* [8868]

Turner Family Scholarships *(Undergraduate, Vocational/Occupational/Scholarship)* [3925]

Laramie Walden Memorial Fund *(Undergraduate/Scholarship)* [3927]

Walmart Associate Scholarships *(Undergraduate/Scholarship)* [9479]

Walton Family Foundation Scholarships *(Undergraduate/Scholarship)* [9481]

Fred C. Wikoff, Jr. Scholarships *(Undergraduate, Vocational/Occupational/Scholarship)* [3928]

Willamette Chapter Scholarship Awards *(Undergraduate/Scholarship)* [6943]

Ethnic group membership

AAA Minority Dissertation Fellowship Program *(Doctorate/Fellowship)* [406]

AAMA Houston Chapter - Medical Student Scholarships *(Professional development/Scholarship)* [1494]

Accenture American Indian Scholarship Program *(Graduate, Undergraduate/Scholarship)* [825]

AGBU Scholarships *(Graduate/Loan)* [1573]

AGI Minority Participation Program Geoscience Student Scholarships (AGI-MPP) *(Graduate, Undergraduate/Scholarship)* [778]

AIGC Fellowships - Graduate *(Graduate/Fellowship)* [826]

AISES Intel Scholarships *(Graduate, Undergraduate/Scholarship)* [832]

Al Muammar Scholarships for Journalism *(Undergraduate/Scholarship)* [1490]

Alberta Blue Cross Scholarships for Aboriginal Students *(Undergraduate/Scholarship)* [211]

AMEC Aboriginal Undergraduate Scholarships *(Undergraduate/Scholarship)* [2453]

American Lebanese Engineering Society Scholarship Program *(Graduate, Undergraduate/Scholarship)* [892]

American Physical Society Minority Undergraduate Scholarships *(Undergraduate/Scholarship)* [996]

AMLN Scholarships *(Graduate, Undergraduate/Scholarship)* [934]

A.T. Anderson Memorial Scholarships *(Graduate, Undergraduate/Scholarship)* [834]

APTA Minority Scholarships - Faculty Development Scholarships *(Postdoctorate/Scholarship)* [999]

APTA Minority Scholarships - Physical Therapist Assistant Students *(All/Scholarship)* [1000]

APTA Minority Scholarships - Physical Therapist Students *(All/Scholarship)* [1001]

Armenian American Citizen's League Scholarships *(Undergraduate/Scholarship)* [1580]

Armenian American Medical Association Scholarships *(Undergraduate/Scholarship)* [1581]

Armenian American Pharmacists' Association Scholarships *(Doctorate, Graduate/Scholarship)* [1582]

Armenian Bar Association Graduate Scholarships in Law *(Graduate/Scholarship)* [1569]

Armenian General Athletic Union Scholarships *(Undergraduate/Scholarship)* [1583]

Armenian Relief Society Scholarships *(Graduate, Undergraduate/Scholarship)* [1584]

ARS Undergraduate Scholarships *(Undergraduate/Scholarship)* [1577]

Michael M. Assarian Scholarships *(Undergraduate/Scholarship)* [1585]

Association of American Indian Physicians Scholarships *(Graduate, Undergraduate/Scholarship)* [1699]

John M. Azarian Memorial Armenian Youth Scholarship Fund *(Undergraduate/Scholarship)* [1586]

Baker Donelson Diversity Scholarships *(Undergraduate/Scholarship)* [1997]

Baker and Hostetler Diversity Fellowships *(Undergraduate/Fellowship)* [1999]

Guthikonda BasavapunnaRao & Umadevi Scholarships *(Graduate/Scholarship)* [8829]

BCA Ethnic Minority Postgraduate Scholarships for Careers in Athletics *(Postgraduate/Scholarship)* [2135]

Harvey Bell Memorial Prize *(Graduate/Prize)* [6564]

BIE-Loan for Service for Graduates *(Graduate/Loan)* [827]

Alex Blaski Memorial Scholarships *(Undergraduate/Scholarship)* [7757]

Hagop Bogigian Scholarship Fund *(Undergraduate/Scholarship)* [1587]

Bohemian Lawyers Association of Chicago Scholarships *(Graduate/Scholarship)* [2162]

Anne-Marie Bonner Scholarships *(Undergraduate/Scholarship)* [5115]

Maria and Czeslaw Borek Scholarships *(Undergraduate/Scholarship)* [7758]

Corris Boyd Scholarships *(Master's/Scholarship)* [1891]

Gladys Kamakakuokalani 'Ainoa Brandt Scholarships *(Graduate, Undergraduate/Scholarship)* [5209]

Cathy L. Brock Memorial Scholarships *(Graduate/Scholarship)* [4787]

Brown Dental Scholarships *(Undergraduate/Scholarship)* [5116]

The Thuy Nguyen Scholarships *(High School/ Scholarship)* [9433]

NHLBI Individual Pre-Doctoral Fellowships *(Doctorate, Graduate/Fellowship)* [6315]

NIAF Scholarships - General Category I *(Undergraduate/Scholarship)* [6369]

Nissan North America, Inc. Scholarships *(Undergraduate/Scholarship)* [809]

NUF Fellowships *(Graduate, Postgraduate, Professional development/Fellowship)* [6553]

NWAG Georgia, USA Scholarships *(High School/ Scholarship)* [6718]

NWAG Nigeria Scholarships *(Undergraduate/ Scholarship)* [6719]

Outstanding Minority Accounting Student Scholarships *(All/Scholarship)* [6753]

PACE/Columbian Lawyers Association of Westchester County Endowed Scholarships *(Undergraduate/Scholarship)* [3010]

Dr. Nicholas Padis Memorial Graduate Scholarships *(Graduate/Scholarship)* [4517]

Pan-Macedonian National Scholarships *(Undergraduate/Scholarship)* [7039]

The PanHellenic Scholarships *(Undergraduate/ Scholarship)* [7041]

Pepperdine University Armenian Student Scholarships *(Undergraduate/Scholarship)* [7200]

Leonard M. Perryman Communications Scholarships for Ethnic Minority Students *(Undergraduate/Scholarship)* [9013]

Eleonora Pidperyhora Scholarship *(Undergraduate/Scholarship)* [7775]

Dr. Adolph Piotrowski Memorial Art Scholarships *(Undergraduate/Scholarship)* [7776]

Peter George Pitsakis Memorial Scholarships *(Undergraduate/Scholarship)* [4518]

Porter Physiology Development Fellowship Awards *(Doctorate/Fellowship)* [1005]

Poundmaker Memorial Scholarships *(Undergraduate/Scholarship)* [6565]

Prince Henry Society Scholarships *(Undergraduate/Scholarship)* [7433]

Guthikonda Ramabrahmam & Balamani *(Graduate/Scholarship)* [8831]

W. Reymonta Scholarships *(Undergraduate/Scholarship)* [7777]

William S. Richardson Commemorative Scholarships *(Graduate/Scholarship)* [5221]

Ameen Rihani Scholarship Program *(Undergraduate/Scholarship)* [1492]

Elliott C. Roberts Scholarships *(Graduate/Scholarship)* [4789]

Jackie Robinson Foundation Minority Scholarships *(Undergraduate/Scholarship)* [822]

R.O.E.A. Dumitru Golea Goldy-Gemu Scholarships *(Undergraduate/Scholarship)* [1165]

Ryerson Scholarships *(Undergraduate/Scholarship)* [5124]

Chester & Maria Sadowski Memorial Scholarships *(Undergraduate/Scholarship)* [7778]

St. James Armenian Church Memorial Scholarships *(All/Scholarship)* [1604]

SAJA Journalism Scholarships *(Graduate, Undergraduate/Scholarship)* [8540]

SALEF Health Career Scholarships *(Graduate, Undergraduate/Scholarship)* [7894]

Scholarships for Aboriginal Canadians *(Undergraduate/Scholarship)* [6550]

Scholarships for Emigres in the Health Sciences *(Undergraduate/Scholarship)* [5157]

Tadeusz Sendzimir Scholarships *(Undergraduate/Scholarship)* [4460]

Gadde Sitaramamma & Tirupataiah Scholarships *(Graduate/Scholarship)* [8832]

Eva Smith Bursary *(Undergraduate/Scholarship)* [5125]

Boleslaw & Irena Sobczak Scholarships *(Undergraduate/Scholarship)* [7779]

Sovereign Nations Scholarships *(Undergraduate/ Scholarship)* [810]

Iwalani Carpenter Sowa Scholarships *(Graduate/ Scholarship)* [5222]

SREB-State Doctoral Scholarships *(Doctorate, Graduate/Scholarship)* [8585]

Morgan Stanley Tribal Scholars Program *(Undergraduate/Scholarship)* [811]

Vallabhaneni Sukundamma & Lakshmaiah Scholarships *(Graduate/Scholarship)* [8833]

Syncrude/Athabasca University Aboriginal Scholarships *(All/Scholarship)* [8791]

Hazaros Tabakoglu Scholarship Fund *(Undergraduate/Scholarship)* [1605]

TANA Foundation Graduate Scholarships *(Graduate/Scholarship)* [8834]

Dr. Peter A. Theodos Memorial Graduate Scholarships *(Graduate/Scholarship)* [4519]

Barbara Thomas Bursary *(Undergraduate/Scholarship)* [5126]

Time Warner Tribal Scholars Program *(Undergraduate/Scholarship)* [812]

Aram Torossian Memorial Scholarships *(Undergraduate/Scholarship)* [1606]

Vera Tran Memorial Scholarships *(Undergraduate/ Scholarship)* [9434]

Richard R. Tufenkian Memorial Scholarships *(Undergraduate/Scholarship)* [1571]

Two Nineteen Scholarships *(Community College, Graduate, Undergraduate/Scholarship)* [7895]

Morris K. Udall Scholarships *(Undergraduate/ Scholarship)* [8991]

Union of Marash Armenian Scholarships *(Graduate, Undergraduate/Scholarship)* [1607]

University of Wisconsin-Madison American Indian Alumni Scholarships *(Undergraduate/Scholarship)* [9373]

Upakar Indian-American Scholarships *(Undergraduate/Scholarship)* [9389]

UPS Diversity Scholarships *(Undergraduate/ Scholarship)* [1356]

Hurad Van Der Bedrosian Memorial Scholarships *(Graduate/Scholarship)* [1608]

Kodali Veeraiah & Sarojini Scholarships *(Graduate/Scholarship)* [8835]

Dimitri J. Ververelli Memorial Scholarships *(Undergraduate/Scholarship)* [4520]

Vorgin-Bell Scholarships *(Graduate, Master's, Undergraduate/Scholarship)* [6848]

VSCPA Educational Foundation Minority Scholarships *(Graduate, Undergraduate/Scholarship)* [9465]

Warner Norcross & Judd LLP Minorty Scholarships *(Undergraduate/Scholarship)* [9483]

Wells Fargo American Indian Scholarships - Graduate *(Graduate/Scholarship)* [828]

Dennis Wong and Associates Scholarships *(Graduate, Undergraduate/Scholarship)* [5223]

York Regional Police Scholarships *(Undergraduate/Scholarship)* [5127]

Youth Affairs Committee Rising Star Scholarships *(Undergraduate/Scholarship)* [5128]

Harry and Angel Zerigian Scholarships *(Undergraduate/Scholarship)* [1609]

Fraternal organization membership

Nancy Ashley Adams/Ashley Adams Koetje Scholarships *(Undergraduate/Scholarship)* [3360]

Adams Family Scholarships *(Undergraduate/ Scholarship)* [3361]

ADHA IOH Sigma Phi Alpha Graduate Scholarships *(Graduate/Scholarship)* [707]

ALD Graduate Fellowships *(Graduate/Fellowship)* [6019]

Margaret M. Alkek Scholarships *(Undergraduate/ Scholarship)* [3362]

Alpha Chi Sigma Scholarship Awards *(Graduate, Undergraduate/Scholarship)* [348]

Alpha Delta Gamma Educational Foundation Scholarships (ADGEF) *(All/Scholarship)* [350]

Alpha Eta Scholarships *(Undergraduate/Scholarship)* [3363]

Alpha Kappa Alpha - Educational Advancement Foundation Financial Need-Based Scholarships *(Graduate, Undergraduate/Scholarship)* [352]

Alpha Kappa Alpha - Educational Advancement Foundation Merit Scholarships *(Graduate, Undergraduate/Scholarship)* [353]

Alpha Rho Leadership Scholarships *(Undergraduate/Scholarship)* [3364]

Anchor Plastics Scholarships *(Graduate, Undergraduate/Scholarship)* [7264]

Jane E. Anderson Scholarships *(Undergraduate/ Scholarship)* [3365]

Margaret J. Andrew Memorial Scholarships *(Undergraduate/Scholarship)* [8156]

Jack Anson Fellowships *(Graduate/Fellowship)* [6738]

Hettie M. Anthony Fellowships *(Postdoctorate/ Fellowship)* [5200]

Atlanta Alumnae Achievement Scholarships *(Undergraduate/Scholarship)* [3366]

Frances Warren Baker Memorial Scholarships *(Undergraduate/Scholarship)* [8157]

Lloyd G. Balfour Fellowships *(Graduate/Fellowship)* [6739]

Avery Bayle Barth Scholarships *(Undergraduate/ Scholarship)* [3367]

Beta Gamma Memorial Scholarships *(Undergraduate/Scholarship)* [3368]

Beta Omega Scholarships *(Undergraduate/Scholarship)* [8158]

Beta Sigma Scholarships *(Undergraduate/Scholarship)* [8159]

Mildred Cater Bradham Social Work Fellowships *(Graduate/Fellowship)* [9801]

Seth R. and Corrine H. Brooks Memorial Scholarships *(All/Scholarship)* [2075]

Walta Wilkinson Carmichael Scholarships *(Undergraduate/Scholarship)* [8160]

Commander James Carr Forensic Science Scholarships *(Undergraduate/Scholarship)* [356]

Christine Kerr Cawthorne Scholarships *(Undergraduate/Scholarship)* [8161]

S. Penny Chappell Scholarships *(Undergraduate/ Scholarship)* [7279]

Chi Chapter Undergraduate Scholarships *(Undergraduate/Scholarship)* [3369]

Charline Chilson Scholarships *(Undergraduate/ Scholarship)* [3407]

Patricia Smith Christensen Scholarships *(Postdoctorate/Scholarship)* [8195]

Clan Ross Foundation Scholarships *(Undergraduate/Scholarship)* [2897]

Thomas Arkle Clark Scholar-Leader of the Year Endowed Scholarships *(Graduate, Undergraduate/Scholarship)* [7254]

Geraldine Clewell Fellowships - Doctoral Student *(Graduate/Fellowship)* [7280]

Geraldine Clewell Fellowships - Masteral *(Graduate/Fellowship)* [7281]

Geraldine Clewell Scholarships - Undergraduate *(Undergraduate/Scholarship)* [7282]

Closs/Parnitzke/Clarke Scholarships *(Undergraduate/Scholarship)* [7283]

Maridell Braham Condon Scholarships *(Undergraduate/Scholarship)* [8162]

Beta Nu/Caryl Cordis D'hondt Scholarships *(Undergraduate/Scholarship)* [8163]

Theta/Caryl Cordis D'hondt Scholarships *(Undergraduate/Scholarship)* [8164]

Cornaro Scholarships for Graduate Studies *(Graduate/Scholarship)* [5191]

CSA Fraternal Life Scholarships *(Undergraduate/ Scholarship)* [3299]

Arlene Davis Scholarships *(Undergraduate/Scholarship)* [3408]

Delta Chi Alumnae Memorial Scholarships *(Undergraduate/Scholarship)* [8165]

Delta Epsilon Sigma Graduate Fellowships *(Graduate/Fellowship)* [3395]

Delta Epsilon Sigma Undergraduate Scholarships *(Undergraduate/Scholarship)* [3396]

Delta Nu Alpha Foundation Scholarships *(Undergraduate/Scholarship)* [3400]

Delta Phi Epsilon Educational Foundation Scholarships *(Undergraduate/Scholarship)* [3402]

Delta Zeta Undergraduate Scholarships *(Undergraduate/Scholarship)* [3409]

Jean Dearth Dickerscheid Fellowships *(Graduate/ Fellowship)* [7284]

Scott Dominguez - Craters of the Moon Chapter Scholarships *(Graduate, Undergraduate/Scholarship)* [1336]

Wilma Sackett Dressel Scholarships *(Undergraduate/Scholarship)* [8166]

Margaret Drew Alpha Fellowships *(Graduate/Fellowship)* [7285]

Durning Sisters Scholarships *(Graduate/Scholarship)* [3370]

Enterprise Rent-A-Car Scholarships *(Graduate, Undergraduate/Scholarship)* [7265]

Epsilon Epsilon Scholarships *(Undergraduate/Scholarship)* [8167]

Epsilon Tau Scholarships *(Undergraduate/Scholarship)* [8168]

Harriet Erich Graduate Fellowships *(Graduate/Fellowship)* [3371]

Faculty Advisor Research Grants *(Professional development/Grant)* [7240]

Falcon Achievement Scholarships *(Undergraduate/Scholarship)* [7371]

Federated Insurance Scholarships *(Graduate, Undergraduate/Scholarship)* [7266]

Foresters Scholarships *(Undergraduate/Scholarship)* [4714]

Genevieve Forthun Scholarships *(Undergraduate/Scholarship)* [7286]

Mary Weiking Franken Scholarships *(Undergraduate/Scholarship)* [7287]

Marian Johnson Frutiger Scholarships *(Undergraduate/Scholarship)* [8169]

Louise Bales Gallagher Scholarships *(Undergraduate/Scholarship)* [3372]

Gamma Iota Scholarships - Gamma Tau *(Undergraduate/Scholarship)* [8170]

Gamma Iota Scholarships - Kappa Eta *(Undergraduate/Scholarship)* [8171]

Gamma Iota Scholarships - Zeta Kappa *(Undergraduate/Scholarship)* [8172]

Gamma Iota Scholarships - Zeta Nu *(Undergraduate/Scholarship)* [8173]

Gamma Sigma Alpha Graduate Scholarships *(Graduate/Scholarship)* [4039]

General Falcon Scholarships *(Undergraduate/Scholarship)* [7372]

Gleaner Life Insurance Scholarship Foundation *(Undergraduate/Scholarship)* [4159]

Richard C. Gorecki Scholarships *(Undergraduate/Scholarship)* [7373]

Lucile Cheever Graubart/Lambda Scholarships *(Undergraduate/Scholarship)* [8174]

Elizabeth M. Gruber Scholarships *(Graduate/Scholarship)* [3410]

Anna E. Hall Memorial Scholarships *(Undergraduate/Scholarship)* [7251]

Tommie J. Hamner Scholarships *(Undergraduate/Scholarship)* [7288]

William H. Harris Memorial Scholarships *(Graduate, Undergraduate/Scholarship)* [7267]

Peg Hart Harrison Memorial Scholarships *(Undergraduate/Scholarship)* [3373]

Edith Head Scholarships *(Undergraduate/Scholarship)* [3411]

Erin Kumelos Heard Memorial Scholarships *(Undergraduate/Scholarship)* [3374]

Lavonne Heghinian Scholarships *(Undergraduate/Scholarship)* [3412]

Houston/Nancy Holliman Scholarships *(Undergraduate/Scholarship)* [3413]

Houston Alumnae Chapter Graduate Fellowships *(Graduate/Fellowship)* [3375]

Sarah Jane Houston Scholarships *(Undergraduate/Scholarship)* [3414]

Huenefeld/Denton Scholarships *(Undergraduate/Scholarship)* [3415]

Hazel D. Isbell Fellowships *(Graduate/Fellowship)* [3376]

Jackman Scholarships *(Undergraduate/Scholarship)* [7289]

Jacque Placette Chapman Master's Fellowships *(Graduate/Fellowship)* [6918]

Elise Reed Jenkins Memorial Scholarships - Gamma Psi *(Undergraduate/Scholarship)* [8176]

Martha Combs Jenkins Scholarships *(Undergraduate/Scholarship)* [7290]

Kappa Chapter Centennial Scholarships *(Undergraduate/Scholarship)* [3377]

Kappa Kappa Gamma Graduate Scholarships *(Graduate/Scholarship)* [5193]

Kappa Kappa Gamma Undergraduate Scholarships *(Undergraduate/Scholarship)* [5194]

Kappa Omicron Nu National Alumni Fellowships *(Graduate/Fellowship)* [5196]

Kappa Omicron Nu Undergraduate Scholarships *(Undergraduate/Scholarship)* [5197]

Kappa Zeta Scholarships *(Undergraduate/Scholarship)* [8177]

Luella Akins Key Scholarships *(Undergraduate/Scholarship)* [3378]

Debbie Khalil Memorial Scholarships *(Graduate, Undergraduate/Scholarship)* [7268]

Treva C. Kintner Scholarships *(Undergraduate/Scholarship)* [7291]

Betsy B. and Garold A. Leach Scholarships for Museum Studies *(Undergraduate/Scholarship)* [3416]

LeaderShape Institute Scholarships *(Undergraduate/Grant)* [5202]

V.A. Leonard Scholarships *(Graduate, Undergraduate/Scholarship)* [357]

LIT Scholarships *(Graduate, Undergraduate/Scholarship)* [5328]

Elsa Ludeke Graduate Scholarships *(Graduate/Scholarship)* [3417]

Eileen C. Maddex Fellowships *(Graduate/Fellowship)* [5198]

Sarah Shinn Marshall Scholarships *(Undergraduate/Scholarship)* [3379]

Martin Sisters Scholarships *(Undergraduate/Scholarship)* [3380]

Nancy B. Woolridge McGee Graduate Fellowships *(Graduate/Fellowship)* [9806]

John L. and Eleanore I. Mckinley Scholarships *(Undergraduate/Scholarship)* [3418]

James H. McLaughlin Scholarships *(Undergraduate/Scholarship)* [6740]

Joan Reagin McNeill Scholarships - Alpha Theta *(Undergraduate/Scholarship)* [8178]

Joan Reagin McNeill Scholarships - Theta Phi *(Undergraduate/Scholarship)* [8179]

Mihaly Russin Scholarship Awards *(Graduate/Scholarship)* [7837]

Thomas S. Morgan Memorial Scholarships *(Graduate, Master's/Scholarship)* [7241]

MPower Scholarships *(Graduate, Undergraduate/Scholarship)* [7269]

Virginia Nicklas Scholarships *(Undergraduate/Scholarship)* [3382]

Evelyn S. Nish Scholarships *(Undergraduate/Scholarship)* [8180]

Northwestern Mutual Financial Network Scholarships *(Graduate, Undergraduate/Scholarship)* [7270]

Order of Omega Doctoral Fellowships *(Doctorate, Graduate/Fellowship)* [6919]

Cissy McDaniel Parker Scholarships *(Undergraduate/Scholarship)* [3384]

Gail Patrick Charitable Trust Scholarships *(Undergraduate/Scholarship)* [3420]

Zoe Gore Perrin Scholarships *(Undergraduate/Scholarship)* [3385]

Phi Alpha Theta Doctoral Scholarships *(Doctorate/Scholarship)* [7243]

Phi Eta Sigma Distinguished Member Scholarships *(Graduate or Professional)* *(Graduate, Professional development/Scholarship)* [7255]

Phi Eta Sigma Distinguished Member Scholarships (Undergraduate) *(Undergraduate/Scholarship)* [7256]

Phi Eta Sigma Undergraduate Scholarship Awards *(Undergraduate/Scholarship)* [7257]

Phi Kappa Phi Fellowships *(Graduate, Undergraduate/Fellowship)* [7259]

Phi Kappa Sigma Need-Based Scholarships *(Undergraduate/Scholarship)* [7261]

Phi Kappa Sigma Participation-Based Scholarships *(Undergraduate/Scholarship)* [7262]

Phi Sigma Epsilon Past National President Scholarships *(Graduate, Undergraduate/Scholarship)* [7271]

Phi Theta Kappa Scholarships *(Undergraduate/Scholarship)* [4752]

Phi Upsilon Omicron Candle Fellowships *(Graduate/Fellowship)* [7292]

Phi Upsilon Omicron Challenge Scholarships *(Undergraduate/Scholarship)* [7293]

Phi Upsilon Omicron Diamond Anniversary Fellowships *(Graduate/Fellowship)* [7294]

Phi Upsilon Omicron Founders Fellowships *(Graduate/Fellowship)* [7295]

Phi Upsilon Omicron Golden Anniversary Scholarships *(Undergraduate/Scholarship)* [7296]

Phi Upsilon Omicron Past Presidents Scholarships *(Undergraduate/Scholarship)* [7297]

Phi Upsilon Omicron Presidents Research Fellowships *(Graduate/Fellowship)* [7298]

Pi Gamma Mu Scholarships *(Graduate/Scholarship)* [7330]

John Pine Memorial Scholarships *(Doctorate/Scholarship)* [7244]

Pryor Graduate Fellowships *(Graduate/Fellowship)* [345]

Cheryl White Pryor Memorial Scholarships *(Undergraduate/Scholarship)* [3386]

Public Agency Training Council Criminal Justice Scholarships *(Undergraduate/Scholarship)* [358]

Rho Chi, AFPE First Year Graduate Fellowships *(Doctorate, Graduate/Fellowship)* [7781]

Rho Chi Society Clinical Research Scholarships *(Postdoctorate/Scholarship)* [7782]

Susan E. Riley Scholarships *(Undergraduate/Scholarship)* [3387]

Jean Wiggin Roach Scholarships *(Undergraduate/Scholarship)* [3388]

Nell Bryant Robinson Scholarships *(Undergraduate/Scholarship)* [7299]

Mary Louise Roller Pan-Hellenic Scholarships *(Undergraduate/Scholarship)* [6741]

Dorothy Worden Ronken Scholarships *(Graduate/Scholarship)* [3421]

Lucile Rust Scholarships *(Undergraduate/Scholarship)* [7300]

Jeanne Graves Ryland Scholarships *(Undergraduate/Scholarship)* [3389]

Julie Anne Sadlier Memorial Scholarships *(Undergraduate/Scholarship)* [3390]

Virginia Hartford Saharov Memorial Scholarships *(Undergraduate/Scholarship)* [3391]

Saints Cyril and Methodius Scholarships *(Undergraduate/Scholarship)* [7838]

Margaret Jerome Sampson Scholarships *(Undergraduate/Scholarship)* [7301]

Edith Scandlyn/Sammie Lynn Scandlyn Puett Memorial Scholarships *(Undergraduate/Scholarship)* [3392]

Mary Turnbull Schacht Memorial Scholarships *(Undergraduate/Scholarship)* [8181]

Lillian P. Schoephoerster Scholarships *(Undergraduate/Scholarship)* [7302]

Detective Cheryl Seiden Memorial Scholarships *(Undergraduate/Scholarship)* [359]

Regina B. Shearn Scholarships *(Graduate, Undergraduate/Scholarship)* [360]

Sigma Kappa Foundation Alumnae Continuing Education Scholarships *(Undergraduate/Scholarship)* [8182]

Sigma Kappa Foundation Founders' Scholarships *(Undergraduate/Scholarship)* [8184]

Sigma Kappa Foundation Gerontology Scholarships *(Undergraduate/Scholarship)* [8185]

Sigma Kappa Foundation Michigan Scholarships *(Undergraduate/Scholarship)* [8186]

Helen D. Snow Memorial Scholarships *(Undergraduate/Scholarship)* [7252]

Sons of Union Veterans of the Civil War Scholarships *(Undergraduate/Scholarship)* [8534]

Elin J. Stene/Xi Scholarships *(Undergraduate/Scholarship)* [8187]

Sutherland/Purdy Scholarships *(Undergraduate/Scholarship)* [7303]

Lorraine E. Swain Scholarships *(Undergraduate/Scholarship)* [8188]

Theta Tau Scholarships *(Undergraduate/Scholarship)* [8189]

Barber Owen Thomas Scholarships *(Undergraduate/Scholarship)* [8190]

Thornberg/Havens Scholarships *(Undergraduate/Scholarship)* [3423]

Richard Cecil Todd and Clauda Pennock Todd Tripod Scholarships *(Graduate, Undergraduate/Scholarship)* [7276]

Jo Anne J. Trow Scholarships *(Undergraduate/Scholarship)* [6020]

Graydon A. Tunstall Undergraduate Student Scholarships (Undergraduate/Scholarship) [7245]
UPE/ACM Scholarship Awards (Graduate, Undergraduate/Award) [9391]
UPE Scholarship Awards (Graduate, Undergraduate/Award) [9392]
Valpak Scholarships (Graduate, Undergraduate/Scholarship) [7272]
Vector Marketing Scholarships (Graduate, Undergraduate/Scholarship) [7273]
Whan Memorial Scholarships (Graduate, Undergraduate/Scholarship) [7274]
Donna Axum Whitworth Scholarships (Undergraduate/Scholarship) [3393]
Alice Hersey Wick Scholarships (Undergraduate/Scholarship) [8192]
Andrea Will Memorial Scholarships (Undergraduate/Scholarship) [8193]
William J. Brennan Graduate Assistant Fellowships (Graduate/Fellowship) [6920]
Rolla F. Wood Graduate Scholarships (Graduate/Scholarship) [7277]
Donnell B. Young Scholarships (Undergraduate/Scholarship) [286]
Youth Partners Accessing Capital (PAC) (Graduate, Undergraduate/Scholarship) [354]
A.F. Zimmerman Scholarships (Graduate, Master's/Scholarship) [7246]

Hispanic American

AAA Minority Dissertation Fellowship Program (Doctorate/Fellowship) [406]
AAAA Operation Jumpstart III Scholarships (Graduate/Scholarship) [433]
AACN Minority Nurse Faculty Scholarships (Graduate/Scholarship) [457]
AAMFT Minority Fellowships (Doctorate, Graduate/Fellowship) [511]
ABA Legal Opportunity Scholarship Funds (Undergraduate/Scholarship) [4566]
Acoustical Society of America Minority Fellowships (Graduate/Fellowship) [39]
Affirmative Action Mini Grants and Student Scholarships (All/Grant) [25]
AHETEMS General Scholarships (Graduate, Undergraduate/Scholarship) [55]
AHETEMS Professional Scholarships (Graduate/Scholarship) [56]
Air Products and Chemicals, Inc. Scholarships (Undergraduate/Scholarship) [1793]
ALPFA Scholarship Programs (Postgraduate, Undergraduate/Scholarship) [1824]
AMA Foundation Minority Scholars Awards (Undergraduate/Scholarship) [922]
American GI Forum of San Jose Scholarships (Undergraduate/Scholarship) [780]
American Society for Microbiology International Fellowships for Latin America and the Caribbean (Postdoctorate/Fellowship) [1297]
AMS/Industry Minority Scholarships (Undergraduate/Scholarship) [931]
APS Scholarships for Minority Undergraduate Physics Majors (Undergraduate/Scholarship) [6485]
APTA Minority Scholarships - Faculty Development Scholarships (Postdoctorate/Scholarship) [999]
APTA Minority Scholarships - Physical Therapist Assistant Students (All/Scholarship) [1000]
APTA Minority Scholarships - Physical Therapist Students (All/Scholarship) [1001]
Frank G. Araujo Memorial Scholarships (Undergraduate/Scholarship) [7623]
Artistic Scholarship Awards (Undergraduate, Vocational/Occupational/Scholarship) [2023]
ASC Graduate Fellowships for Ethnic Minorities (Doctorate, Graduate/Fellowship) [1219]
AWG Minority Scholarships (Undergraduate/Scholarship) [1900]
Michael Baker Inc. Scholarships for Diversity in Engineering (Undergraduate/Scholarship) [1794]
Barbri Scholarships for Bar Preparation (Undergraduate/Scholarship) [4561]

BECA Foundation-CUSM Scholarships (Undergraduate/Scholarship) [2039]
Bill Bernbach Diversity Scholarships (Undergraduate/Scholarship) [434]
Thomas M. Blake Memorial Scholarships (Undergraduate/Scholarship) [3230]
Maria Gonzales Borrero Scholarships (Undergraduate/Scholarship) [4414]
Leon Bradley Scholarships (Undergraduate/Scholarship) [548]
Bridging the GAP for Hispanic Success Awards (Undergraduate/Scholarship) [4545]
BSF General Scholarship Awards (Undergraduate, Vocational/Occupational/Scholarship) [2024]
The California Endowment and AACN Minority Nurse Faculty Scholarships (Graduate/Scholarship) [459]
CANFIT Scholarships (Graduate, Undergraduate/Scholarship) [2228]
Chrysler Foundation Scholarship Awards (Undergraduate/Scholarship) [4546]
Citi/TELACU Scholarships (Undergraduate/Scholarship) [8820]
Columbus Citizens Foundation High School Scholarships (High School/Scholarship) [3013]
Congressional Hispanic Caucus Institute Graduate and Young Professional Fellowships (Doctorate, Graduate/Fellowship) [3224]
Congressional Hispanic Caucus Institute Public Policy Fellowships (Graduate/Fellowship) [3225]
Congressional Hispanic Caucus Institute Scholarships (Community College, Graduate, Undergraduate/Scholarship) [3226]
Connecticut Association of Latinos in Higher Education Scholarships (Undergraduate/Scholarship) [4419]
Lydia Cruz and Sandra Maria Ramos Scholarships (Undergraduate/Scholarship) [3404]
Dallas Hispanic Bar Association Scholarships (Undergraduate/Scholarship) [3337]
Davis Family Scholarships (Undergraduate/Scholarship) [7923]
Ruth DeMoss Scholarships (Undergraduate/Scholarship) [7924]
William Diaz Fellowships (Professional development/Fellowship) [6729]
DRI Law Student Diversity Scholarships (Undergraduate/Scholarship) [2144]
FAIC Latin American and Caribbean Scholars Program (Professional development/Scholarship) [851]
Florida Education Fund McKnight Doctoral Fellowships (Graduate/Fellowship) [3822]
Ford Motor Company Scholarship Program (Undergraduate/Scholarship) [4568]
Foundation of American Institute for Conservation Lecture Grants (Professional development/Grant) [852]
Franchise Law Diversity Scholarship Awards (Undergraduate/Scholarship) [4940]
Aracelis Francis Minority Scholarships in Gerontology (Master's/Scholarship) [1787]
John Hope Franklin Dissertation Fellowships (Doctorate/Fellowship) [990]
Fraser Stryker Diversity Scholarships (Undergraduate/Scholarship) [3998]
The Gates Millennium Scholars (Undergraduate/Scholarship) [4569]
Gerber Fellowships in Pediatric Nutrition (Undergraduate/Fellowship) [6401]
Glendale Latino Association Scholarships (High School, Undergraduate/Scholarship) [4161]
Google Hispanic College Fund Scholarships (Graduate, Undergraduate/Scholarship) [4195]
Father Rutilio Grande Scholarships (Graduate, Undergraduate/Scholarship) [7893]
Great Minds in STEM Scholarships (Graduate, Undergraduate/Scholarship) [4331]
HACU/Wal-Mart Achievers Scholarships (Undergraduate/Scholarship) [4547]
The Richard D. Hailey AAJ Law Student Scholarships (Undergraduate/Scholarship) [4581]
HDR Engineering, Inc. Scholarships for Diversity in Engineering (Undergraduate/Scholarship) [1796]

Hispanic Association of Colleges and Universities Scholarships (Undergraduate/Scholarship) [4548]
Hispanic Metropolitan Chamber Scholarships (Graduate, Undergraduate/Scholarship) [4564]
Hispanic Scholarship Fund College Scholarship Program (HSF) (Graduate, Undergraduate/Scholarship) [4570]
HSBC-North America Scholarship Program (Undergraduate/Scholarship) [4571]
HSF/Atrisco Heritage Foundation Scholarship Program (Graduate, Undergraduate/Scholarship) [4572]
HSF/Citi Fellows Program (Undergraduate/Scholarship) [4573]
HSF/General Motors Scholarship Program (Undergraduate/Scholarship) [4574]
HSF/IDT Hope High School Scholarship Program (Undergraduate/Scholarship) [4575]
HSF/Nissan Community College Transfer Scholarship Program (Undergraduate/Scholarship) [4576]
HSF/Wal-Mart Stores Inc. Scholarship Program (Graduate, Undergraduate/Scholarship) [4577]
The Hyatt Hotels Fund For Minority Lodging Management Students (Undergraduate/Scholarship) [798]
Inter American Press Association Scholarships (Undergraduate/Scholarship) [4846]
Italian Language Scholarships (Undergraduate/Scholarship) [6922]
Kaplan Scholarships (Undergraduate/Scholarship) [4562]
W.K. Kellogg Foundation Doctoral Fellowships in Health Policy (Professional development/Fellowship) [6402]
KPMG Foundation Minority Accounting Doctoral Scholarships (Postdoctorate/Scholarship) [5304]
La Voz Latina Scholarships (Undergraduate/Scholarship) [3157]
The Lagrant Foundation - Graduate Students Scholarships (Graduate/Scholarship) [5315]
The Lagrant Foundation - Undergraduate Students Scholarships (Undergraduate/Scholarship) [5316]
Latin American Educational Foundation Scholarships (Undergraduate, Vocational/Occupational/Scholarship) [5356]
Latinos for Dental Careers Scholarships (All/Scholarship) [2676]
Lewis-Clark State College/American Chemical Society Scholars Program (Undergraduate/Scholarship) [5440]
LITA and LSSI Minority Scholarships (Graduate/Scholarship) [5485]
LITA/OCLC Minority Scholarships (Graduate/Scholarship) [5486]
LLN Scholarships (Community College/Scholarship) [5358]
LULAC GM Scholarships (Graduate, High School, Undergraduate, Vocational/Occupational/Award) [5387]
LULAC National Scholarship Fund (Graduate, High School, Undergraduate, Vocational/Occupational/Scholarship) [5388]
Marathon Oil Corporation College Scholarship Program (Graduate, Undergraduate/Scholarship) [4578]
Howard Mayer Brown Fellowships (Graduate/Fellowship) [941]
Ronald McDonald House Charities of Hispanic Heritage (Undergraduate/Scholarship) [5701]
McNamara Family Creative Arts Project Grants (Graduate, Undergraduate/Grant) [4579]
Medical Library Association Scholarships for Minority Students (Graduate/Scholarship) [5745]
Rixio Medina and Associates Hispanics in Safety Scholarships (Graduate, Undergraduate/Scholarship) [1348]
Mexican American Legal Defense and Educational Fund Law School Scholarships (Undergraduate/Scholarship) [5806]
MillerCoors Engineering and Sciences Scholarships (Undergraduate/Scholarship) [47]

MillerCoors National Scholarships *(Undergraduate/Scholarship)* [48]

Minorities in Government Finance Scholarships *(Graduate, Undergraduate/Scholarship)* [4199]

Minority Scholarship Awards for College Students *(Undergraduate/Scholarship)* [761]

Minority Student Pre-Doctoral Fellowship Program *(Doctorate, Graduate/Fellowship)* [761]

Minority Teachers of Illinois Scholarships (MTI) *(Undergraduate/Scholarship)* [4701]

MLA/NLM Spectrum Scholarship Program *(Undergraduate/Scholarship)* [5746]

Archie Motley Memorial Scholarships for Minority Students *(Graduate/Scholarship)* [5856]

Multicultural Advertising Intern Program *(Graduate, Undergraduate/Internship)* [435]

National Association of Campus Activities Multicultural Scholarship Programs *(Undergraduate/Scholarship)* [6053]

National Association of Multicultural Engineering Program Advocates Beginning Freshmen Awards (NAMEPA) *(Undergraduate/Scholarship)* [6088]

National Association of Multicultural Engineering Program Advocates Transfer Engineering Student Awards (NAMEPA) *(Undergraduate/Scholarship)* [6089]

National Medical Fellowships Need-Based Scholarships *(Undergraduate/Scholarship)* [6403]

National Organization of Italian-American Women Scholarships *(All/Scholarship)* [6425]

NHFA Scholarships *(Graduate/Scholarship)* [6340]

NSHMBA Scholarships *(Graduate/Scholarship)* [6508]

Ohio Newspaper Association Minority Scholarships *(Undergraduate/Scholarship)* [6858]

Order Sons of Italy Foundation General Scholarships *(Graduate, Undergraduate/Scholarship)* [6923]

Casilda Pagan Educational/Vocational Scholarships *(Graduate, Undergraduate/Scholarship)* [4608]

Peierls Rising Star Scholarship Program *(Undergraduate/Scholarship)* [4580]

Rudy Perez Songwriting Scholarships *(Undergraduate/Scholarship)* [1214]

Portuguese American Police Association Scholarships *(Undergraduate/Scholarship)* [7380]

Judith McManus Price Scholarships *(Graduate, Undergraduate/Scholarship)* [1012]

Miguel Pro Scholarships *(Undergraduate/Scholarship)* [9774]

PRSSA Multicultural Affairs Scholarships *(Undergraduate/Scholarship)* [7541]

Rosa Quezada Memorial Education Scholarships *(Undergraduate/Scholarship)* [3231]

Leo S. Rowe Pan American Fund *(Graduate, Undergraduate/Loan)* [6967]

Lucille and Edward R. Roybal Foundation Public Health Scholarships *(Graduate, Undergraduate/Scholarship)* [7827]

SALEF Health Career Scholarships *(Graduate, Undergraduate/Scholarship)* [7894]

Henry Salvatori Scholarships *(Undergraduate/Scholarship)* [6924]

Leo and Trinidad Sanchez Scholarships *(Undergraduate/Scholarship)* [8208]

NASCAR/Wendell Scott Awards *(Graduate, Undergraduate/Scholarship)* [4550]

Carl A. Scott Book Scholarships *(Undergraduate/Scholarship)* [3284]

SHPE Foundation General Scholarships *(High School, Undergraduate, Graduate/Scholarship)* [8132]

John Soto Scholarships *(Undergraduate/Scholarship)* [3232]

David Stevenson Fellowships *(Doctorate, Graduate, Professional development/Fellowship)* [6730]

Summer Research Diversity Fellowships in Law and Social Science *(Undergraduate/Fellowship)* [579]

Robert Toigo Foundation Fellowships *(Master's/Fellowship)* [8911]

Toyota High School Scholarship Program *(Undergraduate/Scholarship)* [4581]

Toyota/TELACU Scholarships *(Undergraduate/Scholarship)* [8822]

TUUT HSF College Scholarship Program *(Undergraduate/Scholarship)* [4582]

Two Nineteen Scholarships *(Community College, Graduate, Undergraduate/Scholarship)* [7895]

United Health Foundation National Association of Hispanic Nurses Scholarships *(Graduate, Undergraduate/Scholarship)* [6084]

University Alliance HSF/UGA College Scholarship Program *(Undergraduate/Scholarship)* [4583]

University of Wisconsin-Madison Hispanic/Latino Alumni Scholarships *(Undergraduate/Scholarship)* [9377]

Valley Alliance of Mentors for Opportunities and Scholarship Program (VAMOS) *(Undergraduate/Scholarship)* [4584]

Marta Vallin Memorial Scholarships *(Undergraduate/Scholarship)* [3233]

Valuing Diversity PhD Scholarships *(Doctorate/Scholarship)* [920]

Wachovia Scholars Program *(Undergraduate/Scholarship)* [4551]

Wachovia/TELACU Excellence in Teaching Scholarships *(Undergraduate/Scholarship)* [8823]

Wells Fargo Scholarship Program *(Graduate, Undergraduate/Scholarship)* [4585]

Western Governors University Scholarship Program *(Undergraduate/Scholarship)* [4586]

Woodrow Wilson-Rockefeller Brothers Fund Fellowships for Aspiring Teachers of Color *(Graduate/Fellowship)* [9621]

Xerox Technical Minority Scholarships *(Graduate, Undergraduate/Scholarship)* [9787]

Military

AAAA Scholarship Program *(Undergraduate/Scholarship)* [1611]

ACHE/American Legion Auxiliary Scholarships *(Undergraduate/Scholarship)* [155]

ACHE/American Legion Scholarships *(Undergraduate/Scholarship)* [156]

Alabama Gi Dependents Educational Benefit Program *(Undergraduate/Scholarship)* [162]

Alabama National Guard Educational Assistance Program *(Undergraduate/Scholarship)* [163]

The American Legion Legacy Scholarships *(Undergraduate/Scholarship)* [894]

Anchor Scholarship Foundation *(Undergraduate/Scholarship)* [8780]

Lt. General Douglas D. Buchholz Memorial Scholarships *(Undergraduate/Scholarship)* [1557]

Dr. Aurelio M. Caccomo Family Foundation Memorial Scholarships *(Undergraduate/Scholarship)* [1467]

Commander Ronald J. Cantin Scholarships *(Undergraduate/Scholarship)* [2921]

Commander Daniel J. Christovich Scholarship Fund *(Undergraduate/Scholarship)* [2922]

Coast Guard Foundation Enlisted Education Grants *(All/Grant)* [2923]

Coast Guard Foundation Scholarships *(Undergraduate/Scholarship)* [2924]

LaRue A. Ditmore Music Scholarships *(Undergraduate/Scholarship)* [9706]

Dolphin Scholarships *(Undergraduate/Scholarship)* [3469]

Sergeant Major Douglas R. Drum Memorial Scholarship Fund *(Undergraduate/Scholarship)* [936]

The Fallen Heroes Scholarships *(Undergraduate/Scholarship)* [2925]

FEEA-NTEU Scholarships *(Graduate, Postgraduate, Undergraduate/Scholarship)* [3725]

Freedom Alliance Scholarships *(Undergraduate/Scholarship)* [4004]

Lily H. Gridley Memorial Scholarships *(Undergraduate/Scholarship)* [9707]

Hope for the Warriors Spouses Scholarships *(Graduate, Master's, Undergraduate, Vocational/Occupational/Scholarship)* [4599]

Keiser College Coast Guard Scholarships *(Undergraduate/Scholarship)* [2927]

Khaki University and Y.M.C.A. Memorial Scholarships *(Undergraduate/Scholarship)* [9334]

First Lieutenant Scott McClean Love Memorial Scholarship - Children of Soldiers *(Undergraduate, Vocational/Occupational/Scholarship)* [1615]

First Lieutenant Scott McClean Love Memorial Scholarship - Spouses of Soldiers *(Undergraduate, Vocational/Occupational/Scholarship)* [1616]

Maine Vietnam Veterans Scholarships *(All/Scholarship)* [5586]

Marine Corps Engineer Association Assistance Fund *(Graduate, High School, Undergraduate/Scholarship)* [5635]

Marine Corps League National Scholarships *(Undergraduate/Scholarship)* [5637]

Military Order of the Purple Heart Foundation Scholarships *(Undergraduate/Scholarship)* [5455]

MOAA American Patriot Scholarships *(Undergraduate/Scholarship)* [5874]

MOAA Base/Post Scholarships *(Undergraduate/Scholarship)* [5875]

North Carolina Heroes Fund Scholarships *(All/Scholarship)* [6767]

Captain Jennifer Shafer Odom Memorial Scholarships - Children of Soldiers *(Undergraduate, Vocational/Occupational/Scholarship)* [1617]

Captain Jennifer Shafer Odom Memorial Scholarships - Spouses of Soldiers *(Undergraduate, Vocational/Occupational/Scholarship)* [1618]

Ohio War Orphan Scholarships *(Undergraduate/Scholarship)* [9773]

Ontario Hockey Association War Memorial Scholarships *(Undergraduate/Scholarship)* [9341]

General John Paul Ratay Educational Grants *(Undergraduate/Grant)* [5876]

Paul Resnick and Bruce Donnelly Scholarships *(Undergraduate/Scholarship)* [2928]

Samsung American Legion Scholarships *(Undergraduate/Scholarship)* [897]

Lewis L. Seaman Junior Enlisted Awards for Outstanding Operational Support *(Professional development/Award)* [1462]

Sentinels of Freedom "Life Scholarships" *(All/Scholarship)* [8090]

Arnold Sobel Scholarships *(Undergraduate/Scholarship)* [2929]

ThanksUSA Scholarships *(Undergraduate, Vocational/Occupational/Scholarship)* [8888]

The Vander Putten Family Scholarships *(All/Scholarship)* [2930]

Veterans of Enduring Freedom (Afghanistan) and Iraqi Freedom Scholarships *(Undergraduate/Scholarship)* [1565]

Ethyl and Armin Wiebke Memorial Scholarships *(Undergraduate/Scholarship)* [9708]

WMA Memorial Scholarships *(Undergraduate/Scholarship)* [9709]

Women's Overseas and Service League Scholarships for Women *(Undergraduate/Scholarship)* [9733]

Minority

AACN Minority Nurse Faculty Scholarships *(Graduate/Scholarship)* [457]

AAPM Minority Undergraduate Summer Experience Fellowships (MUSE) *(Undergraduate/Fellowship)* [529]

Dr. Anderson Abbott Awards *(Undergraduate/Scholarship)* [9320]

Aboriginal Traditional Arts Project Grants *(Professional development/Grant)* [215]

Acoustical Society of America Minority Fellowships *(Graduate/Fellowship)* [39]

Adler Pollock & Sheehan Diversity Scholarships *(Undergraduate/Scholarship)* [50]

AERA Minority Fellowship Program in Education Research *(Postdoctorate/Fellowship)* [716]

AGI Minority Participation Program Geoscience Student Scholarships (AGI-MPP) *(Graduate, Undergraduate/Scholarship)* [778]

Alliance of Black Culinarians Scholarships *(Undergraduate/Scholarship)* [7465]

American Association of Blacks in Energy Scholarships *(Undergraduate/Scholarship)* [441]

American Association for Cancer Research Minority Scholar Awards (Graduate/Award) [450]

American Association of University Women Career Development Grants (Postgraduate/Grant) [10]

American Association of University Women Master's and First Professional Awards (Professional development/Award) [12]

American Association of University Women Selected Professions Fellowships (Professional development/Fellowship) [13]

American Dental Association Minority Dental Student Scholarships (Undergraduate/Scholarship) [705]

American Philological Association Minority Student Summer Fellowships (Undergraduate/Fellowship) [986]

American Society for Environmental History Minority Travel Grants (Graduate, Professional development/Grant) [1245]

William G. Anderson, DO, Minority Scholarships (Undergraduate/Scholarship) [969]

APA Minority Fellowships Program (Postdoctorate/Fellowship) [1646]

APS/NIDDK Minority Travel Fellowship Awards (Graduate, Postdoctorate/Fellowship) [1004]

Judge Sidney M. Aronovitz Memorial Scholarships (High School, Undergraduate/Scholarship) [3314]

ASA Minority Fellowship Program (Doctorate, Master's/Fellowship) [1377]

ASHFA Scholarships for Minority Students (Graduate/Scholarship) [1386]

ASM Undergraduate Research Capstone Program (Undergraduate/Fellowship) [1300]

ASPH/CDC/PRC Minority Health Fellowships (Doctorate/Fellowship) [1862]

Bay Area Minority Law Student Scholarships (Graduate, Undergraduate/Scholarship) [2019]

BCA Ethnic Minority Postgraduate Scholarships for Careers in Athletics (Postgraduate/Scholarship) [2135]

Dennis J. Beck Memorial Scholarships (Undergraduate, Vocational/Occupational/Scholarship) [5091]

Lucie and Thornton Blackburn Scholarships (Undergraduate/Scholarship) [2363]

Corris Boyd Scholarships (Master's/Scholarship) [1891]

Leon Bradley Scholarships (Undergraduate/Scholarship) [548]

Mary Ann Brichta Scholarships (Undergraduate/Scholarship) [9350]

Cathy L. Brock Memorial Scholarships (Graduate/Scholarship) [4787]

George M. Brooker Collegiate Scholarships for Minorities (Graduate, Postgraduate, Undergraduate/Scholarship) [4818]

Patricia Buchanan Memorial Scholarships (Undergraduate/Scholarship) [9351]

Peter Butler III - Rose Fortune Scholarship Program (Undergraduate/Scholarship) [1716]

BWEL Law Student Scholarships (Undergraduate/Scholarship) [2142]

The California Endowment and AACN Minority Nurse Faculty Scholarships (Graduate/Scholarship) [459]

CBC Spouses Flexible Education Scholarships (Graduate, Master's, Undergraduate/Scholarship) [3217]

Justice Robert L. Clifford Fellowships (All/Fellowship) [5930]

Holly A. Cornell Scholarships (Graduate/Scholarship) [1417]

Council on Social Work Education Minority Fellowship Programs (Postdoctorate/Fellowship) [3282]

CPA-F Minority Scholarships (Graduate/Scholarship) [2267]

DBPR Division of CPA - BOA Minority Scholarships (Undergraduate/Scholarship) [3430]

Albert and Jane Dewey Scholarships (Undergraduate/Scholarship) [4426]

Diversified Investment Advisors Leaders in Healthcare Scholarships (Graduate/Scholarship) [4788]

Diversity Executive Leadership Program Scholarships (Professional development/Scholarship) [1184]

Dow Chemical Company Fellowships (Graduate/Fellowship) [6427]

DRI Law Student Diversity Scholarships (Undergraduate/Scholarship) [2144]

EFWA Moss Adams Foundation Scholarships (Graduate, Undergraduate/Scholarship) [3598]

E.I. DuPont Fellowships (Graduate/Fellowship) [6428]

Engineering Diversity Affairs Scholarships (All/Scholarship) [9353]

Ethnic Minority and Women's Enhancement Postgraduate Scholarships (Graduate/Scholarship) [6193]

Fine Arts Association Minority Scholarships (Undergraduate/Scholarship) [3749]

Fredrikson and Byron Foundation Minority Scholarships (Undergraduate/Scholarship) [4002]

Greenlining Institute Fellowships (Graduate/Fellowship) [4349]

Dick and Pat Hazel Minority Scholarships (Professional development/Scholarship) [3061]

Melvin Henderson-Rubio Scholarships (Undergraduate/Scholarship) [9605]

JLTLA Scholarships (Undergraduate/Scholarship) [8981]

MCCA Lloyd M. Johnson, Jr. Scholarships (Undergraduate/Scholarship) [5904]

Sylvia Taylor Johnson Minority Fellowships in Educational Measurement (Doctorate/Fellowship) [3611]

Kegler Brown Minority Merit Scholarships (Undergraduate/Scholarship) [5229]

Law Student Diversity Scholarships (Undergraduate/Scholarship) [5814]

Lawton Minority Retention Grants (Undergraduate/Scholarship) [9362]

League of Latin American Citizens General Electric Scholarships (Undergraduate, Vocational/Occupational/Scholarship) [5386]

LIN Media Minority Scholarships and Training Program (Undergraduate/Scholarship) [5501]

Louisville Institute First Book Grants for Minority Scholars (Doctorate/Grant) [5528]

Master's Scholarships Program (MSP) (Graduate, Master's/Scholarship) [8081]

Howard Mayer Brown Fellowships (Graduate/Fellowship) [941]

McClatchy Scholarships (Undergraduate/Scholarship) [8552]

McJulien Minority Graduate Scholarships (Graduate/Scholarship) [1764]

John McLendon Memorial Minority Postgraduate Scholarships (Postdoctorate/Scholarship) [6062]

Medical Library Association Scholarships for Minority Students (Graduate/Scholarship) [5745]

Dolphus E. Milligan Graduate Fellowships (Graduate/Fellowship) [6429]

Minority Leadership Development Awards (Graduate/Award) [503]

Minority Medical Student Fellowships in HIV Psychiatry (Undergraduate/Fellowship) [1025]

Minority Scholarship Awards for Incoming College Freshmen (Undergraduate/Scholarship) [848]

John P. and Tashia F. Morgridge Scholarships (Undergraduate/Scholarship) [9364]

James B. Morris Scholarships (Undergraduate/Scholarship) [5935]

NASP-ERT Minority Scholarships for Graduate Training in School Psychology (Graduate/Scholarship) [6113]

National Association of Campus Activities Multicultural Scholarship Programs (Undergraduate/Scholarship) [6053]

National Co-op Scholarship Program (Undergraduate/Scholarship) [9750]

National GEM Consortium - MS Engineering Fellowships (Graduate/Fellowship) [6305]

National GEM Consortium - PhD Engineering Fellowships (Doctorate, Graduate/Fellowship) [6306]

National GEM Consortium - PhD Science Fellowships (Doctorate, Graduate/Fellowship) [6307]

National Recreation and Park Association Diversity Scholarships (Undergraduate/Scholarship) [6459]

NBMBAA Graduate Scholarships Program (Graduate/Scholarship) [6152]

NBMBAA PhD Fellowship Program (Doctorate/Fellowship) [6153]

New Jersey Psychological Association Scholarships for Minority Graduate Students (Postgraduate/Scholarship) [6655]

NOBCChE Procter and Gamble Fellowships (Graduate/Fellowship) [6430]

NUF Fellowships (Graduate, Postgraduate, Professional development/Fellowship) [6553]

Ohio Newspaper Association Minority Scholarships (Undergraduate/Scholarship) [6858]

Ohio Space Grant Consortium Special Minority Fellowships (Doctorate, Graduate/Fellowship) [6865]

Outlaw Student's Minority Scholarships (Undergraduate/Scholarship) [8753]

Outstanding Minority Accounting Student Scholarships (All/Scholarship) [6753]

Pathways to Success Scholarships (Undergraduate/Scholarship) [3954]

Leonard M. Perryman Communications Scholarships for Ethnic Minority Students (Undergraduate/Scholarship) [9013]

Pfizer Minority Medical Journalism Scholarships (Postgraduate/Scholarship) [9298]

Justice Stewart G. Pollock Fellowships (All/Fellowship) [5931]

Polsinelli Diversity Scholarships (Undergraduate/Scholarship) [9490]

Porter Physiology Development Fellowship Awards (Doctorate/Fellowship) [1005]

Powers-Knapp Scholarships (Undergraduate/Scholarship) [9367]

Lendon N. Pridgen, GlaxoSmithKline - NOBCChE Fellowships (Graduate/Fellowship) [6431]

Elliott C. Roberts Scholarships (Graduate/Scholarship) [4789]

Jackie Robinson Foundation Minority Scholarships (Undergraduate/Scholarship) [822]

Jackie Robinson Scholarships (Undergraduate/Scholarship) [7808]

Edward S. Roth Manufacturing Engineering Scholarships (Graduate, Undergraduate/Scholarship) [8396]

Royce-Osborn Minority Scholarship Program (Undergraduate/Scholarship) [1326]

William Rucker Greenwood Scholarships (Graduate, Undergraduate/Scholarship) [1904]

Scholarships for Visible Minorities (Undergraduate/Scholarship) [6551]

School of Education Scholarships for Students from Underrepresented Groups (Undergraduate/Scholarship) [9369]

Eastman Kodak Dr. Theophilus Sorrell Fellowships (Graduate/Fellowship) [6432]

SREB-State Doctoral Scholarships (Doctorate, Graduate/Scholarship) [8585]

AALL & Thomson West - George A. Strait Minority Scholarship Endowments (Postgraduate/Scholarship) [505]

Surety Industry Scholarship Program for Minority Students (Undergraduate/Scholarship) [8778]

Ira G. Turpin Scholars Fund (Undergraduate/Scholarship) [8706]

UAA Anchorage Daily News Journalism Scholarships (Undergraduate/Scholarship) [9117]

United Parcel Service Scholarships for Minority Students (Undergraduate/Scholarship) [4811]

University of Wisconsin-Madison/CALS Minority Scholarships (Undergraduate/Scholarship) [9375]

University of Wisconsin-Madison Chancellor's Scholarships (Undergraduate/Scholarship) [9376]

University of Wisconsin-Madison Minority Teacher Loans (Professional development, Undergraduate/Loan, Scholarship) [9378]

Vorgin-Bell Scholarships (Graduate, Master's, Undergraduate/Scholarship) [6848]

VSCPA Educational Foundation Minority Scholarships *(Graduate, Undergraduate/Scholarship)* [9465]

Robert D. Watkins Graduate Research Fellowships *(Postdoctorate/Fellowship)* [1303]

Paul D. White Scholarships *(Undergraduate/Award)* [2000]

Sidney B. Williams, Jr. Scholarships *(Undergraduate/Scholarship)* [882]

Native American

AAA Minority Dissertation Fellowship Program *(Doctorate/Fellowship)* [406]

AAAA Operation Jumpstart III Scholarships *(Graduate/Scholarship)* [433]

Affirmative Action Mini Grants and Student Scholarships *(All/Grant)* [25]

AILA Scholarships *(Graduate/Scholarship)* [830]

Air Products and Chemicals, Inc. Scholarships *(Undergraduate/Scholarship)* [1793]

Alaska Native Medical Center Auxiliary Scholarships *(Undergraduate/Scholarship)* [9131]

AMA Foundation Minority Scholars Awards *(Undergraduate/Scholarship)* [922]

American Indian Fellowship in Business Scholarships *(Graduate, Master's, Undergraduate/Scholarship)* [6180]

American Indian Program Fellowships *(Graduate/Fellowship)* [8260]

AMS/Industry Minority Scholarships *(Undergraduate/Scholarship)* [931]

APS Scholarships for Minority Undergraduate Physics Majors *(Undergraduate/Scholarship)* [6485]

APTA Minority Scholarships - Faculty Development Scholarships *(Postdoctorate/Scholarship)* [999]

APTA Minority Scholarships - Physical Therapist Assistant Students *(All/Scholarship)* [1000]

APTA Minority Scholarships - Physical Therapist Students *(All/Scholarship)* [1001]

ASC Graduate Fellowships for Ethnic Minorities *(Doctorate, Graduate/Fellowship)* [1219]

Elizabeth and Sherman Asche Memorial Scholarships *(Graduate, Undergraduate/Scholarship)* [1695]

Association on American Indian Affairs Emergency Aid Scholarships *(Undergraduate/Scholarship)* [815]

AWG Minority Scholarships *(Undergraduate/Scholarship)* [1900]

Michael Baker Inc. Scholarships for Diversity in Engineering *(Undergraduate/Scholarship)* [1794]

Notah Begay III Scholarship Program *(Undergraduate/Scholarship)* [278]

BIA Higher Education Grants *(Graduate, Postgraduate, Undergraduate/Grant)* [1509]

Bill Bernbach Diversity Scholarships *(Undergraduate/Scholarship)* [434]

Leon Bradley Scholarships *(Undergraduate/Scholarship)* [548]

Buder Scholarships for American Indian Law Students *(Undergraduate/Scholarship)* [9530]

Sam Bull Memorial Scholarships *(Undergraduate/Scholarship)* [227]

Calista Scholarships *(Graduate, Undergraduate, Vocational/Occupational/Scholarship)* [2290]

CANFIT Scholarships *(Graduate, Undergraduate/Scholarship)* [2228]

Catching the Dream Scholarships *(Graduate, Undergraduate/Scholarship)* [817]

CERT College Scholarships *(Graduate, Undergraduate/Scholarship)* [3272]

Cherokee Nation Graduate Scholarships *(Graduate/Scholarship)* [2742]

Cherokee Nation Pell Scholarships *(Undergraduate/Scholarship)* [2743]

Cherokee Nation Scholarships *(Undergraduate/Scholarship)* [2744]

Daughters of the American Revolution American Indian Scholarships *(Undergraduate/Scholarship)* [818]

Vine Deloria Jr. Memorial Scholarships *(Graduate/Scholarship)* [807]

Ruth DeMoss Scholarships *(Undergraduate/Scholarship)* [7924]

William Diaz Fellowships *(Professional development/Fellowship)* [6729]

Sergeant Douglas and Charlotte DeHorse Scholarships *(Graduate, Undergraduate/Scholarship)* [2661]

DRI Law Student Diversity Scholarships *(Undergraduate/Scholarship)* [2144]

Josephine P. White Eagle Graduate Fellowships *(Graduate, Master's, Doctorate/Fellowship)* [4591]

Educational Enrichment Awards *(Undergraduate/Scholarship)* [1510]

Franchise Law Diversity Scholarship Awards *(Undergraduate/Scholarship)* [4940]

Aracelis Francis Minority Scholarships in Gerontology *(Master's/Scholarship)* [1787]

John Hope Franklin Dissertation Fellowships *(Doctorate/Fellowship)* [990]

Fraser Stryker Diversity Scholarships *(Undergraduate/Scholarship)* [3998]

The Gates Millennium Scholars *(Undergraduate/Scholarship)* [4569]

Gerber Fellowships in Pediatric Nutrition *(Undergraduate/Fellowship)* [6401]

William Harrison Gill Education Fund *(Undergraduate/Scholarship)* [2061]

Senator James Gladstone Memorial Scholarships *(Graduate, Undergraduate/Scholarship)* [228]

The Richard D. Hailey AAJ Law Student Scholarships *(Undergraduate/Scholarship)* [491]

HDR Engineering, Inc. Scholarships for Diversity in Engineering *(Undergraduate/Scholarship)* [1796]

Hopi Education Awards *(Doctorate, Undergraduate/Award)* [1511]

Indian Health Service Scholarship Program *(Undergraduate/Scholarship)* [819]

International Order of the King's Daughters and Sons North American Indian Scholarship Program *(Undergraduate/Scholarship)* [820]

W.K. Kellogg Foundation Doctoral Fellowships in Health Policy *(Professional development/Fellowship)* [6402]

Kilbuck Family Native American Scholarships *(Undergraduate/Scholarship)* [2063]

KPMG Foundation Minority Accounting Doctoral Scholarships *(Postdoctorate/Scholarship)* [5304]

The Lagrant Foundation - Graduate Students Scholarships *(Graduate/Scholarship)* [5315]

The Lagrant Foundation - Undergraduate Students Scholarships *(Undergraduate/Scholarship)* [5316]

Lewis-Clark State College/American Chemical Society Scholars Program *(Undergraduate/Scholarship)* [5440]

LITA and LSSI Minority Scholarships *(Graduate/Scholarship)* [5485]

LITA/OCLC Minority Scholarships *(Graduate/Scholarship)* [5486]

Marathon Oil Corporation College Scholarship Program *(Graduate, Undergraduate/Scholarship)* [4578]

Howard Mayer Brown Fellowships *(Graduate/Fellowship)* [941]

Medical Library Association Scholarships for Minority Students *(Graduate/Scholarship)* [5745]

Menominee Tribal Scholarships *(Graduate, Undergraduate/Scholarship)* [5769]

MESBEC Scholarships *(Undergraduate/Scholarship)* [2662]

Minorities in Government Finance Scholarships *(Graduate, Undergraduate/Scholarship)* [4199]

Minority Scholarship Awards for College Students *(Undergraduate/Scholarship)* [847]

Minority Teachers of Illinois Scholarships (MTI) *(Undergraduate/Scholarship)* [4701]

MLA/NLM Spectrum Scholarship Program *(Undergraduate/Scholarship)* [5746]

Archie Motley Memorial Scholarships for Minority Students *(Graduate/Scholarship)* [5856]

Multicultural Advertising Intern Program *(Graduate, Undergraduate/Internship)* [435]

National Association of Campus Activities Multicul-

tural Scholarship Programs *(Undergraduate/Scholarship)* [6053]

National Association of Multicultural Engineering Program Advocates Beginning Freshmen Awards (NAMEPA) *(Undergraduate/Scholarship)* [6088]

National Association of Multicultural Engineering Program Advocates Transfer Engineering Student Awards (NAMEPA) *(Undergraduate/Scholarship)* [6089]

National Medical Fellowships Need-Based Scholarships *(Undergraduate/Scholarship)* [6403]

Native American Community Scholars Awards *(Graduate/Award)* [8243]

Native American Education Grants *(Graduate, Undergraduate/Grant)* [821]

Native American Leadership Education Scholarships (NALE) *(Postdoctorate, Undergraduate/Scholarship)* [2663]

Native American Visiting Student Awards *(Graduate/Award)* [8244]

Ohio Newspaper Association Minority Scholarships *(Undergraduate/Scholarship)* [6858]

Adolph Van Pelt Special Fund for Indians Scholarships *(Undergraduate/Scholarship)* [1696]

Judith McManus Price Scholarships *(Graduate, Undergraduate/Scholarship)* [1012]

Private High School Awards *(Undergraduate/Award)* [1512]

PRSSA Multicultural Affairs Scholarships *(Undergraduate/Scholarship)* [7541]

SAA Native American Scholarships *(Graduate, Professional development, Undergraduate/Scholarship)* [8293]

David W. Schacht Native American Student Scholarships *(Undergraduate/Scholarship)* [2064]

Carl A. Scott Book Scholarships *(Undergraduate/Scholarship)* [3284]

Seldovia Native Association Achievement Scholarships *(Undergraduate, Graduate/Scholarship)* [8075]

Seldovia Native Association General Scholarships *(Undergraduate, Graduate/Scholarship)* [8076]

June M. Seneca Scholarships *(Graduate/Scholarship)* [8088]

Sidley Prelaw Scholars Initiative *(Undergraduate/Scholarship)* [8140]

Allogan Slagle Memorial Scholarships *(All/Scholarship)* [1697]

Helen J. and Harold Gilman Smith Scholarships *(Graduate, Undergraduate/Scholarship)* [2065]

David Stevenson Fellowships *(Doctorate, Graduate, Professional development/Fellowship)* [6730]

Summer Research Diversity Fellowships in Law and Social Science *(Undergraduate/Fellowship)* [579]

Robert Toigo Foundation Fellowships *(Master's/Fellowship)* [8911]

Tribal Business Management Program Scholarships (TBM) *(Undergraduate/Scholarship)* [2664]

Tribal Priority Scholarships *(Graduate, Professional development, Undergraduate/Scholarship)* [1513]

Udall Scholarships *(Undergraduate/Scholarship)* [9197]

United South and Eastern Tribes Scholarship Fund *(Undergraduate/Scholarship)* [9021]

U.S. BIA Indian Higher Education Grants *(Undergraduate/Grant)* [823]

Valuing Diversity PhD Scholarships *(Doctorate/Scholarship)* [920]

John D. Voelker Foundation Native American Scholarships *(Undergraduate/Scholarship)* [9470]

Western Michigan Society of Health-System Pharmacists Scholarships *(Undergraduate/Scholarship)* [9577]

WIEA Scholarships *(Doctorate, Graduate, Undergraduate, Vocational/Occupational/Scholarship)* [9687]

WIGA Scholarships *(Postgraduate, Professional development, Undergraduate/Scholarship)* [9512]

Woodrow Wilson-Rockefeller Brothers Fund Fel-

lowships for Aspiring Teachers of Color *(Graduate/Fellowship)* [9621]
Woksape Oyate: "Wisdom of the People" Distinguished Scholars Awards *(Undergraduate/Scholarship)* [813]
Xerox Technical Minority Scholarships *(Graduate, Undergraduate/Scholarship)* [9787]

Other

APS Scholarships for Minority Undergraduate Physics Majors *(Undergraduate/Scholarship)* [6485]

Religious affiliation

Stephanie Ali Memorial Scholarships *(Undergraduate/Scholarship)* [9321]
Rick Arkans Eagle Scout Scholarships *(High School/Scholarship)* [6247]
Associated Women for Pepperdine Scholarships (AWP) *(Undergraduate/Scholarship)* [7167]
Martha and Robert Atherton Ministerial Scholarships *(Graduate, Master's/Scholarship)* [8993]
James R. and Geraldine F. Bertelsen Scholarships *(Undergraduate/Scholarship)* [7912]
Mary E. Bivins Foundation Religious Scholarship Program *(Graduate, Undergraduate/Scholarship)* [2104]
Olympia Brown and Max Kapp Awards *(Graduate/Scholarship)* [8994]
Catholic Biblical Association of America Scholarships *(Undergraduate/Scholarship)* [2666]
Chautauqua Scholarships Program *(All/Scholarship)* [4969]
Children of Unitarian Universalist Ministers College Scholarships *(Undergraduate/Scholarship)* [8995]
CMSF Scholarships *(Graduate, Undergraduate/Scholarship)* [2781]
The Helena B. Cobb Annual Scholarships *(Undergraduate, Vocational/Occupational/Scholarship)* [9728]
The Helena B. Cobb Four-Year Higher Education Grants *(Undergraduate, Vocational/Occupational/Scholarship)* [9729]
CSF Graduate Fellowships *(Graduate/Fellowship)* [2787]
Mary Mouzon Darby Undergraduate Scholarships *(Undergraduate/Scholarship)* [4627]
Emmett J. Doerr Memorial Distinguished Scout Scholarships *(High School/Scholarship)* [6249]
Dollar-A-Day Academic Scholarships *(Graduate, Undergraduate/Scholarship)* [3467]
Pauly D'Orlando Memorial Art Scholarships *(Graduate, Undergraduate/Scholarship)* [8996]
Eastern Orthodox Scouting Scholarships *(High School/Scholarship)* [6251]
David Eaton Scholarships *(Graduate, Master's/Scholarship)* [8997]

Emmanuel Bible College Scholarships *(Undergraduate/Scholarship)* [1592]
FEF Scholarships *(Graduate/Scholarship)* [3700]
Doris W. Frey Memorial Scholarships *(Undergraduate/Scholarship)* [8603]
Greek Orthodox Archdiocese of America Paleologos Graduate Scholarships *(Graduate/Scholarship)* [4345]
Islamic Scholarship Fund Scholarships (ISF) *(Postgraduate, Undergraduate/Scholarship)* [5078]
Jewish Federation Academic Scholarships *(Graduate, Undergraduate/Scholarship)* [5161]
Rev. and Mrs. A.K. Jizmejian Educational Fund *(Undergraduate/Scholarship)* [1600]
Lily Scholarships in Religion for Journalists *(Professional development/Scholarship)* [7732]
MACC Scholarships *(Professional development/Scholarship)* [5796]
Muslim Sister Scholarships *(Undergraduate/Scholarship)* [8224]
Leonard M. Perryman Communications Scholarships for Ethnic Minority Students *(Undergraduate/Scholarship)* [9013]
David Pohl Scholarships *(Graduate, Master's/Scholarship)* [8998]
Roy H. Pollack Scholarships *(Graduate, Master's/Scholarship)* [8999]
St. James Armenian Church Memorial Scholarships *(All/Scholarship)* [1604]
Scholarships for Lutheran College Students *(Undergraduate/Scholarship)* [2077]
David W. Self Scholarships *(Undergraduate/Scholarship)* [9015]
Joseph Sumner Smith Scholarships *(All/Scholarship)* [9001]
Richard S. Smith Scholarships *(Undergraduate/Scholarship)* [9016]
Marion Barr Stanfield Art Scholarships *(Graduate, Undergraduate/Scholarship)* [9002]
Otto M. Stanfield Law Scholarships *(Graduate/Scholarship)* [9003]
Anne Sturrock Nursing Scholarships *(Undergraduate/Scholarship)* [8624]
Rev. Chuck and Nancy Thomas Scholarships *(Graduate, Master's/Scholarship)* [9004]
Thomas and Glenna Trimble Endowed Scholarships *(Undergraduate/Scholarship)* [7211]
Chester M. Vernon Memorial Eagle Scout Scholarships *(High School/Scholarship)* [6263]
Von Ogden Vogt Scholarships *(Graduate, Master's/Scholarship)* [9005]
Frank L. Weil Memorial Eagle Scout Scholarships *(Undergraduate/Scholarship)* [6265]
Wexner Graduate Fellowships/Davidson Scholars *(Graduate/Fellowship)* [9589]
Brian J. White Endowed Law Scholarships *(Undergraduate/Scholarship)* [7212]

Union affiliation

Tommy Douglas Scholarships *(Undergraduate/Scholarship)* [6548]
Duluth Building and Construction Trades Council Scholarships *(Undergraduate, Vocational/Occupational/Scholarship)* [3527]
Raymond A. Kent-Navy V-12/ROTC Scholarships *(Undergraduate/Scholarship)* [9212]
Farmers Union Marketing and Processing Foundation Stanley Moore Scholarships *(Undergraduate, Vocational/Occupational/Scholarship)* [6784]
Stanley Moore Scholarships *(Undergraduate, Vocational/Occupational/Scholarship)* [6785]
North Dakota Farmers Union Co-op House Scholarships *(Undergraduate/Scholarship)* [6786]
Hubert K. Seymour Scholarships *(Undergraduate/Scholarship)* [6788]
Sons of Union Veterans of the Civil War Scholarships *(Undergraduate/Scholarship)* [8534]
Utility Workers Union of America Scholarship Program *(Undergraduate/Scholarship)* [70]

Veteran

AMVETS National Scholarships - Entering College Freshmen *(Undergraduate/Scholarship)* [1464]
AMVETS National Scholarships - For Veterans *(Undergraduate/Scholarship)* [1465]
AMVETS National Scholarships - JROTC *(Undergraduate/Scholarship)* [1466]
Dr. Aurelio M. Caccomo Family Foundation Memorial Scholarships *(Undergraduate/Scholarship)* [1467]
Disabled War Veterans Scholarships *(Undergraduate/Scholarship)* [1559]
Sergeant Douglas and Charlotte DeHorse Scholarships *(Graduate, Undergraduate/Scholarship)* [2661]
Forsyth County Nursing Scholarships *(Undergraduate/Scholarship)* [9636]
Casey Laine Armed Forces Scholarships *(Undergraduate/Scholarship)* [2951]
Maine Vietnam Veterans Scholarships *(All/Scholarship)* [5586]
H.H. McKnight Memorial Scholarships *(Undergraduate/Scholarship)* [9233]
Mike Nash Memorial Scholarships *(Undergraduate/Scholarship)* [9427]
Bernard Rotberg Memorial Scholarships *(Undergraduate/Scholarship)* [5163]
Sons of Union Veterans of the Civil War Scholarships *(Undergraduate/Scholarship)* [8534]
Veterans of Enduring Freedom (Afghanistan) and Iraqi Freedom Scholarships *(Undergraduate/Scholarship)* [1565]
Women's Army Corps Veterans Association Scholarships *(Undergraduate/Scholarship)* [9711]

This index lists, in a single alphabetic sequence, all of the administering and sponsoring organizations and awards covered in the "Sponsors and Their Scholarships" section. Also included are co-sponsoring organizations and organization acronyms. The numbers that follow citations indicate the book entry numbers for particular organizations and awards, not page numbers. Book entry numbers for administering organizations appear in boldface type.

Nancy Ashley Adams/Ashley Adams Koetje Scholarships [3360]
Adams Family Scholarships [3361]
Ruth D. Adams Fund [3756]
Mamie Adams Memorial Awards [5410]
The Clarke B. Adams Memorial Foundation Lapeer County Community Foundation Fund [5347]
Ed Adams Memorial Scholarships [7753]
Lt. Holly Adams Memorial Scholarships [3091]
Ruth Adams Memorial Scholarships [7615]
Beaver Medical Clinic-Glen Adams Scholarship Awards [7616]
Henry S. and Carolyn Adams Scholarship Fund [3880]
Frederick G. Adams Scholarships [4405]
Henry Adams Scholarships [1262]
Adelante Fund [42]
Adelante Fund Hope Scholarships, CPS Energy Dependents [43]
Adelante Fund Hope Scholarships, San Antonio, TX Students [44]
Adelante Fund UPS Scholarships [45]
Carl Joseph Adelhardt Memorial Scholarships [4050]
Adelson Family Scholarships [7463]
Adelson Scholarships [7464]
ADHA IOH Sigma Phi Alpha Graduate Scholarships [707]
Bob Adkins Memorial Scholarships [7057]
Howard E. and Wilma J. Adkins Memorial Scholarships [1423]
Adler Pollock & Sheehan Diversity Scholarships [50]
Adler Pollock & Sheehan, P.C. [49]
Chris Nance Adler Scholarship Fund [2933]
Administrative Sciences Association of Canada (ASAC) [51]
Adolescent Literacy Pre-doctoral Fellowships [6004]
Herb Adrian Memorial Scholarship Fund [3881]
Adult Students in Scholastic Transition Scholarships (ASIST) [3693]
Advanced Cardiovascular Surgery Fellowships [561]
Advanced Light Source Postdoctoral Fellowship Program [5379]
Advancing Hispanic Excellence in Technology, Engineering, Math and Science (AHETEMS) [53]
Advertising Production Club of New York (APC) [57]
Advertising Production Club of New York High School Scholarships (APC) [58]
Advertising Production Club Scholarship Awards [59]
Advocates for the American Osteopathic Association (AAOA) [62]
Advocates' Society [64]
AE Flight Training Scholarships [6721]
AE Jet Type Rating Scholarships [6722]
AE Technical Training Scholarships [6723]
AeA Scholarships [7904]
AEBC Toronto Chapter Scholarships [335]
AECT Foundation Mentor Endowment Scholarships [1761]
AECT Legacy Scholarships [1762]
AERA-AIR Fellows Program [714]
AERA-ETS Fellowship Program in Measurement [715]
AERA Minority Fellowship Program in Education Research [716]
Aerospace States Association (ASA) [67]
AESF Foundation Scholarships [6127]
AfAA Graduate Student Paper Awards [1688]
AfAA Undergraduate Student Paper Awards [1689]
AFAR Scholarships [746]
AFCEA Math and Science Teachers Scholarships [1553]
AFCEA Scholarship for Working Professionals [1554]
AFFIRM University Scholarships [1775]
Affirmative Action Mini Grants and Student Scholarships [25]
AFL-CIO (UWUA) - Utility Workers Union of America (UWUA) [69]
AFPPA Student Scholarships [1773]
African American Network - Carolinas Scholarship Fund [3882]
African American Studies Fellowships [5668]
African American Success Foundation [71]

African Humanities Fellowships [673]
AFROTC Scholarships [87]
AFSA Chapter 155 Division 1 Scholarships - Category 1 [97]
AFSA Chapter 155 Division 1 Scholarships - Category 2 [98]
AFSA Chapter 155 Division 1 Scholarships - Category 3 [99]
AFSP - Distinguished Investigator Grants [766]
AFSP Postdoctoral Research Fellowships [767]
AFSP Standard Research Grants [768]
AFSP Young Investigator Grants [769]
After-the-Fires Scholarships [7905]
AfterCollege/AACN Nursing Scholarships [458]
AG BELL College Scholarship Awards [2048]
AGBU Scholarships [1573]
AGC Foundation Outstanding Educator Awards [1675]
AGC New York State Chapter Scholarship Program [1677]
AGI Minority Participation Program Geoscience Student Scholarships (AGI-MPP) [778]
Agricultural Institute of Canada [73]
Agriculture Future of America (AFA) [76]
Agriculture Future of America Community Scholarships [77]
Agriculture Future of America Scholarship Program [78]
AGS Foundation for Health in Aging (FHA) [79]
Aha Punana Leo [82]
Patty Ahearn Victoria Elementary Scholarships [7617]
Ahepa Buckeye Scholarship Awards [85]
Ahepa Buckeye Scholarship Foundation [84]
Ahepa District No. 1 Scholarship Program [790]
AHETEMS/ExxonMobil Scholarships [54]
AHETEMS General Scholarships [55]
AHETEMS Professional Scholarships [56]
AHNS-ACS Career Development Awards [784]
AHNS Pilot Research Grants [785]
AHNS Young Investigator Awards [786]
Henry and Maria Ahrens Scholarships [4255]
AIA Alaska Scholarships [838]
AIA and the Global Automotive Aftermarket Symposium Scholarships [1955]
AIA/NEI Scholarships [840]
AIAA Foundation Scholarship Program [836]
AIBS Junior Fellowships [843]
AIBS Senior Fellowships [844]
AIDS Awareness Scholarships [7843]
AIGC Fellowships - Graduate [826]
AILA Scholarships [830]
AIMS Long-term Research Grants [860]
AIMS Short-term Research Grants [861]
AIPS Post-Doctoral Fellowships [863]
AIPS Pre-Doctoral Fellowships [864]
Air Force Association (AFA) [86]
Air Force Association Excellence Scholarships [88]
Air Force Association/Grantham Scholarships [89]
Air Force Association Spouse Scholarships [90]
Air Force ROTC Enhanced HBCU Scholarships [9023]
Air Force Sergeants Association [94]
Air Force Sergeants Association-Chapter 155 (AFSA) [96]
Air Force Sergeants Association Scholarship Program [95]
Air Products and Chemicals, Inc. Scholarships [1793]
Air Traffic Control Association (ATCA) [102]
Air Traffic Control Association Full-time Employee Student Scholarships [103]
Air Traffic Control Association Non-employee Student Scholarships [104]
Air and Waste Management Association (A&WMA) [106]
Air and Waste Management Association - Genesee Finger Lakes Chapter (GFLC-A&WMA) [108]
Air and Waste Management Association - Golden West Section (A&WMA-GWS) [110]
Air and Waste Management Association - Louisiana Section [112]
Air and Waste Management Association - Niagara Frontier Section (AWMA-NFS) [114]
Air and Waste Management Association - Northern

and Central New Jersey Chapter (A&WMA NCNJ) [117]
Air and Waste Management Association - Southern Section (SSAWMA) [119]
Aircraft Electronics Association (AEA) [121]
Aircraft Owners and Pilots Association Scholarships [122]
Airport Minority Advisory Council Educational and Scholarship Program (AMACESP) [146]
Airports Council International North America (ACI-NA) [148]
Airports Council International-North America Scholarships [149]
AISC/Great Lakes Fabricators and Erectors Association Fellowships [871]
AISC/Rocky Mountain Steel Construction Association Fellowships [872]
AISC/Southern Association of Steel Fabricators Fellowships [873]
AISC/Southern Association of Steel Fabricators Scholarships [874]
AISC/Structural Steel Education Council Fellowships [875]
AISC/US Steel Fellowships [876]
AISES Intel Scholarships [832]
AISES Summer Internships [833]
AIST Baltimore Chapter Scholarships [1799]
AIST Detroit Chapter Scholarships [1800]
AIST Northwest Chapter Scholarships [1801]
AIST San Francisco Chapter Scholarships [1802]
AJL Convention Travel Grants [1820]
AJL Scholarship Program [1821]
Ak-Sar-Ben Scholarships [296]
Akao Scholarships for QFD [7552]
Crown Prince Akihito Scholarship Foundation [5132]
Akron Bar Association Foundation [150]
Akron Bar Association Foundation Scholarships [151]
Al Muammar Scholarships for Journalism [1490]
Alabama Architectural Foundation (AAF) [152]
Alabama Architectural Foundation Scholarships [153]
Alabama Commission on Higher Education [154]
Alabama Dietetic Association (ALDA) [167]
Alabama Gi Dependents Educational Benefit Program [162]
Alabama Horse Council (AHC) [174]
Alabama Horse Council Scholarships [175]
Alabama Law Foundation [186]
Alabama National Guard Educational Assistance Program [163]
Alabama Power Scholarships [6809]
Alabama Scholarships for Dependents of Blind Parents [164]
Alabama Student Assistance Programs [165]
Alabama Student Grant Programs [166]
Jonathan Alan Scholarship Fund [9546]
Alaska Aerospace Development Corporation Scholarships [9130]
Alaska Airlines Scholarships [1362]
Alaska Airmen Association [190]
Alaska Broadcasters Association (ABA) [194]
Alaska Community Foundation [196]
Alaska Kidney Foundation-ASN Research Grants [1311]
Alaska Native Medical Center Auxiliary Scholarships [9131]
Alaska Press Club Scholarships [9132]
Alaska Support Industry Alliance Scholarships [9133]
Alaska Visitors Association/Gomar Scholarships [9134]
Alaska Yukon Pioneer Memorial Scholarships [9135]
Alberta 4-H [198]
Alberta Agricultural Economics Association (AAEA) [202]
Alberta Agricultural Economics Association Masters Scholarships [203]
Alberta Agricultural Economics Association Undergraduate Scholarships [204]
Alberta Association of Gerontology (AAG) [205]
Alberta Association of Gerontology Student Awards [206]
Alberta Association of Gerontology Student Awards - Edmonton Chapter [207]
Alberta Award for the Study of Canadian Human

American Association of Neurological Surgeons (AANS) (AANS) **[514]**

American Association of Neuroscience Nurses (AANN) **[517]**

American Association of Occupational Health Nurses (AAOHN) **[521]**

American Association for Paralegal Education (AAFPE) **[525]**

American Association of Physicists in Medicine (AAPM) **[527]**

American Association of Physics Teachers (AAPT) **[532]**

American Association of Plastic Surgeons (AAPS) **[534]**

American Association of Plastic Surgeons Academic Scholars Program [535]

American Association of Poison Control Centers **[536]**

American Association of Police Polygraphists (AAPP) **[538]**

American Association of Professional Apiculturists (AAPA) **[540]**

American Association of Professional Apiculturists Research Scholarships [541]

American Association of Railroad Superintendents (AARS) **[542]**

American Association of School Administrators. (AASA) **[544]**

American Association of School Personnel Administrators (AASPA) **[547]**

American Association of State Troopers (AAST) **[549]**

American Association of State Troopers Scholarship Foundation First Scholarships [550]

American Association of State Troopers Scholarship Foundation Second Scholarships [551]

American Association of Stratigraphic Palynologists Student Scholarships [6]

American Association for the Surgery of Trauma (AAST) **[553]**

American Association of Textile Chemists and Colorists (AATCC) **[558]**

American Association for Thoracic Surgery (AATS) **[560]**

American Association of University Women American Fellowships [9]

American Association of University Women Career Development Grants [10]

American Association of University Women International Fellowships [11]

American Association of University Women Master's and First Professional Awards [12]

American Association of University Women Selected Professions Fellowships [13]

American Association for Women in Community Colleges (AAWCC) **[564]**

American Association for Women in Community Colleges Regional Scholarships [565]

American Association for Women in Community Colleges Scholarship Leaders Institute [566]

American Astronomical Society (AAS) **[567]**

American Astronomical Society Small Research Grants [568]

American Australian Association (AAA) **[573]**

American Australian Association Neurological Fellowships [574]

The American Automobile Association Five Diamond Hospitality Scholarships (AAA) [795]

American Bar Foundation (ABF) **[576]**

American Birding Association (ABA) **[580]**

American Board of Funeral Service Education (ABFSE) **[583]**

American Brain Tumor Association (ABTA) **[585]**

American Bus Association (ABA) **[587]**

American Bus Association Academic Merit Scholarships [591]

American Business Women's Association Sarasota Sunrise Chapter Scholarships [3187]

American Cancer Society Inc. (American Society for the Control of Cancer) [593]

American Cancer Society - Postdoctoral Fellowships [594]

American Cancer Society - Research Scholar Grants [595]

American Center for Mongolian Studies (ACMS) **[599]**

American Ceramic Society (ACerS) **[605]**

American Clan Gregor Society (ACGS) **[607]**

The American Classical League (ACL) **[610]**

American College of Chiropractic Orthopedics (ACCO) **[614]**

American College of Nurse-Midwives Foundation (ACNM) **[616]**

American College of Nursing Practitioners (ACNP) **[620]**

American College of Radiation Oncology (ACRO) **[622]**

American College of Radiation Oncology Resident Scholarships [623]

American Composites Manufacturers Association (ACMA) **[624]**

American Composites Manufacturers Association Scholarships [625]

American Composites Manufacturers Association Western Chapter Scholarships [626]

American Concrete Institute (ACI) **[627]**

American Congress on Surveying and Mapping (ACSM) **[640]**

American Conifer Society (ACS) **[651]**

American Conifer Society Scholarships [652]

American Constitution Society for Law and Policy (ACS) **[653]**

American Copy Editors Society Education Fund (ACES) **[655]**

American Council of the Blind (ACB) **[657]**

American Council of the Blind Scholarships [658]

American Council of Engineering Companies of Illinois (Consulting Engineers Association of Illinois) **[659]**

American Council of Engineering Companies of Illinois Scholarships [660]

American Council on Exercise **[661]**

American Council on Germany (ACG) **[665]**

American Council of Independent Laboratories (ACIL) **[668]**

American Council of Independent Laboratories Scholarships [669]

American Council of Learned Societies (ACLS) **[670]**

American Council of Learned Societies Fellowships [674]

American Counsel Association (ACA) **[682]**

American Counsel Association Scholarships [683]

American Counseling Association (ACA) **[684]**

American Criminal Justice Association (ACJA-LAE) - Lambda Alpha Epsilon (ACJA-LAE) **[686]**

American Criminal Justice Association Scholarships [687]

American Culinary Federation (ACF) **[688]**

American Culinary Federation Chair's Scholarship Grants [689]

American Dental Association (ADA) **[700]**

American Dental Association Dental Assisting Scholarship Program [701]

American Dental Association Dental Hygiene Scholarship Program [702]

American Dental Association Dental Laboratory Technology Scholarship Program [703]

American Dental Association Dental Student Scholarships [704]

American Dental Association Minority Dental Student Scholarships [705]

American Dental Hygienists' Association Institute for Oral Health (ADHA IOH) **[706]**

American Dental Hygienists' Association Institute for Oral Health Fellowships [708]

American Division Veterans Association (ADVA) **[711]**

American Division Veterans Association Scholarships [712]

American Dream Scholarship Program [7890]

American Educational Research Association (AERA) **[713]**

American Enterprise Institute **[717]**

American Enterprise Institute National Research Initiative Fellowships (NRI) [718]

American Epilepsy Society (AES) **[719]**

American Express Professional Development Scholarships [796]

The American Express Scholarship Competition [797]

American Express Travel Scholarships [1363]

American Federation of Police and Concerned Citizen Scholarships [722]

American Federation of Police and Concerned Citizens (AFP&CC) **[721]**

American Fire Sprinkler Association Scholarships [4407]

American Floral Endowment (AFE) **[723]**

American Foreign Service Association (AFSA) **[743]**

American Foreign Service Association Scholarship Fund [744]

American Foundation for Aging Research (AFAR) **[745]**

American Foundation for the Blind (AFB) **[747]**

American Foundation for Pharmaceutical Education (AFPE) **[755]**

American Foundation for Pharmaceutical Education Gateway Research Scholarships [756]

American Foundation for Pharmaceutical Education Pre-Doctoral Fellowships in the Pharmaceutical Sciences [757]

American Foundation for Suicide and Prevention (AFSP) **[765]**

American Foundation for Suicide and Prevention Pilot Grants [770]

American Foundry Society, Inc. **[771]**

American Galvanizers Association (AGA) **[773]**

American Geographical Society (AGS) **[775]**

American Geosciences Institute (AGI) **[777]**

American GI Forum of San Jose **[779]**

American GI Forum of San Jose Scholarships [780]

American Guild of Organists, Canton Chapter Charitable Fund [8656]

American Handel Society (AHS) **[781]**

American Head and Neck Society (AHNS) **[783]**

American Hellenic Educational Progressive Association - District No. 1 Scholarship Foundation **[789]**

American Historical Association (AHA) **[791]**

American History Scholarships [6496]

American Hotel and Lodging Educational Foundation (AH&LEF) **[794]**

American Indian College Fund **[804]**

American Indian Education Foundation **[814]**

American Indian Endowed Scholarships [9503]

American Indian Fellowship in Business Scholarships [6180]

American Indian Graduate Center (AIGC) **[824]**

American Indian Library Association (AILA) **[829]**

American Indian Program Fellowships [8260]

American Indian Science and Engineering Society (AISES) **[831]**

American Institute of Aeronautics and Astronautics Foundation **[835]**

American Institute of Architects - Alaska **[837]**

American Institute of Architects Northeast Illinois (AIA NEI) **[839]**

American Institute of Bangladesh Studies (AIBS) **[842]**

American Institute of Chemical Engineers (AIChE) **[845]**

The American Institute for Conservation of Historic and Artistic Works (AIC) **[850]**

American Institute for Economic Research (AIER) **[853]**

American Institute for Economic Research Student Summer Fellowships [854]

American Institute of Iranian Studies (AIIrS) **[855]**

American Institute for Maghrib Studies (AIMS) **[859]**

American Institute of Pakistan Studies (AIPS) **[862]**

American Institute of Physics **[865]**

American Institute of Physics Congressional Science Fellowships [866]

American Institute of Physics State Department Science Fellowships [867]

American Institute of Polish Culture (AIPC) **[868]**

American Institute of Steel Construction (AISC) **[870]**

American Institute of Wine and Food - Rhode Island **[878]**

American Intellectual Property Law Education Foundation (AIPLEF) **[880]**

American Jersey Cattle Association (National All-Jersey Inc.) **[883]**

American Jewish Historical Society (AJHS) **[886]**

American Judges Association (AJA) **[889]**

American Judges Association Law Student Essay Competition [890]

American Lebanese Engineering Society (ALES) **[891]**

American Lebanese Engineering Society Scholarship Program [892]

American Legion (AL) **[893]**

American Legion Boys/Girls State Scholarships [5411]

American Legion Eagle Scout of the Year Scholarships [6246]

The American Legion Legacy Scholarships [894]

The American Legion National High School Oratorical Scholarships Contest [895]

American Library Association (ALA) **[898]**

American Liver Foundation (ALF) **[902]**

American Liver Foundation Liver Scholar Awards [903]

American Liver Foundation Special Research Initiatives [904]

American Lung Association/AAAAI Allergic Respiratory Diseases Awards [908]

American Lung Association (ALA) **[907]**

American Lung Association Biomedical Research Grants [909]

American Lung Association Clinical Patient Care Research Grants [910]

American Lung Association Dalsemer Research Grants [911]

American Lung Association DeSousa Awards [912]

American Lung Association Lung Cancer Discovery Awards [913]

American Lung Association Senior Research Training Fellowships [914]

American Lung Association Social-Behavioral Research Grants [915]

American Marketing Association-Connecticut Chapter, Anna C. Klune Memorial Scholarships [4408]

American Marketing Association Foundation (AMAF) **[917]**

American Medical Association (AMA) **[921]**

American Men's Studies Association (AMSA) **[925]**

American Meteorological Society (AMS) **[927]**

American MidEast Leadership Network (AMLN) **[933]**

American Military Retirees Association (AMRA) **[935]**

American Montessori Society (AMS) **[937]**

American Musicological Society (AMS) **[939]**

American Nephrology Nurses' Association (ANNA) **[942]**

American Nephrology Nurses' Association Evidence-Based Research Grants [943]

American Nephrology Nurses' Association Research Grants [944]

American Nuclear Society (ANS) **[947]**

American Nuclear Society Incoming Freshman Scholarships [948]

American Nuclear Society Nevada Section Scholarships [7466]

American Nuclear Society Undergraduates Scholarships [949]

American Occupational Therapy Foundation (AOTF) **[950]**

American Orff-Schulwerk Association (AOSA) **[958]**

American Oriental Society (AOS) **[963]**

American Orthopedic Foot and Ankle Society (AOFAS) **[965]**

American Osteopathic Foundation (AOF) **[968]**

American Otological Society (AOS) **[973]**

American Paint Horse Foundation (APHA) **[975]**

American Paint Horse Foundation Scholarships [976]

American Parkinson Disease Association (APDA) **[977]**

American Parkinson Disease Association Medical Students Summer Fellowships [978]

American Pediatric Surgical Nurses Association (APSNA) **[983]**

American Pediatric Surgical Nurses Association Educational Grants [984]

American Philological Association (APA) **[985]**

American Philological Association Minority Student Summer Fellowships [986]

American Philosophical Society (APS) **[988]**

American Physical Society (APS) **[995]**

American Physical Society Minority Undergraduate Scholarships [996]

American Physical Therapy Association (APTA) **[998]**

American Physiological Society (APS) **[1002]**

American Physiological Society Post-doctoral Fellowships in Physiological Genomics (APS) [1003]

American Planning Association (APA) **[1007]**

American Political Science Association (APSA) **[1013]**

American Political Science Association Federal Executives Fellowships [1014]

American Political Science Association Journalists Fellowships [1015]

American Political Science Association/MCI Scholarships [1016]

American Political Science Association Political Scientists Fellowships [1017]

American Polygraph Association (APA) **[1020]**

American Psychiatric Association Alliance (APAA) **[1022]**

American Psychiatric Publishing Inc. (APPI) **[1024]**

American Psychoanalytic Association (APSAA) **[1026]**

American Psychoanalytic Association Fellowships [1027]

American Psychological Association of Graduate Students (APAGS) **[1028]**

American Psychological Foundation (APF) **[1036]**

American Psychology-Law Society (AP-LS) **[1042]**

American Psychology-Law Society Dissertation Awards [1043]

American Psychology-Law Society Early Career Professional Grants-In-Aid [1044]

American Psychology-Law Society Student Grants-In-Aid [1045]

American Public Power Association (APPA) **[1047]**

American Public Transportation Foundation (APFT) **[1049]**

American Public Works Association (APWA) **[1058]**

American Public Works Association-Nevada (APWA) **[1060]**

American Quarter Horse Foundation Scholarships [1063]

American Quarter Horse Youth Association (AQHYA) **[1062]**

American Quilt Study Group (AQSG) **[1064]**

American Radio Relay League Foundation (ARRLF) **[1066]**

American Radio Relay League Louisiana Memorial Scholarships [1067]

American Railway Engineering and Maintenance-of-Way Association Scholarships [1117]

American Railway Engineering and Maintenance of Way Association (AREMA) **[1116]**

American Red Cross **[1134]**

American Rental Association Foundation **[1136]**

American Rental Association Foundation Scholarships [1137]

American Research Center in Egypt (ARCE) **[1140]**

American Research in the Humanities in China Fellowships [675]

American Research Institute in Turkey (ARIT) **[1144]**

American Respiratory Care Foundation **[1154]**

American Road and Transportation Builders Association (ARTBA) **[1156]**

American Roentgen Ray Society (ARRS) **[1158]**

American Roentgen Ray Society Scholarships [1159]

American Romanian Orthodox Youth (AROY) **[1161]**

American-Scandinavian Foundation **[1167]**

American-Scandinavian Foundation Fellowships and Grants to Study in America [1168]

American-Scandinavian Foundation Fellowships to Study in Scandinavia [1169]

American-Scandinavian Foundation Grants to Study in Scandinavia [1170]

American-Scandinavian Foundation Translation Prize [1171]

American School Health Association (ASHA) **[1174]**

American Schools of Oriental Research (ASOR) **[1177]**

American Senior Benefits Association (ASBA) **[1179]**

American Shotcrete Association (ASA) **[1181]**

American Society of Association Executives (The Center for Association Leadership) **[1183]**

American Society of Brewing Chemists (ASBC) **[1185]**

American Society of Business Publication Editors (ASBPE) **[1188]**

American Society of Certified Engineering Technicians **[1190]**

American Society of Cinematographers **[1194]**

American Society for Clinical Laboratory Science (ASCLS) **[1196]**

American Society of Colon and Rectal Surgeons (ASCRS) **[1200]**

American Society of Colon and Rectal Surgeons International Fellowships [1201]

American Society of Colon and Rectal Surgeons Travel Scholarships [1202]

American Society of Comparative Law (ASCL) **[1203]**

American Society of Comparative Law TransCoop Programs [1204]

American Society of Composers, Authors and Publishers Foundation (ASCAP) **[1205]**

American Society of Crime Laboratory Directors (ASCLD) **[1216]**

American Society of Crime Laboratory Directors Scholarships [1217]

American Society of Criminology (ASC) **[1218]**

American Society for Eighteenth-Century Studies (ASECS) **[1220]**

American Society of Electroneurodiagnostic Technologists (ASET) **[1237]**

American Society of Electroneurodiagnostic Technologists Student Education Grants (ASET) [1238]

American Society for Engineering Education (ASEE) **[1240]**

American Society for Enology and Viticulture (ASEV) **[1242]**

American Society for Enology and Viticulture Scholarships [1243]

American Society for Environmental History (ASEH) **[1244]**

American Society for Environmental History Minority Travel Grants [1245]

American Society of Genealogists (ASG) **[1256]**

American Society of Health System Pharmacists (ASHP) **[1258]**

American Society of Heating, Refrigerating and Air-Conditioning Engineers (ASHRAE) **[1261]**

American Society of Heating, Refrigerating, and Air-Conditioning Memorial Scholarships [1263]

American Society of Heating, Refrigerating, and Air-Conditioning Undergraduate Scholarships [1264]

American Society for Horticultural Science **[1271]**

American Society for Horticultural Science Student Travel Grants [1272]

American Society of Interior Designers (ASID) **[1276]**

American Society of International Law (ASIL) **[1279]**

American Society of Landscape Architects (ASLA) **[1281]**

American Society of Landscape Architects Council of Fellow Scholarships [1282]

American Society for Legal History (ASLH) **[1290]**

American Society for Mass Spectrometry (ASMS) **[1292]**

American Society for Microbiology (ASM) **[1294]**

American Society for Microbiology International Fellowships for Africa [1295]

American Society for Microbiology International Fellowships for Asia [1296]

American Society for Microbiology International Fellowships for Latin America and the Caribbean [1297]

American Society for Microbiology Undergraduate Research Fellowships (URF) [1298]

American Society of Military Comptrollers (ASMC) **[1304]**

American Society of Military Comptrollers National Scholarship Program [1305]

American Society of Mining and Reclamation (ASMR) **[1306]**

American Society of Mining and Reclamation Memorial Scholarships [1307]

American Society of Naval Engineers (ASNE) **[1308]**
American Society of Naval Engineers Scholarships (ASNE) [1309]
American Society of Nephrology (ASN) **[1310]**
American Society for Nondestructive Testing Inc. (The American Industrial Radium and X-ray Society) **[1314]**
American Society of Podiatric Medical Assistants **[1318]**
American Society for Quality - Statistic Division **[1320]**
American Society of Radiologic Technologists (ASRT) **[1322]**
American Society of Safety Engineers (ASSE) **[1329]**
American Society of Safety Engineers Construction Safety Scholarships [1331]
The American Society for Theatre Research (ASTR) **[1358]**
American Society of Travel Agents (ASTA) **[1361]**
American Society of Travel Agents AVIS Scholarships [1364]
American Society of Women Accountants (ASWA) **[1373]**
American Sociological Association (ASA) **[1376]**
American Sokol **[1378]**
American Sokol Merit Awards [1379]
American Speech Language Hearing Foundation (ASHF) **[1380]**
American Speech Language Hearing Foundation Clinical Research Grants [1381]
American Speech Language Hearing Foundation Endowed Scholarships [1382]
American Speech Language Hearing Foundation General Scholarships [1383]
American Speech Language Hearing Foundation Scholarships for International Students [1384]
American Speech Language Hearing Foundation Scholarships for Students with Disability [1385]
American Standard Scholarships [7344]
American Statistical Association (ASA) **[1392]**
American Surgical Association (ASA) **[1397]**
American Swedish Institute (ASI) **[1399]**
The American University - School of Public Affairs **[1403]**
American Urological Association Foundation (AUAF) **[1406]**
American Water Resources Association - Colorado Section **[1411]**
American Water Ski Educational Foundation (AW-SEF) **[1413]**
American Water Ski Educational Foundation Scholarships [1414]
American Water Works Association (AWWA) **[1415]**
American Watercolor Society (AWS) **[1420]**
American Watercolor Society Scholarship Program for Art Teachers [1421]
American Welding Society (AWS) **[1422]**
American Welding Society District Scholarships [1424]
American Welding Society International Scholarships [1425]
American Welding Society National Scholarships [1426]
American Welding Society Past Presidents Scholarships [1427]
American Welding Society Research Fellowships [1428]
American Wine Society Educational Foundation (AWSEF) **[1449]**
American Wine Society Educational Foundation Scholarships [1450]
American Woman's Society of Certified Public Accountants (AWSCPA) **[1451]**
Americans for Informed Democracy (AID) **[1453]**
Americans for Informed Democracy Global Scholar Tuition [1454]
AmeriGlide **[1455]**
AmeriGlide Achiever Scholarships [1456]
Anna Ames Clinical Excellence Student Grants [2281]
Amgen Scholars Fellowships [3637]
Arsham Amirikian Engineering Scholarships [1429]
AMLN Scholarships [934]
AMS Centennial Fellowships [2738]

AMS Freshman Undergraduate Scholarships [928]
AMS Graduate Fellowships in the History of Science [929]
AMS Industry/Government Graduate Fellowships [930]
AMS/Industry Minority Scholarships [931]
AMS Teacher Education Scholarships [938]
AMS Undergraduate Named Scholarships [932]
ISPE/M.E. Amstutz Memorial Awards [4690]
AMSUS Dentist Awards [1458]
AMSUS Nursing Awards [1459]
AMSUS Physician Awards [1460]
AMSUS - The Society of Federal Health Professionals **[1457]**
Bernard Amtmann Fellowships [2087]
AMVETS **[1463]**
AMVETS National Scholarships - Entering College Freshmen [1464]
AMVETS National Scholarships - For Veterans [1465]
AMVETS National Scholarships - JROTC [1466]
Anaheim Police Association (APA) **[1468]**
Anaheim Police Survivors and Scholarship Fund [1469]
ANCA Scholarships [1613]
Anchor Environmental **[1470]**
Anchor Environmental Scholarships [1471]
Anchor Plastics Scholarships [7264]
Anchor Scholarship Foundation [8780]
Andersen Nontraditional Scholarships for Women's Education and Retraining [3884]
William G. Anderson, DO, Minority Scholarships [969]
The Anderson Group Summer Institute **[1472]**
The Anderson Group Summer Institute Scholarships [1473]
Judge Isaac Anderson, Jr. Scholarships [8589]
A.T. Anderson Memorial Scholarships [834]
Charles Lee Anderson Memorial Scholarships [3142]
Gladys C. Anderson Memorial Scholarships [748]
Roy Anderson Memorial Scholarships [2990]
Earl I. Anderson Scholarships [1068]
Jane E. Anderson Scholarships [3365]
Kathy D. and Stephen J. Anderson Scholarships [3092]
Ora E. Anderson Scholarships [3875]
Redlands Rotary Club - Donald C. Anderson Scholarships [7620]
Michael P. Anderson Scholarships in Space Science [6484]
Warren M. Anderson Scholarships [4741]
Dr. Andy Anderson Young Professional Awards [7317]
Margaret J. Andrew Memorial Scholarships [8156]
Cindy Andrews Educational Scholarships [7621]
William H. Andrews/HAWS Scholarships [9623]
Richard E. Andrews Memorial Scholarships [582]
Marvin A. Andrews Scholarships/Internships [1517]
Androscoggin County Chamber of Commerce **[1474]**
Androscoggin County Chamber of Commerce Adult Scholarships [1475]
John D. Anello Sr. and Albert A. Silverman Memorial Scholarships [2887]
Angus Foundation **[1476]**
Angus Foundation General Undergraduate Student Scholarships [1477]
Angus Foundation Graduate Student Degree Scholarship Program [1478]
Angus Foundation Scholarships [6374]
Angus/Talon Youth Educational Learning Program Endowment Fund [1479]
Anheuser-Busch NAPABA Law Foundation Presidential Scholarships [6026]
Animals and Society Institute (ASI) **[1480]**
Ann Arbor AWC Scholarships for Women in Computing [1896]
Anne Friedberg Innovative Scholarship Awards [8309]
Leonore Annenberg Teaching Fellowships [9614]
Anonymous Scholarship Fund [9547]
Jack Anson Fellowships [6738]
Hettie M. Anthony Fellowships [5200]
Anxiety and Depression Association of America (ADAA) **[1482]**

AOA Research Grants [63]
AOFAS Research Grants Program [966]
AORN Foundation Scholarship Program [1839]
AOS Research Training Fellowships [974]
AOSA Research Grants [959]
AOSA Research Partnership Grants [960]
APA Minority Fellowships Program [1646]
APACVS Scholarships [1841]
APAGS-CLGBTC Grant Program [1029]
APAGS' Committee on Ethic Minority Affairs (CEMA) Grant Program [1030]
APALA Scholarships [1648]
APBASV Scholarships [1652]
APC Tuition-Assist Scholarship Awards [60]
APDA Postdoctoral Fellowships [979]
APDA Research Grants [980]
APF/COGDOP Graduate Research Scholarships [1037]
APIASF Scholarships [1655]
Aplastic Anemia and Myelosdysplasia Scholarships [2533]
Appalachian School of Law (ASL) **[1485]**
Applied Hospitality Degree Scholarships [2487]
Applied Physics Laboratory Alexander Kossiakoff Scholarships [4912]
Appraisal Institute Education Trust **[1487]**
Appraisal Institute Education Trust Scholarships [1488]
APS/ASU Scholarships [7332]
APS/Maricopa County Community Colleges Scholarships [7333]
APS/NIDDK Minority Travel Fellowship Awards [1004]
APS Scholarships for Minority Undergraduate Physics Majors [6485]
APSA Congressional Fellowships [4131]
APT US&C Scholarships [1847]
APTA Minority Scholarships - Faculty Development Scholarships [999]
APTA Minority Scholarships - Physical Therapist Assistant Students [1000]
APTA Minority Scholarships - Physical Therapist Students [1001]
APTRA Scholarships [1684]
APWA Engineering Scholarships [1059]
Aquatics Booster Club Scholarships [7622]
ARA Scholarship Awards [1961]
Arab American Institute (AAI) **[1489]**
Arab American Medical Association - Houston Chapter (AAMA) **[1493]**
ARAFCS Doctoral Scholarships [1534]
ARAFCS Masters Scholarships [1535]
Frank G. Araujo Memorial Scholarships [7623]
Archaeological Institute of America (AIA) **[1495]**
Fred Archibald Communications Internships [8465]
Architects Association of PEI Scholarships [3180]
Architectural Precast Association (APA) **[1497]**
Architecture, Design and Urban Design Prize [8231]
Arctic Institute of North America (AINA) **[1499]**
Mike Ardaw Scholarships [9137]
AREMA Committee 18 - Light Density & Short Line Railways Scholarships [1118]
AREMA Committee 24 - Education and Training Scholarships [1119]
AREMA Committee 33 - Electric Energy Utilization Scholarships [1120]
AREMA Presidential Spouse Scholarships [1121]
Arent Fox Diversity Scholarships [1503]
Arent Fox LLP **[1502]**
A.R.F.O.R.A. Undergraduate Scholarships for Women [1162]
Arizona Airport Association (AZAA) **[1504]**
Arizona Artist Blacksmith Association (AABA) **[1506]**
Arizona Association of Student Financial Aid Administrators (AASFAA) **[1508]**
Arizona Chapter Gold Scholarships [1365]
Arizona Christian School Tuition Organization (ACSTO) **[1514]**
Arizona Christian School Tuition Organization Scholarships [1515]
Arizona City/County Management Association (ACMA) **[1516]**
Arizona Cowpuncher's Scholarship Organization (ACSO) **[1519]**
Arizona Hydrological Society (AHS) **[1521]**

Arizona Hydrological Society Scholarships [1522]
Arizona Nursery Association (ANA) **[1523]**
Arizona Nursery Association Scholarships [1524]
Arizona Nurses Association (AzNA) **[1525]**
Arizona Nurses Foundation Scholarships [1526]
Arizona Society of Certified Public Accountants (AS-CPA) **[1527]**
Rick Arkans Eagle Scout Scholarships [6247]
Arkansas Association of Family and Consumer Sciences (ARAFCS) **[1533]**
Arkansas Environmental Federation (AEF) **[1536]**
Arkansas Library Association (ArLA) **[1540]**
Arkansas Nurses Association (ARNA) **[1542]**
Arkansas Public Health Association (APHA) **[1545]**
Arkansas Public Health Association Scholarships [1546]
Arkansas Single Parent Scholarship Fund (ASPSF) **[1548]**
Arkansas Society of Professional Sanitarians Scholarships [1547]
Arkansas State University (Mountain Home, Arkansas) (ASU) **[1550]**
Arkansas State University Mountain Home Scholarships [1551]
ArLA Scholarships [1541]
Armed Forces Communications and Electronics Association (AFCEA) **[1552]**
Armed Forces Communications and Electronics Association Fellowships [1555]
Connie "Chelo" Armendariz Memorial Scholarships [7624]
Armenian American Citizen's League Scholarships [1580]
Armenian American Medical Association Scholarships [1581]
Armenian American Pharmacists' Association Scholarships [1582]
Armenian Bar Association **[1568]**
Armenian Bar Association Graduate Scholarships in Law [1569]
Armenian Educational Foundation (AEF) **[1570]**
Armenian General Athletic Union Scholarships [1583]
Armenian General Benevolent Union **[1572]**
Armenian Professional Society (APS) **[1574]**
Armenian Professional Society Scholarship Fund [1575]
Armenian Relief Society - Eastern United States **[1576]**
Armenian Relief Society Scholarships [1584]
Armenian Students' Association of America (ASA) **[1579]**
Robin P. Armstrong Memorial Prize for Excellence in Native Studies Awards [2377]
Louis Armstrong Scholarships [1206]
Army Aviation Association of America (AAAA) **[1610]**
Army Nurse Corps Association (ANCA) **[1612]**
Army Scholarship Foundation **[1614]**
Marvin Arnold and Irene Jaquetta Heye Scholarships [7906]
Paul Arnold Memorial Scholarships [7396]
Tara Lynne Arnold Scholarships [8716]
Aaron Arnoldsen Memorial Golf Tournament **[1619]**
Aaron Edward Arnoldsen Memorial Scholarships [1620]
ARNOVA Emerging Scholar Awards [1858]
Jane B. Aron Doctoral Fellowships [6120]
Judge Sidney M. Aronovitz Memorial Scholarships [3314]
Merle Aronson Point Scholarships [7354]
ARREOLA/CBSPM Scholarships [7907]
ARRL Foundation General Fund Scholarships [1069]
ARRLF Mississippi Scholarships [1070]
ARS Undergraduate Scholarships [1577]
Art Acquisition by Application Project Grants [216]
Art Dealers Association of Canada (ADAC) **[1621]**
Art Graduate Scholarships [239]
Art Institute of Colorado **[1623]**
Art Institute of Colorado Scholarships [1624]
Art Institute's Best Teen Chef in America Culinary Scholarships [1625]
ARTC Glenn Moon Scholarships [4409]
Arthritis Foundation (AF) **[1628]**
Arthritis Foundation Doctoral Dissertation Awards for

Arthritis Health Professionals [1629]
Arthritis Foundation Postdoctoral Fellowships [1630]
Arthur Lockwood Beneventi Law Scholarships [6497]
Artistic Scholarship Awards [2023]
David Arver Memorial Scholarships [123]
Dutch and Ginger Arver Scholarships [124]
Chester Arzell and Helen Miller Montgomery Scholarships [9624]
ASA Graduate Scholarships [1182]
ASA Minority Fellowship Program [1377]
ASA/NSF/BLS Fellowships [1393]
ASAC-CJAS PhD Research Grant Awards [52]
ASBA College Scholarship Program [1180]
ASBC Foundation Graduate Scholarships [1186]
ASBC Foundation Undergraduate Scholarships [1187]
Benjamin Asbell Memorial Scholarships [2315]
ASBPE Young Leaders Scholarships [1189]
ASC Graduate Fellowships for Ethnic Minorities [1219]
ASCE San Diego Section (ASCE) **[1631]**
Ascend **[1634]**
ASCEND/ING Scholarships [1635]
Elizabeth and Sherman Asche Memorial Scholarships [1695]
ASCPA High School Scholarships [1528]
ASECS Graduate Student Research Paper Awards [1221]
ASECS Innovative Course Design Competition [1222]
ASECS Women's Caucus Editing and Translation Fellowships [1223]
Officer Brian A. Aselton Memorial Scholarships [4410]
ASET Educational Seminars, Courses and Program Scholarships [1239]
ASF/Annika Teig/Skidmore, Owings and Merril Fellowships [1172]
ASG Scholar Awards [1257]
ASHA Scholarships [1175]
ASHA Student Research Grants [1176]
Ashburn Institute (AI) **[1637]**
ASHFA Scholarships for Minority Students [1386]
ASHP Student Research Awards [1259]
ASHS Industry Division Student Travel Grants [1273]
ASHS Scholars Awards [1274]
ASI Fellowships [1481]
Asian American Journalists Association (AAJA) **[1639]**
Asian American Lawyers Association of Massachusetts (AALAM) **[1643]**
Asian American Lawyers Associations of Massachusetts Scholarships [1644]
Asian American Psychological Association (AAPA) **[1645]**
Asian American Scholarships [9063]
Asian Pacific American Librarians Association (APALA) **[1647]**
Asian/Pacific Bar Association of Sacramento (ABAS) **[1649]**
Asian/Pacific Bar Association of Sacramento Law Foundation Scholarships [1650]
Asian Pacific Bar Association of Silicon Valley (AP-BASV) **[1651]**
Asian and Pacific Islander American Scholarship Fund (APIASF) **[1654]**
Asian and Pacific Islander Queers Sisters Scholarships [7397]
ASIS Foundation Chapter Matching Scholarships [1657]
ASIS International **[1656]**
ASLA Council of Fellows Scholarships [5330]
ASM/CCID Program in Infectious Disease and Public Health Microbiology [1299]
ASM Undergraduate Research Capstone Program [1300]
ASM Undergraduate Teaching Fellowships (ASM-UTF) [1301]
ASME International **[1658]**
ASMS Research Awards [1293]
ASNT Fellow Awards [1315]
ASNT Fellowship Awards [1316]
ASPH/CDC/PRC Minority Health Fellowships [1862]
ASPH/CDC Public Health Fellowships [1863]

ASPH/CDC Public Health Preparedness Fellowships [1864]
ASPH/EPA Environmental Health Fellowships [1865]
ASPH/NHTSA Public Health Fellowships [1866]
ASPH Public Health Policy Fellowships [1867]
Myron Asplin Foundation Scholarships [4719]
ASPPB Larry J. Bass Jr., PhD. Memorial Scholarship Awards [1031]
ASPRS - The Imaging and Geospatial Information Society **[1664]**
Len Assante Scholarship Fund [6311]
Michael M. Assarian Scholarships [1585]
ASSE Diversity Committee Scholarships [1332]
Darrell and Palchie Asselin Scholarships [3524]
Associate Fellowships [4778]
Associated General Contractors of America (AGC) **[1674]**
Associated General Contractors of America, New York State Chapter **[1676]**
Associated General Contractors of Connecticut Scholarships [3235]
Associated Locksmiths of America (ALOA) **[1678]**
Associated Medical Services (AMS) **[1680]**
Associated Press Television and Radio Association (APTRA) **[1683]**
Associated Women for Pepperdine Scholarships (AWP) [7167]
Associates in Behavioral Health Scholarships [7398]
Association for the Advancement of Baltic Studies (AABS) **[1685]**
Association for the Advancement of Baltic Studies Dissertation Grants for Graduate Students [1686]
Association for Africanist Anthropology (AfAA) **[1687]**
Association of American Geographers (AAG) **[1690]**
Association of American Geographers IGIF Graduate Research Awards [1691]
Association of American Geographers IGIF Student Travel Grants [1692]
Association on American Indian Affairs (AAIA) **[1694]**
Association on American Indian Affairs Emergency Aid Scholarships [815]
Association of American Indian Physicians (AAIP) **[1698]**
Association of American Indian Physicians Scholarships [1699]
Association of American Medical Colleges (AAMC) **[1700]**
Association for Applied and Therapeutic Humor (AATH) **[1702]**
Association for Asian Studies (AAS) **[1708]**
Association for Behavior Analysis International **[1711]**
Association of Black Law Enforcers (ABLE) **[1715]**
Association of Black Women Lawyers of New Jersey **[1717]**
Association of Black Women Physicians (ABWP) **[1719]**
Association of California Nurse Leaders (ACNL) **[1721]**
Association of California Water Agencies (ACWA) **[1726]**
Association of California Water Agencies Scholarships [1727]
Association for Canadian Studies in the United States (ACSUS) **[1730]**
Association of Canadian Universities for Northern Studies (Association universitaire canadienne detudes nordique) **[1733]**
Association of Certified Fraud Examiners (ACFE) **[1737]**
Association of College Unions International (ACUI) **[1739]**
Association of College and University Auditors (ACUA) **[1741]**
Association of College and University Auditors Scholarships [1742]
Association for College and University Clubs (ACUC) **[1743]**
Association for Compensatory Educators of Texas (ACET) **[1745]**
Association for Compensatory Educators of Texas Paraprofessionals Scholarships [1746]

Association for Compensatory Educators of Texas Scholarships [1747]
Association of Desk and Derrick Clubs (ADDC) **[1748]**
Association of Desk and Derrick Clubs Education Trust Scholarships [1749]
Association of Donor Recruitment Professionals (ADRP) **[1750]**
Association of Donor Recruitment Professionals Hughes Scholarships [1751]
Association of Donor Recruitment Professionals Presidential Scholarships [1752]
Association of Drilled Shaft Contractors **[1755]**
Association for Education and Rehabilitation of the Blind and Visually Impaired (AERBVI) **[1758]**
Association for Educational Communications and Technology (AECT) **[1760]**
Association of Electronic Journalists Presidents Scholarships [7572]
Association of Energy Engineers Foundation **[1765]**
Association of Energy Engineers Foundation Scholarship Program [1766]
Association of Environmental & Engineering Geologists (Association of Engineering Geologists) **[1767]**
Association of Faculties of Pharmacy of Canada (AFPC) **[1770]**
Association of Family Practice Physician Assistants (AFPPA) **[1772]**
Association for Federal Information Resources Management (AFFIRM) **[1774]**
Association for Financial Technology (AFT) **[1776]**
Association of Flight Attendants - CWA (AFA) (AFA-CWA) **[1778]**
Association of Flight Attendants Scholarship Fund [1779]
Association of Food and Drug Officials **[1780]**
Association of Former Intelligence Officers (AFIO) **[1783]**
Association for Gerontology Education in Social Work (AGESW) **[1786]**
Association of Government Accountants (AGA) **[1788]**
Association of Government Accountants Undergraduate/Graduate Scholarships for Community Service Accomplishments [1789]
Association of Government Accountants Undergraduate/Graduate Scholarships for Full-time study [1790]
Association of Government Accountants Undergraduate/Graduate Scholarships for Part-time study [1791]
Association of Health Care Journalists Media Fellowships on Health Performance [3017]
Association of Independent Colleges and Universities of Pennsylvania (AICUP) **[1792]**
Association for Iron & Steel Technology **[1798]**
Association of Jewish Libraries (AJL) **[1819]**
Association of Latino Professionals in Finance and Accounting (ALPFA) **[1823]**
Association for Library Service to Children (ALSC) **[1825]**
Association of Moving Image Archivists (AMIA) **[1828]**
Association of Occupational Health Professionals in Healthcare (AOHP) **[1835]**
Association of PeriOperative Registered Nurses (AORN) **[1838]**
Association of Physician Assistants in Cardiovascular Surgery (APACVS) **[1840]**
Association for Preservation Technology International (APT) **[1842]**
Association for Preservation Technology International Student Scholarships [1843]
Association for Psychological Science (APS) **[1844]**
Association for Psychological Science Student Grants (APS) [1845]
Association of Public Treasurers of the United States and Canada (APT US & C) **[1846]**
Association of Registered Nurses of Newfoundland and Labrador (ARNNL) **[1848]**
Association of Rehabilitation Nurses (ARN) **[1854]**
Association of Rehabilitation Nurses Scholarship Program [1855]
Association for Research on Nonprofit Organizations and Voluntary Action (ARNOVA) **[1857]**

Association of School Business Officials of Maryland and the District of Columbia (ASBO-MD&DC) **[1859]**
Association of Schools of Public Health Graduate Training Programs (ASPH) **[1861]**
Association of Science-Technology Centers (ASTC) **[1869]**
Association of Seventh-Day Adventist Librarians (ASDAL) **[1871]**
Association for the Sociology of Religion (ASR) **[1873]**
Association of State Dam Safety Officials (ASDSO) **[1876]**
Association of State Dam Safety Officials Undergraduate Scholarships [1877]
Association of Surgical Technologists (AST) **[1878]**
Association of Texas Professional Educators Foundation **[1883]**
Association of the United States Navy (AUSN) **[1886]**
Association of the United States Navy Scholarships [1887]
Association of Universities and Colleges of Canada (AUCC) **[1888]**
Association of Universities and Colleges of Canada Public Scholarships [1889]
Association of University Programs in Health Administration (AUPHA) **[1890]**
Association for Women in Architecture (AWA) **[1893]**
Association for Women in Architecture Scholarships [1894]
Association for Women in Computing - Ann Arbor (AWC-AA) **[1895]**
Association for Women in Computing - Houston Chapter **[1897]**
Association for Women Geoscientists (AWG) **[1899]**
Association for Women in Mathematics (AWM) **[1906]**
Association for Women in Sports Media (AWSM) **[1909]**
Association for Women in Sports Media Internship Program [1910]
Association for Women Veterinarians Foundation (AWVF) **[1911]**
Association for Women Veterinarians Foundation Student Scholarships [1912]
Association of Zoo Veterinary Technicians (AZVT) **[1913]**
AST National Honor Society Student Scholarships [1879]
ASTR Research Fellowships [1359]
AstraZeneca RURAL Scholarships [2534]
Astronaut Scholarship Foundation (ASF) **[1915]**
Astronaut Scholarship Foundation Scholarships [1916]
ASWA 2-Year College Scholarships [1374]
ASWA Undergraduate Scholarships [1375]
AT&T Business Internship Awards [9257]
Martha and Robert Atherton Ministerial Scholarships [8993]
Athletic Equipment Managers Association (AEMA) **[1917]**
Athletic Equipment Managers Association College Scholarships [1918]
Atkinson Charitable Foundation **[1919]**
Atkinson Fellowships in Public Policy [1920]
ISA Aerospace Industries Division - William H. Atkinson Scholarships [5052]
Atlanta Alumnae Achievement Scholarships [3366]
Atlanta Association of Legal Administrators (AALA) **[1921]**
Atlantic County Bar Association **[1923]**
Atlantic Provinces Library Association (APLA) **[1925]**
Atlantic Provinces Library Association Memorial Awards [1926]
Atlantic Salmon Federation (ASF) **[1928]**
Atlantic Salmon Federation Olin Fellowships [1929]
Atlas Shrugged Essay Contest [7591]
Attorney-CPA Foundation Scholarships [439]
UAA Elaine Atwood Scholarships [9084]
AUA Foundation/Astellas Rising Star in Urology Research Awards [1407]
AUA Foundation Bridge Awards [1408]

AUA Foundation - NIDDK/NCI Surgeon-Scientist Awards [1409]
AUA Foundation Ph.D. Post-Doctoral Fellowships [1410]
Aubespin Scholarships [656]
Auburn Animal Science Department Graduate Student Scholarships [176]
Auburn University College of Veterinary Medicine Scholarships [177]
Audio Engineering Society (AES) **[1930]**
Audio Engineering Society Educational Foundation Scholarships [1931]
Herzog August Bibliothek Wolfenbuttel Fellowships [6693]
Joan Auld Scholarships [3181]
Frank H. Ault Scholarships [7908]
H. Thomas Austern Memorial Writing Competition [3853]
Austin Business Travel Association (ABTA) **[1932]**
Australian-American Health Policy Fellowships [3018]
Autism Society of America **[1934]**
Auto Body Technician Certificate Scholarships [7991]
Automotive Hall of Fame (AHF) **[1936]**
Automotive Industries Association of Canada (AIA) **[1954]**
Automotive Recyclers Association (Automotive Dismantlers & Recyclers Association) **[1960]**
Automotive Technician Scholarship Program [5686]
Automotive Warehouse Distributors Association **[1962]**
Automotive Women's Alliance Foundation (AWA) **[1969]**
Automotive Women's Alliance Foundation Scholarships [1970]
Auxiliary Undergraduate Scholarships [1659]
Delores A. Auzenne Fellowships [3818]
Larry H. Averill Memorial Scholarships [1937]
Dr. Noyes L. Avery, Jr. & Ann E. Avery Scholarships [4271]
AVI Scholarships [1963]
Aviation Distributors and Manufacturers Association (ADMA) **[1971]**
Aviation Distributors and Manufacturers Association Scholarship Fund [1972]
Avista Corporation Minds in Motion Scholarships [5412]
AVS Applied Surface Science Division Awards [1974]
AVS Biomaterial Interfaces Division Awards [1975]
AVS Manufacturing Science and Technology Group Awards [1976]
AVS MEMS and NEMS Technical Group Best Paper Awards [1977]
AVS Science and Technology Society (AVS) **[1973]**
AVS Spectroscopic Ellipsometry Focus Topic Graduate Student Awards [1978]
AVS Thin Film Division Harper Awards [1979]
AWG Minority Scholarships [1900]
AWMA Niagara Frontier Section College Scholarships [115]
AWSCPA National Scholarships [1452]
AXA Achievement Scholarships [1989]
AXA Equitable **[1988]**
Susan Ayers Memorial Scholarships [7467]
William Stone Ayres Scholarships [3479]
John M. Azarian Memorial Armenian Youth Scholarship Fund [1586]
B-Brave McMahon/Stratton Scholarship Fund [3758]
Charles Babbage Institute (CBI) **[1990]**
Tom Babcox Memorial Scholarships [1964]
Bach Organ and Keyboard Music Scholarships [7786]
Bachelor of Science in Nursing Academic Scholarships [6099]
Paula Backscheider Archival Fellowships [1224]
BACUS Scholarships [8637]
Leo Baeck Institute - DAAD Fellowships [4115]
BAEO Children's Scholarship Fund [2106]
BAFTX Early Starters Awards [2175]
BAFTX Graduate Awards [2176]
BAFTX Junior Achievers Awards [2177]
BAFTX Undergraduate Awards [2178]
BAGNC Predoctoral Scholarships [382]
Baha'i Faith Scholarships for Racial Harmony [7625]

The Bailey Family Foundation [1993]
The Bailey Family Foundation College Scholarship Program [1994]
The Bailey Family Foundation High School Scholarships Program [1995]
Jaimes F. Bailey, Jr. Scholarships [5111]
Lincoln C. Bailey Memorial Scholarship Fund [4986]
Bambi Bailey Scholarships [3078]
Barbara Bailey Scholarships [7399]
Don Bailey Scholarships [6309]
Sandra Sebrell Bailey Scholarships [3406]
Marian Wood Baird Scholarships [9407]
Baker, Donelson, Bearman, Caldwell and Berkowitz, P.C. (Memphis, Tennessee) [1996]
Baker Donelson Diversity Scholarships [1997]
Charly Baker and Heath Merriwether Memorial Scholarships [7400]
Baker and Hostetler Diversity Fellowships [1999]
Baker and Hostetler LLP [1998]
Michael Baker Inc. Scholarships for Diversity in Engineering [1794]
Frances Warren Baker Memorial Scholarships [8157]
Richard L. Baker Memorial Scholarships [8717]
Robby Baker Memorial Scholarships [277]
UAA Dr. Jon Baker Memorial Scholarships [9085]
Jerry Baker Scholarships [1430]
ACI Baker Student Fellowships [632]
ACI Elmer Baker Student Fellowships [633]
George C. Balch Scholarships [9054]
Bernt Balchen, Jr. Hardingfele Scholarships [4393]
Malcolm Baldridge Scholarships [4411]
Birgit Baldwin Fellowships [5752]
Norman S. Baldwin Fishery Science Scholarships [4868]
Franklin Mosher Baldwin Memorial Fellowships [5390]
Lynn Ann Baldwin Scholarships [2395]
Donald A. Baldwin Sr. Business Aviation Management Scholarships [6161]
Balestreri/Cutino Scholarships [690]
Lloyd G. Balfour Fellowships [6739]
Ball Horticultural Company Scholarships [724]
Vic and Margaret Ball Student Intern Scholarships [725]
Ballantyne Resident Research Grants [787]
Ballard Family Foundation Scholarships [7909]
Leighton M. Ballew Directing Scholarships [8569]
G. Thomas Balsbaugh Memorial Scholarship Fund [3935]
Baltimore City Community College (BCCC) [2001]
B&W Y-12 Scholarship Fund [3565]
Banff Centre - Leadership Development [2004]
Bank of America Junior Achievement Scholarship Fund [3885]
Bank of Canada [2010]
Bank of Canada Fellowships [2011]
Bank of Canada Governor's Awards [2012]
Brenda S. Bank Educational Workshop Scholarships [8326]
Dr. Johnella Banks Memorial Scholarships [2137]
Harvey Washington Banks Scholarships in Astronomy [6486]
Sharon D. Banks Undergraduate Memorial Scholarships [9739]
Banner Bank Business Scholarships [5413]
Donald W. Banner Corporate Intern Scholarships [4844]
Donald W. Banner Diversity Scholarships for Law Students [2014]
Banner Health System - McKee Medical Center, Loveland: Nightingale Scholarships [2991]
Banner Health System - North Colorado Medical Center, Greeley: Nightingale Scholarships [2992]
Mark T. Banner Scholarships for Law Students [7798]
Banner & Witcoff, Ltd. [2013]
CSF Michael Bany Memorial Scholarships [2793]
Baptist Communicators Association [2015]
Bar Association of San Francisco [2018]
Bernice Barabash Sports Scholarships [5090]
Barakat Trust and Barakat Foundation Scholarships [1491]
Cynthia and Alan Baran Fine Arts and Music Scholarships [3093]

Leslie Baranowski Scholarships for Professional Excellence [4764]
Barbados Cancer Association (BACA) [2020]
Barbados Cancer Association Post-Graduate Scholarships [2021]
Joe Barbarow Memorial Scholarships [7060]
Lewis B. Barber Memorial Scholarships [8590]
Barbri Scholarships for Bar Preparation [4561]
Jack R. Barckhoff Welding Management Scholarships [1431]
Janice K. Barden Aviation Scholarships [6162]
Thomas J. Bardos Science Education Awards for Undergraduate Students [451]
Edgar Barge Memorial Scholarships [4256]
UAA Michael Baring-Gould Memorial Scholarships [9086]
TCDA Carroll Barnes Student Scholarships [8846]
Gina L. Barnhart Memorial Scholarship Fund [3759]
Robbie Baron Memorial Scholarships [3936]
Barrientos Scholarship Foundation (BSF) [2022]
Zachary Barriger Memorial Scholarships [2935]
Gloria Barron Wilderness Society Scholarships [9601]
Laura Beckley Barsotti Memorial Scholarships [4652]
Barta-Lehman Musical Scholarships [7910]
Avery Bayle Barth Scholarships [3367]
Barth Syndrome Foundation (BSF) [2025]
CSF Walter and Marilyn Bartlett Scholarships [2794]
William E. Barto Scholarships [3525]
Elsa Barton Educational Scholarship Fund [1023]
Walt Bartram Memorial Education Award, Region 12 and Chapter 119 [8369]
Guthikonda BasavapunnaRao & Umadevi Scholarships [8829]
Bascom Hill Society Scholarships [9349]
Basic Midwifery Student Scholarship Program [618]
Basic Research Fellowships [586]
Diane Basilone-Engle Memorial Scholarships [2329]
Helen Bassett Commemorative Scholarships [6567]
Charles A. Bassett Endowed Memorial Scholarship Fund [4207]
Bat Conservation International (BCI) [2027]
Bat Conservation International Student Research Scholarships [2028]
H. Burton Bates Jr. Scholarships [9459]
Jim Batten Community Newspaper Internships [9258]
Lewis and Gurry Batten/Sand Plains Educational Trust Scholarships [7061]
Hazel Reed Baumeister Scholarship Program [8197]
Jeannette Bautista Memorial Scholarships [7468]
Baxter Corporation Canadian Research Awards in Anesthesia [2356]
Bob Baxter Scholarships [6448]
Bay Area Minority Law Student Scholarships [2019]
Lawrence Bayer Business Administration Scholarships [9138]
Timothy Baylink Good Fellowship Awards [7626]
John Bayliss Broadcast Foundation Internship Programs [2030]
John Bayliss Broadcast Foundation [2029]
John Bayliss Broadcast Foundation Scholarships [2031]
BBM Canada Scholarships [2365]
BCA Ethnic Minority Postgraduate Scholarships for Careers in Athletics [2135]
BCCC Foundation Scholarships [2002]
BCCC Foundation Workforce Scholarships [2003]
BCEN Undergraduate Scholarships [3633]
BCPA Bursaries [2180]
BDC Visiting Fellowships [2196]
BDPA Education Technology Foundation (BETF) [2032]
Willa Beach-Porter Music Scholarships [2721]
Beacon of Hope Scholarship Foundation [2034]
Beacon of Hope Scholarships [2035]
James Beard Foundation/Art Institute of Colorado Scholarships [1626]
Beard Scholarships [4104]
Beatitudes Fellowships [2037]
Beatitudes Society [2036]
Catherine H. Beattie Fellowships [2705]
Jane Beattie Memorial Scholarships [8362]
Beau Gunn Redlands Baseball For Youth Scholarships [7627]

Michael Beaudry Scholarships [4054]
Suzanne Beauregard Scholarships [4180]
Beaver Medical Clinic-H.E.A.R.T. Scholarship Awards [7628]
Beaver Medical Clinic-Premed Scholarship Awards [7629]
Don C. Beaver Memorial Scholarships [2241]
Beaverbrook Media at McGill Student Paper Prize [2435]
BECA Foundation [2038]
BECA Foundation-CUSM Scholarships [2039]
BECA Foundation General Scholarships Fund [2040]
Bechtel Engineering and Science Scholarships [5645]
Bechtel Group Foundation Scholarships for Safety & Health [1333]
Stan Beck Fellowships [3652]
O.J. Beck, Jr. Memorial Scholarships [2936]
Dennis J. Beck Memorial Scholarships [5091]
Beck-Pfann Memorial Scholarships [7168]
Garvin L. Beck Scholarships [7630]
Dr. Joyce Beckett Scholarships [6040]
Anne Beckingham Scholarships [2474]
Dr. Ann C. Beckingham Scholarships [2535]
Beef Industry Scholarships [6174]
Raymond and Donald Beeler Memorial Scholarships [7631]
Notah Begay III Scholarship Program [278]
Behavioral Gerontology SIG Student Research Awards [1712]
Behavioral Sciences Post-Doctoral Fellowships [3660]
Behavioral Sciences Student Fellowships [3661]
Charles E. Behlke Engineering Memorial Scholarships [9139]
Norbert J. Beihoff Scholarships [2888]
Beinecke Rare Book and Manuscript Library [2042]
N.S. Beinstock Fellowships [7573]
Hannah Beiter Graduate Student Research Grants [2762]
Bel Canto Vocal Scholarship Foundation [2045]
Bel Canto Vocal Scholarship Foundation Vocal Competition [2046]
Belfer-Aptman Dissertation Research Awards [5761]
Alexander Graham Bell Association for the Deaf and Hard of Hearing [2047]
Marc and Ruti Bell Foundation [2051]
Marc and Ruti Bell Foundation Scholarships [2052]
John Bell and Lawrence Thornton Scholarship Fund [4412]
Harvey Bell Memorial Prize [6564]
Ray and Mary Bell Memorial Scholarships [7911]
Beverlee Bell Scholarships in Human Rights and Democracy [3473]
Alfred D. Bell Travel Grants [3859]
Bellevue PFLAG Scholarships [7401]
Belmont University Commercial Music Scholarships [3094]
David Beltran Memorial Scholarships [7632]
UAA Mark A. Beltz Scholarships [9087]
Samuel Flagg Bemis Dissertation Research Grants [8335]
Ben Meadows Company Inc. [2053]
CSF Johnny Bench Scholarships [2795]
Reckitt Benckiser Student Scholarships [6105]
Richard W. Bendicksen Memorial Scholarships [1071]
Bill Bendiner and Doug Morgenson Scholarships [7402]
H. Y. Benedict Fellowships [342]
Benign Essential Blepharospasm Research Foundation (BEBRF) [2056]
Benign Essential Blepharospasm Research Foundation Research Grants [2057]
Louise Bennett-Coverley Scholarships [2110]
The Viscount Bennett Fellowships [2419]
Jean Bennett Memorial Student Travel Grants [6909]
Casey Bennett Scholarships [3740]
Eleanor Bennett Scholarships [8770]
Reverend E.F. Bennett Scholarships [2937]
William Bennett W7PHO Memorial Scholarships [1072]
Pete and Ellen Bensley Memorial Scholarship Fund [3886]

Elizabeth Benson Scholarship Awards [7727]
Benton County Foundation (BCF) **[2058]**
Benton-Meier Neuropsychology Scholarships [1038]
George Oliver Benton Memorial Scholarships [3095]
Linn Benton Scholarships [6952]
Lester G. Benz Memorial Scholarships for College
  Journalism Study [7562]
Fred Berg Awards [3594]
Charlotte V. Bergen Scholarships [1207]
Bergman Scholarships [6783]
The Joseph Berkman, and Michael and Sarah Chip-
  kin Holocaust/Genocide Studies Awards [8738]
Berkowitz Fellowships [8902]
Berks County Community Foundation (BCCF)
  [2067]
ARRS/Leonard Berlin Scholarships in Medical Pro-
  fessionalism [1160]
Richard L. Bernardi Memorial Scholarships [3143]
Stuart L. Bernath Dissertation Grants [8336]
Myrna F. Bernath Fellowships [8337]
Hon. Peggy Bernheim Memorial Scholarships [2190]
Donald H. Bernstein/John B. Talbert, Jr. Scholar-
  ships [3887]
The Berntsen International Scholarships in Survey-
  ing Technology [642]
Thomas M. Berry Jr. Scholarships [9460]
James R. and Geraldine F. Bertelsen Scholar-
  ships [7912]
Beta Gamma Memorial Scholarships [3368]
Beta Omega Scholarships [8158]
Beta Phi Mu **[2069]**
Beta Sigma Phi - Fine Arts Scholarships [8111]
Beta Sigma Scholarships [8159]
Beta Theta Pi **[2074]**
Bethesda Lutheran Communities **[2076]**
Bethune-Cookman University (B-CU) **[2078]**
Bethune-Cookman University Excelsior Scholar-
  ships [2079]
Bethune-Cookman University Presidential Scholar-
  ships [2080]
Harold Bettinger Scholarships [726]
Leonard Bettinger Vocational Scholarships [727]
Beverly Estate Scholarships [3480]
Dr. Noorali & Sabiya Bharwani Endowment [2082]
Hussein Jina Bharwani Memorial Endowment [2083]
Noorali Bharwani Professional Corporation **[2081]**
BIA Higher Education Grants [1509]
Bibliographical Society of America (BSA) **[2084]**
Bibliographical Society of Canada **[2086]**
J.P. Bickell Mining Scholarships [9322]
BIE-Loan for Service for Graduates [827]
Big Sandy Community and Technical College
  [2089]
BIGALA Scholarships (Bisexual Gay and Lesbian
  Alliance) [7845]
James L. Biggane Fellowships in Finance [6677]
Bill & Nell Biggs Scholarships [9140]
James Bilder Scholarships [8591]
Dr. Biljan Memorial Awards [2466]
Bill Bernbach Diversity Scholarships [434]
Biocom Scholarships [7913]
BioCommunications Association (BCA) **[2092]**
Biomagnetic Therapy Association (BTA) **[2097]**
Biomedical Engineering Society (BMES) **[2099]**
BioQuip Undergraduate Scholarships [3653]
BioRx/Hemophilia of North Carolina Educational
  Scholarships [6317]
Birks Family Foundation Scholarships [2536]
Birmingham District Alabama Dietetic Association
  Scholarships [168]
Birmingham Public School (BPS) **[2101]**
Birmingham-Southern College Eagle Scout Scholar-
  ships [6248]
Birmingham Student Scholarship Fund Associa-
  tion [2102]
BISA's Scholarship Assistance Program [2146]
Bisexual Foundation Scholarships [8471]
Bison Transport Scholarships [6897]
Lebbeus F. Bissell Scholarships [4413]
Mary E. Bivins Foundation **[2103]**
Mary E. Bivins Foundation Religious Scholarship
  Program [2104]
Dr. Richard E. Bjork Memorial Graduate Study
  Awards [8739]
Ted Bjornn University of Idaho Graduate Student
  Scholarships [4661]

Ted Bjornn University of Idaho Undergraduate Stu-
  dent Scholarships [4662]
Norman Blachford Point Scholarships [7355]
Black Alliance for Educational Options (BAEO)
  [2105]
Black Business and Professional Association
  (BBPA) **[2108]**
Black Canadian Scholarships [6994]
Black Caucus of the American Library Association
  (BCALA) **[2132]**
Black Coaches and Administrators (BCA) **[2134]**
Thomas F. Black, Jr. Memorial Scholarships [7784]
Black Nurses Association of Greater Washington
  [2136]
William Verbon Black Scholarships [187]
Black Student Fund [2107]
Black Theatre Network **[2139]**
Black Women in Entertainment Law (BWEL) **[2141]**
Black Women Lawyers' Association of Greater Chi-
  cago (BWLA) **[2143]**
Black Women in Sisterhood for Action (BISA)
  [2145]
Lucie and Thornton Blackburn Scholarships [2363]
Reid Blackburn Scholarships [6449]
Eileen Blackey Doctoral Fellowships [6121]
William T. Blackwell Scholarship Fund [6358]
Blair Chiropractic Society **[2148]**
Beatrice K. Blair Scholarships [2149]
Thomas M. Blake Memorial Scholarships [3230]
Margaret Blanchard Dissertation Support
  Fund [9259]
Alex Blaski Memorial Scholarships [7757]
Joan Blend Scholarship Fund [8657]
M. Hildred Blewett Fellowships [997]
Blinded Veterans Association (BVA) **[2150]**
Bloch-Selinger Education Fund [3760]
Blood Assurance Foundation **[2152]**
Lawrence Bloomberg Entrance Awards [8034]
F.A. and Charlotte Blount Scholarships [9625]
Blow Molding Division Memorial Scholarships [8444]
Blues Ambassador Scholarships [7469]
Blues Heaven Foundation (BHF) **[2154]**
Jordan ABDO/Michael Bluett Memorial Scholar-
  ships [8592]
Harry and Edith Blunt Scholarships [608]
BMES Graduate and Undergraduate Student
  Awards [2100]
BMI Foundation **[2156]**
BMO Financial Group Scholarships [2111]
David and Camille Boatwright Endowed Scholar-
  ships [7169]
Sandra Bobbitt Continuing Education Scholar-
  ships [1836]
Edith and Arnold N. Bodtker Grants [3339]
Boeing Business Scholarships [4175]
Boeing Company Scholarships [8112]
Hagop Bogigian Scholarship Fund [1587]
Bohemian Lawyers Association of Chicago **[2161]**
Bohemian Lawyers Association of Chicago Scholar-
  ships [2162]
Bolick Foreign Student Scholarships [9141]
Frances P. Bolton Fellowships [7051]
Dorothy M. Bolyard Memorial Scholarships [7914]
BOMA/NY Scholarships [2207]
Carol Bond Community College Scholarships [6748]
Carol Bond Environmental Educator Scholar-
  ships [6749]
Carol Bond University Scholarships [6750]
Steve Bonk Scholarships [2634]
Lorne and Ruby Bonnell Scholarships [3182]
Barbara Bonnema Memorial Scholarships [7633]
Anne-Marie Bonner Scholarships [5115]
Ellis J. Bonner Scholarships [6080]
Scott Bonners Memorial Scholarships [2330]
Sam L. Booke, Sr. Scholarships [9626]
Admiral Mike Boorda Scholarship Program [6592]
T. Frank Booth Memorial Scholarship Fund [3888]
Diane Booth Memorial Scholarships [3761]
Tom Boots Memorial Scholarships [6601]
Maria and Czeslaw Borek Scholarships [7758]
National Security Education Program - David L.
  Boren Fellowships [9204]
David L. Boren Undergraduate Scholarships [1784]
Dr. Anita Borg Memorial Scholarships - USA [4193]
Maria Gonzales Borrero Scholarships [4414]
Geraldine Geistert Boss Scholarships [4272]

Tom Bost Scholarships [9260]
Boston City Federation "Return to School" Scholar-
  ships [4074]
William (Billbo) Boston Scholarships [7062]
Botanical Society of America (BSA) **[2163]**
Stephen Botein Fellowships [415]
Metropolitan Museum of Art Bothmer Fellow-
  ships [5783]
Dr. George T. Bottomley Scholarships [5707]
Richard J. Bouchard Scholarships [1050]
Miranda Bouldin General Scholarships [5513]
Bound to Stay Bound Books Scholarships (BTSB)
  [1826]
Leo Bourassa Scholarships [9455]
Jim Bourque Scholarships [1501]
Rev. Andrew L. Bouwhuis Memorial Scholarship
  Program [2668]
MAC Louisa Bowen Memorial Scholarships for
  Graduate Students in Archival Administra-
  tion [5854]
William R. Bowen Scholarships [3052]
Kathi Bowles Scholarships for Women in Technol-
  ogy [1898]
Billy Bowling Memorial Scholarships [6810]
Bowling Writers Association of America (BWAA)
  [2165]
CAG Margery Boyce Bursary Awards [2381]
Elizabeth W. Boyce Scholarships [2889]
Dr. Betty J. Boyd-Beu & Edwin G. Beu, Jr. Scholar-
  ships [9142]
W. Scott Boyd Group Grants [4884]
Boyd N. Lyon Scholarships [5554]
Corris Boyd Scholarships [1891]
Dody Boyd Scholarships [3096]
Verna Curry Boyer Scholarships [8718]
Eugene Boyko Scholarships [209]
Boys and Girls Club of Ottawa **[2167]**
Mildred Cater Bradham Social Work Fellow-
  ships [9801]
Carol June Bradley Awards [5955]
Charles Bradley Memorial Scholarships [4397]
Donald Franklin Bradley Memorial Scholar-
  ships [7470]
Ed Bradley Scholarships [7574]
Leon Bradley Scholarships [548]
Edward J. Brady Memorial Scholarships [1432]
W. Philip Braender and Nancy Coleman Braender
  Scholarships [4415]
Susan Brager Occupational Education Scholar-
  ships [7471]
William E. "Buck" Bragunier Scholarships [1556]
Brain Tumor Foundation for Children (BTFC)
  [2170]
UAA Pat Brakke Political Science Scholar-
  ships [9088]
George and Mary Brammer Scholarships [3481]
The Helen and Edward Brancati Teacher Develop-
  ment Scholarships [2644]
Charles F. Brandenburg Memorial Scholar-
  ships [2622]
Gladys Kamakakuokalani 'Ainoa Brandt Scholar-
  ships [5209]
Barbara Brantley Nursing Education Scholar-
  ships [1723]
Erika A. and George E. Brattain Sr. Scholarship
  Fund [9548]
Theodore E.D. Braun Research Travel Fellow-
  ships [1225]
Breakthrough to Nursing Scholarships [3976]
Ann Marie Bredefeld Scholarships [7170]
Kenneth H. Breeden Scholarships [5343]
The Lela Breitbart Memorial Scholarship
  Fund [8892]
Marion Breland-Bailey Awards [1713]
Marion Luna Brem/Pat McNeil Health and Education
  Scholarships [2938]
Brenda Renee Horn Memorial Scholarship [4029]
Breslauer Family Scholarships [7915]
Hilda E. Bretzlaff Foundation (HEBF) **[2172]**
Hilda E. Bretzlaff Foundation Scholarships [2173]
Rick Brewer Scholarships [9261]
Mary Ann Brichta Scholarships [9350]
James Bridenbaugh Memorial Scholarships [728]
Lloyd Bridges Scholarships [2679]
Bridgestone Americas Fellowships [9414]

Sponsor and Scholarship Index

Calvin Alumni Association-Illinois Scholarships [2298]
Calvin Alumni Association-Iowa/Pella Scholarships [2299]
Calvin Alumni Association-Maryland/Baltimore Scholarships [2300]
Calvin Alumni Association-Michigan Lakeshore Scholarships [2301]
Calvin Alumni Association-Michigan, Lansing Scholarships [2302]
Calvin Alumni Association-New Jersey Scholarships [2303]
Calvin Alumni Association-New York, Rochester Scholarships [2304]
Calvin Alumni Association-South Florida Scholarships [2305]
Calvin Alumni Association-South Florida Sophomore Scholarships [2306]
Calvin Alumni Association-Southeast Michigan Scholarships [2307]
Calvin Alumni Association-Southeastern Wisconsin Scholarships [2308]
Calvin Alumni Association Southern California Chapter Scholarships [2309]
Calvin Alumni Association-Southwest Michigan, Kalamazoo Scholarships [2310]
Calvin Alumni Association-Washington, D.C. Scholarships [2311]
Calvin Alumni Association-Washington, Lynden Scholarships [2312]
Calvin Alumni Association-Washington-Seattle/ Tacoma Scholarships [2313]
Camden County Bar Association (CCBA) **[2314]**
Camden County College **[2328]**
Camden County College Employee Memorial Scholarships [2331]
Camden County College Foundation Scholarships [2332]
Camden County Retired Educators Association Scholarships [2333]
Cameco Corp. **[2343]**
Cameco Corporation Scholarships in the Geological Sciences - Continuing Students [2344]
Cameco Corporation Scholarships in the Geological Sciences - Entering Students [2345]
Cameco Northern Scholarships - Technical Institute [2346]
Cameco Northern Scholarships - University [2347]
Stuart Cameron and Margaret McLeod Memorial Scholarships (SCMS) [4814]
Wesley C. Cameron Scholarships [6586]
Dalton Camp Awards [4012]
Thomas R. Camp Scholarships [1416]
Lois Campbell Scholarship Awards [4930]
Lucille Campbell Scholarship Fund [9550]
Robert G. Campbell Scholarships [7636]
Theodore R. Campbell Scholarships [240]
Campus Compact **[2349]**
Campus Discovery **[2351]**
Campus Discovery Scholarships [2352]
Canada Graduate Scholarship Program [8285]
Canada-Ukraine Parliamentary Program Internship Scholarships (CUPP) [9497]
Canada West Equipment Dealers Association **[2353]**
Canadian Anesthesiologists' Society (CAS) **[2355]**
Canadian Anesthesiologists' Society Research Awards [2357]
Canadian Association of Black Lawyers (CABL) **[2362]**
Canadian Association of Broadcasters (CAB) **[2364]**
Canadian Association for Business Economics (CABE) **[2367]**
Canadian Association of Cardiac Rehabilitation **[2369]**
Canadian Association of Cardiac Rehabilitation Graduate Scholarship Awards [2370]
Canadian Association of Chiefs of Police **[2371]**
Canadian Association of Drilling Engineers (CADE) **[2373]**
Canadian Association of Geographers (CAG) **[2376]**
Canadian Association of Geographers Historical Geography Study Group Awards [2379]

Canadian Association on Gerontology (CAG) **[2380]**
Canadian Association for HIV Research (CAHR) **[2383]**
Canadian Association of Insolvency and Restructuring Professionals (CAIRP) **[2385]**
Canadian Association of Law Libraries (CALL) **[2387]**
Canadian Association of Law Libraries CALL Research Grants [2389]
Canadian Association of Law Teachers (CALT) **[2392]**
Canadian Association of Law Teachers Award for Academic Excellence [2393]
Canadian Association of Neuroscience Nurses (CANN) **[2394]**
Canadian Association of Oilwell Drilling Contractors (CAODC) **[2398]**
Canadian Association for the Practical Study of Law in Education (CAPSLE) **[2401]**
Canadian Association for the Practical Study of Law in Education Fellowships [2402]
Canadian Association of Radiation Oncology (CARO) **[2403]**
Canadian Association of Second Language Teachers (CASLT) **[2405]**
Canadian Association of Student Activity Advisors (CASAA) **[2408]**
Canadian Association for Studies in Co-operation Scholarships Lemaire Co-operative Studies Awards (CASC) [2431]
Canadian Association for Theatre Research (CATR) **[2411]**
Canadian Association of University Teachers **[2414]**
Canadian Authors Association-Ottawa Branch **[2416]**
Canadian Bar Association (CBA) **[2418]**
Canadian Blood Services **[2420]**
Canadian Blood Services Graduate Fellowships [2421]
Canadian Blood Services Postdoctoral Fellowships [2422]
Canadian Cartographic Association (CCA) **[2423]**
Canadian Centre for Occupational Health and Safety (CCOHS) **[2425]**
Canadian Civil Liberties Association (CCLA) **[2427]**
Canadian Co-operative Association (CCA) **[2430]**
Canadian Communication Association (CCA) **[2434]**
Canadian Corporate Counsel Association (CCCA) **[2437]**
Canadian Council for Aboriginal Business (CCAB) **[2439]**
Canadian Council on International Law (CCIL) **[2442]**
Canadian Council of Technicians and Technologists (CCTT) **[2444]**
Canadian Council of Technicians and Technologists Scholarships for Technology Students [2445]
Canadian Cystic Fibrosis Foundation (CCFF) **[2446]**
Canadian Diabetes Association (CDA) **[2450]**
Canadian Engineering Memorial Foundation **[2452]**
Canadian Evaluation Society Educational Fund (CESEF) **[2458]**
Canadian Evaluation Society Educational Fund Scholarships [2459]
Canadian Evaluation Society Memorial Scholarships [2475]
Canadian Federation of Independent Grocers (CFIG) **[2460]**
Canadian Federation of Independent Grocers National Scholarships [2461]
Canadian Federation for Sexual Health (CFSH) **[2462]**
Canadian Federation of University Women Etobicoke Bursary [9324]
Canadian Fertility and Andrology Society (CFAS) **[2465]**
Canadian Fire Safety Association (CFSA) **[2467]**
Canadian Gerontological Nursing Association (CGNA) **[2473]**
Canadian Group Psychotherapy Association **[2477]**
Canadian Hard of Hearing Association (CHHA) **[2480]**

Canadian Hard of Hearing Association Scholarships [2481]
Canadian Hemophilia Society (CHS) **[2482]**
Canadian Hospitality Foundation (CHF) **[2486]**
Canadian Hospitality Foundation College Entrance Scholarships [2488]
Canadian Hospitality Foundation University Entrance Scholarships [2489]
Canadian Hydrographic Association **[2491]**
Canadian Hydrographic Association Student Awards [2492]
Canadian Identification Society (CIS) **[2493]**
Canadian Identification Society Essay Scholarship Awards [2494]
Canadian Institute for the Administration of Justice (CIAJ) **[2497]**
Canadian Institute for Advanced Legal Studies **[2499]**
Canadian Institute of Planners (CIP) **[2501]**
Canadian Institute of Ukrainian Studies (CIUS) **[2503]**
Canadian Institutes of Health Research **[2506]**
Canadian Iranian Foundation (CIF) **[2508]**
Canadian Iranian Foundation Scholarships [2509]
Canadian IT Law Association (IT.Can) **[2510]**
Canadian IT Law Association Student Writing Contest [2511]
Canadian Japanese-Mennonite Scholarships [5767]
Canadian Journalism Foundation (CJF) **[2512]**
Canadian Lawyers Abroad (CLA) **[2516]**
Canadian Library Association (CLA) **[2518]**
Canadian Medical Foundation (CMF) **[2522]**
Canadian Meteorological and Oceanographic Society (CMOS) **[2524]**
Canadian National Institute for the Blind (CNIB) **[2530]**
Canadian Nurses Foundation (CNF) **[2532]**
Canadian Nurses Foundation - Baxter Corporation Scholarships [2537]
Canadian Nurses Foundation Northern Scholarships [2538]
Canadian Nurses Foundation Scholarships [2539]
Canadian Occupational Therapy Foundation (COTF) **[2557]**
Canadian Occupational Therapy Foundation Graduate Scholarships [2558]
Canadian Occupational Therapy Foundation Invacare Master's Scholarships [2559]
Canadian Office Products Association (COPA) **[2562]**
Canadian Organic Growers **[2564]**
Canadian Pain Society (CPS) **[2566]**
Canadian Pain Society Post-Doctoral Fellowship Awards [2567]
Canadian Paraplegic Association (CPA) **[2577]**
Canadian Parking Association (CPA) - Association Canadienne du Stationnement (ACS) **[2580]**
Canadian Parking Association Scholarships [2581]
Canadian Picture Pioneers **[2582]**
Canadian Picture Pioneers Scholarships [2583]
Canadian Polar Commission Scholarships [1734]
Canadian Political Science Association **[2584]**
Canadian Poultry Research Council **[2587]**
Canadian Poultry Research Council Postgraduate Scholarships [2588]
Canadian Purchasing Research Foundation **[2589]**
Canadian Purchasing Research Foundation Prize [2590]
Canadian Sanitation Supply Association (CSSA) **[2591]**
Canadian Sanitation Supply Association Scholarships [2592]
Canadian Seniors' Golf Association Scholarships [4181]
Canadian Simmental Association (CSA) **[2595]**
Canadian Society of Biblical Studies (CSBS) **[2597]**
Canadian Society for Clinical Investigation (CSCI) **[2599]**
Canadian Society of Club Managers (CSCM) **[2602]**
Canadian Society for Eighteenth Century Studies (CSECS) **[2604]**
Canadian Society of Exploration Geophysicists (CSEG) **[2606]**
Canadian Society for Medical Laboratory Science (CSMLS) **[2608]**

CfA Postdoctoral Fellowships [4471]
CFERP Masters Fellowships [3030]
CFIDS Association of America NP Student Scholarships [376]
CFT/ACPSOP Scholarships [2798]
CGPF Endowments Conference Scholarships [2478]
Rick Chace Foundation Scholarships [1829]
Chaine des Rotisseurs Scholarships [691]
Jeanne S. Chall Research Fellowships [4975]
Challenge Met Scholarships [1077]
Mariam K. Chamberlain Fellowships in Women and Public Policy [4835]
Logan S. Chambers Individual Scholarships [4885]
Mary Anne Chambers Scholarships [5117]
Chambersburg/Fannett-Metal School District Scholarship Fund [3937]
Chambliss Astronomy Achievement Student Awards [570]
Jason Chaney Memorial Scholarship Fund [9553]
Channabasappa Memorial Scholarships [4918]
Harry H. and Floy B. Chapin Scholarships [3145]
Nancy J. Chapman Scholarships [1753]
S. Penny Chappell Scholarships [7279]
Chapter 6 Fairfield County Scholarships [8379]
Chapter 17 - St. Louis Scholarships [8372]
Chapter 23 - Quad Cities Iowa/Illinois Scholarships [8374]
Chapter 31 - Peoria Endowed Scholarships [8375]
Chapter 52 - Wichita Scholarships [8377]
Chapter 56 - Fort Wayne Scholarships [8378]
Chapter 67 - Phoenix Scholarships [8380]
Chapter 93 - Albuquerque Scholarships [8381]
Chapter 198 - Downriver Detroit Scholarships [8373]
Chapter 311 - Tri City Scholarships [8376]
Chapter One - Detroit Founding Chapter Scholarships [8382]
Charles "Chuck" McAdams Memorial Scholarships [8809]
Charlotte Housing Authority Scholarship Fund (CHASF) [3894]
Charlotte-Mecklenburg Schools Scholarship Incentive Program [3895]
Abram and Sylvia Chasens Teaching and Research Fellowships [395]
Chateau Ste. Michelle Scholarship Fund [2975]
Emilie Du Chatelet Awards [1226]
Chattanooga Bar Association (CBA) **[2735]**
Chautauqua Scholarships Program [4969]
Cesar E. Chavez Scholarships [7637]
CHEA Undergraduate Scholarship Program for Students with Disabilities [2260]
CHEA Vocational Grants [2261]
Cheatham County Scholarships [3100]
Cheerful Giver Scholarships [7918]
Chelsea Publishing Company Inc. **[2737]**
Chemical Heritage Foundation (CHF) **[2739]**
Chemical Heritage Foundation Travel Grants (CHF) [2740]
Chernos Essay Competition [2429]
Cherokee Nation **[2741]**
Cherokee Nation Graduate Scholarships [2742]
Cherokee Nation Pell Scholarships [2743]
Cherokee Nation Scholarships [2744]
Cherry Lane Foundation/Music Alive! Scholarships [1208]
Sgt. Michael F. Cherven Memorial Scholarships [5666]
Buena M. Chesshir Memorial Women's Educational Scholarships [9440]
Cheyenne High School Faculty Memorial Scholarships [7475]
Chi Chapter Undergraduate Scholarships [3369]
Melba Dawn Chiarenza Scholarship Fund [9554]
Chicago Bar Foundation (CBF) **[2745]**
Chicago Division Scholarships [5858]
Chicago FM Club Scholarships [1078]
Chicago Railroad Mechanical Association (CRMA) **[2747]**
Chicana/Latina Foundation (CLF) **[2749]**
Chicana Latina Scholarship Fund [2750]
Child of Alumni Book Voucher Awards [4742]
Child and Family Advocacy Fellowships [9486]
Julia Child Memorial Scholarships [692]
Kevin Child Scholarships [6319]
Childbirth Educator Program Scholarships [5326]

John and Ruth Childe Scholarships [8594]
Childhood Cancer Canada Foundation **[2751]**
Childhood Cancer Foundation Scholarships [2752]
Childhood Cancer Survivor Scholarships [2753]
Children of Evangeline Section Scholarships [8435]
Children of Unitarian Universalist Ministers College Scholarships [8995]
Children's Hospital of Philadelphia **[2754]**
Children's Literature Association (ChLA) **[2761]**
Children's Memorial Hospital Postgraduate Administrative Fellowships [5539]
Children's Scholarship Fund of Charlotte [3896]
Jane Coffin Childs Memorial Fund **[2763]**
Jane Coffin Childs Memorial Fund - Medical Research Fellowships [2764]
Charline Chilson Scholarships [3407]
Chinese American Medical Society (CAMS) **[2765]**
Chinese American Medical Society Summer Research Fellowships Program [2766]
Chinese Professionals Association of Canada (CPAC) **[2769]**
Chinese Professionals Association of Canada BMO Diversity Scholarships [2771]
Chinese Professionals Association of Canada Education Foundation Awards [2772]
Chinese Professionals Association of Canada Journalism Scholarships [2773]
Chinese Professionals Association of Canada Professional Achievement Awards [2774]
Helen Krich Chinoy Dissertation Research Fellowships [1360]
Choose Your Future Scholarships [3101]
Chopin Foundation of the United States **[2776]**
Chopin Foundation of the United States Scholarships [2777]
Chopivsky Fellowships [9498]
Choristers Guild (CG) **[2778]**
Chretien International Research Grants [571]
Patricia Smith Christensen Scholarships [8195]
Frances N. Christian Memorial Endowment Nursing Scholarships [8740]
Almeric Christian Memorial Scholarships [9438]
Christian Missionary Scholarship Foundation (CMSF) **[2780]**
Christian Pharmacist Fellowship International [2783]
Christian Pharmacists Fellowship International (CPFI) **[2782]**
Christian Record Services for the Blind (CRSB) **[2784]**
Christian Scholarship Foundation (CSF) **[2786]**
Christmas Tree Chapter Scholarship Awards [6933]
Commander Daniel J. Christovich Scholarship Fund [2922]
Chrysalis Scholarships [1901]
Chrysler Foundation Scholarship Awards [4546]
Chrysler Technical Scholarship Fund [3358]
CHS - Bursary Program Scholarships [2483]
CHS - Mature Student Bursary Program Scholarships [2484]
CHS Scholarships [2485]
Chugach Gem & Mineral Society Scholarships [9089]
Church Family Scholarships [5418]
Churchill Family Scholarships [5575]
Winston Churchill Foundation **[2788]**
Edward D. Churchill Research Scholarships [562]
The Churchill Scholarships [2789]
CIA Undergraduate Scholarships [1785]
CIBC Scholarships [2115]
CIGNA Healthcare Graduate Scholarships [6290]
CIGNA Healthcare Undergraduate Scholarships [6291]
CIHR Health Law and Policy Fellowships [2791]
CIHR Training Program in Health Law and Policy **[2790]**
Cincinnati High School Scholarships [2799]
Cincinnati Scholarship Foundation (CSF) **[2792]**
Cintas Foundation **[2880]**
Cintas Foundation Fellowships in Architecture [2881]
Cintas Foundation Fellowships in Visual Arts [2882]
CIP Fellow's Travel Scholarships [2502]
Antonio Cirino Memorial Art Education Fellowships [7787]
CISDL Associate Fellows [2730]
CISDL Legal Research Fellows [2731]

CISDL Senior Research Fellows [2732]
Carlos Enrique Cisneros Point Scholarships [7356]
Citi Foundation Scholarship Program [805]
Citi/TELACU Scholarships [8820]
Citizens' Scholarship Foundation of Wakefield **[2884]**
Citizens' Scholarship Foundation of Wakefield Scholarships [2885]
City of Sanibel Employee Dependent Scholarships [8595]
City of Toronto Graduate Scholarships for Women in Mathematics [9325]
City of Toronto Queen Elizabeth II Sesquicentennial Scholarships in Community Health Nursing for Graduates [9326]
City of Toronto Queen Elizabeth II Sesquicentennial Scholarships in Community Health Nursing for Undergraduates [9327]
City of Toronto Scholarships for Aboriginal Students [9328]
City of Toronto Women's Studies Scholarships [9329]
Civic Music Association of Milwaukee **[2886]**
Civil Air Patrol (CAP) **[2892]**
Civil Air Patrol Scholarships for School and Flying [2893]
Civitan International (CI) **[2894]**
Civitan Shropshire Scholarships [2895]
CJF Canadian Journalism Fellowships [2513]
CLA Student Summer Internship Program [2517]
Clackamas Chapter Scholarship Awards [6934]
Clackamas County Farm Bureau Scholarships [6946]
Claes Nobel Academic Scholarships for Members [6502]
Clan Ross Association of the United States **[2896]**
Clan Ross Foundation Scholarships [2897]
Cecil Earl Clapp, Sr. Memorial Scholarships [6811]
David and Deborah Clark Fellowships [6979]
Michelle Clark Fellowships [7576]
Vickie Clark-Flaherty Scholarships [6772]
Willis W. and Ethel M. Clark Foundation Fellowships [2899]
Willis W. and Ethel M. Clark Foundation **[2898]**
Clark High School Academy of Finance Scholarships [7476]
Clark High School Alumni Leadership Circle Scholarships [7477]
Clark High School Teacher Education Academy Scholarships [7478]
Howard A. Clark Horticulture Scholarships [3102]
Robert A. Clark Memorial Educational Scholarships [6510]
Fisher Clark Memorial Endowed Scholarships [5419]
Andrew Blake Clark Memorial Scholarships [9629]
Thomas Arkle Clark Scholar-Leader of the Year Endowed Scholarships [7254]
Athalie Clarke Endowed Scholarships [7174]
Lucy and Charles W.E. Clarke Scholarships [1660]
CLASS Fund Irrigation Scholarship Program [5331]
Classic Wines of California Scholarships [2244]
Classical Association of Canada **[2900]**
J. Clawson Mills Scholarships [5784]
Clay Postdoctoral Fellowships [4472]
CLCA Landscape Educational Advancement Foundation Scholarships [2263]
Brian Dane Cleary Memorial Scholarships [7175]
Lula Faye Clegg Memorial Scholarship Fund [3897]
Bruce Clement Post-Secondary Education Scholarships [6631]
Greg Clerk Awards [2514]
Cleveland Executive Fellowships (CEF) [2903]
Cleveland Leadership Center **[2902]**
Geraldine Clewell Fellowships - Doctoral Student [7280]
Geraldine Clewell Fellowships - Masteral [7281]
Geraldine Clewell Scholarships - Undergraduate [7282]
Justice Robert L. Clifford Fellowships [5930]
James L. Clifford Prize [1227]
David H. Clift Scholarships [900]
Bryan Cline Memorial Soccer Scholarship Program [279]
Clinic for the Rehabilitation of Wildlife (CROW) **[2904]**

Clinical Laboratory Management Association (CLMA) **[2906]**
Clinical Laboratory Management Association High School Senior Scholarships [2907]
Clinical Laboratory Management Association Undergraduate Scholarships [2908]
Clinical Pain Management Fellowship Awards [2568]
Clinical Pharmacy Post-Pharm.D. Fellowships in the Biomedical Research Sciences [758]
Clinical Research Fellowship for Medical Students [3522]
Clinical Research Training Fellowships [373]
Clinical Toxicology Scholarships [537]
Clinician Scientist Development Awards [7127]
UAA Edward Rollin Clinton Memorial for Music [9090]
George H. Clinton Scholarship Fund [7065]
CLN Scholarships [3237]
Closs/Parnitzke/Clarke Scholarships [7283]
Austin M. Cloyd, Matthew G. Gwaltney and Maxine S. Turner Doctoral Scholarships [9461]
Club Managers Association of America (CMAA) **[2909]**
Club Managers Association of America Research Grants (CMAA) [2910]
The Club at Morningside Scholarships [7919]
CMAA Student Conference Travel Grants [2911]
CMSF Scholarships [2781]
CN Scholarships for Women [8307]
CNA Foundation Scholarships [1335]
CNST Scholarships [1735]
Dr. Princeton L. Co Emergency Fund for Dental Hygiene Scholarships [8113]
COACH: Canada's Health Informatics Association **[2914]**
Coaching Association of Canada (CAC) **[2916]**
Coalition of Higher Education Assistance Organizations (COHEAO) **[2918]**
Coast Guard Foundation **[2920]**
Coast Guard Foundation Enlisted Education Grants [2923]
Coast Guard Foundation Scholarships [2924]
Coastal Bend Community Foundation (CBCF) **[2931]**
The Helena B. Cobb Annual Scholarships [9728]
The Helena B. Cobb Four-Year Higher Education Grants [9729]
J.C. and Rheba Cobb Memorial Scholarships [6198]
Gordon W. and Agnes P. Cobb Scholarships [3567]
John Coburn and Harold Winters Student Award in Plasma Science and Technology [1980]
Coca-Cola First Generation Scholarships [806]
Coca-Cola Scholars Foundation **[2965]**
Coca-Cola Scholars Foundation Four-Year Awards for Seniors [2966]
Geri Coccodrilli Culinary Scholarship Fund [4209]
Johnnie L. Cochran, Jr./MWH Scholarships [6292]
Cocke, Szpanka and Taylor Scholarships [9462]
Frank M. Coda Scholarships [1266]
CODY Foundation Fund [3938]
Coeur d'Alene Alumni Scholarships [5420]
Steven L. Coffey Memorial Scholarships [3568]
Thomas D. Coffield Scholarships [4276]
Frank M. Coffin Family Law Fellowships [5569]
Claude T. Coffman Memorial Scholarships [9221]
Donald O. Coffman Scholarships [7405]
Ruth M. Cogan Scholarship Fund [8661]
COHEAO Scholarships [2919]
Marshall A. Cohen Entrance Awards [8039]
Maurice and Marilyn Cohen Fund for Doctoral Dissertation Fellowships in Jewish Studies [3974]
Ardis Cohoon Scholarships [9263]
Warren E. "Whitey" Cole American Society of Highway Engineers Scholarships [3764]
Cole Family Scholarships [7406]
Cole Foundation Undergraduate Scholarship Program [3898]
Arthur H. Cole Grants in Aid [3582]
Paul Cole Scholarships [8420]
Sally Cole Visual Arts Scholarship Fund [3899]
Dennis Coleman Choral Conducting Scholarships [7407]
Colgate-Palmolive/HDA Foundation Scholarships [4555]
College Art Association (CAA) **[2967]**

College Art Association Professional Development Fellowships [2968]
College Art Association Wyeth Publication Grants [2969]
The College Club of Hartford Scholarships [4418]
College of Healthcare Information Management Executives (CHIME) **[2970]**
College of Marin Gay and Lesbian Student Scholarships [7847]
College Student Educators International **[2972]**
College Success Foundation (CSF) **[2974]**
Collegiate Soaring Association (CSA) **[2979]**
Jennet Colliflower Nursing Scholarships [3315]
Irene Culver Collins and Louis Franklin Collins Scholarships [3054]
Captain Winifred Quick Collins Scholarships [6587]
Elmer and Rosa Lee Collins Scholarships [9630]
Erma Collins Scholarships [2116]
Lloyd E. and Rachel S. Collins Scholarships [9631]
Paul Collins Scholarships [4277]
Zoe E. Collymore Page Scholarships [6145]
Colorado Association of Stormwater and Floodplain Managers (CASFM) **[2981]**
Colorado Broadcasters Association (CBA) **[2983]**
Colorado Broadcasters Association Continuing Education Scholarships [2984]
Colorado Christian University Alumni Association **[2985]**
Colorado Hotel and Lodging Association (CH&LA) **[2987]**
Colorado Nurses Association: Nightingale Scholarships [2993]
Colorado Nurses Foundation (CNF) **[2989]**
Colorado Nurses Foundation Nightingale Scholarships [2994]
Colorado Organization of Nursing Leaders Scholarships [2995]
Colorado PROSTART/Art Institute of Colorado Art Scholarships for High School Seniors [1627]
Colorado Society of Certified Public Accountants (COCPA) **[3004]**
ColorMasters Scholarships [4055]
Columbian Lawyers Association of Westchester County **[3008]**
Columbian Lawyers Association of Westchester County Scholarships [3009]
Columbus Citizens Foundation **[3011]**
Columbus Citizens Foundation College Scholarships [3012]
Columbus Citizens Foundation High School Scholarships [3013]
Robert N. Colwell Memorial Fellowships [1666]
Committee 12 - Rail Transit Scholarships [1122]
Committee 27 - Maintenance-of-Way Work Equipment Scholarships [1123]
Committee of 200 (C200) **[3014]**
Commonwealth Fund **[3016]**
Commonwealth Fund/Harvard University Fellowships in Minority Health Policy [3019]
Commonwealth "Good Citizen" Scholarships [1795]
Communal Studies Association (CSA) **[3021]**
Communal Studies Association Research Fellowships [3022]
Communication Disorder/Speech Therapy Scholarships [4075]
Communications Workers of America **[3023]**
Communications Workers of America Scholarships [3024]
Communities Adolescents Nutrition Fitness (CAN-FIT) **[3025]**
Community-based Natural Resource Management Assistantships [3031]
Community and Economic Development Association (CEDA) **[3027]**
Community Forestry and Environmental Research Partnerships (CEFRP) **[3029]**
Community Foundation of Calhoun County (CFCC) **[3032]**
The Community Foundation DBI Scholarships [3103]
Community Foundation of the Eastern Shore (CFES) **[3051]**
Community Foundation of the Fox River Valley **[3072]**
Community Foundation of the Fox River Valley Scholarships [3073]

Community Foundation for Greater Atlanta **[3074]**
Community Foundation for Greater New Haven **[3077]**
Community Foundation of Greene County (CFGC) **[3085]**
The Community Foundation of Middle Tennessee (CFMT) **[3090]**
Community Foundation of Northern Illinois **[3141]**
Community Foundation of Prince Edward Island (CFPEI) **[3179]**
Community Foundation of Sarasota County **[3186]**
Community Foundation of Sarasota County Adult Learner Scholarships [3189]
Community Foundation Scholarships [3146]
Community Foundation for Southeast Michigan (CF-SEM) **[3195]**
The Community Foundation Student Education Loans [3104]
Community Foundation of Western Massachusetts **[3206]**
Community Foundation of Western Massachusetts Community Scholarship Program [3207]
Comparative Perspectives on Chinese Culture and Society Grants [676]
Compassionate Care Scholarships [7408]
Composite Panel Association (CPA) **[3208]**
Alan Compton and Bob Stanley Professional Scholarships [2016]
Tom and Judith Comstock Scholarships [1079]
Desmond Conacher Scholarships [2901]
Richard G. Condon Prize [8469]
Maridell Braham Condon Scholarships [8162]
Conference on Asian Pacific American Leadership (CAPAL) **[3210]**
Conference on Asian Pacific American Leadership Scholarships [3211]
Conference of State Bank Supervisors (CSBS) **[3212]**
Conference of State Bank Supervisors Graduate School Scholarships [3213]
Congressional Black Caucus Foundation (CBCF) **[3214]**
Congressional Hispanic Caucus Institute (CHCI) **[3223]**
Congressional Hispanic Caucus Institute Graduate and Young Professional Fellowships [3224]
Congressional Hispanic Caucus Institute Public Policy Fellowships [3225]
Congressional Hispanic Caucus Institute Scholarships [3226]
Congressional Scholarship Awards [4016]
Congressional Science Fellowships [1302]
Alan H. Conklin Business Aviation Management Scholarships [6163]
CSF T.L. Conlan Memorial Scholarships [2800]
Connecticut Association of Land Surveyors (CALS) **[3227]**
Connecticut Association of Land Surveyors Memorial Scholarships [3228]
Connecticut Association of Latinos in Higher Education (CALAHE) **[3229]**
Connecticut Association of Latinos in Higher Education Scholarships [4419]
Connecticut Building Congress Scholarships [4420]
Connecticut Capitol Scholarship Program [4421]
Connecticut Construction Industries Association (CCIA) **[3234]**
Connecticut League for Nursing (CLN) **[3236]**
Connecticut Mortgage Bankers Scholarships-Social Affairs Committee [4422]
Connecticut Nurserymen's Foundation Scholarships [4423]
Cecilia Connelly Memorial Scholarships in Underwater Archaeology [9698]
Dwight O. Conner and Ellen Conner Lepp/Danhart Scholarships [7066]
Karen Connick Memorial Scholarships [4257]
Louis M. Connor Jr. Scholarships [9264]
Connor/Spafford Scholarships [4182]
Patricia Powder Conolly Memorial Scholarships [5777]
Conservation Department Program Fellowships [8258]
Conservation Guest Scholar Grants [4139]
Constangy, Brooks and Smith, LLP **[3238]**

Sponsor and Scholarship Index

Directors of Health Promotion and Education **[3456]**

Disabled American Veterans (DAV) **[3458]**

Disabled War Veterans Scholarships [1559]

Walt Disney Company Foundation Scholarships [5173]

Dissertation Fellowships in East European Studies [677]

Dissertation Proposal Development Fellowships [8282]

Distinguished Flying Cross Society (DFCS) **[3460]**

Distinguished Flying Cross Society Scholarships [3461]

Distinguished Young Women **[3462]**

Distinguished Young Women Scholarships [3463]

LaRue A. Ditmore Music Scholarships [9706]

Diversified Investment Advisors Leaders in Healthcare Scholarships [4788]

Diversity Dissertation Scholarships [1032]

Diversity Executive Leadership Program Scholarships [1184]

Diversity Fellowship Program (DFP) [5928]

Diversity Scholars Awards [3239]

Robert A. and Barbara Divine Graduate Student Travel Grants [8338]

Dixon Hughes Goodman, LLP **[3464]**

Dixon Hughes Goodman LLP Annual Scholarship [3465]

Dr. Allan A. Dixon Memorial Scholarships [2596]

William Donald Dixon Research Grants [2495]

Daniel B. Dixon Scholarships [326]

Peggy Dixon Two-Year Scholarships [8438]

Mychajlo Dmytrenko Fine Arts Foundation Scholarships [9074]

Grace O. Doane Scholarships [3485]

Charles Dobbins FTA Scholarships [4033]

Julian Dobranowski Memorial Scholarships [7759]

Dr. Feroz Ahmed Memorial Educational Post-Graduate Scholarships [8216]

Doctoral Degree Scholarships in Cancer Nursing [596]

Doctoral Fellowships - Dissertation [4779]

Doctoral Fellowships - Graduate [4780]

Doctors IRA & UDAYA Nursing Scholarships [8598]

Document Management and Graphic Communications Industry Scholarships [3627]

Doddridge County Promise Scholarships [7072]

F. Atlee Dodge Maintenance Scholarships [192]

Robert Winchester Dodson Scholarships [9268]

DOE Computational Science Graduate Fellowships (DOE CSGF) [5306]

Hans H. and Margaret B. Doe Scholarships [7926]

Emmett J. Doerr Memorial Distinguished Scout Scholarships [6249]

Dofflemyer Scholarships [6250]

Dokmo Family Scholarships [7927]

Dole Food Fellowships [6981]

Dollar-A-Day Academic Scholarships [3467]

Dollar-A-Day Scholarship Fund **[3466]**

Dolphin Scholarship Foundation **[3468]**

Dolphin Scholarships [3469]

Scott Dominguez - Craters of the Moon Chapter Scholarships [1336]

Dominican Bar Association (DBA) **[3470]**

Dominio of Canada Insurance Scholarships [7324]

Don Aron Scholarships [6208]

Marian Jones Donaldson Scholarship Fund [3769]

Harvey N. Dondero Communication and Journalism Excellence Scholarships [7482]

Hon. Ralph W.E. Donges Memorial Scholarships [2317]

Doniphan Community Foundation Scholarships [4258]

Harry A. Donn Scholarships [4427]

Mickey Donnelly Memorial Scholarships [7483]

Jim Doogan Memorial Scholarships [9185]

Doraine Pursuit of Educational Excellence Scholarships [2944]

Dorchester Woman's Club Scholarships [4076]

Joseph M. Dorgan Scholarships [3486]

Dr. Michael Dorizas Memorial Scholarships [4514]

Pauly D'Orlando Memorial Art Scholarships [8996]

Dosatron International Inc. Scholarships [731]

Eric Dostie Memorial College Scholarships [6322]

Father Connie Dougherty Scholarships [3191]

Robert E. Dougherty Scholarships [3209]

Sergeant Douglas and Charlotte DeHorse Scholarships [2661]

Douglas-Coldwell Foundation (DCF) **[3472]**

Douglas-Coldwell Foundation Scholarships in Social Affairs [3474]

Chapter 116 - Kalamazoo - Roscoe Douglas Scholarships [8383]

Tommy Douglas Scholarships [6548]

Douglass Foundation Fellowships in American Art [5786]

Harold K. Douthit Regional Scholarships [6857]

Dow Chemical Company Fellowships [6427]

Margaret Dowell-Gravatt, M.D. Scholarships [2059]

Downeast Energy and Building Supply **[3476]**

Downeast Energy Scholarships [3477]

Downeast Feline Scholarships [5577]

Jay Downes Memorial Scholarships [2945]

Rodger Doxsey Travel Prizes [572]

Nettie Dracup Memorial Scholarships [643]

AAGS Joseph F. Dracup Scholarship Awards [644]

Drake University Law School **[3478]**

Drake University Law School Law Opportunity Scholarships - Disadvantage [3487]

Drake University Law School Law Opportunity Scholarships - Diversity [3488]

Drake University Law School Public Service Scholarships [3489]

The Drama Therapy Fund **[3517]**

The Drama Therapy Fund Graduate Research Grants [3518]

The Drama Therapy Fund Graduate Student Research Awards [3519]

Lou Drane Music Scholarships [3940]

The "Drawn to Art" Fellowships [417]

Vivian Drenckhahn Student Scholarships [8477]

Cleveland Drennon, Jr. Memorial Scholarships [9222]

Wilma Sackett Dressel Scholarships [8166]

Margaret Drew Alpha Fellowships [7285]

Charles Drew Scholarships [1754]

Louis Dreyfus Warner-Chappell City College Scholarships [1211]

DRI Law Student Diversity Scholarships [2144]

Thomas J. Drinan Memorial Fellowships [7604]

Drinkwater Family Scholarships [7928]

Mary Ellen Driscoll Scholarships [4183]

Lillian Cooper Droke Memorial Scholarships [5778]

Richard Drukker Memorial Scholarships [6651]

Drum Major Institute Scholars [8144]

Sergeant Major Douglas R. Drum Memorial Scholarship Fund [936]

Janusz & Roma Drzymala Scholarships [7760]

W.E.B. Du Bois Fellowships [6355]

Martin Duberman Fellowships [2702]

Lee Dubin Scholarship Fund [7848]

DuBois Brothers Scholarships [2318]

Charles Dubose Scholarships [4428]

John W. Duckett Jr., AFUD Pediatric Research Scholarships [8432]

Mark Duda Scholarship Fund [3446]

Deborah Gandee Dudding Memorial Scholarships [7073]

Edward Leon Duhamel Freemasons Scholarships [7789]

Doris Duke Charitable Foundation (DDCF) **[3521]**

Doris Duke Conservation Fellows Program [9615]

Aleksander & Stefania Dulemba Scholarships [7761]

Edward J. Dulis Scholarships [5690]

Duluth Building and Construction Trades Council Scholarships [3527]

Duluth Central High School Alumni Scholarships [3528]

Duluth-Superior Area Community Foundation **[3523]**

Dumbarton Oaks Fellowships [3549]

Dumbarton Oaks Junior Fellowships [3550]

Dumbarton Oaks Research Library and Collection **[3548]**

Dunbar Heritage Scholarships [8599]

Duncan Aviation Scholarships [126]

Wade and Marcelene Duncan Scholarships [9635]

Lord Dundonald Chapter Imperial Order Daughters of the Empire Scholarships (IODE) [6996]

Ed Dunkelblau Scholarships [1704]

Travis Dunning Memorial Scholarships [7484]

DuPage County Bar Association (DCBA) **[3552]**

Bus and Mary Ellen Durant Timberline High School Endowed Scholarships [5426]

William R. Durham/Theater Scholarships [3148]

Durning Sisters Scholarships [3370]

Joe Durso Memorial Scholarships [5921]

Dutchess County Bar Association (DCBA) **[3554]**

Roger C. Duvoisin, MD Research Grants [982]

Sue and Ken Dyer Foundation Travel Scholarships [3941]

Joshua Dyke Family Scholarships [8895]

Dystonia Medical Research Foundation (DMRF) **[3556]**

Dystonia Medical Research Foundation Fellowships [3557]

EAA Tuition Scholarships [3647]

EAA Workshop Scholarships [3648]

Josephine P. White Eagle Graduate Fellowships [4591]

Eagles Fly for Leukemia Scholarships [2755]

EAIA Research Grants [3561]

Howard G. and Gladys A. Eakes Memorial Scholarships [4259]

EAPSI Fellowships [6467]

Amelia Earhart Fellowship Program [9811]

Amelia Earhart Memorial Academic Scholarships [6724]

Earl and Countess of Wessex - World Championships in Athletics Scholarships [244]

Fernandez Earle Scholarship Foundation **[3558]**

Fernandez Earle Undergraduate Entrance Scholarships [3559]

Early American Industries Association (EAIA) **[3560]**

Early Career Postdoctoral Fellowships in East European Studies [678]

Early Childhood Educators Scholarship Program [5684]

Robert E. Early Memorial Scholarships [3490]

Earthquake Engineering Research Institute (EERI) **[3562]**

Bob East Scholarships [6450]

East Tennessee Foundation (ETF) **[3564]**

East Tennessee Foundation Scholarships [9223]

Patricia Ann Hughes Eastaugh Memorial Teaching Scholarships [9147]

Easter Seals Ontario **[3571]**

Eastern Communication Association (ECA) **[3574]**

Eastern Orthodox Scouting Scholarships [6251]

Eastern Shore Building Industry Association Scholarships [3055]

Eastman Community Music School (ECMS) **[3577]**

David Eaton Scholarships [8997]

The Christoph Daniel Ebeling Fellowships [418]

Ellen Eberhardt Memorial Scholarships [8720]

ECA Applied Urban Communication Research Grants [3575]

ECA Centennial Scholarships [3576]

John E. Echlin Memorial Scholarships [1939]

ECMS Scholarships [3578]

Ecological Society of America (ESA) **[3579]**

Economic Development Division Graduate Scholarships [1010]

Economic History Association (EHA) **[3581]**

ECT Foundation Master Scholarships [1763]

Edgecliff Alumni Awards [9768]

Edgecliff McAuley Art Scholarships [9769]

Edgecliff McAuley Music Scholarships [9770]

EDiS Company **[3585]**

Editors Association of Canada (EAC) **[3587]**

Vivian Edmonds Scholarships [9269]

S. Randolph Edmonds Young Scholars Competition [2140]

Melanie and Todd Edmonson Memorial Scholarships [3035]

Edmonton Epilepsy Association (EEA) **[3589]**

Edmonton Epilepsy Continuing Education Scholarships [3590]

Edon Farmers Cooperative Association Inc. **[3591]**

Edon Farmers Cooperative Scholarships [3592]

Education Factor Scholarships [5735]

Education is Power Scholarships [6323]

Education Resource Center Scholarships (ERC) [8211]

Educational Administration Scholarship Awards [545]

Educational Audiology Association (EAA) **[3593]**

Educational Audiology Association Doctoral Scholarships [3595]
Educational and Cultural Affairs Alumni Small Grants Program (ECA) [4980]
Educational Enrichment Awards [1510]
Educational Foundation for Women in Accounting (EFWA) **[3597]**
Educational Leadership Foundation Grants [2973]
Educational Portal of the Americas **[3603]**
Educational Portal of the Americas Graduate Scholarships [3604]
Educational Portal of the Americas Undergraduate Scholarships [3605]
Educational and Professional Achievement Scholarships [1933]
Educational Research Center of America (ERCA) **[3606]**
Educational Testing Service **[3608]**
Edward C. Pomeroy Awards for Outstanding Contributions to Teacher Education [466]
Carli Edwards Memorial Scholarships [8114]
Palo Verde High School - Barbara Edwards Memorial Scholarships [7485]
Jimmy Edwards Scholarships [3107]
EERI/FEMA Graduate Fellowships [3563]
EFWA Moss Adams Foundation Scholarships [3598]
John and Alice Egan Multi-Year Mentioning Scholarships [3327]
Bill Egan Scholarship Program [6935]
UAA Governor William A. Egan Scholarships [9091]
EHA Exploratory Travel and Data Grants [3583]
EHA Graduate Dissertation Fellowships [3584]
E.I. DuPont Fellowships [6428]
Christine H. Eide Memorial Scholarships [5496]
John R. Eidson Jr., Scholarships [2946]
Mike Eidson Scholarships [490]
Eight and Forty Lung and Respiratory Disease Nursing Scholarships [896]
Hillel Einhorn New Investigator Awards [8363]
Albert Einstein Distinguished Educator Fellowships [8956]
Harold E. Eisenberg Foundation Scholarships [4906]
Eisenhower World Affairs Institute **[3612]**
EJLB Foundation **[3617]**
EJLB Foundation's Scholar Research Programme [3618]
Farouk El-Baz Student Research Grants [4087]
El Dorado County Mineral and Gem Society **[3619]**
El Dorado County Mineral and Gem Society Scholarships [3620]
El Pomar Fellowships [3622]
El Pomar Foundation **[3621]**
George & Isabelle Elanjian Scholarships [1591]
W. Eldridge and Emily Lowe Scholarships [8219]
Electric Cooperative Pioneer Trust Fund Scholarships [3491]
Electrochemical Society (ECS) **[3623]**
Electronic Document Systems Foundation (EDSF) **[3626]**
Electronic Materials and Processing Division - Postdoctoral Award [1981]
Herman E. Elgar Memorial Scholarships [3492]
Elks National Foundation (ENF) **[3628]**
Elks National Foundation Scholarships [3629]
Mark Jonathan Elliot Scholarship Fund [4722]
Dr. Robert Elliott Memorial Scholarships [5708]
Clay Elliott Scholarship Foundation **[3630]**
Clay Elliott Scholarship Foundation Scholarships [3631]
Pauline Elliott Scholarships [5709]
Robert A. Ellis Scholarships in Physics [6488]
William P. Elrod Memorial Scholarships [8815]
Emerald Empire Chapter Scholarship Awards [6936]
Emergency Medicine Physician Scholarships for Health Information Management Program [8664]
Emergency Nurses Association (ENA) **[3632]**
Emergency Nurses Association Undergraduate Scholarships [3634]
Emerging Teacher-Leaders in Elementary School Mathematics Grants for Grades K-5 Teachers [6221]
CSF Thomas J. Emery Memorial Scholarships [2842]
EMLF Law Student Scholarships [3643]
Emmanuel Bible College Scholarships [1592]

Thomas O. Enders Graduate Fellowships [1732]
Priscilla Maxwell Endicott Scholarships [4429]
Alice Yuriko Endo Memorial Scholarships [5141]
Endocrine Society **[3636]**
Endodontic Educator Fellowship Awards [471]
Endodontic Research Grants [472]
Endourological Society **[3640]**
Endourological Society Fellowships [3641]
Endowment Fund for Education Grants (EFFE) [2093]
Endowment Fund for Education, Loans [2094]
Endowment Fund for Education, Loans/Grants for Educational Materials [2095]
Endowment Fund for Education, Loans/Grants for Equipment [2096]
Energy and Mineral Law Foundation (EMLF) **[3642]**
The Eneslow Pedorthic Institute Scholarships [7139]
Vice Admiral Donald D. Engen Scholarships [6577]
Engineering Departmental Scholarships [9352]
Engineering Diversity Affairs Scholarships [9353]
Engineers for Tomorrow Scholarship Program [5915]
Don English Memorial Scholarships [7486]
Enlisted Association of National Guard of the United States (EANGUS) **[3644]**
Harold E. Ennes Scholarships [8303]
Ennis Arts Association (EAA) **[3646]**
Irene Winifred Eno Grants [1277]
Enterprise Rent-A-Car Scholarships [7265]
Entertainment Software Association (ESA) **[3649]**
Entomological Society of America (ESA) **[3651]**
Lindsay M. Entz Memorial Scholarships [3770]
Environment, Natural Resource and Energy Division Fellowships (ENRE) [1011]
Environmental History of Quebec Scholarships [6617]
Environmental Law Institute (ELI) **[3655]**
Environmental Research and Education Foundation (EREF) **[3657]**
Environmental Research and Education Foundation Scholarships [3658]
Epicurean Charitable Foundation Scholarships [7487]
Epilepsy Foundation **[3659]**
Epilepsy Foundation Post-doctoral Research Fellowships [3662]
Epilepsy Foundation Pre-doctoral Research Training Fellowships [3663]
Epilepsy Foundation Research Grants [3664]
Epilepsy Foundation Research and Training Fellowships for Clinicians [3665]
Epilepsy Newfoundland and Labrador (ENL) **[3671]**
Epsilon Epsilon Scholarships [8167]
Epsilon Tau Pi's Soaring Eagle Scholarships [6252]
Epsilon Tau Scholarships [8168]
Dena Epstein Awards for Archival and Library Research in American Music [5956]
Alan R. Epstein "Reach for the Stars" Scholarships [3317]
Lee Epstein Scholarship Fund [3447]
Equal Access to Justice Scholarships [6134]
Equal Justice Works **[3674]**
Equal Justice Works Fellowship Program [3675]
eQuality Scholarships [7849]
Equity Foundation **[3676]**
Erb Group Companies Service to Community Scholarships [6898]
Robert C. Erb Sr. Scholarships [5710]
ERCA Community Contribution Scholarships [3607]
ERDAS Internships [1667]
Harriet Erich Graduate Fellowships [3371]
E.V. Erickson Field of Interest Education Scholarship Fund [4211]
Bruce T. and Jackie Mahi Erickson Grants [5210]
Alaska Community Foundation Sven E. & Lorraine Eriksson Scholarships [9092]
Kenan T. Erim Fellowships for Archaeological Research at Aphrodisias [1146]
Ernest Hemingway Research Grants [4524]
The Eleonor A. Ernest Scholarships [5095]
Melissa Eleonor Ernest Scholarships [5096]
Robert P. Ernest Scholarships [5097]
Kevin Ernst Memorial Scholarship Fund [4212]
Ernst and Young/Ascend Leadership Scholarship Program [1636]
Jack Ervin EDI Scholarships [6761]
Judge Samuel J. Ervin, III Fellowships [5402]

ESA Foundation Computer and Video Game Scholarship Program [3650]
Boomer Esiason Foundation (BEF) **[3684]**
Boomer Esiason Foundation Scholarship Program [3685]
Charles A. Esser Memorial Scholarships [1518]
Robert Esser Student Achievement Scholarships [4685]
NSPF Ray B. Essick Scholarship Awards [6538]
R. Wayne Estes Endowed Scholarships [7180]
Larry L. Etherton Scholarships [1126]
Ethnic Minority and Women's Enhancement Postgraduate Scholarships [6193]
ETS Postdoctoral Fellowships [3609]
Alex J. Ettl Grants [6469]
Eurasia Foundation **[3690]**
European College of Liberal Arts Scholarships (ECLA) [9075]
Eustace-Kwan Family Foundation Scholarships [8200]
Chick Evans Caddie Scholarships [9575]
Lee S. Evans/National Housing Endowment Scholarships [6344]
Evans and Petree Law Firm Scholarships [9224]
Evans Scholarships [5900]
Ruth Murphy Evans Scholarships [4335]
Clifton W. Everett, Sr. Community Lawyer Fellowships [5403]
CSF Lyle Everingham Scholarships [2843]
CSF Lyle and Arlene Everingham Scholarships [2844]
Evjue Foundation, Inc./Capital Times Scholarships [9354]
Evolving Perceptions Scholarships [6360]
Excel Staffing Companies Scholarships for Excellence in Continuing Education [280]
Excellence in Geographic Information Systems Scholarships [9148]
Executive Women International (EWI) **[3692]**
Executive Women International Scholarship Program (EWISP) [3694]
ExceptionalNurse.com **[3695]**
ExceptionalNurse.com College Scholarships [3696]
Exercise For Life Athletic Scholarships Program [3686]
Explorers Club **[3697]**
Extendicare Scholarships in Gerontology [2540]
Exxon Mobil Aviation and the Avitats International Operators Scholarships [6165]
The William C. Ezell Fellowships [385]
FACS Graduate Fellowships [6129]
FACT Graduating Senior Scholarship Program [3736]
Faculty Advisor Research Grants [7240]
Faculty Doctoral Scholarships [3635]
Faculty Research Visit Grants [4118]
Fadel Educational Foundation (FEF) **[3699]**
Faegre & Benson Diversity Scholarships [3702]
Faegre & Benson LLP **[3701]**
Claire M. Fagin Fellowships [383]
FAIC Latin American and Caribbean Scholars Program [851]
Wayne G. Failor Scholarships [7158]
Fairbanks Chapter Legacy Scholarships [9186]
D.J. Fairgrave Education Trust [3493]
AIST Benjamin F. Fairless Scholarships, American Institute of Mining, Metallurgical and Petroleum Engineers (AIME) [1803]
Falcon Achievement Scholarships [7371]
Fall Fellowships in Korean Studies [5289]
The Fallen Heroes Scholarships [2925]
James Mackenzie Fallows Scholarships Honoring Gertrude Baccus [7645]
Families of Freedom Scholarship Fund **[3703]**
Families of Freedom Scholarship Fund - America Scholarships [3704]
Families USA **[3705]**
Family, Career and Community Leaders of America (FCCLA) **[3708]**
Family and Children's Services of Lebanon County Fund [3942]
Fanconi Anemia Research Fund **[3712]**
Fanconi Anemia Research Grants [3713]
William M. Fanning Maintenance Scholarships [6166]
Farella Braun Martel LLP **[3714]**

Farella Braun Martel LLP Diversity Scholarships [3715]
John S.W. Fargher Scholarships [4800]
Judge McIntyre Faries Scholarships [7181]
Palmer Farley Memorial Scholarships [4372]
Farmers State Bank Scholarships [8721]
Farmington UNICO Scholarships [4430]
W.D. Farr Scholarships [6175]
David Edward Farson Scholarships [7074]
Bertha M. Fase Memorial Scholarship Fund [4213]
Anne M. Fassett Scholarships [8600]
Miklos Faust International Travel Awards [1275]
Fecon Scholarships [3825]
Federal Circuit Bar Association (FCBA) **[3716]**
Federal Communication Bar Association Foundation (FCBA) **[3719]**
Federal Communication Bar Association Foundation Scholarships [3720]
Federal Court Bench and Bar Scholarships [9225]
Federal Court Clerks Association (FCCA) **[3721]**
Federal Employee Education and Assistance Fund (FEEA) **[3723]**
Federal Employee Education and Assistance Fund Scholarships [3724]
Federal Law Enforcement Officers Association (FLEOA) **[3726]**
Federal Managers Association (FMA) **[3728]**
The Federalist Society **[3730]**
Federalsburg Rotary Club Scholarships [3056]
Federated Insurance Scholarships [7266]
Federated Women's Institutes of Ontario **[3733]**
Federation of American Consumers and Travelers (FACT) **[3735]**
Federation of Diocesan Liturgical Commissions (FDLC) **[3737]**
Adrienne Zoe Fedok Art and Music Scholarships [3943]
FEEA-NTEU Scholarships [3725]
Nolan W. Feeser Scholarship Fund [3771]
FEF Scholarships [3700]
Red and Lola Fehr: Nightingale Scholarships [2996]
Virginia Valk Fehsenfeld Scholarships [4279]
FEI Company **[3739]**
Ruth B. Fein Prize [887]
Symee Ruth Feinburg Memorial Scholarships [4431]
Edward R. and Hazel N. Felber Scholarships [9355]
Harold E. Fellows Scholarships [2182]
Fellowships in Aerospace History [792]
Fellowships for Full-time Studies in French [245]
Fellowships in the Humanities and Social Sciences in Turkey [1147]
Fellowships for Intensive Advanced Turkish Language Study in Turkey [1148]
Fellowships and Internships Program in Latin America [8269]
Fellowships in the PMAC-AGPC [7450]
Fellowships to Promote Research on the Legal Framework for Civil Society in Latin America, Africa and Asia [4892]
Reese Felts Scholarships [9270]
John E. Fenton, Jr. Public Service Fellowships [7605]
Jennica Ferguson Memorial Scholarships [6274]
Dr. Joan W. Fernandez Point Scholarships [7359]
William and Dorothy Ferrell Scholarship Program [1759]
Lt. Colonel Romeo and Josephine Bass Ferretti Scholarships [92]
FFB-C Postdoctoral Fellowships [3968]
FHSMAI Scholarship Program [3970]
Mary Lou Fiala Fellowships [4907]
FICE Scholarships [3826]
FICPA Educational Foundation 1040K Race Scholarships [3836]
Field Aviation Co., Inc. Scholarships [127]
Field Museum **[3741]**
Field Museum Graduate Student Fellowships [3742]
UFVA Carole Fielding Student Grants [9202]
Fields Institute **[3743]**
Fields Research Immersion Fellowships [3744]
Beth K. Fields Scholarships [9211]
Filipino Bar Association of Northern California Scholarships (FBANC) [1653]
Film Studies Association of Canada **[3746]**
Film and Video Arts Project Grants [219]
E. Lanier Finch Scholarships [4097]

Herb and Anne Fincher Memorial Scholarships [3057]
Fine Arts Association (FAA) **[3748]**
Fine Arts Association Minority Scholarships [3749]
Fine Arts Association United Way Scholarships [3750]
Dr. Mary Finegold Scholarships [8201]
Sakura Finetek Student Scholarships [6511]
Gordy Fink Memorial Scholarships [7488]
Helen R. Finley-Loescher and Stephen Loescher Scholarships [3149]
Finnegan, Henderson, Farabow, Garrett & Dunner LLP **[3752]**
Finnegan, Henderson, Farabow, Garrett & Dunner, LLP Diversity Scholarships [3753]
Dayton E. Finnigan Scholarships [4336]
Fire Safety Awards [2469]
First Article Prize [3277]
First Church of Christ in Wethersfield - Metcalf Scholarships [4432]
First Community Foundation of Pennsylvania, Williamsport-Lycoming **[3754]**
First Friday Breakfast Club Scholarships [7850]
FIRST Operator Certification Scholarships [3812]
First Security Foundation Business Scholarships [5427]
Martin Fischer Awards [2479]
William A. Fischer Memorial Scholarships [1668]
Fish & Richardson 1L Diversity Fellowships [3800]
Fish & Richardson P.C. **[3799]**
St. Stephen A.M.E. Allison E. Fisher Book Awards [3804]
Fisher Broadcasting Scholarships for Minorities [3802]
Fisher Communications Inc. **[3801]**
Joseph L. Fisher Doctoral Dissertation Fellowships [7743]
Fisher Healthcare Educational Scholarships [6512]
Allison E. Fisher Memorial Fund **[3803]**
Charles N. Fisher Memorial Scholarships [1084]
Arthur and Juna Fisher Memorial Track Scholarships [7646]
Jack B. Fisher Scholarship Fund [8665]
Allison E. Fisher Scholarships [3805]
Ameel J. Fisher Scholarships [9271]
Sergeant Paul Fisher Scholarships [6235]
Carol C. Fitzgerald Scholarship Program [3722]
Dr. Joseph J. Fitzsimmons Scholarships [9055]
Gloria Flaherty Scholarships [4171]
Scott A. Flahive Memorial Scholarship Fund [4214]
Flamenco de la Isla Society **[3807]**
Flamenco Student Scholarships [3808]
Reuben H. Fleet Memorial Scholarships [7929]
Fleming/Blaszcak Scholarships [8447]
Charlie Fleming Education Fund Scholarships [6542]
Laura M. Fleming Scholarships [3903]
FLEOA Foundation Scholarship Program [3727]
Flexible Packaging Academic Scholarships & Summer Internships Program [3810]
Flexible Packaging Association (FPA) **[3809]**
Flexographic Technical Association (FTA) **[3811]**
Flight Attendants/Flight Technician Scholarships [6167]
Grant H. Flint International Scholarships - Category I [8524]
Grant H. Flint International Scholarships - Category II [8525]
Walter & Anna Flis Memorial Scholarships [7762]
Flora English Creative Writing Scholarships [7489]
Dave Florence Scholarship Fund [3448]
Florida Association Directors of Nursing Administration (FADONA) **[3813]**
Florida Association for Media in Education (FAME) **[3815]**
Florida Atlantic Planning Society (FAPS) **[3817]**
Florida Atlantic Planning Society Graduate Fellowships for Academic Excellence [3819]
Florida Automotive Industry Scholarships [1966]
Florida Education Fund (FEF) **[3821]**
Florida Education Fund McKnight Doctoral Fellowships [3822]
Florida Engineering Society (FES) **[3823]**
Florida Engineering Society Junior College Scholarships [3827]

Florida Engineering Society University Scholarships [3828]
Florida Fertilizer and Agrichemical Association (FFAA) **[3833]**
Florida Fertilizer and Agrichemical Association Scholarships [3834]
Florida Institute of Certified Public Accountants (FICPA) **[3835]**
Florida Nursery, Growers and Landscape Association (FNGLA) **[3837]**
Florida Nurses Association (FNA) **[3839]**
Florida Nurses Foundation Scholarships [3840]
Florida Outdoor Writers Association (FOWA) **[3841]**
Florida Outdoor Writers Association Scholarships [3842]
Florida Police Chiefs Association (FPCA) **[3843]**
Florida Public Health Association (FPHA) **[3845]**
Florida Public Health Association Public Health Graduate Scholarships [3846]
Florida Public Health Association Public Health Undergraduate Scholarships [3847]
Florida Public Transportation Association Scholarships (FPTA) [1052]
Floto-Peel Family Scholarship Fund [4215]
Fluid Power Distributor Association (FPDA) **[3848]**
Flying Physicians Association (FPA) **[3850]**
Barney Flynn Memorial Scholarships [2947]
John Flynn Memorial Scholarships [3150]
Paul B. & Aline Flynn Scholarships [8601]
FMA-FEEA Scholarship Program [3729]
Lydia Fohn-Hansen/Lola Hill Memorial Scholarships [9149]
Alice J. Foit Scholarships [8666]
Gail Goodell Folsom Memorial Scholarships [5975]
Frank Fong Scholarships [8290]
Food and Drug Law Institute (FDLI) **[3852]**
Food Processing Suppliers Association (FPSA) **[3854]**
For the Love of Chocolate Foundation Scholarships [3857]
For the Love of Chocolate Scholarship Foundation **[3856]**
Henry Ford Academy Scholarships [8384]
Ford Foundation Dissertation Fellowships [5999]
Ford Foundation Diversity Fellowships [6000]
Ford Foundation Postdoctoral Fellowships [6001]
Ford Foundation Predoctoral Fellowships [6002]
UAA Michael D. Ford Memorial Scholarships [9093]
Ford Motor Company Scholarship Program [4568]
Anne Ford Scholarships [6186]
Foreign, Comparative & International Law - Schaffer Grants for Foreign Law Librarians [499]
George Foreman Tribute to Lyndon B. Johnson Scholarships [7577]
Forest History Society (FHS) **[3858]**
Nancy B. Forest and L. Michael Honaker Master's Scholarships for Research [1033]
Foresters Scholarships [4714]
Leland Stanford Forrest Scholarships [3494]
Forsyth County Nursing Scholarships [9636]
Forsyth County United Way Scholarships [5344]
Fort Atkinson Community Foundation **[3861]**
Genevieve Forthun Scholarships [7286]
Edward Foster Awards [2496]
Foster Care to Success (FC2S) **[3870]**
Emily P. Foster Fellowships [6982]
Barbara Palo Foster Memorial Scholarships [2756]
Dr. Nancy Foster Scholarship Program **[3872]**
Andrew Foster Scholarships [6146]
Charles and Margaret Foster Scholarships [8602]
Dr. Nancy Foster Scholarships [3873]
Jonathan Hastings Foster Scholarships [7930]
Fostering Hope Scholarships Fund [7075]
Foundation for the Advancement of Aboriginal Youth Bursary Program [2440]
Foundation for the Advancement of Aboriginal Youth Scholarships [2441]
Foundation of American Institute for Conservation Lecture Grants [852]
Foundation for Appalachian Ohio **[3874]**
Foundation for the Carolinas (FFTC) **[3879]**
Foundation for the Carolinas Rotary Scholarship Fund [3904]
Foundation for Community Association Research **[3932]**
Foundation for Enhancing Communities **[3934]**

Foundation of the Federal Bar Association (FFBA) **[3965]**

Foundation of the Federal Bar Association Public Service Scholarships [3966]

Foundation Fighting Blindness (FFB) **[3967]**

Foundation of the Hospitality Sales and Marketing Association International **[3969]**

Foundation of the International Association of Defense Counsel (IADC) **[3971]**

Foundation for Jewish Culture **[3973]**

Foundation of the National Student Nurses Association (NSNA) **[3975]**

The Foundation of the National Student Nurses' Association Scholarships [6536]

Foundation for Neonatal Research and Education (FNRE) **[3980]**

Foundation for Neonatal Research and Education Scholarships [3981]

Foundation of the Pennsylvania Medical Society **[3982]**

Foundation for the Preservation of Honey Bees **[3989]**

Foundation for the Preservation of Honey Bees Graduate Scholarships [3990]

Foundation Scholarships [5231]

Foundation for Seacoast Health **[3991]**

Foundation for Seacoast Health Scholarships [3992]

Foundation for Surgical Technology Advanced Education/Medical Mission Scholarships [1881]

Foundation for Surgical Technology Scholarships [1882]

Founders Circle Professional Scholarships [4839]

Founding Fathers Leadership Scholarships [9676]

Howard Fox Memorial Law Scholarships [2068]

Terry Fox Memorial Scholarships [6549]

Captain Ernest Fox Perpetual Scholarships [2926]

FPA Aviation Scholarships [3851]

Paris Fracasso Production Floriculture Scholarships [732]

Brandon Fradd Fellowships in Music Competition [2883]

Fragile X Research Foundation of Canada (FXRFC) **[3993]**

William A. Fraker Student Heritage Awards [1195]

Franchise Law Diversity Scholarship Awards [4940]

Joe Francis Haircare Scholarship Foundation **[3995]**

Joe Francis Haircare Scholarships [3996]

Aracelis Francis Minority Scholarships in Gerontology [1787]

Parker B. Francis Respiratory Research Grants [1155]

Joey and Florence Franco Legacy Scholarships [2245]

Joe Francomano Scholarships [5174]

Mayme and Herb Frank Scholarship Program [1638]

Johnny and Sarah Frank Scholarships [9150]

Michael W. and Jean D. Franke Family Foundation Scholarships [1127]

Loren Frankel Memorial Scholarships [926]

Mary Weiking Franken Scholarships [7287]

The Ginny Frankenthaler Memorial Scholarships [8567]

John Hope Franklin Dissertation Fellowships [990]

James Franklin and Dorothy J. Warnell Scholarship Fund [3192]

Franklin Elementary School PTA Scholarships [7647]

Denise Franklin Journalism Scholarships [9637]

John Hope Franklin Prize [5366]

Franklin Research Grants [991]

Violet and Cyril Franks Scholarships [1039]

John and Victory E. Frantz Scholarship Fund [4216]

Joseph Frasca Excellence in Aviation Scholarships [9191]

Fraser Family Scholarships [7490]

Fraser Milner Casgrain Scholarships [2006]

Fraser Stryker **[3997]**

Fraser Stryker Diversity Scholarships [3998]

Carlyle Fraser/Wilton Looney Scholarships [1940]

FRAXA Postdoctoral Fellowships [4000]

FRAXA Research Foundation **[3999]**

UAA Jan & Glenn Fredericks Scholarships [9094]

Fredrikson and Byron Foundation Minority Scholarships [4002]

Fredrikson and Byron P.A. **[4001]**

Emanuel R. Freedman Scholarships [7012]

Freedom Alliance **[4003]**

Freedom Alliance Scholarships [4004]

Freedom and Justice Foundation **[4005]**

Richard Gregory Freeland, II Educational Scholarships [2147]

Belknap Freeman Carnegie Mellon Scholarships [1128]

Kevin Freeman Travel Grants [5957]

Freepali **[4007]**

Freepali Scholarships [4008]

Malcolm and Mildred Freidberg Fellowships [5670]

The French Culinary Institute Classic Pastry Arts Scholarships [3306]

The French Culinary Institute Culinary Arts Scholarships [3307]

Ruth M. French Graduate or Undergraduate Scholarships [1198]

UAA Ardell French Memorial Scholarships [9095]

Ludo Frevel Crystallography Scholarships [4896]

Doris W. Frey Memorial Scholarships [8603]

Carleton A. Friday Memorial Scholarships [5867]

Dale E. Fridell Memorial Scholarships [8750]

Fried, Frank, Harris, Shriver and Jacobson Fellowships [4010]

Fried, Frank, Harris, Shriver and Jacobson LLP **[4009]**

Marc Friedlaender Fellowships [5671]

CSF William A. Friedlander Scholarships [2845]

A.E. Robert Friedman Scholarships [7035]

Phil Friel Scholarships [5711]

Joel R. Friend Scholarships [2060]

Kennedy T. Friend Scholarships [327]

Friends of Canadian Broadcasting (FCB) **[4011]**

Friends of Coal Scholarships [9566]

Friends of the Jose Carreras International Leukemia Foundation **[4013]**

Friends of Mary Automotive Scholarships [8115]

Friends of Megan Bolton Memorial Fund [3944]

Henry Friesen Awards and Lectures [2601]

Froberg-Suess JD/MBA Scholarships [7182]

Dean A. Froehlich Endowed Scholarships [5428]

Melbourne & Alice E. Frontjes Scholarships [4280]

Fruits and Vegetable Industries Scholarships [5831]

Marian Johnson Frutiger Scholarships [8169]

William and Francis Fry Honorary Fellowships for Contributions to Therapeutic Ultrasound [5003]

FTE Congregational Fellowships [4019]

FTE Dissertation Fellowships [4020]

FTE Doctoral Fellowships [4021]

FTE Ministry Fellowships [4022]

FTE North American Doctoral Fellowships [4023]

FTE Undergraduate Fellowships [4024]

FTE Volunteers Exploring Vocation Fellowships [4025]

Fuchs-Harden Educational Scholarships Fund [4337]

Gerard Swartz Fudge Memorial Scholarships [4653]

Keiko Fukuda Scholarships [9056]

Kathryn Fuller Science for Nature Post-Doctoral Fellowships [9759]

Don and Eileen Fulton Nursing Scholarships [8722]

Daniel G. and Helen I. Fultz Scholarship Fund [3772]

Fund for American Studies (TFAS) **[4015]**

Arkansas Nursing Foundation - Dorothea Fund Scholarships [1543]

Fund for Theological Education (FTE) **[4018]**

Fundacion Educativa Carlos M. Castaneda (FECMC) **[4026]**

Funeral Service Foundation (FSF) **[4028]**

Fur Takers of America (FTA) **[4032]**

Donald M. Furbush Professional Development Grants [4819]

Furman-Tikvah Scholarships [8903]

The Future Colleagues Scholarships [6293]

Future CPA Scholarships [1529]

Future Leader in Radiocommunications Scholarships [7567]

Future Leaders of Manufacturing Scholarships [8385]

FXRFC Medical Research Postdoctoral Fellowships [3994]

Mearl K. Gable II Memorial Grants [4387]

Gaddy Student Scholarships [9638]

Gadsden State/McClellan Campus Nursing Scholarship Awards [3036]

Franciszek Gadzala Memorial Scholarships [7763]

Gaebe Eagle Scout Awards [6253]

Harry Gairey Scholarships [2117]

Farley Moody Galbraith Scholarship Fund [3037]

Thomas W. Gallagher Scholarships Fund [8667]

Louise Bales Gallagher Scholarships [3372]

William E. "Bill" Gallagher Scholarships [7076]

Whitney Laine Gallahar Memorial Scholarship Fund [3038]

Sam Gallant Memorial Scholarships [1530]

The Gallery Collection **[4034]**

The Gallery Collection's Greeting Card Scholarships [4035]

Carolyn Gallmeyer Scholarships [4281]

Mathilda & Carolyn Gallmeyer Scholarships [4282]

Gallo Blue Chip Scholarships [4398]

CSF Priscilla Gamble Scholarships [2846]

Gamewarden Scholarship program [4037]

Gamewarden of Vietnam Association **[4036]**

Gamma Iota Scholarships - Gamma Tau [8170]

Gamma Iota Scholarships - Kappa Eta [8171]

Gamma Iota Scholarships - Zeta Kappa [8172]

Gamma Iota Scholarships - Zeta Nu [8173]

Gamma Sigma Alpha (GSA) **[4038]**

Gamma Sigma Alpha Graduate Scholarships [4039]

Guy P. Gannett Scholarships [5578]

Veronica Gantt Memorial Scholarships [7491]

GAPA Scholarships [4048]

Joel Garcia Memorial Scholarships [2237]

Michael and Gina Garcia Rail Engineering Scholarships [1129]

William R. Gard Memorial Scholarships [6091]

Garden Club of America (GCA) **[4040]**

Garden Club of America Awards in Tropical Botany (GCA) [4041]

Garden Club Council of Winston-Salem and Forsyth County Council [9639]

Garden Conservancy **[4043]**

Garden State Rotary Club of Cherry Hill Scholarships [2335]

Jewels Gardiner Scholarships [2270]

John Gardner Fellowships [9195]

Gardner Foundation Infusion Nurses Society Education Scholarships [4765]

Robert Gardner Memorial Fellowships [4489]

Dwight D. Gardner Scholarships [4801]

Victoria M. Gardner Scholarships [9272]

Eugene Garfield Doctoral Dissertation Fellowships [2070]

Peter M. Gargano Scholarship Fund [3529]

Garikian Scholarship Fund [1593]

Garmin Scholarships [128]

Gerald Garner Memorial Scholarships [7183]

Gail Garner R.I.S.E. Memorial Scholarships [7648]

Eileen J. Garrett Scholarships [7052]

Marcus Mosiah Garvey Scholarships [5118]

Kays Gary Scholarships [9273]

Edwin W. Gaston Scholarships [343]

Gates Cambridge Scholarships [6072]

Bill and Melinda Gates Foundation **[4045]**

The Gates Millennium Scholars [4569]

William H. Gates Public Service Law Scholarships [4046]

Stephen Gates Scholarships [9274]

Raffin Gathercole Scholarships [4051]

David A. and Pamela A. Gault Charitable Fund [8668]

Gauthier Family Scholarship Fund [4217]

A.R.F.O.R.A. Martha Gavrila Scholarships for Women [1164]

GAWP Graduate Scholarships [4099]

Gay Asian Pacific Alliance (GAPA) **[4047]**

Gay, Lesbian, Bisexual, Transgender Alumni Council Scholarships [9356]

Gay and Lesbian Business Association of Santa Barbara (GLBA) **[4049]**

Lowell Gaylor Memorial Scholarships [129]

Florence S. Gaynor Scholarships [6081]

GCABS Youth Scholarship Awards [4147]

GCSAA Scholars Competition [4187]

GCSAA Student Essay Contest [4188]

GE Healthcare Management Scholarship Program [1323]

GED Jump Start Scholarships [8029]

GEF Scholarship Program [4319]
Gehring Memorial Foundation Scholarships [4723]
Victoria S. and Bradley L. Geist Scholarships [4477]
Lawrence Gelfand - Armin Rappaport Fellowships [8339]
Irma Gelhausen Scholarship Fund [5349]
Joseph H. Gellert/Dutchess County Bar Association Scholarships [3555]
Elaine Gelman Scholarship Awards [6106]
Gemological Institute of America Inc. (GIA) **[4053]**
The Gene and John Athletic Scholarships [8746]
General Aviation Manufacturers Association (GAMA) **[4071]**
General Falcon Scholarships [7372]
General Federation of Women's Clubs of Massachusetts **[4073]**
General Mills Foundation Scholarships [808]
Generation III Scholarships [3586]
Geological Association of Canada (GAC) **[4084]**
Geological Association of Canada Student Prizes [4085]
Geological Society of America (GSA) **[4086]**
Geological Society of America Graduate Student Research Grants [4088]
Georgetown Working League **[4089]**
Georgetown Working League Scholarships [4090]
Georgia Association of Broadcasters (GAB) **[4096]**
Georgia Association of Water Professionals (GAWP) **[4098]**
Georgia Engineering Foundation **[4101]**
Georgia Engineering Foundation Scholarships [4102]
Georgia Library Association (GLA) **[4103]**
Georgia Press Educational Foundation (GPEF) **[4106]**
Gerber Fellowships in Pediatric Nutrition [6401]
Gerber Foundation **[4111]**
Gerber Foundation Merit Scholarships [4112]
Doris Y. and John J. Gerber Scholarships [9524]
Daniel Gerber, Sr. Medallion Scholarships [4113]
Walter Gerboth Awards [5958]
German Academic Exchange Service (DAAD) **[4114]**
German Historical Institute (GHI) **[4125]**
German Historical Institute Doctoral and Postdoctoral Fellowships [4126]
German Historical Institute Fellowships at the Horner Library [4127]
German Marshall Fund of the United States (GMF) **[4130]**
German Society of Pennsylvania (GSP) **[4136]**
German Society Scholarships [4137]
German Studies Research Grants [4119]
Eloise Gerry Fellowships [8151]
Getty Foundation **[4138]**
Getty GRI-NEH Postdoctoral Fellowships [4140]
Getty Postdoctoral Fellowships [4141]
Getty Predoctoral Fellowships [4142]
Getty Research Exchange Fellowship Program for Cultural Heritage Preservation [1149]
Getty Scholar Grants [4143]
GFLC-A&WMA Memorial [109]
GFWC Women's Club of South County Scholarships [7790]
Ghana-Canada Association of British Columbia (GCABC) **[4146]**
Mary Ghezzi Nursing Scholarships [8983]
GIA Endowment Scholarships - Distance Education [4056]
GIA Endowment Scholarships - On Campus [4057]
IDSA Gianninoto Graduate Scholarships [4758]
John J. Gibbons Fellowships in Public Interest and Constitutional Law [4149]
Gibbons P.C. **[4148]**
Laverne L. Gibson Memorial Scholarships [7077]
Joy Gibson Scholarships [9275]
L.C. Gifford Distinguished Journalism Scholarships [9276]
Tom Gifford Scholarships [4218]
Dr. Virginia Gilbert Memorial Scholarships [7492]
Shane Gilbert Memorial Scholarships [7078]
Margaret S. Gilbert Scholarship Fund [8669]
Gilbreth Memorial Fellowships [4802]
Gilder Lehrman Institute of American History **[4150]**
Gilder Lehrman Short-Term Fellowships [4151]
Terry M. Giles Honor Scholarships [7184]

Harold Giles Scholarships [8448]
William Harrison Gill Education Fund [2061]
Midwest Chapter Scholarships - Jack Gill [1804]
R.L. Gillette Scholarships [751]
Gilliam Fellowships for Advanced Study [4621]
Benjamin A. Gilman International Scholarships [9096]
Ethel Z. Gilman Scholarships [8804]
Leo Gilmartin Scholarships [7352]
Keith Gilmore Foundation - Diploma Scholarships [4153]
Keith Gilmore Foundation **[4152]**
Keith Gilmore Foundation - Postgraduate Scholarships [4154]
Keith Gilmore Foundation - Undergraduate Scholarships [4155]
Susan Kay Munson Gilmore Memorial Scholarships [3151]
Jack R. Gilstrap Scholarships [1053]
Lawrence Ginocchio Aviation Scholarships [6168]
Nick Giorgione Hope for Hearts Scholarships [7493]
Alex Gissler Memorial Scholarships [5712]
Senator James Gladstone Memorial Scholarships [228]
Elizabeth Glaser Pediatric AIDS Foundation **[4156]**
Jane R. Glaser Scholarships [1405]
John Glaser Scholarships [2971]
Elizabeth Glaser Scientist Awards [4157]
Dr. Helen Preston Glass Fellowships [2541]
Ann and Brad Glassco Scholarships [7649]
GLATA Living Memorial Doctorate Scholarships [4325]
GLATA Living Memorial Undergraduate/Graduate Scholarships [4326]
Glazing Industry Scholarships [7494]
Gleaner Life Insurance Scholarship Foundation [4159]
Gleaner Life Insurance Society **[4158]**
Glendale Latino Association (GLA) **[4160]**
Glendale Latino Association Scholarships [4161]
Jane S. Glenn Memorial Endowed Scholarships [7805]
Glens Falls Foundation **[4162]**
Global Business Travel Association (GBTA) **[4165]**
Global Volcanism Program for Visiting Scientist/Postdoctoral Fellowships [8261]
Globe-Trotters Chapter Scholarships [1805]
Franciszek Glogowski Memorial Scholarships [7764]
Northeastern Ohio Chapter Scholarships - Alfred B. Glossbrenner and John Klusch Scholarships [1806]
Bud Glover Memorial Scholarships [130]
GLP Program Scholarships [4166]
Irene Carlson Gnaedinger Memorial Scholarships [5429]
Dr. Robert H. Goddard Memorial Scholarships [6523]
Glenn Godfrey Memorial Scholarships [5283]
Godparents for Tanzania **[4168]**
Godparents for Tanzania Scholarships [4169]
Max Godwin Endowed Scholarships [8880]
John Goerlich Memorial Scholarships [1941]
Goethe Society of North America **[4170]**
Gogos Scholarships [2980]
Gold Award/Eagle Scout Scholarships [6254]
Gold Country Section & Region II Scholarships [1337]
Gold Key Scholarships [5232]
William Goldberg Diamond Corp. Scholarships [4058]
Daniel B. Goldberg Scholarships [4197]
Golden Belt Community Foundation **[4172]**
Golden Corral Scholarships [6773]
Golden Key Graduate Scholar Awards [6073]
Golden Key International Honour Society (GKIHS) **[4174]**
Golden Key International Honour Society Study Abroad Scholarships [4176]
Golden Key Math Scholarships [4177]
William R. Goldfarb Memorial Scholarships [1085]
Rhode Island Commission on Women/Freda H. Goldman Education Awards [7791]
Dr. Guido Goldman Scholarships [666]
Goldman Sachs/Matsuo Takabuki Commemorative Scholarships [5211]
Alois and Marie Goldmann Scholarship Fund [4669]

American Radio Relay League Scholarships Honoring Barry Goldwater, K7UGA [1086]
Barry M. Goldwater Scholarships [9357]
Golf Canada **[4179]**
Golf Course Superintendents Association of America (GCSAA) **[4186]**
Joshua Gomes Memorial Scholarship Fund [6324]
Gongaware Scholarships [4743]
Charles D. Gonthier Research Fellowships [2498]
Gonzaga University School of Law **[4190]**
Millie Gonzalez Memorial Scholarships [6325]
Kenneth M. Good Graduate Students Fellowship Program [9396]
Goodfellow Nursing Scholarships [5507]
Goodfellow Professional Development Fund [5508]
Goodman & Company Scholarships [9463]
Victor and Ruth N. Goodman Memorial Scholarships [4373]
J.O. Goodman Scholarship Awards [6899]
David B. Goodstein Point Scholarships [7360]
Baxter Corporation - Jean Goodwill Scholarships [20]
James L. and Genevieve H. Goodwin Scholarships [4433]
Google-American Indian Science and Engineering Society Scholarships [4194]
Google Hispanic College Fund Scholarships [4195]
Google Inc. **[4192]**
Richard Goolsby Scholarship Fund [3905]
Lucille May Gopie Scholarships [2118]
L. Gordon, Jr. and June D. Pfefferkorn Scholarships [9640]
Barnett D. Gordon Scholarships [4724]
Pauline LaFon Gore Scholarships [3108]
Richard C. Gorecki Scholarships [7373]
TCDA Bill Gorham Student Scholarships [8848]
Nettie and Jesse Gorov Scholarships [3152]
Consuelo W. Gosnell Memorial Scholarships [6122]
American Association of University Women-Mary Sue Gottcent Memorial Scholarships [8604]
Louis Gottschalk Prize [1228]
Carl W. Gottschalk Research Scholar Grants [1312]
Norma Gotwalt Scholarship Fund [3945]
Charles F. Gould Endowment Scholarships [9151]
Government Documents Special Interest Section - Veronica Maclay Student Grants [509]
Government Finance Officers Association of United States and Canada (GFOA) **[4196]**
Wilford Hayes Gowen Scholarships [9226]
ACI W.R. Grace Scholarships [634]
William L. Graddy Law School Scholarships [8605]
Graduate Fellowship Program - Mahboob Khan/Advanced Micro Devices Fellowships (GFP) [8079]
Graduate Fellowship Program - Research Fellowships (GFP) [8080]
Graduate Fellowships in Alternatives in Scientific Research [4937]
Graduate Realtor Institute Scholarships [5244]
Graduate Research Fellowships [2694]
Graduate Scholarships in Cancer Nursing Practice [597]
Graduate Student Scholarships [246]
Graduate Student Travel Grants [8314]
Graham & Dunn 1L Diversity Fellowships [4203]
Graham and Dunn P.C. **[4202]**
Rachel Graham Memorial Scholarships [7650]
Jim Graham Scholarships [6781]
Grand Canyon Historical Society (GCHS) **[4204]**
Grand Canyon Historical Society Scholarships [4205]
Grand Haven Area Community Foundation **[4206]**
Grand Haven Offshore Challenge Scholarship Fund [4219]
Grand Island Community Foundation **[4254]**
Grand Lodge of Saskatchewan **[4267]**
Grand Rapids Community Foundation (GRCF) **[4269]**
Grand Rapids Scholarship Association [4283]
Grande Prairie 4-H District Scholarships [199]
Father Rutilio Grande Scholarships [7893]
Charles Hall Grandgent Awards [3342]
Grandmothers for Peace International (GPI) **[4310]**
Granger Business Association (GBA) **[4312]**
Granger Business Association College Scholarships [4313]
Russ Grant Memorial Scholarship for Tennis [7079]

Sponsor and Scholarship Index

Sponsor and Scholarship Index

Japan Foundation, New York Doctoral Fellowship Program [5134]
Japan Foundation, New York Research Fellowship Program [5135]
Japan Foundation, New York Short-Term Fellowship Program [5136]
Japanese American Bar Association (JABA) **[5137]**
Japanese American Bar Association Scholarships [5138]
Japanese American Citizens League (JACL) **[5139]**
Japanese Queen Scholarship Organization of Washington **[5148]**
Don Jaques Memorial Fellowships [8003]
Dr. Ali Jarrahi Merit Scholarships [5050]
Carl and Lucille Jarrett Scholarship Fund [3778]
Terry Jarvis Memorial Scholarships [1439]
Dannie Jasmine Scholarships [5944]
Jacob K. Javits Fellowships [6076]
JCC Association **[5150]**
JCC Association Graduate Education Scholarships [5151]
J.D. Graduate Tikvah Scholarships [8904]
J.D. or LL.M. Tikvah Scholarships [8905]
JD/MBA Scholarships [7188]
Right Hon. Michaelle Jean Legacy Scholarships [2122]
Sister Rita Jeanne Scholarships [5169]
Jefferson Graduate Fellowships [5153]
Jefferson Scholars Foundation **[5152]**
Jefferson Science Associates, LLC (JSA) **[5154]**
Erin L. Jenkins Memorial Scholarship Fund [3948]
Elise Reed Jenkins Memorial Scholarships - Gamma Lambda [8175]
Elise Reed Jenkins Memorial Scholarships - Gamma Psi [8176]
John H. Jenkins Research Fellowships in Texas History [8876]
Martha Combs Jenkins Scholarships [7290]
Ruth E. Jenkins Scholarships [7936]
Gaynold Jensen Education Stipends [3443]
Walter J. Jensen Fellowships [7248]
Nancy Lorraine Jensen Memorial Scholarships [8531]
Mike Jensen R.I.S.E. Memorial Scholarships [7656]
Stanley "Doc" Jensen Scholarships [694]
Jerman-Cahoon Student Scholarship Program [1324]
Kenneth Jernigan Scholarships [6276]
Jerome Fellowships [7337]
Harry Jerome Scholarships [2123]
James Jesinski Scholarships [9359]
Jewish Caucus Scholarships [6559]
Jewish Federation Academic Scholarships [5161]
Jewish Foundation for Education of Women (JFEW) **[5156]**
Jewish Guild for the Blind (JGB) **[5158]**
Jewish Vocational Service (JVS) **[5160]**
Jewish War Veterans of the United States of America **[5162]**
Brian Jimenez Memorial Scholarships [7657]
Rev. and Mrs. A.K. Jizmejian Educational Fund [1600]
JLTLA Scholarships [8981]
JMA Architecture Studios Scholarships [7498]
Oliver Joel and Ellen Pell Denny Healthcare Scholarship Fund [9642]
John W. Webb Lecture Awards [1260]
Alvin H. Johnson AMS Dissertation Fellowships [940]
Robert Wood Johnson Clinical Scholarships [5165]
Craig Johnson Family Scholarships [8884]
Robert Wood Johnson Foundation **[5164]**
The Robert Wood Johnson Health Policy Fellowship Program [1019]
Johnson and Johnson: Nightingale Scholarships [2997]
Johnson & Johnson Scholarships [2543]
MCCA Lloyd M. Johnson, Jr. Scholarships [5904]
Margaret G. Johnson and Marge J. Stout Scholarships [5437]
Bernadine Johnson-Marshall and Martha Bell Williams Scholarships [1718]
Joseph C. Johnson Memorial Grants [1191]
Fred Johnson Memorial Scholarships [6176]
Gregory D. Johnson Memorial Scholarships [6378]
V.J. Johnson Memorial Scholarships [552]

Sylvia Taylor Johnson Minority Fellowships in Educational Measurement [3611]
James V. Johnson Scholarship Fund [3908]
Camilla C. Johnson Scholarships [4288]
Chip Johnson Scholarships [8608]
CSF Ella Wilson Johnson Scholarships [2851]
Dr. Bill Johnson Scholarships [8116]
Stella B. Johnson Scholarships [9643]
Johnson and Wales University Scholarships [5175]
Nancy Johnston Memorial Scholarships [8837]
OOIDA Mary Johnston Scholarships [7025]
Mary Jon and J. P. Bryan Leadership in Education Awards [8877]
Louis August Jonas Foundation (LAJF) **[5166]**
George E. Jonas Scholarships [5167]
Robert V.A. Jones Canadians Corporate Counsel Awards [2438]
Greater Baton Rouge Chapter - Don Jones Excellence in Safety Scholarships [1342]
Napoleon A. Jones, III Memorial Scholarships [7937]
Annabel Lambeth Jones Scholarships [3909]
Edward H. Jones Scholarships [3500]
Barbara Jordan Memorial Scholarships [1884]
CSF David J. Joseph Company Scholarships [2852]
Joseph H. Fichter Research Grants [1874]
E.J. Josey Scholarships [2133]
Alice Newell Joslyn Medical Fund [2041]
Journalism Education Association (JEA) **[5168]**
Journyx Inc. **[5170]**
Journyx Scholarships [5171]
Leslie W. Joyce and Paul W. Thayer Graduate Fellowships in I-O Psychology [8355]
JQSOW Scholarships [5149]
JSA/Jefferson Lab Graduate Fellowships [5155]
JSR Foundation Endowed School of Law Scholarships [7189]
Kazimiera Juchniewicz Memorial Scholarships [7765]
Clem Judd Jr. Memorial Scholarships [4483]
George E. Judd Scholarships [8609]
Woodrow Judkins Endowed Scholarships [7190]
Junior Achievement of East Central Ohio, Inc. Scholarship Fund [8679]
Junior Achievement Inc. **[5172]**
Junior Firefighter Scholarships [6555]
Junior Service League **[5177]**
Junior Women of the Contemporary Club Scholarships [7658]
George W. Juno Memorial Scholarships [4062]
Just Out Scholarship Fund [3678]
Juvenile Arthritis Scholarships [4444]
K-12 Edu-Grants [6329]
K & W Cafeterias Scholarships [6775]
Mike Kabo Global Scholarships [4167]
Stefan & Weronika Kacperski Memorial Scholarships [7766]
Annette Kade Fellowships [5787]
Kade-Heideking Fellowships [4128]
Edward G. Kaelber Scholarships [5582]
Daniel Kahikina and Millie Akaka Scholarships [5213]
Kaiser Family Foundation (KFF) **[5179]**
Kaiser Media Fellowships in Health [5180]
Stacy Kaiser Memorial Funds [8984]
David A. Kaiser Memorial Scholarship Fund [8680]
Kaiser Permanente: Nightingale Scholarships [2998]
Kaiser Permanente Northwest Pride Scholarships [3679]
Kamehameha Schools Class of 1968 "Ka Poli O Kaiona" Scholarships [5214]
Kamehameha Schools Class of 1972 Scholarships [5215]
Benjamin Kaminer Endowed Scholarships in Physiology [5618]
Martin S. Kane Memorial Community Service Award Scholarships [3062]
Kansas Association of Broadcasters (KAB) **[5181]**
Kansas Association of Broadcasters Scholarships [5182]
Kansas Board of Regents (KBOR) **[5183]**
Kansas City Division Scholarships [5860]
Kansas Health Information Management Association (KHIMA) **[5186]**
Kansas Optometry Service Scholarships [5184]

Kansas Osteopathic Medical Service Scholarships [5185]
CSF M. Kantor and Brothers Scholarships [2853]
Walter Kapala Scholarships [4445]
Joseph Kaplan Fund [4726]
Don Kaplan Legacy Scholarships [2250]
Kaplan Scholarships [4562]
Kaplan Test Prep and Admission Scholarships for NSHSS Members [6503]
Steve Kaplan TV and Film Studies Scholarships [1212]
Kalmen Kaplansky Scholarships in Economic and Social Rights [3475]
Kappa Chapter Centennial Scholarships [3377]
Kappa Delta Phi Scholarship Program [952]
Kappa Gamma Pi **[5190]**
Kappa Kappa Gamma **[5192]**
Kappa Kappa Gamma Graduate Scholarships [5193]
Kappa Kappa Gamma Undergraduate Scholarships [5194]
Kappa Omicron Nu (KON) **[5195]**
Kappa Omicron Nu Honor Society **[5199]**
Kappa Omicron Nu National Alumni Fellowships [5196]
Kappa Omicron Nu Undergraduate Scholarships [5197]
Kappa Zeta Scholarships [8177]
The ISASI Rudolf Kapustin Memorial Scholarships [4988]
J.S. Karling Graduate Student Research Awards [2164]
Josephine de Karman Fellowship Trust **[5204]**
Josephine de Karman Fellowships [5205]
Philip R. Karr, III Scholarship Fund [4100]
K.A.S.A Memorial Scholarships [7092]
KASF Chair Scholarships [5292]
KASF Designated Scholarships [5293]
KASF General Scholarships [5294]
Ken Kashiwahara Scholarships [7569]
Ken Kashiwara Scholarships [7578]
Katherine Singer Kovacs Book and Essay Awards [8310]
Magoichi & Shizuko Kato Memorial Scholarships [5143]
KATS Graduate Scholarships [5246]
KATS Undergraduate Scholarships [5247]
Ka'u Chamber of Commerce **[5206]**
Ka'u Chamber of Commerce College Scholarships [5207]
Ken and Romaine Kauffman Scholarship Fund [3949]
Lucile B. Kaufman Women's Scholarships [8388]
N.G. Kaul Memorial Scholarships [6687]
William and Beatrice Kavanaugh Scholarships [5100]
Kawano Family Scholarships [7938]
E. Wayne Kay Co-op Scholarships [8389]
E. Wayne Kay Community College Scholarships [8390]
E. Wayne Kay High School Scholarships [8391]
KCC-JEE Graduate Fellowships [5279]
Ke Ali'i Pauahi Foundation **[5208]**
Keats-Shelley Association of America (KSAA) **[5224]**
Doc Keen Memorial Scholarships [8610]
Donald Keene Center of Japanese Culture **[5226]**
Keepers Preservation Education Fund [5583]
Gunild Keetman Scholarships [6957]
Glenn Keever Scholarships [9284]
KEF Academic Scholarships [5284]
KEF College/University Basic Scholarships [5285]
KEF Vocational Education Scholarship [5286]
Kegler, Brown, Hill, and Ritter Company, L.P.A **[5228]**
Kegler Brown Minority Merit Scholarships [5229]
Keiser College Coast Guard Scholarships [2927]
Maude Keisling/Cumberland County Extension Homemakers Scholarships [3112]
Annette and Ernest Keith Scholarships [7659]
John W. Kelley Memorial Scholarships [8729]
Kellogg Community College Foundation **[5230]**
Kellogg Company Career Scholarships [5234]
W.K. Kellogg Foundation Doctoral Fellowships in Health Policy [6402]
Dr. Charles Kelly Memorial Scholarships [7093]

Lavina Laible Scholarships [4289]
Canadian Association for Studies in Co-operation Scholarships Alexander Fraser Laidlaw Fellowships (CASC) [2433]
Casey Laine Armed Forces Scholarships [2951]
Lake Dollars for Scholars Endowment Fund [8683]
Lake George Dollars for Scholars Awards [5318]
Lake George Scholarship Association **[5317]**
Lakselaget **[5319]**
Lakselaget Foundation Scholarships [5320]
Lalor Foundation **[5321]**
Lalor Foundation Post-Doctoral Fellowships [5322]
Lam Research Corp. **[5323]**
Lam Research Corporation Core Values Scholarships [5324]
Lamaku Post-Secondary Scholarships [83]
Lamar University College of Engineering Scholarships [6257]
Lamaze International **[5325]**
Lambda Alumni, UCLA Lesbian & Gay Alumni Association Scholarships Program [7854]
Lambda Iota Tau (LIT) **[5327]**
Allen T. Lambert Scholarships [8042]
John and Lois Lamont Graduate Scholarships [2464]
Frank S. Land Scholarships [3425]
Land-Use Planning Scholarships [6294]
Robert S. Landauer, Sr. Memorial Fellowships [4490]
Gloria Landis Bursary [5398]
UAA Paul G. Landis Scholarships [9104]
Landscape Architecture Foundation (LAF) **[5329]**
Landscape Forms Design for People Scholarships [5334]
Cecil Lane Family Scholarships [178]
Lane Powell PC **[5338]**
The Lanford Family Highway Worker Memorial Scholarship Program [1157]
James D. Lang Memorial Scholarships [2390]
Frank H. Lang Merit Scholarships [5341]
Lang, Richert & Patch **[5340]**
Jason Lang Scholarships [252]
Langfitt-Ambrose Trust Funds [7097]
Language Teacher Bursary Program Awards [253]
Languages In Teacher Education Scholarships [254]
Lanier Technical College (Oakwood, Georgia) **[5342]**
Paul J. Laninga Memorial Scholarship Fund [4226]
Stephen Lankester Scholarships [4290]
Lapeer County Medical Scholarship Fund [5351]
The Otis and Florence Lapham Memorial Scholarships [5101]
Lapper County Community Foundation (LCCF) **[5346]**
Christian Larew Memorial Scholarships [5484]
Peter and Jody Larkin Legacy Scholarships [2251]
Arnold Les Larsen, FAIA, Memorial Scholarships [841]
Larson Aquatic Research Support Scholarships (LARS) [1418]
Joseph C. Larson Entrepreneurial Scholarships [7942]
David B. Larson Fellowships in Health and Spirituality [5275]
Las Limas Community Scholarships [8730]
Las Vegas Chinatown Scholarships [7500]
Las Vegas Elks Scholarships [7501]
Las Vegas Elks Scholarships for the Physically Challenged [7502]
Stanislaw & Aniela Lasek Scholarships [7771]
Laser Technology, Engineering and Applications Scholarships [8639]
Jay and Deborah Last Fellowships [420]
Latham Diversity Scholars [5354]
Latham & Watkins LLP **[5353]**
Austin E. Lathrop Scholarships [9157]
Latin American Educational Foundation (LAEF) **[5355]**
Latin American Educational Foundation Scholarships [5356]
Latina Leadership Network (LLN) **[5357]**
Latinos for Dental Careers Scholarships [2676]
Rick and Beverly Lattin Education Scholarship Fund [4227]
Kenneth Laundy Entrance Scholarships [8043]

Robert J. Lavidge Nonprofit Marketing Research Scholarships [919]
Law Enforcement Memorial Scholarship Fund [3911]
Law Foundation of British Columbia **[5359]**
Law Foundation of British Columbia Graduate Fellowships [5360]
Law Foundation of Ontario **[5361]**
Law Foundation of Ontario Community Leadership in Justice Fellowships [5362]
Law Offices of Michael A. DeMayo, L.L.P. **[5363]**
Law and Social Science Dissertation Fellowship and Mentoring Program [578]
Law and Society Association (LSA) **[5365]**
Law and Society Association Article Prize [5367]
Law and Society Association Dissertation Prize [5368]
Law and Society Association International Prize [5369]
Law and Society Association Student Paper Prize [5370]
Law Society of British Columbia **[5372]**
Law Society of British Columbia Scholarships [5373]
Law Society of New Brunswick **[5374]**
Law Society of Prince Edward Island (LSPEI) **[5376]**
Law Student Diversity Scholarships [5814]
Lawrence Berkeley National Laboratory **[5378]**
Lawrence Livermore National Laboratory **[5381]**
Robert G. Lawrence Prize [2412]
Willie D. Lawson, Jr. Memorial Scholarships [6150]
Dr. James L. Lawson Memorial Scholarships [1092]
Lawton Minority Retention Grants [9362]
Verne Lawyer Scholarships [3503]
Lawyers' Committee for Civil Rights Under Law (LCCRUL) **[5383]**
Sue Kay Lay Memorial Scholarships [2952]
Lazarian Graduate Scholarships [1578]
Richard J. Lazzara Fellowships in Advanced Implant Surgery [396]
LCSC Welding Club Scholarships [5438]
Danny T. Le Memorial Scholarships [9431]
Franklin M. Leach Scholarships [9158]
Betsy B. and Garold A. Leach Scholarships for Museum Studies [3416]
The Leaders of Tomorrow Scholarships [3572]
LeaderShape Institute Scholarships [5202]
Leadership 1000 Scholarships [2976]
Leadership Development Scholarships [524]
League of Attorneys' Wives Scholarships [3504]
LEAGUE Foundation Scholarships [7855]
League of Latin American Citizens (LULAC) **[5385]**
League of Latin American Citizens General Electric Scholarships [5386]
Leakey Foundation **[5389]**
Leakey Foundation Research Grants [5391]
Learn German in Germany Grants [4122]
Learning Disabilities Association of Alberta (LDAA) **[5392]**
Learning Disabilities Association of Kingston (LDAK) **[5394]**
Learning Disabilities Association of Ontario (LDAO) **[5396]**
William C. Leary Memorial Emergency Services Scholarships [8985]
Jack W. Leatherman Family Scholarship Fund [4228]
Leber Rubes Inc. Awards [2470]
Patrick Ledden Honorary Scholarships [7943]
Rebecca Lee, M.D. Scholarships [1720]
Albert J. and Mae Lee Memorial Scholarships [7194]
Ken Lee Memorial Scholarships [7944]
Bruce Lee Scholarships [9064]
Harold Leeming Memorial Scholarships [7663]
The Leesfield/AAJ Law Student Scholarships [493]
Judge William B. Leffler Scholarships [9232]
The Legacy Fellowships [421]
Legacy Inc. **[5399]**
Legacy Inc. College Undergraduate and Graduate Scholarships [5400]
Legacy Scholarship Program [8870]
Legacy Scholarships for Graduate Students [1278]
Legal Aid of North Carolina (LANC) **[5401]**
Legal Research Service Scholarships [3505]
Doreen Legg Memorial Scholarships [7664]

Jay C. and B. Nadine Leggett Charitable Scholarship Fund [8684]
Herbert Lehman Education Scholarships [5971]
Lehman Family Scholarships [7945]
PCH Architects/Steven J. Lehnhof Memorial Architectural Scholarships [7665]
Leiber and Stoller Music Scholarships [1213]
Imelda and Ralph LeMar Scholarship Program [3201]
Lemelson Center Fellowships [8255]
Lemelson Center Travel to Collections Awards [8256]
The Lemon Grove Education Foundation Scholarships [7946]
Stan Lencki Scholarships [5713]
John Lennon Scholarships [2159]
Craig Lensch Memorial Scholarships [2192]
Franklin A. Lentesty Scholarships [6817]
V.A. Leonard Scholarships [357]
Leopold Education Project Scholarships [3158]
Sherman L. & Mabel C. Lepard Scholarships [4291]
Lerner-Scott Dissertation Prizes [6959]
Irwin S. Lerner Student Scholarships [6513]
Les Dames D'Escoffier New York (LDNY) **[5404]**
Les Dames D'Escoffier New York Scholarships [5405]
Lesbian, Gay, Bisexual and Transgender Health, Education and Research Trust (LGBT HEART) **[5406]**
Carol Anne Letheren Entrance Awards [8044]
The Irving Leuchter Memorial Scholarships [6714]
Gerald J. Levandoski Memorial Scholarship Fund [3779]
Myra Levick Scholarships [427]
Harold A. Levin Scholarships [2890]
Jack A. and Louise S. Levine Memorial Scholarships [7666]
Herbert Levy Memorial Endowment Fund Scholarships [8439]
Erwin Lew Memorial Scholarships [8451]
Karen B. Lewis Career Education Scholarships [9441]
Lewis-Clark Coin Club Endowed Scholarships [5439]
Lewis and Clark Fund for Exploration and Field Research [992]
Lewis-Clark State College **[5408]**
Lewis-Clark State College/American Chemical Society Scholars Program [5440]
Lewis-Clark State College Foundation Scholars Scholarships [5441]
Lewis-Clark State College Freshman Scholarships [5442]
Lewis-Clark State College Governor's Cup Scholarships [5443]
Lewis-Clark State College/Idaho Society of CPAs Scholarships Fund [5444]
Lewis-Clark State College Non-Traditional Student Scholarships [5445]
Lewis-Clark State College Presidential Out-of-State Scholarships [5446]
Lewis-Clark State College Presidential Technical Out-of-State Scholarships [5447]
Lewis-Clark State College Provost Scholarships [5448]
Lewis-Clark State College Transfer Scholarships [5449]
Lewis-Clark State College Valley Scholarships [5450]
Marvin Lewis Community Fund (MLCF) **[5470]**
Lloyd Lewis Fellowships in American History [6696]
George T. Lewis, Jr. Academic Scholarship Fund [3912]
Frederick D. Lewis Jr. Scholarships [3506]
Flora Lewis Memorial Scholarships [7015]
S. Evelyn Lewis Memorial Scholarships in Medical Health Sciences [9805]
Jonathan D. Lewis Point Scholarships [7365]
Marvin Lewis Scholarships [5471]
Lewiston Clarkston Kiwanis Club Scholarships [5451]
Lewiston Service League Memorial Scholarships [5452]
Lexington Alumni Scholarships [5473]
Lexington Community Foundation (LCF) **[5472]**

Lexington Community Foundation Annual Scholarships [5474]

Lexington Community Foundation/CCC Scholarships [5475]

LGBT HEART Scholarships [5407]

Ta Liang Memorial Awards [1669]

The Liberace Museum and Foundation **[5481]**

Liberace Scholarship Fund [5482]

Liberty Bell Award Law Scholarships [2736]

Liberty Mutual Scholarships [1346]

Library and Information Technology Association (LITA) **[5483]**

Library Media Teacher Scholarships [2271]

Library Research Grants [4144]

Library Resident Research Fellowships [993]

Richard T. Liddicoat Scholarships [4063]

Dolores Zohrab Liebmann Fund **[5487]**

Dolores Zohrab Liebmann Fund - Graduate School Fellowships [5488]

Dolores Zohrab Liebmann Fund - Independent Research/Study Grants [5489]

Dolores Zohrab Liebmann Fund - Publication Grants [5490]

Life and Health Insurance Foundation for Education **[5491]**

LIFE Lessons Scholarship Program [5492]

Life Sciences Research Foundation (LSRF) **[5493]**

Life Sciences Research Foundation Postdoctoral Fellowship Program [5494]

Lighthouse International (Lighthouse Inc.) **[5495]**

Lighthouse International Scholarships - College-bound Awards [5497]

Lighthouse International Scholarships - Graduate Awards [5498]

Lighthouse International Scholarships - Undergraduate Awards [5499]

Frank R. Lillie Fellowships and Scholarships [5620]

Eli Lilly and Company/Black Data Processing Associates Scholarships [2033]

Lilly Endocrine Scholars Fellowship Awards [3638]

Eli Lilly Graduate Scholarships [2451]

Lilly Reintegration Scholarships [2707]

Lily Scholarships in Religion for Journalists [7732]

Esther Lim Memorial Scholarships [2767]

Lim, Ruger and Kim Scholarships [6027]

LIN Media Minority Scholarships and Training Program [5501]

Tecla Lin & Nelia Laroza Memorial Scholarships [2545]

Lin Television Corp. **[5500]**

Lincoln Forum **[5502]**

AIST Ronald E. Lincoln Memorial Scholarships [1808]

John C. Lincoln Memorial Scholarships [1440]

Linda's Scholarships [5882]

Donald A.B. Lindberg Research Fellowships [5744]

Charles A. Lindbergh Fellowships [8252]

Lindenwood University Scouting Scholarships [6258]

CSF Carl H. Lindner Family Scholarships [2856]

George N. Lindsay Civil Rights Legal Fellowships [5384]

Johnny Lineberry Memorial Scholarships [9645]

Link Foundation/Smithsonian Graduate Fellowships in Marine Science [8262]

F. Maynard Lipe Scholarship Awards [615]

Lawrence Lipking Fellowships at the Newberry Library [6697]

Ruth Lister Scholarships [8986]

LIT Scholarships [5328]

LITA and LSSI Minority Scholarships [5485]

LITA/OCLC Minority Scholarships [5486]

Literary Arts Project Grants [220]

Litherland/FTE Scholarships [5007]

Ian Lithgow Memorial Awards [8045]

Ruth Liu Memorial Scholarships [2768]

Live Out Loud Annual Scholarships [7856]

Lawrence Livermore National Laboratory Fellowships [5382]

David C. Lizarraga Graduate Fellowships [8821]

Nancy Llewellyn, RN Pediatric Nursing Bursaries [1849]

LLN Scholarships [5358]

E.C. Lloyd and J.C.U. Johnson Scholarship Fund [3042]

Patricia Lloyd Scholarship Concert Association (PLSCA) **[5504]**

Lloydminster Region Health Foundation (LRHF) **[5506]**

Lo Family Scholarships [9335]

Loan Forgiveness Scholarships [8634]

Virgil K. Lobring Scholarships [3202]

Local Wound Haemostatics and Hemorrhage Control Scholarships [557]

Leon I. Lock and Barbara R. Lock Scholarship Fund [3950]

William J. Locklin Scholarships [1285]

Lodging Management Program Scholarships (LMP) [800]

Audrey Loftus Memorial Scholarships [9188]

Stephen Logan Memorial Scholarships [4052]

LogiCore Corporation **[5512]**

Abram D. and Maxine H. Londa Scholarships [6661]

London Goodenough Association of Canada (LGAC) **[5514]**

London Goodenough Association of Canada Scholarships [5515]

Lone Star GIA Associate and Alumni Scholarships [4064]

Lawrence A. Long Memorial Law Scholarships [368]

James E. Long Memorial Post Doctoral Fellowships [4913]

L.D. and Elsie Long Memorial Scholarships [9646]

Long-Term Research Fellowship Programs [5672]

Kay Longscope Scholarships [6392]

Megan Nicole Longwell Scholarships [7098]

Audre Lord Scholarships [7857]

Lilly Lorenzen Scholarships [1400]

Suzanne and Caleb Loring Research Fellowships [5673]

Barbara Lotze Scholarships for Future Teachers [533]

Willie T. Loud - CH2M Hill Scholarships [6295]

Sir James Lougheed Awards of Distinction [255]

Louisiana Agricultural Consultants Association (LACA) **[5516]**

Louisiana Agricultural Consultants Association Scholarships [5517]

Louisiana Environmental Health Association (LEHA) **[5518]**

Louisiana Library Association (LLA) **[5521]**

Louisiana Library Association Scholarships [5522]

Louisiana Public Health Association (LPHA) **[5524]**

Louisville Institute **[5526]**

Louisville Institute Dissertation Fellowships [5527]

Louisville Institute First Book Grants for Minority Scholars [5528]

Louisville Institute Project Grants for Researchers [5529]

Louisville Institute Sabbatical Grants for Researchers [5530]

Love of Bonita Empowerment Scholarships [8613]

First Lieutenant Scott McClean Love Memorial Scholarship - Children of Soldiers [1615]

First Lieutenant Scott McClean Love Memorial Scholarship - Spouses of Soldiers [1616]

Loveland Archaeological Society (LAS) **[5531]**

D.J. Lovell Scholarships [8640]

The Lowell H. and Dorothy Loving Undergraduate Scholarships [646]

Diane G. Lowe and John Gomez, IV Scholarships [3117]

Gertie S. Lowe Nursing Scholarship Awards [3043]

H.B. Paul Lowenberg Lions Scholarships [4447]

LPHA Scholarships [5525]

LRF Post-Doctoral Fellowships [5552]

Henry Luce Foundation Dissertation Fellowships in American Art [679]

Elsa Ludeke Graduate Scholarships [3417]

David F. Ludovici Scholarships [3829]

Lugonia Alumni/Harrison Lightfoot Scholarships [7667]

Mollie Lukken Memorial Scholarships [5178]

LULAC GM Scholarships [5387]

LULAC National Scholarship Fund [5388]

Audrey Lumsden-Kouvel Fellowships [6698]

Samuel Lunenfeld Research Institute-Research Training Centre **[5534]**

Lung Health Dissertation Grants [916]

Ann & Robert H. Lurie Children's Hospital of Chicago **[5538]**

Luso-American Education Foundation **[5540]**

Luso-American Education Foundation C-1 General Scholarships [5541]

Luso-American Education Foundation G-1 Grants [5542]

Luso-American Education Foundation G-2 Grants [5543]

Luso-American Education Foundation G-3 Grants [5544]

Luso-American Fraternal Federation B-2 Scholarships [5545]

Luso-American Fraternal Federation B-3 Scholarships [5546]

Luso-American Fraternal Federation B-4 Scholarships [5547]

Norval Neil Luxon Prize for Scholarships to Juniors [9286]

Lycoming County Medical Society Scholarships (LCMS) [3986]

Denny Lydic Scholarships [8952]

Melissa A. Lyles Memorial Scholarships [7503]

Lymphoma Research Foundation (LRF) **[5551]**

Pat Lyon Nursing Fellowships [8916]

Boyd Lyon Sea Turtle Fund **[5553]**

The C. Lyons Fellowship Program [6389]

Linda Lyons Memorial Scholarship Fund [5779]

Verne LaMarr Lyons Memorial Scholarships [6123]

Carie and George Lyter Scholarship Fund [3951]

John Mabry Forestry Scholarships [7587]

MAC Emeritus Scholarships for First-Time Meeting Attendees [5855]

Dr. Mac Scholarships [3118]

Bill MacAloney Legacy Scholarships [2252]

John Macara, Barrister of Goderich, Scholarships [9336]

Catharine Macaulay Prize [1233]

MACC Scholarships [5796]

Katie MacDonald Memorial Scholarships [9018]

Irene and Daisy MacGregor Memorial Scholarships [4448]

Nate Mack/Cindi Turner Scholarships [7504]

Robert Mack Scholarship Foundation **[5555]**

Robert Mack Scholarships [5556]

CEMF Claudette MacKay-Lassonde Graduate Scholarships [2456]

R. Tait Mackenzie Awards [7318]

James Mackenzie Fallows Scholarships Honoring William Cunningham [7668]

Thermoset Division/James I. Mackenzie and James H. Cunningham Scholarships [8452]

Mackenzie Municipal Services Agency **[5557]**

Mackey-Byars Scholarships for Communication Excellence [9287]

Macomb County Bar Foundation (MCBF) **[5559]**

MACPA Scholarships [5652]

Carol E. Macpherson Memorial Scholarship and Alumnae Society Scholarships [9244]

Andrew Macrina Scholarships [695]

Pat and John MacTavish Scholarship Fund [4229]

Eileen C. Maddex Fellowships [5198]

Lawrence Madeiros Scholarships [6330]

James Madison Foundation - Junior Fellowships [5564]

James Madison Foundation - Senior Fellowships [5565]

James Madison Memorial Fellowship Foundation **[5563]**

Gordon and Delores Madson Scholarships [3507]

MAES Founders Scholarships [5798]

MAES General Scholarships [5799]

MAES Graduate Scholarships [5800]

MAES Padrino/Madrina Scholarships [5801]

MAES Pipeline Scholarships [5802]

MAES Presidential Scholarships [5803]

MAF Canada Scholarship Fund [5908]

The Brandon Magalassi Memorial Scholarship Foundation **[5566]**

The Brandon Magalassi Memorial Scholarship Foundation Scholarships [5567]

Jay Magazine Memorial Fund College Scholarships (JMMF) [5759]

John T. & Frances Maghielse Scholarships [4292]

Magnetic Interfaces and Nanostructures Division - The Leo M. Falicov Student Award [1983]

Dr. Edward May Magruder Medical Scholarships [609]

Sonia S. Maguire Outstanding Scholastic Achievement Awards [8782]

Lillian Grace Mahan Scholarship Fund [8685]

Dan and Rachel Mahi Educational Scholarships [5216]

Rick Mahoney Scholarships [5714]

Maiman Student Paper Competition [6912]

Mary Main Memorial Scholarships [4449]

Maine Bar Foundation **[5568]**

Maine Chapter of the International Association of Arson Investigators (IAAI) **[5570]**

Maine Community Foundation **[5572]**

Maine Community Foundation - CWG Scholarship Fund [5584]

Maine Community Foundation - Rice Scholarships [5585]

Maine Graphic Arts Association **[5596]**

Maine Graphic Arts Association Scholarships [5597]

Maine Nutrition Council (MNC) **[5598]**

Maine Nutrition Council Scholarships [5599]

Maine Vietnam Veterans Scholarships [5586]

Maintenance Technical Reward and Career Scholarships [6170]

Major Collaborative Research Initiatives Grants [8286]

Malayalee Engineers Association (MEA) **[5600]**

Malayalee Engineers Association Scholarships [5601]

MALDEF Dream Act Student Activist Scholarships [5805]

Maley/FTE Scholarships [5013]

Maley/FTEE Teacher Scholarships [5008]

Mallet Nursing Scholarships [8120]

Malmberg Fellowships [1401]

Malmberg Scholarships [1402]

Joseph J. Malone Fellowships in Arab and Islamic Studies [6227]

Reba Malone Scholarships [1055]

Sue A. Malone Scholarships [5188]

David C. Maloney Scholarships [6423]

MALSCE Scholarships [5660]

Dr. Julianne Malveaux Scholarships [6093]

Malyon-Smith Scholarships [8472]

Lyle Mamer Fellowships [9724]

MANAA Media Scholarships [5737]

Manchester Scholarship Foundation Scholarships [4450]

Mangasar M. Mangasarian Scholarship Fund [1602]

Norm Manly - YMTA Maritime Educational Scholarships [9795]

Horace Mann Insurance Scholarships [6878]

Raleigh Mann Scholarships [9288]

Mansfield Soccer Association (MSA) **[5602]**

Mansfield Soccer Association Scholarships [5603]

Honorable Carol Los Mansmann Memorial Scholarships [329]

Paul Mansur Scholarships [4952]

Manufacturing Jewelers and Association of America (MJSA) **[5604]**

Many Voices Fellowships [7338]

Manzer-Keener-Wefler Scholarships [8686]

Marathon Oil Corporation College Scholarship Program [4578]

March of Dimes **[5606]**

March of Dimes Graduate Nursing Scholarships [5607]

Stephen T. Marchello Scholarship Foundation **[5608]**

Stephen T. Marchello Scholarships [5609]

Harold and Inge Marcus Scholarships [4805]

The Eric Marder Scholarships [4710]

American Turkish Society Arif Mardin Music Fellowships [8976]

Margaret B. Lindsey Awards for Distinguished Research in Teacher Education [467]

Aurella Varallo Mariani Scholarship Program [5985]

Marine Biological Laboratory **[5610]**

Marine Biological Laboratory Pioneers Fund [5621]

Marine Corps Engineer Association **[5634]**

Marine Corps Engineer Association Assistance Fund [5635]

Marine Corps League Foundation **[5636]**

Marine Corps League National Scholarships [5637]

Marine Technology Society (MTS) **[5638]**

Marine Technology Society ROV Scholarships [5639]

Marine Technology Society Scholarships for Graduate and Undergraduate Students [5640]

Marine Technology Society Student Scholarships for Graduating High School Seniors [5641]

Marine Technology Society Student Scholarships for Two-year Technical, Engineering and Community College Students [5642]

Marines Memorial Association (MMA) **[5644]**

Dr. Frank and Florence Marino Scholarships [4451]

Mariposa Elementary School PTA Scholarships [7669]

Howard T. Markey Memorial Scholarships [3717]

Ed Markham International Scholarships [733]

Markley Family Scholarship Fund [8687]

Markley Scholarships [6046]

Markowski-Leach Scholarship Fund [7858]

Richard Marks Educational Fund [5217]

Kaia Lynn Markwalter Endowed Scholarships [5453]

Marliave Scholarship Fund [1768]

Marmot Leadership Scholarships [7008]

Abraham Lincoln Marovitz Public Interest Law Scholarships [2746]

Carl J. Marrara Memorial Scholarship Fund [3780]

Marsh College Scholarships [4842]

Burton W. Marsh Fellowships [4826]

George Perkins Marsh Prize [1249]

Marsh Risk Consulting Scholarships [1347]

Barry H. Marshal Scholarships [7859]

Marshall-Baruch Fellowships [5649]

Thurgood Marshall College Fund (TMCF) **[5646]**

George C. Marshall Foundation (GCMF) **[5648]**

Marshall Memorial Fellowships [4132]

Ray and Gertrude Marshall Scholarships [696]

Ron Marshall Scholarships [1138]

Sarah Shinn Marshall Scholarships [3379]

Marshall Undergraduate Scholars Program [5650]

E.H. Marth Food and Environmental Scholarships [9674]

Lockheed Martin Graduate Scholarships [1560]

Lewis K. Martin II, M.D. and Cheryl Rose Martin Scholarship Fund [4378]

Lockheed Martin IT Scholarships [1561]

Susan B. Martin Memorial Scholarships [4666]

Bryce-Lietzke Martin Scholarships [7099]

Dick Martin Scholarships [2426]

Edna Martin Scholarships [3119]

Eleanor Jean Martin Scholarships [2546]

Right Honourable Paul Martin Sr. Scholarships [2500]

Martin Sisters Scholarships [3380]

Dottie Martin Teacher Scholarships [6765]

John S. Martinez and Family Scholarship Fund [3081]

Eric Martinez Memorial Scholarships [9019]

Corporal Joseph Martinez U.S. Army Memorial Scholarships [7505]

Michael Marucci Memorial Scholarships [6278]

Michael L. Marx and Donald K. Marshall Scholarships [7860]

Maryland Association of Certified Public Accountants (MACPA) **[5651]**

Maryland Poison Center **[5653]**

Maryland Poison Center Clinical Toxicology Fellowships [5654]

Maryland Speech Language Hearing Association (MSHA) **[5655]**

Maryland Speech Language Hearing Association Scholarships [5656]

Jorge Mas Canosa Freedom Foundation **[5657]**

Mas Family Scholarships [5658]

The Maschhoffs Pork Production Scholarships [6379]

Beverly Mascoll Scholarships [2124]

Val Mason Scholarships [2603]

Masonic-Range Science Scholarships [8484]

Massachusetts Association of Land Surveyors and Civil Engineers (MALSCE) **[5659]**

Massachusetts Association of Women Lawyers (MAWL) **[5661]**

Massachusetts Bar Foundation (MBF) **[5663]**

Massachusetts Bar Foundation Legal Intern Fellowship Program (LIFP) [5664]

Massachusetts Chapter of the International Association of Arson Investigators (MAIAAI) **[5665]**

Massachusetts Federation of Polish Women's Clubs Scholarships [5299]

The Massachusetts Historical Society (MHS) **[5667]**

Massachusetts LGBTQ Bar Association (MLGBA) **[5681]**

Massachusetts Office of Student Financial Assistance **[5683]**

Massachusetts Society of the Cincinnati Fellowships [5674]

Massachusetts State Automobile Dealers Association (MSADA) **[5685]**

S.O. Mast Founder's Scholarships [5622]

The Master Gardeners of Pierce County Scholarships [4339]

Master Municipal Clerks Academy Scholarships [4958]

Master's Degree with a Major in Nursing Academic Scholarships [6100]

Master's Scholarships Program (MSP) [8081]

Mat-Su Health Foundation Scholarships [9159]

Matanuska-Susitna College Regent's Scholarships [9160]

Matching Scholarships Program [3328]

Material Handling Education Foundation Scholarships [5688]

Material Handling Industry (MHIA) **[5687]**

Materials Information Society **[5689]**

Materials Information Society National Merit Scholarships [5693]

Larry Matfay Scholarships [5287]

Katharine & Bryant Mather Scholarships [635]

Noel D. Matkin Awards [3596]

Rene Matos Memorial Scholarships [6338]

The Renardo A. Matteucci Scholarship Fund [3088]

Greg Matthews Memorial Scholarships [7195]

Randall Matthis for Environmental Studies Scholarships [1537]

Antonio Mattos Memorial Scholarships [5548]

Mature Student Scholarships [3673]

Aaron Matusek Memorial Scholarships [7506]

Donald Mauer Scholarships [9289]

Monna Mawson Scholarships [4659]

Edmund F. Maxwell Foundation **[5697]**

Maxwell Graduate Scholarships in Medical Journalism [9290]

Edmund F. Maxwell Scholarships [5698]

Juliann and Joseph Maxwell Scholarships [3120]

Juliann King Maxwell Scholarships for Riverview High School Students [3121]

May-Cassioppi Scholarships [3159]

Howard Mayer Brown Fellowships [941]

John E. Mayfield ABLE Scholarships [3122]

John E. Mayfield Scholarships for Cheatham County Central High School [3123]

John E. Mayfield Scholarships for Harpeth High School [3124]

John E. Mayfield Scholarships Pleasant View Christian School [3125]

John E. Mayfield Scholarships for Sycamore High School [3126]

Bill Maynes Fellowships [3691]

Joseph W. Mayo ALS Scholarships [5587]

Clara Mayo Grants [8474]

Charles D. Mayo Student Scholarships [4944]

Tadeusz Maziarz Scholarships [7772]

John Mazurek Memorial-Morgex Insurance Scholarships [274]

Giuliano Mazzetti Scholarships [8392]

Bill McAdam Scholarships [6331]

Walter Samuel McAfee Scholarships in Space Physics [6490]

Durwood McAlister Scholarships [4107]

McBurney Disability Scholarships [9363]

Heather McCallum Scholarships [2413]

Bill McCarthy Scout Scholarship Fund [8688]

McCaughan Heritage Scholarships [970]

McClatchy Scholarships [8552]

McCleary Law Fellows Program [4634]

Walter A. and Nan C. McCloskey Memorial Scholarships [3781]

Dave McCloud Aviation Memorial Scholarships [9161]

McColl Family Fellowships [776]

David McColm Fellowships in Lung Cancer Research [5536]

Anne O'Hare McCormick Scholarship Fund [6716]

Dwight Mosley Scholarships [9410]
John H. Moss Scholarships [9339]
Wilma Motley Memorial California Merit Scholarships [709]
Archie Motley Memorial Scholarships for Minority Students [5856]
John R. Mott Scholarship Foundation **[5938]**
John R. Mott Scholarships [5939]
Jack D. Motteler Scholarships [7413]
Mt. Hood Chapter Scholarship Awards [6938]
Mountain Memorial Scholarships [5624]
Dorothy Mountain Memorial Scholarships [5532]
Mountain Plains Adult Education Association (MPAEA) **[5940]**
Burton J. Moyer Memorial Fellowships [4491]
MPAC-DC Graduate Policy Fellowships [5960]
MPAEA Memorial Scholarships [5941]
MPAEA Student Scholarships [5942]
MPI CRV Scholarships [5757]
MPower Scholarships [7269]
MPTA Doctoral Scholarships [5913]
MSCPA Undergraduate Scholarships [5910]
MSPT Sports Medicine Scholarships [7509]
Ruth Mu-Lan and James S.C. Chao Scholarships [9065]
Muddy Waters Scholarships [2155]
Brittany Mueller Memorial Scholarships [6603]
Mueller Undergraduate Scholarships [9677]
H.M. Muffly Memorial Scholarships [2999]
Mule Deer Foundation (MDF) **[5943]**
Ryan Mullaly Second Chance Fund **[5945]**
Ryan Mullaly Second Chance Fund Scholarships [5946]
Barbara H. Mullin Memorial Scholarships [9573]
Dudley Mullins/Cabot Corporation Scholarships [7100]
Multi-Country Research Fellowships [3270]
Multicultural Advertising Intern Program [435]
Muncy Rotary Club Scholarship Fund [3785]
Muncy Scholars Award Fund [3786]
Marvin Mundel Memorial Scholarships [4806]
Anthony Munoz Foundation **[5947]**
Harry Munoz Memorial Scholarships [7675]
Rick Munoz Memorial Scholarships [7676]
Anthony Munoz Scholarships [5948]
Margaret Munro Scholarships [2548]
Jack and Gertrude Murphy Fellowships [7983]
Daniel Murphy Scholarship Fund (DMSF) **[5949]**
Daniel Murphy Scholarships [5950]
Linda J. Murphy Scholarships [9704]
NACCED Annual John C. Murphy Scholarships [6066]
Carolyn Murray Memorial Scholarships [2337]
Muscle Shoals Kiwanis/Wal-Mart Scholarships [6818]
Muscular Dystrophy Association (MDA) **[5951]**
Music Library Association (MLA) **[5954]**
Music Project Grants [221]
Muslim Public Affairs Council (MPAC-DC) **[5959]**
Muslim Sister Scholarships [8224]
Dr. Helen K. Mussallem Fellowships [2549]
My Life As A Lawyer Scholarships [3262]
MyApartmentMap **[5961]**
MyApartmentMap Housing Scholarships [5962]
Sam A. Myar Jr. Law Scholarships [9235]
Myasthenia Gravis Foundation of America (MGFA) **[5963]**
Myasthenia Gravis Foundation of America Nursing Fellowships [5964]
Myasthenia Gravis Foundation of America Student Fellowships [5965]
Clarence and Josephine Myers Scholarships [8394]
Mary Fran Myers Scholarships [6569]
The Myositis Association (TMA) **[5966]**
Myotonic Dystrophy Foundation (MDF) **[5968]**
NAACP Legal Defense and Educational Fund (NAACP LDF) **[5970]**
NAAF Aboriginal Health Careers Bursary and Scholarships [5992]
NAAF Post-Secondary Education Scholarships [5993]
NAAMA Scholarships [6024]
NABA National Scholarship Program [6037]
NACA East Coast Graduate Student Scholarships [6047]

NACA East Coast Higher Education Research Scholarships [6048]
NACA East Coast Undergraduate Scholarships for Student Leaders [6049]
NACA Foundation Graduate Scholarships [6050]
NACA Regional Council Student Leadership Scholarships [6051]
NACA Southeast Student Leadership Scholarships [6052]
NACADA Scholarships [5997]
Albert and Alice Nacinovich Music Scholarships [3787]
Irwin Allen Nadal Entrance Awards [8046]
Miles Spencer Nadal Entrance Awards [8047]
Nadine International Inc. Awards [2471]
NAED/Spencer Dissertation Fellowship Program [6005]
NAFA International Dissertation Research Fellowships [6078]
NAFEO Internship Program [6068]
Jack Nagasaka Memorial Scholarships [7677]
NAJA Scholarships [6086]
Gongoro Nakamura Memorial Scholarships [5145]
NALS of Arizona **[5974]**
NALS of Detroit **[5976]**
NALS of Detroit Scholarships [5977]
NALS of Michigan **[5978]**
NALS of Michigan Scholarships [5979]
NAMTA - International Art Materials Trade Association **[5980]**
NAMTA - International Art Materials Trade Association Visual Arts Major Scholarships [5981]
NANBPWC National Scholarships [6095]
Robyn Nance Memorial Scholarships [7678]
Nanometer-Scale Science and Technology Division Graduate Award [1984]
NAPABA Law Foundation Scholarships [6028]
Chereddi NarayanaRao & Radhamanohari Scholarships [8830]
NARFE-FEEA Scholarship Awards Program [6011]
NARRP Student Conference Scholarships [6111]
NASA Aeronautics Scholarships - Undergraduate Program [1241]
NASCOE Scholarships [6070]
NASE Future Entrepreneur Scholarships [6117]
Kermit B. Nash Academic Scholarships [8137]
Elizabeth Nash Foundation **[5982]**
Elizabeth Nash Foundation Scholarships [5983]
Archie Hartwell Nash Memorial Scholarships [3127]
Mike Nash Memorial Scholarships [9427]
Nashville Catholic Business Women's League (NCBWL) **[5984]**
Nashville Unit Scholarships [4534]
NASIG Conference Student Grants [6743]
NASP-ERT Minority Scholarships for Graduate Training in School Psychology [6113]
NASSCO **[5987]**
National 4th Infantry Ivy Division Association **[5989]**
National AAHAM Scholarships [483]
National Aboriginal Achievement Foundation (NAAF) **[5991]**
National Academic Advising Association (NACADA) **[5995]**
The National Academies **[5998]**
National Academy of Education **[6003]**
National Academy of Education Scholarships [6006]
National Academy of Television Arts and Sciences (NATAS) **[6008]**
National Active and Retired Federal Employees Association (NARFE) **[6010]**
National Administrative Law Judiciary Foundation (NALJF) **[6012]**
National Air Filtration Association **[6014]**
National Air Filtration Association Scholarship Fund [6015]
National Alliance of Preservation Commission Student Scholarships [6017]
National Alliance of Preservation Commissions (NAPC) **[6016]**
National Alpha Lambda Delta **[6018]**
National American Arab Nurses Association (NAANA) **[6021]**
National American Arab Nurses Association Scholarships [6022]
National Arab American Medical Association (NAAMA) **[6023]**

National Asian Pacific American Bar Association (NAPABA) **[6025]**
National Association of Abandoned Mine Land Programs (NAAMLP) **[6030]**
National Association of Abandoned Mine Land Programs Scholarships [6031]
National Association of Agricultural Educators (NAAE) **[6032]**
National Association for Armenian Studies and Research Scholarships [1603]
National Association of Biology Teachers (NABT) **[6034]**
National Association of Biology Teachers BioClub Student Awards [6035]
National Association of Black Accountants (NABA) **[6036]**
National Association of Black Social Workers (NABSW) **[6038]**
National Association of Campus Activities (NACA) **[6044]**
National Association of Campus Activities Multicultural Scholarship Programs [6053]
National Association of Campus Activities Scholarships for Student Leaders [6054]
National Association of Chain Drug Stores Foundation **[6059]**
National Association of Collegiate Directors of Athletics (NACDA) **[6061]**
National Association of Container Distributors (NACD) **[6063]**
National Association for County Community and Economic Development (NACCED) **[6065]**
National Association for Equal Opportunity in Higher Education (NAFEO) **[6067]**
National Association of Farm Service Agency County Office Employees (NASCOE) **[6069]**
National Association of Fellowships Advisors (NAFA) **[6071]**
National Association of Health Services Executives (NAHSE) **[6079]**
National Association of Hispanic Nurses (NAHN) **[6083]**
National Association of Junior Auxiliaries (NAJA) **[6085]**
National Association of Multicultural Engineering Program Advocates (NAMEPA) **[6087]**
National Association of Multicultural Engineering Program Advocates Beginning Freshmen Awards (NAMEPA) [6088]
National Association of Multicultural Engineering Program Advocates Transfer Engineering Student Awards (NAMEPA) [6089]
National Association of Music Merchants, the International Music Products Association (NAMM) **[6090]**
National Association of Negro Business and Professional Women's Clubs (NANBPWC) **[6092]**
National Association of Oil and Energy Service Professionals (OESP) **[6096]**
National Association of Orthopaedic Nurses Foundation (NAON) **[6098]**
National Association of Pastoral Musicians Academic Scholarships [6102]
National Association of Pastoral Musicians (NPM) **[6101]**
National Association of Pediatric Nurse Practitioners (NAPNAP) **[6104]**
National Association for Pupil Transportation (NAPT) **[6108]**
National Association of Recreation Resource Planners (NARRP) **[6110]**
National Association of School Psychologists (NASP) **[6112]**
National Association of School Safety and Law Enforcement Officers (NASSLEO) **[6114]**
National Association of School Safety and Law Enforcement Officers Scholarships (NASSLEO) [6115]
National Association for the Self-Employed (NASE) **[6116]**
National Association for the Self-Employed Scholarships [6118]
National Association of Social Workers (NASW) **[6119]**
National Association of State Land Reclamationists (NASLR) **[6124]**

National Association for Surface Finishing (NASF) **[6126]**

National Association of Teacher Educators for Family and Consumer Sciences (NATEFACS) **[6128]**

National Association of Women in Construction (NAWIC) **[6130]**

National Association of Women in Construction Founders Undergraduate Scholarships [6132]

National Association of Women Judges (NAWJ) **[6133]**

National Ataxia Foundation **[6135]**

National Ataxia Foundation Research Fellowships [6136]

National Ataxia Foundation Research Grants [6137]

National Beta Club **[6138]**

National Beta Club Scholarships [6139]

National Biosafety and Biocontainment Training Program (NBBTP) **[6140]**

National Biosafety and Biocontainment Training Program Fellowships [6141]

National Black Coalition of Federal Aviation Employees (NBCFAE) **[6142]**

National Black Coalition of Federal Aviation Employees Scholarships [6143]

National Black Deaf Advocate Scholarships [6147]

National Black Deaf Advocates (NBDA) **[6144]**

National Black Graduate Student Association (NBGSA) **[6149]**

National Black MBA Association **[6151]**

National Black Nurses Association (NBNA) **[6154]**

National Black Nurses Association Scholarships [6155]

National Black Police Association (NBPA) **[6156]**

National Board of Boiler and Pressure Vessel Inspectors (NBBI) **[6158]**

The National Board Technical Scholarships [6159]

National Business Aviation Association Inc. (NBAA) **[6160]**

National Cattlemen's Foundation (NCF) **[6173]**

National Center for American Indian Enterprise Development **[6179]**

National Center for Farmworker Health (NCFH) **[6181]**

National Center for Health Statistics Postdoctoral Research Awards [2714]

National Center for Law and Economic Justice (NCLEJ) **[6183]**

National Center for Learning Disabilities (NCLD) **[6185]**

National Chapter of Canada IODE **[6187]**

National Co-op Scholarship Program [9750]

National Coal Transportation Association (NCTA) **[6189]**

National Coal Transportation Association At Large Scholarships [6190]

National College Scholarship Awards [5088]

National Collegiate Athletic Association (NCAA) **[6191]**

National Collegiate Athletic Association Postgraduate Scholarships [6194]

National Collegiate Cancer Foundation (NCCF) **[6195]**

National Collegiate Cancer Foundation Scholarships [6196]

National Community Pharmacists Association (NCPA) **[6197]**

National Community Pharmacists Association Presidential Scholarships [6199]

National Community Pharmacists Association Summer Internship Programs [6200]

National Conference of Bar Examiners (NCBE) **[6203]**

National Conference of CPA Practitioners (NCC-PAP) **[6205]**

National Conservation District Employees Association (NCDEA) **[6207]**

National Costumers Association (NCA) **[6209]**

National Costumers Association Scholarships [6210]

National Council on Education for the Ceramic Arts (NCECA) **[6211]**

National Council on Public History (NCPH) **[6214]**

National Council on Public History Graduate Student Travel Awards [6215]

National Council on Public History Student Project Awards [6216]

National Council of Teachers of English (NCTE) **[6217]**

National Council of Teachers of Mathematics (NCTM) **[6220]**

National Council on U.S.-Arab Relations (NCUSAR) **[6226]**

National Cowboy & Western Heritage Museum **[6228]**

National Dairy Herd Information Association (NDHIA) **[6230]**

National Dairy Herd Information Association Scholarship Program [6231]

National Dairy Shrine (NDS) **[6232]**

National Defense Industrial Association - Iowa Illinois Chapter **[6234]**

National Defense Industrial Association - Picatinny Chapter **[6236]**

National Defense Science and Engineering Graduate Fellowship (NDSEG) **[6238]**

National Defense Transportation Association (NDTA) **[6240]**

National Dental Hygienists' Association (NDHA) **[6243]**

National Dental Hygienists' Association Scholarships [6244]

National Eagle Scout Association (NESA) **[6245]**

National Electrical Manufacturers Representatives Association (NEMRA) **[6266]**

National Endowment for the Humanities Advanced Fellowships for Research in Turkey [1153]

National Endowment for the Humanities Fellowships [6700]

The National Endowment for the Humanities Fellowships [1142]

National Environmental Health Association (NEHA) **[6268]**

National Environmental Health Association Scholarship Fund [6269]

National Estuarine Research Reserve System (NERRS) **[6270]**

National Federation of the Blind (NFB) **[6272]**

National Federation of the Blind Educator of Tomorrow Awards [6279]

National Federation of Paralegal Associations (NFPA) **[6283]**

National Federation of Republican Women (NFRW) **[6286]**

National Forum for Black Public Administrators (NFBPA) **[6289]**

National Foster Parent Association (NFPA) **[6298]**

National Foundation for Infectious Diseases (NFID) **[6300]**

National Garden Clubs **[6302]**

National GEM Consortium **[6304]**

National GEM Consortium - MS Engineering Fellowships [6305]

National GEM Consortium - PhD Engineering Fellowships [6306]

National GEM Consortium - PhD Science Fellowships [6307]

National Government Publishing Association (NGPA) **[6308]**

National Greenhouse Manufacturers Association Scholarships [734]

National Ground Water Association (NGWA) **[6310]**

The National Guard Association of Texas **[6312]**

National Heart, Lung and Blood Institute (NHLBI) **[6314]**

National Heartburn Alliance NP Student Scholarships [377]

National Hemophilia Foundation **[6316]**

National Hispanic Coalition of Federal Aviation Employees (NHCFAE) **[6337]**

National Hispanic Foundation for the Arts (NHFA) **[6339]**

National Honor Roll Scholarships [2222]

National Honor Society (NHS) **[6341]**

National Housing Endowment **[6343]**

National Huguenot Society (NHS) **[6346]**

National Huguenot Society Scholarships [6347]

National Humanities Center (NHC) **[6348]**

National Humanities Center Fellowships [6349]

National Industrial Belting Association (NIBA) **[6350]**

National Institute of Health (NIH) **[6352]**

National Institute of Health Undergraduate Scholarship Program [6353]

National Institute of Justice (NIJ) **[6354]**

National Investment Company Service Association (NICSA) **[6357]**

National Iranian American Council (NIAC) **[6359]**

National Iranian American Council Fellowships [6365]

National Italian American Bar Association **[6366]**

National Italian American Bar Association Scholarships [6367]

National Italian American Foundation (NIAF) **[6368]**

National Judges Association (NJA) **[6371]**

National Judges Association Scholarships [6372]

National Junior Angus Association (NJAA) **[6373]**

National Junior Horticultural Association Alumni Scholarships [6376]

National Junior Horticultural Association (NJHA) **[6375]**

National Junior Swine Association (NJSA) **[6377]**

National Junior Swine Association Outstanding Member Scholarships [6380]

National Kindergarten Alliance (NKA) **[6384]**

National Kindergarten Alliance Graduate Scholarships [6385]

National Law Enforcement and Firefighters Childrens Foundation (NLEAFCF) **[6386]**

National Legal Aid and Defender Association (NLADA) **[6388]**

National Lesbian and Gay Journalists Association (NLGJA) **[6390]**

National LGBT Bar Association (NLGLA) **[6393]**

National Library of Medicine (NLM) **[6395]**

National Little Britches Rodeo Association (NLBRA) **[6397]**

National Medical Fellowships (NMF) **[6400]**

National Medical Fellowships Need-Based Scholarships [6403]

National Merit Scholarship Corporation (NMSC) **[6404]**

National Merit Scholarship Program [6405]

National Military Family Association (NMFA) **[6410]**

National Military Intelligence Association **[6414]**

National Oceanic and Atmospheric Administration (NOAA) **[6416]**

National Organization of Black Law Enforcement Executives (NOBLE) **[6420]**

National Organization of Black Law Enforcement Executives Fellowship Programs [6421]

National Organization for Human Services (NOHS) **[6422]**

National Organization of Italian-American Women (NOIAW) **[6424]**

National Organization of Italian-American Women Scholarships [6425]

National Organization for the Professional Advancement of Black Chemists and Chemical Engineers (NOBCChE) **[6426]**

National Orientation Directors Association **[6433]**

National Parking Association **[6435]**

National Pathfinder Scholarships [6287]

National Pest Management Association (NPMA) **[6437]**

National Physical Science Consortium (NPSC) **[6439]**

National Potato Council (NPC) **[6441]**

National Poultry and Food Distributors Association (NPFDA) **[6443]**

National Poultry and Food Distributors Association Scholarships [6444]

National Preservation Institute (NPI) **[6445]**

National Preservation Institute Scholarships [6446]

National Press Photographers Association (NPPA) **[6447]**

National Private Truck Council (Private Carrier Conference Inc.) **[6454]**

National Public Employer Labor Relations Association (NPELRA) **[6456]**

National Recreation and Park Association (NRPA) **[6458]**

National Recreation and Park Association Diversity Scholarships [6459]

National Research Council Canada (NRC) **[6460]**

National Restaurant Association Educational Foundation (NRAEF) **[6462]**

National Roofing Contractors Association (NRCA) **[6464]**

National Science Foundation (NSF) **[6466]**

National Sculpture Society (NSS) **[6468]**

National Sculpture Society Scholarships [6470]

National Security Technology Engineering and Science Scholarships [7510]

National Senior Citizens Law Center (NSCLC) **[6471]**

National Sheriffs' Association **[6473]**

National Sheriffs' Association Scholarship Program [6474]

National Sleep Foundation (NSF) **[6475]**

National Slovak Society of the United States of America (NSS) **[6477]**

National Slovak Society of the USA Scholarships [6478]

National Slovak Society of the USA Senior Scholarships [6479]

National Society of Accountants (NSA) **[6480]**

National Society of Accountants Scholarship Program [6481]

National Society of Black Physicists (NSBP) **[6483]**

National Society, Daughters of the American Revolution (DAR) **[6495]**

National Society of High School Scholars **[6500]**

National Society of Hispanic MBAs (NSHMBA) **[6507]**

National Society for HistoTechnology (NSH) **[6509]**

National Space Biomedical Research Institute (NSBRI) **[6520]**

National Space Biomedical Research Institute Postdoctoral Fellowships [6521]

National Space Club (NSC) **[6522]**

National Speleological Society (NSS) **[6524]**

National Sporting Clays Association (NSCA) **[6530]**

National Stone, Sand & Gravel Association **[6532]**

National Student Nurses' Association (NSNA) **[6535]**

National Swimming Pool Foundation (NSPF) **[6537]**

National Swimming Pool Foundation Board of Directors' Scholarship Awards [6539]

National Swimming Pool Foundation Scholarship Awards [6540]

National Taxidermists Association (NTA) **[6541]**

National Technical Honor Society (NTHS) **[6543]**

National Technical Honor Society Scholarships [3710]

National Trust for Historic Preservation **[6545]**

National Union of Public and General Employees (NUPGE) **[6547]**

National Urban Fellows (NUF) **[6552]**

National Volunteer Fire Council (NVFC) **[6554]**

National Wildlife Federation **[6556]**

National Women's Studies Association (NWSA) **[6558]**

National Women's Studies Association Lesbian Caucus Scholarships [6560]

Native American Community Scholars Awards [8243]

Native American Education Grants [821]

Native American Leadership Education Scholarships (NALE) [2663]

Native American Visiting Student Awards [8244]

Native Hawaiian Chamber of Commerce Scholarships [5219]

Native Hawaiian Visual Arts Scholarships [5220]

Native Law Centre of Canada **[6563]**

Native Women's Association of Canada **[6566]**

Natural Hazards Center **[6568]**

Natural Sciences & Engineering Research Council of Canada **[6570]**

Natural Sciences and Engineering Research Council Postgraduate Scholarships [6572]

Naval Helicopter Association Scholarship Fund **[6574]**

Naval Helicopter Association Scholarships [6575]

Naval Intelligence Professionals (NIP) **[6576]**

Naval Research Laboratory (NRL) **[6580]**

Naval Weather Service Association (NWSA) **[6582]**

Naval Weather Service Association Scholarships [6583]

Navy, Army or Air Force ROTC Scholarship Program [3329]

Navy League of the United States (NLUS) **[6584]**

Navy-Marine Corps Relief Society (Dahlgren, Virginia) (NMCRS) **[6591]**

Marek Nawrot Memorial Scholarships [7774]

Nazareth Association **[6596]**

The Nazareth Scholarships [6597]

NBMBAA Graduate Scholarships Program [6152]

NBMBAA PhD Fellowship Program [6153]

NC Hospitality Education Foundation Scholarships - Four Year College or University [6776]

NC Hospitality Education Foundation Scholarships - Graduate [6777]

NC Hospitality Education Foundation Scholarships - High School [6778]

NC Hospitality Education Foundation Scholarships - Two Year Community or Junior College [6779]

N.C. Psychoanalytic Foundation Journalism Scholarships [9297]

NCAEA Scholarships [6746]

NCBWL Scholarships [5986]

NCCPAP and AICPA Scholarships for Graduating High School Seniors [6206]

NCECA Graduate Student Fellowships [6213]

NCF Fort Dodge Animal Health Legacy Scholarships for Undergraduate Students [6177]

NCF Fort Dodge Animal Health Legacy Scholarships for Veterinary Students [6178]

NCLEJ Law School Graduate Fellows and Volunteers [6184]

NCTE Research Foundation Grants [6218]

NDIA Picatinny Chapter Scholarships [6237]

NDSEG Fellowships [6239]

H.N. Neal Memorial Scholarships [2338]

Nebraska Farm Bureau **[6598]**

Nebraska Farm Bureau Young Farmers and Ranchers Greater Horizon Scholarships [6599]

Nebraska High School Rodeo Association **[6600]**

Nebraska Hospital Association (NHA) **[6605]**

Nebraska Hospital Association Tuition Aid and Scholarships [6606]

Nebraska Library Association (NLA) **[6607]**

Nebraska Paralegal Association (NePA) **[6609]**

Nebraska Paralegal Association Student Scholarships [6610]

Nebraska Society of Certified Public Accountants (NSCPA) **[6611]**

J.W. "Bill" Neese Scholarships [4900]

NEH Fellowships for Senior Scholars [2695]

Paul and Ruth Neidhold Business Scholarships [3161]

NELA Scholarships [6624]

Edward J. Nell Memorial Scholarships in Journalism [7563]

Nellie Yeoh Whetten Award [1985]

Dave Nelsen Scholarships [6097]

Charles I. Nelson Endowed Scholarships [7198]

Midwest Chapter Scholarships - Don Nelson [1813]

Bill Nelson Scholarship Endowment [7004]

Hubert A. Nelson Scholarships [3539]

Judge William J. Nelson Scholarships [8615]

NEMLA Book Prize [6798]

NEMLA Summer Fellowships [6799]

NEMRA Educational Scholarship Foundation [6267]

Nephrology Nurse Researcher Awards [945]

Andrew Nerland Endowment Scholarships [9164]

NERRS Graduate Research Fellowships (GRF) [6271]

Dr. Ezra Nesbeth Scholarships [5123]

NESCPA Fifth-Year Scholarships [6612]

NESCPA General Scholarships [6613]

Amelia and Emanuel Nessell Scholarships [3540]

Netherlands-Florida Scholarship Foundation (NFSF) **[6614]**

Netherlands-Florida Scholarship Foundation Scholarships [6615]

Reverend John S. Nettled Scholarships [3045]

Network in Canadian History and Environment (NiCHE) **[6616]**

Networks Scholarships College of Business [4750]

Elizabeth Neuffer Fellowships [5030]

Nevada Black Police Association Scholarships [7511]

Nevada Organization of Nurse Leaders (NONL) **[6618]**

Nevada Parent Teacher Association Scholarships [7512]

Alan H. Neville Memorial Scholarships [337]

New Brunswick Law Foundation Graduate Scholarships in Law [5375]

New Brunswick Nurses Association Scholarships [2550]

New Century Scholars Doctoral Scholarships [1387]

New Century Scholars Research Grants [1388]

New England Club Managers Association (NECMA) **[6620]**

New England FEMARA Scholarships [1096]

New England Library Association (NELA) **[6623]**

New Hampshire Association of Educational Office Professionals (NHAEOP) **[6625]**

New Hampshire Automotive Dealers Association (NHADA) **[6628]**

New Hampshire Sheep and Wool Growers Association (NHSWGA) **[6630]**

New Hampshire Snowmobile Association (NHSA) **[6632]**

New Hampshire Snowmobile Association Scholarships [6633]

New Hampshire Society of Certified Public Accountants (NHSCPA) **[6634]**

New Jersey Association of Osteopathic Physicians and Surgeons (NJAOPS) **[6636]**

New Jersey Association of Osteopathic Physicians and Surgeons Scholarships [6637]

New Jersey Commission on Brain Injury Research (NJCBIR) **[6638]**

New Jersey Hospital Association (NJHA) **[6643]**

New Jersey Library Association (NJLA) **[6645]**

New Jersey Performing Arts Center (NJPAC) **[6647]**

New Jersey Press Foundation (NJPF) **[6650]**

New Jersey Psychological Association (NJPA) **[6654]**

New Jersey Psychological Association Scholarships for Minority Graduate Students [6655]

New Jersey Society of Certified Public Accountants (NJSCPA) **[6656]**

New Jersey State Bar Foundation (NJSBF) **[6659]**

New Mexico Association for Bilingual Education (NMABE) **[6664]**

New Mexico Association for Bilingual Education Scholarships [6665]

New Mexico Manufactured Housing Association Scholarship Program [281]

New York Financial Writers' Association (NYFWA) **[6666]**

New York Financial Writers' Associations Scholarships [6667]

New York School Nutrition Association (NYSNA) **[6668]**

New York State Association of Agricultural Fairs (NYSAAF) **[6670]**

New York State Association of Agricultural Fairs Scholarships [6671]

New York State Government Finance Officers' Association Inc. **[6672]**

New York State Higher Education Services Corp. **[6674]**

New York State Senate **[6676]**

New York State Senate - Legislative Fellowships [6678]

New York State Society of Certified Public Accountants (NYSSCPA) **[6682]**

The New York Times College Scholarships [6685]

The New York Times Company Foundation **[6684]**

New York Water Environment Association (NYWEA) **[6686]**

New York Water Environment Association Scholarships [6688]

New York Women in Communications Foundation **[6689]**

New York Women in Communications, Inc. Foundation Scholarships [6690]

Ted and Ruth Neward Scholarships [8453]

Newberry Consortium on American Indian Studies Faculty Fellowships [6701]

Newberry Consortium on American Indian Studies Graduate Student Fellowships [6702]

Newberry Library ACM/GLCA Faculty Fellowships [6703]

Newberry Library **[6691]**

Newberry Library/British Academy Fellowships for Study in Great Britain [6704]

Newberry Library/Ecole Nationale des Chartes Ex-

change Fellowships [6705]
Newberry Library Short-Term Fellowships in the History of Cartography [6706]
Newberry Library Short-Term Resident Fellowships for Individual Research [6707]
The Shanon Newberry Physical Therapy Scholarship Endowment [8741]
Charlotte W. Newcombe Doctoral Dissertation Fellowships [9618]
Newcomer Supply Student Scholarships [6514]
AAJA/S.I. Newhouse Foundation Scholarships [1642]
Newkirk Center for Science and Society **[6711]**
Newkirk Center for Science and Society Graduate Student Fellowships [6712]
Frank Newman Leadership Awards [2350]
Edsel Newman Scholarships [5476]
Newman University Scouting Scholarships [6260]
Jerry Newson Scholarships [3128]
The Newspaper Guild (TNG) **[6713]**
Newswomen's Club of New York (NCNY) **[6715]**
Alwin B. Newton Scholarships [1268]
Newtonville Woman's Club Scholarships [4079]
NFBPA/CDM Scholarships [6296]
NFDA Professional Women's Conference Scholarships [4031]
NFID Advanced Vaccinology Course Travel Grants [6301]
NFPA/PACE Scholarships [6284]
NFPA and Thomson West Scholarships [6285]
NFPA Youth Scholarships [6299]
NGAT Educational Scholarships [6313]
NGC College Scholarships [6303]
Le Hoang Nguyen College Scholarships (LHN) [9432]
The Thuy Nguyen Scholarships [9433]
NHAEOP Member Scholarships [6626]
NHFA Scholarships [6340]
NHLBI Individual Pre-Doctoral Fellowships [6315]
NHPGA Apprentice Scholarships [5715]
NHS National Scholarships [6342]
NHSCPA Scholarships [6635]
NIAF Scholarships - General Category I [6369]
NIAF Scholarships - General Category II [6370]
NIBA Presidential Scholarships [6351]
Donald E. Nichols Scholarships [1269]
Gunnar Nicholson Endowed Scholarships [7199]
Norman Nicholson Scholarships [2424]
Midwest Chapter Scholarships - Mel Nickel [1814]
"Nickels for Notes" Scholarships [4080]
Herbert W. Nickens Medical Student Scholarships [1701]
Virginia Nicklas Scholarships [3382]
Sharon Nield Memorial Scholarships [2551]
George A. Nielsen Public Investor Scholarships [4200]
Mike Niemeyer Memorial Football Scholarships [7679]
Eric Niemitalo Scholarships in Earth and Environmental Science [8121]
Helen W. Nies Memorial Scholarships [3718]
Nigerian Women Association of Georgia (NWAG) **[6717]**
NIJ Visiting Fellowships [6356]
Ninety-Nines, International Organization of Women Pilots **[6720]**
Evelyn S. Nish Scholarships [8180]
Anderson Niskanen Scholarships [3541]
Nissan North America, Inc. Scholarships [809]
Nixon Family Scholarship Fund [9556]
CSF Corwin Nixon Scholarships [2857]
Louise A. Nixon Scholarships [6608]
NJCBIR Individual Research Grants [6639]
NJCBIR Pilot Research Grants [6640]
NJCBIR Postdoctoral and Graduate Student Fellowships [6641]
NJCBIR Programmatic Multi-Investigator Project Grants [6642]
NJLA Scholarships [6646]
NJSA Visionary Leader Scholarships [6381]
NJSCPA College Scholarships [6657]
NJSCPA High School Scholarships [6658]
NLBRA/Wrangler Academic Scholarships [6398]
NLM Associate Fellowships [6396]
NMCRS Gold Star Scholarship Program [6593]
NMIA Scholarship Program [6415]

NMSC College and University Sponsorship of Merit Scholarship Awards [6406]
NMSC Corporate-Sponsored Achievement Scholarship Awards [6407]
NMSC National Achievement Scholarship Program [6408]
NMSC Special Scholarships [6409]
NNF Scholarship Program [520]
NOAA Graduate Sciences Scholarships [6418]
NOAA Undergraduate Scholarships [6419]
NOBCChE Procter and Gamble Fellowships [6430]
Leonard Noble Educational Scholarships [6515]
Charles S. Noble Scholarships for Study at Harvard [258]
Edna A. Noblin Dawsonville Lions Club Scholarships [5345]
Stuart L. Noderer Memorial Scholarships [7949]
George H. Nofer Scholarships for Law and Public Policy [2049]
NOHIMSS Student Scholarship Program [6805]
Maureen E. Nolan-Cahill Memorial Scholarships [9165]
Alfred H. Nolle Scholarships [344]
Helen Woodruff Nolop Scholarships in Audiology and Allied Fields [3419]
Non Commissioned Officers Association (NCOA) **[6725]**
Non Commissioned Officers Association Scholarships [6726]
Nonprofit Academic Centers Council (NACC) **[6728]**
Nonproliferation Graduate Fellowships Program (NGFP) [7033]
Nor' Easters Scholarships - Four-year Program [6732]
Nor' Easters Scholarships - Two-year Program [6733]
Nor' Easters Snowmobile Club **[6731]**
Norall Scholarship Trust [5477]
Arthur L. Norberg Travel Grants [1991]
Marian Norby Scholarships [8495]
Nordic Ski Association of Anchorage Scholarships [197]
Norfolk Southern Foundation Scholarships [1131]
Norfolk Southern Scholarships [9450]
Norkus Charitable Foundation Scholarships [2727]
Nortel Institute Undergraduate Scholarships [9340]
North Alabama Dietetic Association Scholarships [169]
North American Conference on British Studies (NACBS) **[6734]**
North American Conference on British Studies Dissertation Year Fellowships [6735]
North American Conference on British Studies-Huntington Library Fellowships [6736]
North American Interfraternal Foundation (NIF) **[6737]**
North American Rolex Scholarships [7002]
North American Serials Interest Group (NASIG) **[6742]**
North American Society Fellowships [7319]
North Carolina Adult Education Association (NCAEA) **[6745]**
North Carolina American Water Works Association **[6747]**
North Carolina Association of Certified Public Accountants (NCACPA) **[6751]**
North Carolina Association of Health Care Recruiters (NCAHCR) **[6754]**
North Carolina Association of Health Care Recruiters Scholarships [6755]
North Carolina Commercial Flower Growers Association (NCCFGA) **[6756]**
North Carolina Commercial Flower Growers Association Floriculture Scholarships [6757]
North Carolina Council of Epsilon Sigma Alpha **[6758]**
North Carolina Council of Epsilon Sigma Alpha Scholarships [6759]
North Carolina CPA Foundation Scholarships [6752]
North Carolina Economic Developers Association (NCEDA) **[6760]**
North Carolina Federation of Republican Women (NCFRW) **[6764]**
North Carolina Heroes Fund **[6766]**
North Carolina Heroes Fund Scholarships [6767]

North Carolina League for Nursing Academic Scholarships [3915]
North Carolina Nursery and Landscape Association (NCNLA) **[6768]**
North Carolina Nursery and Landscape Association Horticulture Scholarships [6769]
North Carolina Restaurant and Lodging Association (NCRLA) **[6770]**
North Carolina Simmental Association (NCSA) **[6780]**
North Central, Region 9 Scholarships [8395]
North Dakota Division Scholarships [5862]
North Dakota Farmers Union (NDFU) **[6782]**
North Dakota Farmers Union Co-op House Scholarships [6786]
North Dakota Farmers Union Scholarships [6787]
North Dakota Veterinary Medical Association (ND-VMA) **[6789]**
North Dakota Veterinary Medical Association Scholarships [6791]
North Florida Chapter Safety Education Scholarships [1349]
North Mecklenburg Teachers' Memorial Scholarships [3916]
North Ottawa Hospital Auxiliary Scholarship Fund [4231]
Michelle North Scholarships for Safety [4510]
North Texas GIA Alumni Association Scholarships [4067]
Northampton County Medical Society Alliance (NCMSA) **[6793]**
Northampton County Medical Society Alliance Scholarships [6794]
NorthCoast Medical Scholarship Program [954]
Northeast Alabama District Dietetic Association Scholarships [170]
Northeast Conference on the Teaching of Foreign Languages (NECTFL) **[6795]**
Northeast Modern Language Association (NEMLA) **[6797]**
Northeastern Illinois Chapter Scholarships [1350]
Northern Alberta Development Council Bursary Awards [259]
Northern Alberta Development Council Bursary Partnership Program [260]
The Northern Arizona Native-American Foundation (TNANAF) **[6800]**
Northern Arizona Native-American Foundation Scholarships [6801]
Northern California Chapter of HIMSS Scholarships [4506]
Northern California DX Foundation Scholarships [1097]
Northern Indiana Community Foundation (NICF) **[6802]**
Northern Ohio Chapter of Healthcare Information Management Systems Society (NOHIMSS) **[6804]**
Northern Resident Scholarships [1736]
Northern Tier Hardwood Association (NTHA) **[6806]**
Northern Virginia Alumnae Chapter Scholarships [3383]
Eugene Northrup Scholarships [5457]
Northwest Community Center Scholarships [3162]
Northwest-Shoals Community College Academic Scholarships [6819]
Northwest-Shoals Community College (Muscle Shoals, Alabama) (NW-SCC) **[6808]**
Northwest-Shoals Community College Applied Technology Scholarships [6820]
Northwest-Shoals Community College Athletic Scholarships [6821]
Northwest-Shoals Community College Bank Independent Scholarships [6822]
Northwest-Shoals Community College Fine Arts Scholarships - Art [6823]
Northwest-Shoals Community College Fine Arts Scholarships - Drama [6824]
Northwest-Shoals Community College Fine Arts Scholarships - Music [6825]
Northwest-Shoals Community College High School Academic Scholarships [6826]
Northwest-Shoals Community College Independent Computer Scholarships [6827]
Northwest-Shoals Community College Student Activities Scholarships [6828]

Outdoor Power Equipment Aftermarket Association (OPEAA) **[7003]**
Outdoor Writers Association of America (OWAA) **[7005]**
Outlaw Student's Medical Professions Scholarships [8752]
Outlaw Student's Minority Scholarships [8753]
Outlaw Student's Nursing School Scholarships [8754]
Outlaw Student's Teacher Scholarships [8755]
Outstanding Minority Accounting Student Scholarships [6753]
Outstanding Undergraduate Scholarships, Student Organization for Alumni Relations (SOAR) [9217]
Outward Bound (OB) **[7007]**
Outward Bound Leadership Scholarships for Educators [7009]
Outward Bound Wilderness Leadership Awards for Youth [7010]
Helene M. Overly Memorial Scholarships [9741]
Overseas Press Club Foundation **[7011]**
Overseas Press Club Foundation Harper's Magazine Scholarships [7016]
Overseas Press Club Foundation Reuters Scholarships [7017]
Victoria Ovis Memorial Scholarships [6387]
Charles and Melva T. Owen Memorial Scholarships [6280]
Owner-Operator Independent Drivers Association (OOIDA) **[7024]**
Ozarks Division Scholarships [5863]
PABA Foundation Community Service Scholarships [7308]
PABA Foundation Fellowships [7309]
PABA Foundation Incentive Scholarships [7310]
PABA Foundation Merit Scholarships [7311]
The Pac-10 Postgraduate Scholarships [7027]
PACE/Columbian Lawyers Association of Westchester County Endowed Scholarships [3010]
Pacific 12 Conference (Pac-12) **[7026]**
Pacific Institute for the Mathematical Sciences (PIMS) **[7028]**
Pacific Legal Foundation **[7030]**
Pacific Legal Foundation Faculty Grants [7031]
Pacific NorthWest National Laboratory (PNNL) **[7032]**
The Arthur J. Packard Memorial Scholarship Competition [801]
Dr. Nicholas Padis Memorial Graduate Scholarships [4517]
Casilda Pagan Educational/Vocational Scholarships [4608]
Laurie Page-Peck Scholarship Fund [1914]
Raymond E. Page Scholarships [1286]
AFCEA General Emmett Paige Scholarships [1562]
Painting & Decorating Contractors of America (PDCA) **[7034]**
Ben Palacio Scholarships [9058]
Paleontological Society Student Research Grants [7]
Robert R. Palmer Research Travel Fellowships [1234]
Palo Verde High School Faculty Follies Scholarships [7513]
Palos Fine Arts Association **[7036]**
PAMA Foundation Scholarship Program [7437]
Pan-Macedonian Association USA Inc. **[7038]**
Pan-Macedonian National Scholarships [7039]
Pan Pacific Law Enforcement Scholarships [7978]
PanHellenic Scholarship Foundation **[7040]**
The PanHellenic Scholarships [7041]
ACI Charles Pankow Foundation ACI Student Fellowships [637]
Panther Cafe Scholarships [7514]
Katharine Pantzer Fellowships in the British Book Trades [2085]
Paper-Check.Com **[7042]**
Paper Stock Industries **[7044]**
Paper Stock Industries Chapter of the Institute of Scrap Recycling Industries **[7046]**
Paper Stock Industries Chapter of ISRI Scholarship Program [7047]
Paper Stock Industries/RRF Scholarships [7045]
Parapsychological Association (PA) **[7048]**
Parapsychological Association Research Endowments [7049]

Parapsychology Foundation **[7050]**
Pardee Community Building Scholarships [7515]
Joseph M. Parish Memorial Grants [1192]
Park Law Enforcement Association (PLEA) **[7054]**
William Park Woodside Founder's Scholarships [5694]
Cissy McDaniel Parker Scholarships [3384]
E.U. Parker Scholarships [6281]
Parkersburg Area Community Foundation **[7056]**
Parking Industry Institute Scholarship Program [6436]
Sylvia Parkinson Scholarships [4453]
Parkinson's Disease Foundation (PDF) **[7126]**
Parkinson's Disease Foundation International Research Grants Program [7128]
PARMA Scholarships [7460]
The Paros-Digiquartz Scholarships [5643]
William E. Parrish Scholarships [7242]
Carl Parsell Scholarship Fund [5810]
Elizabeth M. and Winchell M. Parson Scholarships [1661]
Partnership for Pediatric Epilepsy Research [3667]
Pasteur Foundation **[7129]**
Pasteur Foundation Postdoctoral Fellowships [7130]
PATCH **[7131]**
PATCH Early Childhood Education Scholarships [7132]
Senator Norman Paterson Fellowships [2552]
Pathways to Success Scholarships [3954]
James H. Patrenos Memorial Scholarships [8220]
Gail Patrick Charitable Trust Scholarships [3420]
Q.O.(Quint) Patrick Scholarships [9592]
Patriot Education Scholarships [5591]
Marvin R. and Pearl E. Patterson Family Scholarships Fund [4232]
Rachael Patterson Memorial Scholarships [8987]
Alice Conger Patterson Scholarships [9649]
Walter S. Patterson Scholarships [2183]
Patterson Trust Postdoctoral Fellowships in Brain Circuitry [4496]
Joanne Holbrook Patton Military Spouse Scholarships [6411]
Joanne Holbrook Patton Military Spouse Scholarships for Spouses of the Fallen [6412]
Joanne Holbrook Patton Military Spouse Scholarships for Spouses of the Wounded [6413]
Paul and Inger Friend 4-H Scholarships [8731]
Arthur Paulin Automotive Aftermarket Scholarship Awards [1957]
Colorado Nurses Association: Virginia Paulson Memorial Scholarships [3000]
Ray, NORP and Katie, WOKTE Pautz Scholarships [1098]
Kenyon T. Payne Outstanding Student Awards [5838]
PB Rail Engineering Scholarships [1132]
PBR Forces Veterans Association (PBR-FVA) **[7133]**
PDC Scholarships [1351]
PEA Bursaries [7443]
PEA Scholarships [7444]
Peace Frogs Fellowships [6984]
Chuck Peacock Memorial Scholarships [137]
Charles S. Pearce Scholarships [9365]
Scott Pearlman Field Awards for Science and Exploration [3698]
Pearman Family Scholarships [7950]
Robert L. Peaslee-Detroit Brazing and Soldiering Division Scholarships [1442]
Laura Ann Peck Memorial Endowed Scholarships [5460]
Pediatric Endocrinology Nursing Society Academic Education Scholarships [7136]
Pediatric Endocrinology Nursing Society (PENS) **[7135]**
Pediatric Endocrinology Nursing Society Convention Reimbursement Awards [7137]
Pedorthic Footwear Association (PFA) **[7138]**
Pedrozzi Scholarship Foundation **[7144]**
Mario Pedrozzi Scholarships [7145]
Peermusic Latin Scholarships [2160]
Peierls Rising Star Scholarship Program [4580]
Melissa Pellegrin Memorial Scholarships [8504]
Pellegrini Scholarships [8784]
Adolph Van Pelt Special Fund for Indians Scholarships [1696]

Louis Pelzer Memorial Awards [6961]
Margaret Pemberton Scholarships [2138]
Dorothy E. Hofmann Pembroke Scholarships [4454]
Robert B. and Dorothy Pence Scholarships [8616]
Penn-Bird Family Memorial Scholarships [7516]
Penndelphia Scholarship Foundation, [7147], **[7146]**
Florrie Penney, RN Rehabilitation Nursing Bursaries [1850]
Pennies for Art Scholarships [4081]
Pennsboro Alumni Scholarship Fund [7101]
Pennsylvania Heartland Unit Scholarships [4535]
Pennsylvania Land Surveyors Foundation (PSLS) **[7148]**
Pennsylvania Land Surveyors Foundation Scholarships [7149]
Pennsylvania Library Association (PALA) **[7150]**
Pennsylvania Library Association Scholarships for MLS Students [7151]
Pennsylvania Manufacturing Confectioners' Association **[7152]**
Pennsylvania Society of Professional Engineers (PSPE) **[7155]**
Pennsylvania Society of Professional Engineers Scholarships [7156]
Pennsylvania State System of Higher Education Foundation **[7157]**
Pension Real Estate Association (PREA) **[7162]**
Pension Real Estate Association Scholarships [7163]
P.E.O. Chapter Scholarship Fund [4233]
PEO Educational Loan Funds [7306]
People to People International (PTPI) **[7164]**
Peoria Area Amateur Radio Club Scholarships [1099]
Pepperdine University Armenian Student Scholarships [7200]
Pepperdine University Dean's Scholarships [7201]
Pepperdine University Diversity Scholarships [7202]
Pepperdine University Faculty Scholarships [7203]
Pepperdine University School of Law **[7166]**
Pepsi Scholarships [802]
Pepsi Wood County Technical/Caperton Center Scholarship Fund [7102]
Pepsico Scholarships [9066]
Joe Perdue Scholarships [2913]
Joaquin Pereira Memorial Scholarships [5549]
Rudy Perez Songwriting Scholarships [1214]
Peridian International, Inc./Rae L. Price, FASLA Scholarships [5335]
The A.W. Perigard Fund [8487]
Mary Perlmutter Scholarships [2565]
Sanky Perlowin Memorial Scholarships [3453]
Zoe Gore Perrin Scholarships [3385]
Eleanor Perry Memorial Endowed Scholarships [5461]
Chet and Jannett Perry Scholarships [8617]
Perry Township School Memorial Scholarship Fund [8695]
Jim Perry Vocational Scholarships [737]
Leonard M. Perryman Communications Scholarships for Ethnic Minority Students [9013]
Persian Language Study in Tehran Scholarships [856]
Dr. Connell Persico Scholarships [7865]
Persons Case Scholarships [261]
Gilberto and Lennetta Pesquera Medical School Scholarships [4163]
Peter Buck Fellowships Program - Graduate [8263]
Peter Buck Fellowships Program - Postdoctoral [8264]
Peter R. Weitz Prize [4133]
Jerome Peters Family Scholarships [5592]
Kate B. and Hall J. Peterson Fellowships [422]
Lizette Peterson Homer Injury Prevention Grant Awards [8426]
Steve Petix Journalism Scholarships [7951]
William H. and Lena M. Petree Scholarships [9650]
Silvio and Eugenio Petrini Grants [4389]
Petroleum Engineering Scholarships [8436]
Petroleum History Society (PHS) **[7214]**
Petroleum History Society Graduate Scholarships [7215]
Petroleum Packaging Council (PPC) **[7216]**
Petroleum Packaging Council Scholarships [7217]
Jerome S. Petz, S.J., Scholarships [3510]
Pew Charitable Trusts **[7218]**

Kenneth Rogers Memorial Scholarships [5462]
Pat and Cliff Rogers Nursing Scholarships [9170]
Geraldine Ruth Rogers Scholarships [8897]
Mary Stuart Rogers Scholarships [9606]
William C. Rogers Scholarships [4109]
Richard C. Rolfs Scholarships [7418]
Mary Louise Roller Pan-Hellenic Scholarships [6741]
Rome Prize [400]
Dr. Orrin J. Rongstad Wildlife Management Scholarships [9171]
Charles and Ruth Ronin Memorial Scholarships [7709]
Dorothy Worden Ronken Scholarships [3421]
Roofing Industry Alliance for Progress **[7816]**
Alice W. Rooke Scholarships [4459]
Roothbert Fund **[7818]**
Roothbert Fund Scholarships [7819]
ROP - Rob Bruce Memorial Scholarships [7710]
Barnes W. Rose, Jr. and Eva Rose Nichol Scholarship Fund [282]
Carl M. Rose Memorial Scholarship Fund [7109]
Florence C. Rose and S. Meryl Rose Scholarships [5628]
Dr. Wayne F. Rose Scholarship Fund [3790]
David Rose Scholarships [1215]
Esther Katz Rosen Fellowships [1041]
Ollie Rosenberg Educational Trust [3958]
Rosenberg-Ibarra Scholarships [7419]
Ollie Rosenberg Scholarship Travel Fund [3959]
Mandell and Lester Rosenblatt and Robert N. Herbert Undergraduate Scholarships [8417]
Barbara Rosenblum Cancer Dissertation Scholarships [8520]
ASPH/CDC Allan Rosenfield Global Health Fellowships [1868]
Rosenthal Bar Exam Scholarships [2235]
Jean and Tom Rosenthal Scholarship Program [3204]
Marty Rosness Student Scholarships [1505]
Bettsy Ross Educational Fund [6727]
Ross-Fahey Scholarships [6056]
S. Byrl Ross Memorial Scholarship Fund [7110]
Dorothy M. Ross Memorial Scholarships [1948]
The Bea and Harry Ross Scholarship Endowment [8743]
Ross Trust Graduate Student Scholarships [685]
Hon. Rudolph J. Rossetti Memorial Scholarships [2322]
The Rotary Club of Cape Coral Goldcoast Scholarship Fund [2645]
Rotary Club of Corpus Christi Scholarships [2956]
The Rotary Club of Rancho Bernardo Sunrise Abraxas Student Scholarships [7956]
The Rotary Foundation Ambassadorial Scholarships [7821]
The Rotary Foundation **[7820]**
Rotary Public Safety Scholarships [3920]
Bernard Rotberg Memorial Scholarships [5163]
Richard J. Roth Journalism Fellowships [6679]
Edward S. Roth Manufacturing Engineering Scholarships [8396]
Isaac Roth Newspaper Carrier Scholarship Program [6653]
Marjorie Roy Rothermel Scholarships [1663]
Hal Rothman Dissertation Fellowships [1252]
Theodore Rousseau Fellowships [5790]
Marion and Donald Routh Student Research Grants [8427]
Roy Rowan Scholarships [7018]
Rowe Family Fellowships [6985]
Leo S. Rowe Pan American Fund [6967]
Ellis W. Rowe Scholarships [4380]
Robert Roy Awards [2406]
Royal Bank of Canada (RBC) **[7822]**
Royal Palm Audubon Society Environmental Fellowships [3820]
Lucille and Edward R. Roybal Foundation **[7826]**
Lucille and Edward R. Roybal Foundation Public Health Scholarships [7827]
Royce-Osborn Minority Scholarship Program [1326]
RPNAS Baccalaureate Level Program Scholarships [7723]
RPNAS Doctorate Level Program Scholarships [7724]

RPNAS Master's Level Program Scholarships [7725]
RSDSA Research Grants [7719]
RSNA/AAPM Fellowships for Graduate Study in Medical Physics [531]
Rubber Division American Chemical Society **[7828]**
Rubber Division American Chemical Society Undergraduate Scholarships [7829]
Mike Ruben Scholarships [7111]
IRARC Memorial Joseph P. Rubino WA4MMD Scholarships [1103]
Glen Ruby Memorial Scholarships [2613]
William Rucker Greenwood Scholarships [1904]
Paul and Ellen Ruckes Scholarships [753]
Lawrence E. & Mabel Jackson Rudberg Scholarships [3543]
Joe Rudd Scholarships [7813]
Violet D. Ruelokke Primary Health Care Awards [1852]
Drs. Kirkland Ruffin & Willcox Ruffin Scholarships [4381]
Anna M. Rundquist Memorial Scholarships [4340]
Damon Runyon Cancer Research Foundation **[7830]**
Damon Runyon Cancer Research Foundation Fellowships [7831]
Damon Runyon Clinical Investigator Awards [7832]
Damon Runyon-Rachleff Innovation Awards [7833]
Ruppert Educational Grant Program [8207]
Rural Telephone Company **[7834]**
Rural Telephone Company Scholarships [7835]
Hermann G. Rusch Scholarships [697]
Norman K. Russell Scholarships [6434]
Russian Brotherhood Organization of the U.S.A. (RBOUSA) **[7836]**
Russian/Central Asian Student Scholarships [9172]
Michael A. Russo Memorial Scholarships [7711]
The Anthony C. Russo Scholarships [6457]
Lucile Rust Scholarships [7300]
Rutherford Scholars [265]
Alexander Rutherford Scholarships for High School Achievement [266]
IOIA Andrew Rutherford Scholarships [4717]
Ralph and Clara Rutledge Memorial Scholarships [3869]
Charles and Eleonor Rycenga Education Scholarship Fund [4238]
Deborah Jean Rydberg Memorial Scholarships [3168]
Ryerson Scholarships [5124]
Jeanne Graves Ryland Scholarships [3389]
Charles A. Ryskamp Research Fellowships [681]
SAA Native American Scholarships [8293]
SABA Foundation Fellowships [8538]
SACHS Foundation **[7839]**
SACHS Foundation Graduate Scholarships [7840]
SACHS Foundation Undergraduate Scholarships for Colorado Black Students [7841]
Sacks For CF Scholarships [3687]
Julie Anne Sadlier Memorial Scholarships [3390]
Chester & Maria Sadowski Memorial Scholarships [7778]
Safe Schools Coalition (SSC) **[7842]**
Safer Athletic Field Environments Scholarships (SAFE) [8649]
Russell Sage Foundation (RSF) **[7879]**
Russell Sage Foundation Visiting Scholars [7880]
Ruth Sager Scholarships [5629]
SAH Study Tour Fellowships [8297]
Virginia Hartford Saharov Memorial Scholarships [3391]
Don Sahli-Kathy Woodall Graduate Scholarships [8841]
Sons and Daughters Don Sahli-Kathy Woodall Scholarships [8842]
Saint Andrews Scholarships [7882]
Saint Andrew's Society of the State of New York **[7881]**
St. Anthony's Hospitals, Denver: Nightingale Scholarships [3002]
St. Clare's Mercy Hospital School of Nursing Alumni Association Scholarships [1853]
St. Francis Xavier Scholarships [9775]
St. James Armenian Church Memorial Scholarships [1604]

St. Joseph's Hospital School of Nursing Alumnae Scholarships [7112]
St. Louis Division Scholarships [5864]
St. Louis Paralegal Association (SPA) **[7883]**
St. Louis Paralegal Association Student Scholarships [7884]
Saint Paul University Canada **[7886]**
Saint Paul University Excellence Scholarships [7887]
Saint Paul University Financial Aid Bursaries [7888]
Saint Vincent College Eagle Scout Scholarships [6261]
Saints Cyril and Methodius Scholarships [7838]
SAJA Journalism Scholarships [8540]
Casey Sakir Point Scholarships [7366]
Joseph and Amelia Saks Scholarship Fund [3047]
Jane Salanky-Onzik Scholarship Fund [3791]
SALEF Health Career Scholarships [7894]
Bill Salerno, W2ONV, Memorial Scholarships [1104]
Eugene Gene Sallee, W4YFR Memorial Scholarships [1105]
The Sallie Mae 911 Education Fund [7891]
Sallie Mae Fund **[7889]**
Sally Beauty Scholarships for High School Graduates [7439]
Ann S. Salsberg Scholarship Awards [2323]
Salvadoran American Leadership and Education Fund (SALEF) **[7892]**
Henry Salvatori Scholarships [6924]
Samalot - Sebastian Scholarship Fund [3320]
The Walter Samek III Memorial Scholarship Fund [3089]
SAMFund **[7896]**
SAMFund Scholarships [7897]
Samoa O Nevada (SON) **[7898]**
Margaret Jerome Sampson Scholarships [7301]
Ray and Pearl Sams Scholarships [9653]
AIST David H. Samson Scholarships [1816]
Samsung American Legion Scholarships [897]
San Angelo Area Foundation (SAAF) **[7900]**
San Angelo Area Foundation Scholarships [7901]
San Diego City College Study Abroad Scholarships [7957]
The San Diego Foundation **[7902]**
The San Diego Foundation Community Scholarships I [7958]
The San Diego Foundation Community Scholarships II [7959]
San Diego National Bank Scholarships [7960]
San Diego Pan Pacific Law Enforcement Association **[7977]**
San Diego Regional Aviation Association Scholarships [7961]
San Francisco Film Society (SFFS) **[7979]**
San Francisco Foundation **[7981]**
San Pasqual Academy Scholarships [7962]
Barbara Sanchez Scholarships [8348]
Leo and Trinidad Sanchez Scholarships [8208]
Sand Hill Scholars Program [8209]
Major General Jerry Sanders Scholarship Program [1461]
Bill Sanderson Aviation Maintenance Technician Scholarships [4511]
Sanofi Pasteur Scholarships [2553]
Santa Barbara Dance Alliance (SBDA) **[7984]**
Santa Clara La Raza Lawyers Scholarships [5313]
Bert Saperstein Communication Scholarships [7987]
Bert Saperstein Communications Scholarship Fund **[7986]**
Saratoga County Bar Association **[7988]**
Saratoga County Bar Association Law Student Scholarships [7989]
Saskatchewan Government Insurance Actuarial Science Scholarships [7996]
Saskatchewan Government Insurance Anniversary Scholarships [7997]
Saskatchewan Government Insurance (SGI) **[7990]**
Saskatchewan Government Insurance Corporate Scholarships [7998]
Saskatchewan Government Insurance Graduate Student Traffic Safety Research Scholarhips [7999]
Saskatchewan Hockey Association **[8000]**
Saskatchewan Hockey Association Scholarships [8001]
Saskatchewan Pulse Growers **[8002]**

Charles Shafae' Scholarships [7043]

Elizabeth Shafer Memorial Scholarships [7522]

SHAFR Dissertation Completion Fellowships [8342]

Saleem Shah Early Career Development Awards [1046]

Josephine Hooker Shain Scholarships [4094]

Shamberg Scholarships [9491]

Judge Terry Shamsie Scholarships [2958]

The Ivan Shandor Memorial Ukrainian American Bar Association Scholarships [9500]

John M. and Mary A. Shanley Memorial Scholarships [8622]

William Shannon American Council on Exercise Certification Scholarships [664]

William H. Shannon Fellowships [5017]

Commander Dan F. Shanower Scholarships [6579]

Ken and Sandy Sharkey Family Scholarship Fund [4242]

Shastri Indo-Canadian Institute **[8098]**

Lal Bahadur Shastri Student Prize [8099]

W.L. Shattuck Scholarships [4674]

Benjamin G. Shatz Scholarships [7207]

Anne Shaw Fellowships [8890]

Luci Shaw Fellowships [4704]

Dr. Robert and Anna Shaw Scholarships [267]

Dr. Robert Norman Shaw Scholarships [268]

Shaw-Worth Memorial Scholarships [4636]

Regina B. Shearn Scholarships [360]

Dezna C. Sheehan Memorial Educational Scholarships [6516]

Jim Sheerin Scholarships [5719]

Sheet Metal and Air Conditioning Contractors' National Association (SMACNA) **[8100]**

Sheet Metal And Air Conditioning Contractors' National Association College of Fellows Scholarships [8101]

Nettie and Edward Shelah Scholarships [8733]

Shell Incentive Scholarship Fund [8103]

Shell Oil Co. **[8102]**

Shell Process Technology Scholarships [8104]

Shell Technical Scholarships [8105]

Bruce Shelton Scholarships [9654]

Matthew Shepard Scholarships [7870]

Bill and Ann Sheperd Legal Scholarship Fund [3683]

Joseph Henry Shepherd Scholarships [9238]

Robert P. Sheppard Leadership Awards [6506]

David S. Sheridan Canadian Research Awards [2360]

Sheriff's Law Enforcement Association of McLennan County (SLEAMC) **[8106]**

Marion A. and Ruth Sherwood Family Fund Education Scholarships [4243]

Marion A. and Ruth K. Sherwood Family Fund Engineering Scholarships [4244]

Miller G. Sherwood Family Scholarship Fund [4245]

Morgan and Jeanie Sherwood Travel Grants [1253]

Shields-Gillespie Scholarships [962]

Drs. Poh Shien and Judy Young Scholarships [9068]

Milton L. Shifman Endowed Scholarships [5630]

Everett Oscar Shimp Memorial Scholarships [7113]

Pat Shimp Memorial Scholarships [7114]

The Shincho Graduate Fellowships for Study in Japan [5227]

Ethel Shinn Alumni-Vocational Scholarships [5465]

Joseph Shinoda Memorial Scholarship Foundation **[8108]**

Joseph Shinoda Memorial Scholarships [8109]

Jason Shipley Memorial Scholarships [6383]

Clair Shirey Scholarships [9173]

Shohet Scholars Program [4890]

CSF S. David Shor Scholarships [2869]

Shoreline Community College Academic Excellence Scholarships for Graduating High School Seniors [8123]

Shoreline Community College Academic Improvement Scholarships for Graduating High School Seniors [8124]

Shoreline Community College Continuing Students Scholarships [8125]

Shoreline Community College Foundation **[8110]**

Shoreline Community College Part-Time Students Scholarships [8126]

Justice Janie L. Shores Scholarships [189]

Short-Term Fellowships [8271]

Short-term Senior Fellowships in Iranian Studies [858]

SHOT-NASA Fellowships [8346]

Tom Shown Scholarships [9655]

SHPE Foundation **[8129]**

SHPE Foundation Dissertation Scholarships [8131]

SHPE Foundation General Scholarships [8132]

SHPE Foundation Northrop Grumman Scholarships [8133]

SHPE Foundation Professional Scholarships [8134]

SHPE Foundation Verizon Scholarships [8135]

Ralph W. Shrader Diversity Scholarships [1563]

Jack Shrader Memorial Awards [1744]

SHRM Certification Scholarships - Individual [8349]

SHRM Foundation Regional Academic Scholarships [8350]

Phil Shykes Memorial Scholarships [3544]

Mary Isabel Sibley Fellowships [7249]

SICB Fellowships of Graduate Student Travel (FGST) [8359]

SICB Grants-in-Aid of Research Program (GIAR) [8360]

Don and Madalyn Sickafoose Educational Trust [8698]

Sickle Cell Disease Association of America (SCDAA) **[8136]**

Sidley Austin LLP - North America **[8139]**

Sidley Prelaw Scholars Initiative [8140]

Norman Siegel Research Scholar Grants [1313]

Jeff Siegel Scholarships [6669]

Myrtle Siegfried, MD and Michael Vigilante, MD Scholarships [3988]

Siemens Clinical Advancement Scholarship Program [1327]

Siemens Foundation **[8141]**

Siemens Teacher Scholarships [8142]

E.J. Sierleja Memorial Fellowships [4809]

Sierra Student Coalition (SSC) **[8143]**

Sig Memorial Scholarships [30]

Sigma Delta Chi Foundation (SDX) **[8148]**

Sigma Delta Epsilon Fellowships [8154]

Sigma Delta Epsilon, Graduate Women in Science (SDE/GWIS) **[8150]**

Sigma Diagnostics Student Scholarships [6517]

Sigma Kappa Foundation Alumnae Continuing Education Scholarships [8182]

Sigma Kappa Foundation Alzheimer's/Gerontology Scholarships [8183]

Sigma Kappa Foundation **[8155]**

Sigma Kappa Foundation Founders' Scholarships [8184]

Sigma Kappa Foundation Gerontology Scholarships [8185]

Sigma Kappa Foundation Michigan Scholarships [8186]

Sigma Pi Sigma Undergraduate Research Awards [8440]

Sigma Theta Tau International Honor Society of Nursing **[8194]**

Sigma Theta Tau International Scholarships [2554]

Silicon Valley Community Foundation **[8196]**

Silver Nugget Family Scholarships [7523]

Silver Nugget Gaming Ambassadors Scholarships [7524]

APSAIL's Ralph Silverman Memorial Scholarships [1967]

Meyer and Dorothy Silverman Scholarships [3133]

Stuart Silverman Scholarships [7208]

Harvey L. Simmons Memorial Scholarships [7965]

Linda Simmons Memorial Scholarships [195]

Willard B. Simmons Sr. Memorial Scholarships [6202]

Hazel Simms Nursing Scholarships [5352]

Julia Viola Simms Science Scholarships [2128]

Julian Simon Fellowships [7455]

Simon Youth Foundation (SYF) **[8210]**

Simon Youth Foundation Community Scholarships [8212]

Simonton Windows Scholarships [7115]

DW Simpson Actuarial Science Scholarship Program [8214]

DW Simpson Global Actuarial Recruitment **[8213]**

Carole Simpson Scholarships [7583]

CSF Lowe Simpson Scholarships [2870]

Ward Sims Memorial Scholarships [9174]

Sindhi Association of North America **[8215]**

SINFONIA Educational Foundation (SEF) **[8217]**

Single Parent Scholarships [1549]

Aaron B. Singleton Memorial Scholarships [6830]

Sino-American Pharmaceutical Professionals Association (SAPA) **[8221]**

Sino-American Pharmaceutical Professionals Association Scholarships [8222]

Helen J. Sioussat/Fay Wells Scholarships [2184]

S.I.S.T.E.R.S. **[8223]**

Gadde Sitaramamma & Tirupataiah Scholarships [8832]

Wiggsy Sivertsen Scholarships [7871]

Bill Six Memorial Scholarship Fund [7116]

Six Meter Club of Chicago Scholarships [1107]

Leif and Inger Sjoberg Awards [1173]

Sjogren's Syndrome Foundation (SSF) **[8225]**

Skadden Fellowship Foundation **[8228]**

Skadden Fellowships [8229]

R. Skeeles Memorial Scholarship Fund [8699]

Skidmore, Owings and Merrill Foundation **[8230]**

CSF Frank Foster Skillman Scholarships [2871]

Francelene Skinner Memorial Scholarships [5478]

Allogan Slagle Memorial Scholarships [1697]

Lillian and Murray Slatkin Fellowships [6986]

SLEAMC Scholarships [8107]

Robert W. Sledge Fellowships [346]

J. Ward Sleichter and Frances F. Sleichter Memorial Scholarship Fund [3960]

Slifka Foundation Interdisciplinary Fellowships [5791]

Dr. Alfred E. Slinkard Scholarships [8005]

Alfred P. Sloan Foundation **[8234]**

Sloan Northwood University Heavy-Duty Scholarships [1968]

Sloan Research Fellowships [8235]

Thomas J. Slocum Memorial Scholarships to Westwood College of Aviation Technology [139]

The Aaron and Rita Slom Scholarships [8923]

SMART Scholarships [8056]

SME Coal and Energy Division Scholarships [8414]

SME Directors Scholarships [8398]

SME Education Foundation Family Scholarships [8399]

SME Environmental Division Scholarships [8415]

Dr. George M. Smerk Scholarships [1057]

SMFM/AAOGF Scholarship Awards [8410]

Donald Smiley Prize [2585]

Eva Smith Bursary [5125]

The Smith Companies **[8236]**

Hy Smith Endowment Fund [4382]

Ryan and Jamie Smith Essay Contest [8237]

David W. Smith Fellowships [2605]

Gladys Ann Smith Greater Los Angeles Women's Council Scholarships [6588]

Stanley Smith Horticultural Fellowships [6987]

James I. Smith, III Notre Dame Law School Scholarship Fund [331]

Florence L. Smith Medical Scholarships [4383]

Charles Smith Memorial Scholarship Awards [1633]

Boy Scouts of America Troop 3 Scholarships - Art Till/Nathan E. Smith Memorial Scholarships [7714]

Colonel Nate Smith Memorial Scholarships [5731]

Drew Smith Memorial Scholarships [3068]

Tacy Ana Smith Memorial Scholarships [3921]

Mary K. Smith Rector Scholarships [7117]

Smith-Reynolds Founder Fellowships [4526]

The Eileen J. Smith, R.N. Memorial Scholarships [5105]

Smith Scholarship Foundation **[8238]**

Ralph and Josephine Smith Scholarship Fund [3793]

Lillian Smith Scholarship for Teaching Students [9111]

A.O. Smith Scholarships [7349]

Brian Smith Scholarships [2169]

Chapter 63 - Portland Uncle Bud Smith Scholarships [8400]

Esther M. Smith Scholarships [3069]

Helen J. and Harold Gilman Smith Scholarships [2065]

Herman J. Smith Scholarships [6345]

Joseph Sumner Smith Scholarships [9001]

Marian A. Smith Scholarships [8572]

Richard S. Smith Scholarships [9016]

William E. Smith Scholarships [171]

Sponsor and Scholarship Index

Texas Vegetation Management Association (TVMA) **[8883]**
Textile Care Allied Trades Association (TCATA) **[8885]**
Jim and Pat Thacker Sports Communication Internships [9307]
Anil and Neema Thakrar Family Fund [3963]
ThanksUSA **[8887]**
ThanksUSA Scholarships [8888]
The Rodney Thaxton Justice Fund [3322]
Theatre and Performance Art Project Grants [222]
Theatre for Young Audiences USA (TYA/USA) **[8889]**
Dr. Peter A. Theodos Memorial Graduate Scholarships [4519]
Thermo Scientific Educational Scholarships [6518]
Thermoforming Division Memorial Scholarships [8458]
Thermoplastic Materials and Foams Division Scholarships [8459]
Thermoplastics Elastomers Special Interest Group Scholarships [8460]
Thesaurus Linguae Latinae Fellowships (TTL) [987]
Theta Tau Scholarships [8189]
Third Wave Foundation **[8891]**
Barbara Thomas Bursary [5126]
Nadene M. Thomas Graduate Research Scholarships [275]
Dean James Thomas Memorial Scholarships [9680]
E.D. Thomas Post Doctoral Fellowships [4014]
Barber Owen Thomas Scholarships [8190]
C.R. Thomas Scholarships [7118]
Dorothy B. & Charles E. Thomas Scholarships [4302]
Elizabeth R. Thomas Scholarships [8128]
Rev. Chuck and Nancy Thomas Scholarships [9004]
Honorable Raymond Thompson Endowed Scholarships [7210]
F. Christian and Betty Thompson Fellowships [6988]
Madlyn D. Thompson Memorial Scholarships [2340]
Barbara and Howard Thompson Scholarships [5108]
Marjorie Anderson Thompson Scholarships [363]
Thompson Scholarships for Women in Safety [1355]
Dr. Andrew Thomson Prize in Applied Meteorology [2529]
Thomson Reuters/MLA Doctoral Fellowships [5748]
Ken Thomson Scholarships [2632]
Thornberg/Havens Scholarships [3423]
Ross/Nickey Scholarships and Gary E. Thornton Memorial Scholarships [5911]
Thunder Bay Community Foundation **[8893]**
Dorothy J. Thurston Graduate Scholarships [4303]
Thyssen-Heideking Fellowships [4129]
TIAC / Parks Canada Sustainable Tourism Scholarships [8921]
Raymond A. Tice Scholarships I [7967]
Raymond A. Tice Scholarships II [7968]
Tidewater Builders Association (TBA) **[8899]**
Tidewater Builders Association Scholarships [8900]
Tikvah Center for Law and Jewish Civilization **[8901]**
Tikvah Fellowships [8909]
Tikvah Fund **[8908]**
Patricia Tillinghast Memorial Scholarships [879]
Jack E. Tillson Scholarships [5040]
Time Warner Point Scholarships [7367]
Time Warner Tribal Scholars Program [812]
Eben Tisdale Fellowships [4017]
TMA Research Fellowships [5967]
TMCF Scholarships [5647]
Star and Barry Tobias Scholarships [2728]
Mario J. Tocco Hydrocephalus Foundation Scholarships [4654]
Richard Cecil Todd and Clauda Pennock Todd Tripod Scholarships [7276]
CSF Christopher Todd Grant Memorial Scholarships [2875]
Robert Toigo Foundation Fellowships [8911]
Robert Toigo Foundation (RTF) **[8910]**
Daniel B. Toll Memorial Scholarships [2325]
William Tomar Memorial Scholarships [2326]
The Adelle and Erwin Tomash Fellowships [1992]
John Tomasovic, Sr. Scholarships [740]
Tomato Fest Scholarship Grants [699]
George Torkildsen Literary Awards [9757]
Evald Torokvei Foundation Scholarships [9343]

Toronto and Region Conservation Authority (TRCA) **[8912]**
Toronto Rehab Scholarships in Rehabilitation-Related Research [8918]
Toronto Rehabilitation Institute **[8914]**
Toronto Rehabilitation Institute Graduate Student Scholarships - Ontario Student Opportunities Trust Fund (OSOTF) [8919]
Aram Torossian Memorial Scholarships [1606]
Ferdinand Torres Scholarships [754]
Touchstone Special Achievement Scholarships [8557]
Tourism Industry Association of Canada (TIAC) **[8920]**
Touro Synagogue Foundation (TSF) **[8922]**
Judith A. Towle Environmental Studies Fund [5082]
Town and County Club Scholarships [4462]
Joseph Towner Fund for Gay and Lesbian Families [7872]
Charles A. Townsend Scholarships [7119]
Toyota Community Scholars [8927]
Toyota Earth Day Scholarship Program **[8924]**
Toyota Earth Day Scholarships [8925]
Toyota High School Scholarship Program [4581]
Toyota Motor Sales **[8926]**
Toyota/TELACU Scholarships [8822]
The Joyce Tracy Fellowships [424]
Traditional Education Scholarships [8500]
Traditional Student Scholarships [3194]
TRALA Scholarship Program [8964]
Vera Tran Memorial Scholarships [9434]
Reuben Trane Scholarships [1270]
Transatlantic Fellows Program [4134]
Transoft Solutions, Inc. Ahead of the Curve Scholarships (AOTC) [4827]
Transport Workers Union of America (TWU) **[8928]**
Transportation Association of Canada (TAC) **[8930]**
Transportation Association of Canada Foundation Scholarships [8947]
Transportation Clubs International (TCI) **[8948]**
Traub-Dicker Rainbow Scholarships [8747]
Morton M. Traum Surface Science Student Awards [1986]
Travel Fellowships in Architecture, Design and Urban Design [8233]
Travel Grants for Women Researchers [1908]
Trelut Family Legacy Scholarships [2255]
Davis Wright Tremaine 1L Diversity Scholarships [3348]
Marie Tremaine Fellowships [2088]
Triangle Coalition for Science and Technology Education (TCSTE) **[8955]**
Tribal Business Management Program Scholarships (TBM) [2664]
Tribal Priority Scholarships [1513]
Tribeca Film Institute **[8957]**
Tribeca Film Institute Film and Video Fellowships [8958]
Tribeca Film Institute Media Arts Fellowships in Mexico [8959]
Tribeca Film Institute New Media Fellowships [8960]
Thomas and Glenna Trimble Endowed Scholarships [7211]
Tim Triner Letter Carriers Scholarship Fund [8704]
J.P. and Madeline Trinkaus Endowed Scholarships in Embryology [5632]
Tristin Memorial Scholarships [5395]
Johnny Trombly Scholarships [5919]
Mildred E. Troske Music Scholarships [4304]
Charlie Trotter Culinary Education Foundation **[8961]**
Vincent Trotter Health Care Scholarships [7969]
Charlie Trotters's Culinary Education Foundation Culinary Study Scholarships [8962]
Jo Anne J. Trow Scholarships [6020]
Troy University Rodeo Team Scholarships [181]
Truck Renting and Leasing Association (TRALA) **[8963]**
Truckload Carriers Association (TCA) **[8965]**
Truckload Carriers Association Scholarships [8966]
Trudeau Foundation Doctoral Scholarships [8968]
Pierre Elliott Trudeau Foundation **[8967]**
Harry S. Truman Scholarship Foundation (HSTSF) **[8969]**
Harry S. Truman Scholarships [8970]

Trustee, Schawe, and Presidential Scholarships [9776]
Trustee Scholarships [5235]
Trustees College Scholarships [5561]
Trustees Law School Scholarships [5562]
TRW Foundation Scholarships [1951]
TSA Teach Technology Scholarships [8816]
Norman J. Tschantz/Walter C. Deuble Scholarships [8705]
Tschudy Family Scholarships [5468]
TSHP R&E Foundation Scholarship Program [8972]
TSHP Research and Education Foundation **[8971]**
Tucker Family Scholarships [9308]
Jacki Tuckfield Memorial Graduate Business Scholarship Fund [3323]
Barry Tuckwell Scholarships [4953]
Richard R. Tufenkian Memorial Scholarships [1571]
Sam Tughan Scholarships [2593]
Edward Tuinier Memorial Scholarships [741]
Graydon A. Tunstall Undergraduate Student Scholarships [7245]
Earl S. Tupper 3-year Postdoctoral Fellowships in Tropical Biology [8272]
Turf and Ornamental Communicators Association (TOCA) **[8973]**
Turf and Ornamental Communicators Association Scholarship Program [8974]
Turkish Coalition of America (TCA) **[8975]**
Hans Turley Prize in Queer Eighteenth-Century Studies [1235]
Turner Family Scholarships [3925]
Jeff Turner-Forsyth Audubon Society Scholarships [9658]
James A. Turner, Jr. Memorial Scholarships [1447]
J.L. Turner Legal Association (JLTLA) **[8980]**
Mark and Vera Turner Memorial Scholarships [5479]
Emmett H. Turner Scholarships [3137]
Ira G. Turpin Scholars Fund [8706]
Tuscumbia Kiwanis Scholarships [6831]
Lydia Donaldson Tutt-Jones Memorial Research Grant [72]
Vice Adm. Jerry O. Tuttle, USN (Ret.) and Mrs. Barbara A. Tuttle Science and Technology Scholarships [1564]
TUUT HSF College Scholarship Program [4582]
Two Nineteen Scholarships [7895]
Two Year/Community Broadcast Education Association Scholarship Awards [2186]
UAA Accounting Club Scholarships [9114]
UAA Alaska Kidney Foundation Scholarships [9115]
UAA Alumni Association Scholarships [9116]
UAA Anchorage Daily News Journalism Scholarships [9117]
UAA College of Business & Public Policy Scholarships [9118]
UAA Emi Chance Memorial Scholarships [9119]
UAA Friends of the Performing Arts Scholarships [9120]
UAA GCI, Inc. Scholarships [9121]
UAA Kimura Scholarship Fund Illustration Scholarships [9122]
UAA Kimura Scholarship Fund Photography Scholarships [9123]
UAA Pignalberi Public Policy Scholarships [9124]
UAA Quanterra Scholarships [9125]
UAA RRANN Program Scholarships [9126]
UAA Wells Fargo Career Scholarships [9127]
UAF Alumni Association Scholarships [9189]
UAF Community and Technical College **[8982]**
UAL/UABT Scholarship Program [9007]
UC MEXUS Grants for Dissertation Research [9199]
UC MEXUS Short-Term Projects [9200]
UCB, Inc. NP Student Scholarships [380]
The UCSD Black Alumni Scholarship for Arts and Humanities [7970]
The UCSD Black Alumni Scholarships for Engineering, Mathematics and Science [7971]
Morris K. Udall Foundation **[8990]**
Udall Scholarships [9197]
Morris K. Udall Scholarships [8991]
UFCW Scholarships [9011]
Ukrainian Canadian Professional and Business Club Scholarships in Education [2505]
Sandy Ulm Scholarships [3816]
Ric Ulrich and Chuck Pischke Scholarships [7423]
Umialik Scholarships [9177]

Sponsor and Scholarship Index

Vermont Paralegal Organization (VPO) **[9418]**

Vermont Paralegal Organization Scholarships [9419]

Chester M. Vernon Memorial Eagle Scout Scholarships [6263]

Dimitri J. Ververelli Memorial Scholarships [4520]

A. Verville Fellowships [8253]

Vesalius Trust (VT) **[9420]**

Vesalius Trust Student Scholarships [9422]

Veterans of Enduring Freedom (Afghanistan) and Iraqi Freedom Scholarships [1565]

Veterans of Foreign Wars Scout of the Year [6264]

Zelda Walling Vicha Memorial Scholarships [1319]

Jill Vickers Prize [2586]

Vietnam Education Foundation (VEF) **[9423]**

Vietnam Veterans of America (VVA) **[9426]**

Vietnamese American Bar Association of Northern California (VABANC) **[9428]**

Vietnamese American Scholarship Foundation **[9430]**

Vilas Equity Scholarships [9383]

William F. Vilas Scholarships [9384]

Dr. Juan D. Villarreal/HDA Foundation Scholarships [4557]

Villers Fellowships for Health Care Justice [3706]

Philip F. Vineberg Travelling Fellowships in the Humanities [5726]

Vinyl Plastics Division Scholarships [8461]

Violin Society of America (VSA) **[9435]**

Violin Society of America Scholarships [9436]

Virgin Islands Bar Association **[9437]**

Virginia Business and Professional Women's Foundation **[9439]**

Virginia Dental Hygienist's Association Foundation **[9444]**

Virginia Federation of Republican Women (VFRW) **[9446]**

Virginia Foundation for Independent Colleges (VFIC) **[9448]**

Virginia Historical Society (VHS) **[9452]**

Virginia Historical Society Research Fellowships [9453]

Virginia Lakes and Watershed Association (VLWA) **[9454]**

Virginia Museum of Fine Arts **[9456]**

Virginia Museum of Fine Arts Visual Arts Fellowships [9457]

Virginia Society of Certified Public Accountants (VSCPA) **[9458]**

Visiting Doctoral Tikvah Scholarships [8907]

Visiting Fellowships [4783]

Visiting Scholars Fellowships [2043]

Visiting Scholars Program [2699]

VISTAKON Research Grants [389]

Visual Arts and New Media Project Grants [223]

John D. Voelker Foundation **[9469]**

John D. Voelker Foundation Native American Scholarships [9470]

Von Ogden Vogt Scholarships [9005]

Miki Vohryzek-Bolden Student Paper Awards [9583]

The Voice Foundation (VF) **[9471]**

Irma E. Voigt Memorial Scholarships [8191]

Voluntary Protection Programs Participants' Association (VPPPA) **[9473]**

Vorgin-Bell Scholarships [6848]

The Sibyl Jennings Vorheis Memorial Undergraduate Scholarships [3926]

Abe Voron Scholarships [2187]

VPPPA June Brothers Scholarships [9477]

VSCPA Educational Foundation Graduate Scholarships [9464]

VSCPA Educational Foundation Minority Scholarships [9465]

VSCPA Educational Foundation Undergraduate Scholarships [9466]

VSCPA PhD Accounting Scholarships [9467]

VSP Research Grants [390]

Wachovia Scholars Program [4551]

Wachovia/TELACU Excellence in Teaching Scholarships [8823]

Chapter 4 - Lawrence A. Wacker Memorial Awards [8402]

CSF Dee Wacksman Memorial Scholarships [2876]

Bruce Wade Memorial Scholarships for Lesbian, Gay and Bisexual [7875]

Mercedes Laurie Wade Scholarships [2341]

Robert & Barbara Wade Scholarships [5480]

Wadsworth International Fellowships [9562]

Ed Wadsworth Memorial Scholarships [184]

WAEPA Scholarship Program [9763]

Nell and Spencer Waggoner Scholarships [9659]

Gary Wagner, K3OMI Scholarships [1111]

Jack H. Wagner Scholarships [5842]

Selman A. Waksman Endowed Scholarships in Microbial Diversity [5633]

Jane C. Waldbaum Archaeological Field School Scholarships [1496]

Laramie Walden Memorial Fund [3927]

Margaret E. Waldron Scholarship Fund [3794]

Sue Walicki Nursing Scholarships [5109]

Gary Walker Memorial Scholarships [3972]

Arthur BC Walker Scholarships [6494]

Myrtle and Earl Walker Scholarships [8403]

Bruce A. Wallace Memorial Scholarships [2327]

Walmart Associate Scholarships [9479]

Walmart Foundation **[9478]**

Martin Walmsley Fellowships for Technological Entrepreneurship [6891]

WALPA Lake Scholarships [9526]

Patty Walter Memorial Scholarships [3003]

Robert E. Walter Memorial Scholarships [5558]

Sam Walton Community Scholarships [9480]

Walton Family Foundation Scholarships [9481]

Francis Walton Memorial Scholarships [1112]

Harry Walts Memorial Graduate Scholarships [5533]

War Memorial Doctoral Scholarships [6188]

Mary-Claire Ward Geoscience Awards [7458]

Imogene Ward Nursing Scholarships [3814]

Alice Glaisyer Warfield Scholarships [8954]

Judith Warner Memorial Scholarships [7532]

Rachel Warner Memorial Scholarships [6336]

Warner Norcross & Judd LLP (WNJ) **[9482]**

Warner Norcross & Judd LLP Minorty Scholarships [9483]

Earl Warren Civil Rights Training Scholarships [5972]

Earl Warren Shearman and Sterling Scholarships [5973]

Washburn University School of Law **[9484]**

Washington City/County Management Association (WCMA) **[9493]**

Washington City/County Management Association Scholarships [9494]

Washington College Bound Scholarships [9504]

Washington County Farm Bureau Scholarships [6948]

Washington CPA Foundation Scholarships [9514]

The Washington Group (TWG) **[9495]**

Washington Group International Safety Scholarships [1357]

Washington Higher Education Coordinating Board **[9502]**

Washington Higher Education Coordinating Board Educational Opportunity Grants [9505]

Washington Higher Education Coordinating Board Health Professional Scholarships [9506]

Washington Higher Education Coordinating Board - State Need Grants (SNG) [9507]

Washington Hospital Healthcare System (WHHS) **[9508]**

Washington Indian Gaming Association (WIGA) **[9511]**

Washington Reciprocity Out-of-State Scholarships [5469]

Washington Society of Certified Public Accountants (WSCPA) **[9513]**

Washington State Association for Justice (WSAJ) **[9517]**

Washington State Business Education Association **[9522]**

Washington State Governors' Scholarship for Foster Youth [2978]

Washington State Lake Protection Association (WALPA) **[9525]**

Washington State Nurses Association **[9527]**

Washington State Nurses Association Foundation Scholarships (WSNF) [9528]

Washington University Law School **[9529]**

Washington University Law School Chancellor's Graduate Fellowships [9532]

Washington University Law School Olin Fellowships for Women [9533]

Vincent T. Wasilewski Scholarships [2188]

John J. Wasmuth Postdoctoral Fellowships [4541]

Water Environment Federation (WEF) **[9535]**

Water and Sewer Distributors of America (WASDA) **[9537]**

George Waterman Memorial Scholarships [9515]

Stand Watie Scholarships [8529]

Robert D. Watkins Graduate Research Fellowships [1303]

Watson-Brown Foundation **[9539]**

Watson-Brown Scholarships [9540]

Dr. James Watson Fellowship Program [4189]

Jeannette K. Watson Fellowships [9542]

Jeannette K. Watson Fellowships (JKW) **[9541]**

Thomas J. Watson Fellowships [9544]

Thomas J. Watson Foundation (TJW) **[9543]**

Glenn Watson Scholarships [8576]

Watsontown Volunteer Fire Company Scholarships [2342]

The Wax Company Scholarships [185]

Wayne County Bank Scholarships [6832]

Wayne County Foundation, Inc. **[9545]**

Wayne-Meador-Elliott Scholarships [7120]

Kurt Wayne Scholarships [4069]

W.B.H. Dowse Fellowships [5680]

WBSN Foundation Scholarships [9719]

WDA Full-Time Graduate Scholarships [9684]

WDA Part-Time Graduate Scholarships [9685]

WDHOF Scholarships in Marine Conservation [9700]

Richard M. Weaver Fellowships [4849]

Monica M. Weaver Memorial Fund [3795]

Faye and Rendell Webb Scholarships [2962]

TCDA Cloys Webb Student Scholarships [8853]

Allen and Loureena Weber Scholarships [8404]

Art and Dannie Weber Scholarships [9660]

Lester and Eleanor Webster Charitable Trust Fund [8707]

Jerome P. Webster Fellowships [7749]

Webster Society Scholarships [9534]

Kenneth G. Weckel Scholarships [5868]

WEF Canham Graduate Studies Scholarships [9536]

J.L. Weigand, Jr. Legal Education Trust Scholarships [9492]

Frank L. Weil Memorial Eagle Scout Scholarships [6265]

Arthur Weinberg Fellowships for Independent Scholars [6710]

ACI Bertold E. Weinberg Scholarships [638]

Edith Weingarten Scholarship Program [957]

The Bee Winkler Weinstein Scholarship Fund [8748]

William E. Weisel Scholarships [8405]

Weissbuch Family Scholarships [7973]

Polaire Weissman Funds [5793]

Edward Kent Welch Memorial Scholarships [9661]

Welch Scholars Grants [972]

Welder Wildlife Foundation Fellowships [9559]

Rob and Bessie Welder Wildlife Foundation **[9558]**

Sue Marsh Weller Memorial Scholarships [4738]

Dorothy Wellnitz Canadian Scholarships [1139]

Wells Fargo American Indian Scholarships - Graduate [828]

Wells Fargo Scholarship Program [4585]

Wells Fargo Scholarships [7425]

Donald M. Wells Scholarships [4307]

Wellstone Fellowships for Social Justice [3707]

Francis X. Weninger Scholarships [9777]

Wenner-Gren Foundation **[9560]**

Wenner-Gren Foundation Dissertation Fieldwork Grants [9563]

Wenner-Gren Foundation Post-PhD Research Grants [9564]

John R. and Joan F. Werren Scholarships Fund [8708]

Lucille and Charles A. Wert Scholarships [5696]

West Coast Sea Grant Fellowships [2279]

West Michigan Nursery and Landscape Association Scholarship Fund [4249]

West Virginia Coal Association **[9565]**

West Virginia Congress of Parents and Teachers (WV PTA) **[9567]**

West Virginia Educational Foundation Hospitality Business Alliance Scholarships [9570]

West Virginia Hospitality and Travel Association (WVHTA) **[9569]**

West Virginia Hospitality and Travel Association

Woman In Rural Electrification Scholarships (WIRE) [8565]
Woman's Club of Grand Haven Scholarships Fund [4251]
The Woman's Club of Nashville Scholarships [3139]
Women in Cancer Research Scholar Awards [453]
Women in Coaching National Coaching Institute Scholarships [2917]
Women in Defense, a National Security Organization (WID) **[9695]**
Women Divers Hall of Fame (WDHOF) **[9697]**
Women in Federal Law Enforcement (WIFLE) **[9701]**
Women In Defense HORIZONS Scholarships [9696]
Women In Need Scholarships [3601]
Women In Transition Scholarships [3602]
Women Lawyers Association of Greater St. Louis **[9703]**
Women Marines Association **[9705]**
Women in Science and Technology Scholarships [9442]
Women of Today's Manufacturing Scholarships [3175]
Women of WSAJ Bar Preparation Scholarships [9518]
Women's Army Corps Veterans' Association (WACVA) **[9710]**
Women's Army Corps Veterans Association Scholarships [9711]
Women's Association of the Mining Industry of Canada Foundation (WAMICF) **[9712]**
Women's Association of the Mining Industry of Canada Foundation National Geophysics Scholarships [9713]
Women's Association of the Mining Industry of Canada Foundation National Scholarships [9714]
Women's Association of the Mining Industry of Canada Foundation Wood Bursary Awards [9715]
Women's Business Enterprise National Council (WBENC) **[9716]**
Women's Business Support Network (WBSN) **[9718]**
Women's Health Research Foundation of Canada (WHRFC) **[9720]**
Women's Health Research Foundation of Canada Scholarship Program [9721]
Women's Independence Scholarship Programs [8774]
Women's International Network of Utility Professionals (WiNUP) **[9722]**
Women's Italian Club of Boston Scholarships [4083]
Women's Jewelry Association (WJA) **[9725]**
Women's Jewelry Association Member Grants [9726]
Women's Leadership in Agriculture Scholarship Program [6855]
Women's Missionary Council of the Christian Methodist Episcopal Church **[9727]**
Women's National Book Association (WNBA) **[9730]**
Women's Overseas and Service League **[9732]**
Women's Overseas and Service League Scholarships for Women [9733]
Women's Research and Education Institute (WREI) **[9734]**
Women's Sports Foundation (WSF) **[9736]**
Women's Transportation Seminar (WTS) **[9738]**
Carolyn Wones Recruitment Scholarship Grants [3176]
Dennis Wong and Associates Scholarships [5223]
Dr. Harold S. Wood Awards for Excellence [4072]
Wood County Bar Association Memorial Scholarships [7125]
Mary and Elliot Wood Foundation Graduate Scholarship Fund [3930]
Mary and Elliot Wood Foundation Undergraduate Scholarship Fund [3931]
Wood Fruitticher Grocery Company, Inc. Scholarships [173]
Rolla F. Wood Graduate Scholarships [7277]
Ed Wood Memorial Scholarship Awards [6944]
Hugh and Helen Wood Nepales Scholarships [2066]
Geoffrey H. Wood Scholarships [2594]
Irene Woodall Graduate Scholarships [710]

Woodcock Family Education Scholarship Program [284]
Woodex Bearing Company Scholarships [4095]
Frank and Betty Woodhams Memorial Scholarships [5773]
Guy A. Woodings Scholarships [9180]
Carter G. Woodson Institute for African-American and African Studies **[9742]**
Betsy B. Woodward Scholarships [1782]
Woodyard Family Scholarships [4265]
Marilyn Graboys Wool Scholarships [7796]
CSF L and T Woolfolk Memorial Scholarships [2878]
Blance E. Woolls Scholarships [2073]
David T. Woolsey Scholarships [1289]
Hawaii Chapter/David T. Woolsey Scholarships [5337]
Patty Wooten Scholarships [1707]
Worcester District Medical Society (WDMS) **[9745]**
Worcester District Medical Society Scholarship Fund [9746]
John W. Work III Memorial Foundation Scholarships [3140]
Working for Farmers' Success (WFS) **[9747]**
Working for Farmers' Success Scholarships [9748]
The Working Press Internships [8467]
Workshop, Inc. and Stark MRDD Fostering Diversity Through Special Needs Scholarship Fund [8710]
World Association for Cooperative Education (WACE) **[9749]**
World Book Graduate Scholarships in Library and Information Science [2521]
World Council of Credit Unions (WOCCU) **[9751]**
World Forest Institute (WFI) **[9753]**
World Leisure Organization (WLO) **[9755]**
World Wildlife Fund (WWF) **[9758]**
Worldstudio AIGA Scholarships [9761]
Worldstudio Foundation **[9760]**
Worldwide Assurance for Employees of Public Agencies (WAEPA) **[9762]**
Donald Worster Travel Grants [1255]
Wound, Ostomy and Continence Nurses Society (WOCN) **[9764]**
James and Colin Lee Wozumi Scholarships [7427]
WREI Congressional Fellows on Women and Public Policy [9735]
WRI Education Foundation Scholarships - Graduate [9670]
WRI Education Foundation Scholarships - High School Seniors [9671]
WRI Education Foundation Scholarships - Undergraduate [9672]
Jean Wright-Elson Scholarships [7976]
Audrey L. Wright Scholarships [4309]
WSAJ American Justice Essay Scholarships [9519]
WSAJ Diversity Bar Preparation Scholarships [9520]
WSAJ Presidents' Scholarships [9521]
WSCPA Chapter Scholarships [9516]
WSSA Students Paper Competition [9579]
WTVD Endowment Scholarships [9312]
Wyatt, Tarrant and Combs, LLP Scholarships [9242]
WYCUP Scholarships [9752]
Margaret Wyeth Scholarships [3177]
Wyeth-SUS Clinical Scholar Awards [8512]
Xavier Community-Engaged Fellowships [9778]
Xavier University **[9767]**
Xavier University Chancellor Scholarships [9779]
Xavier University Departmental Scholarships [9780]
Xavier University Honors Bachelor of Arts Scholarships [9781]
Xavier University Legacy Scholarships [9782]
Xavier University ROTC Scholarships - Air Force ROTC [9783]
Xavier University ROTC Scholarships - Army ROTC [9784]
Xavier University Williams Scholarships [9785]
Xerox **[9786]**
Xerox Technical Minority Scholarships [9787]
Pang Xiaoyan Scholarships [2775]
M.H. Yager Memorial Scholarships [1953]
Yale Graduate and Professional Students Research Fellowships [2044]
Yamhill County Farm Bureau Scholarships [6950]
Yankee Clipper Contest Club, Inc. Youth Scholarships [1114]
William J. Yankee Memorial Scholarships [1021]

Gwen Yarnell Theatre Scholarships [3751]
Yasme Foundation Scholarships [1115]
Minoru Yasui Memorial Scholarships [5147]
Marusia Yaworska Entrance Scholarships [9501]
Willa Yeck Memorial Scholarship Fund [3450]
Ralph Yetka Memorial Scholarships [9181]
Marilyn Yetso Memorial Scholarships [2759]
Vera Yip Memorial Scholarships [2760]
YMF Scholarships [9791]
Joan C. Yoder Memorial Nursing Scholarships [9182]
York Art Association (YAA) **[9788]**
York Graduate Scholarships [8050]
York Regional Police Scholarships [5127]
York Rite Grand Chapter Royal Arch Masons Scholarships [3426]
Gary Yoshimura Scholarships [7542]
Jack and Edna May Yost Scholarships [3964]
You Go Girl! Scholarships [7428]
Jessie Young Bursary Awards [2397]
Alma H. Young Emerging Scholar Awards [9394]
Young Investigator Grants [6529]
Searle Young Legal Scholars Research Fellowships [3732]
Young Musicians Foundation (YMF) **[9790]**
Young People For Fellowships (YP4) [8147]
Donnell B. Young Scholarships [286]
Elmer Cooke Young - Taylor Young Scholarships [4463]
Young Women's Alliance (YWA) **[9792]**
Yount, Hyde & Barbour Scholarships [9468]
Youth Affairs Committee Rising Star Scholarships [5128]
Youth Empowerment Summit Scholarships [6148]
Youth or the Environment Scholarships [2009]
Youth Leadership Scholarships [2265]
Youth Maritime Training Association (YMTA) **[9794]**
Youth Partners Accessing Capital (PAC) [354]
The Youth Scholarship Program [2719]
Youth Scholarships [8305]
Youth for Understanding (YFU) **[9796]**
Youth for Understanding Scholarships [9797]
Nettie Tucker Yowell Scholarships [9443]
Diane Yu Loan Repayment Assistance Program [6029]
Yukon Delta Fisheries Development Association Scholarships [9183]
Yukon Law Foundation **[9798]**
Yukon Law Foundation Scholarships [9799]
YWA Foundation Scholarships [9793]
Z/I Imaging Scholarships [1673]
Zagunis Student Leader Scholarships [6058]
Lisa Zaken Awards For Excellence [4812]
Dr. Marie E. Zakrzewski Medical Scholarships [5302]
Michael A. Zamperini/W. Clay Burchell Scholarships [7878]
James and Joy Zana Memorial Scholarships [4266]
CSF L.B. Zapoleon Scholarships [2879]
Zarley, McKee, Thomte, Voorhees, Sease Law Scholarships [3516]
Urashi Zen Scholarships [7429]
Zenko Family Scholarship Fund [4252]
Harry and Angel Zerigian Scholarships [1609]
Zeta Chapter Memorial Scholarship Awards [3178]
Zeta Phi Beta Sorority **[9800]**
Zeta Phi Beta Sorority General Graduate Scholarships [9808]
Zeta Phi Beta Sorority General Undergraduate Scholarships [9809]
A.F. Zimmerman Scholarships [7246]
Blanche Raper Zimmerman Scholarships [9665]
Zimmermann Scholarships [8785]
A.R. Zipf Fellowships [3280]
Jacob Ziskind Memorial Fund for Upperclassmen [4728]
Morris L. and Rebecca Ziskind Memorial Scholarships [4655]
Lorraine Zitone Memorial Scholarship Fund [3451]
Zonta Club of Hilo **[9810]**
Zonta International Foundation (ZIF) **[9812]**
Ruth and Sherman Zudekoff Scholarships [3084]
Leo Zupin Memorial Scholarship Fund [4253]
Francis Sylvia Zverina Scholarships [4538]

CPSIA information can be obtained
at www.ICGtesting.com
Printed in the USA
FFOW020525170113
711FF